APPLICATIONS AND CONNECTIONS LEAD TO ALGEBRA SUCCESS!

An Educational Program from
GLENCOE

Today's Algebra Students Require More Than The Basics... They Require Applications And Connections!

Glencoe **realizes that in order to bring success to today's high school students, algebra programs must show the students how the basic principles integrate with their everyday lives. And** *Merrill Algebra 1* **and** *Algebra 2 with Trigonometry,* **do just that by offering a perfect blend of both...applications and connections.**

By introducing algebra concepts with applications and connections, your students will finally come to realize algebra's relevance in our society. And once your students realize the practical applications of algebra, they will remain interested...stay motivated...and want to learn everything they can about this important mathematical topic.

The **Student Edition** is designed to motivate and excite your students about the study of algebra. It contains a vast array of lesson features, challenging activities, and thought-provoking applications that correlate with the four main NCTM Standards:

• **Problem Solving**
• **Communication**
• **Reasoning**
• **Connections**

The **Teacher's Wraparound Edition** organizes each lesson into six easy-to-follow steps... **Introducing, Teaching, Evaluating, Reteaching, Applying,** and **Extending the Lesson.** Right at your fingertips, you have a variety of classroom-proven teaching strategies and activities that help you create the most stimulating environment for learning.

The **Teacher's Classroom Resources** is filled with valuable teaching materials that help you support and enrich the content in every lesson.

Merrill Algebra Answers The Question, "When Am I Ever Going To Use This?"

With *Merrill Algebra 1* **and** *Algebra 2 with Trigonometry,* **your students will finally come to realize the need for learning algebra. The content continuously applies and connects algebra principles with other areas of mathematics, other disciplines, and real-world applications thus giving your students a better understanding of how algebra is relevant to their future lives and careers.**

Algebra 1

CHAPTER 12
Radical Expressions

CHAPTER OBJECTIVES
In this chapter, you will:
* Find exact and approximate values for square roots.
* Simplify radical expressions.
* Solve radical equations.
* Solve problems that can be represented by radical equations.
* Solve problems by using tables.

Have you ever noticed that Mother Nature is a very skilled designer! Just look around and you can find many examples of mathematics in nature's designs.

APPLICATION IN NATURE

The shell of a chambered nautilus is one of the many examples of mathematics occurring in nature's designs. This shell takes on its spiral shape because of the nautilus's growth pattern and the formation of small chambers of increasing size to accommodate this growth. The growth pattern of the nautilus can be studied by looking at the size and shape of the shell's spiral.

One method for studying the spiral is to use a set of right triangles winding around a point to represent the shape of the spiral. These right triangles are drawn so that the sides used to represent the spiral all have the same length, one unit, as shown in the figure below. Notice that each triangle has the same apex (top point). The longest side of each right triangle, called the hypotenuse, is also one of the shorter sides of the next triangle in the set. This design is called a "spiral of square roots" because of the relationship between the lengths of the sides of the right triangles.

The shell of the chambered nautilus is just one example of naturally occurring spirals. The next time you see a daisy, a sunflower, or a pineapple, see if you can find the spirals that are a part of their design.

ALGEBRA IN ACTION

Look at the triangle with sides 1, $\sqrt{1}$, and $\sqrt{2}$ in the figure at the left. Notice that $1^2 + (\sqrt{1})^2 = (\sqrt{2})^2$ since $(\sqrt{1})^2 = 1$ and $(\sqrt{2})^2 = 2$. Similarly, in the next few triangles, $1^2 + (\sqrt{2})^2 = (\sqrt{3})^2$, $1^2 + (\sqrt{3})^2 = (\sqrt{4})^2$, and $1^2 + (\sqrt{4})^2 = (\sqrt{5})^2$. This relationship between the measures of the sides of the right triangles is the basis for the Pythagorean Theorem. If you continue in this manner, what will be the measure of the side labeled $?$ in the figure?

473

A stimulating Chapter Opener introduces your students to every chapter. Algebra 1 chapters begin with real-world applications, and Algebra 2 with interesting careers so that your students become motivated and engaged in learning the upcoming content.

CHAPTER 3
Systems of Equations and Inequalities

CHAPTER OBJECTIVES
In this chapter, you will:
* Solve systems of equations in two or three variables.
* Solve systems of inequalities.
* Use linear programming to find maximum and minimum values of functions.
* Graph linear equations in space.

The breakeven point is the level of sales where the revenue from the sales equals the cost of manufacturing those products. Can you list some of the costs of manufacturing a product or providing a service?

Cost and Revenue of Sales

102

CAREERS IN MARKET RESEARCH

Can you work accurately with detail? Are you patient and persistent? Can you work objectively and systematically to discovery solutions to problems no one has ever solved before? If so, perhaps you could be a successful market research analyst.

These days no company can afford to provide products or services to the public without first making sure exactly what the public wants. So the early steps of any product development rely on market research. A market researcher first designs a survey—that is, decides what questions to ask the public.

Say a fast-food restaurant is being planned for a shopping mall. The researcher will need to ask lots of questions. What kinds of foods will mall shoppers buy—hot things or cold things, full meals or just snacks? Should the new restaurant have real ice cream or frozen yogurt? Which issues rank highest with mall shoppers: nutrition, taste, or speed?

The market research analyst heads a team that asks many, many mall shoppers all these questions and more. Then the team analyzes the data. They may need to perform a second or even a third survey, if results indicate that important questions were omitted. Finally, they present their findings both orally and in writing, with visual aids such as charts and graphs. From their work, businesses can know more surely than ever before what the marketplace wants.

Algebra 2

MORE ABOUT MARKET RESEARCH

Degree Required:
* Bachelor's Degree in Marketing

Some market research analysts like:
* working with people
* lots of travel
* the variety and challenge of their work
* good salaries

Related Math Subjects:
* Statistics
* Calculus
* Applied Math

Some market research analyst dislike:
* working long hours, including evenings and weekends
* working under high pressure
* the competitive nature of this field

For more information on the various careers available in the field of Market Research, write to:
Marketing Research Association
111 East Wacker Drive
Chicago, Illinois 60601

103

8-7 Rational Expressions with Unlike Denominators

Objective   After studying this lesson, you should be able to:
■ add or subtract rational expressions with unlike denominators.

Application

FYI···

The longest-running musical to date is *The Fantasticks*. So far, there have been over 12,000 performances.

Judith Paulsen, the choreographer of a big Broadway musical, has requested that the producer of the show hire enough dancers so that they can be arranged in groups of 4, 6, or 9 with no one sitting out. What is the least number of dancers that can be hired?

If the choreographer wanted to arrange the dancers in groups of 6, then the producer should hire a number of dancers that is a multiple of 6. But since she wants to arrange the dancers in groups of 4, 6, or 9, the producer must be concerned with multiples of all three numbers. The least number of dancers is given by the **least common multiple (LCM)** of the three numbers. The least common multiple is the smallest number that is a common multiple of two or more numbers.

The multiples of 4, 6, and 9 can be found by multiplying 4, 6, and 9 by each whole number.

You can find the LCM by making an organized list.

multiples of 4: $4 \cdot 0, 4 \cdot 1, 4 \cdot 2, 4 \cdot 3, 4 \cdot 4, \ldots, 4 \cdot 9, \ldots$
   0,   4,   8,   12,   16,   36, . . .

multiples of 6: $6 \cdot 0, 6 \cdot 1, 6 \cdot 2, 6 \cdot 3, 6 \cdot 4, 6 \cdot 5, 6 \cdot 6, \ldots$
   0,   6,   12,   18,   24,   30,   36, . . .

multiples of 9: $9 \cdot 0, 9 \cdot 1, 9 \cdot 2, 9 \cdot 3, 9 \cdot 4, 9 \cdot 5, \ldots$
   0,   9,   18,   27,   36,   45, . . .

Compare these multiples. Aside from 0, the least number that is common to all three sets of multiples is 36. Thus, the LCM of 4, 6, and 9 is 36, and the producer should hire 36 dancers.

You can also use prime factorization to find the LCM.

1. Find the prime factorization of each number.

   $4 = 2 \cdot 2$
   $6 = 2 \cdot 3$
   $9 = 3 \cdot 3$

Applications

Most lessons begin with **Applications** that are visually supported by stimulating photographs and graphics. Clearly-labeled application problems are integrated into every exercise set to continuously show your students how algebra is used in our society.

FYI introduces your students to "fast facts," interesting tidbits, and fascinating math-related trivia.

FYI···

The longest-running musical to date is *The Fantasticks*. So far, there have been over 12,000 performances.

Connections

Throughout the text, you will find a variety of **Connections** — examples and problems designed to give your students a more complete understanding of how algebra is applicable to other disciplines.

Example 2
CONNECTION
Geometry

The perimeter of a triangle is 83 inches. The longest side is three times the length of the shortest side and 17 inches more than one-half the sum of the other two sides. Find the length of each side.

EXPLORE   Let a = the measure of the shortest side of the triangle, c = the measure of the longest side of the triangle, and b = the measure of the other side.

PLAN   Write equations for all the information you know.

$a + b + c = 83$ *The perimeter is 83 in.*
$a = 3c$ *The longest side is 3 times the length of shortest.*
$a = \frac{1}{2}(b + c) + 17$ *The longest side is 17 more than half the sum of the lengths of the other sides.*

SOLVE   In order to solve the system, rewrite the equations so that they are all in the form necessary to write an augmented matrix.

$a + b + c = 83$
$a - 3c = 0$
$2a - b - c = 34$ $\begin{bmatrix} 1 & 1 & 1 & 83 \\ 1 & 0 & -3 & 0 \\ 2 & -1 & -1 & 34 \end{bmatrix}$

After applying row operations on the matrix, we get

$\begin{bmatrix} 0 & 1 & 0 & 31 \\ 1 & 0 & 0 & 39 \\ 0 & 0 & 1 & 13 \end{bmatrix}$ ➡ $\begin{bmatrix} 1 & 0 & 0 & 39 \\ 0 & 1 & 0 & 31 \\ 0 & 0 & 1 & 13 \end{bmatrix}$ *Interchange the first and second rows.*

The solution is (39, 31, 13), which means the lengths of the sides of the triangle are 39 inches, 31 inches, and 13 inches.

EXAMINE   The sum of the three lengths (39 + 31 + 13) is 83 inches. The longest side, 39, is 3 times 13, the shortest side. Half the sum of 31 and 13 is 22, which is 17 less than 39, the longest side.

As with other methods of solving systems of equations, there is not always a unique solution. However, when using augmented matrices, you can determine what type of solution you have when a solution is not unique. Study the solution of the system shown below.

$2x - y + 4z = 4$
$x + 2y - 3z = 7$
$x - 8y + 17z = -13$ $\begin{bmatrix} 2 & -1 & 4 & 4 \\ 1 & 2 & -3 & 7 \\ 1 & -8 & 17 & -13 \end{bmatrix}$ ➡ $\begin{bmatrix} 1 & 0 & 1 & 3 \\ 0 & 1 & -2 & 2 \\ 0 & 0 & 0 & 0 \end{bmatrix}$

"This standard emphasizes the importance of...modeling connections between problem situations that may arise in the real world or in disciplines other than mathematics; and mathematical connections between two equivalent representations..."
— NCTM Standards

∼∼∼ HISTORY CONNECTION ∼∼∼

René Descartes

René Descartes (1596–1650) was one of the greatest scientists of the seventeenth century. It was he who used two perpendicular number lines to identify points in a plane. This rectangular coordinate system is called the *Cartesian coordinate system*, in honor of Descartes. The connecting of algebra and geometry through graphing is called *analytic geometry*. Although Descartes is considered to be the founder of analytic geometry, he did not consider himself a mathematician. He is often called the "father of modern philosophy," his great love.

History Connection is only one of the many enjoyable connection features contained throughout the text. This particular feature highlights men and women from various cultures who have played an integral part in the development of mathematics.

Problem-Solving Lessons Engage Your Students In Critical Thinking And Decision Making

Merrill Algebra 1 and *Algebra 2 with Trigonometry* **offer you a vast array of problem-solving lessons and activities that make it fun and easy for your students to apply and retain what they have learned.**

Problem Solving

Each chapter contains numerous problem-solving activities including a **Problem-Solving Strategy Lesson** that gives your students a better understanding of a particular algebra concept. The strategies are then applied and integrated throughout subsequent lessons.

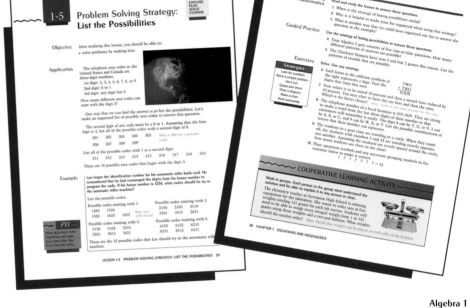

Critical Thinking

Each lesson contains **Critical Thinking** problems which will challenge your students to develop and apply higher order thinking skills.

Critical Thinking

37. A butterfly lands on one of the six squares of the T-shaped figure shown and then randomly moves to an adjacent square. What is the probability that the butterfly ends up on the red square?

Algebra 1

At the end of selective chapters you will find a **College Entrance Exam Preview.** A two-page problem-solving review that gives your students the practice they need to do well on upcoming ACT and SAT examinations.

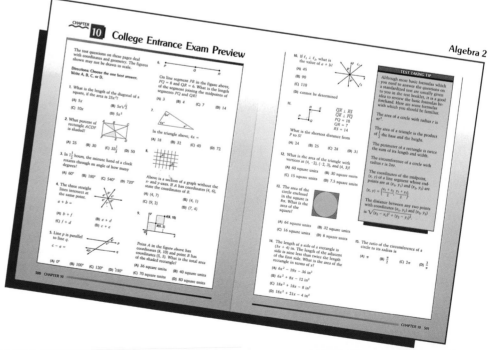

All New Reviews

Merrill Algebra 1 and *Algebra 2 with Trigonometry* provide numerous opportunities to review and reinforce the skills needed to succeed in algebra. Each lesson contains a **Mixed Review**— a blend of previously taught concepts, that are lesson referenced, so that students can easily go back and restudy important mathematical concepts. In addition, each chapter has a **Chapter Summary and Review.** This unique combination of objectives, examples, and exercises helps your students better understand and retain what they have learned.

> "A mathematics curriculum should include a refinement and extension of methods of mathematical problem solving so that students can apply integrated mathematical problem-solving strategies to solve problems from within and outside mathematics."
> —NCTM Standards

Thought-Provoking Problems, Activities, And Technology Features Teach Your Students How To Communicate Mathematically

Glencoe **realizes that in order for students to succeed in mathematics, they must be able to reflect upon and clarify their thinking about mathematical ideas and relationships. For this reason, our program offers numerous problems, activities, and features that develop and enhance your students' communication skills.**

Algebra 1

Communicating Mathematics

Read and study the lesson to complete the following.

1. How do you undo addition? division?

2. Write an example of an equation requiring more than one operation to solve.

3. If n is an even integer, explain how to find the even integer just before it.

Communications

Every exercise set contains several **Communicating Mathematics** problems. These problems provide opportunities for your student to express mathematical concepts verbally, in writing, or through the use of pictures, symbols, models, tables, or graphs.

Algebra 2

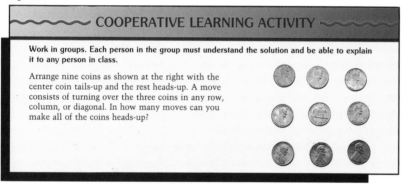

COOPERATIVE LEARNING ACTIVITY

Work in groups. Each person in the group must understand the solution and be able to explain it to any person in class.

Arrange nine coins as shown at the right with the center coin tails-up and the rest heads-up. A move consists of turning over the three coins in any row, column, or diagonal. In how many moves can you make all of the coins heads-up?

A **Cooperative Learning Activity** is contained in every chapter. It provides multiple opportunities for discussion, questioning, listening, and summarizing — all important techniques needed to communicate successfully in mathematics.

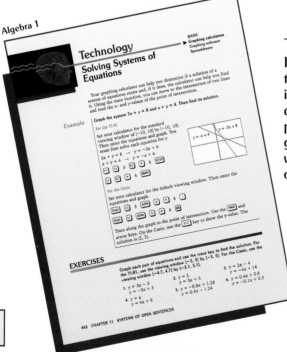

Technology

In addition to integrating the use of the scientific calculator, special high-interest **Technology** features introduce your students to spreadsheets, programming, graphing software, and graphing calculators, and open their world to very powerful applications of mathematics.

"All students need extensive experience listening to, reading about, writing about, speaking about, reflecting on, and demonstrating mathematical ideas."
— NCTM Standards

Computer 37. The BASIC program at the right generates the line of coefficients in Pascal's triangle for $(a + b)^n$. You must input the value of n when running the program.

Use the program to express each binomial in expanded form.

a. $(a + b)^4$ b. $(a + b)^{12}$
c. $(x - y)^6$ d. $(x - y)^{10}$

```
  1  PRINT "ENTER THE VALUE
     OF N"
  5  INPUT Y
 10  FOR N = 0 TO Y
 20  FOR R = 0 TO N
 30  LET C = 1
 40  IF N < N - R + 1 THEN 80
 50  FOR X = N TO N - R + 1
     STEP - 1
 60  LET C = C*X/(N - X + 1)
 70  NEXT X
 80  PRINT C;" ";
 90  NEXT R
100  PRINT
110  NEXT N
120  END
```

Computer exercises give your students experience solving algebra problems using BASIC language.

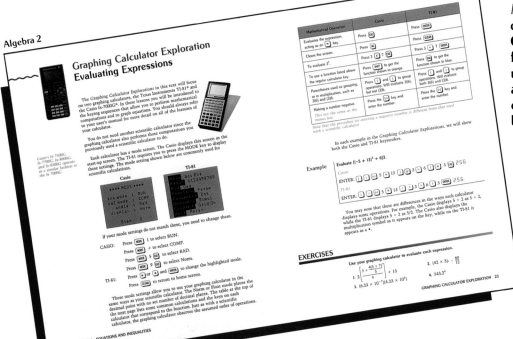

Merrill Algebra 2 with Trigonometry contains 17 interesting **Graphing Calculator Explorations.** These features enable your students to use graphing calculators to explore and investigate mathematical concepts. They contain keystrokes for both TI-81 and Casio models.

"Technology is yet another avenue for mathematical communication, both in transmitting and receiving information."
—*NCTM Standards*

Table of Contents

Merrill Algebra 1

Chapter 1: An Introduction to Algebra
Chapter 2: Rational Numbers
Chapter 3: Equations
Chapter 4: Applications of Rational Numbers
Chapter 5: Inequalities
Chapter 6: Polynomials
Chapter 7: Factoring
Chapter 8: Rational Expressions
Chapter 9: Functions and Graphs
Chapter 10: Graphing Linear Equations
Chapter 11: Systems of Open Sentences
Chapter 12: Radical Expressions
Chapter 13: Quadratics
Chapter 14: Statistics and Probability
Chapter 15: Trigonometry

Merrill Algebra 2 with Trigonometry

Chapter 1: Equations and Inequalities
Chapter 2: Linear Relations and Functions
Chapter 3: Systems of Equations and Inequalities
Chapter 4: Matrices
Chapter 5: Polynomials
Chapter 6: Irrational and Complex Numbers
Chapter 7: Quadratic Equations
Chapter 8: Quadratic Relations and Functions
Chapter 9: Conics
Chapter 10: Polynomial Functions
Chapter 11: Rational Polynomial Expressions
Chapter 12: Exponential and Logarithmic Functions
Chapter 13: Sequences and Series
Chapter 14: Statistics
Chapter 15: Probability
Chapter 16: Trigonometric Functions
Chapter 17: Trigonometric Graphs, Identities, and Equations

The Teacher's Wraparound Edition Makes It Easy For You To Preview, Organize, Present, And Enhance The Content In Every Chapter

Merrill Algebra 1 and *Algebra 2 with Trigonometry* is the only algebra program that offers you the advantages of a Teacher's Wraparound Edition. At your fingertips, you will have a variety of unique teaching strategies that enable you to meet your teaching goals while allowing you to create the best, most captivating atmosphere for learning.

Four **Interleaf Pages** precede each chapter. They provide a quick and easy reference to **Previewing**, **Organizing**, and **Enhancing the Chapter.**

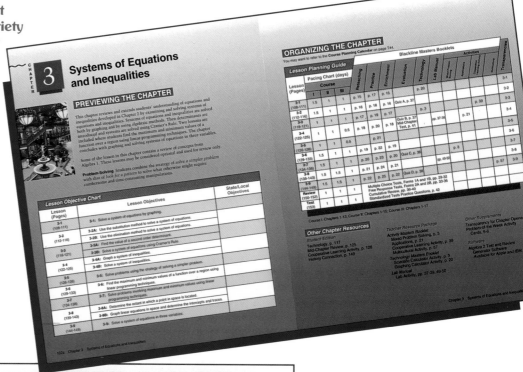

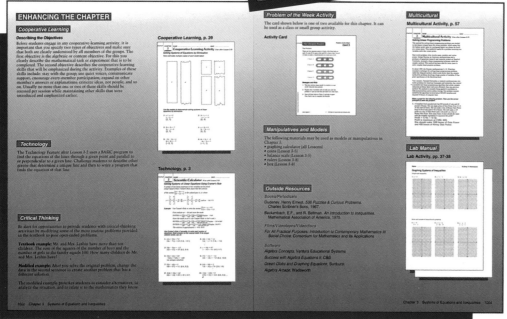

Within the **Interleaf Pages,** you will also find a variety of interesting strategies and activities to enhance your students' learning experience. Some of the topics highlighted include:

- cooperative learning strategies
- list of manipulatives used in the chapter
- technology highlights and suggestions
- critical thinking strategies
- outside resources

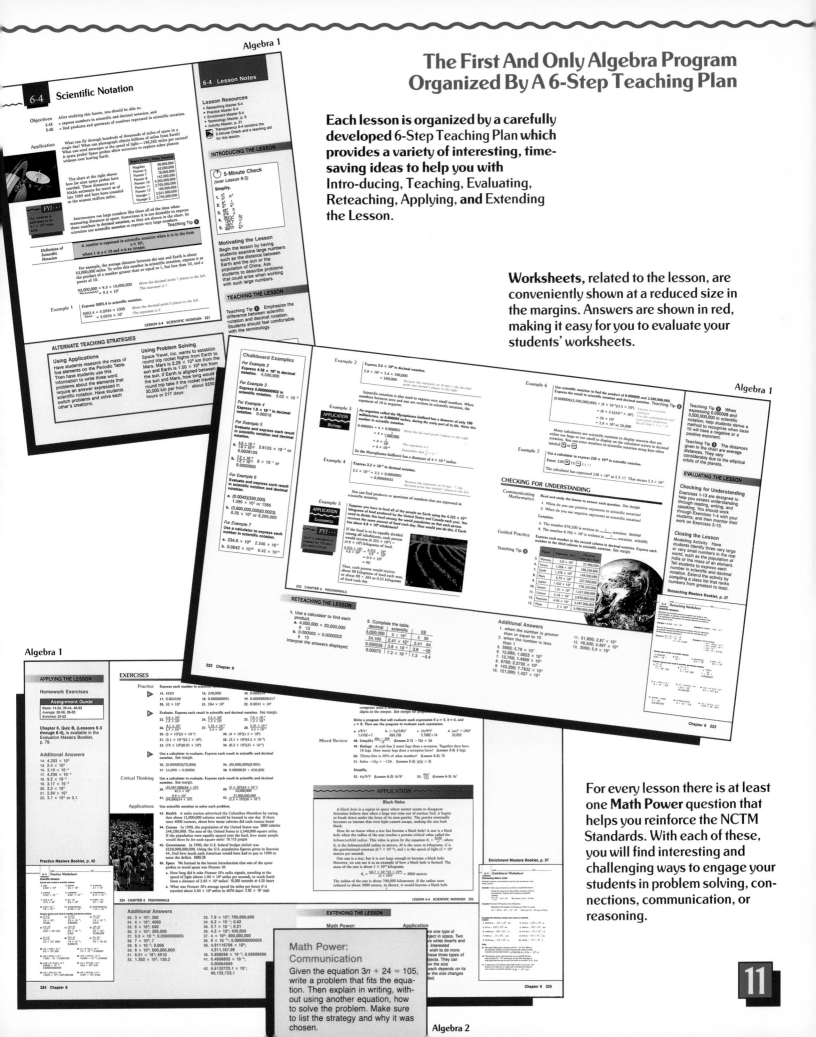

The First And Only Algebra Program Organized By A 6-Step Teaching Plan

Each lesson is organized by a carefully developed 6-Step Teaching Plan which provides a variety of interesting, time-saving ideas to help you with Intro-ducing, Teaching, Evaluating, Reteaching, Applying, **and** Extending the Lesson.

Worksheets, related to the lesson, are conveniently shown at a reduced size in the margins. Answers are shown in red, making it easy for you to evaluate your students' worksheets.

For every lesson there is at least one **Math Power** question that helps you reinforce the NCTM Standards. With each of these, you will find interesting and challenging ways to engage your students in problem solving, connections, communication, or reasoning.

Math Power: Communication

Given the equation $3n + 24 = 105$, write a problem that fits the equation. Then explain in writing, without using another equation, how to solve the problem. Make sure to list the strategy and why it was chosen.

11

Count On Merrill Algebra 1 and Algebra 2 With Trigonometry To Give You The Best, Most Comprehensive Teacher's Resource Package Available

No other algebra program can give you as many unique, challenging, and thought-provoking support materials as *Merrill Algebra 1* and *Algebra 2 with Trigonometry*. At your disposal, you can choose from an abundance of resources to help you support and extend the content in every lesson.

Reteaching Masters Booklet explores lesson concepts using alternative methods such as modeling and graphing.

Practice Masters Booklet gives your students additional practice for the concept exercises found in each lesson. The practice exercises help to reinforce important mathematical skills needed for future success.

Enrichment Masters Booklet contains such things as stimulating games and puzzles to help you extend and enrich the main ideas in the chapter.

Evaluation Masters Booklet provides a thorough representation of the chapter content through a variety of multiple choice and free-response chapter tests, quizzes, a mid-chapter test, and cumulative reviews and tests.

Technology Masters Booklet contains calculator and computer activities to help your students practice using technological tools to develop algebraic skills and applications.

The **Lab Manual** contains 24 activities for both *Merrill Algebra 1* and *Algebra 2 with Trigonometry*. Each activity consists of a full-page transparency master, a full-page student worksheet, and complete teaching instructions.

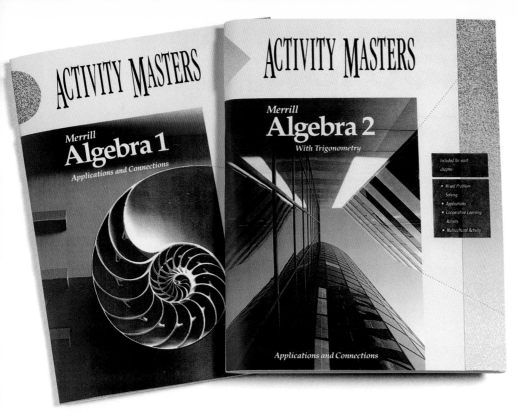

Activities Booklet

Contains four interesting activities for each chapter to help your students get the most out of the lessons.

ACTIVITY MASTERS

ACTIVITY MASTERS

Merrill
Algebra 1
Applications and Connections

Merrill
Algebra 2
With Trigonometry

Applications and Connections

Included for each chapter:

• Mixed Problem Solving
• Applications
• Cooperative Learning Activity
• Multicultural Activity

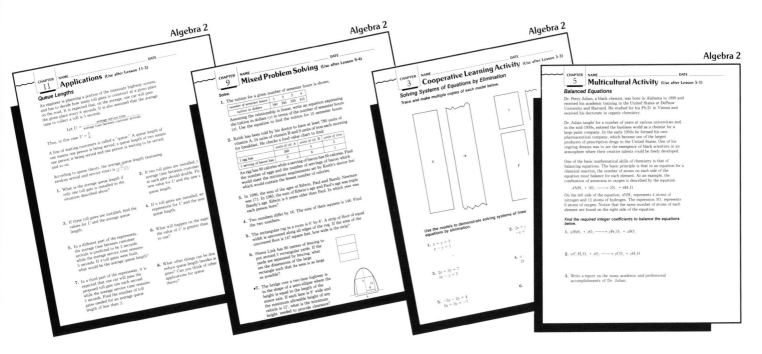

Application activities connect the chapter content to common, everyday situations.

Mixed Problem Solving Activities provide your students with an assortment of verbal problems from throughout the text.

Cooperative Learning Activities present a problem or mini-project that require students to make observations, record data, survey, or make a decision while they apply important interpersonal skills.

Multicultural Activities present a unique cross-cultural array of historical situations that engage students to solve a problem based on the content of the chapter.

An Abundance Of Other Support Materials Provide Alternatives For Stimulating Instruction

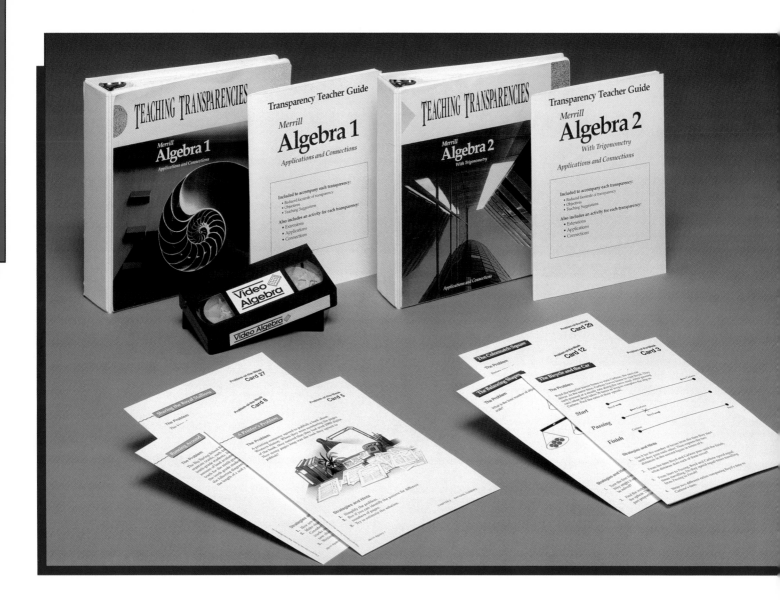

Transparency Package for each text contains a full-color transparency for each lesson and chapter opener. The package contains captivating photographs, graphs, completely-worked examples, and overlays as well as a repeat of the 5-Minute Checks found in the **Teacher's Wraparound Edition.**

A **Transparency Teacher's Guide** contains pictures of the transparencies, objectives, and teaching suggestions with an extension, application, or connection.

Video Algebra is an excellent reteaching tool. Ideal for students who have missed class or for use by a substitute teacher.

Problem-of-the-Week Cards give you another fun and interesting way to motivate your students to think mathematically.

The **Test Generator,** available in both
IBM and Apple formats, provides a valuable test bank for creating your own
tests, worksheets, and answer keys.

Lesson Plans, one for each lesson, help
you plan your daily lessons by making it
easy for you to make the best of the
learning materials for your class.

A **Solutions Manual** provides a complete solution for every problem in the
Student Edition.

Spanish Resources provide a Spanish
translation of the English-language
glossary in the **Student Edition.** Also,
the key chapter objectives are provided
in Spanish.

Give Your Students The Advantage Of Merrill Algebra...Strong Algebra Content... Reinforced By Applications And Connections!

Teacher's Wraparound Edition

Merrill
Algebra 1
Applications and Connections

GLENCOE
Macmillan/McGraw–Hill

Lake Forest, Illinois   Columbus, Ohio   Mission Hills, California   Peoria, Illinois

Send all inquiries to:
Glencoe Division, Macmillan/McGraw-Hill
936 Eastwind Drive
Westerville, OH 43081

ISBN: 0-675-13116-2 (Student Edition)
ISBN: 0-675-13117-0

1 2 3 4 5 6 7 8 9 10 VH 00 99 98 97 96 95 94 93 92 91

Alan G. Foster is chairperson of the mathematics department at Addison Trail High School, Addison, Illinois. He has taught mathematics courses at every level of the high school curriculum. Mr. Foster obtained his B.S. degree from Illinois State University and M.A. in mathematics from the University of Illinois. He is active in professional organizations at the local, state, and national levels. He is a past president of the Illinois Council of Teachers of Mathematics and a recipient of the Illinois Council of Teachers of Mathematics T.E. Rine Award for excellence in the teaching of mathematics. He also was a recipient of the 1987 Presidential Award for Excellence in the Teaching of Mathematics in the state of Illinois. Mr. Foster is a coauthor of *Merrill Geometry, Merrill Algebra Essentials,* and *Merrill Algebra 2.*

Joan M. Gell is a mathematics teacher and department chairperson at Palos Verdes High School in Palos Verdes Estates, California. Ms. Gell has taught mathematics at every level from junior high school to college. She received her B.S. degree in mathematics education from The State University of New York-Cortland, and M.A. degree in mathematics from Bowdoin College in Brunswick, Maine. Ms. Gell has developed and conducted in-service classes in mathematics and computer science and is past president of the California Mathematics Council. She serves as the chairperson of the 1992 MATH-COUNTS Problem Writing Committee. Ms. Gell was a finalist for the 1984 Presidential Award for Excellence in the Teaching of Mathematics in the state of California.

Leslie J. Winters is the Secondary Mathematics Specialist for the Los Angeles Unified School District. He has thirty years of classroom experience in teaching mathematics at every level from junior high school to college. Mr. Winters received bachelor's degrees in mathematics and secondary education from Pepperdine University and the University of Dayton, and master's degrees from the University of Southern California and Boston College. He is a past president of the California Mathematics Council-Southern Section and was a recipient of the 1983 Presidential Award for Excellence in the Teaching of Mathematics in the state of California. Mr. Winters is a coauthor of *Merrill Algebra Essentials* and *Merrill Algebra 2.*

James N. Rath has 30 years of classroom experience in teaching mathematics at every level of the high school curriculum. He is a mathematics teacher and former head of the mathematics department at Darien High School, Darien, Connecticut. Mr. Rath earned his B.A. degree in philosophy from the Catholic University of America and his M.Ed. and M.A. degrees in mathematics from Boston College. He is active in professional organizations at the local, state, and national levels. Mr. Rath is a coauthor of *Merrill Pre-Algebra, Merrill Algebra Essentials,* and *Merrill Algebra 2.*

Berchie W. Gordon is a Mathematics/Computer coordinator for the Northwest Local School District in Cincinnati, Ohio. Dr. Gordon has taught mathematics at every level from junior high school to college. She received her B.S. degree in Mathematics from Emory University in Atlanta, Georgia and M.A.T. in education from Northwestern University, Evanston, Illinois. She has done further study at the University of Illinois and the University of Cincinnati where she received her doctorate in curriculum and instruction. Dr. Gordon has developed and conducted numerous in-service workshops in mathematics and computer applications. She has served as a consultant for IBM. She has traveled nationally to make presentations on the graphing calculator to teacher groups.

CONSULTANTS

Donald W. Collins
Department of Mathematics and Informational
  Sciences
Sam Houston State University
Huntsville, Texas

Gail F. Burrill
Chairperson, Department of Mathematics
Whitnall High School
Greenfield, Wisconsin

EDITORIAL ADVISOR

Jo Helen Williams
Supervisor, Secondary Mathematics
Dayton Public School
Dayton, Ohio

REVIEWERS

Ron Ashby
Mathematics Supervisor
Vigo County School
Terre Haute, IN

Marietta Harris
Curriculum Coordinator
Memphis City School
Memphis, TN

Paul Benz
Mathematics Department Chairman
Clay Junior High School
Carmel, IN

Cathy Jahr
Mathematics Department Chairman
Martin Westview High School
Martin, TN

Grace Berlin
Mathematics Department Chairman/Teacher
Stillwater Junior High School
Stillwater, OK

Joe Lee
Mathematics Department Chairman/Teacher
Parkway West Junior High School
Chesterfield, MO

Hans DeGroat
Secondary Research Teacher
San Diego Unified School District
San Diego, CA

Betty Mayberry
Mathematics Department Head
Riverdale High School
Murfreesboro, TN

Dr. Marva Fears
Mathematics Supervisor
Dekalb County School District
Decauter, GA

Dr. James Reney
Supervisor of Mathematics
Altoona Area School District
Altoona, PA

Terry Hacker
Mathematics Teacher
Oliver Springs High School
Oliver Springs, TN

Lowell Wilson
Mathematics Teacher
George Washington High School
Greenfield, IN

Table of Contents

CHAPTER 1

An Introduction to Algebra — 6

1-1	Variables and Expressions	8
1-2	Evaluating Expressions	12
	Reading Algebra	17
1-3	Open Sentences	18
1-4	Identity and Equality Properties	22
	Mid-Chapter Review	25
1-5	The Distributive Property	26
1-6	Commutative and Associative Properties	31
	History Connection: Sir William Rowan Hamilton	35
1-7	Formulas	36
	Technology: Formulas	40
1-8	Problem-Solving: Explore Verbal Problems	41
	Cooperative Learning Activity	43
	Chapter Summary and Review	44
	Chapter Test	47

CHAPTER 2

Rational Numbers — 48

2-1	Integers and the Number Line	50
	Application: Meteorology	54
2-2	Adding and Subtracting Integers	55
	Puzzle	59
2-3	Inequalities and the Number Line	60
2-4	Comparing and Ordering Rational Numbers	65
2-5	Adding and Subtracting Rational Numbers	69
	Mid-Chapter Review	73
2-6	Multiplying Rational Numbers	74
	History Connection: Sonya Kovalevskaya	78
	Technology: Adding Fractions	79
2-7	Dividing Rational Numbers	80
2-8	Problem-Solving Strategy: Write an Equation	85
	Cooperative Learning Activity	87
	Chapter Summary and Review	88
	Chapter Test	91

APPLICATIONS AND CONNECTIONS

APPLICATIONS

Basketball	26
Golf	56
Business	62
Consumerism	66
Stock Market	69

CONNECTIONS

Geometry	10, 14, 32, 36, 37
Logic	18
Mental Math	27
Set Theory	51
Sequences	76

Technology

Is a quick game of Nintendo one of the ways you unwind? Do you have a library card? Are credit cards a part of your life or your parents' lives? If you answered yes to even one of these questions, perhaps you're already aware of the growing role technology plays in your everyday life.

In fact, calculators and computers have become so essential that it would be rare for your life not to be affected by these amazingly versatile machines. Schools, banks, department stores, hospitals, government offices — even police departments — rely heavily on technology to perform many important tasks.

The Technology pages in this text let you use technology to explore patterns, make conjectures, and discover mathematics. You will learn to use programs written in the BASIC computer language as well as computer software. You will also investigate mathematical concepts using scientific calculators and graphing calculators.

BASIC and Spreadsheets: Formulas 40
BASIC: Adding Fractions 79
MET: Solving Equations 121
BASIC: Successive Discounts 150
MET: Solving Inequalities 191
Spreadsheets: Volume and Surface Area 247
MET: Factoring 285
MET: Rational Expressions 315
Graphing Calculator: Graphing Linear Relations 384
MET: Graphing Linear Equations 427
Graphing Calculator: Systems of Equations 462
MET: Radical Equations 505
Graphing Calculator: Quadratic Equations 530
Graphing Calculator: Regression Lines 588
BASIC: Trigonometric Functions 637

MET (Mathematics Exploration Toolkit) was developed for IBM by Wicat Systems, Inc.

CHAPTER 3 Equations   92

3-1 Solving Equations by Using Addition 94
3-2 Solving Equations by Using Subtraction 99
3-3 Solving Equations by Using Multiplication and Division ... 103
    Mid-Chapter Review 107
3-4 Problem-Solving Strategy: Work Backwards 108
    Cooperative Learning Activity 110
3-5 Solving Equations Using More Than One Operation 111
    Puzzle 115
3-6 Solving Equations with the Variable on Both Sides 116
    Puzzle 120
    Technology: Solving Equations 121
3-7 More Equations 122
    History Connection 125
    Chapter Summary and Review 126
    Chapter Test 129
    College Entrance Exam Preview 130

CHAPTER 4 Applications of Rational Numbers   132

4-1 Ratios and Proportions 134
4-2 Percent 138
4-3 Application: Simple Interest 142
    Application: Compound Interest 145
4-4 Percent of Change 146
    Technology: Successive Discounts 150
4-5 Problem-Solving Strategy: Make a Table or Chart 151
    Cooperative Learning Activity 153
4-6 Application: Mixtures 154
    Mid-Chapter Review 157
4-7 Application: Uniform Motion 158
    Application: Travel Agents 161
4-8 Direct Variation 162
    History Connection: A'h-Mose 165
4-9 Inverse Variation 166
    Chapter Summary and Review 170
    Chapter Test 173

APPLICATIONS AND CONNECTIONS

APPLICATIONS

Aviation 95
Weightlifting 99
Finance 111, 142, 143
Biology 134
Models 135
Travel 136, 158
Sales 140, 146, 147, 148, 154
Chemistry 155
Uniform Motion 159
Space 162
Electronics 163
Music 166
Physics 167, 168

CONNECTIONS

Geometry 105, 117
Number Theory 113

CHAPTER 5 Inequalities 174

5-1 Solving Inequalities Using Addition and Subtraction 176
History Connection: Recorde, Harriot, and Oughtred 180
5-2 Solving Inequalities Using Multiplication and Division ... 181
Reading Algebra 185
5-3 Inequalities with More Than One Operation 186
Mid-Chapter Review 190
Technology: Solving Inequalities 191
5-4 Problem-Solving Strategy: Make a Diagram 192
Cooperative Learning Activity 193
5-5 Compound Sentences 194
5-6 Open Sentences Involving Absolute Value 199
Chapter Summary and Review 204
Chapter Test 207

CHAPTER 6 Polynomials 208

6-1 Problem-Solving Strategy: Look for a Pattern 210
Cooperative Learning Activity 212
6-2 Multiplying Monomials 213
6-3 Dividing Monomials 217
Reading Algebra 220
6-4 Scientific Notation 221
Application: Black Holes 225
6-5 Polynomials 226
Mid-Chapter Review 229
6-6 Adding and Subtracting Polynomials 230
History Connection: Emmy Noether 233
6-7 Multiplying a Polynomial by a Monomial 234
6-8 Multiplying Polynomials 238
Extra 242
6-9 Some Special Products 243
Application: Punnett Squares 246
Technology: Volume and Surface Area 247
Chapter Summary and Review 248
Chapter Test 251
College Entrance Exam Preview 252

POLLS OPEN 7 A.M. CLOSE 8 P.M.

POLLING PLACE

APPLICATIONS
AND CONNECTIONS

APPLICATIONS
Sports 178
Sales 183, 196
Machinery 201
Biology 222
Economics 222
Finance 227
Gardening 240

CONNECTIONS
Geometry 182, 213, 214,
                      231, 235
Statistics 188

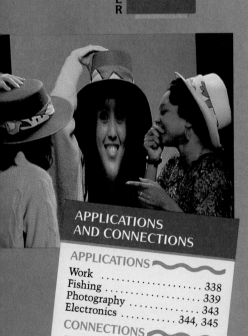

<table>

CHAPTER 7 **Factoring** 254

7-1	Factors and Greatest Common Factor	256
	History Connection: Eratosthenes	260
7-2	Factoring Using the Distributive Property	261
7-3	Factoring by Grouping	265
7-4	Problem-Solving Strategy: Guess and Check	269
	Cooperative Learning Activity	270
7-5	Factoring Trinomials	271
7-6	Factoring Differences of Squares	276
	Mid-Chapter Review	280
7-7	Perfect Squares and Factoring	281
	Technology: Factoring	285
7-8	Summary of Factoring	286
7-9	Solving Equations by Factoring	290
7-10	More Solving Equations by Factoring	295
	Chapter Summary and Review	300
	Chapter Test	303

CHAPTER 8 **Rational Expressions** 304

8-1	Simplifying Rational Expressions	306
	History Connection: Fractions	310
8-2	Multiplying Rational Expressions	311
	Technology: Rational Expressions	315
8-3	Dividing Rational Expressions	316
	Extra	318
8-4	Dividing Polynomials	319
8-5	Rational Expressions with Like Denominators	322
	Mid-Chapter Review	325
8-6	Problem-Solving Strategy: List Possibilities	326
	Cooperative Learning Activity	328
8-7	Rational Expressions with Unlike Denominators	329
8-8	Mixed Expressions and Complex Fractions	334
8-9	Solving Rational Equations	338
8-10	Application: Formulas	343
	Chapter Summary and Review	348
	Chapter Test	351

</table>

APPLICATIONS AND CONNECTIONS

APPLICATIONS

Work	338
Fishing	338
Photography	339
Electronics	343
	344, 345

CONNECTIONS

Geometry	262, 272, 278, 282, 287, 312, 323, 343
Number Theory	297

Special Features

How did algebra get its name? Read the **History Connection** on page 549 to find out. These features contain information about real people from the past and present and from many different cultures who have had a great influence on what you study in algebra today.

What does algebra have to do with genetics? The **Application** on page 246 can answer this question. In these features, you'll discover how algebra is used in most of the subjects you study in school as well as in your everyday life.

How can working together with my classmates help me solve problems? The fun, but challenging, problem presented in each **Cooperative Learning Activity** gives you an opportunity to cooperate, not compete, with other students.

History Connections

Sir William Rowan Hamilton 35
Sonya Kovalevskaya 78
Diophantus 125
A'h Mose 165
Recorde, Harriot, and Oughtred 180
Emmy Noether 233
Eratosthenes 260
Fractions 310
Rene Descartes 393
Benjamin Banneker 409
The K'iu-ch'ang Suan-shu 467
Jaime Escalante 481
Muhammed ibn Musa al Khwarizmi 549
Graunt and Bernoulli 593
Pythagoras 636

Applications

Meteorology 54
Compound Interest 145
Travel Agents 161
Black Holes 225
Punnett Squares 246
Escape Velocity 486

Cooperative Learning

Activities 43, 87, 110, 153, 193, 212, 270, 328, 393, 433, 441, 476, 539, 593, 616

CHAPTER 9 Functions and Graphs   352

9-1 Ordered Pairs 354
9-2 Relations 359
9-3 Equations as Relations 364
9-4 Graphing Linear Relations 369
9-5 Functions 374
    Mid-Chapter Review 375
9-6 Graphing Inequalities in Two Variables 379
    History Connection: René Descartes 383
    Technology: Graphing Linear Relations 384
9-7 Finding Equations from Relations 385
9-8 Problem-Solving Strategy: Use a Graph 389
    Cooperative Learning Activity 391
    Chapter Summary and Review 392
    Chapter Test 395
    College Entrance Exam Preview 396

CHAPTER 10 Graphing Linear Equations   398

10-1 Slope 400
10-2 Equations of Lines in Point-Slope and Standard Form 405
    History Connection: Benjamin Banneker 409
10-3 Slope-Intercept Form 410
10-4 Graphing Linear Equations 415
    Mid-Chapter Review 418
10-5 Writing Slope-Intercept Equations of Lines 419
10-6 Parallel and Perpendicular Lines 423
    Technology: Graphing Linear Equations 427
10-7 Midpoint of a Line Segment 428
10-8 Problem-Solving Strategy: Use a Graph 432
    Cooperative Learning Activity 433
    Chapter Summary and Review 434
    Chapter Test 437

APPLICATIONS AND CONNECTIONS

APPLICATIONS
Cartography 356
Career 366
Meteorology 371
Physics 376
Sales 380
Business 386
Statistics 390
Driving 400
Travel 411
Communication 416
Manufacturing 419

CONNECTIONS
Probability 361
Geometry 423, 428

CHAPTER 11   Systems of Open Sentences   438

11-1	Problem-Solving Strategy: Hidden Assumptions	440
	Cooperative Learning Activity	441
11-2	Graphing Systems of Equations	442
11-3	Substitution	447
11-4	Elimination Using Addition and Subtraction	452
	Mid-Chapter Review	456
11-5	Elimination Using Multiplication	457
	Technology: Systems of Equations	462
11-6	Graphing Systems of Inequalities	463
	History Connection: The *K'iu-ch'ang Suan-shu*	467
	Chapter Summary and Review	468
	Chapter Test	471

CHAPTER 12   Radical Expressions   472

12-1	Problem-Solving Strategy: Use a Table	474
	Cooperative Learning Activity	476
12-2	Square Roots	477
	History Connection: Jaime Escalante	481
12-3	The Pythagorean Theorem	482
	Application: Escape Velocity	486
12-4	Real Numbers	487
	Mid-Chapter Review	491
12-5	Simplifying Square Roots	492
12-6	Adding and Subtracting Radical Expressions	497
12-7	Radical Equations	501
	Technology: Radical Equations	505
12-8	The Distance Formula	506
	Chapter Summary and Review	510
	Chapter Test	513
	College Entrance Exam Preview	514

APPLICATIONS AND CONNECTIONS

APPLICATIONS

Metallurgy	448
Uniform Motion	454, 459
Banking	459
Agriculture	459
Plumbing	464
Construction	479
Electricity	484

CONNECTIONS

Geometry	444, 494, 497, 498, 507
Number Theory	449, 453, 502
Statistics	474

CHAPTER 13 Quadratics 516

13-1	Graphing Quadratic Functions	518
13-2	Solving Quadratic Equations by Graphing	523
13-3	Problem-Solving Strategy: Identify Subgoals	527
	Cooperative Learning Activity	529
13-4	Technology: Quadratic Equations	530
	Solving Quadratic Equations by Completing the Square	531
13-5	Solving Quadratic Equations by Using the Quadratic Formula	536
	Mid-Chapter Review	540
13-6	Using the Discriminant	541
13-7	Application: Solving Quadratic Equations	546
	History Connection: Muhammed ibn Musa al Khwarizmi	549
13-8	The Sum and Product of Roots	550
	Chapter Summary and Review	554
	Chapter Test	557

CHAPTER 14 Statistics and Probability 558

14-1	Statistics and Line Plots	560
14-2	Stem-and-Leaf Plots	565
14-3	Measures of Central Tendency	570
14-4	Measures of Variation	575
14-5	Box-and-Whisker Plots	579
14-6	Scatter Plots	583
	Mid-Chapter Review	587
	Technology: Regression Lines	588
14-7	Probability and Odds	589
	History Connection: Graunt and Bernoulli	593
14-8	Experimental Probability	594
14-9	Problem-Solving Strategy: Solve a Simpler Problem	598
	Cooperative Learning Activity	599
14-10	Compound Events	600
	Chapter Summary and Review	604
	Chapter Test	607

APPLICATIONS AND CONNECTIONS

APPLICATIONS

Finance	520, 576
Construction	533
Physics	538, 551
Manufacturing	547
Transportation	561
Income	566
Meteorology	570
Baseball	571
Sports	572
Fundraising	580
Weather	590
Civics	595

CONNECTIONS

Number Theory	524
Geometry	543, 546

College Entrance Exam Preview

What will you do after you graduate from high school? Go to college? Get a job? Join the armed forces? If college is for you, you need to get ready **now.** That's right — NOW!

To get into most colleges and universities, you need to take the SAT (Scholastic Aptitude Test) or the ACT (American College Test) in your junior or senior year of high school. To help you prepare for these tests and other similar tests, you can use the College Entrance Exam Previews given after every third chapter in this text. They are on pages 130-131, 252-253, 396-397, 514-515, and 642-643.

15 Trigonometry 608

15-1	Angles	610
15-2	Problem-Solving Strategy: Make a Model	615
	Cooperative Learning Activity	616
15-3	30°-60° Right Triangles	617
	Mid-Chapter Review	621
15-4	Similar Triangles	622
15-5	Trigonometric Ratios	626
15-6	Solving Right Triangles	632
	History Connection: Pythagoras	636
	Technology: Trigonometric Functions	637
	Chapter Summary and Review	638
	Chapter Test	641
	College Entrance Exam Preview	642

APPLICATIONS

Recreation	618
Construction	619, 633
Transportation	628
Physics	628
Forestry	633
Fishing	633

Tables	644
Skills Review	647
Glossary	664
Selected Answers	674
Index	698
Photo Credits	710

To The Teacher

The purpose of this 20-page *Teacher's Guide* is to provide an introduction to the format and philosophy of the ***Merrill Algebra Teacher's Wraparound Edition.*** It is also intended to relate some background information on several contemporary issues facing mathematics educators in the 1990s, such as the use of technology and alternative assessment strategies. Suggested time schedules for six-week and nine-week grading periods and clearly-defined instructional objectives are included to further make the learning of algebra smooth for both students and teachers.

Teacher's Guide Table of Contents

How to Use the Six-Step Teaching Plan in *Merrill Algebra* T18

Correlation of NCTM Standards to *Merrill Algebra* T20

Cooperative Learning T22

Problem Solving in Algebra T24

Using Manipulatives in Your Algebra Classroom T25

Integrating Technology into Your Algebra Classroom T26

Using the Graphing Calculator T28

Alternate Assessment Strategies T30

Meeting Individual Needs T32

Learning Objectives T33

Planning Your Algebra Course T36

How to Use the Six-Step Teaching Plan in Merrill Algebra

What do you search for when making a new textbook selection? You may search for a total program that is easy to teach. Your **Merrill Algebra Teacher's Wraparound Edition** delivers the collective teaching experience of its authors, consultants, and reviewers so that you will have the wealth of reliable information you search for. By furnishing you with an effective teaching model, this book saves you preparation time and energy. You, in turn, are free to spend that time and energy on your most important responsibility—your students.

As a professional, you will be pleased to find this program provides you with readily available activities to engage your students throughout the entire class period.

Each chapter begins with **Background Information** that gives

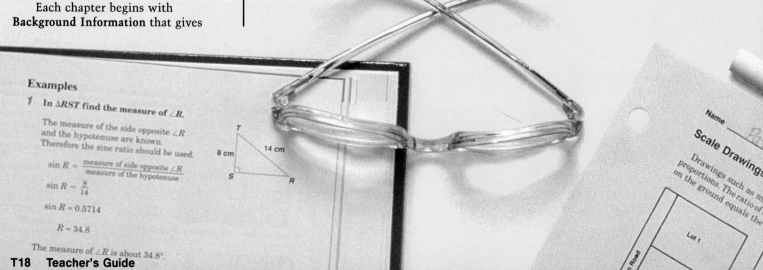

Connections and Applications provide you with real-world examples and exercises found in the chapter.

additional information about the career introduced in the Chapter Opener. A **Class Project** is also provided that is intended to be on-going throughout the chapter. The **Connections and Applications** chart provides you with a list of real-world

examples and exercises found in the chapter.

Each lesson includes a comprehensive six-part teaching plan that, when utilized consistently, makes it easy for you to teach and easy for your students to learn.

Examples

1 In △RST find the measure of ∠R.

The measure of the side opposite ∠R and the hypotenuse are known. Therefore the sine ratio should be used.

$$\sin R = \frac{\text{measure of side opposite } \angle R}{\text{measure of the hypotenuse}}$$

$$\sin R = \frac{8}{14}$$

$$\sin R = 0.5714$$

$$R \approx 34.8$$

The measure of ∠R is about 34.8°.

1 INTRODUCING THE LESSON

INTRODUCING THE LESSON, or the anticipatory set as it is sometimes called, is the first step of the **Merrill Algebra** teaching plan.

INTRODUCING THE LESSON begins with two pre-lesson activities to engage your students. The **5-Minute Check** includes one to five questions from the previous lesson. This allows you to check retention of skills and concepts. **Motivating the Lesson** helps prepare students for learning the day's lesson by piquing their interest. It is intended to help focus the attention of the class so the lesson can begin.

The latter activity may also provide time for students to interact with you, thus enabling you to modify the lesson to fit what students already know. This activity usually can be completed within the first five minutes of class and should be a direct lead-in to the concepts that will be presented. By focusing your students, you will provide the structural framework for what is to come.

2 TEACHING THE LESSON

TEACHING THE LESSON, the second step of the teaching plan, is the heart of any lesson. The primary aim of the **Merrill Algebra** teaching plan is to give you the tools to accomplish the admittedly difficult task of enabling your students to learn algebraic concepts. Effective **Teaching Tips** as well as **Chalkboard Examples** are provided in this part of the teaching cycle.

ALTERNATE TEACHING STRATEGIES provides you various methods of teaching the content of the lesson. These strategies include Using Cooperative Groups, Using Manipulatives, Using Technology, and Using Critical Thinking, just to name a few.

With the materials presented in the TEACHING THE LESSON step of the six-part teaching plan, your efficiency and productivity as a teacher will increase. The TEACHING THE LESSON step brings together the major elements that form a sound teaching approach.

3 EVALUATING THE LESSON

As a teacher, you work hard at making the transfer of knowledge as efficient and productive as it can be. One finding of educational researchers is that teachers who closely guide their students during a lesson are more effective. This third step provides **Checking for Understanding** and **Error Analysis** to assist you in identifying and correcting common student errors. **Closing the Lesson** provides you with a quick way of determining if students have mastered the objectives of the lesson and gives students an opportunity for direct communication in written, spoken, or modeled form.

4 RETEACHING THE LESSON

No matter how thoroughly a subject is covered in the classroom, there usually will be students who do not understand the lesson the first time it is taught. A **RETEACHING THE LESSON** activity is provided for every lesson as a way to teach the same concepts or facts differently so they will be more amenable to students' individual learning styles.

> **R**esearch shows that teachers who closely guide their students during a lesson are more effective.

5 APPLYING THE LESSON

A suggested **HOMEWORK ASSIGNMENT GUIDE** for three levels—Basic, Average, and Enriched—is provided for each lesson. In addition, **Teaching Tips** may be provided that give insight and hints into specific exercises.

6 EXTENDING THE LESSON

Every lesson has an **EXTENDING THE LESSON** activity that enriches and extends the concepts taught in the lesson.

As you review the Teacher's Wraparound Edition to **Merrill Algebra,** you will discover that you and your students are considered very important. With the enormous number of teaching tips and strategies provided by the **Teacher's Wraparound Edition,** you should be able to accomplish the goals of your curriculum with a minimum of time and effort. This is true whether you are teaching algebra for the first time, or whether you are a veteran teacher. The materials allow adaptability and flexibility so that student and curricular needs can be met. ∎

How Merrill Algebra 1 Meets the NCTM Standards

Content that relates to specific NCTM standards are found on the following Student Edition pages:

STANDARD 1:

MATHEMATICS AS PROBLEM SOLVING
10, 14, 18, 26, 27, 32, 36, 37, 41–43, 51, 56, 62, 66, 69, 76, 85, 86, 87, 95, 99, 108–111, 134–136, 140, 142, 143, 146–148, 151–155, 158–163, 166, 168, 178, 182, 183, 188, 192, 193, 196, 201, 210–214, 222, 227, 235, 240, 262, 269, 270, 272, 278, 282, 287, 297, 312, 323, 326–328, 338, 339, 343–345, 356, 361, 366, 371, 376, 380, 386, 389, 390, 397, 400, 411, 416, 419, 432, 433, 440, 441, 444, 448, 449, 453, 454, 459, 464, 474–476, 479, 484, 489, 497, 498, 502, 507, 520, 521, 524, 528, 529, 533, 535, 538, 543, 546, 547, 551, 561, 566, 570–572, 576, 580, 590, 595, 598, 599, 615, 616, 618, 628, 633, 638

STANDARD 2:

MATHEMATICS AS COMMUNICATION
11, 15, 20, 23, 29, 33, 37, 41, 52, 57, 63, 67, 71, 76, 82, 86, 97, 101, 105, 108, 113, 118, 123, 136, 140, 143, 148, 152, 155, 159, 164, 168, 178, 183, 188, 192, 197, 201, 211, 215, 219, 223, 228, 232, 235, 240, 245, 258, 262, 266, 269, 274, 278, 283, 288, 293, 297, 308, 313, 317, 320, 324, 327, 331, 336, 340, 345, 356, 361, 367, 371, 377, 381, 387, 390, 402, 407, 412, 416, 421, 425, 429, 432, 440, 444, 450, 454, 459, 465, 475, 479, 484, 489, 495, 499, 503, 508, 521, 525, 528, 534, 538, 544, 547, 552, 562, 567, 572, 577, 581, 591, 595, 599, 602, 612, 615, 619, 624, 629, 634

STANDARD 3:

MATHEMATICS AS REASONING
12, 16, 18, 21, 24, 30, 34, 39, 54, 58, 64, 68, 72, 77, 84, 98, 102, 107, 114, 119, 124, 137, 141, 149, 157, 161, 164, 169, 179, 184, 185, 189, 198, 199, 203, 216, 219, 224, 228, 233, 237, 241, 245, 264, 268, 275, 279, 284, 289, 294, 298, 309, 314, 317, 320, 324, 332, 337, 341, 347, 358, 363, 368, 372, 378, 382, 388, 404, 408, 414, 417, 422, 426, 430, 446, 451, 455, 460, 466, 480, 490, 496, 500, 504, 509, 522, 526, 535, 539, 545, 549, 553, 564, 569, 574, 578, 582, 587, 592, 596, 603, 614, 620, 625, 630, 635

STANDARD 4:

MATHEMATICAL CONNECTIONS
10, 14, 18, 26, 27, 32, 36, 37, 51, 56, 62, 66, 69, 76, 95, 99, 111, 134–136, 140, 142, 143, 146–148, 154, 155, 158, 159, 162, 163, 166–168, 178, 182, 183, 188, 196, 201, 213, 214, 222, 227, 235, 240, 262, 272, 278, 282, 287, 297, 312, 323, 338, 339, 343–345, 356, 361, 366, 371, 376, 380, 386, 390, 400, 411, 416, 419, 444, 448, 449, 453, 454, 459, 464, 474, 479, 484, 489, 497, 498, 502, 507, 520, 524, 533, 538, 543, 546, 561, 566, 570–572, 580, 590, 595, 618, 619, 628, 633

STANDARD 5:

ALGEBRA

8-22, 26-30, 32, 36-43, 45, 50-53, 55, 56, 60-64, 66, 69, 76, 85-89, 94-129, 134-136, 140, 142, 143, 146-148, 151-155, 158, 159, 162, 163, 166-168, 176-191, 195-207, 210-214, 218-220, 222, 227, 235, 240, 262, 269, 270, 272, 278, 282, 287, 290-299, 302, 312, 323, 326-328, 338-347, 350, 354, 356, 359-362, 366, 369-373, 375, 376, 380, 384, 386, 389-391, 393, 397, 400-405, 410-419, 421-427, 432, 433, 435, 440-449, 453, 454, 459, 463-466, 468, 470, 474-476, 479, 484, 489, 492-504, 506-509, 511, 512, 520, 521, 523-526, 528, 529, 531-540, 546-549, 554, 555, 560-564, 578, 579, 583-587, 598, 599, 604, 606, 615, 616, 637, 638

STANDARD 6:

FUNCTIONS

353, 374-378, 385-391

STANDARD 7:

GEOMETRY FROM A SYNTHETIC PERSPECTIVE

10, 14, 16, 32, 36-40, 105, 117, 118, 166, 182, 185, 247, 278, 279, 354, 383, 414, 423-426, 428-431, 436, 446, 473, 479, 482-486, 494, 497, 498, 507, 510, 543, 546, 547, 555, 610-614, 617-641

STANDARD 8:

GEOMETRY FROM AN ALGEBRAIC PERSPECTIVE

10, 14, 16, 32, 36-40, 105, 117, 118, 166, 182, 185, 203, 213, 214, 231, 232, 235, 236, 237, 245, 247, 263, 264, 267, 268, 272, 275, 278, 279, 282, 284, 287, 298, 354, 383, 414, 423-426, 428-431, 436, 444, 446, 473, 479, 480, 482-486, 490, 494, 496, 497, 498, 504, 507, 508, 510, 534, 535, 543, 544, 545, 546, 547, 549, 555, 578, 587, 610-614, 617-641

STANDARD 9:

TRIGONOMETRY

608-641

STANDARD 10:

STATISTICS

78, 114, 141, 188, 189, 203, 309, 321, 337, 363, 390, 455, 474, 486, 526, 558-588, 625, 631

STANDARD 11:

PROBABILITY

198, 328, 361, 363, 589-603

STANDARD 12:

DISCRETE MATHEMATICS

19-21, 51, 194-196, 389-391, 432, 433, 589-603

STANDARD 13:

CONCEPTUAL UNDERPINNINGS OF CALCULUS

518-522, 554

STANDARD 14:

MATHEMATICAL STRUCTURE

51, 369, 488, 489, 518-524

Cooperative Learning

"The best answer to the question, 'What is the most effective method of teaching?' is that it depends on the goal, the student, the content, and the teacher. But the next best answer is, 'Students teaching other students.' There is a wealth of evidence that peer teaching is extremely effective for a wide range of goals, content, and students of different levels and personalities."

Wilbert McKeachie, et al, 1986

Cooperative learning groups *learn* things together, not just do things together. Studies show that cooperative learning promotes more learning than competitive or individual learning experiences regardless of student age, subject matter, or learning activity. More difficult learning tasks, such as problem solving, critical thinking, and conceptual learning, come out far ahead when cooperative strategies are used. Studies also show that in classroom settings, adolescents learn more from each other about subject matter than from the teacher.

The basic elements of a cooperative learning group are as follows:
(1) Students must perceive that they "sink or swim together."
(2) Students are responsible for everyone else in the group, as well as themselves, in learning the assigned material.
(3) Students must see that they all have the same goal, that they need to divide up the tasks and share the responsibility equally, and that they will be given one evaluation or reward that will apply to all members of the group.

General guidelines and suggestion for implementing cooperative learning in your algebra classroom are provided on this page and the next. In addition, specific guidelines are provided in the teacher material that precedes each chapter. The **Teacher Resource Package**

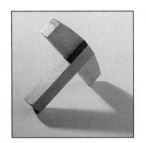

More difficult learning tasks, such as problem solving and critical thinking, come out far ahead when cooperative strategies are used.

also contains a Cooperative Learning Activity in the Activities Booklet that can be used with each chapter.

Preparation and Social Skills

1. *Arrange your room.* Students in groups should face each other as they work together. It is helpful to number the tables so you can refer to groups by number, or have groups choose a name.

2. *Decide on the size of the group.* Groups work best when teams are composed of two to five students. The materials available might dictate the size of the group.

3. *Assign students to groups.* Each group should be mixed socially, racially, ethnically, sexually, and by learning abilities. Occasionally a student may insist on working alone. This student usually changes his or her mind when seeing that everyone else's grades are better, and the groups are having more fun.

4. *Prepare students for cooperation.* This is a critical step. Tell students about the rationale, procedures, and expected outcomes of this method of instruction. Students need to know that you are not forcing them to be friends, but asking them to work together as they will later on in life with people who come together for a specific purpose.

5. *Plan Teaching Materials.* Distributing materials can help you communicate that the activity is to be a group and not an individual activity. You can provide only one set of materials or one copy of the worksheet to the group. Group members will quickly realize that they need to work together if they are to be successful. You can vary this by providing each member with a worksheet but collect only one of them.

6. *Explain group tasks.* For more activities, each group will need someone to take notes, someone to summarize as the group progresses, and someone to make sure everyone is involved. Classes that have less experience using these methods may need these roles assigned to group members at the beginning of each activity. These jobs should be done by different students each time, so that one student does not feel burdened doing the same job all the time.

7. *Explain the day's lesson.* On the chalkboard or overhead, write the following headings:

■ *Form Groups:* List the number of students in each group.

■ *Topic of the Day:* general academic topic.

■ *Task:* title of activity. At this time, go over instructions and relate the work to previous learning.

■ *Goal:* Indicate whether students will all do individual work of which you will select one person's paper or product to grade, or whether they will produce only one product per group. Student signatures on all the work indicates that they will accept the collected work for their grade.

■ *Cooperative Skills:* List the specific group skills you will be checking. Start with one or two basic skills. The following skills start from basic and move to more advanced.

a. Use quiet voices.

b. Encourage each other to participate.

c. Use each other's names. Use eye contact.

d. Ask your teacher for help only after you have decided as a group that you all need help.

e. Stress that all student contributions are valuable.

After students have some experience working in cooperative groups, you can expect group members to exhibit some or all of the following higher level cooperative skills.

a. Express support and acceptance, both verbal and nonverbal, through eye contact, enthusiasm, and praise.

b. Ask for help or clarification about what is happening.

c. Suggest new ideas.

d. Use appropriate humor that stays on task.

e. Describe feelings using "I messages," such as, "I like the way you praised my idea."

f. Summarize and elaborate on what others have contributed.

g. Develop memory aids and analogies that are clever ways of remembering important points.

h. Criticize ideas, not people.

i. Go beyond the first answer to a question.

Teacher Responsibilities During Cooperative Group Work

1. *Monitor student behavior.* Use a formal observation sheet to count the number of times you observe the behavior expected on that particular assignment for each group. Start with a few behaviors at the beginning and move up to many different behaviors when you feel comfortable doing so. Share your observations with each group.

2. *Provide assistance with the task.* Clarify instructions, review concepts, or answer questions. You will find students who see you nearby will automatically start asking questions. Your first response should be, "Have you asked everyone in the group?"

Your role will be supportive supervisor rather than direct supervisor; you will help a group that has gotten stuck and is experiencing a high level of frustration. You might do this by asking a few open-ended questions. In a conflict situation, you might ask the group to identify the reason for the difficulty and ask them to come up with some strategies for handling the conflict.

3. *Intervene to teach cooperative skills.* As you observe that some groups have more problems than others with cooperative skills, you may wish to intervene by asking the group to think about why they are not being effective and have them work toward a solution.

4. *Provide closure for the lesson.* Students should be asked to summarize what they have learned and be able to relate it to what they have previously studied. You may want to review the main points and ask students to give examples. You should also answer any final questions.

5. *Evaluate the group process.* In order for groups to be aware of their progress in learning to work together, they must be given time to evaluate or process how they are working together. Allow a few minutes at the end of the lesson for groups to decide if they achieved the criterion you set up. Have them rate themselves on a

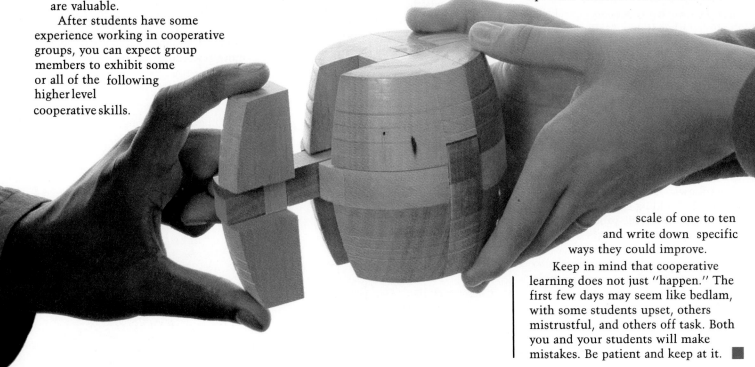

scale of one to ten and write down specific ways they could improve.

Keep in mind that cooperative learning does not just "happen." The first few days may seem like bedlam, with some students upset, others mistrustful, and others off task. Both you and your students will make mistakes. Be patient and keep at it. ■

Problem Solving in Algebra

One of the challenges of teaching mathematics is helping students learn to solve problems. Problem solving involves more than solving verbal problems—it also involves the ability to analyze a new problem and discover a way to solve it.

Algebra is a very useful tool for solving problems. Many verbal problems can be easily solved by translating the problem into an equation. This involves many skills which must be developed gradually—reading and exploring the problem, defining a variable, writing an equation, solving the equation, interpreting the result, and checking the solution. In this text, these skills are introduced in Lessons 1–8 and 2–8.

Not all problems in real-life can be solved by using an equation. Sometimes there is no "clear-cut" method of solution. Thus, it is important for students to learn alternative strategies for solving problems. This text includes numerous *Problem-Solving Strategy* lessons that illustrate various strategies, such as guess-and-check (p. 269). Other strategies are introduced in *Problem-Solving Strategy* lessons on pages 85, 108, 151, 192, 210, 326, 389, 434, 442, 476, 527, 598, and 615. The four-step problem-solving plan can be used to solve *any* type of problem, using *any* strategy.

It is important to create a classroom environment which encourages problem-solving abilities. The following suggestions should be helpful in building students' confidence in solving problems:

- Encourage students to try a variety of strategies. Praise them for suggesting ways to approach a problem, even if the suggestions do not lead to a correct result. Also, spend time "looking back" at problems which were previously

1. EXPLORE *the problem.* Read the problem and identify what is given and what is asked. Jot down important facts from the problem. Sometimes it is helpful to draw a chart or diagram. Think about how the facts are related.

If an equation will be used to solve the problem, choose a variable to represent one of the unspecified numbers in the problem. Read the problem again and use the variable in writing expressions for other unspecified numbers in the problem.

2. PLAN *the solution.* Many different strategies may be used. If an equation will be used to solve the problem, read the problem again. Decide how the unspecified numbers relate to other given information. Write an equation to represent the relationship.

3. SOLVE *the problem.* This involves doing the mathematics and interpreting the answer. If an equation was written, solve the equation and interpret the solution. State the answer to the verbal problem.

4. EXAMINE *the solution.* Check whether the answer makes sense with the conditions of the problem. If not, check your mathematics again. If the mathematics was correct, a mistake was made in "setting up" the problem. In that case, explore the problem again and try a different approach.

solved and discuss alternative ways to solve the problems.

- Assume that students will make mistakes when solving verbal problems. An evaluation system which gives partial credit for thoughtful attempts is recommended. For example, you could award 4 points for a correct solution, 3 points for a solution which has the right process but had a small mathematical error, 2 points for a thoughtful attempt with a mistake in "setting up" the solution, and 1 point for other meaningful attempts.
- Allow sufficient time for the class to explore problems. In some cases it is preferable to spend twice the time on half the problems. Although discussions may seem to move slowly, the extra time will give students more confidence.
- Throughout the year, emphasize the steps for solving problems. A chart listing the steps could be displayed on the bulletin board, along with a problem for students to solve in their spare time. Problems could be chosen from this text, or from other sources such as *The Mathematics Teacher.*

If the suggestions on this page are followed, problem solving will become more rewarding and enjoyable. ■

Using Manipulatives in Your Algebra Classroom

Most teachers agree that the use of manipulative materials helps students build a solid understanding of mathematical concepts and enhances students' achievement in mathematics. The universal anxiety today about achievement in mathematics should prompt educators in this field to heed results from recent studies which indicate that by using manipulative materials at every level, test scores are dramatically improved.

"Manipulative materials are the key to understanding operations and algorithms."[1] Because abstractions are an integral part of algebra and because students derive their abstract ideas primarily from their experience, it is imperative that they experiment with a variety of manipulative materials on the concrete level to develop an understanding of algebraic symbols and concepts.

> **The purpose of using manipulatives is to assist students in bridging the gap from the concrete to the abstract.**

Many teachers find that demonstrations on an overhead projector ease students with little experience in hands-on learning into working with manipulatives. Simply observing such a demonstration, however, is not enough. Follow-up activities that involve the students in the act of physically manipulating such aids are essential if students are to experience the patterns and relations inherent in mathematics.

"The purpose of using manipulatives is to assist students in bridging the gap from their own concrete environment to the abstract level."[2] Affording students the opportunity for meaningful practice through modeling algorithms with manipulatives not only results in greater understanding of the concepts and skills in question but also provides a fun alternative to everyday, routine problem-solving exercises as well.

Merrill Algebra contains many opportunities for students to use manipulatives to discover and explore algebraic concepts. Students actually *do* mathematics and are encouraged to make conjectures based on their observations. The **Merrill Algebra Lab Manual** contains numerous activities that require the use of manipulatives, allowing students to make the connection from the concrete to the abstract.

To make sure that students understand what is expected of each activity, the teacher must discuss its goal and model how the manipulative is to be used to achieve it. Encouraging students to suggest ways in which manipulatives can be used helps them to relate concepts and to develop mathematical insights.

The important thing to keep in mind is that most students do not automatically abstract the concepts they explore with materials; they must be led to see how the concepts relate to traditional algorithms. Summarizing and recording group activity results helps to focus on such relationships and algebraic concepts. Used in this way, manipulative materials are a justifiable means to a desirable end.

No presentation advocating the use of manipulative materials in the algebra classroom would be totally complete without interjecting a note of caution. Despite the fact that manipulative materials are highly touted, and rightly so, they can, if used incorrectly, undo much of the good for which they are intended. Through careless or erroneous use of manipulatives, students might conclude that there are two distinct mathematical worlds—one of manipulatives and another of symbols—and that each has its own rules.

Teachers must, therefore, direct students to see the need for precise and exact connection between the symbols and the manipulatives; otherwise they cannot possibly develop proper mathematical understanding. The point that must be stressed repeatedly in teaching with manipulatives in the algebra classroom is that "symbols and manipulatives must always reflect the same concept."[3]

If mathematics educators sincerely want to challenge their students in the algebra classroom, perhaps they must first endorse the fact that the use of manipulative materials holds the promise of increasing students' understanding of and achievement in mathematics, and then translate that belief into classroom practice. ■

1. Beattie, Ian D., "Modeling Operations and Algorithms," *Arithmetic Teacher*, February 1986, p. 24.
2. Hynes, Michael C., "Selection Criteria," *Arithmetic Teacher*, February 1986, p. 11.
3. Bright, George W., "One Point of View: Using Manipulatives," *Arithmetic Teacher*, February 1986, p. 4.

Integrating Technology Into Your Algebra Classroom

"Students today can't prepare bark to calculate their problems. They depend upon their slates which are more expensive. What will they do when their slate is dropped and it breaks? They will be unable to write!"

Teachers' Conference, 1703

The above quote seems ridiculous today, but in 1703 it was not. Many people may ask, "Couldn't they see enough into the future to know that slates would be required?"; but as the old adage goes, hindsight is twenty-twenty. The difficulty lies in foreseeing the future.

The argument nowadays is in regard to computers and calculators; and while most people agree that technology should be used in the mathematics classroom, few are offering ideas on incorporation, testing, appropriate use, and other areas where teachers have questions. Some use this as an argument against using technology, but that is not the answer to the problem. Instead we must be able to recognize a good idea when we see one and adopt it for our classrooms.

Appropriate Use of Technology

There are many different ideas and definitions of "appropriate use of technology," and rightly so. Every class and every teacher is different. What is appropriate and works for one may not be appropriate or work for another. However, there are some classifications and generalizations that can be made for different grade levels. Keep in mind that many of your students are just learning the technology. You should refrain from getting "high-tech" with them. Give them opportunities for success early so that they can begin to feel comfortable with technology.

Have your students complete an easy calculation for their first encounter. For the students new to technology, this will give them a sense of accomplishment because they can see something they have done; for the more technologically experienced students, this will give them a sense of confidence because they already know what is being done.

At any level of teaching, try to get students to make generalizations about what they see or do with technology.

Using Technology in Your Classroom

Technology opens up many new ideas and opportunities. It is up to you to decide how to present and use technology in your classroom. Many of the standard teaching techniques are appropriate, such as using cooperative groups, or having students work in pairs, but there are also new ways of teaching that are appropriate

when using technology in your classroom. For example, you can assign lab partners in each class. Each pair of students would then work together whenever technology is used. This can also be used if you have a limited supply of equipment.

Teaching Aids

There are many technological teaching aids as well as numerous products to assist in the teaching of technology. One of them is a projection panel for the overhead projector. This can be used in conjunction with a demonstration computer and can project the image from the computer onto a screen or wall.

Overhead projector calculators are also available for most models. They can serve the same purpose as a projection panel and demonstration computer.

Another teaching aid is a template of the computer or calculator keyboard that can be used on the overhead or put on the bulletin board

---

Technology teaches students in a way that piques their interest and leads to questions that show a desire to learn.

for easy reference. (Masters for the TI-34 and TI-81 calculators are provided on pages 9 and 10 in the *Merrill Algebra Lab Manual*.) This can help in conveying the location of keys, especially second function keys on graphing calculators.

Changes in the Classroom

There will be some changes in your classroom with the onset of technology. One will be your role. It most likely will change from leader to guide. Students will begin to do things on their own and it will be up to you to keep them headed in the right direction. Students will also begin to ask more questions, including more higher-order questions, than before.

You may not have all the answers, but the investigation can be enjoyable and enlightening for both you and your students.

Advantages of Technology

Probably the biggest advantage of technology is the amount of time it can save you. The ease of editing errors, the number of graphs and pictures that can be drawn in a short amount of time, the speed of calculating; all these and other time-saving advantages make technology a major plus for the mathematics classroom.

There are numerous other advantages. One is that students will have a deeper understanding of the concepts being taught. As we develop toward a more pictorial society, students are becoming visual learners. Technology teaches them in a way that piques their interest and leads to questions that show a desire to learn.

Another advantage of technology is the cooperative efforts that develop among students. Since students will most likely need to work with others when they become members of the work force, it is best for them to learn to work with others while they are in school. With technology, you can teach your students to work cooperatively, which will benefit them in college and in their careers.

Technology Fears

Perhaps the biggest fear, and certainly one that is most often expressed, is that of the technology taking the place of the teacher. *This will never happen.* There is no way that a computer can do what a teacher does, and in particular, sense what a teacher can. For example, no computer can sense uncertainty of an answer in a student's tone of voice. Few students will be able to turn on a calculator or computer and teach themselves with it. They need teachers to explain the technology and to help make connections.

You can also see the evidence of needing the teacher when you relate the use of technology in education to its use in the business world. Computers have been in the mainstream of business for quite some time now, and there has not been a reduction in the number of persons needed. Yet a large number of business executives will tell you they would not want to do their job without the use of a computer. Many teachers who have incorporated technology into their classrooms are saying the same thing.

Computers and calculators are excellent tools for teaching mathematics concepts. Though there are still some who argue their use in the classroom, none can argue their educational advantage. Technology can teach students in ways that were never before possible. In the past, teachers could only dream of being able to do some of the things that they can now do with ease, thanks to technology. While incorporating technology into your mathematical classroom can be difficult at first, in the long run, it will definitely pay off for both you and your students.

Specific guidelines and instructions for using Casio graphing calculators and the TI-81 graphing calculator are provided on pages T28–29.

Using the Graphing Calculator

Incorporating the graphing calculator into your mathematics classroom may seem like an arduous task, but it may be easier than you think. And the results will be very rewarding. Once your students are familiar with using the technology, they may begin to respond to math in a way that you have never seen before. Because the graphing calculator is a visual teaching tool, many of today's students work well with it. You can definitely use this to your advantage.

There are some things that you can do to make teaching the use of the graphing calculator easier, both for yourself and for your students. For example, one of the most helpful teaching aids is an overhead transparency of the graphing calculator keyboard. If you are using the TI-81 graphing calculator, there is a picture of the calculator in the front of the TI-81 manual. You may want to make an enlarged copy of it and make a transparency of the keyboard from that. The *Merrill Algebra Lab Manual* (pages 9 and 10) also includes a master of both the TI-34 and the TI-81 calculator layout from which you can make a transparency. If you are using a Casio calculator, there is also a picture of it in the Casio manual.

Enlarging these pictures and making overlays of them will help you show your students where keys are if they are having trouble finding them or if you are explaining a lesson and need to demonstrate your keystrokes. You can also make a large poster of the calculator's keyboard and hang it in a visible location in the classroom. One of your students may like to do this for extra credit, or someone may just enjoy doing it.

Using graphing calculators in your classroom can bring your students together and can help them learn to help each other solve problems.

In the beginning, many of your students will be looking at a graphing calculator for the first time in their lives, and they may be scared by what they see. A graphing calculator may seem like something they will not be able to understand or something that will be too difficult for them to use. As a start with the calculator, have them draw a graph that has just a few keystrokes, like $y = x$. This way they can see their accomplishments and they may realize that the calculator is not as difficult to use as they thought. Then go step-by-step with them as they progress into doing more difficult problems with the calculator.

In **Merrill Algebra 1**, there are four graphing calculator lessons. The chapters in which they occur and their titles are listed below.

Chapter 10: Graphing Linear Relations
Chapter 11: Systems of Equations
Chapter 13: Quadratic Equations
Chapter 14: Regression Lines

You will most likely need to have a "get to know the graphing calculator" session before you teach one of the lessons in the text. This session should help the students become comfortable with the calculator and should cover

some basic graphing techniques, like how to graph a function. For example, if you wanted the students to graph the function $y = 2x + 4$, you can have them key in GRAPH 2 ALPHA X + 4 EXE if they are using Casio's and Y= 2 X|T + 4 ENTER if they are using TI-81s. Use the default viewing window of [−10, 10] by [−10, 10] with scale factors of 1 for each axis.

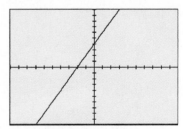

It would also be a good idea to discuss range and scale with your students. Having a thorough understanding of these concepts early will help your students immensely with graphing in the future and with understanding and interpreting graphs now. Ask your students if a range of [−10, 10] by [−5, 5] with scale factors of 1 on each axis is the same as a range of [−20, 20] by [−10, 10] with scale factors of 2 on each axis. Have your students look at each screen on the calculator. Explain to them that it is not the same even though each range looks the same. Have them graph $y = x^2$ in each range value to illustrate the difference. This is a good illustration of the concept of scale. If your students are still having difficulty with the concepts, use visual aids as well as examples. Graph the equation $y = 2x + 4$ in different viewing windows. This is also a good lead-in to the zoom process.

You may also find that the atmosphere and environment of your classroom will change. It may become a cooperative environment instead of a competitive one. Using graphing calculators in your classroom can bring your students together and can help them learn to help each other solve problems. This may change your role from instructor to guide, and your classroom may also change into a "working" environment where the

students experiment to find solutions to problems, not just ask for an answer.

While it may take some time for your students and yourself to feel comfortable using the graphing calculator in class, both of you will probably enjoy using them eventually. The use of technology will also help your students get a good start in the highly technical world that we live in today. ■

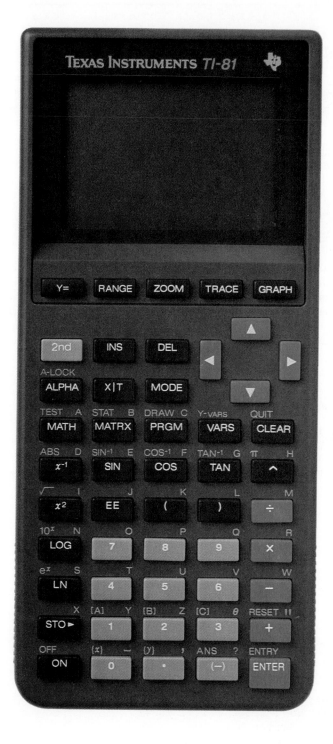

Alternate Assessment Strategies

Most students today will agree that the test is seen as the bottom line of the educational enterprise. Most of them will also agree that the present tests used to determine a student's accomplishment often fall short of the goal of measuring a student's understanding of ideas.

The vast array of testing devices today which, for the most part, center around multiple choice answers, true/false responses, and objective one-word answers, may be little more than mechanical ways of evaluating that focus on a student's ability to cough up answers on cue. They may reveal little to either the student or the teacher of the student's capabilities.

"Mathematics teachers are participating in a major restructuring of the goals and practices of mathematics education. It is essential that assessment strategies be found that can adequately reflect this new conception of the subject."[1]

Many formal assessment strategies may be rooted in informal assessment: that is, the garnering of information concomitant with instruction. Informal assessments are invaluable in the sense that they provide a realistic picture of student ability in a context where such ability is put to immediate use.

When educational goals are confined to the duplication of mathematical procedures, then conventional paper-and-pencil tests are adequate for assessing a learner's level of performance. But as our educational objectives broaden in scope, assessment should go beyond this. Assessments should now be extended for the purpose of guiding the actions of not just the student but of all those persons involved in the learning experience.

What Are the Alternatives?

There is a plethora of devices whereby the teacher of mathematics may expand his or her repertoire of assessment strategies. These include the use of questioning, observation, and journals.

Open-ended Questions Perhaps one of the easiest strategies to employ is that of open-ended questions which will permit students to more fully elaborate their knowledge of mathematical concepts and principles. In an assessment of this nature, students are forced to think for themselves and to express mathematical ideas in language that corresponds with their mathematical development.

The teacher has several options for scoring open-ended questions but the two most frequently used methods are analytic and holistic. Holistic scoring seems to be favored because judgement is based on the response as a whole, as opposed to analytic scoring, which evaluates answers on

Informal assessments provide a realistic picture of student ability in a context where such ability is put to immediate use.

the basis of specific points that have been addressed in the student's responses.

Classroom Observation

Documenting classroom observations is another strategic device for assessing student achievement. During the course of the instructional process, most teachers are quite adept at forming rather accurate opinions concerning the capabilities of their students which, in many instances, a later formal assessment will bear out or validate. Such observations, however, are very often not accorded the status of a test because they have not been formally structured and systematically recorded. Yet the quality of such informal assessment is in many cases superior to that obtained by formal testing. By simply implementing some structure into such observations, teachers can capitalize on this information for assessment purposes and at the same time dispense with other time-consuming and often unproductive forms of evaluation.

Questioning provides an excellent tool for assessing the competence of students as well as for monitoring the development of meaningful understanding. Dialogue of this nature between teacher and student is most beneficial in identifying errors in comprehension (reading and otherwise), in transformation, and in the use of process skills. "Research has indicated that at least 40% of students' errors on written mathematical problems occur before they even get to use the process skills their teachers have so laboriously stressed."[2]

Self-evaluation One of the most valuable strategies we might implement is that of enabling students to monitor their own progress. This procedure calls for the student to write confidential answers to teacher questions regarding the way he or she feels in the class, what he or she would most like help with, and how mathematics class might be changed with an eye toward improving his or her skills.

Along the same lines, utilizing tests to which students have contributed questions not only makes for an effective revision strategy, it also provides students with a sense of ownership in the assessment process.

Portfolios and Journals Yet another means to assess student progress is to require students to periodically submit samples of their work in portfolios. Again, students might be

asked to keep a daily journal in which they describe what they have learned and reflect on the material covered. Regular perusal of the journal can guide teaching procedures and serve as the basis for individual student-teacher conferences.

Daily Assessment Lastly, the mathematics class lends itself quite easily to carrying out practical tests—demonstrating skills in a practice situation. Your **Merrill Algebra Teacher's Wraparound Edition** contains an assessment option in each lesson plan. Student understanding can be evaluated through writing, modeling, or speaking activities. Since the skills are assessed in practice, they provide immediate feedback as well as enhanced motivation for students who are usually most eager to show off (correctly or not!) what they can do.

Although there are undoubtedly situations when the written test is effective, we must guard against using it to the exclusion of other forms of assessment. The examiner must select, from among the many strategic techniques available, that one which will best indicate what his or her students can do. ■

1. Clarke, David J., Doug M. Clarke, and Charles J. Lovitt, "Changes in Mathematics Teaching Call for Assessment Alternatives," *Teaching and Learning Mathematics in the 1990s*, (1990 Yearbook, Reston VA: NCTM, 1990), p. 118.
2. Ibid., p. 123.

Meeting Individual Needs

"We cannot afford to have the majority of our population mathematically illiterate: Equity has become an economic necessity."

NCTM Standards (1989, p. 4)

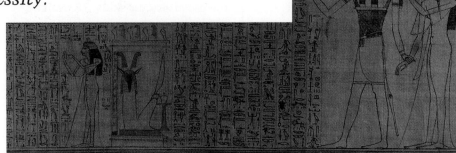

Multicultural Perspective

There is no doubt that the United States is a multicultural society. Changing demographics, and changing economic and social orders are having a tremendous impact on the schools in this country. But, the term *multicultural* represents more than just *many cultures*. There is a multicultural basis to all knowledge, even mathematics.

From the ancient Egyptians, who used the "Pythagorean" theorem fifteen hundred years *before* Pythagoras, to the ancient Chinese, who calculated the value of π to ten places twelve hundred years *before* the Europeans, mathematics as we know it today has been shaped by many cultures. Even the term *algebra* was contributed by an Arabian mathematician, Al-Khowarizmi.

What is the role of the mathematics educator in all this? Students should have the opportunity to learn about persons from all cultures who have contributed to the development of mathematics. In addition, students should learn about persons from all cultures who have been successful in their respective careers. To this end, the *Merrill Algebra Activities Masters Booklet* contains one multicultural worksheet for each chapter.

As educators, we also must prepare all students for the new jobs of the future that will require mathematical literacy. The mathematics teacher must be in the vanguard of those who demand that *all* students be given the opportunity to study the more advanced forms of mathematics. It is our responsibility as educators to make every effort to prepare the students of today to participate in the complex world of tomorrow.

Limited English Proficiency Needs

One of the greatest factors contributing to the under-achievement in mathematics education for the language-minority student is his or her failure to understand the language of instruction. There are, however, strategies which the mathematics teacher can employ to help overcome the obstacles that beset language-minority students.

Ideally, these students would be afforded the opportunity of having new concepts and skills reinforced by discussing them in their native tongue. It may be that a bilingual teacher could meet this need, or perhaps a tutor proficient in the language could be procured to provide such service.

If the student is proficient in his or her native language, perhaps materials written in that language could be provided to supplement classroom instruction.

If the student is not especially literate in his or her own language, perhaps an oral approach using pictorial materials and/or manipulative devices would be feasible.

When a student does not respond to the prescribed expectations of the school, the teacher needs to substitute developmentally equivalent tasks to shape development. If, for example, the student does not participate in classroom discussion, the wise teacher will observe his or her verbal interaction with other students in informal, less structured environments.

Because students coming from diverse cultural backgrounds lack common educational experiences, the teacher soon recognizes that the only way to establish a basis for communication is to begin instruction with content that is familiar to one and all.

"The challenge is to find personally interesting and culturally relevant ways of creating new contexts for children, contexts in which the mastery of school skills can be meaningful and rewarding."[1]

By integrating the development of language in such new contexts, we may be able to open the door to the challenging and exciting world of mathematics for the language-minority student. ■

---

1. Bowman, Barbara T., "Educating Language-Minority Children: Challenges and Opportunities," *Phi Delta Kappan*, October 1989, p. 120.

Learning Objectives

1   An Introduction to Algebra

1-1A: Translate verbal expressions into mathematical expressions.

1-1B: Write an expression containing identical factors as an expression using exponents.

1-2: Use the order of operations to evaluate expressions.

1-3: Solve open sentences by performing arithmetic operations.

1-4: Recognize and use the properties of identity and equality.

1-5: Use the distributive property to simplify expressions.

1-6: Recognize and use the commutative and associative properties when simplifying expressions.

1-7: Translate verbal expressions into equations and formulas.

1-8: Explore problem situations by asking and answering questions.

2   Rational Numbers

2-1A: State the coordinate of a point on a number line.

2-1B: Graph integers on a number line.

2-1C: Add integers by using a number line.

2-2A: Find the absolute value of a number.

2-2B: Add integers without using a number line.

2-2C: Subtract integers.

2-3A: Compare numbers.

2-3B: Write inequalities for graphs on number lines.

2-3C: Graph inequalities on number lines.

2-4A: Compare rational numbers.

2-4B: Write rational numbers in increasing or decreasing order.

2-4C: Find a number between two rational numbers.

2-5A: Add two or more rational numbers.

2-5B: Subtract rational numbers.

2-5C: Simplify expressions that contain rational numbers.

2-6: Multiply rational numbers.

2-7: Divide rational numbers.

2-8A: Define variables and write equations for verbal problems.

2-8B: Write verbal problems from equations.

3   Equations

3-1: Solve equations by using addition.

3-2: Solve equations by using subtraction.

3-3A: Solve equations by using multiplication.

3-3B: Solve equations by using division.

3-4: Solve problems by working backwards.

3-5: Solve equations involving more than one operation.

3-6A: Solve equations with the variable on both sides.

3-6B: Solve equations containing grouping symbols.

3-7A: Solve equations containing fractions or decimals.

3-7B: Solve equations containing more than one variable.

4   Applications of Rational Numbers

4-1: Solve proportions.

4-2: Solve percent problems.

4-3: Solve problems involving simple interest.

4-4A: Solve problems involving percent of increase or decrease.

4-4B: Solve problems involving discount or sales tax.

4-5: Solve problems by making a table or chart.

4-6: Solve mixture problems.

4-7: Solve problems involving uniform motion by using the formula $d = rt$.

4-8: Solve problems involving direct variations.

4-9: Solve problems involving inverse variations.

5   Inequalities

5-1: Solve inequalities by using addition and subtraction.

5-2: Solve inequalities by using multiplication and division.

5-3: Solve inequalities involving more than one operation.

5-4: Solve problems by making a diagram.

5-5A: Solve compound inequalities and graph their solution sets.

5-5B: Solve problems that involve compound inequalities.

5-6: Solve open sentences involving absolute values and graph the solutions.

6 Polynomials

6-1: Solve problems by looking for a pattern.
6-2A: Multiply monomials.
6-2B: Simplify expressions involving powers of monomials.
6-3A: Simplify expressions involving quotients of monomials.
6-3B: Simplify expressions containing negative exponents.
6-4A: Express numbers in scientific and decimal notation.
6-4B: Find products and quotients of numbers expressed in scientific notation.
6-5A: Find the degree of a polynomial.
6-5B: Arrange the terms of a polynomial so that the powers of a certain variable are in ascending or descending order.
6-6: Add and subtract polynomials.
6-7A: Multiply a polynomial by a monomial.
6-7B: Simplify expressions involving polynomials.
6-8A: Use the FOIL method to multiply two binomials.
6-8B: Multiply any two polynomials by using the distributive property.
6-9: Use the patterns for $(a + b)^2$, $(a - b)^2$, and $(a + b)(a - b)$.

7 Factoring

7-1A: Find the prime factorization of an integer.
7-1B: Find the greatest common factor (GCF) for a set of monomials.
7-2: Use the GCF and the distributive property to factor polynomials.
7-3: Use grouping techniques to factor polynomials with four or more terms.
7-4: Solve problems by using guess and check.
7-5: Factor quadratic trinomials.
7-6: Identify and factor polynomials that are the differences of squares.
7-7: Identify and factor perfect square trinomials.
7-8: Factor polynomials by applying the various methods of factoring.
7-9: Use the zero product property to solve equations.
7-10: Solve equations by using various factoring methods and applying the zero product property.

8 Rational Expressions

8-1: Simplify rational expressions.
8-2: Multiply rational expressions.
8-3: Divide rational expressions.
8-4: Divide polynomials by binomials.
8-5: Add and subtract rational expressions with like denominators.
8-6: Solve problems by making an organized list of the possibilities.
8-7: Add or subtract rational expressions with unlike denominators.
8-8: Simplify mixed expressions and complex fractions.
8-9A: Solve rational equations.
8-9B: Solve problems involving work and uniform motion.
8-10A: Solve formulas for a specified variable.
8-10B: Use formulas that involve rational expressions.

9 Functions and Graphs

9-1: Graph ordered pairs on a coordinate plane.
9-2A: Identify the domain, range, and inverse of a relation.
9-2B: Show relations as sets of ordered pairs and mappings.
9-3A: Solve linear equations for a specific variable.
9-3B: Solve linear equations for a given domain.
9-4: Graph linear equations on a coordinate plane.
9-5A: Determine whether a given relation is a function.
9-5B: Calculate functional values for a given function.
9-6: Graph inequalities in the coordinate plane.
9-7: Write an equation to represent a relation, given a chart of values.
9-8: Solve problems by using bar graphs and line graphs.

10 Graphing Linear Equations

10-1: Find the slope of a line, given the coordinates of two points on the line.
10-2A: Write a linear equation in standard form given the coordinates of a point on the line and the slope of the line.
10-2B: Write a linear equation in standard form given the coordinates of two points on the line.
10-3A: Write an equation in slope-intercept form given the slope and y-intercept.
10-3B: Determine the x- and y-intercept of a graph.
10-3C: Determine the x- and y-intercepts of a graph.
10-4: Graph linear equations using the x- and y-intercepts or the slope and y-intercept.
10-5A: Write a linear equation in slope-intercept form given the slope of a line and the coordinates of a point on the line.
10-5B: Write a linear equation in slope-intercept form given the coordinates of two points on the line.
10-6: Write an equation of a line that passes through a given point and is parallel or perpendicular to the graph of a given equation.
10-7: Find the coordinates of the midpoint of a line segment in the coordinate plane given the coordinates of the endpoints.
10-8: Solve problems by using pictographs, circle graphs, and comparative graphs.

11 Systems of Open Sentences

11-1: Solve problems after checking for hidden assumptions.
11-2A: Solve systems of equations by graphing.
11-2B: Determine whether a system of equations has one solution, no solution, or infinitely many solutions by graphing.
11-3: Solve systems of equations by the substitution method.
11-4: Solve systems of equations by the elimination method using addition or subtraction.
11-5: Solve systems of equations by the elimination method using multiplication and addition.
11-6: Solve systems of inequalities by graphing.

12 Radical Expressions

12-1: Solve problems by using a table.
12-2A: Simplify rational square roots.
12-2B: Find approximate values for square roots.
12-3: Use the Pythagorean Theorem.
12-4: Identify irrational numbers.
12-5A: Simplify square roots.
12-5B: Simplify radical expressions that contain variables.
12-6: Simplify radical expressions involving addition and subtraction.
12-7: Solve radical equations.
12-8: Find the distance between two points in the coordinate plane.

13 Quadratics

13-1A: Find the equation of the axis of symmetry and the coordinates of the vertex of the graph of a quadratic function.
13-1B: Graph quadratic functions.
13-2: Find the roots of a quadratic equation by graphing.
13-3: Solve problems by identifying subgoals.
13-4: Solve quadratic equations by completing the square.
13-5: Solve quadratic equations by using the quadratic formula.
13-6: Evaluate the discriminant of a quadratic equation to determine the nature of the roots of the equation.

13-7: Solve problems that can be represented by quadratic equations.
13-8A: Find the sum and product of the roots of a quadratic equation.
13-8B: Write a quadratic equation given its roots.

14 Statistics and Probability

14-1A: Interpret numerical data from a table.
14-1B: Display and interpret statistical data on a line plot.
14-2: Display and interpret data on a stem-and-leaf plot.
14-3: Calculate and interpret the mean, median, and mode of a set of data.
14-4: Calculate and interpret the range, quartiles, and the interquartile range of a set of data.
14-5: Display and interpret data on a box-and-whisker plot.
14-6: Graph and interpret pairs of numbers on a scatter plot.
14-7A: Find the probability of a simple event.
14-7B: Find the odds of a simple event.
14-8: Conduct and interpret probability experiments.
14-9: Solve problems by first solving a simpler but related problem.
14-10: Find the probability of a compound event.

15 Trigonometry

15-1A: Find the complement and the supplement of an angle.
15-1B: Find the measure of the third angle of a triangle given the measure of the other two angles.
15-2: Solve problems by making models.
15-3: Find the measures of the sides of a $30°-60°$ right triangle given the measure of one side.
15-4: Find the unknown measures of the sides of two similar triangles.
15-5A: Compute the sine, cosine, and tangent of an acute angle of a right triangle given the measures of its sides.
15-5B: Find the measure of an acute angle of a right triangle given a trigonometric value or the lengths of two of the sides.
15-6A: Use trigonometric ratios to solve verbal problems.
15-6B: Use trigonometric ratios to solve right triangles.

Planning Your Algebra Course

The charts below give suggested time schedules for three types of courses: I, II, and III, and for two types of grading periods: 9-week and 6-week.

Course I covers Chapters 1–13. It allows for extra time for longer sessions and for reteaching and review. Course II covers Chapters 1–14. Generally, one day is allotted for each lesson, the Chapter Review, and the Chapter Test. Course III covers Chapter 1–15. This course is intended for students who master concepts quickly and retain skills well.

COURSE PLANNING CALENDAR
6-Week Grading Periods

Grading Period	I Chapter	I Days	II Chapter	II Days	III Chapter	III Days
1	1 2	13 13	1 2 3 (Lessons 3-1 to 3-3)	12 12 4	1 2 3 (Lessons 3-1 to 3-5)	11 11 6
2	3 4 5 (Lessons 5-1 to 5-5)	11 11 7	3 (Lesson 3-4 to end) 4 5	6 11 9	3 (Lesson 3-6 to end) 4 5	4 11 9
3	5 (Lesson 5-6 to end) 6 7	3 12 15	6 7	11 13	6 7 8 (Lessons 8-1 to 8-6)	11 12 6
4	8 9	14 13	8 9	13 12	8 (Lesson 8-7 to end) 9 10	6 11 11
5	10 11	12 11	10 11 12 (Lessons 12-1 to 12-6)	11 10 7	11 12 13 Lessons 13-1 to 13-5)	9 10 6
6	12 13	12 13	12 (Lesson 12-7 to end) 13 14	4 12 13	13 (Lesson 13-6 to end) 14 15	5 12 9
Total Days		160		160		160

COURSE PLANNING CALENDAR
9-Week Grading Periods

Grading Period	I Chapter	I Days	II Chapter	II Days	III Chapter	III Days
1	1 2 3 4 (Lessons 4-1 to 4-5)	13 13 11 5	1 2 3 4 (Lessons 4-1 to 4-5)	12 12 10 5	1 2 3 4	11 11 10 11
2	4 (Lesson 4-6 to end) 5 6 7	6 10 12 15	4 (Lessons 4-6 to end) 5 6 7	6 9 11 13	5 6 7 8	9 11 12 12
3	8 9 10	14 13 12	8 9 10 11 (Lessons 11-1 to 11-4)	13 12 11 5	9 10 11 12 (Lessons 12-1 to 12-5)	11 11 9 5
4	11 12 13	11 12 13	11 (Lesson 11-5 to end) 12 13 14	5 11 12 13	12 (Lesson 12-6 to end) 13 14 15	5 11 12 9
Total Days		160		160		160

SYMBOLS

$=$	is equal to	π	pi
$\neq$	is not equal to	$\{\ \}$	set
$>$	is greater than	$\%$	percent
$<$	is less than	$^\circ$	degrees
$\geq$	is greater than or equal to	$a{:}b$	ratio of a to b
$\leq$	is less than or equal to	$f(x)$	f of x, the value of f at x
$\approx$	is approximately equal to	(a, b)	ordered pair a, b
$\cdot$	times	$\overline{AB}$	line segment AB
$-$	negative	AB	measure of $\overline{AB}$
$+$	positive	$\sqrt{\ }$	principal square root
$\pm$	positive or negative	$\cos A$	cosine of A
$-a$	opposite or additive inverse of a	$\sin A$	sine of A
$|a|$	absolute value of a	$\tan A$	tangent of A
$a \overset{?}{=} b$	Does a equal b?		

Metric System

mm	millimeter	h	hour
cm	centimeter	min	minute
m	meter	s	second
km	kilometer	km/h	kilometer per hour
g	gram	m/s	meters per second
kg	kilogram	°C	degrees Celsius
mL	milliliter		
L	liter		

Understanding the Lesson

Each chapter is organized into lessons to make learning manageable. The basic plan of the lesson is easy to follow, beginning with a relevant application, followed by the development of the mathematical concept with plenty of examples, and ending with various types of exercises for you to complete.

Objectives clarify what concepts and skills you are expected to know after studying the lesson and completing the exercises.

Interesting math-related trivia and historical facts, presented in FYI — "for your information" — enhance the relevance of the mathematics content.

To help ensure your success in *Merrill Algebra 1*, completely worked out **examples** are provided for each type of practice exercise.

Connections, in both examples and exercises, highlight ways in which the study of algebra is related to other areas of mathematics like geometry and statistics.

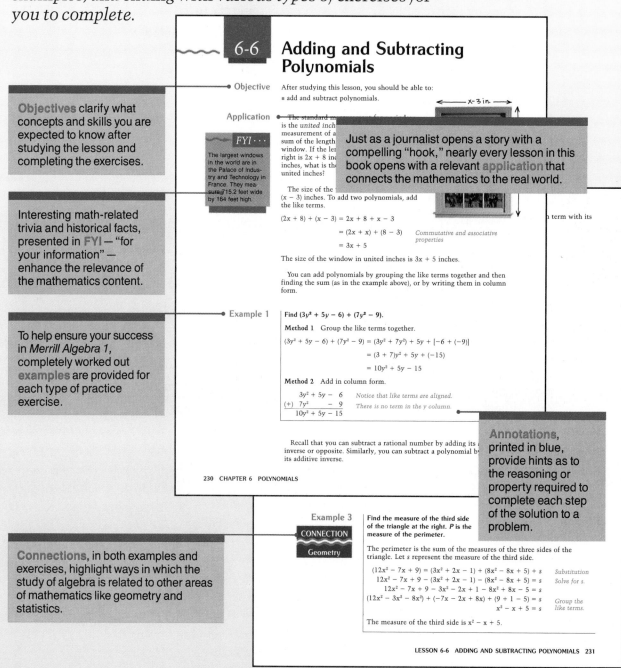

Just as a journalist opens a story with a compelling "hook," nearly every lesson in this book opens with a relevant **application** that connects the mathematics to the real world.

Annotations, printed in blue, provide hints as to the reasoning or property required to complete each step of the solution to a problem.

6-6 Adding and Subtracting Polynomials

Objective
After studying this lesson, you should be able to:
■ add and subtract polynomials.

Application
The standard measurement for a window is the *united inch*. The united inch measurement of a window is the sum of the length and width of the window. If the length of the window at right is $2x + 8$ inches and the width is $(x - 3)$ inches, what is the size of the window in united inches?

FYI ···
The largest windows in the world are in the Palace of Industry and Technology in France. They measure 715.2 feet wide by 164 feet high.

The size of the window is $(2x + 8)$ and $(x - 3)$ inches. To add two polynomials, add the like terms.

$(2x + 8) + (x - 3) = 2x + 8 + x - 3$

$\qquad = (2x + x) + (8 - 3)$ *Commutative and associative properties*

$\qquad = 3x + 5$

The size of the window in united inches is $3x + 5$ inches.

You can add polynomials by grouping the like terms together and then finding the sum (as in the example above), or by writing them in column form.

Example 1
Find $(3y^2 + 5y - 6) + (7y^2 - 9)$.

Method 1 Group the like terms together.

$(3y^2 + 5y - 6) + (7y^2 - 9) = (3y^2 + 7y^2) + 5y + [-6 + (-9)]$

$\qquad = (3 + 7)y^2 + 5y + (-15)$

$\qquad = 10y^2 + 5y - 15$

Method 2 Add in column form.

$\begin{array}{r} 3y^2 + 5y - 6 \\ (+)\ 7y^2 \quad\ - 9 \\ \hline 10y^2 + 5y - 15 \end{array}$ *Notice that like terms are aligned.*
There is no term in the y column.

Recall that you can subtract a rational number by adding its additive inverse or opposite. Similarly, you can subtract a polynomial by adding its additive inverse.

230 CHAPTER 6 POLYNOMIALS

Example 3

CONNECTION
Geometry

Find the measure of the third side of the triangle at the right. *P* is the measure of the perimeter.

The perimeter is the sum of the measures of the three sides of the triangle. Let *s* represent the measure of the third side.

$(12x^2 - 7x + 9) = (3x^2 + 2x - 1) + (8x^2 - 8x + 5) + s$ *Substitution*
$12x^2 - 7x + 9 - (3x^2 + 2x - 1) - (8x^2 - 8x + 5) = s$ *Solve for s.*
$12x^2 - 7x + 9 - 3x^2 - 2x + 1 - 8x^2 + 8x - 5 = s$
$(12x^2 - 3x^2 - 8x^2) + (-7x - 2x + 8x) + (9 + 1 - 5) = s$ *Group the like terms.*
$x^2 - x + 5 = s$

The measure of the third side is $x^2 - x + 5$.

LESSON 6-6 ADDING AND SUBTRACTING POLYNOMIALS 231

2

Communicating Mathematics exercises provide you with an opportunity to check your understanding of the material you have just read using verbal, written, pictorial, graphical, and algebraic methods.

CHECKING FOR UNDERSTANDING

Communicating Mathematics

Read and study the lesson to answer each question.

1. What is the first step when adding or subtracting in column form?
2. What is the best way to check the subtraction of two polynomials?

Guided Practice

Find the additive inverse of each polynomial.

3. $3x + 2y$
4. $-8m + 7n$
5. $x^2 + 3x + 7$
6. $-4h^2 - 5hk - k^2$
7. $-3ab^2 + 5a^2b - b^3$
8. $x^3 + 5x^2 - 3x - 11$

Name the like terms in each group.

9. $5m, 4mn, -3m, 2n, -mn, 8n$
10. $2x^3, 5xy, -x^2y, 14xy, 12xy$
11. $-7ab^2, 8a^2b, 11b^2, 16a^2b, -2b^2$
12. $3p^3q, -2p, 10p^3q, 15pq, -p$

EXERCISES

Practice

Find each sum or difference.

13. $\begin{array}{r} 5ax^2 + 3a^2x - 7a^3 \\ (+)\ 2ax^2 - 8a^2x\ \ \ \ \ \ \ + 4 \\ \hline \end{array}$

14. $\begin{array}{r} a^3\ \ \ \ \ \ \ \ \ \ \ \ - b^3 \\ (+)\ 3a^3 + 2a^2b - b^2 + 2b^3 \\ \hline \end{array}$

15. $\begin{array}{r} 4a + 5b - 6c + \ d \\ 3a - 7b + 2c + 8d \\ (+)\ 2a -\ \ b\ \ \ \ \ \ \ + 7d \\ \hline \end{array}$

16. $\begin{array}{r} 2x^2 - 5x + \ 7 \\ 5x^2 + 7x - \ 3 \\ (+)\ \ x^2 -\ \ x + 11 \\ \hline \end{array}$

17. $\begin{array}{r} 6x^2y^2 - 3xy - 7 \\ (-)\ 5x^2y^2 + 2xy + 3 \\ \hline \end{array}$

18. $\begin{array}{r} 5x^2\ \ \ \ \ \ \ \ - 4 \\ (-)\ 3x^2 + 8x + 4 \\ \hline \end{array}$

19. $\begin{array}{r} 11m^2n^2 + 2mn - 11 \\ (-)\ 5m^2n^2 - 6mn + 17 \\ \hline \end{array}$

20. $\begin{array}{r} 2a - \ 7 \\ (-)\ 5a^2 + 8a - 11 \\ \hline \end{array}$

Sharpening your reasoning skills is a major goal of challenging critical thinking exercises. Exercises of this type frequently appear on scholastic aptitude tests.

Critical Thinking

The sum of the degree measures of the three angles of a triangle is 180. Find the degree measure of the third angle of each triangle given the degree measures of the other two angles.

34. $5 - 2x;\ 7 + 8x$
35. $3x^2 - 5;\ 4x^2 + 2x + 1$
36. $4 - 2x;\ x^2 - 1$
37. $x^2 - 8x + 2;\ x^2 - 3x - 1$

Applications

38. **Travel** Joan Be... average rate of 4... miles per hour... average speed is...

Word problems are easier to solve because applications relate to your own experiences or to things you have read or heard about.

39. **Basketball** On ... Detroit Pistons ... game. The two t... scored 2 less po... score?

Mixed Review exercises help you retain the concepts and skills you have learned. The lesson reference given with each exercise makes it easy for you to re-study the concept.

Mixed Review

40. Evaluate $|x|$ if $x = -2.1$. **(Lesson 2-2)**
41. **Sports** There were 3 times as many sports in the 1976 Summer Olympics as there were in the 1976 Winter Olympics. There were 14 more sports in the Summer Olympics than there were in the Winter Olympics. How many sports were there in the 1976 Summer Olympics? **(Lesson 3-6)**
42. **Bicycling** Adita rode his bicycle 72 kilometers. How long did it take him if his rate was: **a.** 9 km/h? **b.** 18 km/h? **(Lesson 4-7)**
43. Solve $3m < 2m - 7$. **(Lesson 5-1)**
44. Find the degree of $x + 2y^2 + 3z^3$. **(Lesson 6-5)**

HISTORY CONNECTION

Emmy Noether

Emmy Noether (1882–1935) was a German mathematician whose strength was in abstract algebra. In her hands the axiomatic method (using axioms or properties) became a powerful tool of mathematical research. Noether did much of her research while living in Göttingen, Germany, which was then the principal center for mathematics research in Europe. Because she was female, Noether was unable to secure a teaching position at the University of Göttingen. However, her influence there was vast. During World War II, Noether was forced to leave Germany. She became a professor at Bryn Mawr College, in the United States, where she remained until her death. Albert Einstein paid her a great tribute in 1935: "In the judgment of the most competent living mathematicians, (Emmy) Noether was the most significant creative mathematical genius thus far produced since the higher education of women began."

History Connections highlight the mathematics contributions of individuals from many cultures and times.

Getting into the Chapter

Every chapter begins with a two-page application including a large full-color photograph to help you connect the mathematics you will learn in the chapter with your real world experiences.

CHAPTER OBJECTIVES ~~~~~~~

In this chapter, you will:
- Arrange the terms of a polynomial in order.
- Add, subtract, and multiply polynomials.
- Solve polynomial equations.
- Solve problems by looking for a pattern.

The list of chapter objectives lets you know what you can expect to learn in the chapter.

C H A P T E R

6

Polynomials

The Application describes a real-life situation where the algebra in the chapter can be used. It will help you answer the question "When am I ever going to use this?"

APPLICATION IN BIOLOGY

These days, many cities support herds of deer in their metropolitan parks, supplying them with food, medical care, shelter in winter, and protection from predators.

But uncontrolled, an animal population develops *polynomially*. That is, if one animal has x offspring, then it will have an average of x^2 grandoffspring, x^3 great-grandoffspring, x^4 great-great-grandoffspring, and so on, assuming that each animal has an average of x babies in its lifetime. We can represent the number of descendants of one animal with the polynomial expression $x + x^2 + x^3 + x^4 + \ldots$, continuing for any number of generations, assuming that none of the animals dies early. So, if an animal has an average of 13 offspring in its lifetime, then it will probably have 30,940 descendants in four generations.

So this is the problem caused by cities' support of deer in parks. Any natural ecosystem has a delicate balance. In the wild, deer populations are controlled naturally—by predators, disease, starvation, and other forms of natural competition. Since we have eliminated nearly all of the population controls for the deer living in city parks, we now have a responsibility to provide them with new ones or face the consequences of an uncontrolled population.

Population control for deer? This might seem like an unwarranted interference with nature, but this problem is much more complex.

ALGEBRA IN ACTION

A deer has an average of 4 offspring during its lifetime. Complete the chart below to determine the probable number of deer descendants in five generations.

In Algebra in Action, you can begin to actually apply the algebra that is presented in the chapter.

Generation	Polynomial	Number of Deer Descendants
1	x	4
2	$x + x^2$	$4 + 16 = 20$
3	$x + x^2 + x^3$	$4 + 16 + 64 = \underline{?}$
4	$x + x^2 + x^3 + x^4$	$4 + 16 + 64 + \underline{?} = \underline{?}$
5	$x + x^2 + x^3 + x^4 + \underline{?}$	$4 + 16 + 64 + \underline{?} + \underline{?} = \underline{?}$

209

4

Wrapping Up the Chapter

Review pages at the end of each chapter allow you to complete your mastery of the material. The vocabulary, objectives, examples, and exercises help you make sure you understand the skills and concepts presented in the chapter.

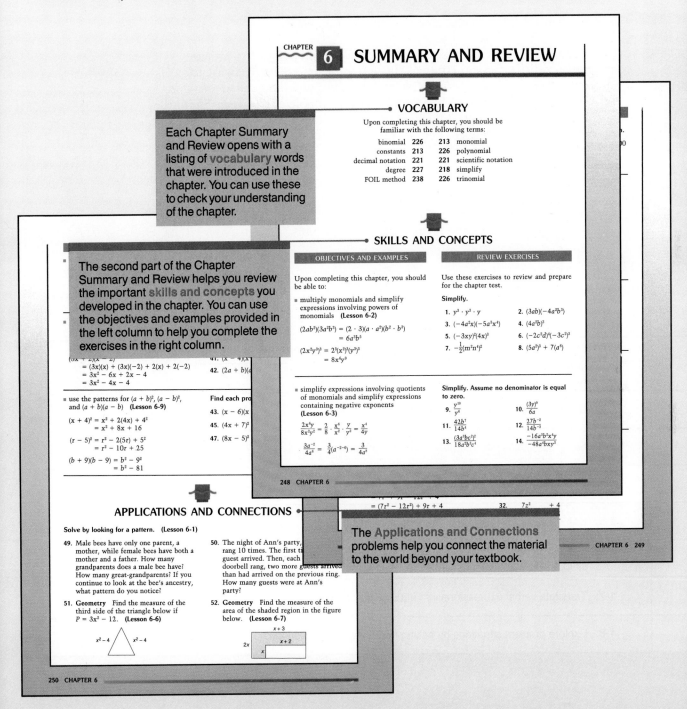

CHAPTER 6 **SUMMARY AND REVIEW**

VOCABULARY

Upon completing this chapter, you should be familiar with the following terms:

binomial	226	213	monomial
constants	213	226	polynomial
decimal notation	221	221	scientific notation
degree	227	218	simplify
FOIL method	238	226	trinomial

SKILLS AND CONCEPTS

OBJECTIVES AND EXAMPLES	REVIEW EXERCISES

Upon completing this chapter, you should be able to:

Use these exercises to review and prepare for the chapter test.

■ multiply monomials and simplify expressions involving powers of monomials **(Lesson 6-2)**

$(2ab^2)(3a^2b^3) = (2 \cdot 3)(a \cdot a^2)(b^2 \cdot b^3)$
$= 6a^3b^5$

$(2x^2y^3)^3 = 2^3(x^2)^3(y^3)^3$
$= 8x^6y^9$

Simplify.

1. $y^3 \cdot y^3 \cdot y$
2. $(3ab)(-4a^2b^3)$
3. $(-4a^2x)(-5a^3x^4)$
4. $(4a^2b)^3$
5. $(-3xy)^2(4x)^3$
6. $(-2c^2d)^4(-3c^2)^3$
7. $-\frac{1}{2}(m^2n^4)^2$
8. $(5a^2)^3 + 7(a^6)$

■ simplify expressions involving quotients of monomials and simplify expressions containing negative exponents **(Lesson 6-3)**

$\frac{2x^4y}{8x^3y^2} = \frac{2}{8} \cdot \frac{x^6}{x^2} \cdot \frac{y}{y^2} = \frac{x^4}{4y}$

$\frac{3a^{-2}}{4a^6} = \frac{3}{4}(a^{-2-6}) = \frac{3}{4a^8}$

Simplify. Assume no denominator is equal to zero.

9. $\frac{y^{10}}{y^8}$
10. $\frac{(3y)^0}{6a}$
11. $\frac{42b^7}{14b^4}$
12. $\frac{27b^{-2}}{14b^{-3}}$
13. $\frac{(3a^3bc^2)^2}{18a^2b^3c^4}$
14. $\frac{-16a^3b^2x^4y}{-48a^2bxy^3}$

248 CHAPTER 6

The second part of the Chapter Summary and Review helps you review the important skills and concepts you developed in the chapter. You can use the objectives and examples provided in the left column to help you complete the exercises in the right column.

$(6x + 2)(x - 2)$
$= (3x)(x) + (3x)(-2) + 2(x) + 2(-2)$
$= 3x^2 - 6x + 2x - 4$
$= 3x^2 - 4x - 4$

41. $(x - 4)(x$
42. $(2a + b)(a$

■ use the patterns for $(a + b)^2$, $(a - b)^2$, and $(a + b)(a - b)$ **(Lesson 6-9)**

$(x + 4)^2 = x^2 + 2(4x) + 4^2$
$= x^2 + 8x + 16$

$(r - 5)^2 = r^2 - 2(5r) + 5^2$
$= r^2 - 10r + 25$

$(b + 9)(b - 9) = b^2 - 9^2$
$= b^2 - 81$

Find each pro

43. $(x - 6)(x$
45. $(4x + 7)^2$
47. $(8x - 5)^2$

Each Chapter Summary and Review opens with a listing of vocabulary words that were introduced in the chapter. You can use these to check your understanding of the chapter.

APPLICATIONS AND CONNECTIONS

Solve by looking for a pattern. **(Lesson 6-1)**

49. Male bees have only one parent, a mother, while female bees have both a mother and a father. How many great-grandparents does a male bee have? How many great-grandparents? If you continue to look at the bee's ancestry, what pattern do you notice?

50. The night of Ann's party, rang 10 times. The first ti guest arrived. Then, each doorbell rang, two more guests arrived than had arrived on the previous ring. How many guests were at Ann's party?

51. **Geometry** Find the measure of the third side of the triangle below if $P = 3x^2 - 12$. **(Lesson 6-6)**

$x^2 - 4$ $x^2 - 4$

52. **Geometry** Find the measure of the area of the shaded region in the figure below. **(Lesson 6-7)**

$x + 3$
$x + 2$
$2x$
x

The Applications and Connections problems help you connect the material to the world beyond your textbook.

CHAPTER 6 249

$= (7r^2 - 12r^2) + 9r + 4$
32. $7z^2 + 4$

250 CHAPTER 6

5

1

An Introduction to Algebra

PREVIEWING THE CHAPTER

This chapter provides the necessary introduction and practice to prepare students for the successful study of algebra. Students are made aware that algebra differs from arithmetic in its extensive use of letters called *variables*. Students are familiarized with the concept of a variable and its use. The skill of translating verbal expressions into mathematical symbols, expressions, and open sentences is developed. Relevant number rules and properties help students realize the organization and structure of algebra. The distributive property is emphasized because of its vital role in performing algebraic functions.

Problem-Solving Strategy   Students learn to explore problems by asking and answering questions about the problem situation.

Lesson Objective Chart

Lesson (Pages)	Lesson Objectives	State/Local Objectives
1-1 (8-12)	**1-1A:** Translate verbal expressions into mathematical expressions.	
	1-1B: Write an expression containing identical factors as an expression using exponents.	
1-2 (13-17)	**1-2:** Use the order of operations to evaluate expressions.	
1-3 (18-21)	**1-3:** Solve open sentences by performing arithmetic operations.	
1-4 (22-25)	**1-4:** Recognize and use the properties of identity and equality.	
1-5 (26-30)	**1-5:** Use the distributive property to simplify expressions.	
1-6 (31-35)	**1-6:** Recognize and use the commutative and associative properties when simplifying expressions.	
1-7 (36-39)	**1-7:** Translate verbal expressions into equations and formulas.	
1-8 (41-43)	**1-8:** Explore problem situations by asking and answering questions.	

ORGANIZING THE CHAPTER

You may want to refer to the **Course Planning Calendar** on page T36.

Lesson (Pages)	Pacing Chart (days) Course I	II	III	Reteaching	Practice	Enrichment	Evaluation	Technology	Lab Manual	Mixed Problem Solving	Applications	Cooperative Learning Activity	Multicultural	Transparencies
1-1 (8-12)	1.5	1.5	1.5	p. 1	p. 1	p. 1						p. 31		1-1
1-2 (13-17)	1.5	1.5	1.5	p. 2	p. 2	p. 2	Quiz A, p. 9							1-2
1-3 (18-21)	1.5	1	1	p. 3	p. 3	p. 3		p. 1						1-3
1-4 (22-25)	1	1	1	p. 4	p. 4	p. 4	Quiz B, p. 9 Mid-Chapter Test, p. 13							1-4
1-5 (26-30)	1.5	1.5	1	p. 5	p. 5	p. 5								1-5
1-6 (31-35)	1.5	1.5	1	p. 6	p. 6	p. 6	Quiz C, p. 10							1-6
1-7 (36-39)	1.5	1	1	p. 7	p. 7	p. 7		p. 16	pp. 17-18		p. 16			1-7
1-8 (41-43)	1	1	1	p. 8	p. 8	p. 8	Quiz D, p. 10			p. 1			p. 46	1-8
Review (45-46)	1	1	1	Multiple Choice Test, Forms 1A and 1B, pp. 1-4 Free Response Tests, Forms 2A and 2B, pp. 5-8										
Test (47)	1	1	1	Cumulative Review, pp. 11-12 Standardized Test Practice Questions, p. 14										

Course I: Chapters 1-13; Course II: Chapters 1-14; Course III: Chapters 1-15

Other Chapter Resources

Student Edition
Technology, p. 40
Reading Algebra, p. 17
Mid-Chapter Review, p. 25
History Connection, p. 35
Cooperative Learning Activity, p. 43

Teacher Resource Package
Activity Masters Booklet
　Mixed Problem Solving, p. 1
　Applications, p. 16
　Cooperative Learning Activity, p. 31
　Multicultural Activity, p. 46
Technology Masters Booklet
　Scientific Calculator Activity, p. 1
　Graphing Calculator Activity, p. 16
Lab Manual
　Lab Activity, pp. 17-18

Other Supplements
Transparency for Chapter Opener
Problem-of-the-Week Activity
　Cards, 1-2
Video Algebra, 1-4, 6-7, 10

Software
Algebra 1 Test and Review
　Generator Software
　Available for Apple and IBM.

ENHANCING THE CHAPTER

Cooperative Learning

An Overview

For successful cooperative-learning experiences, research (Johnson and Johnson) indicates that the teacher's responsibilities include:

1. Deciding on the size of the groups.
2. Assigning students to the groups.
3. Arranging the room.
4. Describing the subject-matter and cooperative-skills objectives.
5. Planning teaching materials to promote group interdependence.
6. Assigning roles to students in the group.
7. Explaining the specific task to be performed.
8. Describing the student's responsibilities to the group.
9. Establishing individual accountability.
10. Explaining the criteria for success.
11. Specifying desired student behaviors.
12. Monitoring students' behavior.
13. Providing task assistance.
14. Intervening to teach cooperative-learning skills.
15. Providing closure to the lesson.
16. Evaluating the quality of students' learning.
17. Assessing how well the group functioned.

Cooperative Learning, p. 31

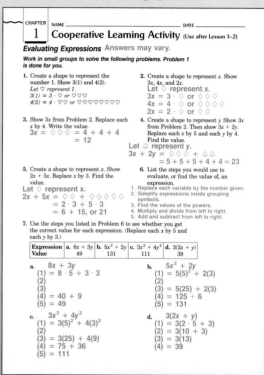

Technology

The Technology Feature after Lesson 1-7 focuses on the use of formulas in the BASIC computer language programs in spreadsheets. Use this feature to discuss with students the order of operations. Like calculators, BASIC follows the same order of operations as algebra. Spreadsheets do not usually employ algebraic logic but instead rely on grouping symbols. You may want to have students practice writing various formulas in BASIC and in spreadsheet form.

Technology, p. 1

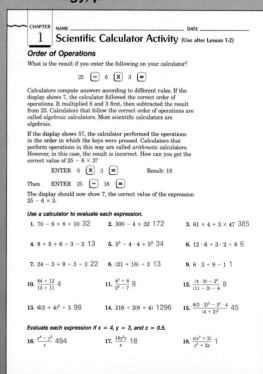

Critical Thinking

The development of critical thinking skills is crucial for any real understanding of the concepts presented in this course. Although there are numerous exercises so labeled throughout the text, you should look for additional opportunities to ask questions that encourage students to classify and compare, identify and extend patterns, make and test predictions, make generalizations and draw conclusions, make conjectures and draw inferences, clarify by giving specific examples, look for more than one solution, look for more than one way to arrive at a solution, justify a solution, and relate a situation to other situations.

Problem of the Week Activity

The card shown below is one of two available for this chapter. It can be used as a class or small group activity.

Activity Card

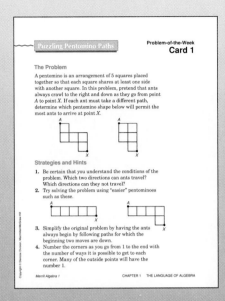

Manipulatives and Models

The following materials may be used as models or manipulatives in Chapter 1.

- scientific calculator (all Lessons)
- coins (Lesson 1-1)
- paper and scissors (Lesson 1-5)
- graph paper (Lesson 1-5)

Outside Resources

Books/Periodicals

Arthur, Lee, Elizabeth James, and Judith Taylor. *Sportsmath - How It Works.* Lothrop, Lee & Shepard.

Brancazio, Peter J.. *Sport Science.* Simon and Schuster.

National Council of Teachers of Mathematics. *Curriculum and Evaluation Standards for School Mathematics.* Reston, VA.: National Council of Teachers of Mathematics, 1989.

National Research Council. *Everybody Counts: A Report to the Nation on the Future of Mathematics Education.* Washington,D.C.: National Academy Press, 1989.

Films/Videotapes/Videodiscs

Fitness and the Athletic Experience, 1988

25 Years of Sports, Universal Archives

Software

Quations, Scholastic

Tobbs Learns Algebra, Sunburst

Multicultural

Multicultural Activity, p. 46

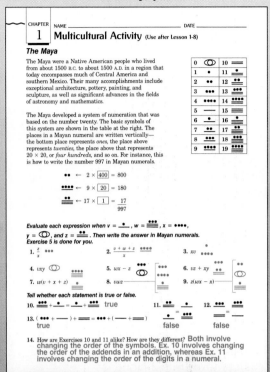

Lab Manual

Lab Activity, pp. 17-18

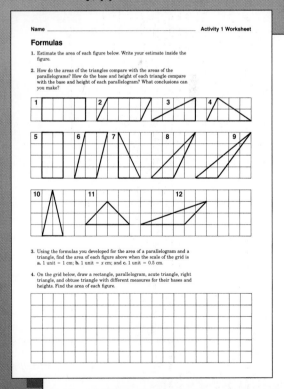

Using the Chapter Opener

Background Information

Our interest in sports is an English tradition brought by early colonists. Physical fitness and gymnastics came with Germans and Scandinavians in the nineteenth century. By the end of the nineteenth century professional baseball and college football were growing in popularity. Tennis and golf were introduced in the 1870s and 1880s, basketball was invented in 1891, and the Olympic Games were revived in 1896. The first regular sports page appeared in 1895. Our study of sports since the 1970s shows that every successful move or technique is based on a law of mathematics and science.

Chapter Project

Materials: ruler, paper, pencil

Tell your students that this project requires them to select and attend, or watch on TV, an up-coming football game. In preparation for the game, have each student draw a chart similar to those shown. Then have them research magazines and newspapers to select one player for each position on their charts. Players selected must be on one of the teams playing in their game. Have them research each player's "Season Totals To Date," record them in columns A and B, and calculate and complete column C. "Season Totals To Date" can also be found by calling the sports desk of a local newspaper. Review each student's research and calculations prior to the game. While watching the game, students are to record and calculate "Today's Game Totals," and calculate "New Season Totals" for each of their players. Finally, have each student report the results of his/her charts to the class.

In this chapter, you will:
- Evaluate expressions and formulas.
- Use mathematical properties to simplify expressions.
- Solve open sentences.
- Translate verbal expressions into mathematical expressions and equations.

Quarterback Name _____	A Pass Attempts	B Pass Completions	C Passing Percentage $C = B \div A$
Season Totals To Date			
Today's Game Totals			
New Season Totals			

1

An Introduction to Algebra

APPLICATION IN SPORTS

Most of our sports developed from skills that we had to use to survive: running, dodging, kicking, throwing, climbing, and so on. Because we were intelligent and aggressive, staying alive became easier. With more free time, we began to find ways to enjoy the use of our survival skills. By combining our natural love of action with vivid imagination, we not only created a wide variety of sports, but we also invented a means to measure our sports achievement: numbers.

Without numbers, we could not evaluate the performances of individuals and teams. Every baseball game is full of numbers used to compare the players and their teams. Which team scored the most runs? Who pitched the fastest? How far was the ball hit? Who has the most home runs? stolen bases? runs batted in? What is a player's batting average? earned run average?

"Who won?" "What was the score?" "How did my favorite player do?" "Has my team moved up in the standings?"

As the volume of numbers used to describe sports increased, we developed tools to measure, calculate, and store them. Radar guns measure the speed of a fastball. Cameras film the swing of the bat and the flight of the ball. Computers compile, calculate, and store numbers for later evaluation.

ALGEBRA IN ACTION

A *batting average* is calculated by dividing the number of hits by the number of at bats. The result is rounded so that the average has three digits after the decimal point. The chart below shows the players with the most hits in the American League in 1990. Copy and complete the chart. Who had the best average?

George Brett

Player	Hits	At Bats	Batting Average
Rafael Palmeiro	191	598	191 ÷ 598 = 0.319
Wade Boggs	187	619	187 ÷ 619 = ? 0.302
Roberto Kelly	183	641	? 0.285
Mike Greenwell	181	610	? 0.297
George Brett	179	544	? 0.329

7

Connections and Applications

Lesson	Connections (C) and Applications (A)		Examples	Exercises
1-1	C:	Geometry	5, 6	33-34
	A:	Electronics		42
		Government		43
1-2	C:	Geometry	2	27-32, 53
	A:	Merchandising		46
		Health		47
		Carpentry		48
1-3	C:	Logic	1	19-22
	A:	Music		40
		Banking		41
		Health		42
1-4	A:	History		33
		Culture		34
		Money		35
1-5	C:	Mental Math	2	
	A:	Basketball	1	
		Retailing		38
		Archaeology		39
1-6	C:	Geometry	1	
	A:	Marketing		43
		America		44
		Weather		46
		Volleyball		45
1-7	C:	Geometry	1, 4	7-12, 20-38
	A:	Travel		40
		Fitness		41
		Physics		42
		Astronomy		43

	A	**B**	**C**
Running Back Name _____	**Number of Carries**	**Yards Gained**	**Average Yards per Carry** $C = B \div A$
Season Totals To Date			
Today's Game Totals			
New Season Totals			

Lesson Resources

• Reteaching Master 1-1
• Practice Master 1-1
• Enrichment Master 1-1
• Activity Master, p. 31
• Video Algebra, 1

 Transparency 1-1 contains the 5-Minute Check and a teaching aid for this lesson.

INTRODUCING THE LESSON

5-Minute Check

Write an arithmetic expression that represents each situation.

1. the sum of 18, 23, and 51
   $18 + 23 + 51$
2. the quotient of 2,910,000 and 550,000
   $2{,}910{,}000 \div 550{,}000$
3. the square of 9 9^2
4. the product of 4, 5, and 6
   $4 \cdot 5 \cdot 6$
5. 10 decreased by the cube of 2 $10 - 2^3$

Motivating the Lesson
Ask students the following questions concerning the United States House of Representatives.
Answers may vary.
1. Do they know how many members of the House represent their state?
2. Each state is divided into Congressional districts. Do they know how many Congressional districts are in their city?
3. Do they know who the representative is for the Congressional district in which they live?

TEACHING THE LESSON

Teaching Tip ① Point out that the term variable is used since the value of the symbol, in this case the letter *p*, can vary.

Objectives

After studying this lesson, you should be able to:

1-1A   ■ translate verbal expressions into mathematical expressions, and
1-1B   ■ write an expression containing identical factors as an expression using exponents.

Application

> *FYI* · · ·
>
> The Constitution guarantees each state representation in Congress regardless of population.

The United States House of Representatives has 435 members. The number of members from each state is determined by the state's population. Each state is divided into congressional districts, which have an average of about 575,000 people. There is one representative from each district.

Alaska, Delaware, North Dakota, South Dakota, Vermont, and Wyoming each have one representative in the House. You can find the number of representatives from other states if you know the populations of those states.

Since you cannot have a fraction of a representative, round to the nearest whole number.

If a state has a population of 2,910,000, it will have $2{,}910{,}000 \div 575{,}000$ or 5 representatives.

If a state has a population of 6,280,000, it will have $6{,}280{,}000 \div 575{,}000$ or 11 representatives.

If a state has a population of *p*, it will have $p \div 575{,}000$ representatives.

Teaching Tip
①   The letter *p* is called a **variable**, and $p \div 575{,}000$ is an **algebraic expression**. In algebra, variables are symbols that are used to represent unspecified numbers. Any letter may be used as a variable. We chose the letter *p* since it is the first letter in the word "population."

6 + 3 and 4 × 5 − 8 are numerical expressions.

An algebraic expression consists of one or more numbers and variables along with one or more arithmetic operations. Here are some other examples of algebraic expressions.

$$b + 4 \qquad \frac{s}{t} - 1 \qquad a \times 4n \qquad 8rs \div 3k$$

In a multiplication expression, the quantities being multiplied are called **factors** and the result is called the **product**.

$$4 \times 5 \times 8 = 160$$
$$\underset{factors}{\nwarrow \uparrow \nearrow} \quad \underset{product}{\uparrow}$$

8   CHAPTER 1   AN INTRODUCTION TO ALGEBRA

ALTERNATE TEACHING STRATEGIES

Using Logical Reasoning
Have students count the money they have and verbally explain the process they use to determine how much money they have. Then have them explain how the process would be done for any number of coins.   (0.01 times the number of pennies) plus (0.05 times the number of nickels) and so on.

Using Applications
Many real-world quantities, such as the speed of a car, can be found by evaluating algebraic expressions. For example, the speed of a car that travels *d* miles in 3 hours is $\frac{d}{3}$ miles per hour. Have students name some other quantities that can be represented by algebraic expressions.

Teaching Tip

② In algebraic expressions, a raised dot or parentheses are often used to indicate multiplication. When variables are used to represent factors, the multiplication sign is usually omitted. Here are five ways to represent the product of *a* and *b*.

$$ab \qquad a \cdot b \qquad a(b) \qquad a \times b \qquad (a)(b)$$

Fraction bars are used to indicate division.

$$\frac{x}{3} \quad \text{means} \quad x \div 3 \text{ Teaching Tip ③}$$

To solve some verbal problems in mathematics, you can create an algebraic expression by translating words into mathematical symbols. The chart below shows some of the words that are used to indicate mathematical operations.

Addition	Subtraction	Multiplication	Division
■ the sum of	■ the difference of	■ the product of	■ the quotient of
■ increased by	■ decreased by	■ multiplied by	■ divided by
■ plus	■ minus	■ times	■ the ratio of
■ more than	■ less than		
■ added to	■ subtracted from		
■ the total of			

Example 1

Write an algebraic expression for *the sum of a and b.*

An algebraic expression is $a + b$.

Example 2

Write an algebraic expression for *a number k divided by a number n.*

An algebraic expression is $\frac{k}{n}$.

Example 3

Write a verbal expression for *4x*.

A verbal expression is the product of 4 and *x*, or 4 times *x*.

Example 4

Write a verbal expression for *z − 6.*

One verbal expression is six less than *z*. Another is the difference of *z* and 6. *Can you think of another?*

In an expression like 10^3, 10 is the **base** and 3 is the **exponent**. The exponent indicates the number of times the base is used as a factor.

$$10^3 \quad \text{means} \quad 10 \cdot 10 \cdot 10 \qquad a^2 \quad \text{means} \quad a \cdot a$$

LESSON 1-1   VARIABLES AND EXPRESSIONS   9

Teaching Tip ②   Note that for a product of a number and a variable, the number is written first. For example, the product of *x* and 5 is 5*x*, not *x*5.

Teaching Tip ③   Ask students how dividing by 3 could be described in terms of multiplication.   Dividing by 3 is the same as multiplying by $\frac{1}{3}$.

Chalkboard Examples

Write an algebraic expression for each verbal expression.

For Example 1
a. *m* increased by 5 $m + 5$

b. the difference of *x* and 9
   $x - 9$

For Example 2
a. the ratio of *a* to *t* $\frac{a}{t}$

b. 7 times the product of *x* and *t* $7xt$

Write two different verbal expressions for each mathematical expression.

For Example 3
a. 9*t*   9 times *t*, product of 9 and *t*

b. 8 + *a*   8 plus *a*, sum of 8 and *a*

For Example 4
a. *m* ÷ *r*   *m* divided by *r*, the quotient of *m* and *r*

b. 7 − 3*y*   difference of 7 and 3 times *y*, 7 minus the product of 3 and *y*

For Example 5
Find the area of each rectangle whose dimensions are given.

length = 5 m, width = 4 m
20 m²

For Example 6
Find the volume of each rectangular solid whose dimensions are given.

length = 4 ft, width = 4 ft, height = 2 ft   32 ft³

An expression in the form x^n is called a power.

Symbols	Words	Meaning
8^1	8 to the first power	8
8^2	8 to the second power or 8 squared	$8 \cdot 8$
8^3	8 to the third power or 8 cubed	$8 \cdot 8 \cdot 8$
8^4	8 to the fourth power	$8 \cdot 8 \cdot 8 \cdot 8$
$6n^5$	6 times n to the fifth power	$6 \cdot n \cdot n \cdot n \cdot n \cdot n$

Teaching Tip ④

Example 5

CONNECTION
Geometry

Find the area of the square at the right.
Teaching Tip ⑤

8 cm

The area of a square is the length of the side squared.
The area of the square is $(8)^2$ or 64 cm².
Area is expressed in units squared.

Example 6

CONNECTION
Geometry

Find the volume of the cube at the right.

3 in.

The volume of a cube is the length of the side cubed.
The volume of the cube is $(3)^3$ or 27 in³.
Volume is expressed in units cubed.

Example 7

Evaluate 2^5. Teaching Tip ⑥

$2^5 = 2 \cdot 2 \cdot 2 \cdot 2 \cdot 2$
  $= 32$

You can use the $\boxed{y^x}$ key on a calculator to raise a number to a power.

Enter: 2 $\boxed{y^x}$ 5 $\boxed{=}$

Display: 2   5   32   **Teaching Tip ⑦**

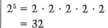

Example 8

Write an algebraic expression for the expression *the cube of k increased by seven*.

An algebraic expression is $k^3 + 7$.

RETEACHING THE LESSON

Have students answer each question with an algebraic expression. Let d represent Dawn's age now.
1. How old will Dawn be in two years? $d + 2$
2. How old is Ellen now if she is five years younger than Dawn? $d - 5$
3. How old is Frank now if he is three times as old as Dawn? $3d$

CHECKING FOR UNDERSTANDING

Communicating Mathematics

Read and study the lesson to answer each question. **3. 3 + a, 3a**

1. If a state has a population of 3,431,000, how would you determine the number of representatives it has? **Divide 3,431,000 by 575,000.**

2. What is the difference between numerical expressions and algebraic expressions? **Algebraic expressions include variables.**

3. How would you represent the sum of 3 and a? the product of 3 and a?

4. Can you find the volume of a cube if you only know the length of a side? How? **Yes; multiply the measure of the side by itself 3 times.**

Guided Practice

Write an algebraic expression for each verbal expression.

5. the product of x and 7 **$7x$**
6. the quotient of r and s **$\frac{r}{s}$**
7. the sum of a and 19 **$a + 19$**
8. a number n decreased by 4 **$n - 4$**
9. a number b to the third power **b^3**
10. 25 squared **25^2**

Write as expressions that use exponents.

11. $5 \cdot 5 \cdot 5$ **5^3**
12. $7 \cdot a \cdot a \cdot a \cdot a$ **$7a^4$**
13. $2(m)(m)(m)$ **$2m^3$**
14. $5 \cdot 5 \cdot 5 \cdot x \cdot x \cdot y$ **5^3x^2y**

Evaluate each expression.

15. 2^4 **16**
16. 5^3 **125**
17. 10^4 **10,000**
18. 3^6 **729**

EXERCISES

Practice

Write a verbal expression for each algebraic expression.

19. $m - 1$ **m minus 1**
20. xy **the product of x and y**
21. n^4 **n to the fourth power**
22. 5^3 **5 cubed**
23. $8y^2$ **8 times y squared**
24. $z^7 + 2$ **z to the seventh power plus 2**

Write an algebraic expression for each verbal expression.

25. a number increased by 17 **$x + 17$**
26. seven times a number **$7x$**
27. twice the cube of a number **$2x^3$**
28. a number to the sixth power **x^6**

Write an algebraic expression for each verbal expression.

29. one-half the square of a number **$\frac{1x^2}{2}$ or $\frac{x^2}{2}$**
30. six times a number decreased by 17 **$6x - 17$**
31. 94 increased by twice a number **$94 + 2x$**
32. three fourths of the square of a number **$\frac{3x^2}{4}$**

APPLYING THE LESSON

Homework Exercises

See the assignment guide on page 11.

Additional Answer

44. 6, −2, 8, 0.5, 16; 13, 7, 30, 3.333, 1000; −7, −11, −18, −4.5, 81; 7.2, 3.2, 10.4, 2.6, 27.04

Enrichment Masters Booklet, p. 1

CONNECTION
Geometry

33. Find the area of the figure at the right. **15 m²**
5 m
3 m

34. Find the volume of the figure at the right. **288 mm³** 12 mm
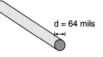
12 mm
2 mm

C Use your calculator to evaluate each expression to the nearest thousandth.

35. $(6.2)^6$
56,800.236

36. $(4.8)^5$
2548.040

37. $5^5 + 6^6 + 7^7$
873,324

38. $2^2 \cdot 3^3 \cdot 4^4 \cdot 5^5$
86,400,000

Write an algebraic expression for each verbal expression.

39. the sum of a and b, decreased by the product of a and b $a + b - ab$

40. the difference of a and b, increased by the quotient of a and b $a - b + \frac{a}{b}$

Critical Thinking

41. Evaluate 4^2 and 2^4. What do you notice? From this example, can you say that the same relationship exists between 2^5 and 5^2? What about between 3^4 and 4^3? **They are equal; no; no.**

42. **64² C.M. or 4096 C.M.**

Applications

42. **Electronics** For a round conductor, the diameter in mils squared (d^2) equals the cross-sectional area in circular mils (C.M.). Find the cross-sectional area in C.M. for the wire shown at the right.

d = 64 mils

43. **Government** The White House has 132 rooms, including a barber shop and a bowling alley. The main building is shaped like a rectangle that is 168 feet long and 85 feet wide. What is the area of the main building of the White House?
14,280 square feet

Computer

Teaching Tip 8

44. BASIC is a computer language. The symbols used in BASIC are similar to those used in algebra.

+ means add.   / means divide.
− means subtract.   ↑ means exponent.
* means multiply.

Numeric variables in BASIC are represented by capital letters. Input the following sets of values for a and b into the program below to find $a + b$, $a - b$, $a \times b$, $a \div b$, and a^b: 2, 4; 10, 3; −9, 2; 5.2, 2. **See margin.**

```
10 INPUT A,B
20 PRINT "A + B = ";A + B
30 PRINT "A - B = ";A - B
40 PRINT "A * B = ";A * B
50 PRINT "A / B = ";A / B
60 PRINT "A ↑ B = ";A ↑ B
```

12 CHAPTER 1 AN INTRODUCTION TO ALGEBRA

EXTENDING THE LESSON

Math Power: Reasoning

Carolyn received d dollars on Sunday. She spent half of this money on Monday, one-third of what was left on Tuesday, and one-fourth of what was left on Wednesday. Write an algebraic expression to represent how much money she spent each day.

a. Monday $\frac{d}{2}$

b. Tuesday $\frac{1}{3}\left(d - \frac{d}{2}\right)$

c. Wednesday $\frac{1}{4}\left[d - \frac{d}{2} - \frac{1}{3}\left(d - \frac{d}{2}\right)\right]$

1-2 Evaluating Expressions

Objective
1-2

After studying this lesson, you should be able to:
- use the order of operations to evaluate expressions.

Application

Janet Graves scored 7 points in each of the first four volleyball games. In the fifth game, she scored 3 points. The following expression represents the number of points she scored in the five games.

$$7 \cdot 4 + 3$$

To find the number of points she scored, evaluate the expression $7 \cdot 4 + 3$. Which of the following methods is correct?

$7 \cdot 4 + 3 = 28 + 3$ *Multiply first.*	$7 \cdot 4 + 3 = 7 \cdot 7$ *Add first.*
$\quad = 31$ *Then add.*	$\quad = 49$ *Then multiply.*

The answers are not equal because a different order of operations was used in each method. Since a numerical expression must have only one value, we use the following order of operations in algebra. **Teaching Tip** ❶

Teaching Tip ❷

Order of Operations

1. **Simplify the expressions inside grouping symbols, such as parentheses and brackets, and as indicated by fraction bars.**
2. **Evaluate all powers.**
3. **Do all multiplications and divisions from left to right.**
4. **Do all additions and subtractions from left to right.**

Therefore, Janet scored $7 \cdot 4 + 3$ or 31 points in the five games.

Let's evaluate another numerical expression.

Example 1

Evaluate $12 \div 3 \cdot 5 - 4^2$.

$12 \div 3 \cdot 5 - 4^2 = 12 \div 3 \cdot 5 - 16$	*Evaluate 4^2.*
$\quad = 4 \cdot 5 - 16$	*Divide 12 by 3.*
$\quad = 20 - 16$	*Multiply 5 by 4.*
$\quad = 4$	*Subtract 16 from 20.*

Algebraic expressions can be evaluated when the value of the variables is known. First, the variables are replaced by their values. Then, the value of the numerical expression is calculated.

LESSON 1-2 EVALUATING EXPRESSIONS 13

ALTERNATE TEACHING STRATEGIES

Using Logical Reasoning

Insert parentheses in different places in the following expression and evaluate. What values do you obtain?

$$5 + 2 \times 3 + 1 + 6 \times 0$$

Answers will vary. A sample answer is as follows.
$(5 + 2) \times (3 + 1) + (6 \times 0) = 28$

INTRODUCING THE LESSON

5-Minute Check

(over Lesson 1-1)
1. Write a verbal expression for $2x - x^2$. **twice a number less the square of the number**
2. Evaluate 3^4. **81**

Write an algebraic expression for each verbal expression.

3. a number increased by 17 **$n + 17$**
4. twice a number decreased by 45 **$2n - 45$**
5. the square of a number decreased by twice the number **$n^2 - 2n$**

Motivating the Lesson

Use exactly four 4's to write a numerical expression that equals each number from 1 to 5. Here is an example for the number 0: $4 - 4 + 4 - 4$.

$1 = \frac{(4 + 4)}{(4 + 4)}$ **Answers may vary.**

$2 = \frac{4}{4} + \frac{4}{4}$

$3 = \frac{(4 + 4 + 4)}{4}$

$4 = 4(4 - 4) + 4$

$5 = \frac{4(4) + 4}{4}$

TEACHING THE LESSON

Teaching Tip ❶ Ask students to explain what it means for a numerical expression to have a unique value. The expression must be equal to "one and only one" value.

Chalkboard Examples

For Example 1
Evaluate each expression.

a. $14 \div 7 \cdot 2 - 3$ **1**

b. $64 \div 8 - 3 \cdot 2$ **2**

For Example 2
The circumference (C) of a circle is given by the formula $C = 2\pi r$, where r is the radius of the circle. Find the circumference of a circle when $r = 8$. Use $\frac{22}{7}$ for π. $\frac{352}{7}$ **units**

For Example 3
Evaluate each expression.

a. $3(3 + 7)^2 \div 5$ **60**

b. $27 \div 3(5 - 3)^2$ **36**

For Example 4
Evaluate $\frac{2}{3}[8(a - b)^2 + 3b]$ if $a = 6$ and $b = 3$.   **54**

For Example 5
Use a calculator to evaluate $\frac{a^6 - 22}{a^3 + x^7}$ if $a = 12$ and $x = 9$. Round to the nearest thousandth.   **0.624**

Example 2

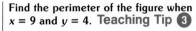

CONNECTION

Geometry

Find the perimeter of the figure when $x = 9$ and $y = 4$. Teaching Tip ③

The perimeter (P) is the sum of the lengths of the sides.

$P = x + y + 6 + 6 + 7$
$P = x + y + 19$

Now replace each variable with its given value.

$P = 9 + 4 + 19$
$P = 32$

The perimeter is 32 cm.

[Figure: pentagon with sides labeled y cm, x cm, 6 cm, 7 cm, 6 cm]

$$50 - 5 \cdot 6 + 3 = 50 - 30 + 3 \text{ or } 23$$
$$50 - 5(6 + 3) = 50 - 5 \cdot 9 \text{ or } 5$$

Example 3

Evaluate $4(1 + 5)^2 \div 8$.

$4(1 + 5)^2 \div 8 = 4(6)^2 \div 8$	*Add 1 and 5.*
$= 4(36) \div 8$	*Evaluate 6^2.*
$= 144 \div 8$	*Multiply 36 by 4.*
$= 18$	*Divide 144 by 8.*

When more than one grouping symbol is used, start evaluating within the innermost grouping symbols.

$$50 - [5(6 + 3)] = 50 - (5 \cdot 9) = 50 - 45 \text{ or } 5$$

Example 4

Evaluate $\frac{2}{3}[8(a - b)^2 + 3b]$ if $a = 5$ and $b = 2$.

$\frac{2}{3}[8(a - b)^2 + 3b] = \frac{2}{3}[8(5 - 2)^2 + 3 \cdot 2]$	*Substitute 5 for a and 2 for each b.*
$= \frac{2}{3}[8(3)^2 + 3 \cdot 2]$	*Subtract 2 from 5.*
$= \frac{2}{3}[8 \cdot 9 + 3 \cdot 2]$	*Evaluate 3^2.*
$= \frac{2}{3}[72 + 6]$	*Multiply 9 by 8 and 2 by 3.*
$= \frac{2}{3}[78]$	*Add 72 and 6.*
$= 52$	*Multiply 78 by $\frac{2}{3}$ and simplify.*

ALTERNATE TEACHING STRATEGIES

Using Questioning

Ask students how they would enter the following expression on a calculator to determine its value.

$$\frac{252 + 463}{768 - 339}$$

 (252 + 463) ÷ (

768 − 339) = 1.667

The fraction bar is another grouping symbol. It indicates that the numerator and denominator should each be treated as a single value.

$$\frac{3 \times 8}{2 \times 4}$$ means $(3 \times 8) \div (2 \times 4)$ or 3

When evaluating an expression with a scientific calculator, it may be necessary to use grouping symbols.

Example 5

Use a calculator to evaluate $\frac{b^7 - 5}{b^2 + c^4}$ if $b = 6$ and $c = 8$.

You can use the x^2 key on a calculator to square a number like 6.

Enter: $(\ 6\ \boxed{y^x}\ 7\ \boxed{-}\ 5\ )\ \div\ (\ 6\ \boxed{x^2}\ \boxed{+}\ 8\ \boxed{y^x}\ 4\ )\ =$

Display: 67.747096

Why is it necessary to have parenthesis around the numerator and denominator? **Teaching Tip 5**

CHECKING FOR UNDERSTANDING

Communicating Mathematics

Read and study the lesson to answer each question.

1. When evaluating the expression $2 + 5 \cdot 3$, what do you do first? **multiply 5 by 3**
2. Name two types of grouping symbols.
   parentheses, brackets, braces, fraction bar

Explain how to evaluate each expression. Do *not* evaluate. **See margin.**

3. $(12 - 6) \cdot 2$
4. $9 - 3^2$
5. $4(5 - 3)^2$
6. $8 + 6 \div (2 + 1)$

Guided Practice

Evaluate each expression.

7. $3 + 8 \div 2 - 5$ **2**
8. $5(9 + 3) - 3 \cdot 4$ **48**
9. $5^3 + 6^3 - 5^2$ **316**
10. $\frac{38 - 12}{2 \cdot 13}$ **1**

Evaluate each expression if $a = 6$, $b = 4$, and $c = 3$.

11. $a + b^2 + c^2$ **31**
12. $3ab - c^2$ **63**
13. $8(a - c)^2 + 3$ **75**
14. $\frac{2ab - c^3}{7}$ **3**

EXERCISES

Practice

Evaluate each expression.

15. $4 + 7 \cdot 2 + 8$ **26**
16. $12 \div 4 + 15 \cdot 3$ **48**
17. $29 - 3(9 - 4)$ **14**
18. $4(11 + 7) - 9 \cdot 8$ **0**
19. $16 \div 2 \cdot 5 \cdot 3 \div 6$ **20**
20. $288 \div [3(9 + 3)]$ **8**

LESSON 1-2 EVALUATING EXPRESSIONS 15

RETEACHING THE LESSON

Have students insert parentheses so that each expression has the indicated value.

1. $56 \div 6 + 2 \div 1$; 7
   $56 \div (6 + 2) \div 1$
2. $2 \cdot 8 - 2 + 6 \div 3$; 14
   $2 \cdot (8 - 2) + 6 \div 3$
3. $2 \cdot 8 - 2 + 6 \div 3$; 0
   $2 \cdot (8 - (2 + 6)) \div 3$
4. $20 - 2 \cdot 3^2 + 12 \div 6$; 0
   $20 - (2 \cdot 3^2 + 12 \div 6)$

Additional Answers

3. Subtract 6 from 12. Then multiply by 2.
4. Square 3. Then subtract from 9.
5. Subtract 3 from 5. Square the result. Then multiply by 4.
6. Add 2 and 1. Divide 6 by the result. Then add 8.

Teaching Tip 5 Have students analyze the necessity of grouping symbols in Example 5 by working the example without using the parentheses keys and then interpreting the resulting value of 284031.8611.

EVALUATING THE LESSON

Checking for Understanding

Exercises 1-14 are designed to help you assess understanding through reading, writing, and speaking. You should work through Exercises 1-6 with your students, and then monitor their work on Exercises 7-14.

Error Analysis

Students may tend to evaluate expressions from left to right, ignoring the correct order of operations. For example, they may evaluate $24 - 8 \div 2$ as $16 \div 2$ or 8 and not $24 - 4$ or 20. Emphasize the importance of looking at the entire expression to determine the correct order of operations before evaluating.

Assignment Guide

Basic: 15-36, 45-53
Average: 16-38, 41, 43, 47-53
Enriched: 21-53

Reteaching Masters Booklet, p. 2

Chapter 1 15

16 Chapter 1

B ▶ Evaluate each expression. **Teaching Tip** ⑥

21. $6(4^3 + 2^2)$ 408
22. $\frac{9 \cdot 4 + 2 \cdot 6}{7 \cdot 7}$ $\frac{48}{49}$; 0.980
23. $\frac{2 \cdot 8^2 - 2^2 \cdot 8}{2 \cdot 8}$ 6
24. $\frac{3}{4}(6) + \frac{1}{3}(12)$ $\frac{17}{2}$; 8.5
25. $25 - \frac{1}{3}(18 + 9)$ 16
26. $7(0.2 + 0.5) - 0.6$ 4.3

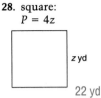
CONNECTION
Geometry

A formula for the perimeter or circumference of each figure is given. Find the perimeter or circumference when $x = 3$, $y = 4$, and $z = 5.5$. Use 3.14 for π.

27. triangle:
$P = x + y + z$
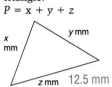
12.5 mm

28. square:
$P = 4z$
22 yd

29. parallelogram:
$P = 2(x + y)$
14 in.

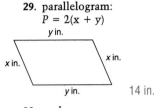

30. isosceles trapezoid:
$P = x + 2y + z$
16.5 cm

31. circle:
$C = \pi y$
12.56 ft

32. oval:
$P = \pi x + 2y$
17.42

FYI · · ·

See Exercise 32. On a regulation track, x is 75 and y is 101.

Evaluate each expression if $a = 6$, $b = 4$, $c = 3$, $d = \frac{1}{2}$, $n = \frac{2}{3}$, $x = 0.2$, and $y = 1.3$.

33. $12d + bc$ 18
34. $a(8 - 3n) + 4d$ 38
35. $ax + bc$ 13.2
36. $x^2 + 6d$ 3.04
C ▶ 37. $(100x)^2 + 10y$ 413
38. $\frac{8b^2c}{x}$ 1920
39. $\frac{a + b^2}{3bc}$ $\frac{11}{18}$; $0.6\overline{1}$
40. $\frac{a^2 - b^2}{2 + d^3}$ $\frac{160}{17}$; 9.412

Write an algebraic expression for each verbal expression. Then, evaluate the expression if $a = 3$, $b = \frac{1}{2}$, and $c = 0$.

41. twice the sum of a and b $2(a + b)$; 7
42. twice the product of a and b $2(ab)$; 3
43. the square of b increased by c $b^2 + c$; $\frac{1}{4}$; 0.25
44. the cube of a decreased by b $a^3 - b$; $26\frac{1}{2}$; 26.5

Critical Thinking 45. If you change one sign in the expression below, the value of the expression will double. Find the sign. Why does this work? See margin.

$$61 - 13 - 12 - 8 - 7 - 6 - 5$$
↑

16 CHAPTER 1 AN INTRODUCTION TO ALGEBRA

Applications

46. **Merchandising** If 12 items are in a dozen, 12 dozen are in a gross, and 12 gross are in a great-gross, how many items are in a great-gross? **1728 items**

47. **Health** Your optimum exercise heart rate per minute is given by the expression $0.7(220 - a)$, where a represents your age. Find your optimum exercise heart rate. **See margin.**

48. **Carpentry** Ana Martinez is putting molding around the ceiling of a paneled family room. If the room measures 12 feet by 16 feet, how many feet of molding are needed? **56 feet**

Mixed Review

50. See margin.

49. Write an algebraic expression for *7 less than w*. **(Lesson 1-1)** $w - 7$

50. Write a verbal expression for y^5. **(Lesson 1-1)**

51. Write $4 \cdot 4 \cdot 4 \cdot 4$ as an expression using exponents. **(Lesson 1-1)** 4^4

52. Write an algebraic expression for *twice a number decreased by 25*. **(Lesson 1-1)** $2n - 25$

CONNECTION
Geometry

53. Find the area of the rectangle. **(Lesson 1-1)** 24 ft^2

6 ft
4 ft

READING ALGEBRA

Suppose you are asked to read each expression below.

$$3x + y \qquad\qquad 3(x + y)$$

In the expression $3(x + y)$, parentheses are used to show that the sum $x + y$ is multiplied by three. In algebraic expressions, terms enclosed by parentheses are treated as one quantity. The expression $3(x + y)$ is read *three times the quantity x plus y*. The expression $3x + y$ is read *three x plus y*.

Try this experiment. Have a classmate close his or her book. Read the expressions below to your classmate. Then have him or her write each one as an algebraic expression.

a. seven times the cube of the quantity b minus 4 $7(b - 4)^3$
b. twice the quantity a plus 3 times the quantity b minus 9 $2(a + 3)(b - 9)$
c. four divided by the difference of a number and 6 $4 \div (n - 6)$

Compare your classmate's answers with the correct answers shown above. How do they compare?

EXTENDING THE LESSON

Math Power: Reasoning

Determine all the possible values for the numerical expression $8 - 2 \cdot 3 + 1$ if you ignore the rules for order of operation.
There are five possible values: 0, 1, 3, 19, and 24.

Reading Algebra

Emphasize the importance of looking for key words when translating verbal expressions into algebraic expressions. For example, the word quantity usually indicates that parentheses or other grouping symbols are to be used.

Lesson Resources

- Reteaching Master 1-3
- Practice Master 1-3
- Enrichment Master 1-3
- Video Algebra, 3

 Transparency 1-3 contains the 5-Minute Check and a teaching aid for this lesson.

INTRODUCING THE LESSON

 5-Minute Check

(over Lesson 1-2)

Evaluate each expression.

1. $5 + 6 \cdot 3 + 7$ 30
2. $3(10 + 6) - 8 \cdot 6$ 0
3. $5(3^2 + 2^3)$ 85

Evaluate if $x = 4$, $y = 2$, and $z = 5$.

4. $3xz - y^3$ 52
5. $6x + y^2 - z^2$ 3

Motivating the Lesson

Jerry, Kerrie, Larry, and Mary went to the movies together. Kerrie has $1.75. She wants to buy a bucket of popcorn, which costs $2.90. Jerry has $1.25, Larry has $1.10, and Mary has $1.18. How can Kerrie determine which of her friends does not have enough money to help her buy the popcorn?   She should add the money that she has ($1.75) to the money that each of the friends has ($1.25, $1.10, and $1.18) and determine which sum is less than $2.90. Since $1.75 + $1.10 < $2.90, Larry is the one who does not have enough money.

TEACHING THE LESSON

Teaching Tip ❶   In mathematics, sentences that can be classified as true or false are called *statements*. In general, *open sentences* are true for some variable replacements and false for others. The original sentence is neither true nor false.

1-3 Open Sentences

Objective
1-3

After studying this lesson, you should be able to:
- solve open sentences by performing arithmetic operations.

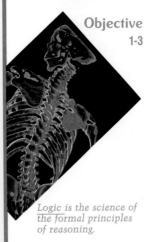

Logic is the science of the formal principles of reasoning.

Which of the following sentences are true? Which are false?

There are over 200 bones in the human body.   *true*
The name Mary is a verb.   *false*
California is larger than New Jersey.   *true*
Twenty-seven divided by 3 is less than 7.   *false*

Note that each of the previous sentences is either true or false. A **statement** is any sentence that is either true or false, but not both. Statements are the building blocks in a system of *logic*. One way of referring to a specific statement is to represent it with a letter such as p or q. Let *p* be the statement *France is a country in Europe.* This statement is true. To find the *negation* of statement *p*, write ~*p* (read "not p"). This represents the statement *France is not a country in Europe.* This statement is false.

Example 1

CONNECTION

Logic

Let *p* represent the statement *5 + 2 = 8*. Let *q* represent the statement *The President of the United States must be born in the U.S.* State whether each statement is *true* or *false*. Then state whether its negation is *true* or *false*.

a. *p* $5 + 2 = 8$ *This statement is false.*
    ~*p* $5 + 2 \neq 8$ *This statement is true.*

b. *q*   The President of the United States must be born in the U.S.   *This statement is true.*
    ~*q*   The President of the United States can be born outside of the U.S.   *This statement is false.*

Open sentences are neither true nor false.

Are the statements below true or false?

Words	Symbols
A number x plus six is equal to eight.	$x + 6 = 8$
A number n is less than ten.	$n < 10$
Seven is greater than twice a number c.	$7 > 2c$

Mathematical sentences like these are called **open sentences**. Before you can determine whether these sentences are true or false, you must know what numbers will replace the variables *x*, *n*, and *c*. Finding the

---

ALTERNATE TEACHING STRATEGIES

Using Connections

This lesson contains many connections to logic. Have students look up the definition of *disjunction*. Then have them rewrite $2x - 7 \leq 9$ as a disjunction. $2x - 7 < 9$ or $2x - 7 = 9$

Using Discussion

Have students list sets of items such as the different types of U.S. coins, the numbers divisible by 8, or subjects that they have taken in school. Then have them state whether or not each set has a definite number of items.

replacements for the variable that make a sentence true is called **solving the open sentence.** Each replacement is called a **solution** of the open sentence.

An open sentence that contains an equals sign, =, is called an **equation.** Sometimes you can solve an equation by simply applying the order of operations.

Example 2

Solve $\dfrac{5 \cdot 3 + 3}{4 \cdot 2 - 2} = t$.

$$\dfrac{5 \cdot 3 + 3}{4 \cdot 2 - 2} = t$$

$$\dfrac{15 + 3}{8 - 2} = t \qquad \textit{Evaluate the numerator and denominator.}$$

$$\dfrac{18}{6} = t \qquad \textit{Divide.}$$

$$3 = t$$

The solution is 3.

A **set** is a collection of objects or numbers. Sets are often shown by using braces. Each object or number in a set is called an **element.**

$1 \in \{1, 2, 3\}$ is read *One is an element of the set containing 1, 2, 3.*

Sets are usually named by capital letters.

$$A = \{1, 2, 3\} \qquad\qquad B = \{1, 2\}$$

Teaching Tip ❷

Since every element of set B is an element of set A, then set B is a **subset** of set A. Other subsets of set A are $\{1\}$, $\{2\}$, $\{3\}$, $\{1, 3\}$, $\{2, 3\}$, and $\{1, 2, 3\}$. A set with no elements is called the **null** or **empty set,** shown by $\{\ \}$ or $\emptyset$. The empty set is a subset of every set.

The set of numbers from which replacements for a variable may be chosen is called a **replacement set.** The set of all replacements for the variable that make an open sentence true is called the solution set for the sentence.

Example 3

Find the solution set for the open sentence $n - 1 < 2$ if the replacement set is $\{1, 2, 3\}$.

If $n = 1$, then the sentence becomes $1 - 1 < 2$. This sentence is true.
If $n = 2$, then the sentence becomes $2 - 1 < 2$. This sentence is true.
If $n = 3$, then the sentence becomes $3 - 1 < 2$. This sentence is false.

Therefore, $\{1, 2\}$ is the solution set.

LESSON 1-3 OPEN SENTENCES 19

Chalkboard Examples

For Example 1

Write the negation of each statement. Then state whether the negation is *true* or *false*.

a. $8 \cdot 4 < 22$ $\quad 8 \cdot 4 \not< 22$ or $8 \cdot 4 \geq 22$; true

b. Labor Day is not celebrated in May. **Labor Day is celebrated in May; false**

For Example 2

a. Solve $m = \dfrac{7 \cdot 7 + 2}{10 + 7}$. $\quad$ 3

b. Solve $\dfrac{4.2 + 2(3.9)}{3.1 + 2.9} = k$. $\quad$ 2

For Example 3

Find the solution set for each open sentence if the replacement set is {0, 2, 4, 6, 8}.

a. $8 - x < 7$ $\quad$ {2, 4, 6, 8}

b. $\dfrac{x + 3}{4} > 3$ $\quad$ { } or $\emptyset$

Teaching Tip ❷ *Set B is a subset of set A* is written $B \subset A$. Thus, $\{1, 2\} \subset \{1, 2, 3\}$.

Reteaching Masters Booklet, p. 3

NAME _____ DATE _____
1-3 Reteaching Worksheet

Reading Algebra: Translating Words into Symbols

Although the expression *7 less than x* and the statement *7 is less than x* look similar, their meanings are very different. The phrase *less than* indicates subtraction, whereas the phrase *is less than* indicates the relationship between two unequal numbers. The symbol $<$ represents this inequality.

Words	Symbols
seven less than x	$x - 7$
Seven is less than x.	$7 < x$

The expressions $x - 7$ and $7 - x$ also have different meanings. In the expression $x - 7$, 7 is subtracted from x. So the value of $x - 7$ is 7 less than the value of x. But in the expression $7 - x$, x is subtracted from 7. Therefore, the value of $7 - x$ is equal to 7 decreased by the value of x.

Symbols	Words
$x - 7$	seven less than x
$7 - x$	seven less than x, or seven decreased by x

The phrases *greater than* and *is greater than* have different meanings and are also represented by different symbols. We use a plus sign to indicate *greater than*, and we use the inequality symbol, $>$, to indicate *is greater than*.

Words	Symbols
ten more than the quantity m minus n	$(m - n) + 10$
ten increased by the quantity $m - n$	$10 + (m - n)$
The quantity m minus n is greater than ten.	$m - n > 10$

Write each expression in symbols.

1. Three greater than twice a number x $\quad 2x + 3$
2. Five is less than the cube of a. $\quad 5 < a^3$
3. Three times x is greater than nine less than x. $\quad 3x > x - 9$

Write each algebraic expression in words.

4. $4m - 1$ one less than the product of four and m.
5. $3(b - 2) + 6$ the product of three and the quantity two less than b increased by 6
6. $a^2 + (a + 5)$ the square of a quantity five greater than a
7. $y > 5$ y is greater than five.
8. $8x - 3 < 3$ Three less than the product of eight and x is less than 3.
9. $(a - b)^2 > (a + b)^2$ The square of the quantity a minus b is greater than the square of the quantity a plus b.

RETEACHING THE LESSON

State whether each sentence is *true, false,* or *open*. If the sentence is open, replace the variable with a value to make the sentence true.

1. $2 + 3 \cdot 5 = 30$ $\quad$ false
2. $2 + 3 \cdot 5 = x$ $\quad$ open; 17
3. $40 - 8 \div 2^2 = 38$ $\quad$ true
4. $x - 8 \div 2^2 = 24$ $\quad$ open; 26

Checking for Understanding

Exercises 1-18 are designed to help you assess understanding through reading, writing, and speaking. You should work through Exercises 1-6 with your students, and then monitor their work on exercises 7-18.

Closing the Lesson

Writing Activity Have students write an equation with the indicated solution set if the replacement set was {0, 1, 2, 3}. Answers may vary. Sample equations are given.
1. {3} $t - 3 = 0$
2. {0, 1} $b^2 = b$
3. Ø $4x = 1$
4. {0, 1, 2, 3} $m = (m - 1) + 1$

Practice Masters Booklet, p. 3

NAME _____ DATE _____

| 1-3 | Practice Worksheet |

Open Sentences

Write the negation of each statement. Then state whether the negation is true or false.

1. There are twenty-four hours in a day.
There are not twenty-four hours in a day; false

2. Carrots are a fruit.
Carrots are not a fruit; true

3. A bicycle does not have four wheels.
A bicycle has four wheels; false

4. Mt. Washington is the tallest mountain in the world.
Mt. Washington is not the tallest mountain in the world; true

List all subsets of each set to show that each statement is true.

5. {a} has 2 subsets.
{a}, Ø

6. {a, b, c} has 8 subsets.
{a}, {b}, {c}, {a, b}, {a, c}, {b, c}, {a, b, c}, Ø

Solve each equation.

7. $x = 36 + 15$ 51

8. $3(4) - 3 = y$ 9

9. $c = 70 - 0.29$ 69.71

10. $4.5 - 1.25 = a$ 3.25

11. $\frac{1}{3} + \frac{2}{3} = y$ 1

12. $\frac{43 - 10}{0.2 + 0.9} = r$ 30

13. $n = \frac{5}{8} + \frac{3}{4}$ $1\frac{3}{8}$

14. $w = \frac{4 \cdot 3 + 2}{1 + 2 \cdot 3}$ 2

15. $v = 120 \div \{6(9 - 5)\}$ 5

16. $m = 4\frac{1}{2} \div 3$ $1\frac{1}{2}$

17. $16.7 - 3.95 = u$ 12.75

18. $k = 2\frac{1}{2} + \frac{1}{6}$ $2\frac{2}{3}$

Find the solution set for each open sentence if the replacement set is {6, 7, 8, 9}.

19. $k + 3 > 8$ {6, 7, 8, 9}

20. $2k - 1 > k + 6$ {8, 9}

CHECKING FOR UNDERSTANDING

Communicating Mathematics

Complete. Teaching Tip ③

1. A ___?___ is a sentence that is either true or false. **statement**
2. ~p refers to the ___?___ of statement p. **negation**
3. $17 = n - 4$ is called an ___?___. **open sentence or equation**
4. {3, 4, 5, 6} is a ___?___ for the sentence $p + 2 > 4$. **replacement set**

Write in symbols.

5. the set containing 3, 4, 5, 6 **{3, 4, 5, 6}**
6. Three is an element of the set containing 3, 4, 5, 6. **3 ∈ {3, 4, 5, 6}**

Guided Practice

State whether each sentence is true or false.

7. $3(11 - 5) > 18$ **false**
8. $0.01 + 0.01 = 0.0002$ **false**
9. $\frac{3 + 15}{6} = \frac{1}{2}(6)$ **true**
10. $\frac{1}{2} + \frac{3}{4} = \frac{3}{2} + \frac{1}{4}$ **false**

Replace the variable to make each open sentence true.

11. $18 + y = 20$ **2**
12. $3 \cdot x = 24$ **8**
13. a is an author of this book. **Foster, Winters, Gell, Rath, or Gordon**
14. There are s states in the U.S. **50**

Solve each equation.

15. $x = 8 + 3$ **11**
16. $y = 12 - 0.03$ **11.97**
17. $a = \frac{3}{4} \cdot 12$ **9**
18. $8.2 - 6.75 = m$ **1.45**

19-24. See margin.

EXERCISES

Practice

A

Logic: Write the negation of each statement. Then state whether the negation is *true* or *false*.

19. The capital of the U.S. is Houston.
20. George Bush is President of the United States.
21. Birds have wings.
22. Oranges are not a citrus fruit.

List all subsets of each set to show that each statement is true. Teaching Tip ④

23. {1, 2} has 4 subsets.
24. {5, 6, 7, 8} has 16 subsets.

Additional Answers

19. The capital of the U.S. is not Houston; true
20. George Bush is not the president of the United States; true or false depending on date
21. Birds do not have wings; false
22. Oranges are a citrus fruit; true

23. {1}, {2}, {1, 2}, Ø
24. {5}, {6}, {7}, {8}, {5, 6}, {5, 7}, {5, 8}, {6, 7}, {6, 8}, {7, 8}, {5, 6, 7}, {5, 6, 8}, {5, 7, 8}, {6, 7, 8}, {5, 6, 7, 8}, Ø

Solve each equation.

25. $a = \frac{12 + 8}{4}$ 5

26. $\frac{21 - 3}{12 - 3} = x$ 2

27. $14.8 - 3.75 = t$ 11.05

28. $n = \frac{84 \div 7}{18 \div 9}$ 6

29. $\frac{2}{13} + \frac{5}{13} = p$ $\frac{7}{13}$

30. $\frac{5}{8} + \frac{1}{4} = y$ $\frac{7}{8}$

31. $d = 3\frac{1}{2} \div 2$ $\frac{7}{4}$

32. $r = 5\frac{1}{2} + \frac{1}{3}$ $5\frac{5}{6}$

Find the solution set for each open sentence if the replacement set is {4, 5, 6, 7, 8}.

33. $x + 2 > 7$ {6, 7, 8}

34. $x - 3 > \frac{x + 1}{2}$ {8}

C

35. $\frac{2(x - 2)}{3} = \frac{4}{7 - 5}$ {5}

36. $9x - 20 = x^2$ {4, 5}

37. $0.3(x + 4) \le 0.4(2x + 3)$
{4, 5, 6, 7, 8}

38. $1.3x - 12 < 0.9x + 4$
{4, 5, 6, 7, 8}

Critical Thinking 39. Write five open sentences that have 2 as a solution.
Answers will vary; some possible answers are $3x = 6$, $b + 5 = 7$, $y > 1$.

Applications 40. **Music** The Oakbrook School chorus has eight voices in each section. The sections are as follows: soprano, alto, tenor, and bass. Write an equation to represent the total number of voices in the chorus. Then, solve the equation. $v = 8 \cdot 4$;
32 voices

41. **Banking** In the beginning of the month, the balance in Marisa Fuentes's checking account was $428.79. After writing checks totaling $1097.31, depositing 2 checks of $691.53 each, and withdrawing $100 from a bank machine, what is the new balance in Marisa's account? **$614.54**

42. **Health** Two out of every three people in the United States wear eyeglasses. If the population of the U.S. was about 250,000,000 in 1990, about how many people were wearing eyeglasses?
about 167,000,000

Mixed Review 43. Write an algebraic expression for *a number h cubed*. (**Lesson 1-1**) h^3

44. Write $\frac{1}{2} \cdot a \cdot a \cdot b \cdot b \cdot b$ as an expression using exponents.
(**Lesson 1-1**) $\frac{1}{2}a^2b^3$

Evaluate each expression. (**Lesson 1-2**)

45. $3 \cdot 6 - 12 \div 4$ 15

46. $\frac{9 \cdot 3 - 4^2}{3^2 + 2^2}$ $\frac{11}{13}$

47. Evaluate $(15x)^3 - y$ if $x = 0.2$ and $y = 1.3$. (**Lesson 1-2**) 25.7

EXTENDING THE LESSON

Math Power:
Communication

Write a verbal statement for each open sentence.

1. $2 + 6x = 26$ Two more than six times a number is equal to 14.

2. $5(r - 4) = 20$ Five times the difference of a number and 4 is 20.

3. $a^3 > 10$ The cube of a number is greater than 10.

4. $7(1 + 3z)^2 \le \frac{z}{2}$ Seven times the quantity one plus three times z squared is half of z.

APPLYING THE LESSON

Homework Exercises

Assignment Guide

Basic: 19-30, 32, 34, 39-47
Average: 21-34, 38-47
Enriched: 25-47

Teaching Tip 3 Remind students that "fill in the blank" questions are really open sentences for which they must find the solution set. Some examples of such questions are given below.

_____ was the first President of the United States. A pentagon has _____ sides. **George Washington; five**

Teaching Tip 4 For Exercises 23 and 24, students may need to be reminded that for a given set, the empty set, Ø, and the set itself are subsets of that set.

Enrichment Masters Booklet, p. 3

NAME _____ DATE _____
1-3   **Enrichment Worksheet**

Solution Sets

Consider the following open sentence.

It is a robot that starred in STAR WARS.

You know that a replacement for the variable *It* must be found in order to determine if the sentence is true or false. If *It* is replaced by either *R2D2* or *C3PO*, the sentence is true.

The set {*R2D2, C3PO*} is called the *solution set* of the open sentence given above. This set includes all replacements for the variable that make the sentence true.

Write the solution set of each open sentence.

1. It is the name of a state beginning with the letter A.   1. {Alabama, Alaska, Arizona, Arkansas}

2. It is a primary color.   2. {red, yellow, blue}

3. Its capital is Harrisburg.   3. {Pennsylvania}

4. It is a New England state.   4. {Maine, New Hamp., Vermont, Mass., Rhode Is., Conn.}

5. $x + 4 = 10$ 5. {6}

6. It is the name of a month that contains the letter r.   6. {Jan, Feb, Mar, Apr, Sept, Oct, Nov, Dec}

7. During the 1970s, she was the wife of a U.S. President.   7. {Pat Nixon, Betty Ford, Rosalyn Carter}

8. It is an even number between 1 and 13.   8. {2, 4, 6, 8, 10, 12}

9. $31 = 72 - k$ 9. {41}

10. It is the square of 2, 3, or 4.   10. {4, 9, 16}

Write an open sentence for each solution set.

11. {A, E, I, O, U}   11. It is a vowel.

12. {1, 3, 5, 7, 9}   12. It is an odd number between 0 and 10.

13. {June, July, August}   13. It is a summer month.

14. {Atlantic, Pacific, Indian, Arctic}   14. It is an ocean.

1-4

Identity and Equality Properties

Lesson Resources

- Reteaching Master 1-4
- Practice Master 1-4
- Enrichment Master 1-4
- Video Algebra, 6

 Transparency 1-4 contains the 5-Minute Check and a teaching aid for this lesson.

INTRODUCING THE LESSON

 5-Minute Check

(over Lesson 1-3)

Solve each equation.

1. $b = \frac{10 + 6}{4}$ 4
2. $15.2 - 4.25 = s$ 10.95
3. $k = \frac{8.6 - 1.16}{(1.2)(2)}$ 3.1
4. $t = \frac{3 \cdot 9 - 5^2}{2^3 + 3^2}$ $\frac{2}{17}$
5. Find the solution set for $3x + 1 \geq 3(x + 1)$ if the replacement set is {2, 3, 4, 5, 6}.   { } or ∅

Motivating the Lesson

To attract customers to a car dealership, the manager decides to sell one of the models at cost so she will make $0.00 in profit on each car sold. How much profit will she make if she sells 2 cars? if she sells 10 cars? if she sells *n* cars?   **$0.00, $0.00, $0.00**

TEACHING THE LESSON

Teaching Tip   Have students explore division by zero on a calculator.

ENTER: 6 ÷ 0 =

DISPLAY: 6   0 ERROR

Why does the display show "ERROR"?
Division by zero is undefined.

Objective
1-4

After studying this lesson, you should be able to:
- recognize and use the properties of identity and equality.

In algebra, there are certain statements, or *properties*, that are true for any number. Solve the equations below.

$$b + 15 = 15 \qquad 4780 + c = 4780$$

What value makes each statement true?

The solution of each equation is 0. Since the sum of any number and 0 is equal to the number, zero is called the **additive identity**.

Additive Identity Property	For any number a, $a + 0 = 0 + a = a$.

Solve the equations below.

$$5x = 5 \qquad z \cdot 655 = 655$$

What value makes each statement true?

The solution of each equation is 1. Since the product of any number and 1 is equal to the number, one is called the **multiplicative identity**.

Multiplicative Identity Property	For any number a, $a \cdot 1 = 1 \cdot a = a$.

Zero is a factor in each of these statements.

$$0(11) = 0 \qquad 2 \cdot 5 \cdot 0 = 0 \qquad 4 \cdot 0 \cdot 27 \cdot 8 = 0$$

When 0 is a factor, what can you say about the product?

ALTERNATE TEACHING STRATEGIES

Using Questioning

True or false?

1. $3 + 0 = 3$ true
2. $1 = 4 \cdot 1$ false
3. $0 = 6 \cdot 0$ true
4. If $3 + 2 = 5$ and $5 = 7 - 2$, then $3 + 2 = 7 - 2$.   true

Using Logical Reasoning

Multiplying by 0 gives a product of 0 (multiplicative property of zero). Does dividing by 0 give a quotient of 0?
No, division by 0 is undefined.
To better understand why division by 0 is undefined, consider the equation $6 \div 0 = a$. The related multiplication equation is $6 = 0 \cdot a$. This equation cannot be solved since no number multiplied by 0 results in a product of 6.

<table>
<tr><td>**Multiplicative Property of Zero**</td><td>For any number a, $a \cdot 0 = 0 \cdot a = 0$. Teaching Tip ①</td></tr>
</table>

Take a look at the statements below.

1. If $10 - 2 = 8$ and $8 = 5 + 3$, then $10 - 2 = 5 + 3$. transitive
2. $5 = 5$ reflexive
3. If $3 + 9 = 12$, then $8 + (3 + 9) = 8 + 12$. substitution Teaching Tip ②
4. If $7 + 3 = 10$, then $10 = 7 + 3$. symmetric

These are examples of the **properties of equality**.

<table>
<tr><td>**Properties of Equality**</td><td>The following properties are true for any numbers a, b, and c.

Reflexive Property: $a = a$
Symmetric Property: If $a = b$, then $b = a$.
Transitive Property: If $a = b$ and $b = c$, then $a = c$.
Substitution Property: If $a = b$, then a may be replaced by b.</td></tr>
</table>

Which property of equality corresponds to each of the four numbered statements above? See above.

Example

Evaluate $6(12 - 48 \div 4) + 9 \cdot 1$. Indicate the property used in each step.

$$6(12 - 48 \div 4) + 9 \cdot 1 = 6(12 - 12) + 9 \cdot 1 \quad \textit{Substitution (=)}$$
$$= 6(0) + 9 \cdot 1 \quad \textit{Substitution (=)}$$
$$= 0 + 9 \cdot 1 \quad \textit{Multiplicative property of zero}$$
$$= 0 + 9 \quad \textit{Multiplicative identity}$$
$$= 9 \quad \textit{Additive identity}$$

1. No; because properties are true for any number.   2. No; because $a + 1 \neq a$.

CHECKING FOR UNDERSTANDING   3. No; because $a \cdot 0 \neq a$.

Communicating Mathematics

Read and study the lesson to answer each question.

1. Can a property ever be false? Why or why not?
2. Can 1 be an additive identity? Why or why not?
3. Can 0 be a multiplicative identity? Why or why not?

LESSON 1-4   IDENTITY AND EQUALITY PROPERTIES   23

Chalkboard Example

For the Example

Evaluate $3[8 \div 2^3 + 7(8 - 2^3)]$. Indicate the property used in each step.

$$3[8 \div 2^3 + 7(8 - 2^3)]$$
$$= 3[8 \div 8 + 7(8 - 8)] \quad \text{Sub.(=)}$$
$$= 3[8 \div 8 + 7(0)] \quad \text{Sub. (=)}$$
$$= 3[1 + 7(0)] \quad \text{Sub. (=)}$$
$$= 3(1 + 0) \quad \text{Mult. prop. of 0}$$
$$= 3(1) \quad \text{Add. ident. prop.}$$
$$= 3 \quad \text{Mult. ident. prop.}$$

EVALUATING THE LESSON

Checking for Understanding

Exercises 1-10 are designed to help you assess understanding through reading, writing, and speaking. You should work through Exercises 1-3 with your students, and then monitor their work on Exercises 4-10.

Reteaching Masters Booklet, p. 4

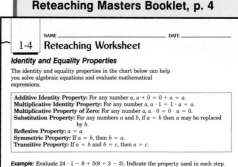

RETEACHING THE LESSON

Replace the variable to make each open sentence true.

1. $(2 + x)^2 = 5^2$ **3**
2. $(2 + x)^2 = 2^2$ **0**
3. $3(2 - a) = 3$ **1**
4. $3(2 - a) = 0$ **2**
5. $m(1) + m(0) = 5$ **5**

24 Chapter 1

Closing the Lesson

Speaking Activity Discuss the following relationships between any two people to determine which ones work with the
a) reflexive property,
b) symmetric property, or
c) transitive property.
1. is taller than   no, no, yes
2. sits next to   no, yes, no
3. has same color eyes as   yes, yes, yes
4. is the father of   no, no, no
5. lives within one mile of   yes, yes, no

APPLYING THE LESSON

Homework Exercises

Assignment Guide

Basic: 11-27, 32-33, 36-39
Average: 13-29, 32-39
Enriched: 15-39
All: Mid-Chapter Review, 1-16

Chapter 1, Quiz B, (Lessons 1-3 through 1-4), is available in the Evaluation Masters Booklet, p. 9.

Practice Masters Booklet, p. 4

1-4 | Practice Worksheet

NAME _____ DATE _____

Identity and Equality Properties

Solve each equation.
1. $7 = x \cdot 1$ 7
2. $p = 0(12)$ 0
3. $y + 0 = 5$ 5

Name the property illustrated by each statement.
4. $0 + b = b$
   Additive identity prop.
5. If $x + y = 3$, then $3 = x + y$.
   Symmetric prop.
6. $x = x$
   Reflexive prop.
7. $4 \cdot 1 = 4$
   Multiplicative identity prop.
8. $1 \cdot y = y$
   Multiplicative identity prop.
9. $6 = 6$
   Reflexive prop.
10. $0 = 0 \cdot 12$
    Multiplicative prop. of zero
11. $5 = 5 + 0$
    Additive identity prop.
12. If $12 = 17 - 5$, then $17 - 5 = 12$.
    Symmetric prop.
13. $7(8 - 3) = 7(5)$
    Substitution prop.
14. $w + (4 + 6) = w + 10$
    Substitution prop.
15. $x + 2 = x + 2$
    Reflexive prop.
16. $(6 + 9)x = 15x$
    Substitution prop.
17. $(7 - 4)(6) = 3(6)$
    Substitution prop.
18. $xyz = 1xyz$
    Multiplicative identity prop.
19. $8 + 5 = (4 + 4) + 5$
    Substitution prop.
20. If $6 + 3 = 9$ and $9 = 3(3)$, then $6 + 3 = 3(3)$.
    Transitive prop.

Evaluate each expression. Indicate the property used in each step.
21. $2 + 6(9 - 3^2) - 2$
    $= 2 + 6(9 - 9) - 2$ Substitution (=)
    $= 2 + 6(0) - 2$ Substitution (=)
    $= 2 + 0 - 2$ Mult. prop. of zero
    $= 2 - 2$ Additive identity
    $= 0$ Substitution (=)
22. $5(13 - 39 \div 3) + 7 \cdot 1$
    $= 5(13 - 13) + 7 \cdot 1$ Substitution (=)
    $= 5(0) + 7 \cdot 1$ Substitution (=)
    $= 0 + 7 \cdot 1$ Mult. prop. of zero
    $= 0 + 7$ Multiplicative identity
    $= 7$ Additive identity
23. $(16 \div 4^2)$
    $= 7(16 \div 16)$ Substitution (=)
    $= 7(1)$ Substitution (=)
    $= 7$ Multiplicative identity

Guided Practice   Name the property illustrated by each statement. 5. symmetric (=)

4. $7 + 6 = 7 + 6$ reflexive (=)
5. If $6 = 3 + 3$, then $3 + 3 = 6$.
6. $3 + (2 + 1) = 3 + 3$ sub. (=)
7. $9 + 5 = (6 + 3) + 5$ sub. (=)
8. If $8 = 6 + 2$ and $6 + 2 = 5 + 3$, then $8 = 5 + 3$. transitive (=)

9-10. See Solutions Manual.
Evaluate each expression. Indicate the property used in each step.

9. $1(8 - 2^3)$ 0
10. $3 + 5(4 - 2^2) - 1$ 2

EXERCISES

Practice   Solve each equation.

11. $0 + x = 7$ 7
12. $a \cdot 1 = 5$ 5
13. $7b = 7$ 1
14. $0(18) = n$ 0

Name the property illustrated by each statement. 15. symmetric (=)

15. If $8 + 1 = 9$, then $9 = 8 + 1$.
16. $0 \cdot 36 = 0$ mult. prop. of zero
17. $1(87) = 87$ mult. ident. prop.
18. $9 + (2 + 10) = 9 + 12$ sub. (=)
19. $14 + 16 = 14 + 16$ refl. (=)
20. $0 + 17 = 17$ add. ident. prop.
21. $(9 - 7)(5) = 2(5)$ sub. (=)
22. $abc = 1abc$ mult. identity prop.
23. $7(0) = 0$ mult. prop. of zero
24. If $3 = 4 - 1$, then $4 - 1 = 3$.
25. If $9 + 1 = 10$ and $10 = 5(2)$, then $9 + 1 = 5(2)$. transitive (=)
                                             24. symmetric (=)

26-31. See Solutions Manual.
Evaluate each expression. Indicate the property used in each step.

26. $5(9 \div 3^2)$ 5
27. $3 + 18(12 \div 6 - 2)$ 3
28. $(19 - 12) \div 7 \cdot 23$ 23
29. $(2^5 - 5^2) + (4^2 - 2^4)$ 7
30. $(9 - 2 \cdot 3)^3 - 27 + 9 \cdot 2$ 18
31. $(13 + \frac{2}{5} \cdot 5)(3^2 - 2^3)$ 15

Teaching Tip ③

Critical Thinking   32. Think about the relationship "is greater than," represented by the symbol >. Does > work with the **a)** reflexive property, **b)** symmetric property, or **c)** the transitive property? Why or why not?
No, no, yes; answers may vary.

Applications   33. **History**   Lincoln's Gettysburg address began "Four score and seven years ago, ..." Write an expression to represent four score and seven. How many years is that? $4(20) + 7$; 87 years

34. **Culture**   Each year in the Chinese calendar is named for one of 12 animals. Every 12 years, the same animal is named. If 1992 is the Year of the Monkey, how many years in the 20th century have been Years of the Monkey? 8 years

35. Money Geraldina makes a call to a teen talkline. The cost of the call is $3.00 for the first minute plus 85¢ for each additional minute. If Geraldina talks for 40 minutes, how much did her call cost? **$36.15**

Mixed Review

36. Write a verbal expression for x^2. (Lesson 1-1) **a number x squared**

37. Evaluate the expression $7(8 - 4) + 11$. (Lesson 1-2) **39**

38. *True* or *false:* $15 \div 3 + 7 < 13$. (Lesson 1-3) **true**

39. Replace the variable to make the sentence $\frac{1}{2}(m) = 10$ true. (Lesson 1-3) **20**

Teaching Tip ③ For Exercise 32, ask students to give counterexamples for parts a and b.

Additional Answers

3. Divide 8 by 2. Multiply 2 by 6. Then add.
4. Square 3. Subtract 3. Then multiply by 3.
5. Add 8 and 6. Divide by 2. Then add 2.

～～～ MID-CHAPTER REVIEW ～～～

Write an algebraic expression for each verbal expression. Use n for the variable. (Lesson 1-1)

1. the cube of a number n^3
2. the square of a number increased by seven $n^2 + 7$

Explain how to evaluate each expression. Do not evaluate. (Lesson 1-2) **See margin.**

3. $8 \div 2 + 6 \cdot 2$
4. $3(3^2 - 3)$
5. $(8 + 6) \div 2 + 2$

Evaluate each expression if $a = 6$, $b = 4$, $c = 3$, and $d = \frac{1}{2}$. (Lesson 1-2)

6. $\frac{2}{3}(b^2) - \frac{1}{3}(a)$ $\frac{26}{3}$
7. $\frac{1}{2}(2b + 10c) - 4$ **15**
8. $d(a + b) - c$ **2**

Solve each equation. (Lesson 1-3)

9. $x = 6 + 0.28$ **6.28**
10. $m = \frac{64 + 4}{17}$ **4**
11. $y = \frac{96 \div 6}{8 \div 2}$ **4**

Find the solution set for each open sentence if the replacement set is {4, 5, 6, 7, 8}. (Lesson 1-3)

12. $10 - x < 7$ {4, 5, 6, 7, 8}
13. $\frac{x + 3}{2} < 5$ {4, 5, 6}
14. $\frac{2x + 1}{7} \geq \frac{x + 4}{5}$ {8}

Name the property illustrated by each statement. (Lesson 1-4)

15. $3abc \cdot 0 = 0$
   multiplicative property of zero
16. If $12xy - 3 = 4$, then $4 = 12xy - 3$.
   symmetric property of equality

EXTENDING THE LESSON

Math Power: Problem Solving

Dentmaster Car Rental charges $21.95 per day and $0.11 a mile to rent one of its cars. Bryan rented a car for one day to visit friends in Altton, 85 miles away, Latton, 80 miles away, or Talton, 75 miles away. If he can only spend $40.00 on his car rental, which friends could he visit?
the friends in Latton or Talton

Mid-Chapter Review

The Mid-Chapter Review provides students with a brief review of the concepts and skills in Lessons 1-1 through 1-4. Lesson numbers are given at the end of problems or instruction lines so students may review concepts not yet mastered.

Enrichment Masters Booklet, p. 4

NAME _____ DATE _____

1-4 **Enrichment Worksheet**

The Conditional Statement

If p and q represent statements, the compound statement "if p then q" is called a *conditional*.

symbol: $p \rightarrow q$ read: either "if p then q" or "p only if q"

The statement p is called the *antecedent*, and the statement q is called the *consequent*.

For each conditional statement identify the antecedent (A) and the consequent (C).

1. If it is nine o'clock, then I am late.
   A: It is 9:00.
   C: I am late.

2. If Karen is home, then we will ask her to come.
   A: Karen is home
   C: We will ask Karen to come.

3. The fish will die if we don't feed them.
   A: We don't feed the fish.
   C: The fish will die.

4. There will be no school if it snows.
   A: It snows, or it is snowing.
   C: There will be no school.

5. There will be no school only if it snows.
   A: There will be no school.
   C: It is snowing.

6. If $y + 2 = 6$ then $y = 4$.
   A: $y + 2 = 6$
   C: $y = 4$

Lesson Resources
- Reteaching Master 1-5
- Practice Master 1-5
- Enrichment Master 1-5
- Video Algebra, 10

 Transparency 1-5 contains the 5-Minute Check and a teaching aid for this lesson.

INTRODUCING THE LESSON

🕐 5-Minute Check
(over Lesson 1-4)

Solve each equation.

1. $0 + r = 5$ **5**
2. $b \cdot 1 = 3$ **3**

Name the property illustrated by each statement.

3. If $3 + 0 = 3$, then $3 = 3 + 0$.   **Symmetric (=)**
4. $3(0) = 3(0)$ **Reflexive (=)**
5. If $8 + 7 = 15$, then $15 = 8 + 7$.   **Symmetric (=)**

Motivating the Lesson

Which of the following expressions represent the area, in square meters, of the large rectangle below?   **2, 3, and 7**

1. $30 + x$ 2. $30 + 6x$
3. $6(5 + x)$ 4. $6(5x)$
5. $30 + x^2$ 6. $11x$
7. $(5 + x)6$ 8. $30x$
9. $5 + 6x$ 10. $22 + 2x$

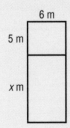

5 m | 6 m
x m

Objective
1-5

After studying this lesson, you should be able to:
- use the distributive property to simplify expressions.

Application

There are four children in the Walker family: Renita, Randy, Robert, and Rochelle. Renita and Robert play basketball; Randy and Rochelle prefer tennis. Mr. and Mrs. Walker buy 2 pairs of basketball shoes for $79.95 each and 2 pairs of tennis shoes for $69.97 each. How much do they spend on athletic shoes?

This problem can be solved in two ways.

1. **Total cost:**
   2 × (cost of basketball shoes plus the cost of tennis shoes)
   $2(\$79.95 + \$69.97) = 2(\$149.92) = \$299.84$

2. **Total cost:**
   (2 × cost of basketball shoes) + (2 × cost of tennis shoes)
   $2(\$79.95) + 2(\$69.97) = \$159.90 + \$139.94 = \$299.84$

Either way you look at it, the Walkers are spending the same amount of money. That's because the following is true.

$$2(\$79.95 + \$69.97) = 2(\$79.95) + 2(\$69.97)$$

This is an example of the **distributive property**.

Distributive Property	For any numbers a, b, and c, $a(b + c) = ab + ac$ and $(b + c)a = ba + ca$; $a(b - c) = ab - ac$ and $(b - c)a = ba - bc$. **Teaching Tip** 

Notice that the distributive property works both ways; that is, it doesn't matter whether a is placed on the right or the left of the expression in parentheses.

Example 1

APPLICATION
Basketball

Find the area of the basketball court in two different ways.

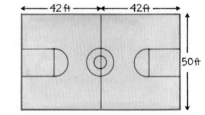

ALTERNATE TEACHING STRATEGIES

Using Manipulatives

Use a rectangular piece of paper as a geometric model to illustrate the distributive property.

The area of the rectangle can be found in two different ways.

Method 1: Multiply the length by the width.
$$A = 8(5 + 4)$$
$$= 8(9) \text{ or } 72$$

Method 2: Add the areas of the smaller rectangles.
$$A = 8(5) + 8(4)$$
$$= 40 + 32 \text{ or } 72$$

Method 1: Multiply the width by the length.

$$A = 50(42 + 42)$$
$$= 50(84)$$
$$= 4200$$

Method 2: Add the areas of the smaller rectangles.

$$A = 50(42) + 50(42)$$
$$= 2100 + 2100$$
$$= 4200$$

The area is 4200 ft².

You can use the distributive property to multiply in your head.

Example 2

Use the distributive property to find each product.

a. $5 \cdot 97 = 5(100 - 3)$
$$= 5 \cdot 100 - 5 \cdot 3$$
$$= 500 - 15$$
$$= 485$$

b. $12(8.5) = 12(8 + 0.5)$
$$= (12)(8) + (12)(0.5)$$
$$= 96 + 6$$
$$= 102$$

The symmetric property of equality allows the distributive property to be rewritten as follows.

If $a(b + c) = ab + ac$, then $ab + ac = a(b + c)$.

A **term** is a number, a variable, or a product or quotient of numbers and variables. Some examples of terms are $5x^2$, $\frac{ab}{4}$, and $7k$. Like terms are terms that contain the same variables, with corresponding variables raised to the same power. Some pairs of like terms are $5x$ and $3x$, $2xy$ and $7xy$, and $7ax^2$ and $11ax^2$.

Note that x and x² are not like terms.

An expression in **simplest form** has no like terms and no parentheses.

Example 3

Simplify $5a + 7a$.

$5a + 7a = (5 + 7)a$ *Distributive property*

$\qquad = 12a$ *Substitution property of equality* **Teaching Tip ❷**

LESSON 1-5 THE DISTRIBUTIVE PROPERTY 27

Teaching Tip ③ When the text refers to a coefficient, it will be referring to the numerical coefficient of the term.

Teaching Tip ④ Emphasize that $9n^2$ and $10n$ cannot be combined into one term because of the different exponents.

Teaching Tip ⑤ Emphasize that the coefficient in $\frac{b}{2}$ is $\frac{1}{2}$. This is often difficult for students.

Reteaching Masters Booklet, p. 5

Example 4 | Simplify $\frac{4}{5}x^2y - \frac{2}{5}x^2y$.

$\begin{aligned}\frac{4}{5}x^2y - \frac{2}{5}x^2y &= \left(\frac{4}{5} - \frac{2}{5}\right)x^2y &&\textit{Distributive property}\\[4pt] &= \frac{2}{5}x^2y &&\textit{Substitution property of equality}\end{aligned}$

Teaching Tip ③   The **coefficient** is the numerical part of a term. For example, in $6ab$, the coefficient is 6. In rs, the coefficient is 1 since, by the multiplicative identity property, $1 \cdot rs = rs$. Like terms may also be defined as terms that are the same or that differ only in their coefficients.

Example 5 | **Name the coefficient in each term.**

a. $19g^2h$ The coefficient is 19.

b. xy^2z^2 The coefficient is 1 since $xy^2z^2 = 1xy^2z^2$.

c. $\frac{2x^3}{5}$ The coefficient is $\frac{2}{5}$ since $\frac{2x^3}{5}$ can be written as $\frac{2}{5}(x^3)$.

Example 6 | Simplify $8n^2 + n^2 + 7n + 3n$. **Teaching Tip ④**

$\begin{aligned}8n^2 + n^2 + 7n + 3n &= 8n^2 + 1n^2 + 7n + 3n &&\textit{Multiplicative identity property}\\ &= (8+1)n^2 + (7+3)n &&\textit{Distributive property}\\ &= 9n^2 + 10n &&\textit{Substitution property of equality}\end{aligned}$

Example 7 | Simplify $\frac{b}{2} + b$. **Teaching Tip ⑤**

$\begin{aligned}\frac{b}{2} + b &= \frac{1}{2}b + 1b &&\textit{Multiplicative identity property}\\[4pt] &= \left(\frac{1}{2} + 1\right)b &&\textit{Distributive property}\\[4pt] &= \left(\frac{1}{2} + \frac{2}{2}\right)b &&\textit{Substitution property of equality}\\[4pt] &= \frac{3}{2}b &&\textit{Substitution property of equality}\end{aligned}$

Example 8 | Use a calculator to simplify $374.2n + 582.6n + 52.38y + 38.02y$.
Teaching Tip ⑥

By the distributive property,
$\begin{aligned}374.2n + 582.6n + 52.38y + 38.02y &= (374.2 + 582.6)n + (52.38 + 38.02)y\\ &= 956.8n + 90.4y.\end{aligned}$

Since $956.8n$ and $90.4y$ are not like terms, the expression $956.8n + 90.4y$ is in simplest form.

RETEACHING THE LESSON

Explain how the multiplication algorithm is just an example of the Distributive Property. Students should demonstrate this by using an example like the following.

$$\begin{array}{r}14\\ \times\ 76\\ \hline 84 = 14 \times 6\\ +\ 980 = 14 \times 70\\ \hline 1064 = 14(70 + 6)\end{array}$$

CHECKING FOR UNDERSTANDING

Communicating Mathematics

Read and study the lesson to answer each question.

1. Write the distributive property in four different ways. **See margin.**

2. The distributive property is sometimes called the distributive property of multiplication over addition (or subtraction). Why do you think it is called that? **Answers will vary.**

Guided Practice

Name the coefficient in each term.

3. $5m$ **5**
4. a^2q **1**
5. $\frac{am}{3}$ **$\frac{1}{3}$**
6. $0.5bm$ **0.5**

Name the like terms in each list of terms.

7. $6b, 6bc, bc$ **$6bc, bc$**
8. $7a, 7a^2, 29a, 7a^3$ **$7a, 29a$**
9. $4xy, 5xy, 6xy^2, 6x^2y$ **$4xy, 5xy$**
10. $2rs^2, r^2s, rs^2$ **$2rs^2, rs^2$**

Simplify each expression, if possible. If not possible, write *in simplest form.*

11. $x + x + x + x + x$ **$5x$**
12. yyy **y^3**
13. $x + \frac{1}{x}$ **in simplest form**
14. $0(x + y)$ **0**

EXERCISES

Practice   **A**

Mental Math: Find each product mentally.

15. $3 \cdot 215$ **645**
16. $4 \cdot 98$ **392**

Use the distributive property to rewrite each expression.

17. $8(3x + 7)$ **$24x + 56$**
18. $4m - 4n$ **$4(m - n)$**

Simplify each expression, if possible. If not possible, write *in simplest form.*
25. in simplest form   26. $12a + 15b$ 30. in simplest form

19. $13a + 5a$ **$18a$**
20. $21x - 10x$ **$11x$**
21. $3(5am - 4)$ **$15am - 12$**
22. $15x^2 + 7x^2$ **$22x^2$**
23. $9y^2 + 13y^2 + 3$ **$22y^2 + 3$**
24. $11a^2 - 11a^2 + 12a^2$ **$12a^2$**
25. $14a^2 + 13b^2 + 27$
26. $5a + 7a + 10b + 5b$
27. $3(x + 2y) - 2y$ **$3x + 4y$**
28. $5x + 3(x - y)$ **$8x - 3y$**
29. $6(5a + 3b - 2b)$ **$30a + 6b$**
30. $5ab^2 + 2a^2b + a^2b^2$
31. $4(3x + 2) + 2(x + 3)$ **$14x + 14$**
32. $x^2 + \frac{7}{8}x - \frac{x}{8}$ **$x^2 + \frac{3}{4}x$**

B

C

Additional Answers

1. $a(b + c) = ab + ac;$
$(b + c)a = ba + bc;$
$a(b - c) = ab - ac;$
$(b - c)a = ba + ca$

Teaching Tip 6   Point out that by using a calculator to simplify expressions like these, students can concentrate more on algebra and less on routine arithmetic.

EVALUATING THE LESSON

Checking for Understanding

Exercises 1-14 are designed to help you assess understanding through reading, writing, and speaking. You should work through Exercises 1-2 with your students, and then monitor their work on Exercises 3-14.

Error Analysis

Students may express $4(x - y)$ as $4x - y$. Remind them that in the first expression, both x and y are multiplied by 4 while in the second, only x is multiplied by 4. Students may also apply the distributive property to multiplication or division problems. They might express $5(2 \cdot x)$ as $10 \cdot 5x$. Emphasize that multiplication only distributes over addition or subtraction.

Assignment Guide

Basic: 15-25, 27, 29, 31, 37-45
Average: 16, 18, 21-32, 35, 37-45
Enriched: 23-45

Practice Masters Booklet, p. 5

NAME _____   DATE _____

1-5 Practice Worksheet

The Distributive Property
Use the Distributive Property to rewrite each expression.

1. $5(2x + 7)$ **$10x + 35$**
2. $6x - 6y$ **$6(x - y)$**
3. $3(m + n)$ **$3m + 3n$**
4. $3p - 3q$ **$3(p - q)$**

Simplify each expression, if possible. If not possible, write in simplest form.

5. $2x + 8x$ **$10x$**
6. $17j + j$ **$18j$**
7. $4ab + ab$ **$5ab$**
8. $2x^2 + 6x^2$ **$8x^2$**
9. $16m - 10m$ **$6m$**
10. $5t^3 - 3t^3$ **$2t^3$**
11. $15i^2 - 15i^2$ **0**
12. $3(5 + 2h)$ **$15 + 6h$**
13. $5(r + 2) + 7r$ **$12r + 10$**
14. $a + b + a + c$ **$2a + b + c$**
15. $6x + 7(y + x)$ **$13x + 7y$**
16. $3(r + 2s) - 3r$ **$6s$**
17. $10c + 5c + 6d + d$ **$15c + 7d$**
18. $(x + 5)y + 2y$ **$xy + 7y$**
19. $7rs + 2rs + 3rs$ **$12rs$**
20. $w + 14w - 6w$ **$9w$**
21. $4.5v + 23v + v$ **$28.5v$**
22. $3r^2 + 6r + 2s^2$ **in simplest form**
23. $c^2 + 4d^2 + d^2 + 3d$ **$c^2 + 3d + 5d^2$**
24. $\frac{1}{3}n + \frac{2}{5}n$ **$\frac{11}{15}n$**
25. $a + \frac{1}{3}b + \frac{4}{3}a + \frac{7}{3}b$ **$\frac{5}{3}a + \frac{5}{3}b$**
26. $35a + 5n + 2(n - 1)$ **$35a + 7n - 2$**

Use a calculator to simplify each expression. See margin.

33. $3.047xy^3 - 0.012y^3 + 5.78xy^3$
34. $1.042a^2 + 8.0879a + 5.265a$
35. $1436x^2 - 789x^2 + 5689x^2$
36. $5.8rs^3 - 4.06rs^3 + 0.92r^2s$

Teaching Tip ⑦

Critical Thinking

37. If $2(b + c) = 2b + 2c$, does $2 + (b \cdot c) = (2 + b)(2 + c)$? Choose values for b and c to show that these may be true or find *counterexamples* to show that they are not. **Answers will vary.**

Applications

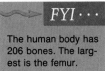

FYI · · ·

The human body has 206 bones. The largest is the femur.

38. **Retailing** Maria and Mark are salesclerks at a local department store. Each earns $4.95 per hour. Maria works 24 hours per week and Mark works 32 hours per week. How much do the two of them earn together each week? **$277.20**

39. **Archaeology** To calculate the height of a person, archaeologists measure the lengths of certain bones. The bones measured are the femur or thigh bone (F), the tibia or leg bone (T), the humerus or upper arm bone (H), and the radius or lower arm bone (R). When the length of one of these bones is known, scientists can use one of the formulas below to determine the person's height (h), in centimeters.

Males	Females
$h = 69.089 + 2.238F$	$h = 61.412 + 2.317F$
$h = 81.688 + 2.392T$	$h = 72.572 + 2.533T$
$h = 73.570 + 2.970H$	$h = 64.977 + 3.144H$
$h = 80.405 + 3.650R$	$h = 73.502 + 3.876R$

a. The femur of a 37-year-old woman measured 47.9 cm. Use a calculator to find the height of the woman to the nearest tenth of a centimeter. **172.4 cm**

b. The humerus of a 49-year-old man measured 35.7 cm. Use a calculator to find the height of the man to the nearest tenth of a centimeter. **179.6 cm**

Computers

Teaching Tip ⑧

40. Use the BASIC program at the right to test whether the distributive property extends to division and exponents. Input different values for A, B, and C.

```
10 INPUT A,B,C
20 PRINT "A = ";A,"B = ";B,"C = ";C
30 PRINT "(A + B)/C = ";(A+B)/C
40 PRINT "A/C + B/C = ";A/C+B/C
50 PRINT
60 PRINT "(A + B)↑C = ";(A+B)↑C
70 PRINT "A↑C + B↑C = ";A↑C+B↑C
```

a. Does $\dfrac{a + b}{c} = \dfrac{a}{c} + \dfrac{b}{c}$? **yes**

b. Does $(a + b)^c = a^c + b^c$? **no**

Mixed Review

41. Write $3 \cdot 3 \cdot a \cdot a \cdot a$ as an expression using exponents. **(Lesson 1-1)** 3^2a^3 or $9a^3$

42. Evaluate $196 \div [4(11 - 4)]$. **(Lesson 1-2)** 7

43. Solve the equation $9.6 + 4.53 = b$. **(Lesson 1-3)** 14.13

44. Name the property shown by the following: If $19 - 3 = 16$, then $16 = 19 - 3$. **(Lesson 1-4)** symmetric (=)

45. Solve the equation $4 + 5 \cdot 0 = y$. **(Lesson 1-4)** 4

EXTENDING THE LESSON

Math Power: Connections

Carita placed six 2-cm by 2-cm squares flat on her desk so that each square had one side in common with at least one other square. What are the possible perimeters for all the figures she can make? (Hint: Make drawings for all the possible figures.) **20 cm, 24 cm, 28 cm**

Additional Answers

33. $8.827xy^3 - 0.012y^3$
34. $1.042a^2 + 13.3529a$
35. $6336x^2$
36. $1.74rs^3 + 0.92r^2s$

Commutative and Associative Properties

Objective
1-6

After studying this lesson, you should be able to:
- recognize and use the commutative and associative properties when simplifying expressions.

Application

John Mattox owns a roofing business. He has a contract to roof three houses for Tradition Homes. These houses require 800, 1050, and 1200 square feet of shingles respectively. How many square feet of shingles are needed to roof the three houses?

To find the sum of the three numbers easily, you can use the **commutative property** and the **associative property**.

Commutative Properties	For any numbers a and b, $a + b = b + a$ and $a \cdot b = b \cdot a$.

The commutative property says that the order in which you add or multiply two numbers does not change their sum or product.

$$800 + 1050 + 1200 = 800 + 1200 + 1050 \qquad \textit{Commutative property (+)}$$

Teaching Tip ① One easy way to evaluate $800 + 1200 + 1050$ is to group, or *associate*, the numbers. The associative property allows you to do this.

Associative Properties	For any numbers a, b, and c, $(a + b) + c = a + (b + c)$ and $(ab)c = a(bc)$.

The associative property says that the way you group three numbers when adding or multiplying does not change their sum or product. Since you can add 800 and 1200 mentally, group them together.

$$
\begin{aligned}
800 + (1200 + 1050) &= (800 + 1200) + 1050 \qquad \textit{Associative property (+)} \\
&= 2000 + 1050 \qquad\qquad\;\; \textit{Substitution property (=)} \\
&= 3050
\end{aligned}
$$

So John needs 3050 square feet of shingles to roof the three houses.

LESSON 1-6 COMMUTATIVE AND ASSOCIATIVE PROPERTIES **31**

ALTERNATE TEACHING STRATEGIES

Using Connections

The commutative and associative properties are used in many different areas of mathematics and science where numerical computations are necessary. For example, both of the properties are used when determining probabilities, interpreting statistics or analyzing mixtures in chemistry. Ask students to make a list of different mathematic or scientific applications for the commutative and associative properties.

1-6 Lesson Notes

Lesson Resources
- Reteaching Master 1-6
- Practice Master 1-6
- Enrichment Master 1-6
- Video Algebra, 6, 7

 Transparency 1-6 contains the 5-Minute Check and a teaching aid for this lesson.

INTRODUCING THE LESSON

🕐 5-Minute Check
(over Lesson 1-5)

Simplify each expression.

1. $8a^3b + 9a^3b - 2a^2b$.
   $17a^3b - 2a^2b$
2. $a(2a + 3b) - ab$ $2a^2 - 2ab$
3. $3m + 2n + 4p + 3n - m$
   $2m + 5n + 4p$
4. $4(3x + 2y) + 6(3y - 2x)$
   $26y$
5. $2(7x + y) + 4(3x + 2y)$
   $26x + 10y$

Motivating the Lesson
Have students list the steps they would follow, in order, when wrapping a gift. Then have them indicate on the list what steps cannot come after other steps. For example, tissue paper cannot be placed in the package after ribbon has been wrapped around the package.

TEACHING THE LESSON

Teaching Tip ① Ask students to explain the difference between the commutative and associative properties. The commutative properties allow a different *ordering* of numbers while the associative properties allow a different *grouping* of numbers.

Example 1

CONNECTION

Geometry

Find the volume of a rectangular prism 4 inches long, $3\frac{1}{2}$ inches wide, and $\frac{1}{2}$ inch high.

Recall that the volume (V) of a rectangular prism is the length (ℓ) times the width (w) times the height (h).

$V = \ell w h$
$\quad = (4)\left(3\frac{1}{2}\right)\left(\frac{1}{2}\right)$
$\quad = (4)\left(\frac{1}{2}\right)\left(3\frac{1}{2}\right) \qquad$ *Commutative property* ($\times$)
$\quad = (2)\left(3\frac{1}{2}\right)$
$\quad = 7$

The volume of the prism is 7 in³.

The commutative and associative properties can be used with the other properties you have studied when simplifying expressions.

Example 2

Simplify $3x + (5 + 6x)$, indicating all of the properties used.

$3x + (5 + 6x) = 3x + (6x + 5) \qquad$ *Commutative property* (+)
$\qquad\qquad\quad = (3x + 6x) + 5 \qquad$ *Associative property* (+)
$\qquad\qquad\quad = (3 + 6)x + 5 \qquad$ *Distributive property*
$\qquad\qquad\quad = 9x + 5 \qquad$ *Substitution property* (=)

The chart below summarizes the properties that are used when simplifying expressions.

The following properties are true for any numbers a, b, and c.		
	Addition	**Multiplication**
Commutative	$a + b = b + a$	$ab = ba$
Associative	$(a + b) + c = a + (b + c)$	$(ab)c = a(bc)$
Identity	0 is the identity. $a + 0 = 0 + a = a$	1 is the identity. $a \cdot 1 = 1 \cdot a = a$
Zero		$a \cdot 0 = 0 \cdot a = 0$
Distributive	$a(b + c) = ab + ac$ and $(b + c)a = ba + ca$	
Substitution	If $a = b$, then a may be substituted for b.	

Example 3

Simplify $5n + 2(n^2 + 4n) + n^2$, indicating all of the properties used.

$5n + 2(n^2 + 4n) + n^2 = 5n + (2n^2 + 8n) + n^2 \qquad$ *Distributive property*
$\qquad\qquad\qquad\qquad = 5n + (8n + 2n^2) + n^2 \qquad$ *Commutative property* (+)
$\qquad\qquad\qquad\qquad = (5n + 8n) + (2n^2 + 1n^2) \qquad$ *Associative property* (+)
$\qquad\qquad\qquad\qquad = (5 + 8)n + (2 + 1)n^2 \qquad$ *Distributive property*
$\qquad\qquad\qquad\qquad = 13n + 3n^2 \qquad$ *Substitution property* (=)

CHECKING FOR UNDERSTANDING

Communicating Mathematics

Name the property illustrated by each statement. See margin.

1. The way you group numbers when adding doesn't change their sum.

2. The order that you multiply numbers doesn't change their product.

Guided Practice

Name the property illustrated by each statement. See margin.

3. $(8 + 4) + 2 = 8 + (4 + 2)$
4. $5 + 3 = 3 + 5$
5. $8(a + b) = 8a + 8b$
6. $(3 + 8) + x = 11 + x$
7. $3x = x \cdot 3$
8. $(a + b) + 3 = a + (b + 3)$
9. $5(ab) = (5a)b$
10. $cb + ab = (c + a)b$
11. $10(x + y) = 10(y + x)$
12. $3(a + 2b) = (a + 2b)3$

Name the property that justifies each step.

13. Simplify $6a + (8b + 2a)$.
  a. $6a + (8b + 2a) = 6a + (2a + 8b)$ commutative property (+)
  b. $\qquad = (6a + 2a) + 8b$ associative property (+)
  c. $\qquad = (6 + 2)a + 8b$ distributive property
  d. $\qquad = 8a + 8b$ substitution property (=)

14. Simplify $8a^2 + (8a + a^2) + 7a$.
  a. $8a^2 + (8a + a^2) + 7a = 8a^2 + (a^2 + 8a) + 7a$ commutative (+)
  b. $\qquad = (8a^2 + a^2) + (8a + 7a)$ associative (+)
  c. $\qquad = (8a^2 + 1a^2) + (8a + 7a)$ mult. identity
  d. $\qquad = (8 + 1)a^2 + (8 + 7)a$ distributive
  e. $\qquad = 9a^2 + 15a$ substitution (=)

EXERCISES

Practice

Name the property illustrated by each statement. See margin.

15. $5a + 2b = 2b + 5a$
16. $1 \cdot a^2 = a^2$
17. $(a + 3b) + 2c = a + (3b + 2c)$
18. $x^2 + (y + z) = x^2 + (z + y)$
19. $ax + 2b = xa + 2b$
20. $(3 \cdot x) \cdot y = 3 \cdot (x \cdot y)$
21. $29 + 0 = 29$
22. $5(a + 3b) = 5a + 15b$
23. $5a + 3b = 3b + 5a$
24. $5a + \left(\frac{1}{2}b + c\right) = \left(5a + \frac{1}{2}b\right) + c$

LESSON 1-6   COMMUTATIVE AND ASSOCIATIVE PROPERTIES   33

Additional Answers

1. Associative property of addition
2. Commutative property of multiplication
3. Associative property of addition
4. Commutative property of addition
5. Distributive property
6. Substitution (=)
7. Commutative property of multiplication
8. Associative property of addition
9. Associative property of multiplication
10. Distributive property
11. Commutative property of addition
12. Commutative property of multiplication
15. Commutative property of addition
16. Multiplicative identity property
17. Associative property of addition
18. Commutative property of addition

Closing the Lesson

Writing Activity Have students list the different properties discussed in Lessons 1-4, 1-5, and 1-6 along with an example of each property.

APPLYING THE LESSON

Homework Exercises

See assignment guide on page 33.

Chapter 1, Quiz C, (Lessons 1-5 through 1-6), is available in the Evaluation Masters Booklet, p. 10.

Teaching Tip ❷ For Exercise 43c, you may want to prepare students for the future work in combinatorics (counting) by pointing out that they are actually counting the number of ways that 3 things—in this case, numbers—can be arranged.

Practice Masters Booklet, p. 6

Name the property illustrated by each statement. See margin.

▷ 25. The quantity m plus n times a equals m times a plus n times a.

26. Zero plus 7 equals 7.

27. The product of one and the quantity a plus b equals a plus b.

28. Three times m plus n times q equals 3 times m plus q times n.

Simplify. 33. $3a + 13b + 2c$ 34. $5 + 9ac + 14b$

29. $5a + 6b + 7a$ $12a + 6b$
30. $8x + 2y + x$ $9x + 2y$
31. $3x + 2y + 2x + 8y$ $5x + 10y$
32. $\frac{2}{3}x^2 + 5x + x^2$ $\frac{5}{3}x^2 + 5x$
33. $3a + 5b + 2c + 8b$
34. $5 + 7(ac + 2b) + 2ac$

▷ 35. $3(4x + y) + 2x$ $14x + 3y$
36. $3(x + 2y) + 4(3x + y)$ $15x + 10y$
37. $\frac{3}{4} + \frac{2}{3}(x + 2y) + x$ $\frac{3}{4} + \frac{5}{3}x + \frac{4}{3}y$
38. $\frac{3}{5}(\frac{1}{2}x + 2y) + 2x$ $\frac{23}{10}x + \frac{6}{5}y$
39. $0.2(3x + 0.2) + 0.5(5x + 3)$
$3.1x + 1.54$
40. $3[4 + 5(2x + 3y)]$
$12 + 30x + 45y$

Critical Thinking 41. Is $24 \div 6 = 6 \div 24$? Is $36 \div 9 = 9 \div 36$? Write a sentence about division and the commutative property. No, no; Division is not commutative.

42. Is $12 - 8 = 8 - 12$? Is $27 - 10 = 10 - 27$? Write a sentence about subtraction and the commutative property. No, no; Subtraction is not commutative.

Applications 43. **Marketing** Betty Castillo is the product manager for Toasty Oatsies cereal. Part of her job is to determine in what size box Toasty Oatsies should be packaged. Betty can choose from among the following sizes: 8″ by 11″ by $2\frac{1}{2}$″, $8\frac{1}{2}$″ × 10″ × 2″, or $7\frac{7}{8}$″ by 11″ by 3″.

a. Name the size that has the greatest volume. $7\frac{7}{8}$″ × 11″ × 3″

b. Write an expression to represent the volume of the largest box in three different ways. See margin.

c. In how many different ways can you write this expression? 6 ways Teaching Tip ❷

44. **America** The United States flag has either 5 stars or 6 stars in each row. Rows of 5 stars alternate with rows of 6 stars. How many rows are there with 6 stars? 5 rows

45. **Volleyball** In the game of volleyball, the top of the net is 7 feet 11 inches from the floor. The bottom of the net is 4 feet 8 inches from the floor. How wide is a volleyball net? 39 inches or 3 feet 3 inches

34 CHAPTER 1 AN INTRODUCTION TO ALGEBRA

Additional Answers

19. Commutative property of multiplication
20. Associative property of multiplication
21. Additive identity property
22. Distributive property
23. Commutative property of addition
24. Associative property of addition
25. Distributive property
26. Additive identity property
27. Multiplicative identity property

28. Commutative property of multiplication

43b. Answers will vary. Possible answers are

$7\frac{7}{8}$″ × 11″ × 3″,

$7\frac{7}{8}$″ × 3″ × 11″,

11″ × $7\frac{7}{8}$″ × 3″,

11″ × 3″ × $7\frac{7}{8}$″,

3″ × $7\frac{7}{8}$″ × 11″, and

3″ × 11″ × $7\frac{7}{8}$″.

46. Weather Meteorologists can predict when a storm will hit their area by examining the travel time of the storm system. To do this, they use the following formula.

$$\begin{array}{ccc} \text{distance of system} & \div \text{ speed of system} & = \text{ travel time of system} \\ \text{(in miles)} & \text{(in miles per hour)} & \text{(in hours)} \end{array}$$

It is 4:00 P.M., and a storm is heading towards the coast at a speed of 30 miles per hour. The storm is about 150 miles from the coast. What time will the storm hit? **9:00 P.M.**

Mixed Review

47. Write an algebraic expression for *twice the square of a number.* **(Lesson 1-1)** $2x^2$

Evaluate each expression if $c = 3$, $x = 0.2$, and $y = 1.3$. **(Lesson 1-2)**

48. $c^2 + y^2$ **10.69**

49. $(15x)^3 - y$ **25.7**

50. Solve the equation $\frac{5}{6} \cdot 18 = m$. **(Lesson 1-3)** **15**

51. Name the coefficient of $\frac{4am^2}{5}$. **(Lesson 1-5)** $\frac{4}{5}$

52. Simplify the expression $9a + 14(a + 3)$. **(Lesson 1-5)** $23a + 42$

Name the property illustrated by each statement. **53. substitution (=)**

53. If $a + b = c$ and $a = b$, then $a + a = c$. **(Lesson 1-4)**

54. $3(4 + 12) = 3(4) + 3(12)$ **(Lesson 1-5)** distributive property

---

HISTORY CONNECTION

Sir William Rowan Hamilton

The use of the term *associative* is often credited to Sir William Rowan Hamilton (1805–1865). Hamilton was a mathematician who studied and taught at Trinity College in Dublin, Ireland. A child prodigy, he was appointed Royal Astronomer of Ireland, Director of the Dunsink Observatory, and Professor of Astronomy at Trinity College at age 22, and was knighted at age 30. Hamilton also holds the distinction of being the first foreign associate named to the National Academy of Sciences in the United States.

EXTENDING THE LESSON

Math Power: Reasoning

Define the operation ∗ as follows: *For any numbers a and b, a ∗ b = a + b + ab.* Use the commutative and associative properties to show that the operation ∗ is commutative.

$$a * b \stackrel{?}{=} b * a$$
$$a + b + ab \stackrel{?}{=} b + a + ba$$
$$a + b + ab = a + b + ba$$

History

History features introduce students to people who were involved in the development of mathematics. You may want to encourage some students to further research Hamilton or to research the term commutative as it applies to mathematics.

Enrichment Masters Booklet, p. 6

NAME _____ DATE _____

1-6 Enrichment Worksheet

Properties of Operations

Let us make up a new operation and denote it by ⊙, so that $a \odot b$ means b^a.
$2 \odot 3 = 3^2 = 9$
$(1 \odot 2) \odot 3 = 2^1 \odot 3 = 3^2 = 9$

1. What number is represented by $2 \odot 3$? $\underline{3^2 = 9}$
2. What number is represented by $3 \odot 2$? $\underline{2^3 = 8}$
3. Does the operation ⊙ appear to be commutative? __no__
4. What number is represented by $(2 \odot 1) \odot 3$? __3__
5. What number is represented by $2 \odot (1 \odot 3)$? __9__
6. Does the operation ⊙ appear to be associative? __no__

Let us make up another operation and denote it by ⊙,
so that $a \odot b = (a + 1)(b + 1)$.
$3 \odot 2 = (3 + 1)(2 + 1) = 4 \cdot 3 = 12$
$(1 \odot 2) \odot 3 = (2 \cdot 3) \odot 3 = 6 \odot 3 = 7 \cdot 4 = 28$

7. What number is represented by $2 \odot 3$? __12__
8. What number is represented by $3 \odot 2$? __12__
9. Does the operation ⊙ appear to be commutative? __yes__
10. What number is represented by $(2 \odot 3) \odot 4$? __65__
11. What number is represented by $2 \odot (3 \odot 4)$? __63__
12. Does the operation ⊙ appear to be associative? __no__
13. What number is represented by $1 \odot (3 \odot 2)$? __12__
14. What number is represented by $(1 \odot 3) \odot (1 \odot 2)$? __12__
15. Does the operation ⊙ appear to be distributive over the operation ⊙? __yes__
16. Let us explore these operations a little further. What number is represented by $3 \odot (4 \odot 2)$? __3375__
17. What number is represented by $(3 \odot 4) \odot (3 \odot 2)$? __585__
18. Is the operation ⊙ actually distributive over the operation ⊙? __no__

INTRODUCING THE LESSON

5-Minute Check
(over Lesson 1-6)

Name the property illustrated by each statement.

1. $by + 3a = yb + 3a$
   commutative property of multiplication
2. $4b + 5c = 5c + 4b$
   commutative property of addition
3. $(2 \cdot a) \cdot b = 2 \cdot (a \cdot b)$
   associative property of multiplication

Simplify.

4. $4x + 5y + 3z + 6x$
   $10x + 5y + 3z$
5. $4(3a + b) + 3a$ **$15a + 4b$**

Motivating the Lesson

How far can Brad travel if he drives 55 miles per hour for 1 hour? for 2 hours? for 3 hours? What will these three distances be if instead he drives 45 miles per hour? Based on these results, write an equation that relates distance traveled (*d*), rate of speed (*r*), and time (*t*).
55 miles, 110 miles, 165 miles; 45 miles, 90 miles, 135 miles; $d = rt$

TEACHING THE LESSON

Teaching Tip ❶ Point out that although *x* and *y* are often used as variables, it is acceptable to use any letter, uppercase or lowercase, as a variable.

1-7 Formulas

Objective
1-7
After studying this lesson, you should be able to:
- translate verbal sentences into equations or formulas.

A **formula** is an equation that states a rule for the relationship between certain quantities.

Application

The First Community Bank shows the time and temperature on an electronic billboard. The temperature is given in degrees Celsius. If the temperature shown is 25°C, what is the temperature in degrees Fahrenheit?

FYI ···

The highest temperature ever recorded was 136.4°F at El Azizia, Libya on Sept. 13, 1922.

Use the formula $F = \frac{9}{5}C + 32$. The variables F and C represent the degree measures in Fahrenheit and Celsius, respectively.

$F = \frac{9}{5}C + 32$

$F = \frac{9}{5}(25) + 32$ *Replace C with 25.*

$F = 45 + 32$

$F = 77$

The temperature is 77°F.

Example 1

CONNECTION

Geometry

The formula for the area of a triangle is $A = \frac{1}{2}bh$. Find the area of a triangle with a base (*b*) of 6 feet and a height (*h*) of 9 feet.

$A = \frac{1}{2}bh$

$= \frac{1}{2}(6)(9)$

$= 3 \cdot 9$

$= 27$

The area of the triangle is 27 ft².

Teaching Tip

❶ Many sentences can be written as equations or formulas. Use variables to represent the unspecified numbers or measures referred to in the sentence. Then write the verbal expressions as algebraic expressions. Some verbal expressions that suggest the *equals sign* are listed below.

- is
- equals
- is equal to
- is the same as
- is as much as
- is identical to

ALTERNATE TEACHING STRATEGIES

Using Communication

Have students write and then compare the algebraic expressions for each verbal expression.

1. square of the sum of *x* and *a*; sum of the square of *x* and the square of *a*   **$(x + a)^2$; $x^2 + a^2$**
2. product of *m*, *n*, and the square of *p*; product of the squares of *m*, *n*, and *p*; square of the product of *m*, *n*, and *p*   **mnp^2, $m^2n^2p^2$, $(mnp)^2$**

Using Connections

This lesson contains many connections to geometry. You may want students to make a list of common formulas from geometry for perimeter, area, and distance.

Example 2

Translate the sentence below into an equation.
The number z is equal to twice the sum of x and y.

The number z is equal to twice the sum of x and y.

| z | = | 2 times | add x and y |

The equation is $z = 2(x + y)$.

Example 3

Translate the sentence below into a formula.
The area of a circle equals the product of π and the square of the radius (r).

The area of a circle equals the product of π and the square of the radius (r).

| A | = | multiply | π and | r^2 |

The formula is $A = \pi r^2$.

Sometimes you can discover a formula by making a model.

Example 4

CONNECTION

Geometry

Find the surface area of a rectangular solid.

Take a rectangular box apart. It could look like the model at the right.

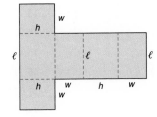

You can find the surface area of the solid by finding the area of each side. Each side is a rectangular surface.

$S = wh + wh + \ell h + \ell h + \ell w + \ell w$
$= 2wh + 2\ell h + 2\ell w$
$= 2(wh + \ell h + \ell w)$

Chalkboard Examples

For Example 1
a. Find the area of a triangle with a base of 5 m and a height of 7.5 m. **18.75 m²**

b. Find the area of a rectangle of length 3.5 mm and width 2.4 mm. **8.4 mm²**

Translate each sentence into an equation or formula.

For Example 2
The number *n* divided by the number *y* equals the number *z*. $\frac{n}{y} = z$

For Example 3
a. The distance (*d*) is equal to the product of the rate (*r*) and the time (*t*). *d = rt*

b. The volume of a cone (*V*) is equal to the area of its base (*a*) times its height (*h*) divided by 3. $V = \frac{ah}{3}$

For Example 4
Find the surface area of a cube with sides of length *s* cm. The length of all sides of the cube are equal to *s*.
$S = 2(s^2 + s^2 + s^2)$
$= 6s^2$

CHECKING FOR UNDERSTANDING

Communicating Mathematics

Read and study the lesson to answer each question. 1. See margin.

1. Is an equation a type of formula, or is a formula a type of equation?
2. In the formula $C = \frac{5}{9}(F - 32)$, what do the *C* and *F* represent?
   degrees Celsius and Fahrenheit

RETEACHING THE LESSON

Match each verbal statement with the corresponding equation.

1. Two less than five times *d* is *r*. **f**
2. Twice the quantity five less than *d* is equal to *r*. **a**
3. The product of two and *d* decreased by five equals *r*. **b**
4. The product of two and the quantity *d* less than 5 is *r*. **d**

   a. $2(d - 5) = r$
   b. $2d - 5 = r$
   c. $5(2 - d) = r$
   d. $2(5 - d) = r$
   e. $2(5) - d = r$
   f. $5d - 2 = r$

NAME _____ DATE _____

1-7 Reteaching Worksheet

Formulas

Verbal sentences can be translated into equations or formulas. A formula is an equation that states a rule for the relationship between certain quantities.

Example: Find the area of a rectangle of length 15 cm and width 12 cm.
$A = lw$
$A = 15 \cdot 12$
$A = 180$
The area of the rectangle is 180 cm².

12 cm
15 cm

The formula for the volume (V) of a rectangular solid is V = lwh. Complete the chart.

l	w	h	V		l	w	h	V
10	3	5	**1. 150**		16	4	6	**3. 384**
4	7	23	**2. 644**		13	13	**4. 3**	507

The formula for the area (A) of the shaded region of the figure at the right is A = πr² − ½bh. Find the area of the shaded region. Use 3.14 for π. Round each answer to the nearest whole number. The base and height of the triangle are equal to the radius of the circle.

5. *r* = 20 **1056**
6. *h* = 33 **2875**
7. *h* = 4.5 **53**
8. *b* = 9 **214**
9. *b* = 10.3 **280**
10. *r* = 7.2 **137**

Write an equation for each sentence.

11. The cube of *a* decreased by the product of *b* and *c* is *d*.
    $a^3 - bc = d$
12. The number 43 equals the sum of the square of *x* and the cube of *y*.
    $43 = x^2 + y^3$
13. The number *b* equals *n* decreased by twice *c*. $b = n - 2c$
14. The product of *x* and *y* decreased by *z* is *a*. $xy - z = a$
15. *Z* is the square of the product of *a* and *b*. $z = (ab)^2$
16. The sum of twice *n* and the square of *x* is *y*. $2n + x^2 = y$

NAME _____ DATE _____

1-7 Practice Worksheet

Formulas

Write an equation for each sentence.

1. Twice y increased by the square of y is equal to x. $2y + y^2 = x$
2. The square of the product a and b is equal to c. $(ab)^2 = c$
3. The square of t increased by r is equal to s. $t^2 + r = s$
4. The cube of e decreased by f is equal to l. $e^3 - f = l$
5. The product of c and n is equal to the square of c. $cn = c^2$
6. The square of the sum of m and n is equal to p. $(m + n)^2 = p$
7. Twice the product of c and d is equal to the cube of e. $2cd = e^3$
8. The cube of x is equal to the product of x and y. $x^3 = xy$
9. The sum of p and its square is equal to q times n. $p + p^2 = qn$

The formula for the area (A) of a trapezoid as shown below is $A = \frac{1}{2}h(a + b)$. Complete the chart.

	h	a	b	A
10.	8	13	21	136
11.	4	5	7	24
12.	9	26	34	270
13.	4	3.1	5.2	16.6
14.	2	1.6	8.6	10.2
15.	11	4	6	55
16.	9	6	12	81
17.	2	$\frac{3}{2}$	$\frac{5}{2}$	4
18.	$5\frac{1}{2}$	$9\frac{1}{2}$	18	$75\frac{5}{8}$
19.	6	8	12	60
20.	40	20	30	1000
21.	8	0.7	1.7	9.6

Guided Practice Write a formula for each sentence. Use the variables indicated.

3. The area (A) of a square is the square of the length of one of its sides (s). $A = s^2$
4. The perimeter (P) of a parallelogram is twice the sum of the lengths of two adjacent sides (a and b). $P = 2(a + b)$
5. The perimeter (P) of a square is 4 times the length of a side (s). $P = 4s$
6. The circumference (C) of a circle is the product of 2, π, and the radius (r). $C = 2\pi r$

CONNECTION
Geometry

Copy each chart. Then use the formula for the surface area (*SA*) of a rectangular solid to complete the chart.

	ℓ	w	h	SA
7.	5	8	6	236
9.	18	10	4	584
11.	$20\frac{1}{2}$	3	8	499

	ℓ	w	h	SA
8.	$5\frac{1}{2}$	12	$3\frac{1}{2}$	$254\frac{1}{2}$
10.	12.9	11	4.6	503.68
12.	21.8	6.5	9.7	832.42

EXERCISES

Practice Write an equation for each sentence.

 A

13. Twice x increased by the square of y is equal to z. $2x + y^2 = z$
14. The square of a decreased by the cube of b is equal to c. $a^2 - b^3 = c$
15. The square of the sum of x and a is equal to m. $(x + a)^2 = m$
16. The number r equals the cube of the difference of a and b. $r = (a - b)^3$
17. The square of the product of a, b, and c is equal to k. $(abc)^2 = k$
18. The product of a, b, and the square of c is f. $abc^2 = f$
19. Twenty-nine decreased by the product of x and y is equal to z. $29 - xy = z$

CONNECTION
Geometry

The formula for the area (A) of a trapezoid as shown at the right is $A = \frac{1}{2}h(a + b)$. Copy and complete each chart.

B

	h	a	b	A
20.	6	24	19	129
21.	11	37	23	330
22.	12	24	40	384
24.	10	19	54	365
26.	$\frac{5}{8}$	$\frac{3}{4}$	$\frac{1}{2}$	$\frac{25}{64}$

	h	a	b	A
23.	$3\frac{1}{3}$	12	$8\frac{1}{4}$	$33\frac{3}{4}$
25.	4	18.9	12.7	63.2
27.	2.4	8.25	3.15	13.68

Additional Answers

1. A formula is a type of equation.

CONNECTION
Geometry

The formula for the area (A) of the shaded region of the figure below is $A = \frac{1}{2}\pi a^2 - a^2$. Find the area of the shaded region for each value of a to the nearest whole number. Use 3.14 for π. **Teaching Tip**

28. 6 **21**   **29.** 4 **9**   **30.** 81 **3740** **31.** 64 **2335**

32. 3.8 **8**   **33.** 5.6 **18**   **34.** 18.3 **191** **35.** 27.4 **428**

CONNECTION
Geometry

C

Write a formula for the area of each figure.

36.

$A = a^2 - b^2$

37.

$A = s^2 + \frac{\pi}{2}s^2$

38.

$A = \frac{1}{2}\pi a^2$

Critical Thinking

39. The area of a triangle is 420 cm². Its base is 30 cm. Use the formula $A = \frac{1}{2}bh$ to find its height. **28 cm**

41. 19,800 ft

Applications

The distance traveled (d) is equal to the rate (r) times the time (t). Write this sentence as a formula and use it to solve each problem.

40. Travel Find the distance from Danville to the beach if it takes 3 hours to drive there at an average rate of 50 miles per hour. **150 mi**

41. Fitness Kimi runs for 30 minutes each day. Find the distance she runs if she averages 660 feet per minute.

42. Physics The speed of sound through air is about 330 meters per second. Find the distance between Carlos and an explosion if it takes 10 seconds for the sound to reach him. **3300 m**

43. Astronomy The speed of light is about 186,000 miles per second. If the sun is about 93 million miles from Earth, about how long does it take for the rays of the sun to reach Earth? **500 seconds or 8 minutes 20 seconds**

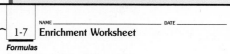

Mixed Review

44. Evaluate $12 \cdot 6 \div 3 \cdot 2 \div 8$. **(Lesson 1-2) 6**

45. Solve the equation $m = 3\frac{1}{3} \div 3$. **(Lesson 1-3) $1\frac{1}{9}$**

46. $b^3, 4b^3$ **46.** Name the like terms in the following list: $a^3, b^3, 3a^2, 4b^3$. **(Lesson 1-5)**

47. $37a + 23b$ **47.** Simplify the expression $16a + 21a + 30b - 7b$. **(Lesson 1-5)**

48. commutative property **48.** State the property shown by $8(2 \cdot 6) = (2 \cdot 6)8$. **(Lesson 1-6)**
of multiplication

EXTENDING THE LESSON

Math Power: Connections

The length and the width of a certain rectangle are whole numbers. Find all possible areas for this rectangle if its perimeter is 16 cm. Use the formulas $A = \ell w$ and $P = 2\ell + 2w$.
The possible dimensions are 1 cm × 7 cm, 2 cm × 6 cm, 3 cm × 5 cm, and 4 cm × 4 cm. Thus, the area could be 7 cm², 12 cm², 15 cm², or 16 cm².

Using Technology

Objective This optional page shows how the BASIC programming language and spreadsheets can be used to perform mathematical computations and to enhance and extend mathematical concepts.

Using Discussion

Point out that most spreadsheets do not follow the rules for order of operation. Usually, spreadsheets evaluate operations from left to right unless grouping symbols are used. For example, the formula for the surface area (*S*) of a rectangular solid, $S = 2(wh + 1h + 1w)$, (found in Example 4 on page 37) would be written as follows in BASIC and in a spreadsheet. For the spreadsheet, assume that the value of length (L) is in cell A3, the value of the width (W) is in cell B3, and the value for the height (H) is in cell C3.

In BASIC:
LET S=2*(W*H+L*H+L*W)

In a spreadsheet:
2*(B3*C3)+(A3*C3)+(A3*B3))

Without the additional parentheses, the spreadsheet would multiply B3 and C3, add A3, multiply this *quantity* by C3, and so on.

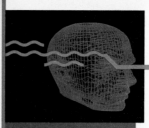

Technology

Formulas

▶ **BASIC**
   Graphing calculator
   Graphing software
▶ **Spreadsheets**

In BASIC, formulas used with READ and DATA statements are helpful when creating charts involving many calculations.

This program makes a chart that finds and records the areas of triangles using the formula $A = \frac{1}{2}bh$.

```
10 PRINT "B","H","A"
20 PRINT
30 READ B, H
40 IF B = 0 THEN 100
50 DATA 4,6,12,10,6,2,5,4
60 DATA 120,91,10,6,15,3,0,0
70 LET A = 0.5*B*H
80 PRINT B,H,A
90 GOTO 30
100 END
```

The READ and DATA statements assign values to the variable *b* for base and *h* for height. Enter and run the program on your computer.

Spreadsheets are computer programs especially designed to create charts involving many calculations. These charts are composed of cells named by column letters and row numbers. In the spreadsheet below, cells A1, B1, and C1 hold the labels B, H, and A for base, height, and area. Cells A3 to A7 hold the values for the base of each triangle. Cells B3 to B7 hold the values for the height of each triangle. Cells C3 to C7 contain the values for the area of each triangle.

```
=====A=======B=======C=======D=======E=======F=====
1:    B        H        A
2:-----------------------------
3:    4        6        12
4:   12       10        60
5:   6,2      5,4       16,74
6:  120       91        5460
7:   10,6     15,3      81,09
```

Each cell in column C holds a formula to compute the area. Cell C3 holds the formula 0.5 * A3 * B3. The formula refers to the cells containing the measures of the base and height of the first triangle.

EXERCISES

1, 3. See margin.   2, 4. See students' work.

1. Write a BASIC program to make a chart for the perimeters of rectangles. Use the formula $P = 2(\ell + w)$. Choose values for the lengths and widths of five rectangles.

2. Set up a spreadsheet to make a chart like the chart in Exercise 1.

3. Write a BASIC program to make a chart for the areas of trapezoids. Use the formula $A = \frac{1}{2}h(a + b)$. Choose values for the heights and bases of five trapezoids.

4. Set up a spreadsheet to make a chart like the chart in Exercise 3.

Additional Answers

1.
```
 10  PRINT "L", "W", "P"
 20  PRINT
 30  READ L, W
 40  IF L = 0 THEN 100
 50  DATA . . .
 60  DATA . . .
 70  LET P = 2 * (L + W)
 80  PRINT L, W, P
 90  GOTO 30
100  END
```

3.
```
 10  PRINT "A", "B", "H",
         "AREA"
 20  PRINT
 30  READ A, B, H
 40  IF A = 0 THEN 100
 50  DATA . . .
 60  DATA . . .
 70  LET A1 = 0.5 * H *
         (A + B)
 80  PRINT A, B, H, A1
 90  GOTO 30
100  END
```

1-8 Problem-Solving: Explore Verbal Problems

Objective
1-8

After studying this lesson, you should be able to:
■ explore problem situations by asking and answering questions.

The four steps that can be used to solve verbal problems are listed below.

Problem-Solving Plan	1. **Explore the problem.** 2. **Plan the solution.** 3. **Solve the problem.** 4. **Examine the solution.**

Let's examine the first step of this plan, exploring the problem. To solve a verbal problem, first read the problem carefully and explore what the problem is about. **Teaching Tip**

■ Identify what information is given.
■ Identify what you are asked to find.
■ Choose a variable to represent one of the unspecified numbers in the problem. This is called *defining the variable.*
■ Use the variable to write expressions for the other unspecified numbers in the problem.

Example

One day John and Inger picked peaches for 4 hours. In all they picked 30 baskets of peaches. Inger picked 6 baskets fewer than John.

Questions	Answers
a. How many baskets were picked in all?	a. 30
b. How long did John and Inger work?	b. 4 hours
c. Who worked longer?	c. They worked the same.
d. Who picked more?	d. John
e. If Inger picked n baskets, how many did John pick?	e. $n + 6$
f. If John picked r baskets, how many did Inger pick?	f. $r - 6$

CHECKING FOR UNDERSTANDING

Communicating Mathematics

Read and study the lesson to answer each question.

1. What is the emphasis of this lesson? **Learning to explore problems.**

2. What happens if you do not understand the problem? **You cannot solve the problem.**

LESSON 1-8 PROBLEM-SOLVING STRATEGY: EXPLORE VERBAL PROBLEMS 41

RETEACHING THE LESSON

Answer each question.

1. John has six fewer pencils than Maria. If Maria has x pencils, how many does John have? **$x - 6$**

2. Marty has 25 books on crafts and hobbies. If he has n books about crafts, how many books about hobbies does he have? **$25 - n$**

3. Bonnie can mow the lawn in 4 hours. In h hours, how much of the lawn will she mow? **$\frac{h}{4}$**

1-8 Lesson Notes

Lesson Resources

• Reteaching Master 1-8
• Practice Master 1-8
• Enrichment Master 1-8
• Activity Master, pp. 1, 46
• Video Algebra, 4

 Transparency 1-8 contains the 5-Minute Check and a teaching aid for this lesson.

INTRODUCING THE LESSON

5-Minute Check
(over Lesson 1-7)

Write an equation for each sentence.

1. Twice the product of r and h plus twice the product of the square of r and h.
   1. $2rh + 2r^2h$ 2. $4(x^2 - 7)$

2. Four times the quantity seven less than x squared.

3. The product of s, t, and the cube of u is w. $stu^3 = w$

4. Thirty-two decreased by the product of a and b is equal to c. $32 - ab = c$

5. The square of the sum of y and c is t. $(y + c)^2 = t$

Reteaching Masters Booklet, p. 8

NAME _____ DATE _____

1-8 **Reteaching Worksheet**

Problem-Solving: Explore Verbal Problems

When solving verbal problems, there are four steps you should follow.

Problem-Solving Plan	*Think:*
1. Explore the problem. 2. Plan the solution. 3. Solve the problem. 4. Examine the solution.	*What do I already know?* *What do I need to find?* *How can I find it?* *Does my solution make sense?*

You can explore a problem situation by asking and answering questions.

Example: One number is twice another number. Their sum is 48.

Questions	Answers
a. How many times as great is one number compared to the other?	a. Two times
b. If the lesser number is n, what is the greater number?	b. $2n$
c. What is the sum of the two numbers?	c. 48

For each situation, answer the related questions.

1. Bob can shovel the snow off the driveway in 2 hours. Laura can shovel the same driveway in 3 hours.
   a. Alone, how much of the driveway can Laura shovel in one hour? $\frac{1}{3}$
   b. Alone, how much of the driveway can Bob shovel in one hour? $\frac{1}{2}$
   c. If they shovel the driveway together using two shovels, can they finish in one hour? No

2. The swim team roster shows that Gene can swim 8 laps in 5 minutes. Sue can swim 10 laps in the same amount of time.
   a. How many laps can Gene swim in 10 minutes? 16
   b. How long does it take Sue to swim 4 laps? 2 minutes
   c. In 30 minutes, Sue will swim how many more laps than Gene? 12

3. A school bus can hold a maximum of 66 students. The bus is five-sixths full. One-fifth of the students on the bus get off at the first stop.
   a. Is the bus full? No
   b. How many students are on the bus when it leaves the school? 55
   c. How many students get off the bus at the first stop? 11

4. Honor students from 3 high schools in Dallas went on a hayride. Each school invited the same number of students, but at the last minute some students could not attend. In the end, 95 students went on the hayride.
   a. If n students could not attend, how many were invited? $n + 95$
   b. Which school invited the most students? They all invited the same number of students.

Motivating the Lesson

Suppose you are your school's newspaper reporter assigned to this afternoon's news conference concerning this year's proposed school budget. Think of five questions you might ask about the budget proposal.

TEACHING THE LESSON

Teaching Tip ❶ Emphasize the importance of establishing a "questioning attitude."

Chalkboard Example

For the Example

Mike is 6 years older than Ray. In 10 years the sum of their ages will be 72.

a. If Ray is y years old now, how old is Mike? $y + 6$

b. If Mike is m years old now, how old will he be in 10 years? $m + 10$

c. What is the sum of their ages now? 52

Practice Masters Booklet, p. 8

NAME _____ DATE _____

| 1-8 | **Practice Worksheet** |

Problem-Solving: Explore Verbal Problems

For each situation, answer the related questions.

1. Otis weighs 15 pounds more than Elbert and Elbert weighs 11 pounds less than Jaime.
 a. Who weighs the most? Otis
 b. Who weighs the least? Elbert
 c. Does Jaime weigh more or less than Otis? less
 d. Otis weighs how much more than Jaime? 4 lb

2. Juanita has written 20 short stories for a publisher. Sabrena has written 6 fewer short stories than Juanita. Glennette has written 2 more stories than Sabrena.
 a. Who has written the most short stories? Juanita
 b. Who has written the fewest short stories? Sabrena
 c. How many more short stories has Juanita written compared to Glennette? 4 short stories
 d. How many more short stories should Sabrena write to match Juanita? 6 short stories

3. Elena is 35 years older than Odette. In 1990, the sum of their ages was 87.
 a. How old was Elena when Odette was born? 35 years
 b. How much older is Elena than Odette in 1991? 35 years
 c. What is the sum of their ages in 1991? 89 years
 d. If Odette's age is x, what is Elena's age? $x + 35$
 e. If Elena's age is y, what is Odette's age? $y - 35$

Guided Practice   **For each situation, answer the related questions.**

3. Louis Limotta checked his cash register at the end of the day. He found that he had 7 fewer $5 bills than $1 bills. He had eleven $10 bills and no larger bills. In all he had $267 in bills.

  a. Did he have more $5 bills or $1 bills? **$1 bills**
  b. How many more? **7**
  c. How much money did he have in all? **$267**
  d. How many $20 bills did he have? **none**
  e. How much money did he have in $1 and $5 bills together? **$157**
  f. When did he check his cash register? **end of the day**
  g. If he had n $5 bills, how much money did he have in $5 bills? **$5n$ dollars**

4. Luisa has 20 books on crafts and cooking. She also has 21 novels. She has 6 more cookbooks than craft books.

  a. Does she have more cookbooks or craft books? **cookbooks**
  b. How many more? **6**
  c. Does she have more novels than craft books? **yes**
  d. How many books does she have in all? **41**
  e. If she has n cookbooks, how many craft books has she? **$20 - n$ or $n - 6$**
  f. Of what kind of book does she have the least? **crafts**

EXERCISES

Practice   **For each situation, answer the related questions.**

Strategies
Look for a pattern.
Solve a simpler problem.
Act it out.
Guess and check.
Draw a diagram.
Make a chart.
Work backwards.

5. Two breakfast cereals, Kornies and Krispies, together cost $3.59. One of them costs 7¢ more than the other.

  a. Which one costs more? **does not say**
  b. What is the difference in their prices? **7¢**
  c. How much would two boxes of each cost? **$7.18**
  d. Would two boxes of the more expensive cereal cost more or less than $3.59? **more**
  e. If the more expensive cereal costs n cents, what is the cost of the other cereal? **$(n - 7)$¢ or $(359 - n)$¢**

6. The Vegetable Mart offers corn at 18¢ per ear, cucumbers at 12¢ each, and tomatoes at 59¢ per basket. Mirna has only $3 to spend and wants one basket of tomatoes and 5 fewer ears of corn than cucumbers.

  a. How many baskets of tomatoes does she want? **1**
  b. How much more is a basket of tomatoes than an ear of corn? **41¢**
  c. After buying the tomatoes, how much money does she have remaining? **$2.41**
  d. Will she buy more cucumbers or ears of corn? **cucumbers**
  e. If she buys n cucumbers, how many ears of corn will she buy? **$n - 5$**

7. Phoebe goes to Pluto's Platters to buy cassette tapes. She bought 3 more rock tapes than classical and 2 fewer western tapes than rock. Including 5 jazz tapes, she bought 18.

   a. Did she buy more classical than rock? **no**
   b. Did she buy more rock than western? **yes**
   c. Which did she buy the most of? **rock**
   d. How many rock, classical, and western tapes did she buy? **13**
   e. If she bought n classical tapes, how many rock tapes did she buy? **$n + 3$**

8. Craig said, "I am 24 years younger than my mom and the sum of our ages is 68 years."

   a. How old was Craig's mother when Craig was born? **24**
   b. How much older than Craig is his mother now? **24 years**
   c. What will be the sum of their ages in 5 years? **78 years**
   d. How old was Craig's mother when Craig was 10 years old? **34**
   e. In ten years, how much younger than his mother will Craig be? **24 years**

9. Selam was working some math problems. She thought that she could finish 3 pages of 24 problems per page in 2 hours. After $1\frac{1}{2}$ hours, she had finished 2 pages.

   a. How many problems had Selam completed in $1\frac{1}{2}$ hours? **48**
   b. How many problems are there in all? **72**
   c. At the rate she is working, will she finish the three pages in 2 hours? **no**

10. Lorena can paint the house in 25 hours. Mia can paint the same house in 30 hours.

    a. Who paints faster, Mia or Lorena? **Lorena**
    b. Working alone, how much of the house can Lorena paint in 20 hours? **$\frac{4}{5}$**
    c. Working alone, how much of the house can Mia paint in x hours? **$\frac{x}{30}$**
    d. If Lorena and Mia work together, how many hours will it take to paint the house? **$13\frac{7}{11}$ hours**

COOPERATIVE LEARNING ACTIVITY

Work in groups of three. Each person in the group must understand your solution and be able to explain it to any person in the class.

In the final round of the game of *Jeopardy*, the contestants have to decide how much money to wager to win the game. During a recent game, the scores were as follows.

Roberta Jackson	Felicia Gonzalez	Peter Thomas
$4800	$5200	$2400

Decide how much each person should wager. Keep in mind that (1) only the person with the most money wins the money, (2) some of the contestants may not get the question right, and (3) you don't know how the other contestants will wager. **Answers will vary.**

LESSON 1-8 PROBLEM-SOLVING STRATEGY: EXPLORE VERBAL PROBLEMS 43

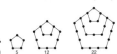

EXTENDING THE LESSON

Math Power: Problem Solving

Working together, Jason and Jenny can clean the house in 12 hours. If Jason worked by himself, how much of the house could he clean in one hour? **$\frac{1}{30}$**

Cooperative Learning Activity

This activity provides students with an opportunity to *learn* things together, not just do things together. You may wish to refer to pages T6-T8 and page 6C for the various elements of cooperative groups and specific goals and strategies for using them.

The Chapter Summary and Review begins with an alphabetical listing of the new terms that were presented in the chapter. Have students define each term and provide an example of it, if appropriate.

The Skills and Concepts presented in the chapter are reviewed using a side-by-side format. Encourage students to refer to the Objectives and Examples on the left as they complete the Review Exercises on the right.

The Chapter Summary and Review ends with exercises that review Applications and Connections.

CHAPTER 1 SUMMARY AND REVIEW

VOCABULARY

Upon completing this chapter, you should be familiar with the following terms:

additive identity	22	18	open sentence
algebraic expression	8	13	order of operations
base	9	10	power
coefficient	28	8	product
element	19	19	replacement set
empty set	19	19	set
equation	19	27	simplest form
exponent	9	19	solution
factor	8	19	subset
formula	36	27	term
like terms	27	8	variable
multiplicative identity	22		

SKILLS AND CONCEPTS

OBJECTIVES AND EXAMPLES	REVIEW EXERCISES
Upon completing this chapter, you should be able to:	Use these exercises to review and prepare for the chapter test.
■ translate verbal expressions into mathematical expressions **(Lesson 1-1)**	**Write an algebraic expression for each verbal expression. Use y as the variable.**
Write an algebraic expression for the verbal expression *twice a number decreased by 17.* $2n - 17$	1. the product of 8 and a number $8y$ 2. twice the cube of a number $2y^3$
■ write an expression containing identical factors as an expression using exponents **(Lesson 1-1)**	**Write as an expression using exponents.**
Write $m \cdot m \cdot m$ as an expression using exponents. m^3	3. $a \cdot a \cdot a \cdot a$ a^4 4. $15 \cdot x \cdot x \cdot x \cdot y \cdot y$ $15x^3y^2$

OBJECTIVES AND EXAMPLES	REVIEW EXERCISES

- use the order of operations to evaluate expressions   (Lesson 1-2)

Evaluate $2x + 2y + z^2$ if $x = 7$, $y = 3$, and $z = 1.5$.

$$2x + 2y + z^2 = 2 \cdot 7 + 2 \cdot 3 + (1.5)^2$$
$$= 14 + 6 + 2.25$$
$$= 22.25$$

Evaluate each expression if $a = 5$, $b = 8$, $c = \frac{2}{3}$, $d = \frac{1}{2}$, and $e = 0.3$.

5. ab^2 320

6. $3ac - bd$ 6

- solve open sentences by performing arithmetic operations   (Lesson 1-3)

$$x = 6(7) + 2^4$$
$$= 42 + 16$$
$$= 58$$

Solve each equation. 8. 15   9. 2.2

7. $a = 29 - 5^2$ 4   8. $5(6) - 3(5) = y$

9. $w = (0.2)(8 + 3)$ 10. $m = \frac{2}{3}\left(3 - \frac{1}{2}\right)$ $\frac{5}{3}$

- recognize and use the properties of identity and equality   (Lesson 1-4)

Name the property illustrated by $(3 + 4) + 2 = 7 + 2$.

substitution property of equality

Name the property illustrated by each statement.

11. $7 + 0 = 7$ additive identity

12. $2(1) = 2$ multiplicative identity

13. If $a + b = 5$, then $5 = a + b$. symmetric

- use the distributive property to simplify expressions   (Lesson 1-5)

$$5b + 3(b + 2) = 5b + 3 \cdot b + 3 \cdot 2$$
$$= 5b + 3b + 6$$
$$= 8b + 6$$

Simplify. 15. $2a + 3b$ 16. $10a + 2b$

14. $10x + x$ $11x$ 15. $2(a + b) + b$

16. $2(3a + 2a + b)$ 17. $9(r + s) - 2s$
 $9r + 7s$

- recognize and use the commutative and associative properties when simplifying expressions   (Lesson 1-6)

Name the property illustrated by $2b + (3c + 1) = (2b + 3c) + 1$.

associative property of addition

$$2x + 4xy + 5x = 2x + 5x + 4xy$$
$$= (2x + 5x) + 4xy$$
$$= 7x + 4xy$$

Name the property illustrated by each statement.

18. $5(a + c) = 5(c + a)$ commutative (+)

19. $10(ab) = (10a)b$ associative (×)

20. $4 + (x + y) = (4 + x) + y$ assoc. (+)

21. $a(b + c) = (b + c)a$ commutative (×)

Simplify.

22. $6a + 7b + 8a + 2b$ $14a + 9b$

23. $\frac{3a^2}{4} + \frac{2ab}{3} + ab$ $\frac{3a^2}{4} + \frac{5ab}{3}$

The Cumulative Review shown below can be used to review skills and concepts presented thus far in the text. Standardized Test Practice Questions are also provided in the Evaluation Masters Booklet.

Evaluation Masters Booklet, pp. 11-12

OBJECTIVES AND EXAMPLES	REVIEW EXERCISES

■ translate verbal sentences into equations or formulas **(Lesson 1-7)**

Write an equation for the sentence *The sum of the square of x and b is equal to a.*

$$x^2 + b = a$$

Write an equation for each sentence.

24. Eighteen decreased by the square of d is equal to f. $18 - d^2 = f$

25. The number c equals the cube of the product of 2 and x. $c = (2x)^3$

APPLICATIONS AND CONNECTIONS

Geometry: Find the perimeter of each figure when $x = 7$, $y = 3$, and $z = 1\frac{1}{2}$. (Lesson 1-2)

26. 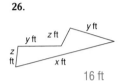 16 ft

27. 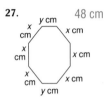 48 cm

28. 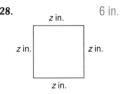 6 in.

Logic: Write the negation of each statement. Then state whether the negation is *true* or *false*. (Lesson 1-3) 29. Ostriches can fly; false. 30. Delaware is not the . . . ; true.

29. Ostriches cannot fly.

30. Delaware is the largest state in the U.S.

Two cans of vegetables together cost $1.08. One of them costs 10¢ more than the other. (Lesson 1-8)

31. Would 2 cans of the less expensive vegetable cost more or less than $1.08? less

32. How much would 3 cans of each cost? $3.24

33. How much is the more expensive vegetable? 59¢

34. **Time** Write an expression to represent the number of seconds in a day. Then evaluate the expression. **(Lessons 1-1, 1-2)** $60 \cdot 60 \cdot 24$; 86,400 seconds

35. **Foods** There are 111 calories in one cup of orange juice. Write an equation to represent the number of calories in 3 cups of orange juice. Then solve the equation. **(Lesson 1-7)** $c = 3 \cdot 111$; 333 calories

36. **Sports** A pitcher's earned-run average is given by the formula $ERA = 9\left(\frac{a}{b}\right)$, where a is the number of earned runs the pitcher has allowed and b is the number of innings pitched. Find a pitcher's ERA if he has allowed 23 earned runs in 180 innings. **(Lesson 1-7)** 1.15

37. **Masonry** What is the maximum number of whole bricks in a wall 25 inches wide and 7 inches high if each brick is 8 inches wide by 2 inches high and there is $\frac{1}{2}$ inch of mortar between each brick? **(Lesson 1-8)** 8 bricks

Write an algebraic expression for each verbal expression. Use x as the variable.

1. a number increased by 17 $x + 17$

2. twice the square of a number $2x^2$

3. the sum of a number and its cube $x + x^3$

4. twice Nica's age decreased by 23 years
$2x - 23$

Evaluate.

5. $(12 - 10)^4$ 16

6. $13 + 4 \cdot 5^2$ 113

7. $0.7(1.4 + 0.6)$ 1.4

8. $\frac{3}{4}(8 + 28)$ 27

9. $23 - 12(1.5)$ 5

10. $6 + 3(3.4)$ 16.2

Evaluate if $m = 8$, $n = 3$, $p = \frac{3}{4}$, $q = \frac{2}{3}$, and $r = 0.5$.

11. $(mn)^2$ 576

12. pq^2 $\frac{1}{3}$; $0.\overline{3}$

13. $n + r^2$ 3.25

Solve each equation.

14. $v = \frac{6^2 - 2^3}{7}$ 4

15. $8(0.03) - 0.05 = y$ 0.19

16. $\frac{3}{4} - \left(\frac{1}{2}\right)^2 = k$ $\frac{1}{2}$

Name the property illustrated by each statement.

18. Commutative Property (+)

17. $t + 0 = t$ Additive Identity Property

18. $7(m + 2n) = 7(2n + m)$

19. $34 \cdot 1 = 34$ Multiplicative Identity Property

20. $3(2a + b) = 6a + 3b$ Distributive Property

21. If $m = a + b$ then $a + b = m$.
Symmetric (=)

22. $3(2) = 2(3)$ Commutative Property (×)

Simplify.

23. $n + 5n$ $6n$

24. $2.5x - x + y + 3.5y$ $1.5x + 4.5y$

25. $3(a + 2) + 5a$ $8a + 6$

26. $4an + \frac{2}{3}am + 8an + \frac{1}{3}am$ $12an + am$

Write an equation for each sentence.

27. The product of π and the square of r is A. $\pi r^2 = A$

28. The sum of a, b, and c is equal to P. $a + b + c = P$

29. If a car travels at an average speed of 60 miles per hour, how far can the car travel in 4 hours? 240 miles

30. Mr. Greenpeas is planning a garden 6 feet wide by 12 feet long. If each plant takes up 1 square foot of space, how many plants can Mr. Greenpeas plant in his garden? 72 plants

31. $s = 2 \cdot 4 \cdot 3$; 24 socks

31. Kenny has 4 pairs of socks in each of the following colors: black, brown, and navy. Write an equation to represent the number of socks Kenny has. Then, solve the equation.

Bonus Simplify.

$$x = \frac{4 + (2 + 6)^2 - \frac{2}{3} + 6 \div 2 + 9^2}{\frac{3}{4} - \frac{2}{3} + 7^2 - 4^2 + 3^2}$$

$\frac{1816}{505}$, $3.\overline{596}$

NAME _____ DATE _____

Chapter 1 Test, Form 1A

Write the letter for the correct answer in the blank at the right of each problem.

1. Write an algebraic expression for 10 less than d.
   A. $10 > d$ B. $10 < d$ C. $10 - d$ D. $d - 10$ 1. __D__

2. Write an algebraic expression for the sum of the cube of a number and 5.
   A. $5x^3$ B. $5 \cdot 3x$ or $15x$ C. $5 + x^3$ D. $5 + 3x$ 2. __C__

3. Write $6 \cdot 6 \cdot m \cdot m \cdot m \cdot y \cdot y \cdot y$ using exponents.
   A. $6^2m^3y^3$ B. $66m^3y^3$ C. $66my^3$ D. 6^2my^3 3. __A__

4. Evaluate: $10(4 + 3 \cdot 2) \div (2 \cdot 6 - 7)$
   A. 4 B. 20 C. 28 D. 100   4. __B__

5. Evaluate $4am - a^2$ if $a = \frac{1}{4}$ and $m = 5$.
   A. $10\frac{1}{4}$ B. $22\frac{1}{4}$ C. $9\frac{3}{4}$ D. 9   5. __C__

6. Evaluate $4v^2 - n(s - v)$ if $n = 3$, $s = 5$, and $v = 2$.
   A. 55 B. 39 C. 183 D. 7   6. __D__

7. Solve: $p = 148 - 3.7$
   A. 145.7 B. 144.3 C. 11.1 D. 111   7. __B__

8. Solve: $\frac{3}{8} + \frac{2}{3} = n$
   A. $\frac{25}{24}$ B. $\frac{5}{11}$ C. $\frac{1}{4}$ D. $\frac{5}{24}$ 8. __A__

9. Which property is illustrated by $4 + (3 - 1) = 4 + 2$?
   A. substitution property B. associative property of addition
   C. additive identity property D. reflexive property   9. __A__

10. Which of the following shows the symmetric property of equality?
    A. If $5 + 2 = 7$ and $7 = 1 + 6$, then $5 + 2 = 1 + 6$.
    B. If $2 + 9 = 11$, then $9 + 2 = 11$.
    C. If $13 = 5 + 8$, then $5 + 8 = 13$.
    D. $(x + y)4 = 4(x + y)$ 10. __C__

11. What is the simplest form of $5x + x + 9$?
    A. $5x^2 + 9$ B. $6x + 9$ C. $5x + 9$ D. $15x$ 11. __B__

12. What is the simplest form of $10y^2 + 2(y^2 + x)$?
    A. $12y^2 + 2x$ B. $12y^2 + x$
    C. $12y^4 + 2x$ D. $12y^4 + x$ 12. __A__

13. What is the simplest form of $9a^2 + 7a + 4a^2 + 2a$?
    A. $22a^6$ B. $13a^4 + 9a^2$
    C. $22a^3$ D. $13a^2 + 9a$ 13. __D__

NAME _____ DATE _____

Chapter 1 Test, Form 1A (continued)

14. Which property is illustrated by $6x^2 - 2x^2 = (6 - 2)x^2$?
    A. distributive property B. associative property of addition
    C. commutative property of addition
    D. reflexive property of equality   14. __A__

15. Which of the following illustrates the commutative property of addition?
    A. $7(ux + 3) = (ux + 3)7$ B. $7(ux + 3) = 7ux + 21$
    C. $7(ux + 3) = 7(xu + 3)$ D. $7(ux + 3) = 7(3 + ux)$ 15. __D__

16. Write an equation for *twice the difference of m and 4 is 25.*
    A. $2m - 4 = 25$ B. $2(m - 4) = 25$
    C. $m^2 - 4 = 25$ D. $(m - 4)^2 = 25$ 16. __B__

17. Write an equation for *k equals the cube of h decreased by j.*
    A. $k = h^3 + j$ B. $k = 3h - j$
    C. $k = j - h^3$ D. $k = h^3 - j$ 17. __D__

18. Janet went to Tape-a-Rama to buy tapes for holiday gifts. She bought 2 more rock tapes than western tapes and 4 more western tapes than classical tapes. Including 2 jazz tapes, she bought 15 total tapes. From which category did she buy the most?
    A. rock B. western C. classical D. jazz   18. __A__

19. Noella has two more brothers than sisters. If Noella has n brothers, how many sisters does she have?
    A. $n - 2$ B. $n + 2$ C. $2 - n$ D. $2n + 2$ 19. __A__

20. Alvin's weight is 2 pounds less than twice his son's weight. Alvin weighs 174 pounds. Which of the following equations can be used to find the son's weight?
    A. $174 = 2 + 2x$ B. $174 = 2 - 2x$
    C. $174 = 2x - 2$ D. $174 = 3x - 2$ 20. __C__

Bonus: **Bonus:**

Simplify: $\frac{5}{4}a + \frac{3}{4}[8(a^2 + 3b^2) - 24b^2] + \frac{1}{4}(8 - 5a)$
    A. $8a^2 + 4a$ B. $6a^2 + 2$ C. $2a^2 + 5a$ D. $5a^2 + 2$ __B__

2 Rational Numbers

PREVIEWING THE CHAPTER

This chapter deals with basic operations as applied to integers and rational numbers. The number line is used as a mathematical model to develop the rules for addition of integers, and students' familiarity with the inverse relationship between addition and subtraction is extended to develop these rules for subtraction. Then the connection is established between these rules for integers and the rules for rational numbers. The properties are used to suggest the rules for multiplication, and the inverse relationship is again recalled to develop the rules for division.

Problem-Solving Strategy Students learn to use variables to write equations for problems and then, to further enhance their understanding, write problems for equations containing variables.

Lesson (Pages)	Lesson Objectives		State/Local Objectives
2-1 (50-54)	**2-1A:** State the coordinate of a point on a number line.		
	2-1B: Graph integers on a number line.		
	2-1C: Add integers by using a number line.		
2-2 (55-59)	**2-2A:** Find the absolute value of a number.		
	2-2B: Add integers without using a number line.		
	2-2C: Subtract integers.		
2-3 (60-64)	**2-3A:** Compare numbers.		
	2-3B: Write inequalities for graphs on number lines.		
	2-3C: Graph inequalities on number lines.		
2-4 (65-68)	**2-4A:** Compare rational numbers.		
	2-4B: Write rational numbers in increasing or decreasing order.		
	2-4C: Find a number between two rational numbers.		
2-5 (69-73)	**2-5A:** Add two or more rational numbers.		
	2-5B: Subtract rational numbers.		
	2-5C: Simplify expressions that contain rational numbers.		
2-6 (74-78)	**2-6:** Multiply rational numbers.		
2-7 (80-84)	**2-7:** Divide rational numbers.		
2-8 (85-87)	**2-8A:** Define variables and write equations for verbal problems.		
	2-8B: Write verbal problems for equations.		

Lesson Objective Chart

ORGANIZING THE CHAPTER

You may want to refer to the **Course Planning Calendar** on page T36.

Lesson Planning Guide — Blackline Masters Booklets

Lesson (Pages)	Course I	Course II	Course III	Reteaching	Practice	Enrichment	Evaluation	Technology	Lab Manual	Mixed Problem Solving	Applications	Cooperative Learning Activity	Multicultural	Transparencies
2-1 (50-54)	1.5	1.5	1.5	p. 9	p. 9	p. 9						p. 32		2-1
2-2 (55-59)	1.5	1.5	1.5	p. 10	p. 10	p. 10	Quiz A, p. 23	p. 2						2-2
2-3 (60-64)	1.5	1.5	1	p. 11	p. 11	p. 11		p. 17						2-3
2-4 (65-68)	1	1	1	p. 12	p. 12	p. 12	Quiz B, p. 23 Mid-Chapter Test, p. 27							2-4
2-5 (69-73)	1.5	1	1	p. 13	p. 13	p. 13							p. 47	2-5
2-6 (74-78)	1.5	1	1	p. 14	p. 14	p. 14	Quiz C, p. 24		pp. 19-20					2-6
2-7 (80-84)	1.5	1.5	1	p. 15	p. 15	p. 15					p. 17			2-7
2-8 (85-87)	1	1	1		p. 16		Quiz D, p. 24			p. 2				2-8
Review (88-90)	1	1	1	Multiple Choice Tests, Forms 1A and 1B, pp. 15-18 Free Response Tests, Forms 2A and 2B, pp. 19-22										
Test (91)	1	1	1	Cumulative Review, pp. 25-26 Standardized Test Practice Questions, p. 28										

Course I: Chapters 1-13; Course II: Chapters 1-14: Course III: Chapters 1-15

Other Chapter Resources

Student Edition

Application, p. 54
Puzzle, p. 59
Mid-Chapter Review, p. 73
History Connection, p. 78
Technology, p. 79
Cooperative Learning Activity, p. 87
Algebraic Skills Review, pp. 647-653, 655

Teacher Resource Package

Activity Masters Booklet
  Mixed Problem Solving, p. 2
  Applications, p. 17
  Cooperative Learning Activity, p. 32
  Multicultural Activity, p. 47

Technology Masters Booklet
  Scientific Calculator Activity, p. 2
  Graphing Calculator Activity, p. 17

Lab Manual
  Lab Activity, pp. 19-20

Other Supplements

Transparency for Chapter Opener
Problem-of-the-Week Activity
  Cards, 3-5
Video Algebra, 5-7, 9, 11-12

Software

Algebra 1 Test and Review
  Generator Software
  Available for Apple and IBM.

ENHANCING THE CHAPTER

Cooperative Learning

Arranging the Room

Providing a physical environment conducive to cooperative-learning activities is important if success is to be achieved when using this mode of learning. How you arrange the room should indicate to students what is expected of them as well as make it easy for both you and the groups to accomplish the defined goals. Since you will want to monitor the groups, they should be arranged in a way that allows you to pass among them, unobtrusively if possible, and also placed far enough apart so that the groups do not interfere with each other's learning. The students in each group must be able to see all of the pertinent materials, to see and converse with one another without disturbing students in other groups, and to exchange ideas and materials with other members of the group in a convenient manner. Experience has demonstrated that among the best arrangements is to have the group members sit in a circle, although any arrangement that enables each group member to have eye contact with an easy access to all other members of the group also would be satisfactory.

Technology

The Technology Feature after Lesson 2-5 uses a BASIC program to add two fractions. Alterations to the program are provided to find the sum in simplest form. Students are asked to change the program so that it finds the difference of two fractions.

Computer languages operate and print rational numbers in decimal form. A few calculators are available that input and output in simplest fraction form.

Critical Thinking

Be alert for opportunities to provide students with high-level thinking activities by modifying some of the more routine problems provided in the textbook to pose open-ended problems.

Textbook example: Ponderosa pines grow about $1\frac{1}{2}$ feet each year. If a pine tree is now 17 feet tall, about how long will it take the tree to become $33\frac{1}{2}$ feet tall?

Modified example: Ponderosa pines grow about $1\frac{1}{2}$ feet each year. A Ponderosa pine is now 17 feet tall. Write as many problems as you can using this data.

The modified example provokes students to consider alternatives, to analyze the situation, and to relate it to the mathematics they know.

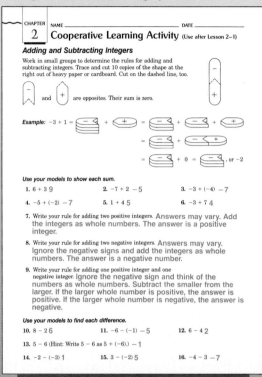

Cooperative Learning, p. 32

Technology, p. 17

The card shown below is one of three available for this chapter. It can be used as a class or small group activity.

Activity Card

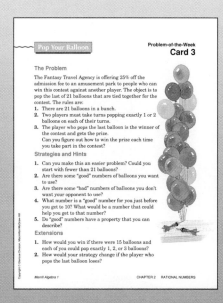

Pop Your Balloon

Problem-of-the-Week
Card 3

The Problem

The Fantasy Travel Agency is offering 25% off the admission fee to an amusement park to people who can win this contest against another player. The object is to pop the last of 21 balloons that are tied together for the contest. The rules are:
1. There are 21 balloons in a bunch.
2. Two players must take turns popping exactly 1 or 2 balloons on each of their turns.
3. The player who pops the last balloon is the winner of the contest and gets the prize.
Can you figure out how to win the prize each time you take part in the contest?

Strategies and Hints
1. Can you make this an easier problem? Could you start with fewer than 21 balloons?
2. Are there some "good" numbers of balloons you want to use?
3. Are there some "bad" numbers of balloons you don't want your opponent to use?
4. What number is a "good" number for you just before you get to 10? What would be a number that could help you get to that number?
5. Do "good" numbers have a property that you can describe?

Extensions
1. How would you win if there were 15 balloons and each of you could pop exactly 1, 2, or 3 balloons?
2. How would your strategy change if the player who pops the last balloon loses?

Merrill Algebra 1   CHAPTER 2 RATIONAL NUMBERS

Manipulatives and Models

The following materials may be used as models or manipulatives in Chapter 2.

• scientific calculator (Lessons 2-2, 2-4)
• newspaper (Lesson 2-5)

Outside Resources

Books/Periodicals

Brady, Maxine. *The Monopoly Book*. David McKay Company, Inc.

Gunther, Noel. *Beyond Boardwalk and Park Place*.

Films/Videotapes/Videodiscs

Algebra: A Way of Thinking About Numbers, Coronet Film and Video

Number concepts, Video Tutor, Inc.

Software

Operations With Integers, Learning Arts

Algebra Tutor With Algebra Action Game, Merit

Multicultural Activity, p. 47

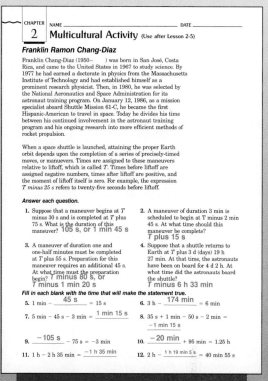

CHAPTER **2** NAME _____ DATE _____

Multicultural Activity (Use after Lesson 2-5)

Franklin Ramon Chang-Diaz

Franklin Chang-Diaz (1950–   ) was born in San José, Costa Rica, and came to the United States in 1967 to study science. By 1977 he had earned a doctorate in physics from the Massachusetts Institute of Technology and had established himself as a prominent research physicist. Then, in 1980, he was selected by the National Aeronautics and Space Administration for its astronaut training program. On January 12, 1986, as a mission specialist aboard Shuttle Mission 61-C, he became the first Hispanic-American to travel in space. Today he divides his time between his continued involvement in the astronaut training program and his ongoing research into more efficient methods of rocket propulsion.

When a space shuttle is launched, attaining the proper Earth orbit depends upon the completion of a series of precisely-timed moves, or maneuvers. Times are assigned to these maneuvers relative to liftoff, which is called T. Times before liftoff are assigned negative numbers, times after liftoff are positive, and the moment of liftoff itself is zero. For example, the expression T minus 25 s refers to twenty-five seconds before liftoff.

Answer each question.

1. Suppose that a maneuver begins at T minus 30 s and is completed at T plus 75 s. What is the duration of this maneuver? **105 s, or 1 min 45 s**

2. A maneuver of duration 3 min is scheduled to begin at T minus 2 min 45 s. At what time should this maneuver be complete? **T plus 15 s**

3. A maneuver of duration one and one-half minutes must be completed at T plus 55 s. Preparation for this maneuver requires an additional 45 s. At what time must the preparation begin? **T minus 80 s, or T minus 1 min 20 s**

4. Suppose that a shuttle returns to Earth at T plus 3 d (days) 19 h 27 min. At that time, the astronauts have been on board for 4 d 2 h. At what time did the astronauts board the shuttle? **T minus 6 h 33 min**

Fill in each blank with the time that will make the statement true.

5. 1 min − **45 s** = 15 s

6. 3 h − **174 min** = 6 min

7. 5 min − 45 s − 3 min = **1 min 15 s**

8. 35 s + 1 min − 50 s − 2 min = **−1 min 15 s**

9. **−105 s** − 75 s = −3 min

10. **−20 min** + 95 min = 1.25 h

11. 1 h − 2 h 35 min = **−1 h 35 min**

12. 2 h − **1 h 19 min 5 s** = 40 min 55 s

Lab Activity, pp. 19-20

Name _____   Activity 2 Worksheet

Multiplying and Dividing Rational Numbers

In groups, act out, videotape, and play back each product.

1. 4(−1)   2. 5(−2)   3. (−3)(+4)

4. What is the sign of the answer for each problem? _____

5. State the rules for multiplying rational numbers. _____

Multiply or divide.

6. (+25)(+12) = _____   7. (−3.2)(+1.5) = _____

8. (−25)(0.5) = _____   9. (+7)(+49) = _____

10. $\left(-\frac{1}{4}\right)(+64)$ = _____   11. $\left(-\frac{3}{8}\right)\left(-\frac{24}{9}\right)$ = _____

12. (10)(−40) = _____   13. (44)(11) = _____

14. $(90)\left(\frac{1}{4}\right)$ = _____   15. (−3)(−6)(−1) = _____

16. (−25) ÷ (5) = _____   17. (4.5) ÷ (0.9) = _____

18. (+6) ÷ (−3) = _____   19. $\left(-\frac{1}{2}\right) ÷ \left(-\frac{3}{8}\right)$ = _____

20. Suppose you wrote 4 checks for $5.00. How much money did you spend? _____
    Is your answer a positive or negative number? _____

21. Taylor High School's defensive lineman sacked North High School's quarterback in 3 consecutive plays for lost yardage of 8 yards each play. How far behind the line of scrimmage is North High School? _____
    Is the lost yardage a positive or negative number? _____

22. During the 4 day U.S. Open Golf Tournament, Jack Nicklaus finished 2 under par each day. What number represented Jack's score at the end of the tournament? _____

23. Mr. Muscle lost $8540 gambling in Las Vegas. He won back one-half of his losses the following day. What were Mr. Muscle's net winnings or losses? (Represent your answer with a positive or negative number.) _____

Using the Chapter Opener

Transparency 2-0 is available in the Transparency Package. It provides a full-color visual and motivational activity that you can use to engage students in the mathematical content of the chapter.

Background Information

The game of Monopoly was created by Charles Darrow in 1933. No other proprietary game has ever been so popular. Mr. Darrow made the first game at home. It became so popular among his family and friends that he began making them their own sets. He then began making and selling sets for $4.00 each. Demand became so great that he attempted to sell it to Parker Brothers. They first turned him down because the game contained "fifty-two fundamental errors" and would never be accepted by the public. They later changed their minds and have since sold over 80 million sets.

In this chapter, you will:
- Simplify expressions.
- Add, subtract, multiply, divide, and compare rational numbers.
- Graph inequalities.
- Write equations for verbal problems.

Chapter Project

Materials: posterboard, markers, scissors, pencil and paper, paper clip (for spinner)

Have students work in small groups to design and produce a Monopoly-type board game that reflects turning points in the life of a familiar individual or in the history of a group of people.

Negative turning points are to be represented by movement backward; positive turning points by movement forward. Individuals or groups can be (1) the students themselves, (2) the hero of a novel, (3) an ethnic group, or (4) anyone facing a current issue in politics, social pressures, sports, the environment, and so on.

Have each group report to the class on its game and its teamwork. Save games for playing when daily class work is completed.

2

Rational Numbers

APPLICATION IN RECREATION

At one time or another, almost everyone in the U.S. has played Monopoly®. It's no wonder that the game has become so popular since its invention by Charles Darrow in the 1930s. Playing Monopoly® lets a person pretend to direct a long business career in just a few hours. The players all start out even, and each one gets the same number of turns. Their success at the game will depend upon their strategy, a good memory, *and* a bit of luck.

In order to play Monopoly®, we must know how to move the playing pieces around the board. To do this, we need to add the numbers on the dice and then move our playing piece the corresponding number of spaces forward. We also need to know how to move our playing piece *backwards* when directed to do so. Thus, we can only play and enjoy Monopoly® by understanding how to add and subtract numbers.

ALGEBRA IN ACTION

Elyse, Tom, Emilio, and Jean have just begun a game of Monopoly®. The chart below shows each of their first three turns. Who is farther around the board after three turns? How can you represent each player's moves using integers?

When you play Monopoly®, what is your favorite playing piece? the top hat? the car? Or do you have your own playing piece, like a lucky coin?

Player	Turn 1	Turn 2	Turn 3
Elyse	Rolls double 5s; rolls 9.	Rolls 6.	Rolls 11; Chance - go back 3.
Tom	Rolls 3.	Rolls 4; Chance - Advance to Illinois Ave. (forward 17).	Rolls 6 - Go directly to jail (back 20).
Emilio	Rolls 6.	Rolls double 3s; rolls 7.	Rolls 8.
Jean	Rolls 8.	Rolls 9; Community Chest - Advance to next utility (forward 11).	Rolls double 2s; rolls 3.

Lesson	Connections (C) and Applications (A)	Examples	Exercises
2-1	C: Set Theory	1	50-53
	A: Oceanography		56
	Football		57
	School		58
2-2	A: Golf	3	
	Business		55
	Mining		56
2-3	A: Business	5	
	School		48
	Population		49
	Armed Forces		50
	History		51
2-4	A: Consumerism	3	
2-5	A: Stock Market	1	53
	Golf		54
	Football		55
	Personal Finance		56
2-6	C: Sequences	6	24-27
	Statistics		46
	A: Sales		47
2-7	C: Statistics		39-42
	A: Basketball		52
	Aviation		53
	Space		54
	World Records		55

49

Lesson Resources

- Reteaching Master 2-1
- Practice Master 2-1
- Enrichment Master 2-1
- Activity Master, p. 32
- Video Algebra, 5, 6

 Transparency 2-1 contains the 5-Minute Check and a teaching aid for this lesson.

INTRODUCING THE LESSON

 5-Minute Check

(over Chapter 1)

Simplify.

1. $6r + 2s + 3r + s$ $9r + 3s$
2. $9(a + b) + 3a$ $12a + 9b$

Evaluate each expression if $a = 5$, $b = 4$, and $c = 3$.

3. $3ac - bc$ 33
4. $b - c + 2ab$ 41

State the property shown.

5. $5 + (x + y) = 5 + (y + x)$
   commutative property

Motivating the Lesson

An outdoor thermometer shows a temperature of 10°C. Twelve hours later, the temperature has dropped 13 degrees. What temperature does the thermometer now show?   −3°C

TEACHING THE LESSON

Teaching Tip ❶   Point out that a number line is not always horizontal. A thermometer is an instrument with a vertical number line.

Objectives

2-1A
2-1B
2-1C

After studying this lesson, you should be able to:
- state the coordinate of a point on a number line,
- graph integers on a number line, and
- add integers by using a number line.

Application

The high temperature in Milwaukee on January 23 was 6°F. The following day, the high temperature was 9° lower. What was the high temperature on January 24?

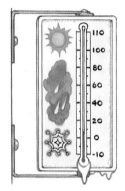

You can solve problems like the one above by using a **number line.** A number line is drawn by choosing a starting position on a line, usually 0, and marking off equal distances from that point. The set of **whole numbers** is often represented on a number line. This set can be written $\{0, 1, 2, 3, \ldots\}$, where " $\ldots$ " means that the set continues indefinitely.

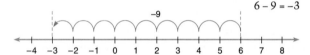

Although only a portion of the number line is shown, the arrowhead indicates that the line and the set of numbers continue.

We can use the expression $6 - 9$ to represent the problem given above. The number line below shows that the value of $6 - 9$ should be 3 less than 0. However, there is no whole number that corresponds to 3 less than 0. You can write the number 3 *less than 0* as −3. This is an example of a **negative** number.

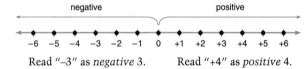

To include negative numbers on a number line, extend the line to the left of zero and mark off equal distances. To avoid confusion, name the points to the right of zero using the *positive sign* (+) and to the left of zero using the *negative sign* (−). Zero is neither positive nor negative.

Any nonzero number written without a sign is understood to be positive.

Teaching Tip ❶

Read "−3" as *negative* 3.   Read "+4" as *positive* 4.

The set of numbers used to name the points on the number line above is called the set of **integers.** This set can be written $\{ \ldots, -3, -2, -1, 0, 1, 2, 3, \ldots \}$.

50   CHAPTER 2   RATIONAL NUMBERS

ALTERNATE TEACHING STRATEGIES

Using Models

Use the number line to introduce the addition of integers. Permit students who know the rules of football to explain Example 3.

When showing addition on a number line, emphasize that negative numbers are indicated by arrows pointing to the left, and positive numbers are indicated by arrows pointing to the right. The first arrow must start at the origin. The second arrow starts at the arrowhead of the first arrow. The sum is at the head of the second arrow.

Sets of numbers are often represented by figures called **Venn diagrams**. The size and shape of a Venn diagram are unimportant. However, usually a rectangle is used to represent the *universal set*, and circles or ovals are used to represent subsets of the universal set.

Sets	Examples
Natural numbers	1, 2, 3, 4, 5, . . .
Whole numbers	0, 1, 2, 3, 4, . . .
Integers	. . . , −2, −1, 0, 1, 2, . . .

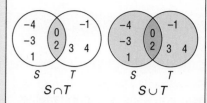

Notice that the natural numbers are a subset of the whole numbers, the whole numbers are a subset of the integers, and the integers are a subset of the universal set, the **real numbers**.

Venn diagrams can also show how various sets are related. Let *A* and *B* be two sets. The **intersection** of *A* and *B* (*A* ∩ *B*) is the set of elements common to *both A and B*. The **union** of two sets *A* and *B* (*A* ∪ *B*) is the set of all elements contained *either in A or in B or in both*.

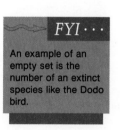

FYI · · ·

An example of an empty set is the number of an extinct species like the Dodo bird.

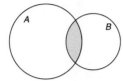

The shaded area is *A* ∩ *B*.

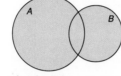

The shaded area is *A* ∪ *B*.

Two sets that have no members in common are said to be **disjoint**. Their intersection is the **empty set**, Ø.

Example 1

CONNECTION

Set Theory

Let *A* = {1, 2, 3, 4, 5}, *B* = {2, 4, 6, 8}, and *C* = {7, 8, 9}. Use a Venn diagram to show *A* ∩ *B*, *A* ∪ *B*, and *A* ∩ *C*.

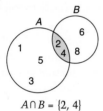
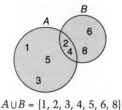
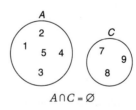

A ∩ *B* = {2, 4} | *A* ∪ *B* = {1, 2, 3, 4, 5, 6, 8} | *A* ∩ *C* = Ø

To **graph** a set of numbers means to locate the points named by those numbers on a number line. The number that corresponds to a point on a number line is called the **coordinate** of that point.

LESSON 2-1 INTEGERS AND THE NUMBER LINE 51

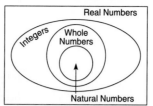

EVALUATING THE LESSON

Checking for Understanding

Exercises 1-24 are designed to help you assess understanding through reading, writing, and speaking. You should work through Exercises 1-4 with your students, and then monitor their work on Exercises 5-24.

Error Analysis

The "−" is used in three ways in math. Students are often interchanging "minus," "negative," and "opposite of."

expression	meaning
−x	opposite of x (relationship)
−3	negative 3 (direction)
5 − 4	5 minus 4 (operation)

The context determines how the "−" is being used. Consider:
−x − 3 − (−2) − y.
opposite of x, minus 3, minus negative 2, minus y.

Reteaching Masters Booklet, p. 9

Example 2

Name the set of numbers graphed.

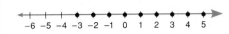

The bold arrow means that the graph continues indefinitely in that direction.

The set is {−3, −2, −1, 0, 1, 2, 3, 4, 5, . . .}.

You can use a number line to add integers. To find the sum of −4 and 6, follow the steps below. **Teaching Tip 2**

Step 1 Draw an arrow starting at 0 and going to −4, the first addend.

Step 2 Starting at −4, draw an arrow to the right 6 units long, the second addend.

Step 3 The second arrow ends at the sum, 2.

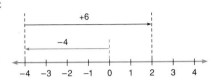

Example 3

Find −2 + (−5) on a number line. **Teaching Tip 3**

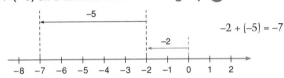

−2 + (−5) = −7

Notice that parentheses are used in the expression −2 + (−5) so that the sign of the number is not confused with the operation symbol.

CHECKING FOR UNDERSTANDING

Communicating Mathematics

Read and study the lesson to answer each question. **See margin.**

1. What are three real-life situations where you would use negative integers?

2. Compare and contrast the intersection and union of sets.

3. How does the set of integers differ from the set of whole numbers?

4. Explain how to use a number line and arrows to find 4 + (−3). What is the sum? **1**

Guided Practice

Name the coordinate of each point.

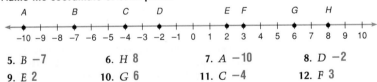

5. B −7	6. H 8	7. A −10
9. E 2	10. G 6	11. C −4

8. D −2
12. F 3

RETEACHING THE LESSON

"Walk out" addition problems by dividing a large strip of paper into squares labeled −9 to 9, with positives on the right and negatives on the left. To "walk out" 2 + (−5), start at zero and walk 2 places to the right (+2). Then walk 5 places to the left (−5) ending on −3. Have students "walk out" 2 + 5, 2 + (−5), (−2) + 5, (−2) + (−5).

Additional Answers

1. Answers may vary. Typical answers are sports, business, and weather.

2. The intersection has elements in both sets. The union has elements in either set or both.

3. Whole numbers are 0, 1, 2, 3 . . .; integers include negative numbers . . .−3, −2, −1, 0, 1, 2, 3 . . .

CONNECTION
Set Theory

Use the Venn diagram to list the members of each set. See margin.

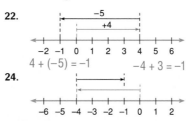

13. A 14. B

15. C 16. $A \cap B$

17. $A \cup B$ 18. $B \cap C$

19. $B \cup C$ 20. $A \cup B \cup C$

Write a corresponding addition sentence for each diagram.

21.

$-3 + 5 = 2$ $-1 + (-4) = -5$

22.

$4 + (-5) = -1$ $-4 + 3 = -1$

23.

24.

EXERCISES

Practice   **Name the set of numbers graphed.** See margin.

A

25.

26.

27.

28.

B   **Graph each set of numbers on a number line.** See margin.

29. $\{-1, 1, 3, 5\}$ 30. $\{-2, -4, -6\}$ 31. $\{-3, 0, 2\}$

32. $\{\ldots, -3, -2, -1, 0\}$ 33. {integers greater than -2}

34. {integers less than 4 and greater than or equal to -2}

Find each sum. If necessary, use a number line.

35. $7 + 6$ **13**   36. $-9 + (-7)$ **−16**   37. $-8 + (-12)$ **−20**

38. $-5 + 0$ **−5**   39. $-9 + 4$ **−5**   40. $6 + (-13)$ **−7**

41. $4 + (-4)$ **0**   42. $9 + (-5)$ **4**   43. $-3 + 9$ **6**

44. $-11 + 11$ **0**   45. $2 + (-7)$ **−5**   46. $-11 + 10$ **−1**

47. $9 + (-4)$ **5**   48. $-6 + (-14)$ **−20**   49. $-13 + (-9)$ **−22**

C   **Draw a Venn diagram to find each of the following.** See margin.

CONNECTION
Set Theory

50. the intersection of {vowels} and {first seven letters of the alphabet}

51. the intersection of {1, 3, 5} and {4, 6, 8, 10}

52. the union of {a, b, c, d} and {14, 15}

53. the union of {letters in the word *dictionary*} and {letters in the word *nation*} and {letters in the word *tidal*}

LESSON 2-1   INTEGERS AND THE NUMBER LINE   53

Additional Answers

4. **Start at 0. Draw an arrow to 4. Then draw another arrow from 4 three units to the left, ending at 1.**

13. $\{3, 6, 9, 12\}$

14. $\{3, 4, 5, 6\}$

15. $\{4, 6, 8, 10, 12\}$

16. $\{3, 6\}$

17. $\{3, 4, 5, 6, 9, 12\}$

18. $\{4, 6\}$

19. $\{3, 4, 5, 6, 8, 10, 12\}$

20. $\{3, 4, 5, 6, 8, 9, 10, 12\}$

25. $\{-3, -2, -1, 0\}$

26. $\{1, 3, 5\}$

27. $\{-1, 0, 1, 2, 3, 4 \ldots\}$

28. $\{-3, -2, -1, 0, 1, 2, 3 \ldots\}$

50. $\{a, e\}$

51. $\varnothing$

52. $\{a, b, c, d, 14, 15\}$

53. $\{d, i, c, t, o, n, a, r, y, l\}$

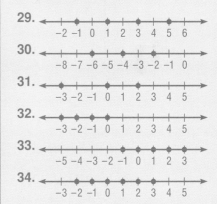
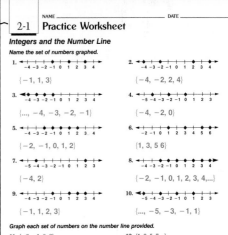

Critical Thinking

Find the next three numbers in each pattern. 54. 9, 1, −7   55. −6, −1, 4

54. 33, 25, 17, __?__, __?__, __?__   55. −21, −16, −11, __?__, __?__, __?__

Applications

For Exercises 56 and 57, write an open sentence using addition. Then solve each problem. **See margin.**

56. **Oceanography**   A scuba diver was exploring mineral deposits at a depth of 75 meters. She went up 30 meters. At what depth was she then? **−45 m**

57. **Football**   A football team gains 4 yards on the first down and loses 20 yards on the second down. What was the net gain or loss after the two plays? **16 yd loss**

Teaching Tip ④

58. **School**   Thirty students are in the French club. Twenty-one students are in the drama club. Six are in both. Make a Venn diagram of this situation. How many are in at least one club? **45 students**

Mixed Review

59. Write $\frac{3}{4} \cdot x \cdot y \cdot y \cdot y \cdot y \cdot y$ as an expression using exponents. **(Lesson 1-1)** $\frac{3}{4}xy^5$

60. Solve $y = 7 - 4$.   **(Lesson 1-3)** 3

61. Simplify $23y^2 + 32y^2$.   **(Lesson 1-5)** $55y^2$

62. Write as an equation: *the sum of x and the square of a is equal to n.* **(Lesson 1-7)** $x + a^2 = n$

APPLICATION

Meteorology

Windchill factor is an estimate of the cooling effect the wind has on a person in cold weather. The chilling effect of cold increases as the speed of the wind increases. Meteorologists use a chart like the one at the right to predict the windchill factor.

Wind speed in mph	Actual temperature (°Fahrenheit)						
	30	20	10	0	−10	−20	−30
	Equivalent temperature (°Fahrenheit)						
0	30	20	10	0	−10	−20	−30
5	27	16	6	−5	−15	−26	−36
10	16	4	−9	−21	−33	−46	−58
15	9	−4	−18	−31	−45	−58	−72

Use the windchill chart to find each windchill factor.

1. 30°F, 10 mph **16°F**   2. 20°F, 5 mph **16°F**   3. 0°F, 15 mph **−31°F**

EXTENDING THE LESSON

Math Power: Reasoning

Have students study the following number pattern.
−15, −12, −9, −6
Ask students to identify the pattern that exists in this sequence. Each number is 3 more than the number that preceded it. Have students identify the 10th term in the number pattern. **12**

Application

The following formula was used to determine the values found in the windchill chart. A good calculator activity would be to have students calculate additional windchill temperatures or check given values. Windchill formula = $0.0817(3.71 \times \sqrt{v} + 5.81 - 0.25v)(t - 91.4) + 91.4$
v = wind speed in mph
t = Fahrenheit temperature

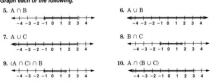

Adding and Subtracting Integers

Objectives

After studying this lesson, you should be able to:

2-2A ■ find the absolute value of a number,

2-2B ■ add integers without using a number line, and

2-2C ■ subtract integers.

Application

Simplex, Inc.
1992 Budget

Expenses $713,000

Expenses $425,000

?

First Half   Second Half

In the first half of 1992, Skillplex Incorporated's expenses were $713,000 under budget. In the second half, their expenses were $425,000. How close to the 1992 budget were Skillplex's expenses?

To find how close Skillplex was to the budget, we would add −$713,000 and +$425,000. But it would be really hard to draw a number line big enough to find sums like −713,000 + 425,000! Some concepts that we can illustrate on a number line will help us find easier ways to add and subtract integers.

Looking at 4 and −4 on a number line, you can see that they are the same number of units from 0. Two numbers that are the same distance from 0 on a number line are said to have the same **absolute value**.

4 units   4 units

−5 −4 −3 −2 −1 0 1 2 3 4 5

Definition of Absolute Value	The absolute value of a number is the number of units it is from 0 on a number line. Teaching Tip ❶

The symbol for the absolute value of a number is two vertical bars around the number.

$|-14| = 14$ is read *The absolute value of −14 is 14.* **Teaching Tip**

$|-8 + 7| = 1$ is read *The absolute value of the expression −8 + 7 is 1.*

Note that absolute value bars can serve as grouping symbols.

Example 1

Evaluate the expression $-|m + 4|$ if $m = -6$.

$-|m + 4| = -|-6 + 4|$ *Substitution property of equality*
$= -|-2|$
$= -(2)$ *The absolute value of $|-2|$ is 2.*
$= -2$

You can use absolute value to find sums of integers.

$3 + 2 = 5$

Notice that the sign of each addend is positive. The sum is positive.

Teaching Tip ❸

$-3 + (-2) = -5$

Notice that the sign of each addend is negative. The sum is negative.

LESSON 2-2   ADDING AND SUBTRACTING INTEGERS   **55**

ALTERNATE TEACHING STRATEGIES

Using Questioning

Some students may have difficulty understanding the distinction between the use of "−" to identify a negative number and to represent the opposite of a number. Ask the following questions.

1. If $y = 4$, what is $-y$?   −4
2. If $m = -6$, what is $-m$?   6
3. If $-x = 5$, what is x?   −5

Using Calculators

Scientific calculators have a built-in operation that gives the absolute value of all expressions entered. If the expression entered has a positive or zero value, the calculator displays the expression. If the value of the expression entered is negative, the calculator displays the opposite value.

INTRODUCING THE LESSON

5-Minute Check
(over Lesson 2-1)

1. Graph {2, 3, 4} on a number line.

−2 −1 0 1 2 3 4 5 6

2. Show the addition $4 + (-7)$ on a number line.   −3

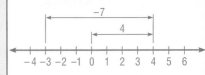

−7

4

−4 −3 −2 −1 0 1 2 3 4 5 6

Find each sum.

3. $9 + (-24)$ −15
4. $(-18) + (-47)$ −65
5. $-27 + 45$ 18

Motivating the Lesson

A scuba diver swimming at a depth of 30 meters descends another 10 meters. Draw a diagram that shows the path of the diver. At what depth is the diver now swimming?
40 meters

TEACHING THE LESSON

Teaching Tip ❶   Another way to state the definition for absolute value is as follows: "The distance a number is from 0 on the number line is called its absolute value."

These examples suggest the following rule.

Adding Integers with the Same Sign	To add integers with the same sign, add their absolute values. Give the result the same sign as the addends.

Example 2

Find the sum: $-5 + (-7)$.

$$-5 + (-7) = -(|-5| + |-7|)$$
$$= -(5 + 7)$$
$$= -12$$

Teaching Tip ④

Both numbers are negative, so the sum is negative. Add the absolute values.

You can use absolute value to add integers with different signs.

$$4 + (-9) = -5$$

Notice that $9 - 4$ is 5. Which integer, 4 or -9, has the greater absolute value? What is its sign? What is the sign of the sum?

$$-5 + 8 = 3$$

Notice that $8 - 5$ is 3. Which integer, -5 or 8, has the greater absolute value? What is its sign? What is the sign of the sum?

These examples suggest the following rule.

Adding Integers with Different Signs	To add integers with different signs, subtract the lesser absolute value from the greater absolute value. Give the result the same sign as the addend with the greater absolute value.

In golf, a score of 0 is called *even par*. A score of 4 under par is written as -4. A score of 1 over par is written as $+1$ or 1.

Example 3

APPLICATION

Golf

FYI · · ·

Before 1850, golf balls were made of leather and stuffed with feathers.

Zero is its own opposite.

In two consecutive rounds of golf, Nancy Lopez shot 3 over par and 4 under par. Calvin Peete shot 5 over par and 1 under par. Which player had the better score at the end of the second round?

Lopez: $+3 + (-4) = -(|-4| - |3|)$ *−4 has the greater absolute value,*
$$= -(4 - 3) \qquad \text{so the sum is negative.}$$
$$= -1 \quad \text{Lopez is 1 under par.}$$

Peete: $5 + (-1) = +(|5| - |-1|)$ *5 has the greater absolute value,*
$$= +(5 - 1) \qquad \text{so the sum is positive.}$$
$$= 4 \quad \text{Peete is 4 over par. So, Lopez had the better score.}$$

Teaching Tip
⑤ What is the result when you add two numbers like 3 and -3? If the sum of two numbers is 0, the numbers are called **additive inverses** or **opposites**.

-3 is the additive inverse, or opposite, of 3. $\qquad -3 + 3 = 0$

7 is the additive inverse, or opposite, of -7. $\qquad 7 + (-7) = 0$

These examples suggest the following rule. **Teaching Tip**

Additive Inverse Property	For every number a, $a + (-a) = 0$.

Additive inverses are used when you subtract numbers.

Subtraction	Addition	Subtraction	Addition
additive inverses		*additive inverses*	
$7 - 3 = 4$	$7 + (-3) = 4$	$8 - (-2) = 10$	$8 + 2 = 10$
same result		*same result*	

It appears that subtracting a number is equivalent to adding its additive inverse.

Subtracting Integers	To subtract a number, add its additive inverse. For any numbers a and b, $a - b = a + (-b)$.

The $\boxed{+/-}$ key, called the **change-sign key**, changes the sign of the number on the display.

Example 4

Find the difference: $-4 - (-7)$.

Method 1
To subtract -7, add $+7$.
$-4 - (-7) = -4 + (+7)$
$\qquad\qquad = 3$

Method 2
Use a calculator.

Enter: $4 \boxed{+/-}\ \boxed{-}\ 7\ \boxed{+/-}\ \boxed{=}$ ∃

Example 5

Simplify $7x - 12x$.

$7x - 12x = 7x + (-12x)$ *To subtract 12x, add −12x.*
$\qquad\quad\ = [7 + (-12)]x$ *Distributive property*
$\qquad\quad\ = -5x$

CHECKING FOR UNDERSTANDING

Communicating Mathematics

Read and study the lesson to answer each question. **3. Answers will vary.**

1. Use an integer to show how far under budget Skillplex's expenses were for 1992. **$288,000; −288,000**

2. In Example 3, by how many strokes is Lopez leading? **5 strokes**

3. Have a friend write an integer on a piece of paper. Without knowing what it is, explain how to find its absolute value without a number line.

4. If you add a positive integer and a negative integer, how do you determine whether the sum is positive or negative?
Look at the addend with the greater absolute value.

Error Analysis

Students often interpret "−x" to be a negative number. Use a table of values to show otherwise.

x	$-x$	$\lvert x\rvert$	$-\lvert x\rvert$
3	−3	3	−3
−2	2	2	−2
−1.5	1.5	1.5	−1.5
0	0	0	0
2	−2	2	−2
−7	7	7	−7

Closing the Lesson

Speaking Activity Ask students the following questions.
1. What integer is its own additive inverse? **0**
2. A number x is added to the absolute value of x. If the sum is 0, what conclusion can you draw about the number x? **It is a negative integer.**

Teaching Tip ⑦ For exercise 55, develop the idea that Ken's stock has realized a net gain of $9.

Guided Practice

State the additive inverse and absolute value of each integer.

5. +8 **−8, 8**   6. −24 **24, 24**   7. 0 **0, 0**

State the sign of each sum.

8. −6 + (−11) **−**   9. −8 + (+16) **+**   10. −27 + 31 **+**

State the number named.

11. −(−5) **5**   12. −(+7) **−7**   13. −(4) **−4**

Find each sum or difference.

14. −13 + (−8) **−21** 15. −10 + 4 **−6**   16. −21 − (−14) **−7**

EXERCISES

Practice Find each sum or difference.

17. 18 + 22 **40**   18. −6 + (−13) **−19**   19. −3 + (+16) **13**
20. 27 − 19 **8**   21. 8 − 13 **−5**   22. 17 − (−23) **40**
23. 14 + (−9) **5**   24. −5 + 31 **26**   25. −18 + (−11) **−29**
26. 0 − 21 **−21**   27. 19m + 12m **31m**   28. 8h − 23h **−15h**
29. −25 + 47 **22**   30. −104 + 16 **−88**   31. 97 + (−79) **18**
32. −18p − 4p **−22p**   33. 24b − (−9b) **33b**   34. 41y − (−41y) **82y**

35. 4 + (−12) + (−18) **−26**   36. 7 + (−11) + 32 **28**

Evaluate each expression if $a = -5$, $k = 3$, and $m = -6$.

37. $a + 13$ **8**   38. $k - 7$ **−4**   39. $15 + m$ **9**
40. $k + (-18)$ **−15**   41. $m + 6$ **0**   42. $\lvert m\rvert$ **6**
43. $\lvert 7 + a\rvert$ **2**   44. $\lvert m - 4\rvert$ **10**   45. $\lvert a + k\rvert$ **2**
46. $\lvert k\rvert + \lvert m\rvert$ **9**   47. $-\lvert -24 + m\rvert$ **−30**   48. $-\lvert a + (-11)\rvert$ **−16**

Find each sum or difference.

49. $\lvert -285 + (-641)\rvert$ **926**   50. $\lvert -931\rvert - (-643)$ **1574**
51. $-\lvert -423 - (-148)\rvert$ **−275**   52. $-\lvert\lvert -843\rvert + \lvert -231\rvert\rvert$ **−1074**

Critical Thinking Complete.

53. If $n > 0$, then $\lvert n\rvert = \underline{\ ?\ }$. **$n$**   54. If $n < 0$, then $\lvert -n\rvert = \underline{\ ?\ }$. **$-n$**

Applications

Teaching Tip ⑦

For each problem, write an open sentence using addition or subtraction. Then solve the problem.

55. $s = 30 - 6 + 15$; $39

55. **Business** Ken Martin purchased a share of stock for $30. The next day the price of the stock dropped $6. On the third day, the price rose by $15. How much was Ken's stock worth at the end of the third day?

56. **Mining** The entrance to a silver mine is 4275 feet above sea level. The mine is 6324 feet deep. What is the elevation at the bottom of the mine? $m = 4275 - 6324$; 2049 feet below sea level

Computer

57. This program creates patterns of addition. Use the patterns to study and review addition of integers. Enter each addend and the steps between the addends from one sentence to the next. For example, to create the sentences $3 + (-4) = -1$, $3 + (-2) = 1$, and $3 + 0 = 3$, enter 3, 0 (because 3 is the first addend and it will not change) and then enter -4, 2 (because -4 is the second addend and it will increase by 2 each time).

```
10 PRINT "ENTER THE FIRST
   ADDEND AND STEP"
20 INPUT A1, S1
30 PRINT "ENTER THE SECOND
   ADDEND AND STEP"
40 INPUT A2, S2
50 FOR I = 1 TO 10
60 LET X1=A1+(I-1)*S1
70 LET X2=A2+(I-1)*S2
80 PRINT X1;"+";X2;"=";
   X1+X2
90 NEXT I
100 END
```

Use the program to find each set of sums. **Teaching Tip** ⑧

a. $-1 + 3$ **2**
$-3 + 0$ **−3**
$-5 + (-3)$ **−8**
etc.

b. $-20 + 5$ **−15**
$-15 + 10$ **−5**
$-10 + 15$ **5**
etc.

c. $-12 + 7$ **−5**
$-11 + 4$ **−7**
$-10 + 1$ **−9**
etc.

d. How are the steps between the addends related to the steps between the sums? **See margin.**

Mixed Review

58. Evaluate $0.2(0.6) + 3(0.4)$. **(Lesson 1-2)** **1.32**

59. Solve $\frac{14 + 28}{4 + 3} = y$. **(Lesson 1-3)** **6**

60. Simplify $\frac{3}{4}y + \frac{x}{4} + 3x$. **(Lesson 1-5)** $3\frac{1}{4}x + \frac{3}{4}y$

61. Name the property illustrated by $a + (2b + 5c) = (a + 2b) + 5c$. **(Lesson 1-6)** **associative (+)**

62. Graph $\{-3, -2, 2, 3\}$ on a number line. **(Lesson 2-1)** **See students' work.**

63. Find $-3 + 12$ on a number line. **(Lesson 2-1)** **9**

∿ PUZZLE ∿

Magic squares are square arrays of numbers. The sum of the numbers in each row, column, and diagonal is the same.

1	2	−3
−4	0	4
3	−2	−1

The sum of the numbers in each row, column, and diagonal of this magic square is 0.

New magic squares can be formed by adding the same number to each entry in the magic square above. In the squares below, how was each entry obtained? Find each new magic square.

3	4	−1
−2	2	6
5	0	1

Add 2.

−2	−1	−6
−7	−3	1
0	−5	−4

Add −3.

−6	−5	−10
−11	−7	−3
−4	−9	−8

Add −7.

LESSON 2-2 ADDING AND SUBTRACTING INTEGERS **59**

EXTENDING THE LESSON

Math Power: Reasoning

Is $|a| + |b|$ always equal to $|a + b|$? Prove your answer with an example. **No. Examples will vary. Sample is $|5| + |-2|$ and $|5 + (-2)|$.**

Puzzle

Explain that a new magic square can be obtained by adding 2 to each number in the magic square above. Discuss how the entries in the other two magic squares can be obtained. After the students have filled in all the missing entries, have them check whether they have actually obtained magic squares.

Chapter 2 **59**

INTRODUCING THE LESSON

 5-Minute Check

(over Lesson 2-2)

Name the property of equality illustrated by each of the following.

1. If $a = 3$, then $3 = a$. **symmetric**
2. If $r = s + t$ and $s + t = 9$, then $r = 9$. **transitive**
3. $6.3 = 6.3$ **reflexive**

Solve.

4. $a + (-6.8) = -4.3$ $a = 2.5$
5. $3n - 11 = -5 - 6n$ $n = \frac{2}{3}$

Motivating the Lesson

Cut a picture of an appliance such as a washing machine or refrigerator from a sales flyer. Note the sale price on the back of the picture. Display the picture to the class. Have students take turns asking questions about the sale price of the item using the terms "greater than" and "less than". Students should use responses from one another's questions to guess the price.

TEACHING THE LESSON

Teaching Tip ❶ Students may benefit from making concrete comparisons involving height, weight, or length to prove that exactly one of the three comparison sentences is true. For example, use three students in the classroom whose heights are different to demonstrate the comparison sentences.

2-3 Inequalities and the Number Line

Objectives

After studying this lesson, you should be able to:

2-3A ▪ compare numbers,
2-3B ▪ write inequalities for graphs on number lines, and
2-3C ▪ graph inequalities on number lines.

Application

The Lincoln High School hockey team played ten games during its regular season. During the season, each win is worth 2 points, each tie is worth 1 point, and each loss is 0 points. To qualify for the playoffs, a team must have more than 14 points. If Lincoln's team finished the regular season with 6 wins, 3 ties, and 1 loss, did they qualify for the playoffs?

You can solve this problem by determining if Lincoln's team received more than 14 points. Since $6(2) + 3(1) + 1(0) = 12 + 3 + 0$ or 15, and 15 is *more than* 14, Lincoln's team qualified for the playoffs.

The statement *15 is more than 14* can be symbolized in two ways.

$15 > 14$, which means 15 *is greater than* 14.
$14 < 15$, which means 14 *is less than* 15.

Note that the < and > point to the lesser number.

A mathematical sentence that uses > or < to compare two expressions is called an **inequality**. If >, <, and = are used to compare the same two numbers, then only one of the three sentences is true. **Teaching Tip** ❶

Comparison Property	For any two numbers a and b, exactly one of the following sentences is true. **Teaching Tip** ❷
	$a < b$ $a = b$ $a > b$

Example 1

Replace __?__ with <, >, or = to make -14 __?__ $3 + (-20)$ a true sentence.

-14 __?__ $3 + (-20)$
-14 __?__ -17 *Simplify.*

Since -14 is greater than -17, the true sentence is $-14 > 3 + (-20)$.

In Chapter 1 you learned that the reflexive, symmetric, and transitive properties hold for equality. Do these properties hold for inequalities? Check each property using specific numbers.

Reflexive: Is $6 > 6$? *no*   Is $6 < 6$? *no*
Symmetric: If $8 > 3$, is $3 > 8$? *no*   If $3 < 8$, is $8 < 3$? *no*
Transitive: If $7 > 1$ and $1 > -4$, is $7 > -4$? *yes*

Check to see if the transitive property is true for other examples.

ALTERNATE TEACHING STRATEGIES

Using Manipulatives

Use items available at students' desks, such as pencils, paper, or backpacks to demonstrate the comparison and transitive properties by comparing lengths of pencils, weights of backpacks, and thickness of paper.

From these and other examples, we can conclude that only the transitive property holds for < and >.

Transitive Property of Order	For all numbers *a*, *b*, and *c*, 1. if $a < b$ and $b < c$, then $a < c$, and 2. if $a > b$ and $b > c$, then $a > c$.

The symbols $\neq$, $\leq$, and $\geq$ can also be used to compare numbers. The chart below shows several inequality symbols and their meanings.

Teaching Tip ③

Symbol	Meaning
<	is less than
>	is greater than
≠	is not equal to
≤	is less than or equal to
≥	is greater than or equal to

Example 2

Is $5.1 \leq -2.4 + 8.3$ *true* or *false*?

$5.1 \overset{?}{\leq} -2.4 + 8.3$ *Is 5.1 less than or equal to −2.4 + 8.3?*
$5.1 \leq 5.9$ *Simplify.*

Since 5.1 is less than 5.9, the sentence is true.

Consider the graphs of -3, -1, $2\frac{1}{2}$, and 4.5 shown on the number line below.

Teaching Tip ④ The following statements can be made about the numbers and their graphs.

The graph of -3 is to the left of the graph of -1.	$-3 < -1$
The graph of -1 is to the left of the graph of $2\frac{1}{2}$.	$-1 < 2\frac{1}{2}$
The graph of $2\frac{1}{2}$ is to the right of the graph of -3.	$2\frac{1}{2} > -3$
The graph of 4.5 is to the right of the graph of $2\frac{1}{2}$.	$4.5 > 2\frac{1}{2}$

Comparing Numbers on the Number Line	If *a* and *b* represent any numbers and the graph of *a* is to the left of the graph of *b*, then $a < b$. If the graph of *a* is to the right of the graph of *b*, then $a > b$.

Some points on a number line cannot be named by integers. The number line below is separated into fourths to show the graphs of some common fractions and decimals. The numbers graphed on this number line are examples of **rational numbers**.

Teaching Tip ② The comparison property is sometimes called the trichotomy property.

Teaching Tip ③ You may wish to introduce the symbols for is not less than ($\not<$) and is not greater than ($\not>$) to your students.

Teaching Tip ④ Stress the importance of the direction a number is graphed in relation to another number. For example, the inequality $-1 < -2$ is false, but $-1 > -2$ is true. On the number line, -1 is to the right of -2.

Chalkboard Examples

For Example 1
Replace ? with <, >, or = to make each sentence true.

a. $-11 \underline{\ ?\ } -20 + 9$ =

b. $-15 + 6 \underline{\ ?\ } 0$ <

c. $5 \underline{\ ?\ } 8 + (-12)$ >

For Example 2
Indicate whether each sentence is *true* or *false*.

a. $-3.4 + 2.1 \geq 5.3 + (-9.2)$
true

b. $6.7 + (-4.4) \leq -5.6 + 3.2$
false

Chalkboard Examples

For Example 3

Graph the solution set of x < 3.

For Example 4.

Graph the solution set of $n \geq -\frac{5}{4}$.

For Example 5

If x represents the number of raffle tickets sold, and x < 8, graph the solution set.

Teaching Tip **5** Remind students of the importance of the stipulation that *b* is not equal to zero.

Reteaching Masters Booklet, p. 11

NAME _____ DATE _____

2-3 **Reteaching Worksheet**

Inequalities and the Number Line

A mathematical sentence containing > or < is called an **inequality**. The chart at the right shows several inequality symbols and their meanings.

Symbol	Meaning
<	is less than
>	is greater than
≠	is not equal to
≤	is less than or equal to
≥	is greater than or equal to

To find the solution set for an inequality, determine what replacements for *x* make the inequality true. Study the graph for the solution set of x < 3.

A circle indicates that 3 is not included in the solution set.

You can use the transitive property of order and the definition of a rational number when solving problems involving inequalities.

Transitive Property of Order	Definition of a Rational Number
For all numbers *a*, *b*, and *c*, 1. If a < b and b < c, then a < c. 2. If a > b and b > c, then a > c.	Any number that can be written in the form $\frac{a}{b}$ where *a* and *b* are integers and $b \neq 0$, is a rational number.

Write an inequality for each graph.

1. _____ x ≥ 2
2. _____ x > −6
3. _____ x ≠ −1
4. _____ x ≤ 5

Fill in each blank with <, >, or = to make each sentence true.

5. −4 ___ 8 <
6. −32 + 11 ___ 21 <
7. −81 ___ 1 + 80 <
8. $14 - \left(-\frac{4}{2}\right)$ ___ 12 >
9. $-\frac{29}{2}$ ___ 14 − 28.5 =
10. −5 + (−6) ___ 12 − 1 >

Graph the solution set of each inequality on a number line.

11. y > −2
12. m ≤ 4
13. x ≠ 3
14. a < −1

Write an algebraic expression for each verbal expression.

15. *a* is no more than five. a ≤ 5
16. *x* is not negative. x ≥ 0

Definition of a Rational Number

A rational number is a number that can be expressed in the form $\frac{a}{b}$, where *a* and *b* are integers and *b* is not equal to zero. **Teaching Tip** **5**

Notice that all integers are rational numbers.

Examples of rational numbers expressed in the form $\frac{a}{b}$ are shown below.

Rational Number	3	$-2\frac{3}{4}$	0.125	0	$0.33\overline{3}$
Form $\frac{a}{b}$	$\frac{3}{1}$	$-\frac{11}{4}$	$\frac{1}{8}$	$\frac{0}{1}$	$\frac{1}{3}$

Recall that equations like x − 4 = 9 are open sentences. Inequalities like x < 5 are also considered to be open sentences. To find the solution set of x < 5, determine what replacements for x make x < 5 true. All numbers less than 5 make the inequality true. This can be shown by the solution set {all numbers less than 5}. Not only does this include integers like 4, 0, and −3, but it also includes all of the rational numbers less than 5. Examples of rational numbers less than 5 are $\frac{1}{3}$, $-4\frac{2}{5}$, and −2.

Example 3

Graph the solution set of x < 5.

The heavy arrow indicates that all numbers to the left of 5 are included. The *circle* indicates that the point corresponding to 5 is *not* included in the graph of the solution set.

Example 4

Graph the solution set of $n \geq -\frac{3}{2}$.

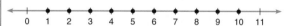

The solution set is $\left\{-\frac{3}{2}\right.$ and all numbers greater than $\left.-\frac{3}{2}\right\}$. The *dot* indicates that the point corresponding to $-\frac{3}{2}$ *is* included in the graph of the solution set.

Example 5

APPLICATION

Business

When cars are ordered from a certain distributor, the order must be for no more than 10 cars. Determine the number of cars that could be in an order from this distributor. Then graph the solution set.

An order from this distributor must be for no more than 10 cars. Since it is not possible to order a fractional number of cars or a negative number of cars, the number of cars in an order must be a whole number that is less than or equal to 10. Since a dealer would not place an order for 0 cars, the solution set is {1, 2, 3, 4, 5, 6, 7, 8, 9, 10}.

RETEACHING THE LESSON

Write an algebraic expression for each verbal expression.

1. The cost is under $195.
   c < 195
2. *x* is positive. x > 0
3. *x* is non-negative. x ≥ 0
4. Tom is at least 18 years old.
   T ≥ 18
5. The stream is no more than 50 feet across. s ≤ 50

CHECKING FOR UNDERSTANDING

Communicating Mathematics

Complete.

1. If $a \le b$, then a is less than b or $a \underline{}$ b. **is equal to**

2. A dot is used to indicate that a point is $\underline{}$ in a graph on a number line. **included**

3. Numbers of the form $\frac{a}{b}$, where a and b are integers and $b \ne 0$, are called $\underline{}$. **rational numbers**

4. The definition of a rational number states that b cannot be zero. Why must this condition be included in the definition?
Because you cannot divide by 0.

Guided Practice

Determine whether each sentence is *true* or *false*.

5. $7 < 4$ **F**

6. $-3 \le 3$ **T**

7. $-9 > -4$ **F**

8. $-5\frac{2}{3} \ne -6\frac{2}{3}$ **T**

9. $-4 < 2 - 8$ **F**

10. If $1 < 3$, then $1 > 3$. **F**

If *n* is a whole number, write the solution set for each inequality.

11. $n > 3$
{4, 5, 6, . . . }

12. $n \le 4$
{0, 1, 2, 3, 4}

13. $n \ne 6$
{0, 1, 2, 3, 4, 5, 7, . . . }

Determine whether each number is included on the graph below.

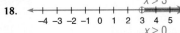

14. -1 **yes**

15. 4 **no**

16. 4.1 **yes**

17. $-1\frac{1}{2}$ **yes**

EXERCISES

Practice

A

Write an inequality for each graph.

18.
 $x > 3$

19. $x \ne -3$

20. $x \ge 0$

21. $x < -3$

22. $x \ne 4$

23. $x \le 2$

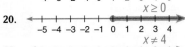
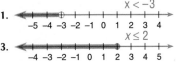

B

Graph the solution set of each inequality on a number line. **See margin.**

24. $n > 5$

25. $y < -2$

26. $x \ne -1$

27. $y \le 6$

28. $x \ge -2$

29. $x < -10$

30. $a \ge -3$

31. $y \ne 3$

Write an algebraic expression for each verbal expression.

32. x is at most thirty. $x \le 30$

33. y is at least negative 5. $y \ge -5$

34. m is no less than ten. $m \ge 10$

35. b is negative. $b < 0$

LESSON 2-3 INEQUALITIES AND THE NUMBER LINE 63

Additional Answers

24.
25.
26.
27.

28.
29.
30.
31.

EVALUATING THE LESSON

Checking for Understanding
Exercises 1-17 are designed to help you assess understanding through reading, writing, and speaking. You should work through Exercises 1-4 with your students, and then monitor their work on Exercises 5-17.

Closing the Lesson
Speaking Activity Have students determine how many whole numbers satisfy the inequality $x < 5$. **5**

Then ask students how many rational numbers satisfy the inequality.
an infinite number

APPLYING THE LESSON

Homework Exercises

Assignment Guide
Basic: 18-38, 46-50, 52-57
Average: 21-42, 46-57
Enriched: 24-57

Practice Masters Booklet, p. 11

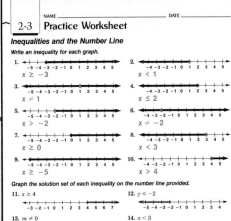

Additional Answer

45.

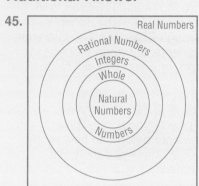

NAME _____ DATE _____

2-3 **Enrichment Worksheet**

Equivalent Sets

Two sets are **equal**, or identical, if they contain exactly the same elements. The order in which we name the elements is unimportant. Thus, {a, b, c, d} and {c, a, d, b} are equal sets. Two sets are **equivalent** if for every element of one set there is one and only one element in the other set; that is, there exists a one-to-one matching between the elements of the two sets. The one-to-one matchings below show that the sets are equivalent.

 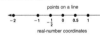

Consider these equivalent sets:

Set of whole numbers = {0, 1, 2, 3, 4, 5, ...}.

Set of even whole numbers = {0, 2, 4, 6, 8, 10, ...}.

Are there more whole numbers or more even whole numbers? Or might there be the same number of each, even though we have no counting number to tell how many?

A one-to-one matching of the whole numbers and the even whole numbers appears at the right. Each whole number n is matched with the even number $2n$, and each even number $2n$ is matched with the whole number n. Therefore, the two sets are equivalent. This means that there are as many even whole numbers as there are whole numbers.

Use a one-to-one matching to show that the two sets are equivalent.

1. {Amy, Betsy, Carol, Dorothy} and {Al, Bob, Carl, David}

2. {1, 2, 3, 4, 5, ...} and {3, 6, 9, 12, 15, ...}

3. {−1, −2, −3, −4, ...} and {1, 2, 3, 4, ...}

4. {1, 2, 3, 4, 5, ...} and {1, 3, 5, 7, 9, ...}

Replace each ? with <, >, or = to make each sentence true.

36. $-5 \underline{\ ?\ } 7$ <

37. $-2 \underline{\ ?\ } -3$ >

38. $-7 - 2 \underline{\ ?\ } -9$ =

39. $-5 \underline{\ ?\ } 0 - 3$ <

40. $3 \underline{\ ?\ } \frac{15}{3}$ <

41. $8 \underline{\ ?\ } 4.1 + 3.9$ =

42. $5 \underline{\ ?\ } 8.4 - 1.5$ <

43. $\frac{4}{3}(6) \underline{\ ?\ } 4\left(\frac{3}{2}\right)$ >

44. $\frac{27.155}{3} \underline{\ ?\ } 2(4.459)$ >

45. Draw a Venn diagram to show the relationship among the following sets of numbers: natural numbers, whole numbers, integers, rational numbers, and real numbers. **See margin.**

Critical Thinking
Teaching Tip ⑥

46. Three numbers x, y, and z satisfy the following conditions: $y - z < 0$, $x - y > 0$, and $z - x < 0$. Which one is the greatest? **x**

47. If $x < y$ and $x < z$, what conclusion can be made about y and z? **none**

Applications

48. **School** Less than half the students in Mrs. Chen's science class are boys. If there are 34 students in the class, what is the greatest number of boys that could be in the class? **16 boys**

49. **Population** At least one-fourth of the residents of Riverdale are over the age of 60. If Riverdale has 19,200 residents, what is the least number of residents that could be over the age of 60? **4800 residents**

50. **Armed Forces** A battalion of 880 people is made up of four companies. Each company is made up of five platoons. Each platoon contains four squads. If each company has the same number of people, as do each platoon and each squad, how many people are in each squad? **11 people**

51. **History** In 1883, the original Metropolitan Opera House opened in New York City. Seven decades and two years later, Marian Anderson became the first African-American soloist to sing with the Metropolitan Opera. When did this event take place? **1955**

Mixed Review

52. Evaluate $5y + 3$ if $y = 1.3$. **(Lesson 1-2) 9.5**

53. Name the like terms: $\frac{m^2n}{2}$, $3mn$, $5m^2n$, $\frac{mn^2}{4}$. **(Lesson 1-5)** $\frac{m^2n}{2}$, $5m^2n$

54. Find the next three numbers in the pattern $1, 3, 9, 27, \underline{\ ?\ }, \underline{\ ?\ }, \underline{\ ?\ }$. **(Lesson 2-1) 81, 243, 729**

55. Write a corresponding addition sentence for the diagram shown at the right. **(Lesson 2-1)**

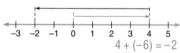

$4 + (-6) = -2$

56. Find the sum: $82 + (-78)$. **(Lesson 2-2) 4**

57. Evaluate $a - 12$ if $a = -8$. **(Lesson 2-2) −20**

EXTENDING THE LESSON

Math Power:
Problem Solving

If $x = \{-2, -10, 18\}$, what value of x would make the following sentence true?

$$|2^2 - x| < \frac{3}{4}(12) + x$$

−2; replacing the value with either −10 or −18 would make $\frac{3}{4}(12) + x$ negative.

Comparing and Ordering Rational Numbers

Objectives

After studying this lesson, you should be able to:

2-4A ■ compare rational numbers,

2-4B ■ write rational numbers in increasing or decreasing order, and

2-4C ■ find a number between two rational numbers.

Application

Paul and Vivian work at a neighborhood fast-food restaurant after school. They each make \$4.95 per hour and work 20 hours per week. Paul saves $\frac{3}{8}$ of his wages and Vivian saves $\frac{4}{11}$ of her wages. Who saves more money?

When two fractions are compared, the cross products are the products of the terms on the diagonals.

You know that $\frac{6}{9}$ is less than $\frac{7}{9}$ because the denominators are the same and 6 is less than 7. But how can you compare $\frac{3}{8}$ and $\frac{4}{11}$? You can use *cross products* to compare rational numbers.

Comparison Property for Rational Numbers	For any rational numbers $\frac{a}{b}$ and $\frac{c}{d}$, with $b > 0$ and $d > 0$: 1. if $\frac{a}{b} < \frac{c}{d}$, then $ad < bc$, and 2. if $ad < bc$, then $\frac{a}{b} < \frac{c}{d}$. **Teaching Tip**

This property also holds if < is replaced by >, ≤, ≥, or =.

Use this property to compare $\frac{3}{8}$ and $\frac{4}{11}$.

Find the product of 3 and 11. $\frac{3}{8}$? $\frac{4}{11}$ *Find the product of 8 and 4.*

$$3(11)\ ?\ 8(4)$$

$$33 > 32$$

Since $33 > 32$, we can conclude that $\frac{3}{8} > \frac{4}{11}$. Thus, Paul is saving more money.

Example 1
Teaching Tip

Replace the _?_ with <, >, or = to make $\frac{6}{11}$ _?_ $\frac{7}{12}$ a true sentence.

$\frac{6}{11}$? $\frac{7}{12}$ *Find the cross products.*

$$6(12)\ ?\ 11(7)$$

$$72 < 77$$

The true sentence is $\frac{6}{11} < \frac{7}{12}$.

ALTERNATE TEACHING STRATEGIES

Using Calculators

Use a calculator to determine which of the two items is the better buy. First change each ratio to a decimal by dividing the numerator by the denominator. Round the result to the nearest thousandth. Then compare the decimals.

1. A dozen oranges for \$1.59 or a half-dozen for \$0.85. **dozen**

2. A 1-pound package of lunch meat for \$1.98 or a 12-ounce package for \$1.80. **1-pound package**

Lesson Resources

- Reteaching Master 2-4
- Practice Master 2-4
- Enrichment Master 2-4
- Evaluation Master, p. 23

Transparency 2-4 contains the 5-Minute Check and a teaching aid for this lesson.

INTRODUCING THE LESSON

5-Minute Check
(over Lesson 2-3)

1. Graph the solution set of $y > -3$ on a number line.

$-3\ -2\ -1\ 0\ 1\ 2\ 3\ 4\ 5\ 6\ 7$

Write an algebraic expression for each verbal expression.

2. p is positive. $p > 0$
3. r is less than 5. $r < 5$

Replace each _?_ with <, >, or = to make each sentence true.

4. $-\frac{4}{3}$ _?_ -2 >
5. 6 _?_ $4.6 + 1.7$ <

Motivating the Lesson

Rita earned \$20.00 for 4 hours of work. If Jason's hourly wage is \$4.75, would his pay for 4 hours of work be greater than, less than, or equal to Rita's? **less than**

TEACHING THE LESSON

Teaching Tip ❶ Emphasize the need for b and d to be positive. For example, insert the inequality symbol to make $-\frac{3}{4}$ _?_ $-\frac{1}{3}$ true. If $b < 0$, then $\frac{3}{-4}$ _?_ $-\frac{1}{3}$ gives $9 > 4$. This implies $-\frac{3}{4} > -\frac{1}{3}$, which is incorrect.

Reteaching Masters Booklet, p. 12

Every rational number can be expressed as a terminating or repeating decimal. You can use a calculator to write rational numbers as decimals so they can be easily compared.

Example 2

Use a calculator to write the fractions $\frac{3}{5}$, $\frac{2}{3}$, and $\frac{6}{11}$ as decimals. Then write the fractions in order from greatest to least.

$\frac{3}{5} = 0.6$ *This is a terminating decimal.*

$\frac{2}{3} = 0.66666\ldots$ or $0.\overline{6}$ *This is a repeating decimal.*

$\frac{6}{11} = 0.545454\ldots$ or $0.\overline{54}$ *This is also a repeating decimal.*

Since $0.\overline{6} > 0.6$ and $0.6 > 0.\overline{54}$, $\frac{2}{3} > \frac{3}{5} > \frac{6}{11}$.

Example 3

APPLICATION
Consumerism

Super Saver Mart advertised a 9.4-ounce tube of toothpaste for $1.61. Is this a better buy than another brand's 6-ounce tube for 95¢? **Teaching Tip 3**

Compare the cost per ounce, or **unit cost** of each tube. Let's assume that the quality of the two items is the same. Then the item with the lesser unit cost is the better buy.

$$\text{unit cost} = \text{total cost} \div \text{number of units}$$

Use a calculator to find the unit cost of each brand. In each case, the unit cost is expressed in cents per ounce.

unit cost of first brand: 1.61 ÷ 9.4 = 0.17127659

unit cost of second brand: 0.95 ÷ 6 = 0.15833333

Since $0.16¢ < 0.17¢$, the 6-ounce tube for 95¢ is the better buy.

Teaching Tip 4

Given any two integers, can you always find another integer between them? Consider the integers 3 and 4. There is no integer between them. What about any two rational numbers? Can you always find another rational number between them? One point that lies between any two numbers is the point midway between them. The coordinates of the points on the number line below are $\frac{1}{3}$ and $\frac{1}{2}$.

To find the coordinate of the point midway between $\frac{1}{3}$ and $\frac{1}{2}$, find the average of the two numbers.

$$\text{average: } \frac{1}{2}\left(\frac{1}{3} + \frac{1}{2}\right) = \frac{1}{2}\left(\frac{5}{6}\right) \text{ or } \frac{5}{12}$$ **Teaching Tip 5**

This process can be continued indefinitely. The property described above is called the **density property**.

RETEACHING THE LESSON

A rational number that is between $\frac{a}{b}$ and $\frac{c}{d}$ is $\frac{a+c}{b+d}$, where a, b, c, and d are integers. If $b = d$, $\frac{a+c}{b+d}$ is not the average of $\frac{a}{b}$ and $\frac{c}{d}$, and its graph is not equidistant from the graph of $\frac{a}{b}$ and $\frac{c}{d}$.

For each pair of rational numbers $\frac{a}{b}$ and $\frac{c}{d}$, find $\frac{a+c}{b+d}$ and show that it is between the given pair of numbers.

1. $\frac{2}{3}, \frac{4}{5}$ $\frac{6}{8}$; $0.\overline{6} < 0.75 < 0.8$

2. $\frac{3}{10}, \frac{1}{2}$ $\frac{4}{12}$; $0.3 < 0.3\overline{3} < 0.5$

3. $\frac{3}{8}, \frac{7}{10}$ $\frac{10}{18}$; $0.375 < 0.5\overline{5} < 0.7$

Density Property for Rational Numbers	Between every pair of distinct rational numbers, there are infinitely many rational numbers.

Example 4

Find a rational number between $\frac{3}{4}$ and $\frac{6}{7}$.

Find the average of the two rational numbers.

$$\frac{1}{2}\left(\frac{3}{4} + \frac{6}{7}\right) = \frac{1}{2}\left(\frac{21}{28} + \frac{24}{28}\right)$$

$$= \frac{1}{2}\left(\frac{45}{28}\right)$$

$$= \frac{45}{56}$$

Enter: 3 ÷ 4 + 6 ÷ 7

Enter: = ÷ 2 =

Display: 0.8035714

A rational number between $\frac{3}{4}$ and $\frac{6}{7}$ is $\frac{45}{56}$ or 0.804.

CHECKING FOR UNDERSTANDING

Communicating Mathematics

Read and study the lesson to answer each question. See margin.

1. On page 66, we discussed terminating decimals and repeating decimals. What is a nonterminating, nonrepeating decimal?

2. Explain how to find three rational numbers between $\frac{1}{5}$ and $\frac{1}{4}$.

Guided Practice

Name the greater rational number.

3. $\frac{3}{4}, \frac{4}{5}$ $\frac{4}{5}$

4. $\frac{11}{12}, \frac{7}{8}$ $\frac{11}{12}$

5. $\frac{9}{10}, \frac{10}{11}$ $\frac{10}{11}$

6. $\frac{7}{8}, \frac{8}{9}$ $\frac{8}{9}$

7. $\frac{6}{5}, \frac{7}{6}$ $\frac{6}{5}$

8. $\frac{11}{9}, \frac{12}{10}$ $\frac{11}{9}$

Which is the better buy?

9. a 21-ounce can of baked beans for 79¢ or a 28-ounce can for 97¢

10. a 10-ounce jar of coffee for $4.27 or an 8-ounce jar for $3.64

EXERCISES

Practice

Replace each _?_ with <, >, or = to make each sentence true.

11. $\frac{6}{7}$ _?_ $\frac{7}{8}$ <

12. $\frac{8}{7}$ _?_ $\frac{9}{8}$ >

13. $\frac{7}{19}$ _?_ $\frac{6}{17}$ >

14. $\frac{8}{15}$ _?_ $\frac{9}{16}$ <

15. $\frac{5}{14}$ _?_ $\frac{25}{70}$ =

16. $\frac{0.4}{3}$ _?_ $\frac{1.2}{8}$ <

LESSON 2-4 COMPARING AND ORDERING RATIONAL NUMBERS 67

Additional Answers

1. A decimal that does not repeat and does not end.

2. Add $\frac{1}{5}$ and $\frac{1}{4}$ and divide by 4.

17. $\frac{20}{27}, \frac{19}{24}, \frac{17}{21}$

18. $\frac{17}{19}, \frac{32}{35}, \frac{45}{49}$

19. $\frac{9}{43}, \frac{3}{14}, \frac{5}{23}$

EVALUATING THE LESSON

Checking for Understanding

Exercises 1-10 are designed to help you assess understanding through reading, writing, and speaking. You should work through Exercises 1-2 with your students, and then monitor their work on Exercises 3-10.

Closing the Lesson

Writing Activity Have students make a table with the headings Whole Number, Integer, and Rational Number. Then ask them to classify each of the following numbers under the appropriate heading: $-\frac{1}{2}$, 0, $\frac{4}{2}$, $-6\frac{1}{3}$, $\frac{4}{5}$, -14.1, 0.34, $\frac{27}{54}$, and $\frac{-56}{2}$.

APPLYING THE LESSON

Homework Exercises

See Assignment Guide on page 67.

Chapter 2, Quiz B, (Lessons 2-3 through 2-4), is available in the Evaluation Masters Booklet, p. 23.

Enrichment Masters Booklet, p. 12

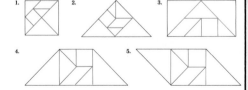

B Write the fractions in order from least to greatest. **See margin.**

17. $\frac{17}{21}, \frac{20}{27}, \frac{19}{24}$
18. $\frac{17}{19}, \frac{32}{35}, \frac{45}{49}$
19. $\frac{3}{14}, \frac{5}{23}, \frac{9}{43}$

20-25. Answers may vary; sample answers are given.

C Find a number between the given numbers.

20. $\frac{1}{2}$ and $\frac{6}{7}$ $\frac{19}{28}$; 0.679
21. $\frac{4}{7}$ and $\frac{9}{4}$ $\frac{79}{56}$; 1.411
22. $\frac{2}{9}$ and $\frac{8}{11}$ $\frac{47}{99}$; 0.475

23. $\frac{19}{30}$ and $\frac{31}{45}$ $\frac{119}{180}$; $0.66\overline{1}$
24. $\frac{7}{6}$ and $\frac{21}{18}$ none
25. $-\frac{3}{8}$ and $\frac{9}{10}$ 0

Critical Thinking

26. Find the coordinates of B and C if the distances between each pair of points are equal.

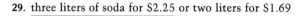

A   B   C   D

$\frac{1}{24}$ $\frac{1}{6}$ $\frac{7}{24}$ $\frac{5}{12}$

27. To find a number between $\frac{3}{4}$ and $\frac{6}{7}$, John added as follows.

$$\frac{3+6}{4+7} = \frac{9}{11} \qquad \frac{9}{11} \text{ is between } \frac{3}{4} \text{ and } \frac{6}{7}.$$

He claimed that this method will always work. Do you agree? **yes**

Applications

Which is the better buy?

28. a half-pound bag of cashews for $2.93 or a $\frac{3}{4}$-pound bag for $4.19

29. three liters of soda for $2.25 or two liters for $1.69

30. a 27-ounce loaf of bread for 93¢ or a 20-ounce loaf for 79¢

31. a dozen oranges for $1.59 or half a dozen oranges for 85¢

32. five pounds of green beans for $3.50 or 2 pounds for $1.38

33. a 48-ounce bottle of dishwashing liquid for $2.39 or a 22-ounce bottle for $1.09

Mixed Review

34. Write a mathematical expression for *seven more than r*.   **(Lesson 1-1)**
$r + 7$ **or** $7 + r$

Name the property illustrated by each statement.

35. $A(1) = A$ **(Lesson 1-4)** multiplicative identity

36. $3 + 4 = 4 + 3$ **(Lesson 1-6)** commutative $(+)$

Replace the $\underline{?}$ with <, >, or = to make each sentence true. **(Lesson 2-3)**

37. $12 \underline{?} 15 - 27$ >
38. $(-7.502)(0.511) \underline{?} -3.115$ <

EXTENDING THE LESSON

Math Power: Connections

Draw two rectangles with equal dimensions. Then show that $\frac{3}{5} > \frac{1}{3}$.

Adding and Subtracting Rational Numbers

Objectives

After studying this lesson, you should be able to:

2-5A ▪ add two or more rational numbers,

2-5B ▪ subtract rational numbers, and

2-5C ▪ simplify expressions that contain rational numbers.

Application

On Monday, stock in Paxtel Corporation rose $3\frac{1}{8}$ points. The next day, because of a rumor about a merger with another company, the stock dropped $1\frac{3}{4}$ points. What was the net change in the price of the Paxtel stock?

Rational numbers can be added using a number line. Consider the sum of $\frac{1}{4}$ and $-\frac{3}{8}$. First replace $\frac{1}{4}$ with $\frac{2}{8}$, because the number line is separated into eighths. Then add $\frac{2}{8}$ and $-\frac{3}{8}$.

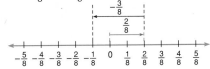

The sum of $\frac{1}{4}$ and $-\frac{3}{8}$ is $-\frac{1}{8}$.

Using a number line to show the addition of rational numbers is very inconvenient. However, the rules used to add integers can also be used to add rational numbers. If two rational numbers have the same sign, add their absolute values. Give the result the same sign as the addends. If two rational numbers have different signs, subtract the lesser absolute value from the greater absolute value. Give the result the same sign as the addend with the greater absolute value. **Teaching Tip ❶**

Example 1

APPLICATION

Stock Market

Find the net change in the price of the Paxtel stock.

Find the net change by finding the sum of $3\frac{1}{8}$ and $-1\frac{3}{4}$.

$$3\frac{1}{8} + \left(-1\frac{3}{4}\right) = 3\frac{1}{8} + \left(-1\frac{6}{8}\right)$$ *Because the least common denominator is 8, replace $-1\frac{3}{4}$ with $-1\frac{6}{8}$.*

$$= +\left(\left|3\frac{1}{8}\right| - \left|-1\frac{6}{8}\right|\right)$$ *$3\frac{1}{8}$ has the greater absolute value.* **Teaching**
So, the sign of the sum is positive. **Tip ❷**

$$= +\left(3\frac{1}{8} - 1\frac{6}{8}\right)$$ *Since the addends have different signs, find the difference of their absolute values.*

$$= +\left(2\frac{9}{8} - 1\frac{6}{8}\right)$$ *Replace $3\frac{1}{8}$ with $2\frac{9}{8}$. Then subtract.*

$$= 1\frac{3}{8}$$ *The net change is up $1\frac{3}{8}$ points.*

ALTERNATE TEACHING STRATEGIES

Using Applications

Evan had $105.63 in his checking account. He wrote checks for $32.46 and $43.28. Then he deposited a check for $48.50. What is his new balance? **$78.39**

Using Problem Solving

Insert parentheses so that a true equation results.
$10 - 4 \times 2 - 1 = 3$
$10 - (4 \times 2 - 1) = 3$

Lesson Resources

- Reteaching Master 2-5
- Practice Master 2-5
- Enrichment Master 2-5
- Activity Master, p. 47
- Video Algebra, 6

 Transparency 2-5 contains the 5-Minute Check and a teaching aid for this lesson.

INTRODUCING THE LESSON

🕐 5-Minute Check
(over Lesson 2-4)

Find the larger of the two numbers.

1. $\frac{3}{15}, \frac{5}{17}$ $\frac{5}{17}$

2. $\frac{7}{12}, \frac{6}{11}$ $\frac{7}{12}$

Determine a rational number between the given numbers.

3. $-\frac{3}{4}, \frac{5}{6}$ 0

4. $\frac{1}{2}, \frac{6}{7}$ $\frac{19}{28}$

Find the unit price.

5. 8 ounces of coffee sells for $3.84. **$0.48**

Motivating the Lesson

Have students read the stock report from a recent newspaper. Discuss the meanings of such headings as "High", "Low", and "Chg". Have each class member select and monitor a particular stock during a one-week period.

TEACHING THE LESSON

Teaching Tip ❶ Students are often confused with the various sets of numbers. Emphasize that a rational number is a ratio of two integers.

Teaching Tip ❷ Although the positive sign is not necessary in $+\left(\left|3\frac{1}{8}\right| - \left|-1\frac{6}{8}\right|\right)$, encourage students, at first, to place the sign outside the parentheses. Emphasize this step in analyzing what sign the sum will have.

Example 2 | **Find the sum: $-1.354 + (-0.765)$.**

$$-1.354 + (-0.765) = -(|-1.354| + |-0.765|)$$

The numbers have the same sign.

$$= -(1.354 + 0.765)$$

Add their absolute values.

$$= -2.119$$

When adding three or more rational numbers, you can use the commutative and associative properties to rearrange the addends.

Example 3 | **Find the sum: $-\frac{4}{3} + \frac{5}{8} + \left(-\frac{7}{3}\right)$.**

$$-\frac{4}{3} + \frac{5}{8} + \left(-\frac{7}{3}\right) = \left[-\frac{4}{3} + \left(-\frac{7}{3}\right)\right] + \frac{5}{8}$$

Commutative and associative properties of addition

$$= -\frac{11}{3} + \frac{5}{8}$$

The least common denominator is 24.

$$= -\frac{88}{24} + \frac{15}{24}$$

$-\frac{11}{3} = -\frac{88}{24}$ and $\frac{5}{8} = \frac{15}{24}$

$$= -\frac{73}{24}$$

$$= -3\frac{1}{24}$$

Example 4 | **Find the sum: $28.32 + (-56.17) + 32.41 + (-75.13)$.**

Group the positive numbers together and the negative numbers together.

$$28.32 + (-56.17) + 32.41 + (-75.13)$$
$$= 28.32 + 32.41 + (-56.17) + (-75.13)$$
$$= (28.32 + 32.41) + [(-56.17) + (-75.13)]$$
$$= 60.73 + (-131.30)$$
$$= -70.57$$

To subtract rational numbers, use the same process you used to subtract integers.

Example 5 | **Find the difference: $-\frac{7}{8} - \left(-\frac{3}{16}\right)$.**

$$-\frac{7}{8} - \left(-\frac{3}{16}\right) = -\frac{7}{8} + \frac{3}{16}$$

To subtract $-\frac{3}{16}$, add $+\frac{3}{16}$.

$$= -\frac{14}{16} + \frac{3}{16}$$

The least common denominator is 16.

$$= -\frac{11}{16}$$

70   CHAPTER 2   RATIONAL NUMBERS

Example 6 | Evaluate $y - 0.5$, if $y = -0.8$.

$$y - 0.5 = -0.8 - 0.5 \quad \textit{Replace y with } -0.8.$$
$$= -1.3$$

CHECKING FOR UNDERSTANDING

Communicating Mathematics Describe how you could use the commutative and associative properties to find each sum mentally. **See margin.**

1. $1.6x - 4y + (-3y) + 0.4x$

2. $-4\frac{1}{4} + 6\frac{1}{3} + 2\frac{2}{3} + \left(-3\frac{3}{4}\right)$

Guided Practice Find the least common denominator of each pair of numbers.

3. $\frac{1}{2}, \frac{3}{4}$ **4**

4. $\frac{3}{4}, \frac{5}{6}$ **12**

5. $\frac{2}{9}, \frac{5}{6}$ **18**

6. $\frac{4}{7}, \frac{3}{5}$ **35**

Find each sum or difference.

7. $\frac{17}{21} + \left(-\frac{13}{21}\right)$ $\frac{4}{21}$

8. $4.57 + (-3.69)$ **0.88**

9. $-72.5 - 81.3$ **−153.8**

10. $\frac{1}{6} - \frac{2}{3}$ $-\frac{1}{2}$

11. $-\frac{2}{7} + \frac{3}{14} + \frac{3}{7}$ $\frac{5}{14}$

12. $-3a + 12a + (-14a)$ **−5a**

EXERCISES

Practice Find each sum or difference.

 A

13. $-\frac{11}{9} + \left(-\frac{7}{9}\right)$ **−2**

14. $\frac{5}{11} - \frac{6}{11}$ $-\frac{1}{11}$

15. $-\frac{7}{12} + \frac{5}{12}$ $-\frac{1}{6}$

16. $-4.8 + 3.2$ **−1.6**

17. $-38.9 + 24.2$ **−14.7**

18. $-1.7 - 3.9$ **−5.6**

B

19. $\frac{2}{7} - \frac{3}{14}$ $\frac{1}{14}$

20. $-\frac{1}{8} + \left(-\frac{5}{2}\right)$ $-\frac{21}{8}$ or $-2\frac{5}{8}$

21. $\frac{2}{3} + \left(-\frac{2}{9}\right)$ $\frac{4}{9}$

22. $-0.007 + 0.06$ **0.053**

23. $-0.0005 + (-0.3)$ **−0.3005**

24. $-\frac{3}{5} + \frac{5}{6}$ $\frac{7}{30}$

25. $\frac{3}{8} + \left(-\frac{7}{12}\right)$ $-\frac{5}{24}$

26. $-\frac{7}{15} + \left(-\frac{5}{12}\right)$ $-\frac{53}{60}$

27. $-4.5 - 8.6$ **−13.1**

28. $89.3 - (-14.2)$ **103.5**

29. $-5\frac{7}{8} - 2\frac{3}{4}$ $-8\frac{5}{8}$

30. $7\frac{3}{10} - \left(-4\frac{1}{5}\right)$ $11\frac{1}{2}$

31.
$$\begin{array}{r} -15m \\ + \quad 6m \\ \hline -9m \end{array}$$

32.
$$\begin{array}{r} -13c \\ - \quad 28c \\ \hline -41c \end{array}$$

33.
$$\begin{array}{r} 5.8k \\ + (-3.6k) \\ \hline 2.2k \end{array}$$

34.
$$\begin{array}{r} -0.23x \\ + (-0.5\ x) \\ \hline -0.73x \end{array}$$

LESSON 2-5 ADDING AND SUBTRACTING RATIONAL NUMBERS **71**

Additional Answers

1. Group the decimals together: $(1.6x + 0.4x) + [(-4y) + (-3y)]$. Then add: $2x + (-7y)$ or $2x - 7y$.

2. Group the fractions with common denominators: $\left[-4\frac{1}{4} + \left(-3\frac{3}{4}\right)\right] + \left(6\frac{1}{3} + 2\frac{2}{3}\right)$. Then add: $-8 + 9$ or 1.

Evaluate each expression.

35. $a - (-7)$, if $a = 1.9$ **8.9**

36. $h - (-1.3)$, if $h = -18$ **−16.7**

37. $w - 3.7$, if $w = -1.8$ **−5.5**

38. $\frac{11}{2} - m$, if $m = -\frac{5}{2}$ **8**

39. $\frac{11}{4} - x$, if $x = \frac{27}{8}$ **$-\frac{5}{8}$**

40. $-\frac{12}{7} - z$, if $z = \frac{16}{21}$ **$-\frac{52}{21}$**

▶ **C** **Find each sum.** Teaching Tip ❸

41. $5y + (-12y) + (-21y)$ **−28y**

42. $-3z + (-17z) + (-18z)$ **−38z**

43. $\frac{7}{3} + \left(-\frac{5}{6}\right) + \left(-\frac{2}{3}\right)$ **$\frac{5}{6}$**

44. $-\frac{3}{5} + \frac{6}{7} + \left(-\frac{2}{35}\right)$ **$\frac{1}{5}$**

45. $\frac{3}{4} + \left(-\frac{5}{8}\right) + \frac{3}{32}$ **$\frac{7}{32}$**

46. $6.7 + (-8.1) + (-7.3)$ **−8.7**

47. $-4.13 + (-5.18) + 9.63$ **0.32**

48. $-14a + 36k + 12k + (-83a)$
−97a + 48k

Critical Thinking **Use a calculator to find each sum. Express each result in decimal form.**

49. $-0.37 + \left(-\frac{21}{8}\right)$ **−2.995**

50. $-8.66 + 6\frac{7}{8}$ **−1.785**

51. $7.43 + \left(-\frac{9}{4}\right)$ **5.18**

52. $-11\frac{7}{16} + 7.225$ **−4.2125**

Applications 53. **Stock Market** Ted Burton invested his savings in 50 shares of stock. In 3 days, the stock gained $3\frac{1}{8}$ points, lost $\frac{3}{4}$ of a point, and gained another $\frac{1}{8}$ of a point. What was the net gain of the value of one share of Ted's stock? **$2\frac{1}{2}$ points**

54. **Golf** In four rounds of a recent golf tournament, Julie shot 3 under par, 2 over par, 4 under par, and 1 under par. What was her score for the tournament? **6 under par, or −6**

55. **Football** On *Monday Night Football*, the Philadelphia Eagles made the following yardage on their first seven plays: +3, −7, +15, −5, +32, +6, and −14. What was their net yardage? **+30 yards**

56. **Personal Finance** On Tuesday, Delia Puente wrote checks for $35.76 and $41.32. On Wednesday, she deposited $135.59 into her checking account. On Friday, she wrote a check for $63.17. What was the net increase or decrease in Delia's account for the week? **−$4.66**

Mixed Review

57. Evaluate $\frac{4d^2}{4ce}$ if $c = 3$, $d = \frac{1}{2}$, and $e = \frac{2}{3}$. (Lesson 1-2) $\frac{1}{8}$

Name an integer that describes each situation. (Lesson 2-1)

58. 650 meters above sea level $+650$ **59.** 25°F below zero -25

60. Write an open sentence using addition and solve. (Lesson 2-2)

An elevator in the Empire State Building went up to the 36th floor. Then it came down 11 floors. At what floor was it then?

61. Graph the solution set of $m < 1$ on a number line. (Lesson 2-3)

62. Which is the better buy: a 184-gram can of peanuts for 91¢ or a 340-gram can for $1.89? (Lesson 2-4)

60. $36 + (-11) = f$; 25th floor   **61.** See margin.

Additional Answers

61.
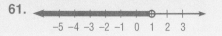
-5 -4 -3 -2 -1 0 1 2 3

Additional Answers for Mid-Chapter Review

1.
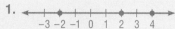
-3 -2 -1 0 1 2 3 4

2.
-5 -4 -3 -2 -1 0 1 2

3.
-1 0 1 2 3 4 5 6

MID-CHAPTER REVIEW

Graph each set of numbers on a number line. (Lesson 2-1) See margin.

1. $\{-2, 2, 4\}$ **2.** $\{-4, -3, -2, -1\}$ **3.** $\{4, 5, 6, \dots\}$

Find each sum or difference. (Lesson 2-2)

4. $43 + (-67)$ -24 **5.** $-23 + (-47)$ -70 **6.** $-93 + 39$ -54

7. $13 - 31$ -18 **8.** $-23 - (-12)$ -11 **9.** $-47 - 35$ -82

10. $-\frac{8}{13} + \left(-\frac{11}{13}\right)$ $-\frac{19}{13}$ **11.** $-\frac{3}{8} + \frac{5}{24}$ $-\frac{1}{6}$ **12.** $-3.948 - 4.826$ -8.774

Replace each __?__ with <, >, or = to make each sentence true. (Lesson 2-3, 2-4)

13. $6 \underline{\;?\;} 4 + 2$ $=$ **14.** $10 \underline{\;?\;} \frac{27}{3}$ $>$ **15.** $8\left(\frac{3}{4}\right) \underline{\;?\;} 6\left(\frac{2}{3}\right)$ $>$

16. $\frac{2}{3} \underline{\;?\;} \frac{3}{5}$ $>$ **17.** $-\frac{7}{6} \underline{\;?\;} -\frac{21}{18}$ $=$ **18.** $\frac{1.1}{4} \underline{\;?\;} \frac{2.2}{5}$ $<$

Solve. (Lesson 2-4, 2-5)

19. Stock Market Last week, the following day-to-day changes were recorded in the Dow Jones stock exchange: Monday, $+5\frac{3}{8}$; Tuesday, $-6\frac{1}{4}$; Wednesday, $+11\frac{1}{8}$; Thursday, $+3\frac{5}{8}$; Friday, $-7\frac{1}{2}$. What was the net change for the week? $+6\frac{3}{8}$

20. Consumerism Haloke wants to buy soda for a party. Eight 1-liter bottles of Brand X cost $3.92. Six 1-liter bottles of Brand Y cost $3.08. A 2-liter bottle of Brand Z costs $1.09. Which soda is the least expensive per liter? Brand X

LESSON 2-5 ADDING AND SUBTRACTING RATIONAL NUMBERS   73

EXTENDING THE LESSON

Math Power: Reasoning

Insert one set of parentheses so that the value of the expression shown becomes $-\frac{37}{60}$.

$\left(-\frac{3}{4}\right) - \left(-\frac{1}{5}\right) - \frac{3}{5} - \left(-\frac{2}{3}\right)$

$\left(-\frac{3}{4}\right) - \left(-\frac{1}{5} - \frac{3}{5} - \left(-\frac{2}{3}\right)\right)$

Mid-Chapter Review

The Mid-Chapter Review provides students with a brief review of the concepts and skills in Lessons 2-1 through 2-5. Lesson numbers are given at the end of problems or instruction lines so students may review concepts not yet mastered.

Enrichment Masters Booklet, p. 13

NAME _____ DATE _____

2-5 **Enrichment Worksheet**

Rounding Fractions

Rounding fractions is more difficult than rounding whole numbers or decimals. For example, think about how you would round $\frac{4}{9}$ inches to the nearest quarter-inch. Through estimation, you might realize that $\frac{4}{9}$ is less than $\frac{1}{2}$. But, is it closer to $\frac{1}{2}$ or to $\frac{1}{4}$? Here are two ways to round fractions. Example 1 uses only the fractions; Example 2 uses decimals.

Example 1:

Subtract the fraction twice. Use the two nearest quarters.

$\frac{1}{2} - \frac{4}{9} = \frac{1}{18}$ $\frac{4}{9} - \frac{1}{4} = \frac{7}{36}$

Compare the differences.

$\frac{1}{18} < \frac{7}{36}$

The smaller difference shows you which fraction to round to.

$\frac{4}{9}$ rounds to $\frac{1}{2}$.

Example 2:

Change the fraction and the two nearest quarters to decimals.

$\frac{4}{9} = 0.4\overline{4}$, $\frac{1}{2} = 0.5$, $\frac{1}{4} = 0.25$

Find the decimal halfway between the two nearest quarters.

$\frac{1}{2}(0.5 + 0.25) = 0.375$

If the fraction is greater than the halfway decimal, round up. If not, round down.

$0.4\overline{4} > 0.3675$. So, $\frac{4}{9}$ is more than half way between $\frac{1}{4}$ and $\frac{1}{2}$.

$\frac{4}{9}$ rounds to $\frac{1}{2}$.

Round each fraction to the nearest one-quarter. Use either method.

1. $\frac{1}{3}$ $\frac{1}{4}$ **2.** $\frac{3}{7}$ $\frac{1}{2}$ **3.** $\frac{7}{11}$ $\frac{3}{4}$ **4.** $\frac{4}{15}$ $\frac{1}{4}$

5. $\frac{7}{20}$ $\frac{1}{4}$ **6.** $\frac{31}{50}$ $\frac{1}{2}$ **7.** $\frac{9}{25}$ $\frac{1}{4}$ **8.** $\frac{23}{30}$ $\frac{3}{4}$

Round each decimal or fraction to the nearest one-eighth.

9. 0.6 $\frac{5}{8}$ **10.** 0.1 $\frac{1}{8}$ **11.** 0.45 $\frac{1}{2}$ **12.** 0.85 $\frac{7}{8}$

13. $\frac{5}{7}$ $\frac{3}{4}$ **14.** $\frac{3}{20}$ $\frac{1}{8}$ **15.** $\frac{23}{25}$ $\frac{7}{8}$ **16.** $\frac{5}{9}$ $\frac{1}{2}$

Lesson Resources
- Reteaching Master 2-6
- Practice Master 2-6
- Enrichment Master 2-6
- Evaluation Master, p. 24
- Lab Manual, pp. 19-20
- Video Algebra, 7

 Transparency 2-6 contains the 5-Minute Check and a teaching aid for this lesson.

INTRODUCING THE LESSON

5-Minute Check
(over Lesson 2-5)

1. Find a rational number between $\frac{3}{4}$ and $\frac{7}{8}$. $\frac{13}{16}$

Find each sum or difference.

2. $3.1 + (-4.56)$ -1.46
3. $-\frac{23}{3} + 2\frac{1}{5}$ $-5\frac{7}{15}$

Evaluate each expression if $a = -1\frac{2}{3}$ and $b = \frac{1}{3}$.

4. $a - b$ -2
5. $|a + b|$ $1\frac{1}{3}$

Motivating the Lesson

Ask students to identify clothing suited to an air temperature of 77 degrees Fahrenheit. Then have them describe what they would wear if air temperature measured 25 degrees Celsius. Develop the idea that these two temperatures are equal amounts. The formula used to convert Fahrenheit degrees to Celsius degrees is $C° = \frac{5}{9}(F° - 32)$.

TEACHING THE LESSON

Teaching Tip   Before studying this procedure, you may wish to review each of the properties involved.

2-6 Multiplying Rational Numbers

Objective
2-6

After studying this lesson, you should be able to:
- multiply rational numbers.

Application

Lourdes Ortiz wants to buy a washer and dryer from Bargain TV and Appliances. If she buys on the "90 days same as cash" plan, she will have to make 4 equal payments of $237.11 each. What is the net effect on her bank account?

One way to solve this problem is to use repeated addition. Think of a bank withdrawal of $237.11 as -237.11. Then $4(-237.11)$ can be expressed as follows.

$$(-237.11) + (-237.11) + (-237.11) + (-237.11) = -948.44$$

Therefore, the net effect on Ms. Ortiz's bank account would be $-\$948.44$.

Since this method would not work if we wanted to find the product of $\frac{2}{3}$ and $-\frac{4}{5}$, we can use the following procedure to show that this product is negative.

$0 = \frac{2}{3}(0)$ *Multiplication property of zero* **Teaching Tip** ❶

$0 = \frac{2}{3}\left[\frac{4}{5} + \left(-\frac{4}{5}\right)\right]$ *Substitution and additive inverse properties*

$0 = \frac{2}{3}\left(\frac{4}{5}\right) + \frac{2}{3}\left(-\frac{4}{5}\right)$ *Distributive property*

$0 = \frac{8}{15} + \frac{2}{3}\left(-\frac{4}{5}\right)$ *Substitution property*

By the additive inverse property, 0 is equal to $\frac{8}{15} + \left(-\frac{8}{15}\right)$. Therefore, $\frac{2}{3}\left(-\frac{4}{5}\right)$ must equal $-\frac{8}{15}$.

This example suggests the following rule.

Multiplying Two Numbers with Different Signs	The product of two numbers having different signs is negative.

Example 1

Multiply $(-0.6)5$.

$(-0.6)5 = -3$ *Since one factor is negative, the product is negative.*

ALTERNATE TEACHING STRATEGIES

Using Logical Reasoning

The formula used to convert degrees Fahrenheit to degrees Celsius is $C° = \frac{5}{9}(F° - 32)$. What is the greatest Fahrenheit temperature whose equivalent Celsius temperature is a negative integer?   **31 degrees**

Example 2

Simplify $(-3a)(4b)$.

$(-3a)(4b) = (-3)(4)ab$ *Commutative and associative properties* (×)

$\qquad\qquad = -12ab$

You already know that the product of two positive numbers is positive. What is the sign of the product of two negative numbers? To find the product of -6 and -8.5, you can use a procedure similar to the one used on the previous page.

$0 = -6(0)$	*Multiplicative property of zero*
$0 = -6[8.5 + (-8.5)]$	*Substitution and additive inverse properties*
$0 = -6(8.5) + (-6)(-8.5)$	*Distributive property*
$0 = -51 + (-6)(-8.5)$	*Substitution property* (=)

By the additive inverse property, 0 is equal to $-51 + 51$. Therefore, $(-6)(-8.5)$ must be equal to $+51$.

This example suggests the following rule.

Multiplying Two Numbers with the Same Sign	**The product of two numbers having the same sign is positive.**

Example 3

Multiply $\left(-\frac{2}{3}\right)\left(-\frac{1}{5}\right)$.

$\left(-\frac{2}{3}\right)\left(-\frac{1}{5}\right) = \frac{2}{15}$ *The sign of the product is positive. Why?*

Example 4

Simplify $6x(-7y) + (-3x)(-5y)$.

$6x(-7y) + (-3x)(-5y) = -42xy + 15xy$

$\qquad\qquad\qquad\qquad\quad = -27xy$

Notice that multiplying a number by -1 results in the opposite of the number.

$$-1(3) = -3 \qquad\qquad (1.7)(-1) = -1.7 \qquad\qquad (-1)-4n = 4n$$

Multiplicative Property of -1	**The product of any number and -1 is its additive inverse.** $-1(a) = -a$ and $a(-1) = -a$

LESSON 2-6 MULTIPLYING RATIONAL NUMBERS 75

Teaching Tip ②   The product of any pair of negative numbers is positive. An even number of negative factors can be paired exactly to produce a positive result. An odd number of negative factors cannot be paired exactly, so a negative result is produced.

EVALUATING THE LESSON

Checking for Understanding

Exercises 1-8 are designed to help you assess understanding through reading, writing, and speaking. You should work through Exercises 1-3 with your students, and then monitor their work on Exercises 4-8.

Reteaching Masters Booklet, p. 14

To find the product of three or more numbers, first group the numbers in pairs.

Example 5   Multiply $\left(-\frac{1}{2}\right)(-6)(5)\left(-\frac{2}{5}\right)(-2)$. **Teaching Tip ②**

$\left(-\frac{1}{2}\right)(-6)(5)\left(-\frac{2}{5}\right)(-2) = \left[\left(-\frac{1}{2}\right)(-6)\right]\left[(5)\left(-\frac{2}{5}\right)\right](-2)$ *Associative property (×)*
$= (3)(-2)(-2)$ *Substitution property (=)*
$= [(3)(-2)](-2)$ *Associative property (×)*
$= (-6)(-2)$ *Substitution property (=)*
$= 12$

A **sequence** is a set of numbers in a specific order. The **terms** of a sequence are the numbers in it. The first term of a sequence is represented by a, the second term a_2, and so on up to the nth term, a_n.

Example 6

CONNECTION
Sequences

Find the twenty-fifth term in the sequence $8, 5, 2, -1, \ldots$.

Notice that each term in the sequence is found by adding -3 to the term preceding it.

$8 + (-3) = 5$ ➡ $5 + (-3) = 2$ ➡ $2 + (-3) = -1$

To find the twenty-fifth term, you can add -3 to 8 twenty-four times, or you can use the formula $a_n = a + (n - 1)d$, where n is the number of the term you want to find and d is the difference between terms.

$a_n = a + (n - 1)d$
$= 8 + (25 - 1)(-3)$ *Replace n with 25 and d with -3.*
$= 8 + (24)(-3)$
$= 8 + (-72)$
$= -64$

So the twenty-fifth term is -64.

CHECKING FOR UNDERSTANDING

Communicating Mathematics

Read and study the lesson to answer each question.

1. Under what conditions is ab positive?
   Either a and b are both positive or they are both negative.
2. Under what conditions is ab negative?
   Either a or b is negative, but not both.
3. Under what conditions is ab equal to zero?
   Either a or b is zero or both are zero.

76   CHAPTER 2   RATIONAL NUMBERS

RETEACHING THE LESSON

1. Write the sign of each product.
   a. $(-)(-)$ $+$
   b. $(-)(-)(-)(+)(+)$ $-$
   c. product of 7 negative and 3 positive factors $-$
2. Find each product.
   a. $(-1)^8$ $+1$
   b. $(-1)^{19}$ -1
   c. $\left(-\frac{3}{4}\right)\left(-\frac{2}{3}\right)\left(-\frac{1}{2}\right)$ $-\frac{1}{4}$
   d. $(-2)(-12)(0)(-6)$ 0

Guided Practice

Determine whether each product is positive or negative. Then find the product.

4. $3(-2)$ -6

5. $(-2)(-8)$ $+16$

6. $\left(\frac{7}{3}\right)\left(\frac{7}{3}\right)$ $+\frac{49}{9}$

7. $(-3)(4)(-2)$ $+24$

8. $\left(-\frac{4}{5}\right)\left(-\frac{1}{5}\right)(-5)$ $-\frac{4}{5}$

EXERCISES

Practice

Find each product.

9. $5(12)$ 60

10. $(-6)(11)$ -66

11. $(-6)(-5)$ 30

12. $\left(\frac{3}{5}\right)\left(-\frac{4}{7}\right)$ $-\frac{12}{35}$

13. $\left(-\frac{7}{8}\right)\left(-\frac{1}{3}\right)$ $\frac{7}{24}$

14. $(-5)\left(-\frac{2}{5}\right)$ 2

15. $(-2.93)(-0.003)$ 0.00879

16. $(-6)(4)(-3)$ 72

17. $\left(\frac{3}{5}\right)\left(\frac{2}{3}\right)(-3)$ $-\frac{6}{5}$

18. $\left(-\frac{7}{12}\right)\left(\frac{6}{7}\right)\left(-\frac{3}{4}\right)$ $\frac{3}{8}$

19. $(-6.8)(-5.415)(3.1)$ 114.1482

20. $(-4)(0)(-2)(-3)$ 0

21. $(4)(-2)(-1)(-3)$ -24

22. $\frac{3}{5}(5)(-2)\left(-\frac{1}{2}\right)$ 3

23. $\frac{2}{11}(-11)(-4)\left(-\frac{3}{4}\right)$ -6

Complete.

24. Find the 19th term of the sequence for which $a = 11$ and $d = -2$. -25

25. Find the 16th term of the sequence for which $a = 1.5$ and $d = 0.5$. 9

26. Find the 43rd term of the sequence $-19, -15, -11, \ldots$. 149

27. Find the 58th term of the sequence $10, 4, -2, \ldots$. -332

Simplify.

28. $5x(-6y) + 2x(-8y)$ $-46xy$

29. $-4(4) + (-2)(-3)$ -10

30. $5(-2) - 3(-8)$ 14

31. $(-2x)(-4y) - (-9x)(10y)$ $98xy$

32. $4(7) - 3(11)$ -5

33. $(-1.9)(3.04) - (-5.4)(-11.6)$ -68.416

34. $\left(-\frac{1}{2}\right)\left(-\frac{1}{2}\right) - \frac{2}{3}\left(\frac{3}{2}\right)$ $-\frac{3}{4}$

35. $\frac{5}{6}\left(\frac{6}{7}\right) - \left(\frac{5}{6}\right)\left(-\frac{6}{7}\right)$ $\frac{10}{7}$

36. $5(3t - 2t) + 2(4t - 3t)$ $7t$

37. $4[3x + (-2x)] - 5(3x + 2x)$ $-21x$

38. $\frac{5}{6}(-24a + 36b) + \left(-\frac{1}{3}\right)(60a - 42b)$ $-40a + 44b$

39. $1.2(4x - 5y) - 0.2(-1.5x + 8y)$ $5.1x - 7.6y$

40. $9(2ab - 3c) - (4ab - 6c)$ $14ab - 21c$

Critical Thinking
Teaching Tip ③

41. If a^2 is positive, what can you conclude about a? $a > 0$ or $a < 0$

42. If a^3 is positive, what can you conclude about a? $a > 0$

43. If a^3 is negative, what can you conclude about a? $a < 0$

44. If a multiplication involves an even number of negative factors, what must be true of the product? It is positive.

45. If a multiplication involves an odd number of negative factors, what must be true of the product? It is negative.

Closing the Lesson

Speaking Activity Without finding each product, have students indicate whether the product will be positive, negative, or 0.

1. $(-4)(-3)$ positive
2. $(-1.3)(4)(-2.54)$ positive
3. $\left(-\frac{3}{4}\right)\left(-\frac{1}{2}\right)(0)\left(-\frac{7}{10}\right)$ 0
4. $\left(\frac{2}{5}\right)\left(-\frac{3}{8}\right)\left(\frac{5}{9}\right)$ negative

APPLYING THE LESSON

Homework Exercises

Assignment Guide

Basic: 9-37, 41-46, 49-54
Average: 15-39, 41-54
Enriched: 16-54

Chapter 2, Quiz C, (Lessons 2-5 through 2-6), is available in the Evaluation Masters Booklet, p. 24.

Teaching Tip ③   Students having difficulty solving Exercises 41-45 should be encouraged to substitute values for each of the variables.

Practice Masters Booklet, p. 14

46. Statistics Neil's algebra average dropped three fourths of a point for each of eight consecutive months. If his average was 82 originally, what was his average at the end of eight months? **76**

47. Sales Mirna bought a pair of shoes that cost $32.87 with tax. If she gave the clerk two twenty-dollar bills, how much should Mirna receive in change? **$7.13**

Computer 48. Temperature is commonly measured in degrees Celsius or degrees Fahrenheit. In this program C represents Celsius temperature and F represents Fahrenheit temperature. The formula in line 20 converts the

```
10 FOR F = -50 TO 50
20 LET C = 5/9*(F-32)
30 IF C<> F THEN 50
40 PRINT "F = ";F,"C = ";C
50 NEXT F
60 END
```

Fahrenheit temperature to Celsius. There is one temperature at which the value of F is the same as C. Use this program to find that temperature. **−40**

Mixed Review 49. Simplify $x^2 + 3x + 2x + 5x^2$. **(Lesson 1-6)** $6x^2 + 5x$

50. Find the next three numbers in the sequence $-6, -3, 0, \underline{\ ?\ }, \underline{\ ?\ }, \underline{\ ?\ }$. **(Lesson 2-1)** **3, 6, 9**

51. Find the sum: $-197 + |-483|$. **(Lesson 2-2)** **286**

$\{-4, -3, -2, \dots\}$ 52. Write the solution set of $y \geq -4$ if y is an integer. **(Lesson 2-3)**

53. Which number is greater, $\frac{1}{3}$ or $\frac{1}{4}$? **(Lesson 2-4)** $\frac{1}{3}$

54. Find the difference: $41y - (-41y)$. **(Lesson 2-5)** **82y**

HISTORY CONNECTION

Sonya Kovalevskaya

Sonya Kovalevskaya (1850–1891) was born in Russia in the midst of sweeping reforms. However, the situation for women was very oppressive. Kovalevskaya was inspired by a paternal uncle who instilled in her a reverence for mathematics. As a child, an error caused her room to be wallpapered by notes from the calculus lectures of a prominent Russian mathematician. Later, she astonished her professors by the speed with which she grasped mathematical ideas. In 1883, Sonya Kovalevskaya became a professor at the University of Stockholm. A Swedish newspaper wrote of her appointment, "Today we do not herald the arrival of some . . . prince of noble blood. No, the Princess of Science, Madam Kovalevskaya, has honoured our city with her arrival. She is to be the first woman lecturer in all Sweden."

EXTENDING THE LESSON

Math Power: Problem Solving

Negative three is added to a certain number 27 times. If the result is −29, what was the original number? **52**

History Connection

The History Connection features introduce students to persons or cultures who were involved in the development of mathematics. You may want students to further research Kovalevskaya or to research her work with sequences.

Enrichment Masters Booklet, p. 14

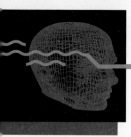

Technology

Adding Fractions

► **BASIC**
Graphing calculator
Graphing software
Spreadsheets

Computers add integers and decimals automatically. However, you have to write a special program for a computer to add fractions. The BASIC program below instructs the computer to add two fractions based on the following definition.

$$\frac{a}{b} + \frac{c}{d} = \frac{ad + bc}{bd}$$

```
10 PRINT "ENTER THE NUMERATOR AND THE
   DENOMINATOR OF THE FIRST FRACTION."
20 INPUT A,B
30 PRINT "ENTER THE NUMERATOR AND THE
   DENOMINATOR OF THE SECOND FRACTION."
40 INPUT C,D
50 LET N = A * D + B * C
60 LET X = B * D
70 PRINT "THE SUM IS ";N;"/";X
80 END
```

This program does not always give the sum in simplest form. You can add the following lines to the program so the sum will always be given in simplest form.

```
70 IF N < X THEN 100
80 LET Y = X
90 GOTO 110
100 LET Y = N
110 FOR I = Y TO 1 STEP - 1
120 IF INT (N/I) < > N/I THEN 140
130 IF INT (X/I) = X/I THEN 150
140 NEXT I
150 LET N = N/I
160 LET X = X/I
170 PRINT "THE SUM IS ";N;"/";X
180 END
```

EXERCISES

Use the program to find each sum in simplest form.

1. $\frac{2}{3} + \frac{4}{9}$ $\frac{10}{9}$ 2. $\frac{8}{11} + \frac{1}{22}$ $\frac{17}{22}$ 3. $\frac{4}{6} + \frac{1}{4}$ $\frac{11}{12}$ 4. $\frac{7}{16} + \frac{9}{10}$ $\frac{107}{80}$ 5. $\frac{5}{12} + \frac{7}{18}$ $\frac{29}{36}$

6. Write a program similar to the one above to subtract two fractions.
   changes: 50 LET N = A * D − B * C
           170 PRINT "THE DIFFERENCE IS";N;"/";X

TECHNOLOGY: ADDING FRACTIONS   79

Using Technology

Objective This optional page shows how the BASIC programming language can be used to perform mathematical computations and to enhance and extend mathematical concepts.

Teaching Suggestions

Have students substitute many different numerical values for *a*, *b*, *c*, and *d* in the formula $\frac{a}{b} + \frac{c}{d} = \frac{ad + bc}{bd}$.

Ask them why the sum generated by this formula is not necessarily in simplest form. Explain that Lines 70-180 can be used to obtain a sum that is in simplest form. You may want to have students who are knowledgeable in BASIC programming explain how these lines work.

The program assumes the numerators and denominators of the original fractions are integers and the denominators do not equal zero.

Lesson Resources

- Reteaching Master 2-7
- Practice Master 2-7
- Enrichment Master 2-7
- Activity Master, p. 17
- Video Algebra, 7

 Transparency 2-7 contains the 5-Minute Check and a teaching aid for this lesson.

INTRODUCING THE LESSON

🕐 5-Minute Check

(over Lesson 2-6)

Find each product.

1. $\left(-\frac{2}{3}\right)\left(\frac{5}{4}\right)$ $-\frac{5}{6}$
2. $(0.1)(-1.1)(-0.01)$ 0.0011

Evaluate each expression if $x = -3$ and $y = \frac{4}{3}$.

3. $2xy + 4x$ -20
4. $-2(x - 6xy)$ -14

5. What is the 28th term of the sequence $-17, -13, -9, -5, \ldots$?   91

Motivating the Lesson

Have students look up the term "inverse" in the dictionary. Develop student understanding of the term by having a volunteer mime a sequence of three actions. Ask another volunteer to mime the inverse of these actions.

TEACHING THE LESSON

Teaching Tip ❶   Remind students that division by 0 is not possible. In addition, $\frac{0}{n} = 0$ regardless of the sign of n if $n \neq 0$.

2-7 Dividing Rational Numbers

Objective
2-7

After studying this lesson, you should be able to:
- divide rational numbers.

Other kinds of averages include median and mode, which are presented in Chapter 14.

The **mean** is a number that represents a set of data. The mean is found by adding the elements in the set and then dividing that sum by the number of elements in the set.

Application

Norm Taylor and Sandy Kim play golf every Tuesday. During the month of July, their scores were as shown.

Scores	
Norm	Sandy
-1	-3
$+1$	-2
-3	-1
-2	-3
$+5$	-1

Who had the better average?

Find each person's mean score.

Norm: $\dfrac{-1 + 1 + (-3) + (-2) + 5}{5} = \dfrac{0}{5}$, or 0

So Norm's mean score is 0, or even par.

Sandy: $\dfrac{-3 + (-2) + (-1) + (-3) + (-1)}{5} = -10 \div 5$

We can divide 10 by 5 to find the quotient. But how do we know if the quotient is positive or negative?

You have already learned that addition and subtraction are inverse operations. In the same way, multiplication and division are inverse operations. So the rule for finding the sign of the quotient of two numbers is the same as the rule for finding the sign of the product.

Dividing Rational Numbers	The quotient of two numbers is positive if the numbers have the same sign. The quotient of two numbers is negative if the numbers have different signs. Teaching Tip ❶

So Sandy's average is $-10 \div 5 = -2$ or 2 under par, and she has the better average.

Example 1

Find the quotient of -45 and -9.

This division problem may be written as $-45 \div (-9)$ or $\dfrac{-45}{-9}$.

$\dfrac{-45}{-9} = 5$ *The fraction bar indicates division.*
The quotient is positive.

ALTERNATE TEACHING STRATEGIES

Using Applications

The temperatures in Fairbanks, Alaska over a five-day period were $-10°$, $-8°$, $4°$, $-12°$, and $1°$. What was the average temperature over the five days? $-5°$

Using Communication

Devise a way of communicating the relationship between any number and its additive inverse and its multiplicative inverse using symbols. Make a drawing of your symbols to share with the class.

Recall that it is possible to subtract a number by adding its additive inverse. In a similar manner, it is possible to divide a number by multiplying by its multiplicative inverse. Two numbers whose product is 1 are called **multiplicative inverses** or **reciprocals**. Teaching Tip ②

The reciprocal of $\frac{4}{3}$ is $\frac{3}{4}$ because $\frac{4}{3} \cdot \frac{3}{4}$ is 1.

The reciprocal of -5 is $-\frac{1}{5}$ because $-5\left(-\frac{1}{5}\right)$ is 1.

The reciprocal of x is $\frac{1}{x}$ because $x \cdot \frac{1}{x}$ is 1.

Zero has no reciprocal because any number times 0 is 0, not 1.

These examples can be summarized in the multiplicative inverse property.

Multiplicative Inverse Property	For every nonzero number a, there is exactly one number $\frac{1}{a}$ such that $$a\left(\frac{1}{a}\right) = \frac{1}{a}(a) = 1.$$

Recall that you can change any division expression to an equivalent multiplication expression. To divide by any nonzero number, multiply by the reciprocal of that number.

Division Rule	For any numbers a and b, with $b \neq 0$, $$a \div b = \frac{a}{b} = a\left(\frac{1}{b}\right) = \frac{1}{b}(a).$$

Example 2

Divide $-\frac{3}{4} \div 8$.

$-\frac{3}{4} \div 8 = -\frac{3}{4} \cdot \frac{1}{8}$ *Multiply by $\frac{1}{8}$, the reciprocal of 8.*

$\qquad = -\frac{3}{32}$ *Since one factor is negative, the product is negative.*

If a fraction has one or more fractions in the numerator or denominator, it is called a **complex fraction**. To simplify a complex fraction, rewrite it as a division sentence.

Example 3

Simplify $\frac{\frac{3}{11}}{6}$.

Rewrite the fraction as $\frac{3}{11} \div 6$, since fractions indicate division.

$\frac{3}{11} \div 6 = \frac{3}{11} \cdot \frac{1}{6}$ *Multiply by $\frac{1}{6}$, the reciprocal of 6.*

$\qquad = \frac{3}{66}$ or $\frac{1}{22}$

Teaching Tip ② After discussing the idea of reciprocals, stress their important use in dividing fractions.

Chalkboard Examples

For Example 1
Find the quotient.

a. -32 and -8 4

b. 81 and -9 -9

For Example 2
Divide.

a. $-\frac{3}{4} \div \frac{5}{8}$ $-1\frac{1}{5}$

b. $-\frac{1}{5} \div \frac{3}{10}$ $-\frac{2}{3}$

For Example 3
Simplify.

a. $\frac{\frac{5}{8}}{25}$ $\frac{1}{40}$

b. $\frac{\frac{4}{9}}{8}$ $\frac{1}{18}$

Example 4 | Simplify $\frac{4a + 32}{4}$. **Teaching Tip 3**

Method 1	Method 2
$\frac{4a + 32}{4} = (4a + 32) \div 4$ *To divide by 4, multiply by $\frac{1}{4}$.* $= (4a + 32)\left(\frac{1}{4}\right)$ *Distributive property* $= 4a\left(\frac{1}{4}\right) + 32\left(\frac{1}{4}\right)$ $= a + 8$	$\frac{4a + 32}{4} = \frac{4a}{4} + \frac{32}{4}$ $= a + 8$

You can use the comparison property for rational numbers to compare two negative fractions, or a positive fraction and a negative fraction. Note that the fractions below are equivalent.

Note that $-\frac{3}{4} \neq \frac{-3}{-4}$.

$$\frac{-3}{4} \qquad \frac{3}{-4} \qquad -\frac{3}{4}$$

Since the comparison property requires that the denominators must be positive, rewrite each negative fraction with a negative numerator.

Example 5 | Replace the __?__ with <, >, or = to make $-\frac{1}{4}$ __?__ $-\frac{1}{5}$ a true sentence.

Rewrite $-\frac{1}{4}$ as $\frac{-1}{4}$ and $-\frac{1}{5}$ as $\frac{-1}{5}$.

$$\frac{-1}{4} \; \underset{?}{\frown} \; \frac{-1}{5} \qquad \textit{Find the cross products.}$$

$$-5 < -4$$

The true sentence is $-\frac{1}{4} < -\frac{1}{5}$.

CHECKING FOR UNDERSTANDING

Communicating Mathematics

Read and study the lesson to answer each question. 1,3. See margin.

1. Why are multiplication and division called inverse operations?

2. What is the reciprocal of $\frac{1}{5}$? **5**

3. Explain in one sentence how to divide rational numbers.

4. Words that have the same meaning are called *synonyms*. Write a synonym for each term. **a. opposite   b. reciprocal   c. average**

   a. additive inverse   b. multiplicative inverse   c. mean

RETEACHING THE LESSON

Here's an easy way to use signed numbers to find an average A of a set of n numbers. Guess an average G. Subtract G from each number to find its deviation. Find the total of the deviations, then divide by n to get the average deviation D. $A = G + D$.

scores	deviations for G = 80	G = 75
92	12	17
60	−20	−15
84	4	9
73	−7	−2
81	1	6
total	−10	15
	$D = -2$	$D = 3$
	$A = 80 + (-2)$	$A = 75 + 3$

Name the reciprocal of each number.

5. $3\frac{1}{3}$

6. -5 $-\frac{1}{5}$

7. 0 none

8. -1 -1

9. $\frac{2}{3}$ $\frac{3}{2}$

10. $-\frac{1}{15}$ -15

11. $3\frac{1}{4}$ $\frac{4}{13}$

12. $-2\frac{3}{7}$ $-\frac{7}{17}$

13. $-6\frac{5}{11}$ $-\frac{11}{71}$

Simplify.

14. $\frac{-30}{-5}$ 6

15. $\frac{-48}{8}$ -6

16. $\frac{-200x}{50}$ $-4x$

17. $\frac{45b}{9}$ $5b$

18. $\frac{-\frac{5}{6}}{8}$ $-\frac{5}{48}$

19. $\frac{3a + 9}{3}$ $a + 3$

EXERCISES

Practice   **Simplify.**

20. $\frac{30}{-6}$ -5

21. $\frac{-55}{11}$ -5

22. $\frac{-96}{-16}$ 6

23. $\frac{-450n}{10}$ $-45n$

24. $\frac{-36a}{-6}$ $6a$

25. $\frac{63a}{-9}$ $-7a$

26. $-49 \div (-7)$ 7

27. $-16 \div 8$ -2

28. $65 \div (-13)$ -5

29. $-\frac{3}{4} \div 9$ $-\frac{1}{12}$

30. $\frac{-1}{3} \div (-4)$ $\frac{1}{12}$

31. $-9 \div \left(-\frac{10}{17}\right)$ $\frac{153}{10}$

32. $\frac{\frac{7}{8}}{-10}$ $-\frac{7}{80}$

33. $\frac{7}{-\frac{2}{5}}$ $-\frac{35}{2}$

34. $\frac{-5}{\frac{2}{7}}$ $-\frac{35}{2}$

35. $\frac{6a + 24}{6}$ $a + 4$

36. $\frac{20a + 30b}{-2}$ $-10a - 15b$

37. $\frac{-5x + (-10y)}{-5}$ $x + 2y$

38. $\frac{70x - 30y}{-5}$ $-14x + 6y$

Find the mean for each set of data.

39. $4, 6, 9, 12, 5$ $7\frac{1}{5}$ or 7.2

40. $10, 3, 8, 15$ 9

41. $10, 4, -21, 6, -3, 8, 5, 5, 2, -2$ $1\frac{2}{5}$ or 1.4

42. $2.5°, 6°, 18.5°, 29.5°, 32.5°, 28°, 24.5°, 20°, 16.5°, 5°, -2°, -1°$ $15°$

Replace each ? with <, >, or = to make each sentence true.

43. $-\frac{6}{5}$ _?_ $-\frac{7}{6}$ $<$

44. $-\frac{9}{7}$ _?_ $-\frac{7}{5}$ $>$

45. $-\frac{3}{4}$ _?_ $-\frac{2}{3}$ $<$

46. $-\frac{13}{11}$ _?_ $-\frac{15}{13}$ $<$

47. $-\frac{1}{3}$ _?_ $-\frac{2}{7}$ $<$

48. $-\frac{7}{6}$ _?_ $-\frac{21}{18}$ $=$

LESSON 2-7   DIVIDING RATIONAL NUMBERS   83

Error Analysis

Since division is not commutative, determining the major division bar in a complex fraction is crucial. Consider $\frac{\frac{3}{4}}{8}$.

Is this $\frac{\frac{3}{4}}{8}$ or $\frac{3}{\frac{4}{8}}$?

Their values are $\frac{3}{32}$ and 6, respectively. The author of the fraction should indicate the major fraction bar by some emphasis (bolder, longer, or wider). If no major fraction bar is indicated, the lowest one is the major one by default.

Example: $\frac{64}{\frac{8}{\frac{4}{2}}}$ defaults to $\frac{\frac{64}{8}}{\frac{4}{2}}$ or

$64 \div 8 \div 4 \div 2 = 1$

Assignment Guide

Basic: 20-42, 49-53, 56-61
Average: 26-45, 49-61
Enriched: 32-61

Practice Masters Booklet, p. 15

NAME _____ DATE _____

2-7   **Practice Worksheet**

Dividing Rational Numbers

Simplify.

1. $\frac{-63}{9}$ -7

2. $\frac{36}{-6}$ -6

3. $\frac{-42}{-7}$ 6

4. $\frac{-144x}{12}$ $-12x$

5. $\frac{-54z}{-9}$ $6z$

6. $\frac{56a}{-8}$ $-7a$

7. $-36 \div (-4)$ 9

8. $-24 \div 6$ -4

9. $75 \div (-15)$ -5

10. $-\frac{2}{3} \div 6$ $-\frac{1}{9}$

11. $-\frac{5}{6} \div (-20)$ $\frac{1}{24}$

12. $-8 \div \left(-\frac{9}{14}\right)$ $\frac{112}{9}$

13. $\frac{\frac{3}{4}}{-6}$ $-\frac{1}{8}$

14. $\frac{6}{-\frac{2}{9}}$ -27

15. $\frac{-7}{\frac{2}{5}}$ $-\frac{35}{2}$

16. $\frac{5x + 25}{5}$ $x + 5$

17. $\frac{18t + 12r}{-3}$ $-6t - 4r$

18. $\frac{5a - 10}{-5}$ $-a + 2$

19. $\frac{18x + 12}{-6}$ $-3x - 2$

20. $\frac{-4c + (-16d)}{4}$ $-c - 4d$

21. $\frac{8k - 12h}{-4}$ $-2k + 3h$

22. $-323 \div (-17)$ 19

23. $-5 \div \frac{3}{7}$ $-\frac{35}{3}$

24. $-\frac{7}{4} \div (-8)$ $\frac{7}{32}$

Find the mean for each set of data.

25. $4, 5, 3, 6, 10, 8$ 6

26. $10, 9, 7, 2$ 7

27. $0, -1, -2, -3, 3, 2, 1$ 0

28. $4.2, 5.8, 6.1, 5.5, 3.9$ 5.1

29. $8, -9, -11, 16, 7, -8$ $\frac{1}{2}$

30. $3.6, 2.9, 3.4, 2.7, 3.4$ 3.2

31. $125, 250, 225$ 200

32. $17, 9, 7, 8, 11, 13, 21, 18$ 13

Additional Answers

1. Multiplication undoes division, and division undoes multiplication.

3. To divide rational numbers, multiply the dividend by the multiplicative inverse or reciprocal of the divisor.

Speaking Activity Have students explain the steps they would follow when comparing $\frac{3}{-5}$ and $\frac{8}{-9}$ by finding cross products. Encourage students to justify each step in the procedure.

APPLYING THE LESSON

Homework Exercises

See Assignment Guide on page 83.

Teaching Tip ④ In Exercise 53, students may enjoy finding the take off/landing rate of a local or state airport and comparing this figure to that of Atlanta's Hartsfield Airport.

Enrichment Masters Booklet, p. 15

Critical Thinking
49-51. See margin.

49. The $\boxed{1/x}$ key on a calculator is called the *reciprocal key*. When this key is pressed, the calculator replaces the number on the display with its reciprocal. Enter 0 and then press the reciprocal key. What happened? Why?

50. Enter a number and then press the reciprocal key twice. What happened? Predict what will happen if you press the key n times.

51. Enter 7.328 $\boxed{1/x}$ $\boxed{\times}$ 7.328 $\boxed{=}$. What is the result? Why?

Applications

52. **Basketball** According to NBA standards, a basketball should bounce back $\frac{2}{3}$ of the distance from which it is dropped. How high should a basketball bounce when it is dropped from a height of $3\frac{3}{4}$ yards? $2\frac{1}{2}$ yd
Teaching Tip ④

53. **Aviation** The busiest airport in the world is Atlanta's Hartsfield Airport. On average, an airplane takes off or lands every 39.66 seconds. At this rate, how many airplanes take off or land in 17 hours? Round to the nearest whole number. **1543 airplanes**

54. **Space** Halley's Comet flashes through the sky every 76.3 years. It last appeared in 1986. In what year of the 23rd century is Halley's Comet expected to reappear? **2214**

55. **World Records** The longest loaf of bread ever baked was 2132 feet $2\frac{1}{2}$ inches. If this loaf were cut into $\frac{1}{2}$-inch slices, how many slices of bread would there have been? **51,173 slices**

Mixed Review

56. Write an equation for the sentence *The number b equals x decreased by the cube of m.* **(Lesson 1-7)** $b = x - m^3$

57. Evaluate $|-8 + k|$ if $k = 3$. **(Lesson 2-2)** 5

58. *True or false:* $0.6 \leq 1 - 0.4$. **(Lesson 2-3)** true

59. Which is the better buy: a 1-pound package of lunch meat for $1.98 or a 12-ounce package for $1.80? **(Lesson 2-4)**

60. Find the sum: $9m + 43m + (-16m)$. **(Lesson 2-5)** $36m$

61. Find the product: $4\left(-\frac{7}{8}\right)$. **(Lesson 2-6)** $-\frac{7}{2}$

84 CHAPTER 2 RATIONAL NUMBERS

EXTENDING THE LESSON

Math Power: Reasoning

Matt had an average of 72 on three 100-point tests. What score would he need on his next test to raise his average to 75? **84**

Additional Answers

49. ERROR; The reciprocal of 0 is $\frac{1}{0}$. Dividing by 0 is not defined.

50. The original number shows on the display. If n is even, the original number is displayed. If n is odd, the reciprocal of the number is displayed.

51. 1; a number times its reciprocal equals 1.

Objectives

2-8A
2-8B

After studying this lesson, you should be able to:
■ define variables and write equations for verbal problems, and
■ write verbal problems for equations.

In Chapter 1, you learned how to explore verbal problems before solving them. In this lesson, you will study how to plan the solution to a verbal problem by writing an equation.

First, explore the problem. Then plan the solution by doing the following.

■ Read the problem again. Decide how the unspecified numbers relate to each other and to the other given information.
■ Write an equation to represent the relationship.

Example 1

Teaching Tip ❶
Teaching Tip ❷

Write an equation for the following problem.

Six years ago, twice Jennifer's age was 16 years. How old is she now?

Let j = Jennifer's age now.

Then, $j - 6$ = Jennifer's age six years ago.

twice Jennifer's age six years ago is 16 years

$$2 \cdot \qquad (j - 6) \qquad = \quad 16$$

So, the equation is $2(j - 6) = 16$.

You can make up your own verbal problem if you are given an equation or two. First, you need to know what the variable in the equation represents. Then you can use the equation to establish the conditions of the problem.

Example 2

Write a problem based on the given information.

Let w = Steve's weight in pounds. **Teaching Tip ❸**
Then, $w - 12$ = Toshiro's weight in pounds.
$w + (w - 12) = 118$

Here's a sample problem.

Toshiro weighs 12 pounds less than Steve. The sum of their weights is 118 pounds. How much does Steve weigh? How much does Toshiro weigh?

RETEACHING THE LESSON

Define a variable, then write an equation for each problem. Do not solve.

1. Four times Mary's age 3 years ago is 56. How old is Mary now? x = Mary's age now; $4(x - 3) = 56$

2. Carrie is 3 years older than Gary. The sum of their ages in 6 years will be 41. How old is Gary? x = Gary's age now; $(x + 6) + (x + 3 + 6) = 41$

3. The sum of Sherry's age and her dad's age is 60. In 12 years Sherry will be half as old as her dad. Find Sherry's age. x = Sherry's age now; $x + 12 = \frac{1}{2}(60 - x + 12)$

4. Larry is 5 years younger than Teri. In 8 years the sum of their ages will be 55. Find Teri's age. x = Teri's age; $(x + 8) + (x - 5 + 8) = 55$

INTRODUCING THE LESSON

 5-Minute Check
(over Lesson 2-7)

Divide.

1. $-\frac{2}{3} \div 6$ $\quad -\frac{1}{9}$

2. $1\frac{1}{5} \div -36$ $\quad -\frac{1}{30}$

Simplify.

3. $\dfrac{\frac{5}{8}}{4}$ $\quad \frac{5}{32}$

4. $\dfrac{12 - 8b}{2}$ $\quad 6 - 4b$

5. $\dfrac{-70x + (-15)}{5}$ $\quad -14x - 3$

Motivating the Lesson

Pose the following problem to students. Peter is older than his wife. Since the age of 21, his age has always been the reverse of the digits of his wife's age. How much older is Peter than his wife? **9 years**

After students have solved the problem, discuss the strategies they used to find the answer.

TEACHING THE LESSON

Teaching Tip ❶ Point out that variables can often be defined in more than one way. In Example 1, you could let j equal the smaller number. Then, Jennifer's age now would be $j + 6$. The equation would be $2(j) = 16$. Her age six years ago was 8. Therefore, her age now is $8 + 6$ or 14.

Teaching Tip ❷

Chalkboard Examples

For Example 1
Write an equation for the following problem. One number is 12 greater than a second number. The sum of these two numbers is 86. Find the numbers. $n + (n + 12) = 86$

For Example 2
Write a problem based on the given information. Let x = Mary's age now, $x - 5 = 17$. Sample answer: Five years ago Mary was 17 years old. How old is she now?

EVALUATING THE LESSON

Checking for Understanding

Exercises 1-10 are designed to help you assess understanding through reading, writing, and speaking. You should work through Exercises 1-3 with your students, and then monitor their work on Exercises 4-10.

Additional Answers

1. explore, plan, solve, examine
2. The first time you read for overall sense; the second time you read for detail.
11. Let k = Kimiko's age now; $k - 27 = 21$
12. Let p = number of pounds lost each week; $145 - 6p = 125$
13. Let x = number of years for a tree to become $33\frac{1}{2}$ feet tall; $17 + 1\frac{1}{2}x = 33\frac{1}{2}$
14. Let c = Cecile's age now; $3(c - 4) = 42$
15. Let t = number of tapes; $t + \left(\frac{1}{2}t + 4\right) = 31$

CHECKING FOR UNDERSTANDING

Communicating Mathematics

Read and study the lesson to answer each question. 1–2. See margin.

1. What are the four steps in the problem-solving plan?

2. Why should you read a verbal problem twice before trying to solve it?

3. Write an equation for Example 1 given the following information.
Let $j + 6$ = Jennifer's age now.
Then, j = Jennifer's age 6 years ago. $2j = 16$

Guided Practice

Write an expression for each problem.

$947 + 117$

4. This year's senior class has 117 fewer students than last year's class. This year's class has 947 students. How many were in last year's class?

5. Buzz Jackson is now 49 years old. How old was he n years ago? $49 - n$

6. The length of a rectangle is 4 feet more than the width. The width is w feet. Find the length. $w + 4$

7. Sheldon is 8 years older than Atepa. If Sheldon is n years old, how old is Atepa? $n - 8$

8. Tess types 42 words per minute. How many minutes would it take for her to type a 3000-word paper? $3000 \div 42$ or $\frac{3000}{42}$

9. Anthony makes $5.65 per hour as a sales clerk at Tom's Sporting Goods. How much does he make for working n hours? $\$5.65n$

10. Alonso has 8 more than twice as many red pens as blue pens. He has b blue pens. How many red pens does he have? $2b + 8$

FYI · · ·

The longest typing marathon on a manual typewriter was 123 hours.

EXERCISES

Practice

Define a variable, then write an equation for each problem. Do *not* try to solve. See margin.

11. When she graduated from college twenty-seven years ago Kimiko was 21. How old is she now?

12. For 6 consecutive weeks, Connie lost the same amount of weight. Six weeks ago she weighed 145 pounds. She now weighs 125 pounds. How many pounds did Connie lose each week?

13. Ponderosa pines grow about $1\frac{1}{2}$ feet each year. If a pine tree is now 17 feet tall, about how long will it take the tree to become $33\frac{1}{2}$ feet tall?

14. Four years ago, three times Cecile's age was 42, her father's age now. How old is Cecile now?

15. Kerri has 31 CDs and tapes altogether. If she has 4 more than half as many CDs as tapes, how many tapes does Kerri have?

16. Sonia is 3 years older than Melissa. The sum of their ages in 4 years will be 59 years. How old is Sonia now?

Additional Answers

16. Let a = Sonia's age now; $(a + 4) + (a - 3 + 4) = 59$
17. Let q = number of quarters; $q + (q + 4) + (q + 4 - 7) = 28$
18. Let x = daughter's age now; $(53 - x) + 8 = 2(x + 8)$
19. Twice Quincy's age 7 years ago was 58. How old is Quincy now?
20. Elena is 4 years older than Willie. In 10 years, the sum of their ages will be 54. How old is Willie now?

21. Ramón's car weighs 250 pounds more than Seth's. The sum of the weights of the cars is 7140 pounds. How much does each car weigh?
22. Jason is 7 inches taller than Manuel. The sum of Jason's height and twice Manuel's is 193 inches. How tall is Manuel?
23. Reggie is 31 cm shorter than Soto. The sum of Soto's height and twice Reggie's is 502 cm. How tall is Soto?

Strategies

Look for a pattern.
Solve a simpler problem.
Act it out.
Guess and check.
Draw a diagram.
Make a chart.
Work backwards.

17. Shannon has 4 more dimes than quarters and 7 fewer nickels than dimes. She has 28 coins in all. How many quarters does Shannon have?

18. The sum of Mrs. Blakely's age and her daughter Karen's age is 53 years. In 8 years, Mrs. Blakely will be twice as old as Karen. How old is Karen now?

Write a problem based on the given information. See margin.

19. Let a = Quincy's age now.
$2(a - 7) = 58$

20. Let w = Willie's age now.
$w + 4$ = Elena's age now.
$(w + 10) + (w + 4 + 10) = 54$

21. Let s = weight of Seth's car in pounds.
$s + 250$ = weight of Ramón's car in pounds.
$s + (s + 250) = 7140$

22. Let m = Manuel's height in inches.
$m + 7$ = Jason's height in inches.
$2m + (m + 7) = 193$

23. Let s = Soto's height in centimeters.
$s - 31$ = Reggie's height in centimeters.
$s + 2(s - 31) = 502$

COOPERATIVE LEARNING ACTIVITY

Work in groups of four. Each person in the group must understand the solution and be able to explain it to any person in the class.

Leah has promised to make at least 15 pounds of chocolate fudge for a graduation party. She will have to buy baking chocolate, milk, butter, and sugar. The grocery carries only one size of each ingredient: a box of baking chocolate is $2.69, a carton of milk is 69¢, a pound of butter is $1.09, and a box of sugar is 75¢.

With one box of chocolate and one carton of milk, Leah can make up to 6 pounds of fudge. With one more box of chocolate, she can make up to 9 pounds. With another carton of milk, she can make up to 12 pounds. There are 4 sticks of butter to a pound, and each stick makes exactly $4\frac{1}{2}$ pounds of fudge. Each box of sugar makes $1\frac{1}{2}$ pounds of fudge.

1. If she buys just enough of everything to come out even, can Leah buy all that she needs for $20? **yes**

2. What will her grocery bill be? **$19.54**

3. How many pounds of fudge can she make? **18 pounds**

LESSON 2-8 PROBLEM-SOLVING STRATEGY: WRITE AN EQUATION 87

EXTENDING THE LESSON

Math Power: Problem Solving

The sum of Mrs. Black's age and her daughter's age is 54 years. In 8 years, Mrs. Black will be twice as old as her daughter. What equation could be used to find out how old her daughter is now? $(54 - x) + 8 = 2(x + 8)$

Cooperative Learning Activity

This activity provides students with an opportunity to *learn* things together, not just do things together. You may wish to refer to pages T6 - T8 and page 6C for the various elements of cooperative groups and specific goals and strategies for using them.

Closing the Lesson

Writing Activity Have students each write a problem using the following information. Let h = Chris's height now, $h - 6$ = Ryan's height. Let students switch problems with a classmate and solve.

APPLYING THE LESSON

Homework Exercises

Assignment Guide
Basic: 11-21
Average: 11-21
Enriched: 11-23

Chapter 2, Quiz D, (Lessons 2-7 through 2-8), is available in the Evaluation Masters Booklet, p. 24.

Practice Master Booklet, p. 16

2-8 NAME _____ DATE _____

Practice Worksheet

Problem Solving: Write an Equation

Define a variable, then write an equation for each problem. Answers may vary. **Do not try to solve.** One possible answer is given for each problem.

1. Three years ago, twice Frank's age was 14 years. How old is he now?
Let a = Frank's age now.
$2(a - 3) = 14$

2. A number increased by 14 is 27. Find the number.
Let n = the number.
$n + 14 = 27$

3. Carla has twice as much money as Peter. Together they have $105. How much does Carla have?
Let m = number of dollars Peter has. Then $2m$ = number of dollars Carla has. $m + 2m = 105$

4. Seventy-two decreased by twice a number is 30. Find the number.
Let n = the number.
$72 - 2n = 30$

5. The sum of two numbers is 64. The greater number is 32 more than the other number. Find the numbers.
Let x = the greater number. Then $x - 32$ = the other number.
$x + (x - 32) = 64$

6. George is 5 cm taller than John . The sum of the heights is 405 cm. How tall is George?
Let h = John's height. Then $h + 5$ = George's height.
$h + (h + 5) = 405$

7. The product of a number and 5 is 80. Find the number.
Let n = the number.
$5n = 80$

8. Forty-five divided by a number is 9. Find the number.
Let n = the number.
$\frac{45}{n} = 9$

9. Jana's mother was 27 when Jana was born. The sum of their ages is now 51. How old is Jana?
Let a = Jana's age now. Then $a + 27$ = Jana's mothers age now.
$a + (a + 27) = 51$

10. The Lions played 27 basketball games. They won twice as many as they lost. How many did they win?
Let d = number of games lost. Then $2d$ = number of games won.
$d + 2d = 27$

Write a problem based on the given information. Answers may vary. One possible problem is given for each answer.

11. Let x = May's age now. Then, $x - 3$ = May's age 3 years ago. $2(x - 3) = 18$
Three years ago, twice May's age was 18 years. How old is she now?

12. Let t = greater of two numbers. Then, $t - 5$ = lesser of two numbers.
$t + (t - 5) = 25$
One of two numbers is 5 less than the other. The sum of the two numbers is 25. Find the numbers.

The Chapter Summary and Review begins with an alphabetical listing of the new terms that were presented in the chapter. Have students define each term and provide an example of it, if appropriate.

The Skills and Concepts presented in the chapter are reviewed using a side-by-side format. Encourage students to refer to the Objectives and Examples on the left as they complete the Review Exercises on the right.

The Chapter Summary and Review ends with exercises that review Applications and Connections.

Additional Answers

1.

2.

CHAPTER **2** SUMMARY AND REVIEW

VOCABULARY

Upon completing this chapter, you should be familiar with the following terms:

absolute value	55	81	multiplicative inverses
additive inverses	56	50	negative
complex fraction	81	50	number line
coordinate	51	56	opposites
cross products	65	61	rational numbers
disjoint	51	50	whole numbers
graph	51	51	real numbers
inequality	60	81	reciprocals
integers	50	51	union
intersection	51	66	unit cost
mean	80	51	Venn diagrams

SKILLS AND CONCEPTS

OBJECTIVES AND EXAMPLES	REVIEW EXERCISES

Upon completing this chapter, you should be able to:

Use these exercises to review and prepare for the chapter test.

■ graph integers on a number line **(Lesson 2-1)**

Graph $\{\ldots, -1, 0, 1, 2\}$.

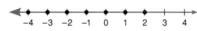

Graph each set of numbers on a number line. See margin.

1. $\{5, 3, -1, -3\}$

2. $\{-3, -2, -1, 0, \ldots\}$

■ add integers **(Lessons 2-1, 2-2)**

$-14 + (-9) = -23$
$20 + (-4) = 16$
$-7 + 3 = -4$

Find each sum.

3. $17 + (-9)$ **8**　　4. $-9 + (-12)$ **−21**

5. $-12 + 8$ **−4**　　6. $-17 + (-31)$ **−48**

■ subtract integers **(Lesson 2-2)**

$7 - 9 = -2$
$-6 - 5 = -11$
$-4 - (-8) = 4$

Find each difference.

7. $14 - 36$ **−22**　　8. $8 - (-5)$ **13**

9. $-7 - (-11)$ **4**　　10. $-13x - (-7x)$ **−6x**

OBJECTIVES AND EXAMPLES	REVIEW EXERCISES

- find the absolute value of a number **(Lesson 2-2)**

Evaluate $|m - 2|$ if $m = -3$.

$$|m - 2| = |-3 - 2|$$
$$= |-5|$$
$$= 5$$

Evaluate each expression.

11. $|4 - x|$, if $x = -2$ **6**

12. $|x| - 2.6$, if $x = -5$ **2.4**

13. $-|a + (-12)|$, if $a = -3$ **−15**

- graph inequalities on number lines **(Lesson 2-3)**

Graph the solution set of $x \geq -3$.

Graph the solution set of each inequality on a number line.

14. $x < 2$

15. $x \neq -4$

- compare numbers **(Lessons 2-3, 2-4)**

$$\frac{2}{3} \underline{\ ?\ } \frac{4}{5}$$

$$5 \cdot 2 \underline{\ ?\ } 3 \cdot 4$$

$$10 < 12$$

$$\frac{2}{3} < \frac{4}{5}$$

Replace each $\underline{\ ?\ }$ with <, >, or = to make each sentence true.

16. $-9 \underline{\ ?\ } -11$ **>**   17. $-13 \underline{\ ?\ } 13$ **<**

18. $-7 \underline{\ ?\ } \frac{-3.6}{0.6}$ **<**   19. $\frac{3}{8} \underline{\ ?\ } \frac{4}{11}$ **>**

20. $-\frac{10}{11} \underline{\ ?\ } \frac{11}{12}$ **<**   21. $-\frac{9}{11} \underline{\ ?\ } -\frac{7}{8}$ **>**

- find a number between two rational numbers **(Lesson 2-4)**

The average of $\frac{3}{5}$ and $\frac{7}{12}$ is as follows.

$$\frac{1}{2}\left(\frac{3}{5} + \frac{7}{12}\right) = \frac{1}{2}\left(\frac{71}{60}\right)$$

$$= \frac{71}{120}$$

Find a number between the given numbers.

22. $\frac{2}{9}$ and $\frac{5}{8}$ $\frac{61}{144}$ **Answers may vary; sample answers are given.**

23. $\frac{3}{5}$ and $\frac{7}{12}$ $\frac{71}{120}$

24. $-\frac{1}{2}$ and $\frac{7}{11}$ **0**

26–28. See margin.

- add or subtract rational numbers **(Lesson 2-5)**

$-0.37 + (-0.812) = -1.182$

Find each sum or difference.

25. $\frac{6}{7} + \left(-\frac{13}{7}\right)$ **−1**   26. $-\frac{4}{3} + \frac{5}{6} + \left(-\frac{7}{3}\right)$

27. $3.72 - (-8.65)$ 28. $-4.5y - 8.1y$

- multiply rational numbers **(Lesson 2-6)**

$-4(-2) + 6(-3) = 8 + (-18)$
$$= -10$$

Simplify. **32. 51**

29. $(-11)(9)$ **−99**   30. $(-8)(-12)$ **96**

31. $\frac{3}{5}\left(-\frac{5}{7}\right)$ **−$\frac{3}{7}$**   32. $-3(7) + (-8)(-9)$

33. $\frac{1}{2}(6a + 8b) - \frac{2}{3}(12a + 24b)$ **−5a − 12b**

Alternate Review Strategy

To provide a brief in-class review, you may wish to read the following questions to the class and require a verbal response.

1. What integer describes a loss of 3 yards? **−3**
2. What is the sum of 38 and −47? **−9**
3. Which is the greater amount, 14 or 8 − 24? **14**
4. What is a number between $-\frac{3}{8}$ and $\frac{9}{10}$? **0**
5. What is the sum of 8, −2, and −4? **2**
6. What is the product of −12 and 5? **−60**
7. What is the quotient of −48 and −12? **4**
8. Tim's height is represented by h. What expression could be used to represent Joe's height if Joe is 4 inches taller than Tim? **$h + 4$**

Additional Answers

26. $-\frac{17}{6}$
27. **12.37**
28. **−12.6y**

Evaluation Masters Booklet, pp. 25-26

OBJECTIVES AND EXAMPLES	REVIEW EXERCISES

■ divide rational numbers **(Lesson 2-7)**

$$\frac{-12}{-\frac{2}{3}} = -12 \div \left(-\frac{2}{3}\right)$$

$$= -12\left(-\frac{3}{2}\right)$$

$$= 18$$

Simplify.

34. $\frac{-54}{6}$ -9

35. $\frac{63b}{-7}$ $-9b$

36. $\frac{\frac{4}{5}}{-7} - \frac{4}{35}$

37. $\frac{33a + 66}{-11}$ $-3a - 6$

APPLICATIONS AND CONNECTIONS

Set Theory: Draw a Venn diagram to find each of the following. **(Lesson 2-1)** See margin.

38. the union of {vowels} and {last ten letters of the alphabet}

39. the intersection of {1, 3, 5, 7} and {1, 2, 3, 4, 5}

40. **Aquatics** A submarine descended to a depth of 432 meters and then rose 189 meters. How far below the surface of the water was the submarine? **(Lesson 2-1)** 243 meters

41. **Savings** Pam was trying to save money for a ten-speed bicycle. She opened a savings account with a deposit of $75. Then she withdrew $37 for a new pair of shoes. What is her new balance? **(Lesson 2-2)** $38

Sequences: Complete. (Lesson 2-6)

42. Find the next five terms of the sequence 3, 4.5, 6, ... 7.5, 9, 10.5, 12, 13.5

43. Find the 20th term of the sequence for which $a = 7$ and $d = -4$. -69

44. Find the 24th term of the sequence $-6, -1, 4, \ldots$ 109

45. **Consumerism** Which is the better buy: 0.75 liter of soda for 89¢ or 1.25 liters of soda for $1.31? **(Lesson 2-4)**

46. **Statistics** Find the mean for the following set of data: 4, 7.2, 4, 9, 21, 15, 6, 6.3, 29, 0. **(Lesson 2-7)** 10.15

47. **Metallurgy** The gold content of jewelry is given in karats. For example, 24-karat gold is pure gold, but 18-karat gold is $\frac{18}{24}$ or 0.75 gold. **(Lessons 2-6, 2-7)**
   a. Ten-karat gold is what fraction gold? What fraction is *not* gold? $\frac{5}{12}, \frac{7}{12}$
   b. If a piece of jewelry is $\frac{2}{3}$ gold, how would you describe it in karats? 16 karats

Define a variable, then write an equation for each problem. Do *not* try to solve. (Lesson 2-8)

48. Minal weighs 8 pounds less than Claudia. Together they weigh 182 pounds. How much does Minal weigh? Let w = Minal's weight; $w + (w + 8) = 182$.

49. Three times a number decreased by 21 is 57. Find the number. Let n = the number; $3n - 21 = 57$.

Additional Answers

38. {a, e, i, o, q, r, s, t, u, w, x, y, z}

39. {1, 3, 5}

NAME _____ DATE _____

Cumulative Review (Chapters 1–2)

Write an algebraic expression for each verbal expression.

1. 7 more than the square of a number   1. $n^2 + 7$

2. 5 less than 4 times a number   2. $4n - 5$

Evaluate each expression.

3. $6 - 2^2 + 14 \cdot 3 \div 7$ 3. 8

4. $3a^2(a^2 - b^2)$ if $a = 4$ and $b = 3$ 4. 336

Solve each equation.

5. $a = \frac{3}{5} \cdot 15$ 5. 9

6. $\frac{84 \div 14}{27 \div 9} = m$ 6. 2

Name the property illustrated by each statement.

7. If $x = 7 + 2$ and $7 + 2 = w$, then $x = w$.   7. Trans.

8. $6 + (7 \cdot 5) = 6 + 35$ 8. Subst.

9. $3(4a + b) = 12a + 3b$ 9. Distrib.

10. $(7 + x) + a = (x + 7) + a$ 10. Comm.; Add.

Simplify.

11. $6a^2 + 11a^2 - 3$ 11. $17a^2 - 3$

12. $2(2x + y) + 6(x + 2y)$ 12. $10x + 14y$

Write an equation for each sentence.

13. y is the product of a and b increased by c.   13. $y = ab + c$

14. The number m equals the square of the difference of n and p.   14. $m = (n - p)^2$

Replace each ? with <, >, or = to make each sentence true.

15. -3 ? -6 15. $>$

16. $\frac{4}{13}$? $\frac{3}{11}$ 16. $>$

17. Name the set of numbers graphed below.

-6 -5 -4 -3 -2 -1 0 1 2 3 4 5

17. {integers less than 3}

NAME _____ DATE _____

Cumulative Review (Chapters 1–2)

18. Graph {-3, -1, 0, 2} on the number line provided.
18. -4 -3 -2 -1 0 1 2 3

19. Graph the solution set for $w \le 3$ on the number line.
19. -3 -2 -1 0 1 2 3 4

Find each sum or difference.

20. $19 + (-4)$ 20. 15

21. $-15 + a$ if $a = -10$ 21. -25

22. $-\frac{2}{7} + \frac{11}{14}$ 22. $\frac{1}{2}$

23. $-1.8 + (-1.4)$ 23. -3.2

24. $-13 + 6 + (-8)$ 24. -15

25. $4m + (-3m) + (-12m)$ 25. $-11m$

26. $-38 - 17$ 26. -55

27. $-3.2 - (-8.4)$ 27. 5.2

Simplify.

28. $5(-7) + (-3)(6)$ 28. -53

29. $3(5t - t) + 4(2t + t)$ 29. $24t$

30. $\left(-\frac{1}{3}\right)\left(\frac{3}{7}\right) + \left(\frac{5}{6}\right)\left(\frac{12}{35}\right)$ 30. $\frac{1}{7}$

31. $\frac{5a - 10}{5}$ 31. $a - 2$

Define a variable then write an equation for each problem. Do not try to solve.

32. Wayne bought a suit on sale and saved $15.35. The regular price was $139.29. What was the sale price?   32. Let s = sale price. $s = 139.29 - 15.35$

33. Lisa is 5 years older than Susan. The sum of their ages is 25. How old is Susan?   33. Let s = Susan's age. $s + (s + 5) = 25$

Graph each set of numbers on a number line. **See margin.**

1. $\{1, 2, 5\}$

2. {all numbers less than 2}

Find each sum or difference.

3. $-11 + (-13)$ **-24**

4. $12 - 19$ **-7**

5. $1.654 + (-2.367)$ **-0.713**

6. $-41 - (-52)$ **11**

7. $6.32 - (-7.41)$ **13.73**

8. $12x + (-21x)$ **$-9x$**

9. $\frac{3}{7} + \left(-\frac{9}{7}\right)$ **$-\frac{6}{7}$**

10. $-\frac{7}{16} - \frac{3}{8}$ **$-\frac{13}{16}$**

11. $18b + 13xy - 46b$
$13xy - 28b$

12. $[4 + (-13)] - 12$ **-21**

13. $\frac{5}{8} + \left(-\frac{3}{16}\right) + \left(-\frac{3}{4}\right)$ **$-\frac{5}{16}$**

Evaluate each expression.

14. $-x - 38$, if $x = -2$ **-36**

15. $\left|-\frac{1}{2} + z\right|$, if $z = \frac{1}{4}$ **$\frac{1}{4}$**

16. $-|a| + |b|$, if $a = 6$ and $b = -2$ **-4**

17. $d - (-3.8)$, if $d = 0$ **3.8**

Replace each __?__ with $<$, $>$, or $=$ to make each sentence true.

18. 2 __?__ -7 **$>$**

19. -4 __?__ -3 **$<$**

20. $\frac{5.4}{18}$ __?__ $-4 + 1$ **$>$**

21. $(4.1)(0.2)$ __?__ 8.2 **$<$**

22. $\frac{7}{6}$ __?__ $\frac{13}{12}$ **$>$**

23. $-\frac{12}{17}$ __?__ $-\frac{9}{14}$ **$<$**

Find a number between the given numbers.

24. $\frac{5}{11}$ and $\frac{13}{7}$ **$\frac{89}{77}$**

25. $-\frac{2}{3}$ and $-\frac{9}{14}$ **$-\frac{55}{84}$**

26. $-\frac{13}{2}$ and $\frac{12}{7}$ **0**

Simplify.

27. $\frac{8(-3)}{2}$ **-12**

28. $(-5)(-2)(-2) - (-6)(-3)$
-38

29. $\frac{2}{3}\left(\frac{1}{2}\right) - \left(-\frac{3}{2}\right)\left(-\frac{2}{3}\right)$ **$-\frac{2}{3}$**

30. $\frac{70a - 42b}{-14}$ **$-5a + 3b$**

31. $\frac{3}{4}(8x + 12y) - \frac{5}{7}(21x - 35y)$
$-9x + 34y$

32. $\frac{\frac{11}{5}}{-6}$ **$-\frac{11}{30}$**

33. Define a variable and write an equation for the following problem.

Each week for several weeks, Save-a-Buck stores reduced the price of a sofa by \$18.25. The original price was \$380.25. The final reduced price was \$252.50. For how many weeks was the sofa on sale?
Let w = number of weeks on sale; $380.25 - 18.25w = 252.50$.

Bonus Find the sum: $4|(-5 + 2)|^2 + (-72)$. **-36**

Using the Chapter Test
This page may be used as a test or as a review. In addition, two multiple-choice tests and two free-response tests are provided in the Evaluation Masters Booklet. Chapter 2 Test, Form 1A is shown below.

Evaluation Masters Booklet, pp. 15-16

NAME _____ DATE _____

Chapter 2 Test, Form 1A

Write the letter for the correct answer in the blank at the right of each problem.

1. What set of numbers is graphed below?

   A. {negative integers}   B. $\{..., -3, -2, -1, 0\}$
   C. $\{-4, -3, -2, -1, 0, ...\}$ D. none of these

   1. **B**

2. Which of the following is the graph of {integers greater than -2}?

   A.   B.
   C.   D.

   2. **D**

3. The graph shows the solution set for which of the following inequalities?

   A. $x < 1$ B. $x \le 1$ C. $x \le -1$ D. $x > 1$

   3. **A**

4. Use a number line to find the sum of -9 and (-13).
   A. -22 B. 22   C. -4 D. 4

   4. **A**

5. What is the value of $-387 + 432$?
   A. -45 B. 45   C. -9 D. 9

   5. **B**

6. Find the value of $-|w + 12|$ if $w = -82$.
   A. -70 B. 70   C. -94 D. 94

   6. **A**

7. Find $-0.007 + 0.02$.
   A. -0.09 B. 0.13   C. -0.027 D. 0.013

   7. **D**

8. Simplify $16a + (-7a) + (-12a) + a$.
   A. 0   B. $-20a$ C. $-2a$ D. $-3a$

   8. **C**

9. What is the value of $435 - (-278)$?
   A. -713 B. 713   C. -157 D. 157

   9. **B**

10. Which fractions are written in order from least to greatest?
    A. $\frac{4}{25}, \frac{3}{19}, \frac{5}{27}$ B. $\frac{3}{19}, \frac{5}{27}, \frac{4}{25}$ C. $\frac{5}{27}, \frac{4}{25}, \frac{3}{19}$ D. $\frac{3}{19}, \frac{4}{25}, \frac{5}{27}$

    10. **D**

11. A rational number between $\frac{2}{9}$ and $\frac{11}{40}$ is:
    A. $\frac{2}{11}$ B. $\frac{9}{31}$ C. $\frac{179}{360}$ D. $\frac{179}{720}$

    11. **D**

NAME _____ DATE _____

Chapter 2 Test, Form 1A (continued)

Exercises 12 to 14: What symbol can replace the __?__ to make each sentence true.

12. -4 __?__ $\frac{4}{3}$ A. $=$ B. $<$ C. $>$ 12. **B**

13. $(2.1)(-1)$ __?__ -5 A. $=$ B. $<$ C. $>$ 13. **C**

14. $\frac{3}{4}$ __?__ $\frac{5}{7}$ A. $=$ B. $<$ C. $>$ 14. **C**

15. Subtract: $-\frac{2}{3} - \left(-\frac{4}{5}\right)$
    A. $-\frac{22}{25}$ B. $-\frac{2}{15}$ C. $\frac{3}{4}$ D. $\frac{2}{15}$ 15. **D**

16. Multiply: $\left(-\frac{1}{3}\right)\left(-\frac{6}{7}\right)$
    A. $\frac{7}{10}$ B. $\frac{2}{7}$ C. $-\frac{2}{7}$ D. $-\frac{7}{10}$ 16. **B**

17. Divide: $-\frac{1}{4} \div 6$
    A. $-\frac{1}{24}$ B. $-\frac{3}{2}$ C. $\frac{1}{24}$ D. $\frac{3}{2}$ 17. **A**

18. Simplify $\frac{-4}{\frac{3}{8}}$.
    A. $-\frac{3}{2}$ B. $-\frac{3}{32}$ C. $-\frac{32}{3}$ D. $\frac{3}{2}$ 18. **C**

19. Simplify $\frac{24k - 6}{-6}$.
    A. $-4k - 6$ B. $-4k + 1$ C. $-24k - 1$ D. $24k - 1$ 19. **B**

20. Which equation can be used to solve the following problem? The Sears Tower in Chicago is 40 feet taller than the Empire State Building in New York. The sum of their heights is 2868 feet. How tall is the Empire State Building?
    A. $x + 40 = 2868$ B. $x = 2868 - 40$
    C. $x + (x + 40) = 2868$ D. $x - 40 = 2868$ 20. **C**

Bonus: What is the opposite of the reciprocal of the multiplicative inverse of the additive inverse of 5?   **Bonus:** **5**

Test Generator Software is provided in both Apple and IBM versions. You may use this software to create your own tests, based on the needs of your students.

Additional Answers

1.

2.

CHAPTER 3

Equations

PREVIEWING THE CHAPTER

This chapter addresses the crucial skills and concepts involved in solving equations. Balance scales are used as a model to develop an understanding of equivalent equations, and then, in carefully sequenced lessons, the addition, subtraction, multiplication, and division properties of equality are presented and applied to solving equations. Students learn to use more than one property to solve equations with the variable on either side or on both sides. The chapter concludes with a lesson on solving equations that contain more than one variable.

Problem-Solving Strategy In Lesson 3-4, students learn that some problems can best be solved by applying the strategy of *working backwards.*

Lesson Objective Chart

Lesson (Pages)	Lesson Objectives	State/Local Objectives
3-1 (94-98)	**3-1:** Solve equations by using addition.	
3-2 (99-102)	**3-2:** Solve equations by using subtraction.	
3-3 (103-107)	**3-3A:** Solve equations by using multiplication.	
	3-3B: Solve equations by using division.	
3-4 (108-110)	**3-4:** Solve problems by working backwards.	
3-5 (111-115)	**3-5:** Solve equations involving more than one operation.	
3-6 (116-120)	**3-6A:** Solve equations with the variable on both sides.	
	3-6B: Solve equations containing grouping symbols.	
3-7 (122-125)	**3-7A:** Solve equations containing fractions or decimals.	
	3-7B: Solve equations containing more than one variable.	

ORGANIZING THE CHAPTER

You may want to refer to the **Course Planning Calendar** on page T36.

Lesson Planning Guide / Blackline Masters Booklets

Lesson (Pages)	Course I	Course II	Course III	Reteaching	Practice	Enrichment	Evaluation	Technology	Lab Manual	Mixed Problem Solving	Applications	Cooperative Learning Activity	Multicultural	Transparencies
3-1 (94-98)	1.5	1.5	1.5	p. 16	p. 17	p. 16						p. 33		3-1
3-2 (99-102)	1	1	1	p. 17	p. 18	p. 17	Quiz A, p. 37	p. 3 p. 18						3-2
3-3 (103-107)	1.5	1	1	p. 18	p. 19	p. 18								3-3
3-4 (108-110)	1	1	1		p. 20		Quiz B, p. 37 Mid-Chapter Test, p. 41							3-4
3-5 (111-115)	1.5	1.5	1.5	p. 19	p. 21	p. 19			pp. 21-22				p. 48	3-5
3-6 (116-120)	1.5	1	1	p. 20	p. 22	p. 20	Quiz C, p. 38		pp. 33-34					3-6
3-7 (122-125)	1	1	1	p. 21	p. 23	p. 21	Quiz D, p. 38			p. 3	p. 18			3-7
Review (126-128)	1	1	1	Multiple Choice Tests, Forms 1A and 1B, pp. 29-32 / Free Response Tests, Forms 2A and 2B, pp. 33-36										
Test (129)	1	1	1	Cumulative Review, pp. 39-40 / Standardized Test Practice Questions, p. 42										

Course I: Chapters 1-13, Course II: Chapters 1-14, Course III: Chapters 1-15

Other Chapter Resources

Student Edition
Mid-Chapter Review, p. 107
Cooperative Learning Activity, p. 110
Puzzle, p. 115
Puzzle, p. 120
Technology, p. 121
History Connection, p. 125
Algebraic Skills Review, p. 661
   (ex. 1-24)

Teacher Resource Package
Activity Masters Booklet
   Mixed Problem Solving, p. 3
   Applications, p. 18
   Cooperative Learning Activity, p. 33
   Multicultural Activity, p. 48
Technology Masters Booklet
   Scientific Calculator Activity, p. 3
   Graphing Calculator Activity, p. 18
Lab Manual
   Lab Activity, pp. 21-22, 33-34

Other Supplements
Transparency for Chapter Opener
Problem-of-the-Week Activity
   Cards, 6-7
Video Algebra, 8-11, 17

Software
Algebra 1 Test and Review
   Generator Software
   Available for Apple and IBM.

ENHANCING THE CHAPTER

Cooperative Learning

Deciding on the Size of Groups

The number of students in each cooperative-learning group can range from two to six. Because group skills must be learned by students, few will have the skills required for a large group. Therefore, in the beginning, it is advisable to begin with small groups of two or three students each. A small group can be more effective because it takes less time for the members to get organized, and it provides more opportunity for each member to participate and to develop cooperative-learning skills. Once students begin to exhibit these group skills, you may choose to organize larger groups for some tasks. A larger group provides more opportunities to have members with different group skills to be helpful to the whole group. It also can decrease the time required to do the assigned task since there are more members with more talents to do the work.

Technology

The Technology Feature after Lesson 3-6 employs the *Mathematical Exploration Toolkit* (MET). MET is a powerful calculator, symbolic manipulator, and graphing utility for IBM and IBM-compatible microcomputers. Students will need some help getting started with the MET program. HELP screens are available at any point in the program by pressing the F1 key. Features using MET will appear from time to time in this text. These features can serve to introduce students to MET's commands and capabilities.

MET offers an authoring language within the Defer Sequence mode. No previous programming experience is required. Defer Sequences can be used as classroom demonstrations or student laboratory modules. Consult the MET manual to learn how to create Defer Sequences or to use those provided with the software package.

Critical Thinking

When considering Bloom's taxonomy of thinking processes — knowledge, comprehension, application, analysis, synthesis, and evaluation — many people envision critical-thinking skills as being applied only at the levels of analysis, synthesis, and evaluation. This is not necessarily so. For example, when a student gives an answer to an exercise that calls only for demonstration of knowledge and comprehension of content, before you say whether the answer is correct, ask the student to explain how the answer was arrived at and to justify the answer. Then before you respond, ask other students if they agree or disagree with the explanation and justification. By utilizing this procedure on a regular basis, you signal to students that it is they, not you, who are responsible for doing the thinking.

Cooperative Learning, p. 33

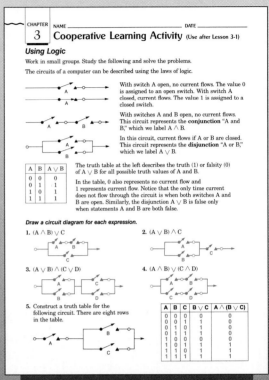

Technology, p. 3

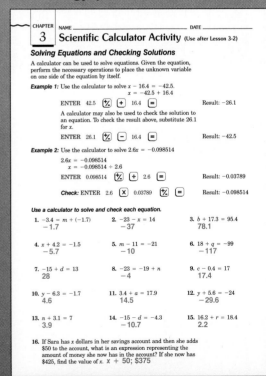

Problem of the Week Activity

The card shown below is one of two available for this chapter. It can be used as a class or small group activity.

Activity Card

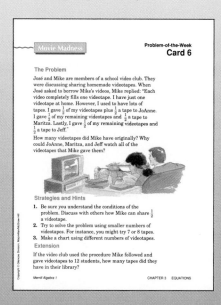

Movie Madness

Problem-of-the-Week
Card 6

The Problem

José and Mike are members of a school video club. They were discussing sharing homemade videotapes. When José asked to borrow Mike's videos, Mike replied: "Each video completely fills one videotape. I have just one videotape at home. However, I used to have lots of tapes. I gave $\frac{1}{2}$ of my videotapes plus $\frac{1}{2}$ a tape to JoAnne. I gave $\frac{1}{2}$ of my remaining videotapes and $\frac{1}{2}$ a tape to Maritza. Lastly, I gave $\frac{1}{2}$ of my remaining videotapes and $\frac{1}{2}$ a tape to Jeff."

How many videotapes did Mike have originally? Why could JoAnne, Maritza, and Jeff watch all of the videotapes that Mike gave them?

Strategies and Hints

1. Be sure you understand the conditions of the problem. Discuss with others how Mike can share $\frac{1}{2}$ a videotape.
2. Try to solve the problem using smaller numbers of videotapes. For instance, you might try 7 or 8 tapes.
3. Make a chart using different numbers of videotapes.

Extension

If the video club used the procedure Mike followed and gave videotapes to 12 students, how many tapes did they have in their library?

Merrill Algebra 1

CHAPTER 3   EQUATIONS

Manipulatives and Models

The following materials may be used as models or manipulatives in Chapter 3.

- scale (Lesson 3-1)
- meterstick (Lessons 3-1, 3-3)
- triangular prism (Lesson 3-1)
- coins (Lesson 3-2)
- tape measure (Lesson 3-3)
- index cards (Lesson 3-7)

Outside Resources

Books/Periodicals

Fisher, Leonard Everett. *Number Art-Thirteen 1 2 3s From Around the World.* Four Winds Press.

Zaslavsky, Claudia. *Africa Counts.* Prindle, Weber and Schmidt.

Films/Videotapes/Videodiscs

Pre-Algebra, Video Tutor, Inc.

Numbers, What They Mean, 1985

Software

Equation Math, MECC

The Factory, Sunburst

Mathematical Exploration Toolkit, IBM

Multicultural

Multicultural Activity, p. 48

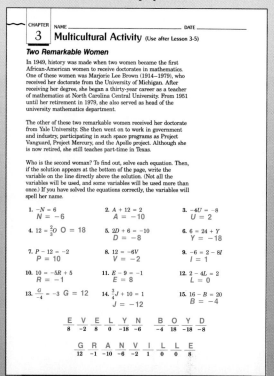

CHAPTER **3** NAME _____ DATE _____

Multicultural Activity (Use after Lesson 3-5)

Two Remarkable Women

In 1949, history was made when two women became the first African-American women to receive doctorates in mathematics. One of these women was Marjorie Lee Brown (1914–1979), who received her doctorate from the University of Michigan. After receiving her degree, she began a thirty-year career as a teacher of mathematics at North Carolina Central University. From 1951 until her retirement in 1979, she also served as head of the university mathematics department.

The other of these two remarkable women received her doctorate from Yale University. She then went on to work in government and industry, participating in such space programs as Project Vanguard, Project Mercury, and the Apollo project. Although she is now retired, she still teaches part-time in Texas.

Who is the second woman? To find out, solve each equation. Then, if the solution appears at the bottom of the page, write the variable on the line directly above the solution. (Not all the variables will be used, and some variables will be used more than once.) If you have solved the equations correctly, the variables will spell her name.

1. $-N = 6$
   $N = -6$
2. $A + 12 = 2$
   $A = -10$
3. $-4U = -8$
   $U = 2$
4. $12 = \frac{2}{3}O$ $O = 18$
5. $2D + 6 = -10$
   $D = -8$
6. $6 = 24 + Y$
   $Y = -18$
7. $P - 12 = -2$
   $P = 10$
8. $12 = -6V$
   $V = -2$
9. $-6 = 2 - 8I$
   $I = 1$
10. $10 = -5R + 5$
    $R = -1$
11. $E - 9 = -1$
    $E = 8$
12. $2 - 4L = 2$
    $L = 0$
13. $\frac{G}{-4} = -3$ $G = 12$
14. $\frac{3}{4}J + 10 = 1$
    $J = -12$
15. $16 - B = 20$
    $B = -4$

E	V	E	L	Y	N		B	O	Y	D
8	-2	8	0	-18	-6		-4	18	-18	-8

G	R	A	N	V	I	L	L	E
12	-1	-10	-6	-2	1	0	0	8

Lab Manual

Lab Activity, pp. 21-22

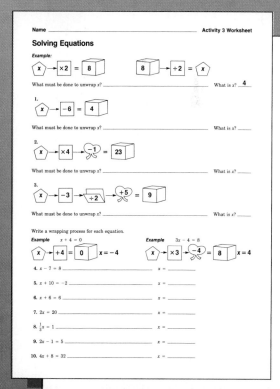

Name _____   Activity 3 Worksheet

Solving Equations

Example:

$x \rightarrow \times 2 = 8$ $8 \rightarrow \div 2 = x$

What must be done to unwrap x? _____   What is x? __4__

1. $x \rightarrow -6 = 4$

What must be done to unwrap x? _____   What is x? _____

2. $x \rightarrow \times 4 \rightarrow -1 = 23$

What must be done to unwrap x? _____   What is x? _____

3. $x \rightarrow -3 \rightarrow \div 2 \rightarrow +5 = 9$

What must be done to unwrap x? _____   What is x? _____

Write a wrapping process for each equation.

Example $x + 4 = 0$ *Example* $3x - 4 = 8$

$x \rightarrow +4 = 0$ $x = -4$ $x \rightarrow \times 3 \rightarrow -4 = 8$ $x = 4$

4. $x - 7 = 8$ _____ $x = $ _____
5. $x + 10 = -2$ _____ $x = $ _____
6. $x + 6 = 6$ _____ $x = $ _____
7. $2x = 20$ _____ $x = $ _____
8. $\frac{1}{3}x = 1$ _____ $x = $ _____
9. $2x - 1 = 5$ _____ $x = $ _____
10. $4x + 8 = 32$ _____ $x = $ _____

Using the Chapter Opener

Transparency 3-0 is available in the Transparency Package. It provides a full-color visual and motivational activity that you can use to engage students in the mathematical content of the chapter.

Background Information

Robert Recorde studied and taught mathematics at both Oxford and Cambridge. He died in prison a year after writing the *Whetstone of Witte*. The title was evidently a play on words. Algebra was referred to as the ''cossike practice'' and ''cos'' is Latin for *whetstone,* a stone for sharpening tools. So the use of whetstone may have been Recorde's way of calling his publication not only an algebra book, but a book on which to sharpen one's mathematical wit. In *Whetstone,* Recorde was the first to use the equal sign as a pair of parallel lines, ''bicause noe 2. thynges can be more equalle.''

In this chapter, you will:
- Solve equations using one or more operations.
- Solve equations containing fractions or decimals.
- Solve problems that can be represented by equations.
- Work backwards to solve problems.

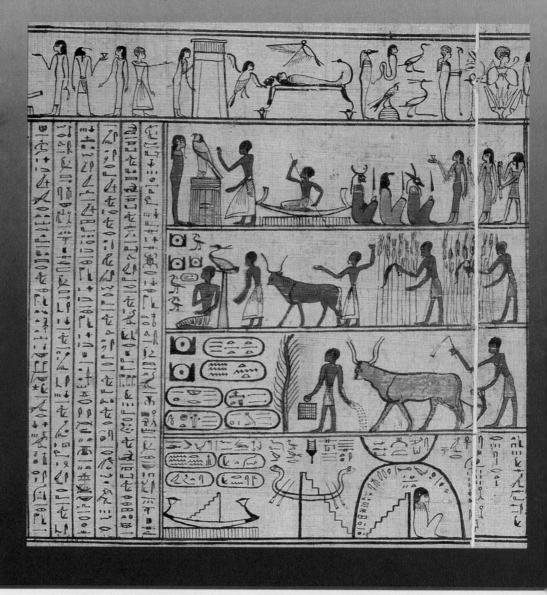

Chapter Project

Materials: posterboard, markers, ruler, paper, pencil

Using early systems of numeration can be both fun and educational. It also provides an opportunity to mesh math with art and drawing. Have students work in cooperative groups to research and adopt one early numbering system. The following is a list of systems from which each group might choose.

African	Inca
Arabic	Mayan
Armenian	Old English
Babylonian	Roman
Chinese	Runes
Egyptian	Sanskrit
Gothic	Thai
Greek	Tibetan
Hindu/Brahmi	

After completing their research, have each group draw a complete set of numbers in its selected system on posterboard. Then have each group develop simple addition and subtraction problems in its adopted system.

Finally, have each group teach the class its chosen system, to include practice problems to perform under the supervision of group members.

Equations

They may not have had skateboards, compact disks, or VCRs, but 4500 years ago, Babylonian teenagers did have algebra homework!

APPLICATION IN HISTORY

Just like you, students in ancient Babylon had algebra homework, although they did not write their assignments in notebooks filled with lined paper. Instead, they wrote on clay tablets using the ends of little sticks to make wedge-shaped marks. About one thousand years later, in Egypt, students wrote their algebra assignments on papyrus, a parchment-like material that was easier to write on than a clay tablet.

If you could read either of these assignments today, you might not recognize them as algebra assignments. Neither the ancient Babylonians nor the ancient Egyptians used letters for unknown values in their algebraic equations. One reason for this is that the alphabet of today had not yet been invented! So, instead of letters, they made little pictures that stood for the unknowns. This would be the same as if you wrote entire words instead of letters like x and y in your equations. Algebraic symbolism using letters did not gain wide acceptance until the Greek mathematician, Diophantus, introduced the *syncopated* style of writing equations.

ALGEBRA IN ACTION

Diophantus made numerous contributions in the area of algebraic symbolism. The chart below shows examples of his syncopated equations along with their modern algebraic form. How would Diophantus have written the equation $2x + 9 = x - 3$? $\zeta\beta\theta\iota\sigma\zeta\Delta\gamma$

Diophantus' Equation	Modern Meaning
$\zeta\iota\sigma\beta$	$x = 2$
$\zeta\gamma\iota\sigma\theta$	$x + 3 = 9$
$\zeta\gamma\beta\iota\sigma\theta$	$3x + 2 = 9$
$\zeta\theta\Lambda\gamma\iota\sigma\beta$	$9x - 3 = 2$
$\zeta\beta\Lambda\theta\iota\sigma\zeta\gamma$	$2x - 9 = x + 3$

Lesson	Connections (C) and Applications (A)	Examples	Exercises
3-1	A: Aviation	2	
	Spelunking		43
	Gardening		44
	Sales		45
	Weather		46
3-2	A: Weightlifting	1	
	Baseball		40
	Skiing		41
	Finance		42
	Farming		43
3-3	C: Geometry	5	49-51
	A: Sports		58
	Sales		59
3-5	C: Number Theory	4	8-14, 33-37
	A: Finance	1	
	Sales		39
	Baseball		40
	Statistics		41
	Running		42
3-6	C: Geometry	2	12-14
	A: Sales		39
	Running		40
	Soccer		41
	Travel		42
3-7	A: Construction		39
	Sales		40

93

Lesson Resources

- Reteaching Master 3-1
- Practice Master 3-1
- Enrichment Master 3-1
- Activity Master, p. 33
- Video Algebra, 8

 Transparency 3-1 contains the 5-Minute Check and a teaching aid for this lesson.

INTRODUCING THE LESSON

🕐 5-Minute Check
(over Chapter 2)

Simplify.

1. $-\frac{38}{2}$ -19
2. $\frac{30}{-5}$ -6
3. $\frac{-200x}{50}$ $-4x$

Write an equation for each problem.

4. A number decreased by 14 is 72. What is the number? $x - 14 = 72$

5. Jon is twice as old as Peter. The sum of their ages is 51. Find their ages. $x + 2x = 51$

Motivating the Lesson

Display a scale to the class. Place two classroom objects such as a pencil and a piece of chalk on the sides of the scale. Have students explain the result. Develop the idea that the scale is balanced when its sides hold equal weights. Challenge students to find two different objects that are equal in weight. Check the validity of student predictions by placing the objects on the scale.

3-1 Solving Equations by Using Addition

Objective
3-1

After studying this lesson, you should be able to:
- solve equations by using addition.

Application

Record Universe and Music Madhouse each sell CDs for $10.95. If each store raises its price by $2, they will still be selling CDs for the same price.

$$10.95 = 10.95$$
$$10.95 + 2 = 10.95 + 2$$

This example illustrates the **addition property of equality**.

Addition Property of Equality	For any numbers *a*, *b*, and *c*, if $a = b$, then $a + c = b + c$.

Note that c can be positive or negative.

$$15 + 3 = 15 + 3 \qquad\qquad 15 + (-3) = 15 + (-3)$$

Think of an equation as a scale in balance. A scale balances when each side holds equal weight. If you add weight to only one side, as shown in the center illustration below, then the scale is no longer in balance. However, if you add the same weight to each side, the scale will balance.

If the same number is added to each side of an equation, then the result is an **equivalent equation**. Equivalent equations are equations that have the same solution.

$$11 = x + 3 \qquad \text{\textit{The solution to this equation is 8.}}$$
$$11 + 5 = x + 3 + 5 \qquad \text{\textit{Using the addition property of equality, add 5 to each side.}}$$
$$16 = x + 8 \qquad \text{\textit{The solution to this equation is also 8.}}$$

Remember, x means $1 \cdot x$. The coefficient of x is 1.

To **solve an equation** means to isolate the variable having a coefficient of 1 on one side of the equation. You can do this by using the addition property of equality.

ALTERNATE TEACHING STRATEGIES

Using Models

Use white squares to represent positive integers and red squares to represent negative integers. A white square "cancels" a red square and vice versa. Have students use the squares to model $r + 5 = -2$. Tell them to solve the equation by manipulating the squares until the left side is empty.

Using Manipulatives

Have students use a meter stick and a triangular prism to make their own scales. Tell them to place the stick on the prism at the 50-cm mark. Discuss with the class what happens when equivalent weights are moved towards and away from the fulcrum of the scale.

Example 1

Solve $r + 16 = -7$.

$$r + 16 = -7$$
$$r + 16 + (-16) = -7 + (-16) \qquad \textit{Add } -16 \textit{ to each side.}$$
$$r + 0 = -23 \qquad \textit{The sum of } -16 \textit{ and } 16 \textit{ is } 0.$$
$$r = -23$$

To check that -23 is the solution, substitute -23 for r in the original equation.

Check: $\quad r + 16 = -7$ **Teaching Tip ❶**
$$-23 + 16 \stackrel{?}{=} -7 \quad \textbf{Teaching Tip ❷}$$
$$-7 = -7 \quad \checkmark$$

The solution is -23.

Recall from Lesson 2-7 how to solve a problem by writing and solving an equation.

Example 2

APPLICATION
Aviation

A traffic helicopter descended 160 meters to observe road conditions. It leveled off at 225 meters. What was its original altitude? **Teaching Tip ❸**

EXPLORE   Read the problem to find out what is asked. Then define a variable.

The problem asks for the helicopter's original altitude.
Let a = the helicopter's original altitude.
Then $a - 160$ = the helicopter's altitude after it descends 160 meters.

PLAN   Write an equation.

The problem states that the helicopter leveled at 225 meters. So, the equation is $a - 160 = 225$.

SOLVE   Solve the equation and answer the problem.

$$a - 160 = 225$$
$$a - 160 + 160 = 225 + 160 \qquad \textit{Add } 160 \textit{ to each side.}$$
$$a + 0 = 385 \qquad \textit{The sum of } -160 \textit{ and } 160 \textit{ is } 0.$$
$$a = 385$$

The original altitude was 385 meters.

EXAMINE   Check to see if the answer makes sense.

If the original altitude was 385 meters, then the new altitude is $385 - 160$ or 225 meters.

LESSON 3-1 SOLVING EQUATIONS BY USING ADDITION **95**

Teaching Tip ❶ Emphasize the importance of utilizing the answer check. For the example, show how $r = -9$ produces a false statement in the last line of the check.
$$r + 16 = -7$$
$$-9 + 16 = -7$$
$$7 \neq -7$$

Teaching Tip ❷ Explain the symbol $\stackrel{?}{=}$ to students. For example, $a \stackrel{?}{=} b$ means "Is a equal to b?"

Teaching Tip ❸ Emphasize the importance of using the four-step problem-solving plan to properly analyze each verbal problem.

Chalkboard Examples

For Example 1
Solve.

a. $p + (-12) = -5$ 7

b. $q + (-31) = -9$ 22

c. $y + (-8) = -13$ -5

For Example 2
An airplane descended 550 feet to reach a cruising altitude of 2700 feet. What was the plane's original altitude? 3250 feet

For Example 3
Solve.

a. $-5 - x = 12$ -17

b. $-9 - p = 30$ -39

c. $-15 - q = 45$ -60

Teaching Tip ④   Point out that the minus sign preceding the variable can be read as "the opposite of". For example, $-k = 21$ means the opposite of k is positive 21. Therefore, k is negative 21; that is $k = -21$.

Teaching Tip ⑤   Encourage students to do the algebraic manipulation in the problem first. Then calculators can be used.

Teaching Tip ⑥   Emphasize that to enter a negative number on a calculator, you must first press the absolute value of the number and then press the change-sign key. To enter a positive number, simply press the number.

Reteaching Masters Booklet, p. 16

Solving some equations requires additional steps.

Example 3 | Solve $-8 - y = 13$. **Teaching Tip ④**

$$-8 - y = 13$$
$$-8 + 8 - y = 13 + 8 \qquad \text{\textit{Add 8 to each side.}}$$
$$-y = 21 \qquad \text{\textit{The opposite of y is positive 21.}}$$
$$y = -21 \qquad \text{\textit{Therefore, y is negative 21.}}$$

Check: $-8 - y = 13$
$$-8 - (-21) \stackrel{?}{=} 13$$
$$-8 + 21 \stackrel{?}{=} 13$$
$$13 = 13 \;\checkmark$$

The solution is -21.

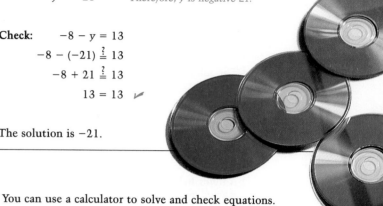

You can use a calculator to solve and check equations.

Example 4 | Use a calculator to solve $t + (-3.28) = -17.56$.

$$t + (-3.28) = -17.56$$
$$t + (-3.28) + 3.28 = -17.56 + 3.28$$
$$t = -17.56 + 3.28 \qquad \text{\textit{Use a calculator to simplify.}}$$

Teaching Tip ⑤

Enter: 17.56 [+/−] [+] 3.28 [=]   **Teaching Tip ⑥**

Display: −14.28

Check: $t + (-3.28) = -17.56$
$$-14.28 + (-3.28) \stackrel{?}{=} -17.56$$

Enter: 14.28 [+/−] [+] 3.28 [+/−] [=]

Display: −17.56 ✔

The solution is -14.28.

RETEACHING THE LESSON

Use the addition property of equality to solve each equation. Check each answer.

1. $m + (-5) = 8$ 13
2. $n + 6 = 15$ 9
3. $p + 14 = -6$ −20
4. $q + (-7) = -13$ −6
5. $12 + r = -14$ −26
6. $-9 + t = 15$ 24
7. $-11 + u = -19$ −8

CHECKING FOR UNDERSTANDING

Communicating Mathematics

Read and study the lesson to answer each question.

1. What will happen if Record Universe and Music Madhouse each lower their prices on CDs by $3? **They will still be selling CDs for the same price.**

2. Write three equivalent equations. **Answers will vary.**

3. What is the key on your calculator called? What does it do? **See margin.**

Guided Practice

State the number you would add to each side of the equation to solve it.

4. $y + 21 = -7$ **−21**

5. $13 + x = -16$ **−13**

6. $y - 5 = 11$ **5**

7. $z + (-9) = 34$ **9**

8. $-10 + k = 34$ **10**

9. $y - 13 = 45$ **13**

Solve and check each equation.

10. $m + 10 = 7$ **−3**

11. $a - 15 = -32$ **−17**

12. $5 + a = -14$ **−19**

13. $y + (-7) = -19$ **−12**

14. $9 = x + 13$ **−4**

15. $b + (-14) = 6$ **20**

EXERCISES

Practice

Solve and check each equation.

A

16. $k + 11 = -21$ **−32**

17. $0 = t + (-1.4)$ **1.4**

18. $-11 = a + 8$ **−19**

19. $-12 + z = -36$ **−24**

20. $14 + c = -5$ **−19**

21. $x - 13 = 45$ **58**

22. $p + 12 = -4$ **−16**

23. $r + (-8) = 7$ **15**

24. $-12 + b = 12$ **24**

25. $r + (-11) = -21$ **−10**

26. $h + (-13) = -5$ **8**

27. $-11 = k + (-5)$ **−6**

B

28. $-7 = -16 - k$ **−9**

29. $-27 = -6 - p$ **21**

30. $-14 - a = -21$ **7**

31. $-23 = -19 + n$ **−4**

32. $-4.1 = m + (-0.5)$ **−3.6**

33. $r - 6.5 = -9.3$ **−2.8**

34. $x + 4.2 = 1.5$ **−2.7**

35. $-1.43 + w = 0.89$ **2.32**

36-37. See margin for equations.
Write an equation and solve. Then check each solution.

36. A number increased by 5 is equal to 34. Find the number. **29**

37. A number decreased by 14 is −46. Find the number. **−32**

Additional Answer

3. The key is the change sign key. It changes the sign of the number on the display.

Closing the Lesson

Modeling Activity Have students use a scale and classroom objects to model the addition property of equality.

APPLYING THE LESSON

Homework Exercises

See assignment guide on page 97.

Additional Answers

36. $n + 5 = 34$
37. $n - 14 = -46$
38. $n - 13 = -5$
39. $n + (-45) = 77$
40. $23 - n = 42$
41. $n + 9 = -23$
51. Let d = number of dimes; $d + (d + 8) + 15 = 51$.

Write an equation and solve. Then check each solution.

38. Thirteen subtracted from a number is -5. Find the number. **8**

39. A number increased by -45 is 77. Find the number. **122**

40. Twenty-three minus a number is 42. Find the number. **-19**

41. The sum of two numbers is -23. One of the numbers is 9. What is the other number? **-32**

Critical Thinking

42. What value of x makes the statement $x + x = x$ true? **0**

Applications

Define a variable, write an equation, and solve each problem.

FYI · · ·

Spelunking is the hobby of exploring caves. The greatest recorded depth to which a team of spelunkers has descended is 5036 feet, recorded in October 1983.

43. Spelunking Four cave explorers descended to a depth of 112 meters below the cave entrance. They discovered a large cavern whose ceiling was 27 meters above them. At what depth below the cave entrance was the cavern ceiling? **85 meters**

44. Gardening The area of Mr. Hooper's triangular courtyard is 1520.2 square feet. The area occupied by a circular fountain in the middle of the courtyard is 132.7 square feet. A walkway covers 253.6 square feet. If the remaining area is used for gardens, how much area will Mr. Hooper have for his gardens? **1133.9 square feet**

45. Sales Jeff Simons sold 27 cars last month. This is 36 fewer cars than he sold during the same time period one year ago. What were his sales one year ago? **63 cars**

46. Weather The temperature at mid-afternoon was 12°C. By early evening, the temperature was -7°C. What was the temperature change? **-19°C**

Mixed Review

47. Evaluate $\dfrac{6ab^2}{x^3 + y^2}$ if $a = 6$, $b = 4$, $x = 0.2$, and $y = 1.3$. **(Lesson 1-2)**
339.223

48. Find the sum: $-21 + 52$. **(Lesson 2-2) 31**

49. Find the difference: $-67.1 - (-38.2)$. **(Lesson 2-5) -28.9**

50. Simplify $\dfrac{7a + 35}{-7}$. **(Lesson 2-7) $-a - 5$**

51. Define the variable, then write an equation. Juan has 15 pennies and 8 more nickels than dimes. He has 51 coins in all. How many dimes does he have? **(Lesson 2-8) See margin.**

Enrichment Masters Booklet, p. 16

EXTENDING THE LESSON

Math Power: Reasoning

Have students work out the following problem in groups. Would you rather have 100 pounds of dimes or a ton of pennies? Students will need to do some research to determine the weight of a dime and a penny to solve the problem.

Since there are 11 dimes per ounce and 9 pennies per ounce, 100 pounds of dimes equals $1760 while 2000 pounds of pennies equals $2880.

Solving Equations by Using Subtraction

Objective
3-2

After studying this lesson, you should be able to:
■ solve equations by using subtraction.

You are now familiar with the addition property of equality that states that when the same number is added to each side of an equation, an equivalent equation results. If the same number is subtracted from each side of an equation, the result is also an equivalent equation. Consider the following example.

Example 1

APPLICATION
Weightlifting

Nolan Young has bench pressed 190 pounds. He is working toward a goal of pressing 215 pounds. How many more pounds does he need to bench press to reach his goal?

Let x = the number of pounds still needed. Since an amount must be added to 190 pounds to reach the goal of 215 pounds, the equation is $190 + x = 215$.

$$190 + x = 215$$
$$190 - 190 + x = 215 - 190$$
$$x + 0 = 25$$
$$x = 25$$

Nolan needs to press 25 pounds more.

The property that is used to subtract the same number from each side of an equation is called the **subtraction property of equality**.

Subtraction Property of Equality	For any numbers a, b, and c, if $a = b$, then $a - c = b - c$.

Most equations can be solved in two ways. Recall that subtracting a number is the same as adding its inverse.

Example 2

Solve $x + 15 = -6$ in two ways.

Method 1:
$$x + 15 = -6$$ *Use the subtraction property of equality.*
$$x + 15 - 15 = -6 - 15$$ *Subtract 15 from each side.*
$$x = -21$$

(continued on the next page)

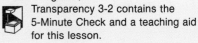

3-2 Lesson Notes

Lesson Resources
- Reteaching Master 3-2
- Practice Master 3-2
- Enrichment Master 3-2
- Technology Master, pp. 3, 18
- Video Algebra, 8
- Transparency 3-2 contains the 5-Minute Check and a teaching aid for this lesson.

INTRODUCING THE LESSON

5-Minute Check
(over Lesson 3-1)

Solve.
1. $m + 10 = 7$ -3
2. $18 + j = 54$ 36
3. $r + 15 = -6$ -21
4. The temperature was $-3°$F at 2:00 A.M. and $35°$F at noon. What was the total increase in temperature? $38°$F
5. The sum of two integers is -42. One integer is 12. Find the other integer. -54

Motivating the Lesson
Read the following to the class. "Jon cannot not go to the dance." Discuss the meaning of this statement. Develop the idea that a double negative makes a statement positive. Have students create their own statements that use a double negative.

TEACHING THE LESSON

ALTERNATE TEACHING STRATEGIES

Using Calculators
Windchill factor is an estimate of the cooling effect the wind has on a person in cold weather. In order to calculate the windchill, one needs to know the wind speed in mph (v) and the Fahrenheit temperature (t). The windchill formula is $0.0817(3.71\sqrt{v} + 5.81 - 0.25v)(t - 91.4) + 91.4$.

Have students use their calculators to determine the windchill when the actual temperature is $40°$F and the wind speed is 15 mph. $22°$F

Chalkboard Examples

For Example 1
Ryan needs to sell 120 candy bars for a fundraiser. He has already sold 85 bars. How many more candy bars must he sell in order to reach his goal?   35

For Example 2
Solve.

a. $r + 21 = -2$ -23

b. $p + 5 = -10$ -15

c. $t + 13 = -14$ -27

Teaching Tip ① The equation in Example 3 can be solved by adding -8 to each side, that is, by performing the inverse operation. However, most students can solve it more easily by first writing the equation in a simpler form, as shown.

Teaching Tip ② The equation in Example 4 can be solved directly by adding 7.5 to each side, as was done in Lesson 3-1. However, students should feel at ease with writing $y + (-7.5)$ as $y - 7.5$.

Reteaching Masters Booklet, p. 17

Check: $x + 15 = -6$

$-21 + 15 \stackrel{?}{=} -6$

$-6 = -6$ ✔

Method 2: $x + 15 = -6$ *Use the addition property of equality.*

$x + 15 + (-15) = -6 + (-15)$ *Add -15 to each side.*

$x = -21$ *The solutions are the same.*

The solution is -21.

Sometimes an equation can be solved more easily if it is first rewritten in a different form.

Example 3   Solve $b - (-8) = 23$.

This equation is equivalent to $b + 8 = 23$.   *Why?* **Teaching Tip ①**

$b + 8 = 23$

$b + 8 - 8 = 23 - 8$ *Subtract 8 from each side.*

$b = 15$

Check: $b - (-8) = 23$

$15 - (-8) \stackrel{?}{=} 23$

$15 + 8 \stackrel{?}{=} 23$

$23 = 23$ ✔

The solution is 15.

Example 4   Solve $y + (-7.5) = -12.2$.

This equation is equivalent to $y - 7.5 = -12.2$.   *Why?* **Teaching Tip ②**

$y - 7.5 = -12.2$

$y - 7.5 + 7.5 = -12.2 + 7.5$ *Add 7.5 to each side.*

$y = -4.7$

Check: $y + (-7.5) = -12.2$

$-4.7 + (-7.5) \stackrel{?}{=} -12.2$

$-12.2 = -12.2$ ✔

The solution is -4.7.

RETEACHING THE LESSON

State the number you subtract from each side of the equation to solve it. Then solve. Check each solution.

1. $a + 5 = 14$ $5; 9$
2. $b + 7 = 2$ $7; -5$
3. $c + (-3) = 9$ $-3; 12$
4. $d + (-7) = 4$ $-7; 11$
5. $e + 6 = -4$ $6; -10$
6. $f + (-8) = -5$ $-8; 3$
7. $g + (-12) = 12$ $-12; 24$

CHECKING FOR UNDERSTANDING

Communicating Mathematics

Read and study the lesson to answer each question.

1. Explain why it was not really necessary to state a subtraction property of equality. **Because subtraction is the inverse of addition.**

2. In Example 1, if Nolan's goal was 225 pounds, how many more pounds would he need to bench press to reach his goal? **35 lb**

Guided Practice

State the number you would subtract from each side of the equation to solve it.

3. $m + 16 = 14$ **16**

4. $k + 9 = -16$ **9**

5. $t + 5 = 8$ **5**

6. $y + 9 = -53$ **9**

7. $z + (-3) = -8$ **−3**

8. $x + (-4) = -37$ **−4**

Rename each expression by using its inverse operation.

9. $m + (-8)$ **$m - 8$**

10. $y - (-11)$ **$y + 11$**

11. $z + (-31)$ **$z - 31$**

12. $p - (-47)$ **$p + 47$**

Solve and check each equation.

13. $y + 16 = 7$ **−9**

14. $b + 15 = -32$ **−47**

15. $x + (-8) = -31$ **−23**

16. $d - (-27) = 13$ **−14**

EXERCISES

Practice

Solve and check each equation.

17. $18 + m = -57$ **−75**

18. $y + 3 = -15$ **−18**

19. $y + 2.3 = 1.5$ **−0.8**

20. $2.4 = m + 3.7$ **−1.3**

21. $h - 26 = -29$ **−3**

22. $-15 + d = 13$ **28**

23. $16 - y = 37$ **−21**

24. $41 = 32 - r$ **−9**

25. $k + (-13) = 21$ **34**

26. $z + (-17) = 0$ **17**

27. $m - (-13) = 37$ **24**

28. $-27 - b = -7$ **−20**

29. $t - (-16) = 9$ **−7**

30. $y + (-13) = -27$ **−14**

31. $-\frac{5}{8} + w = \frac{5}{8}$ **$\frac{5}{4}$; 1.25**

32. $x - \left(-\frac{5}{6}\right) = \frac{2}{3}$ **$-\frac{1}{6}$; −0.1$\overline{6}$**

LESSON 3-2 SOLVING EQUATIONS BY USING SUBTRACTION **101**

EVALUATING THE LESSON

Checking for Understanding

Exercises 1-16 are designed to help you assess understanding through reading, writing, and speaking. You should work through Exercises 1-2 with your students, and then monitor their work on Exercises 3-16.

Closing the Lesson

Writing Activity Read the following problem to the class. Have students write an equation using addition and another equation using subtraction to solve the problem.

Marla needs to prepare 126 letters for a mail survey. She has 82 letters ready to be mailed. How many more letters does she need to prepare? **44 letters**

APPLYING THE LESSON

Homework Exercises

Assignment Guide

Basic: 17-32, 39-41, 44-49
Average: 22-35, 39-49
Enriched: 27-49

Practice Masters Booklet, p. 18

| 3-2 | Practice Worksheet |

NAME _____ DATE _____

Solving Equations by Using Subtraction

Solve and check each equation.

1. $13 + c = -38$ **−51**

2. $z + 5 = -16$ **−21**

3. $z + 3.2 = 1.9$ **−1.3**

4. $4.2 = n + 7.3$ **−3.1**

5. $y - 7 = 8$ **15**

6. $-12 + x = 9$ **21**

7. $19 - k = 32$ **−13**

8. $51 = 42 - t$ **−9**

9. $-12 = 7 - h$ **19**

10. $m + (-15) = 31$ **46**

11. $e + (-14) = 0$ **14**

12. $j - (-17) = 36$ **19**

13. $-17 - d = -8$ **−9**

14. $-20 = 15 - s$ **35**

15. $f - (-11) = 8$ **−3**

16. $l + (-15) = -29$ **−14**

17. $-9 = -17 - n$ **−8**

18. $52 = 41 - u$ **−11**

19. $\frac{9}{10} = k + \frac{7}{10}$ **$\frac{1}{5}$**

20. $-\frac{7}{8} - x = -\frac{7}{12}$ **$-\frac{7}{24}$**

21. $-0.5 + f = 0.5$ **1**

22. $y - (-1.5) = 0.5$ **−1**

Teaching Tip For Exercises 33-38, you may want to have students compare the equations used to solve each problem. Develop the idea that due to inverse operations, there are generally two different methods of solving a particular word problem.

Additional Answers

33. $n + 9 = -23$
34. $82 + n = -34$
35. $n + (-56) = -82$
36. $n - 45 = -78$
37. $n - (-67) = -34$
38. $n - (-23) = 35$

45.

Enrichment Masters Booklet, p. 17

NAME _____ DATE _____

3-2 | **Enrichment Worksheet**

Identities

Any equation that is true for every value of the variable is called an **identity**. When you try to solve an identity, you end up with a statement that is always true. Here is an example.

$$8 - (5 - 6x) = 3(1 + 2x)$$
$$8 - 5 + 6x = 3 + 6x$$
$$3 + 6x = 3 + 6x$$

State whether each equation is an identity. If it is not, find its solution.

1. $2(2 - 3x) = 3(3 + x) + 4$
   $x = -1$

2. $5(m + 1) + 6 = 3(4 + m) + (2m - 1)$
   identity

3. $(5t + 9) - (3t - 13) = 2(11 + t)$
   identity

4. $14 - (6 - 3c) = 4c - c$
   no solution

5. $3y - 2(y + 19) = 9y - 3(9 - y)$
   $y = -1$

6. $3(3h - 1) = 4(h + 3)$
   $h = 3$

7. Start with the true statement $3x - 2 = 3x - 2$. Use it to create an identity of your own. **Answers will vary.**

8. Start with the false statement $1 = 2$. Use it to create an equation with no solution. **Answers will vary.**

Write an equation and solve. See margin for equations.

Teaching Tip

33. The sum of two integers is -23. One of the integers is 9. What is the other integer? -32

34. Eighty-two increased by some number is -34. Find the number. -116

35. A number increased by -56 is -82. Find the number. -26

36. What number decreased by 45 is -78? -33

37. What number decreased by -67 is -34? -101

38. The difference of a number and -23 is 35. Find the number. 12

Critical Thinking

39. Suppose the solution of an equation is a number n. Is it possible for $-n$ to also be a solution of this equation? If so, name an example. **Yes; typical answers are $n^2 = 9$ and $|n| = 15$.**

Applications **Define a variable, write an equation, and solve each problem.**

40. **Baseball** In a mid-season slump, the Yankees scored only 17 runs in 9 games. Their opponents scored 41 runs. By how many runs did their opponents outscore them? **24 runs**

41. **Skiing** Lisa Thorson skied down the slalom run in 139.8 seconds. This was 13.7 seconds slower than her best time. What was her best time? **126.1 seconds**

42. **Finance** Shares of stock in Olympia Motors were listed at $37\frac{3}{4}$ per share when the market opened. When the market closed, the shares had dropped $2\frac{1}{8}$ points. What was the new listing? **$35\frac{5}{8}$ points**

43. **Farming** A rancher lost 47 cattle because of the summer drought. His herd now numbers 396. How large was the herd before the drought? **443 cattle**

Mixed Review

44. Is the sentence $0.101 > 0.110$ *true* or *false*? **(Lesson 1-3)** false

45. Graph $\{0, 2, 6\}$ on a number line. **(Lesson 2-1)** See margin.

46. Find a number between $-\frac{8}{17}$ and $\frac{1}{9}$. **(Lesson 2-4)** Answers may vary; a typical answer is 0.

47. Simplify $3(-4) + 2(-7)$. **(Lesson 2-6)** -26

48. Solve $x + (-7) = 36$. **(Lesson 3-1)** 43

49. Solve $r - 21 = -37$. **(Lesson 3-1)** -16

EXTENDING THE LESSON

Math Power: Connections

Todd went to the store and bought three rolls of tape for $0.89 each, two packs of notebook paper for $1.39 each, and a notebook. If he spent $9.34, not including tax, how much did he spend on the notebook? **$3.89**

Solving Equations by Using Multiplication and Division

Objectives

After studying this lesson, you should be able to:

3-3A   ▪ solve equations by using multiplication, and

3-3B   ▪ solve equations by using division.

Application

Sheet metal is often used as a roofing material. The pitch of a roof is important for the sheet metal technician to know. The pitch is equal to the rise, or height of the roof, divided by the span, or width of the roof.

$$\text{pitch} = \frac{\text{rise}}{\text{span}}$$

Hector Reyes is a sheet metal technician for Reliable Roofing Company. He wants to find the pitch of a roof with a rise of 11 feet and a span of 22 feet.

Let p = the pitch of the roof. Then, p = rise ÷ span or 11 ÷ 22.

$$p = \frac{11}{22}$$

$$p = \frac{1}{2}$$

The pitch is $\frac{1}{2}$.

Suppose Hector knew that the pitch of a certain roof was $\frac{5}{12}$ and the span was 24 feet. How would he find the rise? Let r = the rise. Then solve the equation $\frac{5}{12} = \frac{r}{24}$.

To solve this equation, you would use the **multiplication property of equality**.

Multiplication Property of Equality	For any numbers a, b, and c, if $a = b$, then $ac = bc$.

Lesson Resources

- Reteaching Master 3-3
- Practice Master 3-3
- Enrichment Master 3-3
- Video Algebra, 9, 11
- Transparency 3-3 contains the 5-Minute Check and a teaching aid for this lesson.

INTRODUCING THE LESSON

⏱ 5-Minute Check
(over Lesson 3-2)

Solve.

1. $7 + n = -28$ -35
2. $t - 11 = 46$ 57
3. $x - (-24) = -37$ -61
4. $a + 9.35 = 2.73$ -6.62
5. $-24 - g = -74$ 50
6. $m + 9.382 = 17.941$ 8.559

Motivating the Lesson

Read the following to the class. "Mr. Leebow bought 15 computer disks and a carrying case for $28.50. If the carrying case cost $6.75, what was the cost of each disk?" Have students identify the procedure they would use to solve the problem. Determine the procedure identified that involves the least number of steps.

ALTERNATE TEACHING STRATEGIES

Using Cooperative Groups

Give groups of four a tape measure or meter stick to find the length and width of five classroom objects. Tell them to use this information to write a series of clues about each item measured. Have the groups switch clues and identify the objects described; then have them find the area of each item.

Using Discussion

Ask students to explain why in the division property of equality the divisor must be a nonzero number. Division by zero is not defined in the set of real numbers.

Teaching Tip ❶ Emphasize to students that each side is multiplied by 24 since $24 \times \frac{1}{24} = 1$.

Teaching Tip ❷ Reemphasize that the most practical approach to solving each equation is to isolate the variable on the left or right side of the equal sign.

Teaching Tip ❸ Be sure students develop the habit of checking the solution.

Teaching Tip ❹ Point out that mixed numbers are less difficult to work with if they are changed to improper fractions or decimals.

Teaching Tip ❺ You may wish to show Example 3 using the division property of equality.

$$24 = -2a$$
$$\frac{24}{-2} = \frac{-2a}{-2}$$
$$-12 = a$$

The solution is -12.

Chalkboard Examples

Solve.

For Example 1

a. $\frac{3}{4} = \frac{a}{12}$ 9

b. $\frac{2}{7} = \frac{b}{14}$ 4

c. $\frac{3}{5} = \frac{c}{30}$ 18

For Example 2

a. $(3\frac{1}{2})t = 5\frac{1}{4}$ $1\frac{1}{2}$

b. $(1\frac{3}{4})m = 4\frac{1}{2}$ $2\frac{4}{7}$

c. $(-5\frac{2}{5})y = -4\frac{1}{20}$ $\frac{3}{4}$

For Example 3

a. $-5t = 60$ -12

b. $15 = 6n$ $2\frac{1}{2}$

c. $-17\frac{1}{2} = 7x$ $-2\frac{1}{2}$

d. $-3v = -129$ 43

Example 1   Solve $\frac{5}{12} = \frac{r}{24}$.

$$\frac{5}{12} = \frac{r}{24}$$
$$24\left(\frac{5}{12}\right) = \left(\frac{r}{24}\right)24 \qquad \textit{Multiply each side by 24.} \text{ \textbf{Teaching Tip} ❶}$$
$$10 = r \text{ \textbf{Teaching Tip} ❷}$$

Check: $\frac{5}{12} = \frac{r}{24}$ **Teaching Tip** ❸

$$\frac{5}{12} \overset{?}{=} \frac{10}{24} \qquad \textit{Replace r with 10.}$$
$$\frac{5}{12} = \frac{5}{12} \quad \checkmark$$

The solution is 10, so the rise of the roof is 10 feet.

Example 2   Solve $\left(2\frac{1}{3}\right)m = 3\frac{1}{9}$.

$$\left(2\frac{1}{3}\right)m = 3\frac{1}{9}$$
$$\frac{7}{3}m = \frac{28}{9} \qquad \textit{Rewrite the mixed numbers as improper fractions.} \text{ \textbf{Teaching Tip} ❹}$$
$$\frac{3}{7}\left(\frac{7}{3}m\right) = \frac{3}{7}\left(\frac{28}{9}\right) \qquad \textit{Multiply each side by } \frac{3}{7}, \textit{ the reciprocal of } \frac{7}{3}.$$
$$m = \frac{4}{3} \qquad \textit{Check this result.}$$

The solution is $\frac{4}{3}$.

Example 3   Solve $24 = -2a$.

$$24 = -2a$$
$$-\frac{1}{2}(24) = -\frac{1}{2}(-2a) \qquad \textit{Multiply each side by } -\frac{1}{2}.$$
$$-12 = a \qquad \textit{Check this result.}$$

The solution is -12.

The equation $24 = -2a$ was solved by multiplying each side by $-\frac{1}{2}$. The same result could have been obtained by dividing each side by -2. This method uses the **division property of equality**. **Teaching Tip** ❺

Division Property of Equality	For any numbers *a*, *b*, and *c*, with $c \neq 0$, if $a = b$, then $\frac{a}{c} = \frac{b}{c}$.

The division property of equality is often easier to use than the multiplication property of equality.

Example 4

Solve $-6x = 11$.

$$-6x = 11$$
$$\frac{-6x}{-6} = \frac{11}{-6} \qquad \textit{Divide each side by } -6.$$
$$x = -\frac{11}{6}$$

Check:
$$-6x = 11$$
$$-6\left(-\frac{11}{6}\right) \overset{?}{=} 11$$
$$11 = 11 \quad ✔$$

The solution is $-\frac{11}{6}$.

Example 5

CONNECTION
Geometry

The area of the rectangle at the right is 28 cm². Find the length.

3 cm
ℓ

$$A = \ell w$$
$$28 = \ell(3)$$
$$\frac{28}{3} = \frac{3\ell}{3}$$
$$9.\overline{3} = \ell$$

The length of the rectangle is $9.\overline{3}$ cm.

CHECKING FOR UNDERSTANDING

Communicating Mathematics

Read and study the lesson to answer each question. 3-4. See students' work.

1. Write a formula for the pitch of a roof. Let p = the pitch, r = the rise, and s = the span. $p = \frac{r}{s}$

2. Can the division property of equality ever be used in place of the multiplication property of equality? When? Yes; whenever it is more convenient.

3. Write the multiplication property of equality in your own words.

4. Write the division property of equality in your own words.

LESSON 3-3 SOLVING EQUATIONS BY USING MULTIPLICATION AND DIVISION   105

RETEACHING THE LESSON

State the operation and the number you would apply to each side to solve each equation. Then solve. Check each solution.

1. $4n = -20$ $\times \frac{1}{4}$ or $\div 4$; -5

2. $\frac{x}{3} = 6$ $\times 3$ or $\div \frac{1}{3}$; 18

3. $\frac{m}{-6} = 12$ $\times (-6)$ or $\div \left(-\frac{1}{6}\right)$; -72

4. $12 = -3a$ $\times \left(-\frac{1}{3}\right)$ or $\div (-3)$; -4

5. $1.2x = 6$ $\times \left(\frac{1}{1.2}\right)$ or $\div 1.2$; 5

6. $\frac{c}{2.4} = 12$ $\times 2.4$ or $\div \frac{1}{2.4}$; 28.8

Chalkboard Examples

For Example 4
Solve.

a. $-12p = 48$ -4

b. $-17r = -51$ 3

c. $24x = -144$ -6

d. $25t = -225$ -9

For Example 5
The area of a rectangle is 195 cm². The length of the rectangle is 13 cm. What is the width of the rectangle?   15 cm

EVALUATING THE LESSON

Checking for Understanding

Exercises 1-16 are designed to help you assess understanding through reading, writing, and speaking. You should work through Exercises 1-4 with your students, and then monitor their work on Exercises 5-16.

Closing the Lesson

Speaking Activity   Have students identify specific instances when algebra is used in geometry. Ask them to create problems to illustrate their answer.

Reteaching Masters Booklet, p. 18

NAME _____ DATE _____
3-3 **Reteaching Worksheet**

Solving Equations by Using Multiplication and Division
You can solve equations in which a variable has a coefficient by using the multiplication and division properties of equality.

Multiplicative Property of Equality	For any numbers a, b, and c, with $c \neq 0$, if $a = b$, then $ac = bc$.
Division Property of Equality	For any numbers a, b, and c, with $c \neq 0$, if $a = b$, then $\frac{a}{c} = \frac{b}{c}$.

Example 1: Solve $\frac{1}{4}n = 16$.
$$\frac{1}{4}n = 16$$
$$4\left(\frac{1}{4}n\right) = 4(16)$$
$$n = 64$$

Check: $\frac{1}{4}n = 16$
$$\frac{1}{4}(64) \overset{?}{=} 16$$
$$16 = 16 ✔$$

Example 2: Solve $8n = 64$.
$$8n = 64$$
$$\frac{8n}{8} = \frac{64}{8}$$
$$n = 8$$

Check: $8n = 64$
$$8(8) \overset{?}{=} 64$$
$$64 = 64 ✔$$

Solve and check each equation.

1. $-3r = -24$ 8
2. $8s = -64$ -8
3. $-3t = 51$ -17
4. $\frac{1}{4}w = -16$ -64
5. $6x = \frac{3}{4}$ $\frac{1}{8}$
6. $1\frac{1}{4}y = -3\frac{3}{4}$ -3

Write an equation and solve.

7. Twelve times a number is 96. What is the number? $12n = 96$; 8
8. One half of a number is fifteen. What is the number? $\frac{1}{2}n = 15$; 30
9. Negative four times a number is -112. What is the number? $-4n = 112; -28$
10. Regina paid \$53.50 for 5 basketball tickets. What is the cost of each ticket? $5t = 53.50$; \$10.70

Complete.

11. If $4x = 100$, then $8x = $ ____. 200
12. If $6y = 36$, then $3y = $ ____. 18
13. If $-10a = 53$, then $-5a = $ ____. 26.5
14. If $2g + h = 12$, then $4g + 2h = $ ____. 24

Chapter 3   105

Homework Exercises

Assignment Guide

Basic: 17-48, 57-58, 60-63
Average: 26-54, 57-63
Enriched: 28-63
All: Mid-Chapter Review, 1-11

Additional Answers

44. $8n = 216$
45. $-12n = -156$
46. $-7n = 1.476$
47. $\frac{1}{4}n = -16.325$
48. $\frac{4}{3}n = 4.82$

Practice Masters Booklet, p. 19

Guided Practice

State the number by which you would multiply each side to solve each equation.

5. $\frac{b}{3} = -6$ **3**
6. $\frac{x}{5} = 10$ **5**
7. $\frac{3}{4}n = 30$ **$\frac{4}{3}$**
8. $-\frac{5}{9}x = 15$ **$-\frac{9}{5}$**
9. $-8n = 24$ **$-\frac{1}{8}$**
10. $1 = \frac{k}{9}$ **9**

State the number by which you would divide each side to solve each equation.

11. $4x = 24$ **4**
12. $35 = 4y$ **4**
13. $-36 = 4z$ **4**
14. $-5x = 14$ **-5**
15. $-8x = -9$ **-8**
16. $-6x = -36$ **-6**

EXERCISES

Practice

Solve and check each equation.   22. $-\frac{52}{3}$; $-17.\overline{3}$ 37. $\frac{250}{3}$; $83.\overline{3}$

A

17. $-4r = -28$ **7**
18. $-8t = 56$ **-7**
19. $5x = -45$ **-9**
20. $-5s = -85$ **17**
21. $9x = 40$ **$\frac{40}{9}$; $4.\overline{4}$**
22. $-3y = 52$
23. $3w = -11$ **$-\frac{11}{3}$; $-3.\overline{6}$**
24. $434 = -31y$ **-14**
25. $42.51x = 8$ **0.188**
26. $5c = 8$ **$\frac{8}{5}$**
27. $17b = -391$ **-23**
28. $0.49x = 6.277$ **12.810**
29. $\frac{k}{8} = 6$ **48**
30. $11 = \frac{x}{5}$ **55**
31. $-10 = \frac{b}{-7}$ **70**
32. $\frac{h}{11} = -25$ **-275**
33. $-65 = \frac{f}{29}$ **-1885**
34. $\frac{c}{-8} = -14$ **112**
35. $\frac{2}{5}t = -10$ **-25**
36. $\frac{4}{9}t = 72$ **162**
37. $-\frac{3}{5}y = -50$

B

38. $-\frac{11}{8}x = 42$
39. $-\frac{13}{5}y = -22$
40. $\frac{5}{2}x = -25$ **-10**

38. $-\frac{336}{11}$; $-30.\overline{54}$
41. $3x = 4\frac{2}{3}$ **$\frac{14}{9}$; $1.\overline{5}$**
42. $-5x = -3\frac{2}{3}$ **$\frac{11}{15}$; $0.7\overline{3}$**
43. $\left(-4\frac{1}{2}\right)x = 36$ **-8**

39. $\frac{110}{13}$; 8.462

Write an equation and solve. **See margin for equations.**

44. Eight times a number is 216. What is the number? **27**
45. Negative twelve times a number is -156. What is the number? **13**
46. Negative seven times a number is 1.476. What is the number? **-0.211**
47. One fourth of a number is -16.325. What is the number? **-65.3**
48. Four thirds of a number is 4.82. What is the number? **3.615**

CONNECTION

Geometry

Teaching Tip 6

Find the missing measure.   49. **15**   50. **7**   51. **$7\frac{1}{2}$**

49. $A = ?$ in²

3 in.
5 in.

50. $A = 49$ cm²

7 cm
? cm

51. $A = 32\frac{1}{2}$ ft²

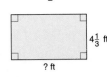
$4\frac{1}{3}$ ft
? ft

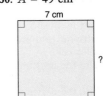

NAME _____ DATE _____

3-3   **Practice Worksheet**

Solving Equations by Using Multiplication and Division

Solve and check each equation.

1. $-6d = -42$ 7
2. $-7t = 49$ -7
3. $8x = -40$ -5
4. $-6s = -72$ 12
5. $32z = 896$ 28
6. $8k = 36$ $\frac{9}{2}$
7. $884 = -26y$ -34
8. $7c = -10$ $-\frac{10}{7}$
9. $18e = -216$ -12
10. $0.26f = 0.0312$ 0.12
11. $\frac{c}{4} = 16$ 64
12. $-18 = \frac{m}{6}$ -108
13. $31 = -\frac{1}{6}m$ -186
14. $6 = \frac{4}{-7}t$ $-\frac{21}{2}$
15. $-\frac{5}{8}w = -9$ $\frac{72}{5}$
16. $\frac{3}{5}x = 15$ 25
17. $-12 = \frac{2}{3}z$ -18
18. $\frac{c}{-7} = -13$ 91
19. $\frac{5}{9}k = -10$ -18
20. $-\frac{3}{5}l = -40$ $\frac{200}{3}$
21. $5n = 2\frac{3}{4}$ $\frac{11}{20}$
22. $-3x = 1\frac{1}{2}$ $-\frac{1}{2}$

C Complete.

52. If $3x = 15$, then $9x = \underline{}$. **45**

53. If $10y = 46$, then $5y = \underline{}$. **23**

54. If $2a = -10$, then $-6a = \underline{}$. **30**

55. If $12b = -1$, then $4b = \underline{}$. $-\frac{1}{3}; -0.\overline{3}$

56. If $7k - 5 = 4$, then $21k - 15 = \underline{}$. **12**

Critical Thinking

57. A number is multiplied by two, then squared, then divided by the multiplicative identity. The result is zero. What was the number? **0**

Applications   **Define a variable, write an equation, and solve each problem.**

58. **Sports**   Joyce Conners paid $47.50 for five football tickets. What was the cost per ticket? **$9.50**

59. **Sales**   A store sells a six-pack of ginger ale for $2.28. Each time Mika buys ginger ale, he sells the empty cans to a recycler at a rate of 1¢ per can. How many cans of ginger ale did Mika buy if the total amount he spent was $7.40? **20 cans**

Mixed Review

60. Simplify $4[1 + 4(5x + 2y)]$.   **(Lesson 1-6)** $4 + 80x + 32y$

61. Find the next three numbers in the pattern $37, 26, 15, \underline{}, \underline{}, \underline{}$.   **(Lesson 2-1)** $4, -7, -18$

Solve.   **(Lessons 3-1 and 3-2)**

62. $d + (-6) = -9$ **-3**   63. $x - (-33) = 14$ **-19**

MID-CHAPTER REVIEW

Solve and check each equation.

1. $4.4 = b + 6.3$ **-1.9**

2. $z + (-18) = 34$ **52**

3. $y - 7 = -32$ **-25**

4. $r - (-31) = 16$ **-15**

5. $-19 - s = 41$ **-60**

6. $6x = -42$ **-7**

7. $-13 = \frac{b}{-8}$ **104**

8. $\frac{3}{4}x = -12$ **-16**

9. $\left(5\frac{1}{2}\right)x = 33$ **6**

10. **Budgeting**   The total of Jon Young's gas bill and electric bill was $210.87. His electric bill was $95.25. How much was his gas bill? **$115.62**

11. **Plumbing**   Two meters of copper tubing weighs 0.25 kilograms. How much will 50 meters of the same tubing weigh? **6.25 kg**

EXTENDING THE LESSON

Math Power: Problem Solving

JoAnn bought 18 cupcakes for a party. She had writing put on seven of the cupcakes at an extra cost of 20 cents each. If the total cost of the cupcakes was $11.30, how much did each plain cupcake cost?   **55 cents**

Mid-Chapter Review

The Mid-Chapter Review provides students with a brief review of the concepts and skills in Lessons 3-1 through 3-3. Lesson numbers are given at the end of problems or instruction lines so students may review concepts not yet mastered.

Teaching Tip 6   Before students solve Exercises 49-51, you may wish to have them measure the sides of the classroom and find its area.

Enrichment Masters Booklet, p. 18

NAME _____   DATE _____

3-3   Enrichment Worksheet

Division by Zero?

You may remember being told, "Division by zero is not possible" or "division by zero is undefined" or "we never divide by zero." Have you wondered why this is so? Consider the two equations

$$\frac{5}{0} = n \qquad \frac{0}{0} = m$$

Because multiplication is the inverse of division, these lead to

$$0 \cdot n = 5 \qquad 0 \cdot m = 0$$

There is no number that will make the first equation true. Any number at all will satisfy the second equation.

For each expression, give the values that must be excluded from the replacement set in order to prevent division by zero.

1. $\frac{x+1}{x-1}$ $x = 1$

2. $\frac{2(x+1)}{2x-1}$ $x = \frac{1}{2}$

3. $\frac{(x+1)(x-1)}{(x+2)(x-2)}$ $x = -2$ or $x = 2$

4. $\frac{x+y+3}{(3x-1)(3y-1)}$ $x = \frac{1}{3}, y = \frac{1}{3}$

5. $\frac{x^2+y^2+z^2}{2xyz}$ $x = 0, y = 0, z = 0$

6. $\frac{(x+y)^2}{x-y}$ values where $x = y$

Many demonstrations or "proofs" that lead to impossible results include a step involving division by zero. Explain what is wrong with each "proof" below.

7. $0 \cdot 1 = 0$ and $0 \cdot 2 = 0$.
Therefore, $\frac{0}{0} = 1$ and $\frac{0}{0} = 2$.
Therefore, $1 = 2$.
The second step involves division by zero.

8. Assume that $a = b$.
Then $ab = a^2$.
Therefore, $ab - b^2 = a^2 - b^2$.
Next it is shown that $a^2 - b^2 = (a + b)(a - b)$.
$(a + b)(a - b) = (a + b)a - (a + b)b$
$= a^2 + ba - ab - b^2$
$= a^2 + 0 - b^2$
$= a^2 - b^2$
Therefore, $ab - b^2 = (a + b)(a - b)$.
Also, $b(a - b) = ba - b^2 = ab - b^2$.
Therefore, $b(a - b) = (a + b)(a - b)$.
Therefore, $b = a + b$.
Therefore, $b = 2b$.
Therefore, $1 = 2$.
In moving to the third from the last step, each side is divided by $(a - b)$. Because $a = b$, that is dividing by zero.

Lesson Resources

INTRODUCING THE LESSON

⏱ 5-Minute Check
(over Lesson 3-3)

Solve.

1. $\frac{k}{8} = -24$ -192
2. $39 = -3b$ -13
3. $\left(1\frac{1}{3}\right)p = 2\frac{1}{6}$ $1\frac{5}{8}$
4. $\left(4\frac{2}{3}\right)r = 1\frac{2}{9}$ $\frac{11}{42}$
5. $-15s = 165$ -11

Motivating the Lesson

Read the following problem to students. Have them identify various ways of solving the problem. Then have students use a method described to find the answer.

Each week for 7 weeks, a store reduced the price of a VCR by $8.99. The original price of the VCR was $329.00. Tom wants a VCR but only has saved $295.00. How long does he have to wait to purchase the VCR? **4 weeks**

TEACHING THE LESSON

Teaching Tip ① Review the four steps in the problem-solving plan: explore, plan, solve, and examine. Emphasize the importance of checking the answers to all problems.

3-4 Problem-Solving Strategy: Work Backwards

Objective
3-4

After studying this lesson, you should be able to:
■ solve problems by working backwards.

Teaching Tip ①

Problem

Four families went to a baseball game. A vendor selling bags of popcorn came by. The Wilson family bought half of the bags of popcorn plus one. The Martin family bought half of the remaining bags of popcorn plus one. The Perez family bought half of the remaining bags of popcorn plus one. And the Royster family bought half of the remaining bags of popcorn plus one, leaving the vendor with no bags of popcorn. If the Roysters bought 2 bags of popcorn, how many bags did the four families buy?

Sometimes you can work backwards to solve problems. Make a table to show what happened.

Family	Bags Left	+	Bags Bought	=	Original Number of Bags
Royster	0		1 + 1		2
Perez	2		1 + 3		6
Martin	6		1 + 7		14
Wilson	14		1 + 15		30

So the families bought 30 bags of popcorn.

Most problems can be solved using one of several strategies. You may find the following strategies helpful as you solve the problems in this lesson.

- work backwards
- make a table
- guess and check
- act it out

- solve a simpler (or a similar) problem
- look for a pattern
- make a diagram
- eliminate possibilities

CHECKING FOR UNDERSTANDING

Communicating Mathematics

Read and study the lesson to answer each question. See margin.

1. How could you use the guess-and-check strategy to solve the problem?

2. How can you check the solution to the problem?

ALTERNATE TEACHING STRATEGIES

Using Critical Thinking

Have students review the eight problem-solving strategies listed in the lesson. Ask students to identify the type of problem that lends itself to each problem-solving strategy. For example, it is often helpful to make a table or diagram when solving problems that involve a great deal of information.

Additional Answers

1. Pick a total number of bags. Then work through the problem from beginning to end. If there are bags left, pick another number.
2. Start at the beginning with 30 bags and work through the problem from beginning to end.

Solve by working backwards.

3. An ice sculpture is melting at a rate of half its weight every hour. After 8 hours, it weighs $\frac{5}{16}$ of a pound. How much did it weigh in the beginning? **80 pounds**

4. A number is decreased by 35, then multiplied by 6, then added to 87, then divided by 3. The result is 67. What is the number? **54**

5. Kristin spent one fifth of her money for gasoline. Then she spent half of what was left for a haircut. She bought lunch for $7. When she got home, she had $13 left. How much did Kristin have originally? **$50**

EXERCISES

Practice

Solve. Use any strategy. **7, 11. See margin.**

6. The digits below are in a special order. What order is it?

0, 2, 3, 6, 7, 1, 9, 4, 5, 8

reverse alphabetical order

7. Four dominoes are shown below. Arrange the dominoes into a domino donut so that all sides equal the same sum.

Example:

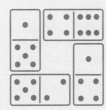

FYI · · ·

The most dominoes set up and toppled by one person is 281,581. It took about 13 minutes for all of them to fall.

8. A bacteria population triples in number each day. If there are 2,187,000 bacteria on the seventh day, how many bacteria were there on the first day? **3000 bacteria**

9. **Number Theory** A number that is *balanced* has exactly one digit that is the sum of all of the other digits. For example, 1236 is balanced because $1 + 2 + 3 = 6$. What is the greatest three-digit balanced number? **981**

10. Paper plates can be purchased in packages of 15 or 25. Joe Spanato bought 7 packages and got 125 plates. How many packages of 25 did he buy? **2 packages**

11. Explain the placement of numbers in the grid at the right. (*Hint:* Think of the words that the numbers represent.)

1	6	2
5	4	9
8	7	3

12. In Mary Ann's garden, all of the flowers are either pink, yellow, or white. Given any three of the flowers, at least one of them is pink. Given any three of the flowers, at least one of them is white. Can you say that given any three of the flowers, at least one of them must be yellow? Why? **Yes; answers may vary.**

LESSON 3-4 PROBLEM-SOLVING STRATEGY: WORK BACKWARDS 109

Chalkboard Example

For the Example

A school cafeteria sells more garden salads than soup but not as much as pizza. Fewer sandwiches are sold than soup. Order the lunch items from most popular to least popular.
pizza, garden salad, soup, sandwiches

EVALUATING THE LESSON

Checking for Understanding

Exercises 1-5 are designed to help you assess understanding through reading, writing, and speaking. You should work through Exercises 1-2 with your students, and then monitor their work on Exercises 3-5.

Closing the Lesson

Speaking Activity Have students describe in their own words three different strategies that can be used to solve a problem.

APPLYING THE LESSON

Homework Exercises

Assignment Guide
Basic: 1-15
Average: 1-15
Enriched: 1-15

Additional Answer

11. **Top row: 3-letter words**
    Middle row: 4-letter words
    Bottom row: 5-letter words
    All words are in alphabetical order.

RETEACHING THE LESSON

Two germs live in a tin can. At 4:00 they begin to double in number every minute. At 5:00 the can is completely full of germs.

1. When was the can
   a. half full? **4:59**
   b. $\frac{1}{4}$ full? **4:58**
   c. $\frac{1}{8}$ full? **4:57**

2. How many germs does the can hold? 2^{61}

Additional Answer

7. **Answers may vary; an example follows.**

All sums are 11.

Chapter 3, Quiz B, (Lessons 3-3 through 3-4), is available in the Evaluation Masters Booklet, p. 37.

Strategies

Look for a pattern.
Solve a simpler problem.
Act it out.
Guess and check.
Draw a diagram.
Make a chart.
Work backwards.

13. Patty Lee invited 17 people to her party. She gave each person a number from 2 to 18, and kept the number 1 for herself. After a while, Patty noticed that the sum of the numbers on each couple dancing was a perfect square. What was the number of Patty's partner? 15

14. What is the least number of colors needed to paint the regions in the picture? No two regions that share a border can be colored the same color. 4

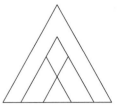

15. Mr. McCutcheon has been asked to direct the school play. After holding auditions, he finds four boys and five girls capable of being in the play. Unfortunately, Paul won't join the cast unless Kim is in it; Kim won't join if either Carlos or John is in it; neither Carlos nor John will join unless Marquita is in it; if either Marquita or Kim is in the cast, Lori will not be in it; unless Lori is in it, Renee won't be in it. Maria and Kevin agree to be in the play no matter what cast is chosen. If the cast has two boys and three girls, who should Mr. McCutcheon choose? Kevin, Kim, Maria, Marquita, and Paul

COOPERATIVE LEARNING ACTIVITY

Work in groups of three. Each person in the group must understand the solution and be able to explain it to any person in the class.

The names of eight colors—*blue, brown, green, maroon, orange, red, white,* and *yellow*—can be placed in sections of the wheel at the right. Use the following clues to fill each section.

1. No two words next to each other are the same length.

2. No two words with double letters are next to each other.

3. The word in Section 1 has no letters in common with the words in either section next to it.

4. The word in Section 3 has the same number of letters as the word in Section 7; the same is true for Sections 4 and 8.

5. The words *red, yellow,* and *blue* do not all appear in the same half of the wheel.

Practice Masters Booklet, p. 20

3-4 NAME _____ DATE _____
Practice Worksheet

Problem Solving: Work Backwards

Solve by working backwards.

1. A number is doubled. Then 5 is subtracted from the result and the new result is divided by 3. The final result is 25. What is the number? 40

2. A number is increased by 25. Then the result is multiplied by 2 and 27 is subtracted from the new result. The final result is 223. What is the number? 100

3. The price on a camera is now four-fifths of the price it was two weeks ago. Now the price is $250. What was the price two weeks ago? $312.50

4. An icicle is melting at the rate of three-fourths of its weight every hour. After 3 hours, it weighs five-eighths of a pound. How much did it weigh in the beginning? 40 lb

5. Each year a computer part is worth about two thirds of its value the previous year. Now this part is worth $60. What was its value two years ago? $135

6. A store reduced the price 50% on one of its bicycles. The bicycle still did not sell so it was reduced another 25%. The bicycle finally sold for $180, which was four-fifths of the last price. What was the original price of the bicycle? $600

EXTENDING THE LESSON

Math Power: Problem Solving

Marta walked 8 blocks north and 3 blocks east from her home to school. After school, she walked 2 blocks south and 1 block west to the library. From the library, she traveled 1 block south and 2 blocks east to visit a friend. How far does Marta have to walk to return home? **5 blocks south and 4 blocks west**

Cooperative Learning Activity

This activity provides students with an opportunity to *learn* things together, not just *do* things together. You may wish to refer to pages T6 - T8 and page 6C for the various elements of cooperative groups and specific goals and strategies for using them.

3-5 Solving Equations Using More Than One Operation

Objective
3-5

After studying this lesson, you should be able to:
- solve equations involving more than one operation.

Application

If you are playing in the outfield during a baseball game and a fly ball is hit in your direction, there are several steps that you must take in order to catch the ball. Some of these steps include the following.

1. Watch the direction that the ball is going in.
2. Begin running in that direction.
3. Estimate where the ball will land.
4. Gauge your running speed to be there in time.
5. Have your glove in the correct position to catch the ball.

Solving some types of equations requires more than one step. To solve an equation with more than one operation, undo the operations in reverse order. In other words, work backwards.

Example 1

APPLICATION
Finance

Bonnie Huston sold some stock for $42 per share. This was $10 per share more than twice what she paid for it. What was the price when she bought the stock?

EXPLORE   Read the problem and define a variable.

Let p = the price Bonnie paid.

PLAN   Write an equation.

$42	equals	$10	more than	twice what she paid

$$42 = 10 + 2p$$

SOLVE   Solve the equation and answer the problem.

Work backwards to solve the equation.

$$42 = 10 + 2p$$
$$42 - 10 = 10 - 10 + 2p$$ *Undo the addition first. Use the subtraction property of equality.*
$$32 = 2p$$
$$\frac{32}{2} = \frac{2p}{2}$$ *Then undo the multiplication. Use the division property of equality.*
$$16 = p$$

Bonnie originally paid $16 per share.

EXAMINE   Check to see if the answer makes sense.

Twice $16 is $32. Ten more than twice $16 is $42.

LESSON 3-5 SOLVING EQUATIONS USING MORE THAN ONE OPERATION **111**

ALTERNATE TEACHING STRATEGIES

Using Cooperative Groups

Give small groups of students a recent financial page from a newspaper. Each group member should select a stock and write a problem about it. Students then switch papers and solve each other's problem.

Using Connections

Have students list the sums of two consecutive odd integers from 1-20. Tell students to analyze the list to identify any relationships between the sums. Then have students describe their findings in a short paragraph.

3-5 Lesson Notes

Lesson Resources

- Reteaching Master 3-5
- Practice Master 3-5
- Enrichment Master 3-5
- Lab Manual, pp. 21-22
- Activity Master, p. 48
- Video Algebra, 10, 11, 17

 Transparency 3-5 contains the 5-Minute Check and a teaching aid for this lesson.

INTRODUCING THE LESSON

5-Minute Check
(over Lesson 3-3)

Solve.

1. $\frac{2}{3}a = 48$ **72**
2. $\frac{4x}{5} = -32$ **−40**
3. $(1\frac{3}{4})y = -6\frac{1}{8}$ **−3$\frac{1}{2}$**
4. $-12\frac{1}{2} = -1\frac{3}{4}m$ **7$\frac{1}{7}$**
5. $-65.8 = 8.27t$ **−7.96**
6. Suzanne bought 7 books for $55.23. If all the books cost the same amount, what was the price of 1 book? **$7.89**

Motivating the Lesson

Ask the class what day of the week it will be in 1000 days. Students should identify the equation $7w = 1000$, where w is the number of weeks. Take the remainder and count forward that many days. In this case, the remainder is 6, so count forward 6 days from today.

TEACHING THE LESSON

Chalkboard Example

For Example 1
Heather bought a winter coat for $6 less than half its original price. Heather paid $65 for the coat. What was the original price? **$142**

Teaching Tip ❶   You may wish to show an alternate method for solving Example 2.
$$\frac{x}{4} + 9 = 6$$
$$4\left(\frac{x}{4} + 9\right) = 4(6)$$
$$x + 36 = 24$$
$$x + 36 - 36 = 24 - 36$$
$$x = -12$$
The solution is -12.

Teaching Tip ❷   You may wish to have students explore other methods of problem solving, such as guess-and-check.

Example 2   Solve $\frac{x}{4} + 9 = 6$. **Teaching Tip ❶**

$$\frac{x}{4} + 9 = 6$$

$$\frac{x}{4} + 9 - 9 = 6 - 9 \qquad \textit{First, subtract 9 from each side. Why?}$$

$$\frac{x}{4} = -3$$

$$4\left(\frac{x}{4}\right) = 4(-3) \qquad \textit{Then, multiply each side by 4.}$$

$$x = -12$$

Check: $\frac{x}{4} + 9 = 6$

$$\frac{-12}{4} + 9 \stackrel{?}{=} 6$$

$$-3 + 9 \stackrel{?}{=} 6$$

$$6 = 6 \quad ✔$$

The solution is -12.

Example 3   Solve $\frac{d - 4}{3} = 5$.

$$\frac{d - 4}{3} = 5$$

$$3\left(\frac{d - 4}{3}\right) = 3(5) \qquad \textit{Multiply each side by 3. Why?}$$

$$d - 4 = 15$$

$$d - 4 + 4 = 15 + 4 \qquad \textit{Add 4 to each side.}$$

$$d = 19$$

Check: $\frac{d - 4}{3} = 5$

$$\frac{19 - 4}{3} \stackrel{?}{=} 5$$

$$\frac{15}{3} \stackrel{?}{=} 5$$

$$5 = 5 \quad ✔$$

The solution is 19.

Consecutive numbers are numbers in counting order such as 3, 4, 5. Beginning with an even integer and counting by two will result in *consecutive even integers*. For example, -6, -4, -2, 0, and 2 are consecutive even integers. Beginning with an odd integer and counting by two will result in *consecutive odd integers*. For example, -1, 1, 3, and 5 are consecutive odd integers.

The study of odd and even numbers as well as the study of numbers in general is called **number theory**.

Example 4

CONNECTION
Number Theory

Find three consecutive even integers whose sum is −12.

Let x = the least even integer.
Then $x + 2$ = the next greater even integer,
and $x + 4$ = the greatest of the three even integers.

$x + (x + 2) + (x + 4) = -12$ **Teaching Tip ②**
$$3x + 6 = -12$$
$$3x + 6 - 6 = -12 - 6$$
$$3x = -18$$
$$\frac{3x}{3} = \frac{-18}{3}$$
$$x = -6$$

$x + 2 = -6 + 2$ $x + 4 = -6 + 4$
$\quad x = -4$ $x = -2$

The integers are −6, −4, and −2.   *Does the answer make sense?*

CHECKING FOR UNDERSTANDING

Communicating Mathematics

Read and study the lesson to complete the following.

1. How do you undo addition? division? subtract, multiply

2. Write an example of an equation requiring more than one operation to solve. Answers will vary.

3. If n is an even integer, explain how to find the even integer just before it. Subtract 2; $n - 2$.

Guided Practice

Explain how to solve each equation. Then solve. See margin.

4. $3x - 7 = 2$ 3

5. $8 + 3x = 5$ −1

6. $\frac{a + 2}{5} = 10$ 48

7. $-\frac{4}{13}y - 7 = 6$ $-42\frac{1}{4}$; −42.25

CONNECTION
Number Theory

List three consecutive integers that satisfy each condition.

8. the least one is −2   −2, −1, 0

9. even, the greatest one is 10   6, 8, 10

10. odd, the least one is −7   −7, −5, −3

For each sentence, define a variable. Then write an equation.

11. The sum of two consecutive integers is 17. $x + (x + 1) = 17$

12. The sum of three consecutive even integers is 48.

13. The sum of two consecutive odd integers is −36. $x + (x + 2) = -36$

14. Seventeen decreased by twice a number is 5. $17 - 2x = 5$

12. $x + (x + 2) + (x + 4) = 48$

LESSON 3-5 SOLVING EQUATIONS USING MORE THAN ONE OPERATION   113

RETEACHING THE LESSON

Solve these equations by undoing the multiplication or division first. Be sure to multiply or divide each side completely (all terms) by the number.

1. $42 = 10 + 2p$ 16

2. $\frac{x}{4} + 9 = 6$ −12

3. $\frac{d - 4}{3} = 5$ 19

Additional Answers

4. Add 7 to each side. Then divide each side by 3.

5. Subtract 8. Then divide by 3.

6. Multiply by 5. Then subtract 2.

7. Add 7. Then multiply by $-\frac{13}{4}$.

EVALUATING THE LESSON

Checking for Understanding

Exercises 1-14 are designed to help you assess understanding through reading, writing, and speaking. You should work through Exercises 1-3 with your students, and then monitor their work on Exercises 4-14.

Error Analysis

Students may choose to undo multiplication before undoing addition. For example,

incorrect	correct
$2x + 6 = 20$	$2x + 6 = 20$
$\frac{2x}{2} + 6 = \frac{20}{2}$	$\frac{2x}{2} + \frac{6}{2} = \frac{20}{2}$
$x + 6 = 10$	$x + 3 = 10$
$x = 4$	$x = 7$

Emphasize that the whole side (all terms) must be divided. The distributive property shows why using the multiplication property of equality is equivalent to multiplying each term by the number.

Closing the Lesson

Speaking Activity Have students explain whether the sum of two consecutive even numbers can ever equal the sum of two consecutive odd numbers.

Reteaching Masters Booklet, p. 19

NAME _____ DATE _____

3-5   **Reteaching Worksheet**

Solving Equations Using More Than One Operation

When solving some equations you must perform more than one operation on both sides. First, determine what operations have been done to the variable. Then undo these operations in the reverse order.

Example 1: How would you solve $\frac{n}{3} - 7 = 28$?

$\frac{n}{3} - 7 = 28$ First, n was divided by 3;   To solve, first add 7 to each side.
         Then 7 was subtracted.   Then multiply each side by 3.

Procedure for Solving a Two-Step Equation	1. Undo any indicated additions or subtractions. 2. Undo any indicated multiplications or divisions involving the variable.

Example 2: $5x + 3 = 23$ *Addition of 3 is indicated.*   **Check:**
$5x + 3 - 3 = 23 - 3$ *Therefore, subtract 3 from each side.* $5x + 3 = 23$
$5x = 20$ *Multiplication by 5 is also indicated.* $5(4) + 3 \stackrel{?}{=} 23$
$\frac{5x}{5} = \frac{20}{5}$ *Therefore, divide each side by 5.* $20 + 3 \stackrel{?}{=} 23$
$x = 4$ $23 = 23$ ✔

Solve and check each equation.

1. $5z + 16 = 51$ 7

2. $14n - 8 = 34$ 3

3. $0.6x - 1.5 = 1.8$ 5.5

4. $\frac{4b + 8}{-2} = 10$ −7

5. $16 = \frac{d - 12}{14}$ 236

6. $8 + \frac{3n}{12} = 13$ 20

7. $\frac{7}{8}p - 4 = 10$ 16

8. $\frac{g}{-5} + 3 = -13$ 80

9. $-4 = \frac{7x - (-1)}{-8}$ $\frac{31}{7}$, or $4\frac{3}{7}$

Define a variable, write an equation, and solve each problem.

10. Find three consecutive integers whose sum is 96. $n + (n + 1) + (n + 2) = 96$; 31, 32, 33

11. Find two consecutive odd integers whose sum is 176. $n + (n + 2) = 176$; 87, 89

EXERCISES

Practice Solve.

15. $4t - 7 = 5$ **3**

16. $6 = 4n + 2$ **1**

17. $4 + 7x = 39$ **5**

18. $34 = 8 - 2t$ **−13**

19. $-3x - 7 = 18$ $-\frac{25}{3}$; **−8.3̄**

20. $0.2n + 3 = 8.6$ **28**

21. $\frac{3}{4}n - 3 = 9$ **16**

22. $7 = 3 - \frac{n}{3}$ **−12**

23. $7 = \frac{x}{2} + 5$ **4**

24. $\frac{y}{3} + 6 = -45$ **−153**

25. $\frac{c}{-4} - 8 = -42$ **136**

26. $\frac{d + 5}{3} = -9$ **−32**

27. $\frac{3 + n}{7} = -5$ **−38**

28. $5 = \frac{m - 5}{4}$ **25**

29. $16 = \frac{s - 8}{-7}$ **−104**

30. $\frac{4d + 5}{7} = 7$ **11**

31. $\frac{7n + (-1)}{8} = 8$ $\frac{65}{7}$; **9.286**

32. $\frac{-3n - (-4)}{-6} = -9$ $-\frac{50}{3}$; **−16.6̄**

CONNECTION
Number Theory

Define a variable, write an equation, and solve each problem. Some problems may have no solution.

33. Find three consecutive integers whose sum is 87. **28, 29, 30**

34. Find four consecutive integers whose sum is 130. **31, 32, 33, 34**

35. Find two consecutive even integers whose sum is 115. **no solution**

36. The lengths of the sides of a triangle are consecutive odd integers. The perimeter is 27 meters. What are the lengths of the sides? **7 m, 9 m, 11 m**

37. Find four consecutive even integers such that twice the least increased by the greatest is 96. **30, 32, 34, 36**

Critical Thinking

38. Write an expression for the sum of three consecutive odd integers where $2n - 1$ is the smallest integer. $(2n - 1) + (2n + 1) + (2n + 3)$

Applications

Define a variable, write an equation, and solve each problem.

39. Sales Karen has 6 more than twice as many newspaper customers as when she started selling newspapers. She now has 98 customers. How many did she have when she started? **46 customers**

40. Baseball One season, Reggie Walker scored 9 more than twice the number of runs he batted in. He scored 117 runs that season. How many runs did he bat in? **54 runs**

41. Statistics Namid has an average of 76 on four tests. What score does he have to get on the 100-point final test if it counts double and he wants to have an average of 80 or better? Is it possible for Namid to have an average of 85? **88; no**

42. Running In cross-country, a team's score is the sum of the place numbers of the first five finishers on the team. The captain of a team placed second in a meet. The next four finishers on the team placed in consecutive order. The team score was 40. In what places did the other members finish? **8th, 9th, 10th, 11th**

Computer
Teaching Tip ④

43. The BASIC program at the right finds three consecutive odd or even integers for a given sum. Not all numbers can be expressed as the sum of three consecutive odd or even integers. Line 40 checks for these numbers. Use the program to answer the following questions.

```
10 PRINT "ENTER THE SUM."
20 INPUT S
30 LET N = (S-6)/3
40 IF N = INT(N) THEN 70
50 PRINT "NO SOLUTION."
60 GOTO 80
70 PRINT "THE NUMBERS ARE ";
   N;",";" N+2;"," AND ";N+4
80 END
```

a. Find five sums of three consecutive odd integers. What do these sums have in common? **They are multiples of 3 and odd.**

b. Find five sums of three consecutive even integers. What do these sums have in common? **They are multiples of 3 and even.**

c. Find five numbers that are not the sum of three consecutive odd or even integers. What do these numbers have in common? **They are not divisible by three.**

Mixed Review

44. Name the property illustrated by the following statement. If $6 = 2a$ and $a = 3$, then $6 = 2 \cdot 3$. **(Lesson 1-4)** substitution (=)

45. Evaluate $m + 17$ if $m = -6$. **(Lesson 2-2) 11**

46. Which is greater, $\frac{0.06}{0.4}$ or $\frac{0.9}{5}$? **(Lesson 2-4)** $\frac{0.9}{5}$

Solve. **(Lessons 3-1, 3-3)**

47. $d - 27 = -63$ **−36**

48. $-7w = -49$ **7**

49. Half of the students in a class are boys. Four boys have blond hair. One-fourth of the boys have blond hair. How many students are in the class? **(Lesson 3-4) 32 students**

PUZZLE

Copy.

Arrange the digits 1 through 8 in the grid at the right so that no two consecutive integers occupy neighboring squares horizontally, vertically, or diagonally.

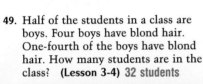

EXTENDING THE LESSON

Math Power: Connections

A rectangular garden is fenced on all four sides. If the garden is 6 feet longer than it is wide, what are its dimensions if 156 feet of fencing is needed to enclose it?
42 feet by 36 feet

Puzzle

Encourage students to use the guess-and-check strategy to complete the puzzle. There are several solutions. One possible solution is provided.

Teaching Tip ③ When scoring a cross-country meet, the first-place finisher is awarded 1 point, second place 2 points, third place 3 points, and so on. The team with the lowest score wins.

Teaching Tip ④ Be sure students try both positive and negative sums. You may need to remind them that zero is even and that negative integers are also odd or even. Show that line 30 is the solution of the equation $S = (n) + (n + 2) + (n + 4)$ which represents the sum of three odd or even integers.

Enrichment Masters Booklet, p. 19

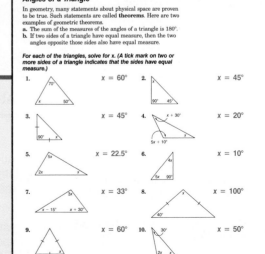

Solving Equations with the Variable on Both Sides

Lesson Resources

- Reteaching Master 3-6
- Practice Master 3-6
- Enrichment Master 3-6
- Lab Manual, pp. 33-34
- Video Algebra, 10, 11

 Transparency 3-6 contains the 5-Minute Check and a teaching aid for this lesson.

INTRODUCING THE LESSON

 5-Minute Check

(over Lesson 3-5)

Solve.

1. $\frac{y}{4} + 7 = -4$ -44

2. $-3 + \frac{2r}{3} = 13$ 24

3. $\frac{(t-5)}{4} = 19$ 81

4. A rectangle is 5 times as long as it is wide. The difference of its length and width is 9 inches. Find its perimeter.   **27 in.**

5. Find three consecutive integers whose sum is 54.   **17, 18, 19**

Motivating the Lesson

Divide the class into two groups. Think of a trait, such as people wearing red sneakers, and count the number of students in each half of the class that exhibit the trait. Tell the class that you are thinking of a trait and they need to identify it. Also tell them how many students in each half show the trait. Students should examine each half of the class and use the clue to guess the trait. They can check the validity of their guess by having students move between halves. Each time a student moves to a different half, you must again announce how many students in each half show the trait. Continue in this manner until the trait has been identified.

Objectives

3-6A
3-6B

After studying this lesson, you should be able to:
- solve equations with the variable on both sides, and
- solve equations containing grouping symbols.

Application

FYI · · ·

Dallas serves as the headquarters of more oil companies than any other U.S. city. More cars are produced in the Detroit area than anywhere else in the U.S.

Many equations contain variables on each side. To solve these types of equations, first use the addition or subtraction property of equality to write an equivalent equation that has all of the variables on one side. Then solve the equation.

In 1980, the population of Detroit, Michigan was 1,203,000. During the 1970s, the population decreased at an average rate of 31,100 people per year. In 1980, the population of Dallas, Texas was 905,000. During the 1970s, the population increased at an average rate of 6100 people per year. Suppose the population of each city continued to increase or decrease at these rates. In how many years would the populations of the two cities be the same?

After y years, the population of Detroit would be $1,203,000 - 31,100y$. After y years, the population of Dallas would be $905,000 + 6100y$. The populations would be the same when the two expressions are equal.

Use a calculator.

Teaching Tip ①

Add 31,100y to each side.

Subtract 905,000 from each side.

Divide each side by 37,200.

$$1,203,000 - 31,100y = 905,000 + 6100y$$
$$1,203,000 - 31,100y + 31,100y = 905,000 + 6100y + 31,100y$$
$$1,203,000 = 905,000 + 37,200y$$
$$1,203,000 - 905,000 = 905,000 - 905,000 + 37,200y$$
$$298,000 = 37,200y$$
$$\frac{298,000}{37,200} = \frac{37,200y}{37,200}$$
$$8 \approx y$$

At these rates, the populations would be the same after about 8 years.

Example 1 Solve $\frac{3}{5}x + 3 = \frac{1}{5}x - 7$.

$$\frac{3}{5}x + 3 = \frac{1}{5}x - 7$$
$$\frac{3}{5}x - \frac{1}{5}x + 3 = \frac{1}{5}x - \frac{1}{5}x - 7 \qquad \text{\textit{Subtract} } \tfrac{1}{5}x \text{ \textit{from each side.}}$$
$$\frac{2}{5}x + 3 = -7$$
$$\frac{2}{5}x + 3 - 3 = -7 - 3 \qquad \text{\textit{Subtract 3 from each side.}}$$

ALTERNATE TEACHING STRATEGIES

Using Applications

Acceleration is the rate at which an object's speed is changing with respect to time. The formula used to compute acceleration is $a = \frac{f - s}{t}$, where f is final speed, s is starting speed, and t is time needed to make the change.

Therefore, a bicycle that goes from 6 mph to 16 mph in 5 seconds is accelerating at a rate of 2 mph per second.

$$\frac{2}{5}x = -10$$

$$\frac{5}{2}\left(\frac{2}{5}x\right) = \frac{5}{2}(-10) \qquad \textit{Multiply each side by } \frac{5}{2}.$$

$$x = -25 \qquad \textit{Check this result.}$$

The solution is -25.

Many equations also contain grouping symbols. When solving equations of this type, first use the distributive property to remove the grouping symbols.

Example 2

CONNECTION
Geometry

The perimeter of a rectangle is 148 inches. Find its dimensions if the length is 17 inches greater than three times the width.

Let w = the width in inches.
Then $3w + 17$ = the length in inches.
Recall that the formula for perimeter can be expressed as $2w + 2\ell = P$.

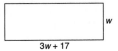

w

$3w + 17$

$$2w + 2(3w + 17) = 148 \qquad \textbf{Teaching Tip ②}$$
$$2w + 6w + 34 = 148 \qquad \textit{Use the distributive property.}$$
$$8w + 34 = 148 \qquad \textit{Simplify.}$$
$$8w + 34 - 34 = 148 - 34$$
$$8w = 114$$
$$\frac{8w}{8} = \frac{114}{8}$$
$$w = \frac{114}{8} \text{ or } 14\frac{1}{4} \qquad \textit{Check this result.}$$

$$3w + 17 = 3\left(\frac{114}{8}\right) + 17 \text{ or } 59\frac{3}{4}$$

The width is $14\frac{1}{4}$ inches and the length is $59\frac{3}{4}$ inches.

Some equations may have no solution. That is, there is no value of the variable that will result in a true equation.

Example 3

Solve $2x + 5 = 2x - 3$.

$$2x + 5 = 2x - 3$$
$$2x - 2x + 5 = 2x - 2x - 3$$
$$5 = -3$$

Teaching Tip ③

Since $5 = -3$ is a false statement, this equation has no solution.

LESSON 3-6 SOLVING EQUATIONS WITH THE VARIABLE ON BOTH SIDES 117

Some equations may have *every number* in their solution sets. An equation that is true for every value of the variable is called an **identity**.

Example 4

Solve $3(x + 1) - 5 = 3x - 2$.

$3(x + 1) - 5 = 3x - 2$
$3x + 3 - 5 = 3x - 2$
$3x - 2 = 3x - 2$ *Reflexive property of equality* **Teaching Tip** ⑤

Since the expressions on each side of the equation are the same, this equation is an identity. The statement $3(x + 1) - 5 = 3x - 2$ is true for all values of x.

CHECKING FOR UNDERSTANDING

Communicating Mathematics

Read and study the lesson to answer each question.

1. Do some research: In 1988, what were the populations of Detroit and Dallas? Were they nearly the same? **1,036,000; 987,000; yes**

2. What do you think are the reasons why the populations of Detroit and Dallas were or were not the same in 1988? **Rates of population change are not constant.**

3. What is the difference between an identity and an equation with no solution? **See margin.**

Guided Practice

Explain how to solve each equation. Do *not* solve. **See margin.**

4. $3x + 2 = 4x - 1$ 5. $8y - 10 = -3y + 2$

6. $4(3 + 5w) = -11$ 7. $-7(x - 3) = -4$

Solve and check each equation.

8. $6x + 7 = 8x - 13$ **10**   9. $3(h + 2) = 12$ **2**

10. $7 - 3x = x - 4(2 + x)$ **no solution**   11. $-3(x + 5) = 3(x - 1)$ **−2**

EXERCISES

Practice

CONNECTION
Geometry

Find the dimensions of each rectangle. The perimeter is given.   **Teaching Tip** ⑥

12. $P = 920$ m

w

$w + 60$

200 m × 260 m

13. $P = 370$ yd

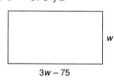

w

$3w - 75$

65 yd × 120 yd

14. $P = 220$ ft

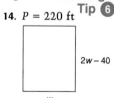

$2w - 40$

w

50 ft × 60 ft

Solve and check each equation.

15. $3 - 4x = 10x + 10$ $-\frac{1}{2}; -0.5$

16. $17 + 2n = 21 + 2n$ **no solution**

17. $14b - 6 = -2b + 8$ $\frac{7}{8}; 0.875$

18. $\frac{2}{3}n + 8 = \frac{1}{3}n - 2$ -30

19. $18 - 3.8x = 7.36 - 1.9x$ **5.6**

20. $\frac{3}{4}n + 16 = 2 - \frac{1}{8}n$ -16

21. $6(y + 2) - 4 = -10$ -3

22. $3x - 2(x + 3) = x$ **no solution**

23. $7 + 2(x + 1) = 2x + 9$ **identity**

24. $6 = 3 + 5(y - 2)$ $\frac{13}{5}; 2.6$

25. $4(x - 2) = 4x$ **no solution**

26. $5x - 7 = 5(x - 2) + 3$ **identity**

27. $5 - \frac{1}{2}(b - 6) = 4$ **8**

28. $5n + 4 = 7(n + 1) - 2n$ **no solution**

29. $4(2x - 1) = -10(x - 5)$ **3**

30. $-8(4 + 9x) = 7(-2 - 11x)$ $\frac{18}{5}; 3.6$

31. $4(2a - 8) = \frac{1}{7}(49a + 70)$ **42**

32. $2(x - 3) + 5 = 3(x - 1)$ **2**

33. $-3(2n - 5) = \frac{1}{2}(-12n + 30)$ **iden.**

34. $2[x + 3(x - 1)] = 18$ **3**

Define a variable, write an equation, and solve each problem.

35. Twice a number increased by 12 is 31 less than three times the number. Find the number. **43**

36. Twice the greater of two consecutive odd integers is 13 less than three times the lesser. Find the integers. **17, 19**

37. Three times the greatest of three consecutive even integers exceeds twice the least by 38. Find the integers. **26, 28, 30**

Critical Thinking

38. Is the inequality $x > -x$ sometimes true, never true, or always true? Is the inequality $x < -x$ sometimes true, never true, or always true?
Sometimes true; when $x > 0$, $x > -x$; when $x = 0$, $x = -x$, when $x < 0$, $x < -x$.

Applications

Define a variable, write an equation, and solve each problem.

39. **Sales** Last year, Marla Ames sold 7 sedans more than twice the number of vans Toshio Kanazawa sold. Marla sold 83 sedans. How many vans did Toshio sell? **38 vans**

40. **Running** One member of a cross-country team placed fourth in a meet. The next four finishers on the team placed in consecutive order, but farther behind. The team score was 70. In what places did the other members finish? **15th, 16th, 17th, and 18th**

LESSON 3-6   SOLVING EQUATIONS WITH THE VARIABLE ON BOTH SIDES   119

Additional Answers

6. Multiply $3 + 5w$ by 4.
Subtract 12 from each side.
Divide each side by 20.

7. Multiply $x - 3$ by -7.
Subtract 21 from each side.
Divide each side by -7.

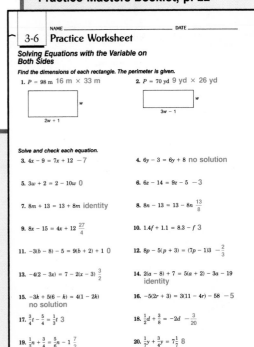

41. Soccer A soccer field is 75 yards shorter than 3 times its width. Its perimeter is 370 yards. Find its dimensions. **65 yd × 120 yd**

42. Travel Paloma Rey drove to work on Wednesday at 40 miles per hour and arrived one minute late. She left home at the same time on Thursday, drove 45 miles per hour, and arrived one minute early. How far does Ms. Rey drive to work? (*Hint:* Convert hours to minutes.) **12 miles**

Mixed Review

43. Write the following sentence as an equation. $a = m + n^2$

A is equal to the sum of m and the square of n. **(Lesson 1-7)**

44. Find the sum: $\frac{3}{4} + \left(-\frac{7}{12}\right)$. **(Lesson 2-5)** $\frac{1}{6}$

45. Find the product: $(-2.93)(-0.003)$. **(Lesson 2-6)** **0.00879**

Solve. **(Lessons 3-1 through 3-3 and 3-5)**

46. $y - 7.3 = 5.1$ **12.4**

47. $w - (-37) = 28$ **−9**

48. $\frac{9}{2}r = -30$ $-\frac{20}{3}; -6.\overline{6}$

49. $7n - 4 = 17$ **3**

120 CHAPTER 3 EQUATIONS

EXTENDING THE LESSON

Math Power: Connections

The lengths of the sides of a seven-sided figure are consecutive odd integers. The sum of the shortest and longest sides is 34 cm. Find the perimeter of the figure. **119 cm**

Puzzle

Encourage students to write an equation in which Mercuria's method is set "equal" to her mother's method since they both arrived at the same answer.

$$\frac{9}{5}C + 32 = 2C + 30$$
$$C = 10$$

Substitute this value into the expression on the left side of the equation to find that F = 50.

120 Chapter 3

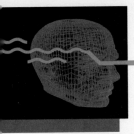

Technology
Solving Equations

The *Mathematics Exploration Toolkit* can help you practice the steps for solving equations. Since the computer performs all calculations and simplifying steps, you can concentrate on deciding which steps to choose. You will use the CALC commands listed below. You may enter the abbreviations in parentheses instead of typing the entire command.

Command	Purpose
ADD	Add the same expression to each side of the equation.
SUBTRACT (sub)	Subtract the same expression from each side of the equation.
MULTIPLY (mul)	Multiply each side of the equation by the same expression.
DIVIDE (div)	Divide each side of the equation by the same expression.
SIMPLIFY (simp) or [F5]	Simplify the equation.

Example 1 Solve $6x = 3x + 18$.

Enter	Result
6x=3x+18	$6x = 3x + 18$
sub 3x	$6x - 3x = 3x + 18 - 3x$
simp	$3x = 18$
div 3	$\frac{3x}{3} = \frac{18}{3}$
simp	$x = 6$

Example 2 Solve $2(x - 2) = 3x - (4x - 5)$.

Enter	Result
2(x−2)=3x−(4x−5)	$2(x - 2) = 3x - (4x - 5)$
simp	$2x - 4 = -x + 5$
add x	$2x - 4 + x = -x + 5 + x$
simp	$3x - 4 = 5$
add 4	$3x - 4 + 4 = 5 + 4$
simp	$3x = 9$
div 3	$\frac{3x}{3} = \frac{9}{3}$
simp	$x = 3$

EXERCISES

Use CALC to solve each equation. Record each step and solution.

1. $5x = x - 12$ −3
2. $7 - x + 5 = -3 + 4x$ 3
3. $3(1 - 6x) = 2x + 1$ $\frac{1}{10}$
4. $2 - (3x - 1) = 2(1 - 2x)$ −1
5. $x = 4 - 5(x - 1) + 6x$ no solution
6. $3(x - 2) - 1 = x - (7 - 2x)$
   all numbers

Objective This optional page shows how graphing software can be used to perform mathematical computations and to enhance and extend mathematical concepts.

Teaching Suggestions

Point out that there are many effective ways to solve an equation. The order of the steps may vary. Encourage them to use only the CALC commands shown. The command SOLVEFOR will solve equations automatically but will not provide the practice intended. You may wish to follow up this lesson by having students use SOLVEFOR and the command STEPS which reveals the steps used by the computer. Have students compare the steps they chose to those used by the computer.

3-7 More Equations

- Reteaching Master 3-7
- Practice Master 3-7
- Enrichment Master 3-7
- Activity Master, pp. 3, 18
- Video Algebra, 10

Transparency 3-7 contains the 5-Minute Check and a teaching aid for this lesson.

INTRODUCING THE LESSON

5-Minute Check

(over Lesson 3-6)

Solve.

1. $8m + 3 = 5m + 15$ 4
2. $\frac{2}{3}t - 7 = 5 - \frac{2}{3}t$ 9
3. $\frac{3}{4}x + \frac{1}{2} = \frac{1}{3}x - \frac{1}{4}$ $-\frac{9}{5}$
4. $4(x + 3) - 5 = 7(x - 1) + 9$
   $\frac{5}{3}$
5. $6(4 + y) - 3 = 4(y - 3) + 2y$ no solution

Motivating the Lesson

Display a supermarket flyer to the class. Have a student volunteer use the flyer to list 5 items to be purchased along with the cost of each item. Have students find the total of the purchases. Challenge other volunteers to identify 5 different items from the flyer that will total the same sum.

TEACHING THE LESSON

Chalkboard Example

For Example 1
Solve.

a. $\frac{3x}{4} - \frac{(x - 5)}{3} = \frac{x}{2}$ 20

b. $\frac{(t - 12)}{5} + \frac{3t}{4} = \frac{(t + 6)}{2}$ 12

c. $\left(\frac{3}{4}\right)n - \left(\frac{2}{3}\right)(n + 6) = \left(\frac{1}{2}\right)(n - 6) + 14$ -36

Objectives
3-7A
3-7B

After studying this lesson, you should be able to:
- solve equations containing fractions or decimals, and
- solve equations containing more than one variable.

Application

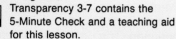

FYI · · ·

Studies show that boys spend most of their money on food (43%) while girls spend most of their money (41%) on clothes.

Kelly and Todd Washington went shopping with their parents for back-to-school clothes. At the end of the day, the Washingtons had bought the same number of skirts, shirts, slacks, and jeans. They spent $311.67. How many of each item did they buy?

	Price List	
Use the price list	Skirts	$29.99
at the right to write	Shirts	19.99
an equation.	Slacks	24.95
	Jeans	28.96

Let x = the number of each item that the Washingtons bought.

$$29.99x + 19.99x + 24.95x + 28.96x = 311.67$$

Since each decimal involves hundredths, multiply each side by 100 to clear the decimals.

$$100(29.99x + 19.99x + 24.95x + 28.96x) = 100(311.67)$$
$$100(29.99x) + 100(19.99x) + 100(24.95x) + 100(28.96x) = 100(311.67)$$
$$2999x + 1999x + 2495x + 2896x = 31,167$$
$$10,389x = 31,167$$
$$x = 3$$

So the Washingtons bought 3 skirts, 3 shirts, 3 pairs of slacks, and 3 pairs of jeans. *Check this result.*

You can also solve equations containing fractions by first using the multiplication property of equality to eliminate the fractions.

Example 1

Solve $\frac{2x}{5} + \frac{x}{4} = \frac{26}{5}$.

$$\frac{2x}{5} + \frac{x}{4} = \frac{26}{5}$$ *The least common denominator is 20.*

$$20\left(\frac{2x}{5} + \frac{x}{4}\right) = 20\left(\frac{26}{5}\right)$$ *Multiply each side of the equation by 20.*

$$20\left(\frac{2x}{5}\right) + 20\left(\frac{x}{4}\right) = 20\left(\frac{26}{5}\right)$$ *Use the distributive property.*

$$8x + 5x = 104$$ *The fractions are eliminated.*

$$13x = 104$$

$$x = 8$$

122   CHAPTER 3   EQUATIONS

ALTERNATE TEACHING STRATEGIES

Using Manipulatives

Use a sheet of $8\frac{1}{2} \times 11$ paper to make a series of prisms. (The prisms will only consist of sides, not tops or bottoms.) Measure and estimate the dimensions and calculate the approximate volume of each figure. Study the relationship between the number of sides of a figure and its volume. Make a general statement about this relationship.

Check: $\dfrac{2x}{5} + \dfrac{x}{4} = \dfrac{26}{5}$

$$\dfrac{2(8)}{5} + \dfrac{8}{4} \stackrel{?}{=} \dfrac{26}{5}$$

$$\dfrac{16}{5} + \dfrac{8}{4} \stackrel{?}{=} \dfrac{26}{5}$$

$$\dfrac{64}{20} + \dfrac{40}{20} \stackrel{?}{=} \dfrac{104}{20}$$

$$\dfrac{104}{20} = \dfrac{104}{20} \quad ✔$$

The solution is 8.

Some equations contain more than one variable. You will often be asked to solve such equations for a specific variable.

Example 2

Solve for x in $ax + b = dx + c$. **Teaching Tip** ❶

$$ax + b = dx + c$$
$$ax + b - b = dx + c - b$$
$$ax = dx + c - b$$
$$ax - dx = dx - dx + c - b$$
$$(a - d)x = c - b$$
$$\dfrac{(a - d)x}{a - d} = \dfrac{c - b}{a - d} \qquad \textit{Division by zero is undefined.}$$
$$\qquad\qquad\qquad\qquad \textit{Therefore } a - d \neq 0, \textit{ or } a \neq d.$$
$$x = \dfrac{c - b}{a - d}$$

CHECKING FOR UNDERSTANDING

Communicating Mathematics

Read and study the lesson to answer each question.

1. What happens when you multiply each side of the equation $\dfrac{a}{16} + \dfrac{1}{2} = \dfrac{1}{8}$ by 16? **The fractions are eliminated.**

2. Can the same result be achieved by multiplying each side by 32? **yes**

3. How would you change the equation in the Application on p. 122 if the number of shirts was 2 times the number of jeans? **See margin.**

Guided Practice

State the number by which you can multiply each side to eliminate the fractions or decimals. Then rewrite each equation. **See margin.**

4. $1.2s + 8.1 = 3.5 - 2s$ **10**

5. $8.17y = 4.2 - 3.7y$ **100**

6. $\dfrac{3}{4}x - 7 = 8 + \dfrac{2}{3}x$ **12**

7. $\dfrac{2}{5}x = 7 - \dfrac{3}{4}x$ **20**

Solve and check each equation.

8. $0.2x + 1.7 = 3.9$ **11**

9. $5.3 - 0.3x = -9.4$ **49**

10. $\dfrac{4 - x}{5} = \dfrac{1}{5}x$ **2**

11. $\dfrac{5}{8}x + \dfrac{3}{5} = x$ **$\dfrac{8}{5}$; 1.6**

RETEACHING THE LESSON

For each equation state a number by which you can multiply each side to eliminate the fractions or decimals. Then solve. Check each solution.

1. $\dfrac{2x}{5} + \dfrac{x}{10} = 10$ $\quad$ **10; 20**

2. $\dfrac{m}{2} - \dfrac{m}{3} = 4$ $\quad$ **6; 24**

3. $0.2x - 0.04 = 1.16$ $\quad$ **100; 6**

Additional Answers

3. Change 19.99x to 19.99(2x) or 39.98x in the equation.

4. 10; $12s + 81 = 35 - 20s$

5. 100; $817y = 420 - 370y$

6. 12; $9x - 84 = 96 + 8x$

7. 20; $8x = 140 - 15x$

Closing the Lesson

Modeling Activity Have students write each letter from *a* to *d* on an index card. Tell them to write the numbers 1-5, two +, and an = on other index cards. Have a volunteer arrange these cards to make an equation in the form $ax + b = cx + d$. Then have the class rearrange the cards to solve for the particular variable asked for by the volunteer who made the equation.

APPLYING THE LESSON

Homework Exercises

Assignment Guide

Basic: 12-31, 38-39, 42-46
Average: 15-34, 38-46
Enriched: 18-46

Chapter 3, Quiz D, (Lesson 3-7), is available in the Evaluation Masters Booklet, p. 38.

Practice Masters Booklet, p. 23

NAME _____ DATE _____

3-7 **Practice Worksheet**

More Equations

Solve and check each equation.

1. $\frac{x+3}{2} = 15$ 27

2. $\frac{2r-3}{3} = \frac{3}{5}$ $\frac{12}{5}$

3. $1.2x + 4.3 = 2.1 - x$ -1

4. $\frac{3}{5}x - 2 = 6 + \frac{1}{4}x$ $\frac{160}{7}$

5. $\frac{7}{8} - \frac{1}{3}n = \frac{1}{2}n - \frac{3}{4}$ $\frac{39}{20}$

6. $0.4r - 1.2 = 0.3r + 0.6$ 18

7. $4.2z = -4(0.6z - 1.2)$ $\frac{8}{11}$ or $0.\overline{72}$

8. $4.4s + 6.2 = 8.8s - 1.8$ $\frac{20}{11}$ or $1.8\overline{1}$

9. $\frac{5}{2}t - t = 3 + \frac{3}{2}t$ no solution

10. $\frac{m}{3} - \frac{1}{2} = \frac{m}{2} - \frac{1}{3}$ -1

Solve for x.

11. $7x = t$ $x = \frac{t}{7}$

12. $\frac{x-c}{2} = d$ $x = c + 2d$

13. $ax - c = b$ $x = \frac{b+c}{a}$

14. $fx + 3y = 2z$ $x = \frac{2z-3y}{f}$

15. $e = rx$ $x = \frac{e}{r}$

16. $2p = kx - q$ $x = \frac{2p+q}{k}$

Solve for y.

17. $ry + s = tx - m$ $y = \frac{tx - m - s}{r}$

18. $x + 3y = 1$ $y = \frac{1-x}{3}$

19. $x - 2y = 1$ $y = \frac{x-1}{2}$

20. $\frac{2}{3}y + k = j$ $y = \frac{3j - 3k}{2}$

EXERCISES

Practice **Solve and check each equation.**

12. $\frac{y+5}{3} = 7$ 16

13. $\frac{3n-2}{5} = \frac{7}{10}$ $\frac{11}{6}$; $1.8\overline{3}$

14. $1.9s + 6 = 3.1 - s$ -1

15. $28 - 2.2y = 11.6y + 262.6$ -17

16. $\frac{3}{4}x - 4 = 7 + \frac{1}{2}x$ 44

17. $\frac{3}{8} - \frac{1}{4}x = \frac{1}{2}x - \frac{3}{4}$ $\frac{3}{2}$; 1.5

B

18. $5.4y + 8.2 = 9.8y - 2.8$ 2.5

19. $1.03x - 4 = -2.15x + 8.72$ 4

20. $3y - \frac{4}{5} = \frac{1}{3}y$ $\frac{3}{10}$; 0.3

21. $\frac{7+3t}{4} = -\frac{1t}{8}$ -2

22. $\frac{3}{2}y - y = 4 + \frac{1}{2}y$ no solution

23. $\frac{x}{2} - \frac{1}{3} = \frac{x}{3} - \frac{1}{2}$ -1

Solve for x.

24. $5x = y$ $\frac{y}{5}$

25. $\frac{x+a}{3} = c$ $3c - a$

26. $ax + b = cx$ $\frac{-b}{a-c}$

27. $ex - 2y = 3z$ $\frac{3z+2y}{e}$

Solve for y.

28. $ay - b = c$ $\frac{c+b}{a}$

29. $ay + z = am - ny$ $\frac{am-z}{a+n}$

30. $a(y+1) = b$ $\frac{b}{a} - 1$

31. $\frac{3}{5}y + a = b$ $\frac{5}{3}(b-a)$

Define a variable, write an equation, and solve each problem.

32. Five eighths of a number is three more than half the number. Find the number. 24

33. One half of a number increased by 16 is four less than two thirds of the number. Find the number. 120

34. Five more than two thirds of a number is the same as three less than one half of the number. Find the number. -48

35. One fifth of a number plus five times that number is equal to seven times the number less 18. Find the number. 10

C

36. The sum of two numbers is 25. Twelve less than four times one of the numbers is 16 more than twice the other number. Find both numbers. 12 and 13

37. The difference of two numbers is 12. Two fifths of one of the numbers is six more than one third of the other number. Find both numbers. 18 and 30 or 150 and 162

Critical Thinking

38. Explain how to solve the following equation. See margin.

$$\frac{3}{x+1} = \frac{1}{x+1} - 7$$

Applications

Define a variable, write an equation, and solve each problem.

39. **Construction** A rectangular playground is 60 meters longer than it is wide. It is enclosed by 920 meters of fencing. Find its length. 260 m

40. **Sales** Luisa stopped by the grocery store to buy 2 cans of peas at $.69 each, 1 carton of orange juice at $2.49, and some tomato sauce at $.95 each. The grocery was having "Double Coupon Day," and Luisa had a 25¢ coupon for the orange juice. If Luisa spent $6.22, how many cans of tomato sauce did she buy? 3 cans

Additional Answer

38. Multiply each term by $x + 1$. Then use the distributive property to multiply 7 by $x + 1$ and solve the equation. $x = -\frac{9}{7}$

41. The program at the right solves equations of the form $ax + b = cx + d$.

```
10 PRINT "ENTER A,B,C,D:"
20 INPUT A,B,C,D
30 PRINT A;"X + ";B;" = ";
40 PRINT C;"X + ";D
50 IF A-C <> 0 THEN 110
60 IF D-B <> 0 THEN 90
70 PRINT "THIS IS AN
   IDENTITY."
80 GOTO 120
90 PRINT "NO SOLUTION."
100 GOTO 120
110 PRINT "X = ";
    (D-B)/(A-C)
120 END
```

Write each equation below in the form ax + b = cx + d. Then run the program to find the solution.

a. $2(2x + 3) = 4x + 6$ **identity**

b. $5x - 7 = x + 3$ $\frac{5}{2}$; **2.5**

c. $6 - 3x = 3x - 6$ **2**

d. $6.8 + 5.4x = 4.6x + 2.8$ **−5**

e. $5x - 8 - 3x = 2(x - 3)$ **no solution**

Teaching Tip ❷ Discuss lines 50 and 60. Point out that the symbol <> means "is not equal to." Note that if A − C equals zero but D − B does not equal zero, there are no solutions. If both A − C and D − B equal zero, all numbers are solutions.

Mixed Review

42. Replace the ___?___ with <, >, or = to make the sentence true.

$(-6.01)(-4.122)$ ___?___ $\frac{9.624}{2.2}$ **(Lesson 2-3)** >

43. Simplify $\frac{\frac{3}{11}}{-6}$. **(Lesson 2-7)** $-\frac{1}{22}$

44. Write a problem based on the following information.
Let n = number of nickels that Yvette has.
$n - 17$ = number of pennies that Yvette has.
$n + (n - 17) = 63$ **(Lesson 2-8) See students' work.**

Solve. (Lessons 3-5 and 3-6)

45. $2 - 7s = -19$ **3**

46. $3x - 5 = 7x + 7$ **−3**

HISTORY CONNECTION

DIOPHANTUS

Diophantus of Alexandria was one of the greatest mathematicians of the Greek civilization. It is believed that he lived in the third century, but no one knows for sure. Diophantus is best known for writing a book called *Arithmetica*, in which some algebraic symbols were used for what may have been the first time.

Little is known of Diophantus' life except for a problem printed in a work called the *Greek Anthology*. Although the problem was not written by Diophantus, it is believed to accurately describe his life.

Diophantus passed one sixth of his life in childhood, one twelfth in youth, and one seventh more as a bachelor. Five years after his marriage, there was born a son who died four years before his father, at half his father's (final) age. How old was Diophantus when he died? **84 years**

EXTENDING THE LESSON

Math Power:
Problem Solving

Experiment with a sheet of $8\frac{1}{2} \times 11$ paper to make a figure with the greatest number of sides possible. Then use another sheet of paper to create a figure with the least number of sides possible.

History Connection

The History Connection features introduce students to persons or cultures who were involved in the development of mathematics. You may want students to further research Diophantus and his use of quadratic equations.

Enrichment Masters Booklet, p. 21

NAME _____ DATE _____

3-7 Enrichment Worksheet

Diophantine Equations

The first great algebraist, Diophantus of Alexandria (about 300 A.D.), devoted much of his work to the solving of indeterminate equations. An indeterminate equation has more than one variable and an unlimited number of solutions. An example is $x + 2y = 4$.

When the coefficients of an indeterminate equation are integers and you are asked to find solutions that must be integers, the equation is called *diophantine*. Such equations can be quite difficult to solve, often involving trial and error—and some luck!

Solve each diophantine equation by finding at least one pair of positive integers that makes the equation true. Some hints are given to help you.

1. $2x + 5y = 32$
  a. First solve the equation for x. $x = 16 - \frac{5y}{2}$
  b. Why must y be an even number? If y is odd, then x won't be an integer.
  c. Find at least one solution. Any of these: (11, 2), (6, 4), (1, 6)

2. $5x + 2y = 42$
  a. First solve the equation for x. $x = \frac{42 - 2y}{5}$
  b. Rewrite your answer in the form $x = 8 +$ some expression.
     $x = 8 + \frac{2 - 2y}{5}$
  c. Why must $(2 - 2y)$ be a multiple of 5? Otherwise, x won't be an integer.
  d. Find at least one solution. Any of these:
     (8, 1), (6, 6), (4, 11), (2, 16)

3. $2x + 7y = 29$
  (11, 1) or (4, 3)

4. $7x + 5y = 118$
  Any of these: (14, 4), (9, 11), (4, 18)

5. $8x - 13y = 100$
  (19, 4), (32, 12) or any pair when $y = 4n$ and n is a positive odd number

6. $3x + 4y = 22$
  (6, 1) or (2, 4)

7. $5x - 14y = 11$
  (5, 1), (19, 6) or any pair when $y = 5m - 4$ and m is a positive number

8. $7x + 3y = 40$
  (4, 4) or (1, 11)

SUMMARY AND REVIEW

VOCABULARY

Upon completing this chapter, you should be familiar with the following terms:

consecutive numbers	112	118	identity
equivalent equation	94	112	number theory

SKILLS AND CONCEPTS

OBJECTIVES AND EXAMPLES	REVIEW EXERCISES

Upon completing this chapter, you should be able to:

Use these exercises to review and prepare for the chapter test.

■ solve equations by using addition **(Lesson 3-1)**

$$x - 3 = 5$$
$$x - 3 + 3 = 5 + 3$$
$$x = 8$$

$$4 = 8 - y$$
$$4 - 8 = 8 - 8 - y$$
$$-4 = -y$$
$$4 = y$$

Solve and check each equation. 6. −12

1. $x - 16 = 37$ **53**   2. $k + 13 = 5$ **−8**
3. $15 - y = 9$ **6**   4. $-13 = 6 - k$ **19**
5. $19 = -8 + d$ **27**   6. $m + (-5) = -17$
7. Thirteen less than some number is 64. What is the number? **77**
8. The sum of a number and −35 is 98. Find the number. **133**

■ solve equations by using subtraction **(Lesson 3-2)**

$$m + 16 = 8$$
$$m + 16 - 16 = 8 - 16$$
$$m = -8$$

$$q - (-2) = -10$$
$$q + 2 = -10$$
$$q + 2 - 2 = -10 - 2$$
$$q = -12$$

Solve and check each equation.

9. $z + 15 = -9$ **−24**   10. $19 = y + 7$ **12**
11. $p + (-7) = 31$ **38**   12. $r - (-5) = -8$ **−13**
13. $y + (-9) = -35$ **−26** 14. $m - (-4) = 21$ **17**
15. Some number added to −16 is equal to 39. What is the number? **55**
16. A number decreased by −11 is −176. Find the number. **−187**

OBJECTIVES AND EXAMPLES	REVIEW EXERCISES

solve equations by using multiplication or division (Lesson 3-3)

$$-14x = 42$$
$$\frac{-14x}{-14} = \frac{42}{-14}$$
$$x = -3$$

$$\frac{m}{6} = -8$$
$$6\left(\frac{m}{6}\right) = (-8)6$$
$$m = -48$$

Solve and check each equation.

17. $-7r = -56$ 8 **18.** $23y = 1035$ 45

19. $534 = -89r$ −6 **20.** $\frac{x}{5} = 7$ 35

21. $\frac{3}{4}x = -12$ −16 **22.** $1\frac{2}{3}n = 1\frac{1}{2}$ $\frac{9}{10}$; 0.9

23. Six times a number is −96. Find the number. −16

24. Seven eighths of a number is 14. What is the number? 16

---

solve equations involving more than one operation (Lesson 3-5)

$$2x + 16 = 18$$
$$2x + 16 - 16 = 18 - 16$$
$$\frac{2x}{2} = \frac{2}{2}$$
$$x = 1$$

Solve and check each equation.

25. $3x - 8 = 22$ 10 **26.** $-4y + 2 = 32$ $-\frac{15}{2}$; −7.5

27. $0.5n + 3 = -6$ −18 **28.** $-6 = 3.1t + 6.4$ −4

29. $\frac{x}{-3} + 2 = -21$ 69 **30.** $\frac{r-8}{-6} = 7$ −34

---

solve equations with the variable on both sides and equations containing grouping symbols (Lesson 3-6)

$$2(c + 1) = 8c - 22$$
$$2c + 2 = 8c - 22$$
$$2c - 8c + 2 = 8c - 8c - 22$$
$$-6c + 2 = -22$$
$$-6c + 2 - 2 = -22 - 2$$
$$\frac{-6c}{-6} = \frac{-24}{-6}$$
$$c = 4$$

Solve and check each equation.

31. $5a - 5 = 7a - 19$ 7

32. $-3(x + 2) = -18$ 4

33. $4(2y - 1) = -10(y - 5)$ 3

34. $11.2n + 6 = 5.2n$ −1

35. Twice a number increased by 12 is 31 less than three times the number. Find the number. 43

---

solve equations containing fractions or decimals (Lesson 3-7)

$$\frac{2}{5}y + \frac{y}{2} = 9$$
$$10\left(\frac{2}{5}y + \frac{y}{2}\right) = 10(9)$$
$$4y + 5y = 90$$
$$\frac{9y}{9} = \frac{90}{9}$$
$$y = 10$$

Solve and check each equation.

36. $\frac{2}{3}x + 5 = \frac{1}{2}x + 4$ −6

37. $2.9m + 1.7 = 3.5 + 2.3m$ 3

38. $\frac{3t + 1}{4} = \frac{3}{4}t - 5$ no solution

39. $2.85y - 7 = 12.85y - 2$ −0.5

Alternate Review Strategy

To provide a brief in-class review, you may wish to read the following questions to the class and require a verbal response.

Solve.

1. $r - 17 = 23$ 40
2. $m + 28 = 5$ −23
3. $-8p = -96$ 12
4. Ron returned an overdue book to the library. He had to pay $0.55. If he paid $0.10 per day for each of the first 3 days the book was overdue and $0.05 per day thereafter, how many days was Ron's book overdue? 8
5. $3x + 7 = 43$ 12
6. $5(c + 2) = 3c - 20$ −15
7. $\frac{2b}{3} + \frac{b}{2} = 14$ 12

The Cumulative Review shown below can be used to review skills and concepts presented thus far in the text. Standardized Test Practice Questions are also provided in the Evaluation Masters Booklet.

Evaluation Masters Booklet, pp. 39-40

■ solve equations containing more than one variable **(Lesson 3-7)**

Solve for x in $\frac{ax + 1}{2} = b$.

$$2\left(\frac{ax + 1}{2}\right) = 2(b)$$
$$ax + 1 = 2b$$
$$ax + 1 - 1 = 2b - 1$$
$$\frac{ax}{a} = \frac{2b - 1}{a}$$
$$x = \frac{2b - 1}{a}$$

Solve for x.

40. $\frac{x + y}{c} = d$ *cd − y*

41. $5(2a + x) = 3b$ $\frac{3b - 10a}{5}$

42. $\frac{2x - a}{3} = \frac{a + 3b}{4}$ $\frac{7a + 9b}{8}$

43. $\frac{2}{3}x + a = a + b$ $\frac{3}{2}b$

APPLICATIONS AND CONNECTIONS

Geometry: Find the missing measure. (Lesson 3-3)

44. $A = 42\frac{1}{4}$ ft² $6\frac{1}{2}$; 6.5

$6\frac{1}{2}$ ft

? ft

45. $A = 17.85$ cm² 5.1

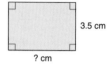

3.5 cm

? cm

Solve by working backwards. (Lesson 3-4)

46. The Broadview Library charges fines for overdue books as follows: 10¢ per day for each of the first three days, and 5¢ per day thereafter. Bill Rogers paid a fine of $1.50. How many days was his book overdue? **27 days**

47. Pia has a beaker filled with water. She uses half of the water and gives half of the remainder to Kwon. She has 225 mL left in the beaker. How much water was originally in the beaker? **900 mL**

Number Theory: Define a variable, write an equation, and solve each problem. (Lesson 3-5)

48. Find two consecutive even integers whose sum is 94. **46, 48**

49. Find three consecutive odd integers whose sum is 81. **25, 27, 29**

Geometry: Find the dimensions of each rectangle. The perimeter is given. (Lesson 3-6)

50. $P = 70$ in.

$w - 5$

15 in. × 20 in. w

51. $P = 188$ m

w

$5w + 1$

15.5 m × 78.5 m

52. **Games** Darlene's score at the end of the first game was −7.8. At the end of the second game, her score was 19.2. How many points did Darlene score during the second game? **27 points** **(Lesson 3-1)**

53. **Gardening** The lengths of the sides of Mrs. Garcia's garden are consecutive even integers. The perimeter is 156 feet. What are the lengths of the four sides? **(Lesson 3-5)** **36 ft, 38 ft, 40 ft, 42 ft**

NAME _____ DATE _____

Cumulative Review (Chapters 1–3)

1. Write an algebraic expression for a number decreased by 21.

2. Evaluate $d^2 - x$ if $d = -\frac{1}{3}$ and $x = \frac{1}{2}$.

3. Solve: $a = 3\frac{1}{2} \div 2$

State the property illustrated by each of the following.

4. $6(0) = 0$

5. $(a + 3) + 2 = a + (3 + 2)$

Simplify.

6. $6(4a + 7b - 6b)$

7. $3x^2 + 7x + x^2 + z^2$

8. Write as an equation: m is the product of r and d decreased by s.

9. There are 150 juniors and seniors attending Monroe High School. If there are x juniors, how many seniors are there?

10. Define a variable and write an equation. Then solve the following problem: A number is 6 less than another number. Their sum is 86. Find the numbers.

11. Graph $\{\dots, -1, 0, 1, 2, 3\}$ on the number line.

Find each sum or difference.

12. $51 + (-14)$

13. $-15 + (-10)$

14. $-\frac{2}{3} + \frac{3}{4}$

15. $-3.9 + (-2.5) + (-8.7)$

16. $38 - (-9)$

17. $m - 20$ if $m = -5$

1. _____ $n - 21$

2. _____ $-\frac{7}{18}$

3. _____ $1\frac{3}{4}$

4. _____ Mult. of Zero

5. _____ Assoc.; Add

6. _____ $24a + 6b$

7. _____ $4x^2 + 7x + z^2$

8. _____ $m = rd - s$

9. _____ $150 - x$

10. _____ $n =$ larger number
$n + (n - 6) = 86$
_____ 40, 46

11. number line graph $-1\ 0\ 1\ 2\ 3\ 4\ 5\ 6$

12. _____ 37

13. _____ -25

14. _____ $\frac{1}{12}$

15. _____ -15.1

16. _____ 47

17. _____ -25

NAME _____ DATE _____

Cumulative Review (Chapters 1–3)

Solve each equation.

18. $y + 5 = -10$

19. $a - 12 = 25$

20. $-27 = -6 - p$

Define a variable, write an equation and solve each problem.

21. Jane is reading a book that is 350 pages long. She has read 85 pages. How many pages does she have left to read?

22. In the 1988 Olympics, Carl Lewis won the 100-meter run in a time of 9.92 seconds. This time is 0.08 seconds faster than the winning time for the race in 1964, run by Bob Hayes. What was Hayes's winning time?

23. 35 less than some number is -43. Find the number.

Simplify.

24. $\left(\frac{2}{3}\right)\left(-\frac{3}{5}\right)\left(-\frac{1}{2}\right)$

25. $6(-3) + 7(-8)$

26. $\frac{56}{-7}$

27. $\frac{-12x + (-14y)}{-2}$

Solve each equation.

28. $\frac{n}{4} = -6$

29. $8 - 7x = 11$

30. $7a + 2 = 3a - 10$

31. $q = mn + p$ for m

32. A rectangular city lot has a perimeter of 540 feet. The width of the lot is 150 feet less than its length. Find the length and the width.

33. Find three consecutive odd integers such that the sum of the least and greatest is 78.

18. _____ -15

19. _____ 37

20. _____ 21

21. _____ $x =$ pages left
$85 + x = 350$
_____ 265

22. _____ $x =$ Hayes's time
$9.92 = x - 0.08$
_____ 10.0 seconds

23. _____ $n =$ number
$n - 35 = -43$
_____ -8

24. _____ $\frac{1}{5}$

25. _____ -74

26. _____ -8

27. _____ $6x + 7y$

28. _____ -24

29. _____ $-\frac{3}{7}$

30. _____ -3

31. _____ $\frac{q - p}{n} = m$

32. _____ 210 ft, 60 ft

33. _____ 37, 39, 41

3 TEST

Solve and check each equation.

1. $m + 13 = -9$ **−22**

2. $k + 16 = -4$ **−20**

3. $y + (-3) = 14$ **17**

4. $x + (-6) = 13$ **19**

5. $k - (-3) = 28$ **25**

6. $-5 - k = 14$ **−19**

7. $r - (-1.2) = -7.3$ **−8.5**

8. $b - \frac{2}{3} = -\frac{5}{6}$ **$-\frac{1}{6}$, −0.1$\overline{6}$**

9. $-3y = 63$ **−21**

10. $\frac{3}{4}y = -27$ **−36**

11. $3x + 1 = 16$ **5**

12. $5.2n + 0.7 = 2.8 + 2.2n$ **0.7**

13. $5(8 - 2n) = 4n - 2$ **3**

14. $3(n + 5) - 6 = 3n + 9$ **all numbers**

15. $7x + 9 = 3(x + 3)$ **0**

16. $-2(3n - 5) + 3n = 2 - n$ **4**

17. $\frac{3}{4}n - \frac{2}{3}n = 5$ **60**

18. $\frac{t - 7}{4} = 11$ **51**

19. $\frac{2r - 3}{-7} = 5$ **−16**

20. $8r - \frac{r}{3} = 46$ **6**

Define a variable, write an equation, and solve each problem.

21. The sum of two integers is -11. One integer is 8. Find the other integer. **−19**

22. The difference of two integers is 26. The lesser integer is -11. What is the greater integer? **15**

23. Four times a number decreased by twice the number is 100. What is the number? **50**

24. Find two consecutive integers such that twice the lesser integer increased by the greater integer is 50. **no solution**

Solve for x.

25. $x + r = q$ **$q - r$**

26. $\frac{x + y}{b} = c$ **$bc - y$**

27. $yx - a = cx$ **$\frac{a}{y - c}$**

Solve.

28. **Skiing** Gary Carson skied down the slalom run in 131.3 seconds. This was 21.7 seconds faster than his sister Jenny. What was Jenny's time? **153 seconds**

29. **Golfing** Joe's golf score was 68. This was 4 less than Maria's golf score. What was Maria's score? **72**

30. **Riding** Alma rides her bicycle for three fourths of an hour every day. Find the distance she rides if she averages 13.65 miles per hour. **10.238 miles**

Bonus A sporting goods store sells T-shirts for one price and sweatshirts for a different price. Editon spent the same amount on 5 T-shirts as he spent on 2 sweatshirts. If he spent a total of $115 on the 5 T-shirts and 2 sweatshirts, what is the cost of each T-shirt? **$11.50**

Using the Chapter Test

This page may be used as a test or as a review. In addition, two multiple-choice tests and two free-response tests are provided in the Evaluation Masters Booklet. Chapter 3 Test, Form 1A is shown below.

Evaluation Masters Booklet, pp. 29-30

NAME _____ DATE _____

Chapter 3 Test, Form 1A

Write the letter for the correct answer in the blank at the right of each problem.

1. What is the solution of $y + (-18) = -3$?
   A. -21 B. 21 C. -15 D. 15 1. __D__

2. What is the solution $5 + x = -19$?
   A. -14 B. 14 C. 24 D. -24 2. __D__

3. What is the solution of $m - 13 = 8$?
   A. 21 B. -21 C. 5 D. -5 3. __A__

4. What is the solution of $t - (-3) = 41$?
   A. -38 B. 38 C. -44 D. 44 4. __B__

5. What is the solution of $-38 = g - (-11)$?
   A. -27 B. 27 C. -49 D. 49 5. __C__

6. What is the solution of $3 - w = -14$?
   A. -11 B. 11 C. -17 D. 17 6. __D__

7. The difference of two integers is 26. The lesser integer is -50. What is the greater integer?
   A. 76 B. -76 C. 24 D. -24 7. __D__

8. What is the solution of $5w = -75$?
   A. -15 B. -80 C. 15 D. 80 8. __A__

9. What is the solution of $-\frac{3}{8}y = -24$?
   A. -9 B. 9 C. -64 D. 64 9. __D__

10. What is the solution of $\frac{s}{8} = 32$?
    A. 4 B. 256 C. $\frac{1}{256}$ D. $\frac{1}{4}$ 10. __B__

11. What is the solution $-\frac{n}{4} + 5 = -16$?
    A. 40 B. 44 C. 59 D. 84 11. __D__

12. What is the solution of $8 - 3x = -16$?
    A. $-\frac{8}{3}$ B. $\frac{8}{3}$ C. 8 D. -8 12. __C__

NAME _____ DATE _____

Chapter 3 Test, Form 1A (continued)

13. What is the solution of $\frac{a + 2}{5} = -9$?
    A. 47 B. -47 C. -55 D. 55 13. __B__

14. What is the solution of $-3(h - 6) = 5(2h + 3)$?
    A. $-\frac{3}{13}$ B. $\frac{3}{13}$ C. $-\frac{9}{13}$ D. $\frac{9}{13}$ 14. __B__

15. What is the solution of $3(x - 1) - x = 3 + 2(x - 3)$?
    A. 0 B. 4 C. There are no solutions.
    D. The equation is an identity. 15. __D__

16. What is the solution of $2n - \frac{5}{6} = \frac{3}{4}n$?
    A. $-\frac{10}{7}$ B. -5 C. $\frac{2}{3}$ D. $\frac{10}{21}$ 16. __C__

17. What is the solution of $1.8x - 5 = 4.3x - 7.75$?
    A. 1.1 B. -1.1 C. 0.11 D. -0.11 17. __A__

18. Six is subtracted from a number. Then the result is divided by 4. The new result is added to 10 to give a final result of 30. What is the number?
    A. 4 B. 80 C. 86 D. 16 18. __C__

19. Find the greatest of four consecutive integers if the least integer decreased by twice the greatest integer is 14.
    A. -20 B. -26 C. -5 D. -17 19. __D__

20. What is the solution for x of $ax - 5 = b$?
    A. $a(b + 5)$ B. $\frac{b - 5}{a}$ C. $\frac{b + 5}{a}$ D. $a(b - 5)$ 20. __C__

Bonus:
Solve for n: $an + bn = w$

Bonus:
$n = \frac{w}{a + b}$

Test Generator Software is provided in both Apple and IBM versions. You may use this software to create your own tests, based on the needs of your students.

Using the College Entrance Exam Preview

The questions on these pages may be used to help students prepare for college entrance exams such as the SAT test. These questions require careful analysis and a thorough understanding of the concepts.

These pages can be used as an overnight assignment.

After students have completed the pages, discuss how each problem can be solved, or provide copies of the solutions from the *Merrill Algebra 1 Solutions Manual.*

The test questions on these pages deal with number concepts and basic operations.

Directions: Choose the best answer. Write A, B, C, or D.

1. Which of the following numbers is *not*
D   a prime number?

  (A) 17   (B) 23   (C) 37   (D) 87

2. How many integers between 325 and
B   400, inclusive, are divisible by 4?

  (A) 18   (B) 19   (C) 20   (D) 24

3. How many integers between 99 and
B   201 are divisible by 2 or 5?

  (A) 60   (B) 61   (C) 70   (D) 71

4. How many integers are between, but
B   not including, 5 and 1995?

  (A) 1988   (B) 1989
  (C) 1990   (D) 2000

5. A person is standing in line, thirteenth
B   from the front and eleventh from the
   back. How many people are in the line?

  (A) 22   (B) 23   (C) 24   (D) 25

6. What number is missing from the
C   sequence 2, 5, 15, 18, 54, 171, 174,
   522?

  (A) 36   (B) 56   (C) 57   (D) 25

7. Which of the following is the least?
C
  (A) 0.77 (B) $\frac{7}{9}$ (C) $\frac{8}{11}$ (D) $\frac{3}{4}$

8. Which fraction is greater than $\frac{1}{4}$ but
A   less than $\frac{1}{3}$?

  (A) $\frac{4}{13}$ (B) $\frac{1}{5}$ (C) $\frac{5}{12}$ (D) $\frac{3}{4}$

9. Which of the following fractions is
C   less than $\frac{1}{5}$?

  (A) $\frac{3}{14}$ (B) $\frac{21}{100}$ (C) $\frac{2}{11}$ (D) $\frac{101}{501}$

10. Which of the following is the greatest?
D   (A) $\frac{1}{2}$ (B) $\frac{5}{11}$ (C) $\frac{4}{9}$ (D) $\frac{7}{13}$

11. What digit is represented by ■ in this
A   subtraction problem?

$$
\begin{array}{r}
80\blacktriangle \\
-\ 602 \\
\hline
\blacksquare 98
\end{array}
$$

  (A) 1   (B) 2   (C) 3   (D) 4

12. The difference between $42\frac{3}{8}$ minutes
D   and $41\frac{2}{3}$ minutes is approximately
   how many seconds?

  (A) 18   (B) 63   (C) $22\frac{1}{2}$ (D) 43

13. A patient must be given medication
C   every 5 hours, starting at 10:00 A.M.
   Thursday. What is the first day on
   which the patient will receive
   medication at noon?

  (A) Thursday   (B) Friday
  (C) Saturday   (D) Sunday

14. Which group of numbers is arranged
C from greatest to least?

(A) $3, \frac{1}{4}, -1, -0.5$

(B) $-1, -0.5, \frac{1}{4}, 3$

(C) $3, \frac{1}{4}, -0.5, -1$

(D) $-0.5, \frac{1}{4}, -1, 3$

15. Find the smallest positive integer
B which gives a remainder of 3 when
divided by 4, 6, or 8.

(A) 51   (B) 27   (C) 15   (D) 26

16. $8(916) + 916 =$
B

(A) $4(916) + 3(916)$

(B) $5(916) + 4(916)$

(C) $6(916) + 4(916)$

(D) $3(916) + 4(916)$

17. Alan owes Benito $4, Benito owes Carl
D $12, and Carl in turn owes Alan some
money. If all three debts could be
settled by having Benito pay $3 to
Alan and $5 to Carl, how much does
Carl owe Alan?

(A) $4   (B) $5   (C) $6   (D) $7

18. A person has 100 green, 100 orange,
A and 100 yellow jelly beans. How many
jars can be filled if each jar must
contain 8 green, 5 orange, and 6
yellow jelly beans?

(A) 12   (B) 15   (C) 16   (D) 25

19. Which is the difference of two
B consecutive prime numbers less
than 30?

(A) 5   (B) 6   (C) 7   (D) 8

20. If $(-9)(-9)(-9) = (-9)(-9)(-9)n$,
A then $n =$

(A) 1   (B) 0   (C) -9 (D) 9

21. The sum of five consecutive integers
C is always divisible by

(A) 2   (B) 4   (C) 5   (D) 10

22. $16 - 12 \div 2^2 \times 3 =$
C

(A) $\frac{1}{3}$ (B) 3   (C) 7   (D) 15

23. Which group of numbers is arranged
A in descending order?

(A) $\frac{5}{7}, \frac{7}{12}, \frac{6}{11}, \frac{3}{13}$

(B) $\frac{7}{12}, \frac{5}{7}, \frac{6}{11}, \frac{3}{13}$

(C) $\frac{5}{7}, \frac{6}{11}, \frac{7}{12}, \frac{3}{13}$

(D) $\frac{3}{13}, \frac{7}{12}, \frac{6}{11}, \frac{5}{7}$

4 Applications of Rational Numbers

PREVIEWING THE CHAPTER

In this chapter, students learn to apply the process of mathematical modeling to real-world problem situations, making the connection with the equation-solving skills and concepts that they mastered in the preceding chapter. The first four lessons review and extend the students' ability to solve problems involving proportion, percent, simple interest, percent increase or decrease, discount, and sales tax. Two application lessons then address problems involving mixtures and uniform motion. The chapter concludes with lessons involving direct and inverse variation.

Problem-Solving Strategy   In Lesson 4-5, students learn that many problems can be solved more easily when they organize the given data in a table or chart.

Lesson Objective Chart

Lesson (Pages)	Lesson Objectives	State/Local Objectives
4-1 (134-137)	**4-1:** Solve proportions.	
4-2 (138-141)	**4-2:** Solve percent problems.	
4-3 (142-145)	**4-3:** Solve problems involving simple interest.	
4-4 (146-149)	**4-4A:** Solve problems involving percent of increase or decrease.	
	4-4B: Solve problems involving discount or sales tax.	
4-5 (151-153)	**4-5:** Solve problems by making a table or chart.	
4-6 (154-157)	**4-6:** Solve mixture problems.	
4-7 (158-161)	**4-7:** Solve problems involving uniform motion by using the formula $d = rt$.	
4-8 (162-165)	**4-8:** Solve problems involving direct variations.	
4-9 (166-169)	**4-9:** Solve problems involving inverse variations.	

ORGANIZING THE CHAPTER

You may want to refer to the **Course Planning Calendar** on page T36.

Lesson Planning Guide

Lesson (Pages)	Pacing Chart (days) Course I	II	III	Reteaching	Practice	Enrichment	Evaluation	Technology	Lab Manual	Mixed Problem Solving	Applications	Cooperative Learning Activity	Multicultural	Transparencies
4-1 (134-137)	1	1	1	p. 22	p. 24	p. 22		p. 4					p. 49	4-1
4-2 (138-141)	1	1	1	p. 23	p. 25	p. 23	Quiz A, p. 51				p. 19			4-2
4-3 (142-145)	1	1	1	p. 24	p. 26	p. 24								4-3
4-4 (146-149)	1	1	1	p. 25	p. 27	p. 25	Quiz B, p. 51					p. 34		4-4
4-5 (151-153)	1	1	1		p. 28		Mid-Chapter Test, p. 55							4-5
4-6 (154-157)	1	1	1	p. 26	p. 29	p. 26			pp. 23-24					4-6
4-7 (158-161)	1	1	1	p. 27	p. 30	p. 27	Quiz C, p. 52							4-7
4-8 (162-165)	1	1	1	p. 28	p. 31	p. 28								4-8
4-9 (166-169)	1	1	1	p. 29	p. 32	p. 29	Quiz D, p. 52	p. 19		p. 4				4-9
Review (170-172)	1	1	1	Multiple Choice Tests, Form 1A and 1B, pp. 43-46 Free Response Tests, Forms 2A and 2B, pp. 47-50										
Test (173)	1	1	1	Cumulative Review, pp. 53-54 Standardized Test Practice Questions, p. 56										

Blackline Masters Booklets · **Activities**

Course I: Chapters 1-13; Course II: Chapters 1-14; Course III: Chapters 1-15

Other Chapter Resources

Student Edition
Application, p. 145
Technology, p. 150
Cooperative Learning Activity, p. 153
Mid-Chapter Review, p. 157
Application, p. 161
History Connection, p. 165
Algebraic Skills Review, p. 654

Teacher Resource Package
Activity Masters Booklet
 Mixed Problem Solving, p. 4
 Applications, p. 19
 Cooperative Learning Activity, p. 34
 Multicultural Activity, p. 49
Technology Masters Booklet
 Scientific Calculator Activity, p. 4
 Graphing Calculator Activity, p. 19
Lab Manual
 Lab Activity, pp. 23-24

Other Supplements
Transparency for Chapter Opener
Problem-of-the-Week Activity
 Cards, 8-10
Video Algebra, 17, 31, 33, 45

Software
Algebra 1 Test and Review
 Generator Software
 Available for Apple and IBM.

ENHANCING THE CHAPTER

Cooperative Learning

Describing the Objectives

Before any group activity begins, two types of objectives should be specified by the teacher and clearly understood by the members of the groups. The first objective is the academic or content objective; for example, a mathematical task or experiment that is to be completed. The second type of objective describes the cooperative-learning skills that will be stressed during the activity; for example, stay with the groups, use quiet voices, express support, encourage every-member participation, expand on other members' answers or explanations, criticize ideas and not people, and so on. Usually no more than one or two such skills should be stressed per session. By giving a clear explanation of the expected results, you will help to focus students' attention appropriately and will increase the probability of a successful session.

Technology

The Technology Feature after Lesson 4-3 uses a BASIC program to explore the affect of successive and combined discounts. The order in which discounts are applied is compared as well. Many consumers have misconceptions about this topic. The computer provides a way to explore many examples in order to reinforce a concept.

Spreadsheets and calculators are excellent tools to explore financial problems. Encourage students to experiment with many examples before formulating a conjecture. Algebra provides the means to prove the conjecture.

Critical Thinking

According to studies conducted by researchers Edward Silver and Margaret Smith, one technique that some teachers have found to be effective in stimulating critical thinking and productive discussion is to present problems that have multiple methods of solution. For example, provide a problem similar to those presented in the chapter. Have students work independently or in small groups to solve the problem using any method they want to use. If you wish, you could require them to find more than one method. Then have the methods presented to the class and discussed, focusing on the unique features of each method and the similarities and differences between them.

Cooperative Learning, p. 34

CHAPTER 4 NAME _____ DATE _____
Cooperative Learning Activity (Use after Lesson 4-4)

The Record Industry

Work in pairs to solve the problems.

Many expenses are involved in producing records, tapes, and CDs, and getting them to the consumer. For example, a record publisher must provide a studio, backup musicians, a producer, technicians, and recording equipment, as well as pay the artist. Then a wholesaler provides storage and transportation. A rackjobber provides records to a number of retailers in an area. And finally the retailer has expenses involved in sales, advertising, marketing, and so on.

Example: An album costs $4.18 to produce. The publisher uses markups to determine the cost to the consumer, as follows.

a. Publisher to wholesaler, 20% markup:
$4.18 + 0.20($4.18) = $4.18 + $0.84 = $5.02
b. Wholesaler to rackjobber, 15% markup:
$5.02 + 0.15($5.02) = $5.02 + $0.75 = $5.77
c. Rackjobber to retailer, 15% markup:
$5.77 + 0.15($5.77) = $5.77 + $0.87 = $6.64
d. Retailer to consumer, 40% markup:
$6.64 + 0.40($6.64) = $6.64 + 2.66 = $9.30

The consumer must pay $9.30 for the record.

Answer the following questions.

1. Use the markups given in the example to find the price a consumer pays for an album that costs the publisher $5.00 to produce. $11.12

2. If a double record album sells at a record store for $15.98, how much did it cost the publisher to produce? $7.19

3. Each time a song is played on the air, the radio station must pay $0.06 to the royalty society. Of this amount, the society keeps 15% for its expenses. Then 75% of the remainder is paid to the publisher and 25% is paid to the songwriter. A network of 75 stations each played "I've Got the Lonesome-For-You Blues" 4 times a day during the first 2 weeks after its release, 11 times a day during the next 2 weeks, 20 times a day for the next 3 weeks, and 8 times a day for the next 3 weeks. How much would the royalty society, the publisher, and the songwriter each receive? $538.65; $2289.26; $763.09

Technology, p. 19

CHAPTER 4 NAME _____ DATE _____
Graphing Calculator Activity (Use after Lesson 4-9)

Inverse Variation

The time it takes a car to drive a certain distance varies inversely as the rate of speed of the car. If Arun drives 200 miles at a constant rate of 55 miles per hour, how long does it take Arun to reach his destination?

This problem can be represented by an equation of the form $time = \frac{distance}{rate}$. If y = time and x = rate, the problem can be solved with a graphing calculator. Place the calculator in computation mode.

a. **Set the range** for x and for y. Choose 0 for the minimum values and convenient numbers for the maximum values.
b. **Graph** $y = \frac{200}{x}$.
c. **Trace** the coordinates.
d. **Zoom in** to trace the coordinates more accurately.

Round the x-value and the y-value to the nearest tenth. When x is 55 mi/h, y is approximately 3.6 hours. It takes Arun about 3.6 hours to travel 200 miles.

Use a graphing calculator to solve each problem.

1. Use the graph above and the trace feature to fill in the chart for a 200-mile trip.

Rate in miles per hour	Time in hours
20	10
35	5.7
40	5
58	3.4

2. Suppose Arun wants to calculate the same mileage chart for a 350-mile trip. What equation should he graph? About how long would it take him to travel the 350 miles if his constant rate of speed is 48 mi/h? $y = \frac{350}{x}$; 7.3 h

Use the graphing method above to find the missing rate or time.

3. distance: 260 mi
rate: 52 mi/h
time: __?__ 5h

4. distance: 3500 mi
rate: __?__ 583.3 mi/h
time: 6 h

5. distance: 176 ft
rate: 44 ft/s
time: __?__ 4 s

Problem of the Week Activity

The card shown below is one of the three available for this chapter. It [c]an be used as a class or small group activity.

Activity Card

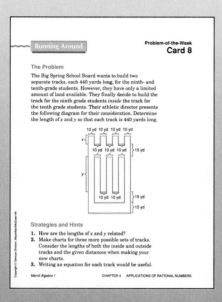

Manipulatives and Models

[T]he following materials may be used as models or manipulatives in [C]hapter 4.

- scientific calculator (all Lessons)
- gears (Lesson 4-1)
- mail-order catalogs (Lesson 4-2)
- nuts (Lesson 4-6)
- balance (Lesson 4-7)
- washers (Lesson 4-7)
- 500-mL beaker (Lesson 4-8)
- spoon or stirring rod (Lesson 4-8)
- stringed instrument (Lesson 4-9)

Outside Resources

Books/Periodicals

[H]ilton, Jean Laity. *Algebra - A New Way of Looking at Numbers.* Weybright and Talley, Inc. 1968.

[W]illiams, Edward. *Survival Mathematics.* Barron's Educational Series, Inc. 1983.

Films/Videotapes/Videodiscs

Percent - Why and How, Coronet Film and Video

Percents, Video Tutor, Inc.

Software

Math Tutor Percents, Ratios, and Proportions, Scholastic

Edu-Ware Algebra Series - Volume 2, Edu-Ware

Multicultural

Multicultural Activity, p. 49

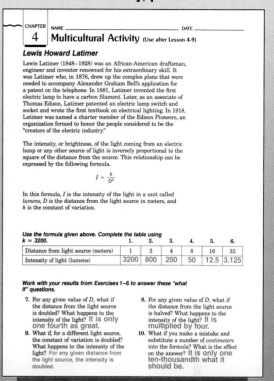

Lab Manual

Lab Activity, pp. 23-24

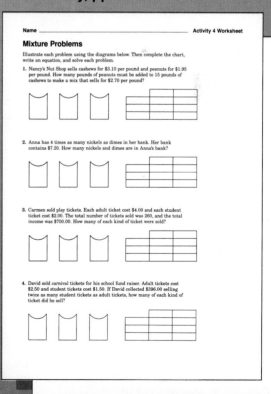

Using the Chapter Opener

Transparency 4-0 is available in the Transparency Package. It provides a full-color visual and motivational activity that you can use to engage students in the mathematical content of the chapter.

Background Information

National consumer advertising began in the U.S. in the mid-1800s. Circulation of newspapers and magazines had grown large enough and covered a wide enough geographical area to justify the financial investments. Advertising has since been so successful because it requires a literate audience. The national system of public education for all children has provided the literate audience. In 1869, over 50% of five- to seventeen-year-olds were enrolled in school. By 1900, this figure had risen to 80%. Advertising stimulates competition, which results in greater choices for consumers.

Chapter Project

Materials: newspapers, magazines, paper and pencil

Organize students into cooperative groups of advertising analysts. Have each group select one product or service. Then have each group collect several ads for the product or service that represent as many different mathematical approaches to sales and discounts as possible.

For example, a $\frac{1}{3}$-off sale vs. a 25% discount vs. a $50 rebate represent different approaches.

Instruct groups to determine which sale offers the lowest price. In addition, have them determine which sale offers the best product or extent of service. Finally, assign each group to report on, and give reasons for, (1) the best price, (2) the best product, and (3) the one they would purchase.

4 Applications of Rational Numbers

APPLICATION IN CONSUMER AWARENESS

The job of every ad writer is to create an advertisement that catches your eye. Ads using large type and flashy photos of exciting and glamorous locations promise you almost anything if you will just buy the product. Somehow, you must read through all of the glitz to find real bargains on things that you actually need. That is the only way that *you* can control your money instead of letting the ad writers do it for you.

How can you tell what discounts and financing actually mean in dollars and cents? Is a 20% discount on an item selling for $12.95 more than $\frac{1}{4}$ off the price of an item selling for $15.98? When is a discount more appealing than a rebate? What is a.p.r. financing? What is the finance charge on your parents' charge card, if they have one? How much money will it *really* cost you to buy an item using that charge card if it will take you more than one month to pay off the balance?

To find answers to these questions, you must understand the language of mathematics and become *math literate*. This will help you to actually read advertisements, and let you, not the advertiser, determine the things that you really need.

ALGEBRA IN ACTION

Three electronic stores are selling the same car stereo system at a discount. Their advertisements are shown below. From which store should you buy the system to get the best price?
Electronics Inc.

How do you know which is the best deal? Just being able to read an advertisement is not enough anymore. Now, you must also understand the mathematics in the advertisement!

Lesson	Connections (C) and Applications (A)	Examples	Exercises
4-1	A: Biology	2	35
	Models	3	
	Travel	6	
	Drafting		36
	Cartography		37
	Machinery		38
4-2	A: Sales	5	32
	Education		31
	Metallurgy		30
	Research		33
	Statistics		34
	Personal Finance		38
4-3	A: Finance	1, 2, 3	11-19
4-4	A: Sales	1, 2, 3, 4	26-29
4-6	A: Sales	1	4, 9, 11, 20
	Chemistry	2	15
	Money		3
	Advertising		5
	Finance		6, 14
	Entertainment		7, 12
	Food		8
	Pharmacy		10
	Automotives		13
	Physiology		19
4-7	A: Travel	1, 2	
	Uniform	3	6-16
	Motion		
	Finance		22
4-8	A: Space	1	
	Electronics	3	24
	Consumerism		25
	Travel		26, 32
	Chemistry		27
	Sales		31
4-9	A: Music	1	
	Physics	3, 4	26-28
	Chemistry		22-23, 32
	Harmonics		24-25
	Employment		33

133

Lesson Resources

- Reteaching Master 4-1
- Practice Master 4-1
- Enrichment Master 4-1
- Technology, p. 4
- Video Algebra, 31
- Activity Master, p. 49

 Transparency 4-1 contains the 5-Minute Check and a teaching aid for this lesson.

INTRODUCING THE LESSON

🕐 5-Minute Check
(over Chapter 3)

Solve.

1. $\frac{1}{2}x + 4 = \frac{1}{3}x$ -24

2. $\frac{5 - y}{6} = \frac{1}{6}y$ $2\frac{1}{2}$

3. $\frac{x + 3}{5} = \frac{2}{5}x$ 3

Solve for x.

4. $x + p = 2b$ $2b - p$

5. $ax - b = c$ $\frac{c + b}{a}$

Motivating the Lesson

Use student understanding of equivalent fractions as a springboard for introducing proportions through the following activity. Write $\frac{3}{4}$ on the board. Have students identify a number of equivalent fractions. Continue the activity by having one student name a fraction and then having other students call out an equivalent fraction. A new fraction can be named when a student cannot think of an equivalent fraction. Continue in this way until all students have had a turn naming a fraction.

TEACHING THE LESSON

Teaching Tip ❶   The proportion $\frac{a}{b} = \frac{c}{d}$ is generally read "a is to b as c is to d".

Teaching Tip ❷   A proportion may also be written as $a{:}b = c{:}d$. In this form, it is easy to see that a and d are the extremes, since they are at the extreme ends. The means are the middle terms.

4-1 Ratios and Proportions

Objective
4-1

After studying this lesson, you should be able to:
- solve proportions.

Application

FYI · · ·

With a single throw of the net, 120 million fish were caught in the Barents Sea in August of 1982.

The title of the newspaper article implies that the fish in the creek were counted one by one. In fact, counting each fish individually would be difficult and might endanger the fish. The *capture-recapture* method uses **ratios** to determine the fish population.

A **ratio** is a comparison of two numbers by division. Ratios can be expressed in the following ways.

$$a \text{ to } b \qquad x{:}y \qquad \frac{3}{7}$$

Ratios are most often expressed as fractions in simplest form. A ratio that is equivalent to a whole number is written with a denominator of 1.

Example 1

> **What is the ratio of 20 inches to 4 feet?**
>
> The units must be the same, so change feet to inches: 4 feet = 48 inches. The ratio is $\frac{20}{48}$ or $\frac{5}{12}$.

Teaching Tip ❶

An equation of the form $\frac{a}{b} = \frac{c}{d}$ stating that two ratios are equal is called a **proportion**. Every proportion consists of four terms.

$$\underset{\uparrow \atop second}{\overset{first \atop \downarrow}{\frac{a}{b}}} = \underset{\uparrow \atop fourth}{\overset{third \atop \downarrow}{\frac{c}{d}}}$$

The first and fourth terms, a and d, are called the **extremes**. **Teaching Tip ❷**

The second and third terms, b and c, are called the **means**.

Means-Extremes Property of Proportions	In a proportion, the product of the extremes is equal to the product of the means. If $\frac{a}{b} = \frac{c}{d}$, then $ad = bc$.

To solve a proportion, <u>cross-multiply</u>.

ALTERNATE TEACHING STRATEGIES

Using Manipulatives

Have students bring in several cases of gears. After studying the moving gears, ask students to determine the relationship between each gear pair. Challenge students to write a ratio to represent each relationship.

Using Logical Reasoning

In the proportion $\frac{e}{f} = \frac{g}{h}$, e is less than g, and e, f, g, and h are nonzero. What can be said about the relationship between f and h? $h > f$

Example 2

APPLICATION

Biology

Twenty fish are captured, tagged, and then released into Black Creek. Later, 29 are recaptured. Of these, 3 were tagged. Estimate the number of fish in the creek.

Let f = the approximate number of fish in the creek.

$$\frac{\text{tagged fish}}{\text{approximate number of fish in creek}} = \frac{\text{captured fish that were tagged}}{\text{captured fish}}$$

$$\frac{20}{f} = \frac{3}{29}$$

$20(29) = 3f$ *Cross multiply.*

$580 = 3f$

$193\frac{1}{3} = f$

A good estimate would be that there are about 193 fish in the creek.

Models are often made to **scale**. A scale is a ratio that compares the size of the model to the actual size of the object being modeled.

Example 3

APPLICATION

Models

A model car is made to the following scale: 1 inch to 10 inches. If the door of the actual car is 33 inches long, what is the door length of the model?

$$\frac{1}{10} = \frac{x}{33}$$ **Teaching Tip ③**

$33 = 10x$ *Means-extremes property*

$3\frac{3}{10} = x$ *Check this result.*

The door length of the model car is $3\frac{3}{10}$ inches.

Example 4

Use a calculator to solve the proportion $\frac{6}{2.56} = \frac{9.32}{m}$.

By the means-extremes property, $6m = (2.56)(9.32)$. Multiply the means. Then divide by 6.

Enter: 2.56   ⊠   9.32   ⊡   6   ⊜

Display: 3.9765333

Rounded to the nearest hundredth, the solution is 3.98.

Example 5

Solve $\frac{x}{5} = \frac{x + 3}{10}$.

$$\frac{x}{5} = \frac{x + 3}{10}$$

$10x = 5(x + 3)$ *Means-extremes property*

$10x = 5x + 15$ *Distributive property*

$5x = 15$

$x = 3$ *Check this result.*

The solution is 3.

RETEACHING THE LESSON

Solve these proportions by multiplying each side by the LCD to clear fractions. First tell by what number each side can be multiplied to clear fractions. Then solve.

1. $\frac{x}{5} = \frac{12}{15}$ 15; $x = 4$

2. $\frac{6}{9} = \frac{10}{x}$ 9x; $x = 15$

Teaching Tip ③   You may wish to explain that this type of problem can be solved using the following method.

$$\frac{1}{10} = \frac{x}{33}$$

$$33\left(\frac{1}{10}\right) = 33\left(\frac{x}{33}\right)$$

$$3\frac{3}{10} = x$$

Chalkboard Examples

For Example 1

Write each ratio as a fraction in simplest form.

a. 16 inches to 3 feet $\frac{4}{9}$

b. 11 m to 1600 cm $\frac{11}{16}$

For Example 2

Sixteen fish are captured, tagged, and then released into Spring Lake. Later, 13 fish are recaptured. Of these, 4 were tagged. Estimate the number of fish in the lake.   52

For Example 3

A model airplane is made to the following scale: 1 inch to 24 inches. If the wing of the actual plane is 18 feet long, how long will the model wing be?   9 inches

---

Reteaching Masters Booklet, p. 22

A ratio of two measurements having different units of measure is called a **rate**. For example, 20 miles per gallon is a rate. Proportions are often used to solve problems involving rates.

Example 6

APPLICATION
Travel

A 96-mile trip requires 6 gallons of gasoline. At that rate, how many gallons would be required for a 152-mile trip?

EXPLORE   Let n = number of gallons required for a 152-mile trip.

PLAN   Write a proportion for the problem. **Teaching Tip** ④

$\frac{96 \text{ miles}}{6 \text{ gallons}} = \frac{152 \text{ miles}}{n \text{ gallons}}$ *Notice that both ratios compare miles to gallons.*

SOLVE
$$\frac{96}{6} = \frac{152}{n}$$
$$96n = 912$$
$$n = 9.5$$

A 152-mile trip would require 9.5 gallons of gasoline.

EXAMINE   A trip of about 100 miles requires 6 gallons of gasoline. A trip of about 150 miles would require about $1\frac{1}{2}$ times the amount of gasoline or 9 gallons. Therefore, for a 152-mile trip a solution of 9.5 gallons is reasonable.

CHECKING FOR UNDERSTANDING

Communicating Mathematics

Read and study the lesson to complete the following.

1. A ratio of two measurements having different units of measure is called a ___?___. rate

2. In a proportion, the product of the means equals the product of the ___?___. extremes

3. A ___?___ is a comparison of two numbers by division. ratio

4. In a proportion, the second and third terms are called the ___?___. means

Guided Practice

Write each ratio as a fraction in simplest form.

5. 3 grams to 11 grams $\frac{3}{11}$
6. 21 meters to 16 meters $\frac{21}{16}$
7. 12 ounces to 6 ounces $\frac{2}{1}$
8. 8 feet to 28 inches $\frac{24}{7}$
9. 16 cm to 40 mm $\frac{4}{1}$
10. 35 minutes to 2 hours $\frac{7}{24}$

Solve each proportion.

11. $\frac{3}{4} = \frac{x}{8}$ 6
12. $\frac{2}{10} = \frac{1}{y}$ 5
13. $\frac{10}{a} = \frac{20}{28}$ 14

EXERCISES

Practice

Solve each proportion. 23. $\frac{52}{41}$; 1.268   24. $\frac{3}{5}$; 0.6   25. $-\frac{149}{6}$; $-24.8\overline{3}$

A

14. $\frac{3}{15} = \frac{b}{45}$ 9

15. $\frac{6}{8} = \frac{7}{x}$ $\frac{28}{3}$; 9.$\overline{3}$

16. $\frac{x}{9} = \frac{-7}{16}$ $-\frac{63}{16}$; -3.938

17. $\frac{5}{2n} = \frac{-2}{1.6}$ -2

18. $\frac{x + 2}{5} = \frac{7}{5}$ 5

19. $\frac{6}{14} = \frac{7}{x - 3}$ $\frac{58}{3}$; 19.$\overline{3}$

B

20. $\frac{3}{5} = \frac{x + 2}{6}$ $\frac{8}{5}$; 1.6

21. $\frac{14}{10} = \frac{5 + x}{x - 3}$ 23

22. $\frac{9}{x - 8} = \frac{4}{5}$ $\frac{77}{4}$; 19.25

23. $\frac{4 - x}{3 + x} = \frac{16}{25}$

24. $\frac{x - 12}{6} = \frac{x + 7}{-4}$

25. $\frac{x + 9}{5} = \frac{x - 10}{11}$

Use a calculator to solve each proportion.

C

26. $\frac{4.3}{25.8} = \frac{1}{2n}$ 3

27. $\frac{2}{0.19} = \frac{12}{0.5n}$ 2.28

28. $\frac{n}{8} = \frac{0.21}{2}$ 0.84

29. $\frac{x}{4.085} = \frac{5}{16.33}$ 1.251

30. $\frac{2.405}{3.67} = \frac{g}{1.88}$ 1.232

31. $\frac{3s}{9.65} = \frac{21}{1.066}$ 63.368

Critical Thinking

Find the ratio of a to b.

32. $10a = 25b$ $\frac{5}{2}$

33. $4a + 2b = 16a$ $\frac{1}{6}$

34. $\frac{3a}{5} = \frac{12b}{7}$ $\frac{20}{7}$

Applications

35. **Biology**   In a game preserve, 239 deer are caught, marked, and then released. Later, out of 198 deer caught, 42 are marked. Estimate the total deer population in the preserve. **1127 deer**

36. **Drafting**   The scale on the blueprint for a house is 1 inch to 3 feet. If the living room on the blueprint is $5\frac{1}{2}$ inches by 7 inches, what are the dimensions of the actual room? **$16\frac{1}{2}$ feet by 21 feet**

37. **Cartography**   The scale on a map is 1 centimeter to 57 kilometers. Fargo and Bismarck are 4.7 centimeters apart on the map. What is the actual distance between these cities? **267.9 km**

38. **Machinery**   In the belt drive shown below, pulley A is 30 inches in diameter and pulley B is 15 inches.

    a. What is the ratio of the diameter of A to the diameter of B? **2:1**

A   B

    b. How many times does pulley B turn while pulley A turns once? **twice**

Mixed Review

39. Evaluate $3^2 + 4(8 - 2) - 6(3) + 4 \div 2 + (8 - 2)^2$.   **(Lesson 1-2)** **53**

40. Simplify $6(2x + y) + 2(x + 4y)$.   **(Lesson 1-6)** **$14x + 14y$**

$18px - 15bg$ 41. Find the sum: $-17px + 22bg + 35px + (-37bg)$.   **(Lesson 2-5)**

42. **Cooking**   If there are four sticks of butter in a pound of butter, and each stick of butter is $\frac{1}{2}$ cup, how many cups of butter are there in a pound of butter?   **(Lesson 2-6)** **2 cups**

43. Solve: $-\frac{7}{6} + k = \frac{5}{6}$.   **(Lesson 3-1)** **2**

LESSON 4-1   RATIOS AND PROPORTIONS   137

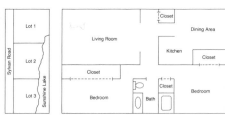

Lesson Resources

- Reteaching Master 4-2
- Practice Master 4-2
- Enrichment Master 4-2
- Activity Master, p. 19
- Video Algebra, 31

 Transparency 4-2 contains the 5-Minute Check and a teaching aid for this lesson.

INTRODUCING THE LESSON

🕐 5-Minute Check
(over Lesson 4-1)

Write each as a fraction in simplest terms.

1. $16 : 24$ $\frac{2}{3}$

2. $15 : 5$ $\frac{3}{1}$

Solve each proportion.

3. $\frac{x}{20} = \frac{3}{5}$ 12

4. $\frac{8}{y} = \frac{4}{7}$ 14

5. $\frac{z-5}{8} = \frac{3}{4}$ 11

Motivating the Lesson

Ask students to state one quick way to find the following percents of any number.

1. **50%**   Take one-half of the number.
2. **25%**   Take one-half of the number twice.
3. **1%**   Move the decimal point two places to the left.
4. **10%**   Move the decimal point one place to the left.

TEACHING THE LESSON

Teaching Tip ❶ This problem can also be solved by finding a ratio that is equivalent to $\frac{11}{50}$ and has a denominator of 100. This ratio is $\frac{11 \cdot 2}{50 \cdot 2} = \frac{22}{100}$.

Teaching Tip ❷ Make sure students understand that $100\% = 1$, or the whole amount.

Objective
4-2

After studying this lesson, you should be able to:
- solve percent problems.

Application

 The Epcot Poll, taken at Disney World's Epcot Center, is one of the world's largest ongoing opinion polls. From 1982 to 1990, more than 500,000 people were polled.

The chart at the right illustrates how 50 people responded to a poll that asked the question, "How did you spend your vacation?" What is the rate of people staying at home per 100 people?

How People Spend Their Vacation	
Visit family/friends	15
Travel/sightsee	13
Stay at home	11
Summer/winter resort	8
No vacation/don't know	3

You can solve this problem by using a proportion. The ratio of people who stay at home to the total polled is $\frac{11}{50}$. Write a proportion that sets $\frac{11}{50}$ equal to a ratio with a denominator of 100.

$$\frac{11}{50} = \frac{n}{100}$$ **Teaching Tip ❶**
$$22 = n$$

People stayed at home at a rate of 22 per 100, or 22 percent. The word **percent** means *per hundred*, or *hundredths*. The symbol for percent is %.

$$22\% = \frac{22}{100} = 0.22$$ **Teaching Tip ❷**

Example 1

Change $\frac{3}{5}$ to a percent.

Use a proportion.	Use a calculator.
$\frac{3}{5} = \frac{n}{100}$	$\frac{3}{5} = \frac{n}{100}$
$300 = 5n$	$100\left(\frac{3}{5}\right) = n$
$60 = n$	**Enter:** 3 ÷ 5 × 100 =
	Display: 60

Thus, $\frac{3}{5}$ is equal to $\frac{60}{100}$ or 60%.

Proportions are often used to solve percent problems. One of the ratios in these proportions is always a comparison of two numbers called the **percentage** and the **base**. The other ratio, called the **rate**, is a fraction with a denominator of 100.

$$\begin{array}{c} percentage \rightarrow \\ base \rightarrow \end{array} \frac{3}{5} = \frac{60}{100} \leftarrow rate$$

ALTERNATE TEACHING STRATEGIES

Using Applications

Have students list five occupations in which salary is dependent upon commission. Have students research these occupations to find the usual rate of commission. Challenge students to analyze their lists to find a relationship between the dollar value of the item sold and the size of the commission awarded an employee.

Using Manipulatives

Have students use catalogs to find five items they would like to purchase. Students should list each item and its selling price. Then have students determine the price of each item when reduced by 15%.

Teaching Tip ③ $\dfrac{\text{Percentage}}{\text{Base}} = \text{Rate}$ or $\dfrac{\text{Percentage}}{\text{Base}} = \dfrac{r}{100}$ Teaching Tip ④

The $\dfrac{percentage}{base}$ represents $\dfrac{part}{whole}$.

Example 2

50 is what percent of 60?

Use the percent proportion.

$\dfrac{\text{Percentage}}{\text{Base}} = \dfrac{r}{100}$ Teaching Tip ⑤

$\dfrac{50}{60} = \dfrac{r}{100}$ *The percentage is 50.*
          The base is 60.

$5000 = 60r$

$83\dfrac{1}{3} = r$ Teaching Tip ⑥

Thus, 50 is $83\dfrac{1}{3}\%$ of 60. The decimal solution is $83.\overline{3}\%$.

You can also write an equation to solve problems with percents.

Example 3

a. What number is 36% of 150?   **b. 40% of what number is 30?**

Teaching Tip ⑦

$x = \dfrac{36}{100} \cdot 150$ $\dfrac{40}{100} \cdot x = 30$

$x = 54$ $x = 75$

Thus, 54 is 36% of 150.   Thus, 40% of 75 is 30.

Most calculators have a key labeled ⬚%⬚. This key can be used when solving problems involving percents. The keying sequences vary for different types of calculators. One possible keying sequence is shown in the next example.

Example 4

Find 18% of 46.3.

Enter: 18 ⬚%⬚ ⬚×⬚ 46.3 ⬚=⬚   *You may not need to press the ⬚=⬚ key.*

Display: 8.334

Thus, 18% of 46.3 is 8.334.

Teaching Tip ③ Some students confuse the terms percentage and percent. If you prefer, you could use the word part instead of percentage. Then the percent proportion will be:
$\dfrac{part}{base} = \dfrac{r}{100}$

Teaching Tip ④ The formula $\dfrac{P}{B} = R$ can easily be rewritten as $P = R \times B$. This form is used if the rate and base are known and the percentage is to be found. If the rate is given as a percent, you can write it as a decimal. Example: Find 20% of 18.
$P = R \times B$
$= 0.20(18)$
$= 3.6$

Teaching Tip ⑤ In the percent proportion, to change the fraction to a percent using a calculator, divide the percentage by the base, then multiply by 100. Using a calculator, the solution to Example 2 would be as follows:
ENTER: 50 ⬚÷⬚ 60 ⬚×⬚ 100 ⬚=⬚
DISPLAY: 83.333333

Teaching Tip ⑥ Emphasize that when a problem asks for the percent, the students must find the value of r.

Teaching Tip ⑦ The equation can also be written $x = 0.36(150)$.

Reteaching Masters Booklet, p. 23

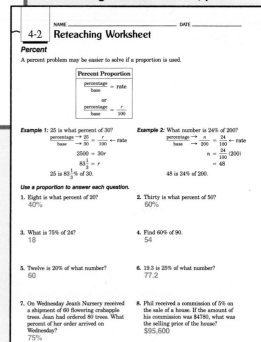

NAME _____ DATE _____

4-2 Reteaching Worksheet

Percent

A percent problem may be easier to solve if a proportion is used.

Percent Proportion
$\dfrac{percentage}{base} = \text{rate}$
or
$\dfrac{percentage}{base} = \dfrac{r}{100}$

Example 1: 25 is what percent of 30?
percentage → 25
base → 30 $= \dfrac{r}{100}$ ← rate
$2500 = 30r$
$83\dfrac{1}{3} = r$
25 is $83\dfrac{1}{3}\%$ of 30.

Example 2: What number is 24% of 200?
percentage → $\dfrac{n}{200} = \dfrac{24}{100}$ ← rate
base →
$n = \dfrac{24}{100}(200)$
$= 48$
48 is 24% of 200.

Use a proportion to answer each question.

1. Eight is what percent of 20?
   40%

2. Thirty is what percent of 50?
   60%

3. What is 75% of 24?
   18

4. Find 60% of 90.
   54

5. Twelve is 20% of what number?
   60

6. 19.3 is 25% of what number?
   77.2

7. On Wednesday Jean's Nursery received a shipment of 60 flowering crabapple trees. Jean had ordered 80 trees. What percent of her order arrived on Wednesday?
   75%

8. Phil received a commission of 5% on the sale of a house. If the amount of his commission was $4780, what was the selling price of the house?
   $95,600

RETEACHING THE LESSON

Here's a form for all percent problems.
$\dfrac{\text{part}}{\text{base or whole}} = \dfrac{\#\text{ of percent}}{100}$
Percent is based on 100. A certain part (percentage) out *of* the whole or base is examined. The base follows the word "of."

Percent problems give two of the three quantities: part, base, and number of percent. So there are three types of percent problems:
1. find the part (percentage),
2. find the base, or
3. find the number of percent.

Chalkboard Examples

For Example 1
Change to a percent.

a. $\frac{9}{10}$ 90%

b. $\frac{4}{5}$ 80%

For Example 2
Solve.

a. 30 is what percent of 50?
60%

b. 46 is what percent of 80?
57.5%

For Example 3
Solve.

a. 70% of what number is
56?   80

b. 45% of what number is
270?   600

For Example 4
Solve.

a. Find 17% of 32.6.   5.542

b. Find 42% of 180.   75.6

For Example 5
**Fred bought a stereo that usually
sells for $220. He received a
20% discount. How much did
Fred pay for the stereo?** $176

Practice Masters Booklet, p. 25

Example 5

APPLICATION
Sales

Jim Byars earns 3% commission on his sales of new cars. If he earned $861 in commissions last week, what was the dollar amount of his total sales?

EXPLORE   Let x = total sales in dollars.

PLAN   3% of total sales equals $861.

$$\frac{3}{100} \cdot \quad x \quad = \quad 861$$ *How could you solve this by using a decimal instead of a fraction?*

SOLVE $\frac{3}{100}x = 861$

            $3x = 86,100$

            $x = 28,700$

The total sales amount was $28,700.

EXAMINE   Enter: 3 [%] [×] 28,700 [=] 861

CHECKING FOR UNDERSTANDING

Communicating Mathematics

Read and study the lesson to answer each question. 2. See margin.

1. In the percent proportion, what is the rate? $\frac{r}{100}$

2. Name three areas in your everyday life where percent is used.

Guided Practice

Write each ratio as a percent.

3. $\frac{31}{100}$ 31%   4. $\frac{3}{10}$ 30%   5. $\frac{1}{25}$ 4%

6. $\frac{7}{20}$ 35%   7. $\frac{3}{8}$ $37\frac{1}{2}$%; 37.5%   8. $\frac{9}{5}$ 180%

Solve.

9. What is 40% of 60? 24

10. Seventy-five is what percent of 250? 30%

11. Twenty-one is 35% of what number? 60

12. Fifty-two is what percent of 80? 65%

EXERCISES

Practice

A

Use a proportion to answer each question. 15. $12\frac{1}{2}$%; 12.5%

13. Six is what percent of 15? 40%   14. What percent of 50 is 35? 70%

15. Five is what percent of 40?   16. What percent of 75 is 225? 300%

140   CHAPTER 4   APPLICATIONS OF RATIONAL NUMBERS

Additional Answer

2. **Answers may vary; typical
answers are sales, statistics,
and test scores.**

B Use an equation to answer each question.

17. What number is 40% of 80? **32**
18. 17.65 is 25% of what number? **70.6**
19. Fourteen is what percent of 56? **25%**
20. What percent of 72 is 12? $16\frac{2}{3}\%$; $16.\overline{6}\%$

Solve.

21. Thirty-six is 45% of what number? **80**
22. Find 81% of 32. **25.92**
23. Find 4% of $6070. **$242.80**
24. Fifty-five is what percent of 88? $62\frac{1}{2}\%$; **62.5%**
25. $54,000 is 108% of what amount? **$50,000**

C

26. Find 112% of $500. **$560**
27. Find 0.12% of $5200. **$6.24**
28. What is 98.5% of $140.32? **$138.22**

Critical Thinking

29. If a is 225% of b, then b is what percent of a? $44.\overline{4}\%$

Applications

30. **Metallurgy** In a 180-kilogram sample of ore, there was 3.2% metal. How many kilograms of metal were in the sample? **5.76 kilograms**

31. **Education** Janice scored 85% on the last test. She answered 34 questions correctly. How many questions were on the test? **40 questions**

32. **Sales** The sales tax on a $20 purchase was $0.90. What was the rate of sales tax? $4\frac{1}{2}\%$; **4.5%**

33. **Research** Suppose 6% of 8000 people polled regarding an election expressed no opinion. How many people had an opinion? **7520 people**

34. **Statistics** Circle graphs are often used to describe sets of data. They show the relationship between parts of the data and the whole. The circle graph at the right was made using the information in the chart on page 138.

   a. What do most people do on their vacation?
   b. What do people do least often on their vacation?
   c. What is the sum of the percents in the circle graph? **100%**
   a. visit family/friends   b. go to a summer/winter resort

Mixed Review

35. Write the following sentence as an equation. The sum of twice m and the square of n is y. **(Lesson 1-7)** $2m + n^2 = y$

36. Find the difference: $18 - (-34)$. **(Lesson 2-2)** **52**

37. Solve $y + \frac{7}{16} = -\frac{5}{8}$. **(Lesson 3-2)** $-\frac{17}{16}$

38. **Personal Finance** Isabel saves $18 in 4 weeks. How long will it take her to save $81 at the same rate? **(Lesson 4-1)** **18 weeks**

EVALUATING THE LESSON

Checking for Understanding

Exercises 1-12 are designed to help you assess understanding through reading, writing, and speaking. You should work through Exercises 1-8 with your students, and then monitor their work on Exercises 9-12.

Closing the Lesson

Speaking Activity Have students explain the following: An amount is increased by 10%. The result is decreased by 10%. Is the final result equal to the original amount? Encourage students to use specific values to help find the answer.

APPLYING THE LESSON

Homework Exercises

Assignment Guide
Basic: 13-20, 29-38
Average: 15-24, 29-38
Enriched: 17-38

Chapter 4, Quiz A, (Lessons 4-1 through 4-2), is available in the Evaluation Masters Booklet, p. 51.

Enrichment Masters Booklet, p. 23

NAME _____ DATE _____

4-2 **Enrichment Worksheet**

Using Percent

Use what you have learned about percent to solve each problem.

A TV movie had a "rating" of 15 and a 25 "share." The rating of 15 means that 15% of the nation's total TV households were tuned in to this show. The 25 share means that 25% of the homes with TVs turned on were tuned to the movie. How many TV households had their TVs turned off at this time?

To find out, let T = the number of TV households
and x = the number TV households with the TV off.
Then $T - x$ = the number of TV households with the TV on.
Since $0.15T$ and $0.25(T - x)$ both represent the number of households tuned to the movie,
$$0.15T = 0.25(T - x)$$
$$0.15T = 0.25T - 0.25x.$$
Solve for x.
$$0.25\,x = 0.10T$$
$$x = \frac{0.10T}{0.25} = 0.40T$$

Forty percent of the TV households had their TVs off when the movie was aired.

Answer each question.

1. During that same week, a sports broadcast had a rating of 22.1 and a 43 share. Show that the percent of TV households with their TVs off was about 48.6%. $0.221T = 0.43T - 0.43x$ $x = \frac{0.221T - 0.43T}{-0.43} = 0.486T$

2. Find the percent of TV households that were tuned off during a show with a rating of 18.9 and a 29 share. **34.8%**

3. Show that if T is the number of TV households, r is the rating, and s is the share, then the number of TV households with the TV off is $\frac{(s-r)T}{s}$. Solve $rT = s(T - x)$ for x.

4. If the fraction of TV households with no TV on is $\frac{s-r}{s}$ then show that the fraction of TV households with TVs on is $\frac{r}{s}$. $1 - \frac{s-r}{s} = \frac{r}{s}$

5. Find the percent of TV households with TVs on during the most watched serial program in history: the last episode of M*A*S*H, which had a 60.3 rating and a 77 share. $\frac{60.3}{77} = 78.3\%$

6. A local station now has a 2 share. Each share is worth $50,000 in advertising revenue per month. The station is thinking of going commercial free for the three months of summer to gain more listeners. What would its new share have to be for the last 4 months of the year to make more money for the year than it would have made had it not gone commercial free? **greater than 3.5**

EXTENDING THE LESSON

Math Power: Problem Solving

At Joe's Clothing, the manager increased the price of a coat x percent and then reduced the price x percent. At the local department store, the same coat that originally sold for the same price was reduced x percent and then the price was increased by x percent.

If you purchased the coat now, which store would have the cheaper price? **Both are the same.**

Lesson Resources
- Reteaching Master 4-3
- Practice Master 4-3
- Enrichment Master 4-3

 Transparency 4-3 contains the 5-Minute Check and a teaching aid for this lesson.

INTRODUCING THE LESSON

 5-Minute Check

(over Lesson 4-2)

Solve.

1. What number increased by 40% equals 14? **10**
2. What number increased by $33\frac{1}{3}\%$ equals 52? **39**
3. Twenty is 20% less than what number? **25**

Find the customer price for each item.

4. Ten-Speed Bike: $148.00
   Discount: 18% **$121.36**
5. Shoes: $44.00
   Discount: 10%
   Sales Tax: 4% **$41.18**

Motivating the Lesson

Develop student understanding of discount through the following activity. One student announces a particular money amount to the class. The next student must identify 50% of this amount. The next student announces 50% of the new amount. Play continues until you reach fractions of cents.

TEACHING THE LESSON

Teaching Tip ❶ Remind students that interest rate is annual. Therefore, time should be expressed in years when working with the simple interest formula.

4-3 Application: Simple Interest

Objective

After studying this lesson, you should be able to:
- solve problems involving simple interest.

The formula $I = prt$ is used to solve problems involving **simple interest**. In the formula, I represents the interest, p represents the amount of money invested, called the *principal*, r represents the annual interest rate, and t represents time in years.

Example 1

APPLICATION
Finance

Kiko Murimoto opened a LifeBank savings account that earns 7% annual interest. After 6 months, she received $52.50 in interest. How much money had Kiko deposited when she opened the account?

EXPLORE Let p = the amount of money Kiko deposited.

PLAN $I = prt$ **Teaching Tip ❶**
$52.50 = p(0.07)(0.5)$ *Change 7% to 0.07 and 6 months to 0.5 year.*

SOLVE $52.50 = 0.035p$ *Multiply 0.07 by 0.5.*
$1500 = p$ *Divide each side by 0.035.*

Kiko had deposited $1500 in the bank.

EXAMINE When p is 1500, $I = (1500)(0.07)\left(\frac{1}{2}\right)$ or $52.50.

Example 2

APPLICATION
Finance

Marilyn Mallinson invested $30,000, part at 6% annual interest and the rest at 7.5% annual interest. Last year, she earned $1995 in interest. How much money did she invest at each rate?

EXPLORE Let n = the amount of money invested at 6%.
Then $30,000 - n$ = the amount of principal invested at 7.5%.

PLAN   *interest on 6% investment*
$n(0.06)(1)$ or $0.06n$

   interest on 7.5% investment
$(30,000 - n)(0.075)(1)$ or $2250 - 0.075n$

SOLVE *interest at 6%* + *interest at 7.5%* = *total interest*
$0.06n + (2250 - 0.075n) = 1995$
$-0.015n + 2250 = 1995$ *Add 0.06n and −0.075n.*
$-0.015n = -255$
$n = 17,000$ *Check this solution.*

Marilyn invested $17,000 at 6% and $30,000 - 17,000$ or $13,000 at 7.5%.

ALTERNATE TEACHING STRATEGIES

Using Cooperative Groups

Many banks offer checking accounts that earn interest. Have students survey local banks to determine the type of programs offered. Tell them to be sure of any stipulations associated with each type of checking account, such as minimum daily balance and cost of checks.

Group members should present and discuss their findings. The group should then identify the bank that offers an account best suited to an individual who intends on maintaining a daily balance of $500 and who will write a maximum of 10 checks per month.

Example 3

APPLICATION

Finance

Joe Parker invested $7625, part at 8% annual interest and the rest at 6.5% annual interest. In the same amount of time, he earned three times as much interest from the 6.5% investment as he did from the 8% investment. How much money did he have invested at 6.5%?

EXPLORE Let n = the amount invested at 6.5%.
     Then $7625 - n$ = the amount invested at 8%.

PLAN   *interest at 6.5% = 3 times interest at 8%*
     $0.065n$ = $3[0.08(7625 - n)]$

SOLVE $0.065n = 3(610 - 0.08n)$
    $0.065n = 1830 - 0.24n$
    $0.305n = 1830$
      $n = 6000$

    Joe invested $6000 at 6.5%.

EXAMINE Since $(0.065)(6000) = \$390$ and $(0.08)(7625 - 6000) = \$130$, and $\$390 = 3(\$130)$, the investment at 6.5% earned three times as much as the one at 8%.

CHECKING FOR UNDERSTANDING

Communicating Mathematics

Read and study the lesson to answer each question. 2. See margin.

1. In Example 1, suppose Kiko adds the $52.50 in interest to the principal. What will the interest be the next year? **$108.68**

2. Suppose an investor invested $5000 at 8% and $2000 at 12%. Why do you think they invested the greater amount at the lower rate?

Guided Practice

Use $I = prt$ to find the missing quantity.

3. Find I if $p = \$8000$, $r = 6\%$, and $t = 1$ year. **$480**

4. Find I if $p = \$5000$, $r = 12\frac{1}{2}\%$, and $t = 5$ years. **$3125**

5. Find t if $I = \$1890$, $p = \$6000$, and $r = 9\%$. **$3\frac{1}{2}$ years**

6. Find t if $I = \$2160$, $p = \$6000$, and $r = 8\%$. **$4\frac{1}{2}$ years**

7. Find r if $I = \$2430$, $p = \$9000$, and $t = 2$ years, 3 months. **12%**

8. Find r if $I = \$780$, $p = \$6500$, and $t = 1$ year. **12%**

9. Find p if $I = \$756$, $r = 9\%$, and $t = 3\frac{1}{2}$ years. **$2400**

10. Find p if $I = \$196$, $r = 10\%$, and $t = 7$ years. **$280**

EXERCISES 11. $6400 at 8%, $3600 at 12% 12. $1200 at 10%, $6000 at 14%

Applications: Finance

Teaching Tip ②

11. Michelle Limotta invested $10,000 for one year, part at 8% annual interest and the rest at 12% annual interest. Her total interest for the year was $944. How much money did she invest at each rate?

12. Steve Devine invested $7200 for one year, part at 10% annual interest and the rest at 14% annual interest. His total interest for the year was $960. How much money did he invest at each rate?

Chalkboard Examples

For Example 1

Jon opened a savings account that earns 8% annual interest. After 9 months, he received $72 in interest. How much money had Jon deposited when he opened the account? **$1200**

For Example 2

Mary Bly invested $12,000, part at 12% annual interest and the rest at 13.25% annual interest. Her total interest last year was $1540. How much money was invested at each rate? **$4000 at 12%, $8000 at 13.25%**

For Example 3

Joan Brook invested some money in bonds at 6% interest and an amount $8000 less than that in stocks at 5% interest. Her total interest for the year is $1690. How much did she invest at 5%? **$11,000 at 5%**

Assignment Guide

Basic: 11-17, 21-26
Average: 12-18, 20-26
Enriched: 13-26

Additional Answer

2. The investment at the higher rate may be too risky.

Reteaching Masters Booklet, p. 24

NAME _____ DATE _____

4-3 **Reteaching Worksheet**

Application: Simple Interest

The formula $I = prt$ is used to solve simple interest problems. I represents the interest, p represents the principal invested, r represents the annual interest rate, and t represents the time in years.

Example: Landa Johns opened a savings account at 9% annual interest. At 6 months, with no other deposits, she had received $112.50 interest. How much money did Landa originally deposit?

Explore Let p = money Landa deposited.

Plan $I = prt$
   Change 9% to 0.09.
   Change 6 months to $\frac{1}{2}$ year.
   $\$112.50 = p(0.09)\left(\frac{1}{2}\right)$

Solve $\$112.50 = 0.045p$
    $2500 = p$
   Landa had deposited $2500.

Examine When p is 2500, I is $(2500)(0.09)\left(\frac{1}{2}\right)$ or $112.50.

Use $I = prt$ to find the missing quantity.

1. Find I if $p = \$1500$, $r = 12\%$, and $t = 2$ years. **$360**

2. Find p if $I = \$6500$, $r = 18\%$, and $t = \frac{1}{2}$ year. **$72,222.22**

3. Elizabeth has $3000 in her savings account. How much interest will she earn in 3 years if the interest rate is $5\frac{1}{2}\%$? **$495**

4. Paul invested $500 for one year at 8% and another sum at 12%. His total interest for the year was $580. How much did Paul invest at 12%? **$4500**

5. Hector has invested $3000 at 9%. He has another $5000 to invest. At what rate of interest must Hector invest the $5000 in order to earn a total of $1250 in interest for one year? **19.6%**

6. Alice invested $1000 at 7%. When she withdrew her investment, she had earned $500 in interest. How long was the money invested? **$7\frac{1}{7}$ years**

RETEACHING THE LESSON

Use "high-low guesses" to solve interest-mixture problems. See Exercises 11-20. For Exercise 11, All $10,000 @ 8% yields $800. All $10,000 @ 12% yields $1200. $5000 @ each rate yields $1000. To get $944 interest, try more money at 8%, say $6000.
$6000 @ 8% = $480
$4000 @ 12% = <u>$480</u>
total interest: 960

Now try $6500 @ 8%: $520
    $3500 @ 12%: <u>$420</u>
        $940
Continue this squeeze to get the final answer of $3600 @ 12% and $6400 @ 8%.

Checking for Understanding

Exercises 1-10 are designed to help you assess understanding through reading, writing, and speaking. You should work through Exercises 1-2 with your students, and then monitor their work on Exercises 3-10.

Error Analysis

Students sometimes subtract quantities in the wrong order when trying to express two parts of a total using one variable. For example, if two numbers have a sum of 20 and x = one number, then they may state that $x - 20$ = other number. But the second number is the rest of the total (20) so the form is total − one number = second number, or $20 - x$ in this example.

Closing the Lesson

Speaking Activity Discuss with the students the difference between interest that is compounded annually and interest that is compounded daily. Have them determine which format is most advantageous to the customer.

Practice Masters Booklet, p. 26

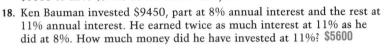

B

13. Fred Ferguson invested $5000 for one year, part at 9% annual interest and the rest at 12% annual interest. The interest from the investment at 9% was $198 more than the interest from the investment at 12%. How much money did he invest at 9%? **$3800**

14. Angela Raimondi wants to invest $8500, part at 14% annual interest and part at 12% annual interest. If she wants to earn the same amount of interest from each investment, how much should she invest at 14%? (Round the answer to the nearest cent.) **$3923.08**

15. In one year, Cholena Youngblood earned the same amount of interest from an investment at 8% annual interest as an investment at 12% annual interest. She had invested $1500 more at 8%. How much money did she have invested at 12%? **$3000**

16. John and Iris Johnson have $8000 to invest. They want to earn $850 interest for the year. Their money can be invested at annual interest rates of 10% or 11%. What is the minimum amount at 11%, with the rest at 10%, that will earn them $850 in interest? **$5000**

17. Carlos and Bonita Díaz have invested $2500 at 10% annual interest. They have $6000 more to invest. At what rate must they invest the $6000 to have $9440 at the end of the year? **11.5%**

C

18. Ken Bauman invested $9450, part at 8% annual interest and the rest at 11% annual interest. He earned twice as much interest at 11% as he did at 8%. How much money did he have invested at 11%? **$5600**

19. If Li Fong had earned one fourth of a percent more in annual interest on an investment, the interest for one year would have been $45 greater. How much did he invest at the beginning of the year? **$18,000**

Computer
Teaching Tip ③

20. The program at the right calculates a percentage increase and then a percentage decrease of the new total at the same rate. First, enter the original amount. Then, enter the percent of increase and decrease.

```
10 PRINT "ENTER THE AMOUNT,"
20 INPUT A
30 PRINT "ENTER THE PERCENT,"
40 INPUT R
50 LET A1 = A + A * (R/100)
60 LET A2 = A1 - A1 * (R/100)
70 PRINT A;" INCREASES TO ";A1
80 PRINT "THEN DECREASES TO ";A2
90 END
```

The program will print the amount after the increase and the amount after both the increase and decrease.

a. Copy and complete the chart.

Original Amount	Percent	After Increase	After Decrease
$100	10%	$110	$99
$40	20%	$48	$38.40
$500	15%	$575	$488.75
$6500	5%	$6825	$6483.75

b. Compare the original amounts and the final amounts. What do you notice? **The final amount is less than the original amount.**

Critical Thinking

21. Polly Crawford deposited $1000 in a savings account at 8% annual interest computed semiannually. If no withdrawals or deposits were made, what was the amount in the account at the end of eighteen months? **$1124.86**

144 CHAPTER 4 APPLICATIONS OF RATIONAL NUMBERS

22. Solve $\frac{5}{6} \cdot 18 = m$. (Lesson 1-3) 15

23. Replace the __?__ in $(-6.01)(-4.122)$ __?__ 25.005 with $<$, $>$, or $=$ to make the sentence true. (Lesson 2-3) $<$

24. Find a number between $-\frac{11}{19}$ and $\frac{5}{14}$. (Lesson 2-4) Answers may vary; a typical answer is 0.

Work backwards to solve the problem. (Lesson 3-4)

25. Two barrels, X and Y, contain water. X contains more water than Y. John pours from X into Y as much water as Y already contains. Then he pours from Y into X as much water as X already contains. Finally, John pours from X into Y as much water as Y already contains. Both barrels now contain 64 gallons of water. How many gallons of water were in each barrel at the beginning? X, 88 gal; Y, 40 gal

26. Twenty-eight is 20% of what number? (Lesson 4-2) 140

APPLICATION

Compound Interest

Compound interest is the amount of interest paid or earned on the original principal *plus* the accumulated interest. Thus, the interest becomes part of the principal. Suppose you deposited $500 in a savings account for 3 years at a rate of 6% annual interest.

	amount deposited +	interest	= new principal
End of first year	$500	+ $500(0.06) =	$530
End of second year	$530	+ $530(0.06) =	$561.80
End of third year	$561.80	+ $561.80(0.06) =	$595.51 *Rounded to the nearest cent.*

A formula that can be used to find compound interest is $T = p(1 + r)^t$, where T is the total amount in the account (principal plus interest), p is the principal, r is the annual interest rate divided by the number of times interest is compounded yearly, and t is the number of times interest is compounded.

Example

Alonso invested $750 for 1 year at 8% annual interest. If interest is compounded semiannually, how much will he have at the end of the year?

$$T = p(1 + r)^t$$
$$= 750\left(1 + \frac{0.08}{2}\right)^{2 \cdot 1} \quad \textit{interest compounded twice per year for 1 year}$$
$$= 750(1.04)^2 \quad \textit{Use a calculator to evaluate.}$$
$$= 811.20 \quad \text{Alonso will have \$811.20 at the end of the year.}$$

Now try this.

Ana invests $600 in a savings account at 12% compounded semiannually. Jim invests $600 in an account at 12% compounded quarterly. At the end of two years, who will have more money? How much more? Jim; $2.57

EXTENDING THE LESSON

Math Power: Problem Solving

Les invested some money at 10.5% simple interest paid yearly. Gail invested $6000 more than Les at 7.5% simple interest. Gail earned $210 more interest than Les in one year. How much money did each invest? Les - $8000; Gail - $14,000

Application

Explain that compound interest differs from simple interest in that simple interest is computed only on the original principal regardless of the time involved. Point out that students should seek compound interest over simple interest because it will always earn more.

Lesson Resources

- Reteaching Master 4-4
- Practice Master 4-4
- Enrichment Master 4-4
- Activity Master, p. 34

 Transparency 4-4 contains the 5-Minute Check and a teaching aid for this lesson.

INTRODUCING THE LESSON

 5-Minute Check

(over Lesson 4-3)

Solve.

1. Which earns more interest, $1000 at 8% interest for one year or $2000 at 2% interest for two years? **They both earn the same amount.**
2. Which earns more interest, $1500 at 10% interest for one year or $500 at 4% interest for ten years? **$500 at 4%**
3. Find I, if $P = \$8000$, $r = 6\%$, and $t = 1$ year. **$480**
4. Find P, if $I = \$196$, $r = 10\%$, and $t = 7$ years. **$280**
5. Find r, if $I = \$780$, $P = \$6500$, and $t = 1$ year. **12%**

Motivating the Lesson

Have students consider the following: A pair of sneakers is reduced 10%. The sales tax on the sneakers is 6%. Is the final price of the sneakers equal to the original price less 4%? **No, because the sales tax is calculated on the sales price not the original price of the sneakers.**

TEACHING THE LESSON

Teaching Tip ❶ Point out that the difference is always compared to the original price.

Objectives

After studying this lesson, you should be able to:

4-4A ▪ solve problems involving percent of increase or decrease, and

4-4B ▪ solve problems involving discount or sales tax.

Application

A pair of jeans that originally cost $40 is on sale for $30. You can write a ratio that compares the amount of decrease to the original price. This ratio can be written as a percent.

$$\frac{amount\ of\ decrease}{original\ price} \rightarrow \frac{10}{40} = \frac{r}{100} \rightarrow r = 25$$

The amount of decrease is $\frac{25}{100}$ or 25% of the original price. So, we can say that the **percent of decrease** is 25%.

The **percent of increase** can be found in a similar manner, as shown in the following example.

Example 1

The base price of the 1991 Buyer's Car of the Year was **$15,925**. The base price of the same car in 1994 is **$19,705**. Find the percent of increase.

EXPLORE The price increased from $15,925 to $19,705. The amount of increase was $3780.

PLAN You need to write a ratio that compares the amount of increase with the original price. Then, express the ratio as a percent.

$$\frac{amount\ of\ increase}{original\ price} \quad \frac{3780}{15,925} = \frac{r}{100} \textbf{ Teaching Tip ❶}$$

SOLVE
$$\frac{3780}{15,925} = \frac{r}{100}$$
$$378,000 = 15,925r \quad \textit{Use a calculator to divide}$$
$$23.736263 = r \quad \textit{each side by 15,925.}$$

The percent of increase is about 24%.

EXAMINE Use a calculator to find 24% of $15,925.

Enter: 24 [%] [×] 15,925 [=] 3822

$15,925 + $3822 = $19,747

Since 24% > 23.736%, the answer is reasonable.

ALTERNATE TEACHING STRATEGIES

Using Calculators

Some calculators can easily compute answers for discount problems. The procedure to follow usually is (original price) − (discount rate)% + (tax rate)% = customer price.

Using Questioning

Have students prepare a questionnaire aimed at gathering information about how merchants determine selling prices of items. Students should then use the questionnaire to interview local merchants anonymously. Challenge the class to review the results of the survey to determine general markup percentages used in various industries.

Sometimes an increase or decrease is given as a percent, rather than an amount. Two applications of percent of change are discounts and sales tax. Keep in mind that a discount of 35% means that the price is decreased by 35%. Sales tax of 5% means that the price is increased by 5%.

Example 2

APPLICATION
Sales

Amy bought a television set that had an original price of $295.95. Because she worked at the store, she received a 20% discount. What was the discounted price?

EXPLORE   The original price was $295.95, and the discount was 20%.

PLAN   You want to find the amount of discount, then subtract that amount from $295.95. The result is the discounted price.

SOLVE   20% of $295.95 = 0.20(295.95)   *Note that $20\% = \frac{20}{100} = 0.20$.*
                       = 59.19

Subtract this amount from the original price.
$295.95 − $59.19 = $236.76 **Teaching Tip ②**

The discounted price was $236.76.

EXAMINE   Here's another way to solve the problem. The discount was 20%, so the discounted price was 80% (100% − 20%) of the original price.

Find 80% of $295.95.   0.80(295.95) = 236.76

This method produces the same discount price, $236.76.

Example 3

APPLICATION
Sales

Frank bought a new tennis racket for $79.99. He also had to pay sales tax of $5\frac{1}{2}\%$. What was the total price?

EXPLORE   The price was $79.99 and the tax rate was $5\frac{1}{2}\%$.

PLAN   First find $5\frac{1}{2}\%$ of $79.99. Then add the result to $79.99.

SOLVE $5\frac{1}{2}\%$ of $79.99 = 0.055(79.99)   *Note that $5\frac{1}{2}\% = 0.055$.*
                        = 4.39945   *Round 4.39945 to 4.40.*

Add this amount to the original price.
$79.99 + $4.40 = $84.39

The total price was $84.39.

EXAMINE   The tax rate is $5\frac{1}{2}\%$, so the total price was 100% + $5\frac{1}{2}\%$ or 105.5% of the purchase price. Find 105.5% of $79.99.

(1.055)(79.99) = 84.38945

Thus, the total price of $84.39 is correct.

LESSON 4-4   PERCENT OF CHANGE   147

RETEACHING THE LESSON

Make certain students realize that two steps are required to solve problems involving percent of change. First, they must subtract to find the amount of change. Then, they must compare that amount, increasing or decreasing, to the *original.* In each exercise at the right, require students to show both steps to find the percent of increase or decrease.

1. old: $74.00
    new: $79.18   7%
2. old: $62.00
    new: $65.72   6%
3. old: $139.40
    new: $164.49   18%
4. old: $65.48
    new: $60.24   8%

Example 4

APPLICATION

Sales

Connie's Clothing prices their goods 25% above the wholesale price. If the retail price of a jacket is $79, what was the wholesale price?

The *wholesale price* is the price the store pays for their goods.
The *retail price* is the price at which the goods are sold in the store.

EXPLORE   Let j = wholesale price of jacket.
Then $0.25j$ = amount of markup.
Note that 25% = 0.25.

PLAN $\underbrace{wholesale\ price}$ + $\underbrace{markup}$ = $\underbrace{retail\ price}$

$$j \quad + \quad 0.25j \quad = \quad 79 \qquad \textbf{Teaching Tip ③}$$

SOLVE $(1 + 0.25)j = 79$ *Distributive property*
$$1.25j = 79$$
$$j = 63.2$$

The wholesale price was $63.20.

EXAMINE   If the wholesale price is $63.20 and the retail price is $79, the markup is $15.80. Since $15.80 is 25% of $63.20, the solution is correct.

CHECKING FOR UNDERSTANDING   1-4. See margin.

Communicating Mathematics

Read and study the lesson. Then explain how to solve each problem.

1. percent of increase, if you know the old and new prices

2. discount, if you know the percent of discount

3. sales tax, if you know the rate of tax

4. wholesale price, if you know the retail price and the percent of markup

Guided Practice

Copy and complete the chart. The first line is given as a sample.

	Original Amount	Later Amount	Did the amount increase (I) or decrease (D)?	Amount of Increase or Decrease	Percent of Increase or Decrease
	$50	$70	I	$20	40%
5.	$100	$94	D	$6	6%
6.	$100	$108	I	$8	8%
7.	$200	$172	D	$28	14%
8.	$313.49	$358.95	I	$45.46	14.5%
9.	$47.89	$60.10	I	$12.21	25.5%
10.	$72	$36	D	$36	50%

Notice that 20 is 40% of 50.

Additional Answers

1. Subtract old price from new price. Divide the result by old price. Move decimal point 2 places to right.

2. Multiply percent of discount by original price. Subtract result from original price.

3. Multiply tax rate by original price. Add result to original price.

4. Divide retail price by 1 plus percent of markup.

EXERCISES

Practice

A

11. What number increased by 40% equals 14? **10**
12. What number decreased by $66\frac{2}{3}\%$ is 18? **54**
13. Fourteen is 50% less than what number? **28**
14. Twenty is 20% more than what number? **16$\frac{2}{3}$**
15. What is 30% more than 30? **39**
16. What is 75% less than 80? **20**

B

17. A price decreased from $50 to $40. Find the percent of decrease. **20%**
18. A price increased from $40 to $50. Find the percent of increase. **25%**
19. A price plus 5% tax is equal to $3.15. Find the original price. **$3.00**
20. An item sells for $36 after a 25% discount. Find the original price. **$48**

Teaching Tip ④

Find the final price of each item. When there is a discount and sales tax, compute the discount price first.

21. stereo: $345.00
    discount: 12% **$303.60**
22. clothing: $74.00
    sales tax: 6.5% **$78.81**

C

23. shoes: $44.00
    discount: 10%
    sales tax: 4% **$41.18**
24. tires: $154.00
    discount: 20%
    sales tax: 5% **$129.36**

Critical Thinking

25. An amount is increased by 10%. The result is decreased by 10%. Is the final result equal to the original amount? **no**

Applications: Sales

26. Zoe got a discount of $4.50 on a new radio. The discounted price was $24.65. What was the percent of discount to the nearest percent? **15%**
27. Chapa paid $92.04 for new school clothes. This included 4% sales tax. What was the cost of the clothes before taxes? **$88.50**
28. The wholesale price of a stove was $550. The retail price was 20% greater than the wholesale price. The retail price was then discounted by 10% during a sale. What was the sale price? **$594**
29. Tires-4-Less allows a 10% discount if a purchase is paid for within 30 days. An additional 5% discount is given if the purchase is paid for within 15 days. Bob Cordoba buys a set of tires that originally cost $360. If he pays the entire amount at the time of purchase, how much does he pay for his tires? (*Hint:* Compute the discounts separately.) **$307.80**

Mixed Review

30. Simplify $9a + 16b + 14a$. **(Lesson 1-5)** $23a + 16b$
31. Simplify $\frac{77b}{-11}$. **(Lesson 2-7)** $-7b$
32. Solve $-5 = 4 - 2(x - 5)$. **(Lesson 3-6)** $\frac{19}{2}$
33. Eighteen is what percent of 60? **(Lesson 4-2)** **30%**
34. Use $I = prt$ to find t if $I = \$3528$, $P = \$8400$, and $r = 10\frac{1}{2}\%$. **(Lesson 4-3)** **4 years**

EXTENDING THE LESSON

Math Power: Reasoning

A coat that sells for $80 is discounted 20%. The sales tax is 6%. Is it better for the buyer to have the discount applied before the sales tax is added or after the sales tax is added? **no difference**

APPLYING THE LESSON

Homework Exercises

Assignment Guide
Basic: 11-20, 25-34
Average: 12-22, 25-34
Enriched: 13-34

Chapter 4, Quiz B, (Lessons 4-3 through 4-4), is available in the Evaluation Masters Booklet, p. 51.

Teaching Tip ④ Before students work on Exercises 21-24, you may wish to discuss why it is necessary to deduct an amount of discount from an item before computing the sales tax on the item.

Enrichment Masters Booklet, p. 25

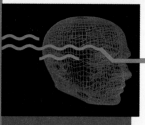

Technology
Successive Discounts

▶ **BASIC**
Graphing Calculator
Graphing Software
Spreadsheets

Application

Bonnie's Appliances sells microwave ovens for $250. One oven is discounted 20% because it is scratched. Then the store puts all microwave ovens on sale at a discount of 15%. What is the final sale price of the scratched microwave?

The regular price of microwave ovens is $250. The scratched microwave oven is $250 − $250(0.20) or $250(0.80) or $200. On sale, the scratched microwave oven is $200(0.85) or $170.

The two successive discounts are summarized as follows.

$$(\$250 \times 0.80) \times 0.85 = \$170$$

A combined discount would be 20% + 15% or 35%. This is 65% of the original amount.

$$\$250 \times 0.65 = \$162.50$$

The program below can help you determine whether two successive discounts or one combined discount will produce the lower price.

```
10 PRINT "ENTER ORIGINAL PRICE AND TWO DISCOUNTS AS
   DECIMALS."
20 INPUT P,X1,X2
30 LET S1 = P * (1 − X1) * (1 − X2)    successive discounts
40 LET S2 = P * (1 − (X1 + X2))        combined discount
50 PRINT "SUCCESSIVE DISCOUNTS: $ ";S1
60 PRINT "COMBINED DISCOUNT: $";S2
70 IF S2 < S1 THEN PRINT "A COMBINED DISCOUNT HAS A
   LOWER SALE PRICE."
80 IF S1 < S2 THEN PRINT "SUCCESSIVE DISCOUNTS HAVE A
   LOWER SALE PRICE."
90 IF S1 = S2 THEN PRINT "THERE IS NO DIFFERENCE."
100 END
```

EXERCISES

Find the sale price of each item using successive discounts and then one combined discount. 5. See margin.

1. price, $49; discounts, 20% and 10% **$35.28; $34.30**

2. price, $185; discounts, 25% and 10% **$124.88; $120.25**

3. price, $12.50; discounts, 30% and 12.5% **$7.66; $7.19**

4. price, $156.95; discounts, 30% and 15% **$93.39; $86.32**

5. What is the relationship between the sale price using successive discounts and the sale price using combined discounts?

Problem-Solving Strategy: Make a Table or Chart

EXPLORE
PLAN
SOLVE
EXAMINE

Objective
4-5

After studying this lesson, you should be able to:
- solve problems by making a table or chart.

Many problems can be solved more easily if you organize the information in a table or chart.

Example 1
Teaching Tip ❶

After college, Mark Brandauer is offered two jobs. Job A has a starting salary of $17,500 per year with a guaranteed raise of $3000 per year. Job B has a starting salary of $20,000 with a guaranteed raise of $2000 per year. Which job would pay more after 5 years?

Make a chart to show the effect of each option over a 5-year period.

Year	1	2	3	4	5
Job A	$17,500	$20,500	$23,500	$26,500	$29,500
Job B	$20,000	$22,000	$24,000	$26,000	$28,000

Job A would pay more after 5 years.

When solving logic problems in which several clues are given, it is often helpful to use a table called a *matrix*.

Example 2
Teaching Tip ❷

Five students each have a favorite food. No two of them have the same favorite. Using the clues below, which food goes with each person?

1. Adrienne's favorite food is not pizza.
2. Benito hates pizza and hamburgers.
3. One of the students' favorite foods is chicken wings.
4. Cindy's favorite is french fries.
5. Darryl is allergic to onion rings.
6. Eddie's favorite is onion rings.

Set up a table to solve the problem. Write all of the names and categories in the table. Place a Y (yes) or N (no) wherever you can. No two have the same favorite food, so once you write a Y in a box, you can write an N in all of the other boxes in that row and column. Then complete the table.

(Continued on page 152)

LESSON 4-5 PROBLEM-SOLVING STRATEGY: MAKE A TABLE OR CHART 151

ALTERNATE TEACHING STRATEGIES

Using Cooperative Groups

Have small groups of students create a logic problem such as the one shown in Example 2. Once the problems have been written, have the groups exchange problems and solve.

Lesson Resources

- Practice Master 4-5
 Transparency 4-5 contains the 5-Minute Check and a teaching aid for this lesson.

INTRODUCING THE LESSON

🕐 5-Minute Check
(over Lesson 4-4)

Solve.

1. What is 30% more than 30? **39**
2. What is 25% more than 28? **35**
3. What is 15% less than 40? **34**
4. What is 50% less than 88? **44**
5. What is 75% more than 12? **21**

Motivating the Lesson

Poll students to determine their favorite food served in the school cafeteria. Compile the results of the survey and rank the foods in order of preference.

TEACHING THE LESSON

Teaching Tip ❶ Emphasize to students that the first step in making a chart is to identify the type of information you wish to present.

Teaching Tip ❷ Most charts and tables compare two different variables or types of information. The chart in Example 1 compares years of work with annual salary. The table in Example 2 compares students with favorite foods.

Name	Pizza	Hamburgers	Chicken Wings	French Fries	Onion Rings
Adrienne	N	Y	N	N	N
Benito	N	N	Y	N	N
Cindy	N	N	N	Y	N
Darryl	Y	N	N	N	N
Eddie	N	N	N	N	Y

Adrienne's favorite is hamburgers, Benito's favorite is chicken wings, Cindy's favorite is french fries, Darryl's favorite is pizza, and Eddie's favorite is onion rings.

CHECKING FOR UNDERSTANDING

Communicating Mathematics

Read and study the lesson to answer each question.

1. Over the 5-year period described in Example 1, which job would pay the most total money? **Job B**

2. Would the matrix solution in Example 2 work if more than one person had the same favorite food? Why or why not? **See margin.**

Guided Practice

Use a table or chart to solve each problem. **5. 3:30 P.M.**

3. Carla Agosto and Ken Takamura are both electricians. Ms. Agosto charges $15 for a service call, plus $15 per hour. Mr. Takamura charges $35 for a service call, plus $10 per hour. If they work the same number of hours and are paid the same amount of money, how many hours did they work? **4 hours**

Amelia-September, Brandon-July, Lianna-January, Jason-December

4. Four friends have birthdays in January, July, September, and December. Amelia was not born in the winter. Brandon celebrates his birthday near Independence Day. Lianna's is the month after Jason's. In what month was each one born?

5. Fly Boy Aviation Products uses two machines to make 33,000 airplane bolts very quickly. Machine A can make 3000 bolts per hour and Machine B can make 1800 bolts per hour. Machine A starts at 7:30 A.M. and Machine B starts at 10:30 A.M. At what time is the job completed?

6. Mr. Smith, Mr. Jones, and Mr. Chang are a butcher, a baker, and a candlestick maker, but not in that order. The baker is married to Mr. Smith's sister. Mr. Chang is not the candlestick maker. Mr. Jones is a bachelor. Mr. Smith is a regular customer of the butcher's. Who does what?
Smith-candlestick maker, Jones-butcher, Chang-baker

Chalkboard Examples

For Example 1

After art school, Lisa Malony is offered two jobs. Job A has a starting salary of $17,500 per year with a guaranteed raise of $1000 per year. Job B has a starting salary of $15,000 per year with a guaranteed raise of $2500 per year. Which job would pay more after 3 years?   **Job B**

For Example 2

On Wednesday, the school cafeteria sold more hamburgers than stew, but less hamburgers than salads. The number of french fry orders was nearly double that of any other item on the menu while more chili was sold than stew. Rank the lunch items from greatest quantity sold to least amount sold.   **french fries, salads, hamburgers, chili, stew**

EVALUATING THE LESSON

Checking for Understanding

Exercises 1-6 are designed to help you assess understanding through reading, writing, and speaking. You should work through Exercises 1-2 with your students, and then monitor their work on Exercises 3-6.

Additional Answers

2. No, since you could no longer write an N in all the other boxes in a row and column that has a Y in one of its boxes.

10a.

n	number of dots
1	1
2	3
3	6
4	10
5	15
6	21

The number of dot n + (the number of dots for the next smallest value of n).

RETEACHING THE LESSON

Solve.

There are 60 algebra students and 80 band members at Smallville High. 34 algebra students are band members. How many algebra students are not in the band? How many band members do not take algebra? How many students take algebra or band?   **26; 46; 106**

EXERCISES

Practice

Strategies

Look for a pattern.
Solve a simpler problem.
Act it out.
Guess and check.
Draw a diagram.
Make a chart.
Work backwards.

Solve. Use any strategy.

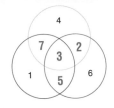

7. Place the numbers 1 through 7 in the seven compartments formed by the three circles at the right so that the sums of the numbers in each circle are the same. The numbers 1, 4, and 6 have already been placed for you.

8. Lindsay, Paul, and Kelly each have hair of a different color. One has blonde hair, one has red hair, and one has brown hair. If Lindsay is a blonde, Paul has red hair. If Lindsay has red hair, Paul has brown hair. If Paul is not a blonde, Kelly has red hair. What color hair does each person have? **Lindsay-brown, Paul-blonde, Kelly-red**

9. Imagine you are playing a game of tic-tac-toe. What is the greatest number of squares that can be left empty when the game is won? **4**

10. Numbers that can be represented by geometric figures are called *figurate numbers*. One type of figurate number is a *triangular number*. Triangular numbers are those that can be represented by a triangular array of dots, with *n* on each side.

$n = 1$ $n = 2$ $n = 3$ $n = 4$

a. Make a table that compares *n* with the number of dots in the array. What pattern do you notice? **See margin.**

b. What is the 10th triangular number? **55**

COOPERATIVE LEARNING ACTIVITY

Work in groups of four. Each person in the group must understand the solution and be able to explain it to any person in the class.

Eight squares cover the large square at the right. All of the eight squares are the same size. The square marked 1 is completely shown; however, you can only see a part of the other seven squares. Number the squares in order from the top layer to the bottom.

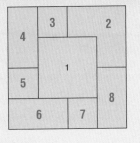

EXTENDING THE LESSON

Math Power: Connections

Figure A, B, C, and D are all quadrilaterals. The length of all sides of Figure B are equal. Figures A, B, and C all have 2 pairs of parallel sides. All the angles in Figures B and C are right angles. Identify each figure as a parallelogram, rectangle, square, or trapezoid.
A: parallelogram, B: square, C: rectangle, D: trapezoid

Cooperative Learning Activity

This activity provides students with an opportunity to *learn* things together, not just do things together. You may wish to refer to pages T6 - T8 and page 6C for the various elements of cooperative groups and specific goals and strategies for using them.

Closing the Lesson

Speaking Activity Ask students to explain how a table or chart is helpful when solving a problem. Challenge them to identify real life situations in which they might choose to make a visual to help solve a problem.

APPLYING THE LESSON

Homework Exercises

Assignment Guide

Basic: 7-10
Average: 7-10
Enriched: 7-10

Practice Masters Booklet, p. 28

NAME _____ DATE _____

4-5 Practice Worksheet

Problem-Solving: Make a Table or Chart

Use a table or chart to solve each problem.

1. There are 19 different ways you can buy a set of four attached stamps. One way is given below. Make a drawing of the other ways.

2. Colleen Brennan fenced in a rectangular lot 225 ft by 350 ft for her ten horses. She placed posts every 25 ft around the lot. How many posts did she use? **46 posts**

3. Hobbs Rental Car charges $35 per day and 12¢ per mile. Wonder Rental Car charges $40 per day and 10¢ per mile. How far must a person drive per day for Wonder to be more economical than Hobbs? **More than 250 miles**

4. Jill Reno and Art Nolan are both plumbers. Jill charges $35 per visit, plus $10 per hour. Art charges $20 per visit, plus $12.50 per hour. If they work the same number of hours and are paid the same amount of money, how many hours did they work? **6 hours**

5. Mike, Sandy, Neal and Joan go to different schools. The names of the schools are Johnson, Springer, Norton, and Monroe. Mike goes to the Springer School. None goes to the school that has the same beginning letter as his or her name. Neither Neal or Joan has ever been to Monroe School. Which school does each person attend?
Mike: Springer
Sandy: Monroe
Neal: Johnson
Joan: Norton

Lesson Resources

- Reteaching Master 4-6
- Practice Master 4-6
- Enrichment Master 4-6
- Lab Manual, pp. 23-24
- Video Algebra, 33

 Transparency 4-6 contains the 5-Minute Check and a teaching aid for this lesson.

INTRODUCING THE LESSON

 5-Minute Check

(over Lesson 4-4)

Solve.

1. A price decreased from $36 to $27. What is the percent of decrease? **25%**

2. A price increased from $68 to $85. What is the percent of increase? **25%**

3. A price increased from $78 to $104. What is the percent of increase? $33\frac{1}{3}$**%**

4. An item sells for $48 after a 20% discount. What was the original price of the item? **$60**

5. An item sells for $85 after a 15% discount. What was the original price of the item? **$100**

Motivating the Lesson

Ask students to identify all the combinations of dimes and nickels that have a total value of $0.50. Encourage students to describe the methods used to determine the combinations. **5 dimes and 0 nickels, 4 dimes and 2 nickels, 3 dimes and 4 nickels, 2 dimes and 6 nickels, 1 dime and 8 nickels, 0 dimes and 10 nickels**

TEACHING THE LESSON

Teaching Tip ❶ Emphasize to students that in mixture problems they are trying to find the perfect blend or balance of several parts to achieve the desired result.

4-6 Application: Mixtures

Objective 4-6

After studying this lesson, you should be able to:

- solve mixture problems.

Teaching Tip

It is often helpful to make a chart to organize the information.

❶ Mixture problems involve a combination of two or more parts into a whole. While studying mixture problems, you will be asked to find information about one or more of these parts when information about the whole is given. You can use equations to solve problems like this.

Example 1

APPLICATION

Sales

Delectable Dan's Cookie Company sells two kinds of cookies daily: chocolate chip at $6.50 per dozen and white chocolate macadamia at $9.00 per dozen. On Thursday, Dan sold 85 dozen more chocolate chip than white chocolate macadamia cookies. The total sales for both were $4055.50. How many dozen of each were sold?

EXPLORE Let w = the number of dozens of white chocolate macadamia cookies sold. Then $w + 85$ = the number of dozens of chocolate chip cookies sold. **Teaching Tip ❷**

PLAN

	Number of Dozens	Price per Dozen	Total Price
White Chocolate	w	$9.00	$9w$
Chocolate Chip	$w + 85$	$6.50	$6.5(w + 85)$

$$\underbrace{\text{total sales of}}_{\text{white chocolate macadamia}} + \underbrace{\text{total sales of}}_{\text{chocolate chip}} = \underbrace{\text{total}}_{\text{sales}}$$

$$9w \qquad + \quad 6.5(w + 85) = 4055.5$$

SOLVE

$$9w + 6.5w + 552.5 = 4055.5$$
$$15.5w + 552.5 = 4055.5$$
$$15.5w = 3503$$
$$w = 226$$

There were 226 dozen white chocolate macadamia cookies sold. There were 226 + 85, or 311 dozen chocolate chip cookies sold.

EXAMINE If 226 dozen white chocolate macadamia cookies were sold, the total sales of those cookies would be 226($9) or $2034. If 311 dozen chocolate chip cookies were sold, the total sales of those cookies would be 311($6.50) or $2021.50.

Since $2034 + $2021.50 = $4055.50, the solution is correct.

ALTERNATE TEACHING STRATEGIES

Using Manipulatives

Have students create nut mixtures from peanuts and cashews brought to class. After the mixing is complete, students should set up an equation to represent each particular combination.

Sometimes mixture problems are expressed in terms of percents.

Example 2

Kendra is doing a chemistry experiment that calls for a 30% solution of copper sulfate. She has 40 mL of 25% solution. How many milliliters of 60% solution should Kendra add to obtain the required 30% solution?

EXPLORE Let x = the amount of 60% solution to be added.

PLAN

	Amount of Solution (mL)	Amount of Copper Sulfate
25% solution	40	0.25(40)
60% solution	x	0.60x
30% solution	40 + x	0.30(40 + x)

$$\underbrace{\text{amount of copper sulfate in 25\% solution}}_{} + \underbrace{\text{amount of copper sulfate in 60\% solution}}_{} = \underbrace{\text{amount of copper sulfate in mixture}}_{}$$

$$0.25(40) + 0.60x = 0.30(40 + x)$$

SOLVE
$$10 + 0.6x = 12 + 0.3x$$
$$0.3x = 2$$
$$x \approx 6.7 \quad \text{\textit{Round to the nearest tenth.}}$$

Kendra should add 6.7 mL of the 60% solution to the 40 mL of 25% solution. *Examine this solution.*

CHECKING FOR UNDERSTANDING

Communicating Mathematics

Read and study the lesson to answer each question. 1. See margin.

1. If Example 1 had stated that Dan sold 85 dozen less white chocolate cookies than chocolate chip, how would you define the variable?

2. In Example 2, suppose Kendra had added an 80% solution of copper sulfate. Write an equation to represent this situation.
$$0.25(40) + 0.80x = 0.30(40 + x)$$

Guided Practice

Copy and complete each chart. Write an equation to represent the situation.

3. **Money** Rodolfo has $2.55 in dimes and quarters. He has eight more dimes than quarters. How many quarters does he have?

	Number	Total Value
Quarters	x	0.25x
Dimes	x + 8	0.10(x + 8)

$$0.25x + 0.10(x + 8) = 2.55$$

4. **Sales** Peanuts sell for $3.00 per pound. Cashews sell for $6.00 per pound. How many pounds of cashews should be mixed with 12 pounds of peanuts to obtain a mixture that sells for $4.20 per pound?

	Pounds	Total Price
$3.00 peanuts	12	36
$6.00 cashews	x	6x
$4.20 mixture	12 + x	4.20(12 + x)

$$6x + 36 = 4.20(12 + x)$$

RETEACHING THE LESSON

Solve. Use the chart to help organize the information.

type	# ·	unit value	=	total value
A				
B				
total				

One hundred pigs and chickens in a field have 280 legs. Find the number of pigs and the number of chickens. **60 chickens, 40 pigs**

Additional Answer

1. Let c = number of dozens of chocolate chip cookies sold. Then c − 85 = number of dozens of white chocolate cookies sold.

Chalkboard Examples

For Example 1

Barrett's bookstore sells pencils for $0.10 each and erasers for $0.15 each. Last Tuesday, the store sold 17 more pencils than erasers for a total of $23.45. How many of each item were sold?
104 pencils, 87 erasers

For Example 2

Molly has 48 mL of a solution that is 25% acid. How much water should she add to obtain a solution that is 15% acid?
32 mL of water

EVALUATING THE LESSON

Checking for Understanding

Exercises 1-6 are designed to help you assess understanding through reading, writing, and speaking. You should work through Exercises 1-2 with your students, and then monitor their work on Exercises 3-6.

Reteaching Masters Booklet, p. 26

5. **Advertising** An advertisement for an orange drink claims that the drink contains 10% orange juice. How much pure orange juice would have to be added to 5 quarts of the drink to obtain a mixture containing 40% orange juice? $0.10(5) + 1.00n = 0.40(5 + n)$

	Quarts	Amount of Orange Juice
10% juice	5	0.10(5)
Pure juice	n	1.00n
40% juice	5 + n	0.40(5 + n)

6. **Finance** Paul Yu is investing $6000 in two accounts, part at 4.5% and the remainder at 6%. If the total annual interest earned from the two accounts is $279, how much did Paul deposit at each rate? $0.045x + 0.06(6.000 − x) = 279$

	Amount	Yearly Interest
At 4.5%	x	0.045x
At 6%	6000 − x	0.06(6000−x)

EXERCISES

7. 5 adults, 16 children

Applications

7. **Entertainment** At the Golden Oldies Theater, tickets for adults cost $5.50 and tickets for children cost $3.50. How many of each kind of ticket was purchased if 21 tickets were bought for $83.50?

8. **Food** A liter of cream has 9.2% butterfat. How much skim milk containing 2% butterfat should be added to the cream to obtain a mixture with 6.4% butterfat? **0.63 liter**

9. **Sales** Anne Leibowitz owns "The Coffee Pot," a specialty coffee store. She wants to create a special mix using two coffees, one priced at $6.40 per pound and the other at $7.28 per pound. How many pounds of the $7.28 coffee should she mix with 9 pounds of the $6.40 coffee to sell the mixture for $6.95 per pound? **15 pounds**

10. **Pharmacy** A pharmacist has 150 dL of a 25% solution of peroxide in water. How many deciliters of pure peroxide should be added to obtain a 40% solution? **37.5 dL**

11. **Sales** Ground chuck sells for $1.75 per pound. How many pounds of ground round selling for $2.45 per pound should be mixed with 20 pounds of ground chuck to obtain a mixture that sells for $2.05 per pound? **15 pounds**

12. **Entertainment** The Martins are going to Funtasticland, an amusement park. The total cost of tickets for a family of two adults and three children is $79.50. If an adult ticket costs $6.00 more than a child's ticket, find the cost of each. **child's-$13.50; adult-$19.50**

13. **Automotives** A car radiator has a capacity of 16 quarts and is filled with a 25% antifreeze solution. How much must be drained off and replaced with pure antifreeze to obtain a 40% antifreeze solution? **3.2 quar**

$25,600 at 5%;
$8000 at 8%

14. Finance Editon Longwell invested $33,600, part at 5% interest and the remainder at 8% interest. If he earned twice as much from his 5% investment as his 8% investment, how much did he invest at each rate?

20 liters **15. Chemistry** A solution is 50% alcohol. If 10 liters are removed from the solution and replaced with 10 liters of pure alcohol, the resulting solution is 75% alcohol. How many liters of the solution are there?

Critical Thinking **16.** Write a mixture problem for the equation $1.00x + 0.28(40) = 0.40(x + 40)$. **Answers may vary; see margin for sample answer.**

Mixed Review **17.** Define a variable, then write an equation for the following problem. In a football game, Diego gained 134 yards running. This was 17 yards more than the previous game. How many yards did he gain in both games? **(Lesson 2-8) See margin.**

18. Solve $-7h = -91$. **(Lesson 3-3) 13**

19. Physiology The brain of the average adult weighs about 2% of that person's total body weight. What is the approximate weight of the brain of a 160-pound person? **(Lesson 4-2) 3.2 pounds**

20. Sales Charlene paid $45.10, including $7\frac{1}{2}$% tax, for a pair of jeans. What was the cost of the jeans before tax? **(Lesson 4-4) $41.95**

MID-CHAPTER REVIEW

Solve each proportion. (Lesson 4-1)

1. $\frac{6}{5} = \frac{18}{t}$ 15

2. $\frac{21}{27} = \frac{x}{18}$ 14

3. $\frac{19.25}{a} = \frac{5.5}{2.94}$ 10.29

Answer the following. (Lesson 4-2)

4. Find 37.5% of 80. 30

5. Sixteen is 40% of what number? 40

6. Thirty-seven is what percent of 296? $12\frac{1}{2}$%

Solve. (Lesson 4-3)

7. **Finance** Isaac deposited an amount of money in the bank at 7% interest. After 3 months he received $14 interest. How much money had Isaac deposited in the bank? $800

Find the final price of each item. (Lesson 4-4)

8. 10-speed bike: $148.00 discount: 18% $121.36

9. books: $38.50 sales tax: 6% $40.81

Use a table to solve the problem. (Lesson 4-5)

10. **Consumer Awareness** The telephone company charges a base rate of $5.12 for a 20-minute long-distance telephone call. If Bob Hartschorn was charged $5.32 for a 22-minute call, how much should he be charged for an hour call? $9.12

EXTENDING THE LESSON

Math Power: Problem Solving

Magazines are mailed to 6240 employees using either a $0.25 stamp, a $0.41 stamp, or both a $0.25 and a $0.41 stamp. The total cost of postage is $2944.68. How many of each stamp were used if 630 more mailings cost $0.66 than $0.25, and the balance cost $0.41 each? 5714 at $0.25, 3698 at $0.41

Mid-Chapter Review

The Mid-Chapter Review provides students with a brief review of the concepts and skills in Lessons 4-1 through 4-6. Lesson numbers are given at the end of problems or instruction lines so students may review concepts not yet mastered.

Homework Exercises

Assignment Guide

Basic: 7-12, 16-20
Average: 8-13, 16-20
Enriched: 9-20
All: Mid-Chapter Review 1-10

Additional Answers

16. How many grams of salt must be added to 40 grams of a 28% salt solution to obtain a 40% salt solution?

17. Let y = number of yards Diego gained in both games; $134 + (134 - 17) = y$.

Enrichment Masters Booklet, p. 26

4-6 NAME _____ DATE _____
Enrichment Worksheet

Partnerships

Two or more people who agree to combine their money, goods, or skill in some business often do so by forming a *partnership*. Gains and losses in a partnership are usually divided in proportion to the amount of money each person has invested.

Sharon and Tina start a business to print restaurant menus using Tina's computer. For supplies and software, Sharon invests $1200 and Tina, $800. If their profit after the first year is $500, what is each person's share?

The entire investment is $1200 plus $800, or $2000.

Sharon's share is $\frac{\$1200}{\$2000}$, of $\frac{3}{5}$. Tina's share is $\frac{\$800}{\$2000}$, or $\frac{2}{5}$.

Answer each question.

1. In the problem above, what is Sharon's share of the profit? $300

2. What is Tina's share? $200

3. Sal and Mario were partners in a construction business. Sal put in $5000 and Mario, $4000. Their profit in 3 years was $4500. What was each partner's share? Sal: $2500; Mario: $2000

4. Tim, Bob, and Alice entered into a business partnership for 2 years. Tim put in $3600, Bob put in $2400, and Alice put in $2000. If their profit was $3000, what was each person's share? Tim: $1350; Bob: $900; Alice: $750

5. Fred, Vito, and Hal began with a capital of $28,000. Fred furnished $7000; Vito, $6000; and Hal, the remainder. If they gained 14% on their investment, what was each person's share? Fred: $980; Vito: $840; Hal: $2100

6. A storeroom belonging to Taylor, Bartinelli, & Wong was entirely destroyed by fire. They received $9675 insurance. What was each person's share, if Taylor owned 15%, Bartinelli, 40%, and Wong the remainder? Taylor: $1451.25; Bartinelli: $3870; Wong: $4353.75

7. Divide a profit of $7200 between two partners so that the ratio of the shares is 4 to 5. $3200, $4000

8. Divide a profit of $18,000 among three partners so that the ratio of the shares is 1:2:3. $3000, $6000, $9000

Lesson Resources

- Reteaching Master 4-7
- Practice Master 4-7
- Enrichment Master 4-7
- Video Algebra, 17

 Transparency 4-7 contains the 5-Minute Check and a teaching aid for this lesson.

INTRODUCING THE LESSON

🕐 5-Minute Check

(over Lesson 4-6)

Solve.

1. Lois has 27 coins in nickels and dimes. In all she has $1.90. How many of each coin does she have? **16 nickels, 11 dimes**

2. Tim has twice as much money in nickels as in dimes. He has 30 coins in all. How many of each coin does he have? **24 nickels and 6 dimes**

3. Gary has 42 coins in nickels, dimes, and quarters. If he has 8 more nickels than dimes and has $7.15 in all, how many of each coin does he have? **5 dimes, 13 nickels, 24 quarters**

4. How much pure copper must be added to 50.255 kg of an alloy containing 12% copper to raise the copper content to 21%? **5.725 kg**

Motivating the Lesson

Open the lesson by asking what units of measure should be used for each rate described below.
1. the speed of a person running
2. the speed of a caterpillar
3. the rate of growth of a child
4. the speed of light

TEACHING THE LESSON

Teaching Tip 1 Remind students that the actual solution of a uniform motion problem is a number with an appropriate unit of measure, not the equation containing the isolated variable.

Objective
4-7

After studying this lesson, you should be able to:
- solve problems involving uniform motion by using the formula $d = rt$.

When an object moves at a constant speed, or rate, it is said to be in **uniform motion**. The formula $d = rt$ is used to solve uniform motion problems. In the formula, d represents distance, r represents rate, and t represents time.

Example 1

APPLICATION
Travel

An airplane flies 1000 miles due east in 2 hours and 1000 miles due south in 3 hours. What is the average speed of the airplane?

EXPLORE	Let r = the average rate of speed at which the airplane travels. The airplane flies a total of 2000 miles in 5 hours.
PLAN	$d = rt$ $2000 = 5r$ *Replace d with 2000 and t with 5.*
SOLVE	$400 = r$ The average speed is 400 miles per hour.
EXAMINE	When r is 400, $2000 = 5(400)$. So, the answer is correct.

When solving uniform motion problems, it is often helpful to draw a diagram and to organize relevant information in a chart.

Example 2

APPLICATION
Travel

Don and Donna Wyatt leave their home at the same time, traveling in opposite directions. Don travels at 80 kilometers per hour and Donna travels at 72 kilometers per hour. In how many hours will they be 760 kilometers apart?

EXPLORE Draw a diagram to help analyze the problem.

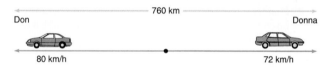

PLAN Organize the information in a chart. Let t represent the number of hours.

	r	$\cdot$ t	$=$ d	
Don	80	t	$80t$	*Don travels 80t km.*
Donna	72	t	$72t$	*Donna travels 72t km.*

Don's distance + Donna's distance = total distance
$$80t \quad + \quad 72t \quad = \quad 760$$

ALTERNATE TEACHING STRATEGIES

Using Cooperative Groups

Divide the class into small groups. Have each group write three word problems involving uniform motion. Groups should then switch problems and solve.

Using Charts

Much controversy has arisen over the maximum speed limit allowed on the nation's highways. Members of the transportation industry feel that raising the limit from 55 mph to 65 mph would save both time and money. Have students make a chart comparing these rates and their respective distances during a 24-hour period of travel.

SOLVE

$$152t = 760$$
$$t = 5 \quad \text{Check this solution.}$$

Teaching Tip ❶

In 5 hours, Don and Donna will be 760 kilometers apart.

Example 3

APPLICATION

Uniform Motion

At 8:00 A.M. Felicia leaves home on a business trip driving 35 miles per hour. A half hour later, José discovers that Felicia forgot her briefcase. He drives 50 miles per hour to catch up with her. If José is delayed 15 minutes with a flat tire, when will he catch up with Felicia?

EXPLORE   Let x = the time Felicia drives until José catches up with her.

PLAN

	r	$\cdot$ t	$= d$
Felicia	35	x	$35x$
José	50	$\left(x - \frac{3}{4}\right)$	$50\left(x - \frac{3}{4}\right)$

Felicia travels for x hours.

José starts $\frac{1}{2}$ hour later and is delayed $\frac{1}{4}$ hour (flat tire). José travels for $\left(x - \frac{3}{4}\right)$ hours.

José and Felicia travel the same distance.

Felicia's distance = José's distance

$$35x \quad = \quad 50\left(x - \frac{3}{4}\right)$$

SOLVE

$$35x = 50x - \frac{75}{2}$$
$$-15x = -\frac{75}{2}$$
$$x = 2\frac{1}{2} \quad \text{Check this solution.}$$

Felicia has been traveling for $2\frac{1}{2}$ hours when José catches up to her. José reaches Felicia at 8 A.M. + $2\frac{1}{2}$ hours or 10:30 A.M.

CHECKING FOR UNDERSTANDING

Communicating Mathematics

Read and study the lesson to answer each question. **See margin.**

1. In the formula $d = rt$, what do the d, r, and t represent?

2. Why is it sometimes helpful to use charts and diagrams?

Guided Practice

Use $d = rt$ to answer each question.   3a. 120 mi   b. 180 mi   c. 10 mi

d. $\frac{2}{3}k$ mi

3. Makya is driving 40 miles per hour. How far will she travel:
   a. in 3 hours?   b. in $4\frac{1}{2}$ hours?   c. in 15 minutes?   d. in k minutes?

4. Juan traveled 270 kilometers. What was his rate if he made the trip:
   a. in 5 hours?   b. in x hours?   a. 54 km/h   b. $\frac{270}{x}$ km/h

5. Patsy traveled 360 miles. How long did it take her if her rate was:
   a. 40 miles per hour?   b. 30 miles per hour?   c. x miles per hour?
   a. 9 hours   b. 12 hours   c. $\frac{360}{x}$ hours

LESSON 4-7 APPLICATION: UNIFORM MOTION   159

Additional Answers

1. d = distance, r = rate, t = time

2. to organize information and model the situation

EVALUATING THE LESSON

Checking for Understanding

Exercises 1-5 are designed to help you assess understanding through reading, writing, and speaking. You should work through Exercises 1-2 with your students, and then monitor their work on Exercises 3-5.

Reteaching Masters Booklet, p. 27

NAME _____   DATE _____

4-7	Reteaching Worksheet

Application: Uniform Motion

When an object moves without changing speed, or rate, it is said to be in **uniform motion.** The formula $d = rt$ is used to solve uniform motion problems such as the one below. In the formula, d represents distance, r represents rate, and t represents time.

Example: Bill Gutierrez left home driving at a speed of 54 miles per hour. How many hours did it take him to reach his destination 243 miles away?

Explore Let t = the time to drive 243 miles.

Plan $d = rt$
   $243 = 54t$

Solve $4\frac{1}{2} = t$
   It will take Bill $4\frac{1}{2}$ hours to drive 243 miles

Examine When t is $4\frac{1}{2}$ hours, d is $54 \cdot 4\frac{1}{2}$ or 243 miles.

Solve.

1. Mr. Anders and Ms. Rich each drove home from a Chicago business meeting. Mr. Anders traveled east at 100 kilometers per hour and Ms. Rich traveled west at 80 kilometers per hour. In how many hours were they 1000 kilometers apart?
   $5\frac{5}{9}$ h

2. Two planes left Kennedy Airport in New York City. One plane flew to London at a rate of 600 mi/h for 6 hours. The second plane flew in the opposite direction to Los Angeles at a rate of 650 mi/h for $3\frac{1}{2}$ hours. What is the distance between Los Angeles and London? 5875 miles

3. An express train left Austin and arrived in Waco 45 minutes later. A commuter train stopped at every station and made the same trip in 52 minutes. The distance between Austin and Waco is 100 miles. What was the rate of speed for each train?
   $133\frac{1}{3}$ mi/h; $115\frac{5}{13}$ mi/h

4. Justin left home at 8:00 A.M. riding his bike at 6 miles per hour. His brother Manuel left 2 hours later riding his bike at 8 miles per hour. At what time will Manuel catch up to Justin if Manuel is delayed 15 minutes by a freight train?
   5 P.M.

Closing the Lesson

Modeling Activity Have each student create a diagram that presents a motion problem. An example might be a drawing of two cars moving in opposite directions with labels showing the starting time of each as well as their rate. Tell students to switch drawings and then create and solve a motion problem from their classmate's diagram.

APPLYING THE LESSON

Homework Exercises

Assignment Guide
Basic: 6-14, 17-22
Average: 8-15, 17-22
Enriched: 10-22

Chapter 4, Quiz C, (Lessons 4-5 through 4-7), is available in the Evaluation Masters Booklet, p. 52.

Practice Masters Booklet, p. 30

4-7	NAME _____ DATE _____
	Practice Worksheet

Application: Uniform Motion

Solve.

1. At the same time Henry leaves Los Angeles for San Francisco, Christy leaves San Francisco for Los Angeles. The distance between the two cities is 380 miles. Christy's average speed is 9 miles per hour faster than Henry's. How fast is Henry driving if they pass each other in 4 hours?
43 mi/h

2. Two trains leave Raleigh at the same time, one traveling north, the other south. The first train travels at 50 miles per hour and second at 60 miles per hour. In how many hours will the trains be 275 miles apart?
2.5 h

3. A train leaves a city heading west and travels at 50 miles per hour. Three hours later, a second train leaves from the same place and travels in the same direction at 65 miles per hour. How long will it take for the second train to overtake the first train?
10 h

4. A ship travels from New York to Southampton, England at 33 miles per hour. A plane traveling 605 miles per hour takes 104 hours less time to make the same trip. How far apart are the two cities?
3630 mi

5. You are 36 miles from a friend. You both start riding your bicycles toward each other at the same time. You travel 15 miles per hour and your friend travels 3 miles per hour slower. How far will you travel before you meet your friend?
20 mi

6. Phil and Inez start from the same place at the same time and walk in opposite directions on Tremont Street. Inez walks twice as fast as Phil. After 30 minutes they are 24 blocks apart. How far does Phil walk?
8 blocks

---

6. At 1:30 P.M., an airplane leaves Tucson for Baltimore, a distance of 2240 miles. The plane flies at 280 miles per hour. A second airplane leaves Tucson at 2:15 P.M., and is scheduled to land in Baltimore 15 minutes before the first airplane. At what rate must the second airplane travel to arrive on schedule? **320 mph**

$3\frac{1}{2}$ hours

7. Two trains leave York at the same time, one traveling north, the other south. The first train travels at 40 miles per hour and the second at 30 miles per hour. In how many hours will the trains be 245 miles apart?

8. Rosita drove from Boston to Cleveland, a distance of 616 miles, to visit her grandparents. Her rest, gasoline, and food stops took 2 hours. What was her average speed if the trip took 16 hours altogether? **44 mph**

9. Two cyclists are traveling in the same direction on the same bike path. One travels at 20 miles per hour and the other at 14 miles per hour. After how many hours will they be 15 miles apart? $2\frac{1}{2}$ hours

10. At the same time Kris leaves Washington, D.C. for Detroit, Amy leaves Detroit for Washington, D.C. The distance between the cities is 510 miles. Amy's average speed is 5 miles per hour faster than Kris's. How fast is Kris driving if they pass each other in 6 hours? **40 mph**

B

11. *The Harvest Moon* leaves the pier at 9:00 A.M. at 8 knots (nautical miles per hour). A half hour later, *The River Nymph* leaves the same pier in the same direction traveling at 10 knots. At what time will *The Nymph* overtake *The Moon*? **11:30 A.M.**

12. Art leaves at 10:00 A.M., traveling at 50 miles per hour. At 11:30 A.M., Jennifer starts in the same direction at 45 miles per hour. When will they be 100 miles apart? **4:30 P.M.**

13. Guillermo is driving 40 miles per hour. After he has driven 30 miles, his brother Jorge starts driving in the same direction. At what rate must Jorge drive to catch up with Guillermo in 5 hours? **46 mph**

14. Two airplanes leave Dallas at the same time and fly in opposite directions. One airplane travels 80 miles per hour faster than the other. After three hours, they are 2940 miles apart. What is the rate of each airplane? **450 mph, 530 mph**

C

240 km

15. An express train travels 80 kilometers per hour from Wheaton to Ward. A local train, traveling at 48 kilometers per hour, takes 2 hours longer for the same trip. How far apart are Wheaton and Ward?

16. Marcus Jackson runs a 440-yard run in 55 seconds and Alfonso Rey runs it in 88 seconds. To have Marcus and Alfonso finish at the same time, how much of a headstart should Marcus give Alfonso? State your answer in yards. **165 yd**

RETEACHING THE LESSON

Have a small group of students use a triple-beam balance and 4 stacks of uniform washers. Each stack should contain a different number of washers tied together with strong thread so students cannot weigh just one washer at a time.

# of washers (*n*)	weight (*W*)

Count and record the number of washers in each stack. Weigh the first stack. Use this result to predict the weights of each of the three remaining stacks. Then weigh these stacks. Write and solve a proportion for the first stack to find the constant of variation *K* in $W = Kn$. What does it represent as a rate? **weight of 1 washer**

17. Two trains are 240 miles apart traveling toward each other on parallel tracks. One travels at 35 miles per hour and the other travels at 45 miles per hour. At the front of the faster train is a bee that can fly at 75 miles per hour. The bee flies from one train to the other until the trains pass each other. When the trains pass, how far has the bee flown? **225 miles**

18. Mary Baylor drove to work on Thursday at 40 miles per hour and arrived one minute late. She left at the same time on Friday, drove at 45 miles per hour, and arrived one minute early. How far does Ms. Baylor drive to work? **12 miles**

Mixed Review

20. See margin.

19. Write an algebraic expression for *five less than w*. **(Lesson 1-1)** $w - 5$

20. Name the property illustrated by $5(3 - 3) = 0$. **(Lesson 1-4)**

21. Find the sum: $-15 + 23$. **(Lesson 2-1)** 8

22. **Finance** A stockbroker has invested part of $25,000 at 10.5% interest and the rest at $12\frac{1}{4}\%$ interest. If the annual income earned from these investments is $2,843.75, find the amount invested at each rate. **(Lesson 4-6)** **$12,500 at each rate**

〜〜〜〜〜〜〜〜〜〜 **APPLICATION** 〜〜〜〜〜〜〜〜〜〜

Travel Agents

Many travelers rely on travel agents to make the best arrangements for them. Travel agents arrange for transportation, hotel accomodations, car rentals, and vacation packages. They may also give advice on weather conditions, time-zone changes, tourist attractions, and restaurants. For the international traveler, travel agents provide information on customs regulations, required papers (like passports and visas), and monetary exchange rates.

Suppose you wanted to fly from Atlanta, Georgia, to Frankfurt, Germany. The timetable at the right shows that Lufthansa Airlines has a number of nonstop flights from Atlanta to Frankfurt. One flight leaves Atlanta at 5:00 P.M. and arrives in Frankfurt at 7:25 A.M. Your travel agent would point out that the time in Frankfurt is 6 hours ahead of the time in Atlanta. With this information, you can determine the length of the flight. The time from 5:00 P.M. to 7:25 A.M. is about $14\frac{1}{2}$ hours. So the flight is about $14\frac{1}{2} - 6$ or $8\frac{1}{2}$ hours long.

From: **ATLANTA, GA.**

Frankfurt, West Germany
4615 mi
LUFTHANSA GERMAN AIRLINES FROM ATLANTA
TO FRANKFURT

56	5:00p	7:25a	447	Nonstop
24	6:25p	8:45a	445	Nonstop
7	7:10p	11:35a	441	Nonstop
3	9:15p	11:35a	443	Nonstop
1	9:15p	11:35a	439	Nonstop

The timetable also shows that the air distance between the two cities is 4615 miles. Using the formula for uniform motion, you can find the average speed of the airplane.

$$d = rt$$
$$4615 = 8.5r$$
$$540 = r \qquad \text{The average speed would be 540 miles per hour.}$$

EXTENDING THE LESSON

Math Power: Connections

Ben who is bicycling at the rate of *x* mph has a head start of 2 miles on Rachel who is bicycling at the rate of *y* mph ($y > x$). In how many hours will Rachel overtake Ben? $\dfrac{2}{y - x}$ **hours**

Additional Answer

20. multiplicative property of zero.

Lesson Resources

- Reteaching Master 4-8
- Practice Master 4-8
- Enrichment Master 4-8
- Video Algebra, 45

 Transparency 4-8 contains the 5-Minute Check and a teaching aid for this lesson.

INTRODUCING THE LESSON

🕐 5-Minute Check

(over Lesson 4-7)

Solve.

1. Adam is driving 75 km/h. How far will he travel in 3 hours? **225 km**
2. Sue is driving 45 mph. How far will she travel in 4 hours? **180 miles**
3. Juan traveled 270 miles. What is his rate if he made the trip in 9 hours? **30 mph**
4. David rode his bicycle 36 km. What is his rate if he began riding 4 hours ago? **9 km/h**
5. Courtney traveled 320 miles. What is her rate if she made the trip in 8 hours? **40 mph**

Motivating the Lesson

Put 400 mL of water in a 500 mL beaker. Then add an object such as a spoon or glass stirring rod to the beaker. Ask students to describe what happens. **The water level rises.** Add additional spoons or rods to the beaker and observe. Challenge students to identify the relationship between the water level and the objects. **The rise of water level is directly proportional to the number of spoons or rods added to the beaker.**

4-8 Direct Variation

Objective
4-8

After studying this lesson, you should be able to:
- solve problems involving direct variations.

Application

Yana is taking part in a work-study program offered by Jackson High School. After school, he works as an assistant manager at Victory Sporting Goods, where he earns $5.95 per hour. The table below relates the number of hours that he works (x) and his pay (y).

x	5	10	15	20	25
y	$29.75	$59.50	$89.25	$119	$148.75

Teaching Tip ❶

Yana's income depends *directly* on the number of hours that he works. The relationship between the number of hours worked and his income is shown by the equation y = 5.95x. This type of equation is called a **direct variation**. We say that y *varies directly as x*.

Definition of Direct Variation	A direct variation is described by an equation of the form $y = kx$, where $k \neq 0$.

Teaching Tip ❷

In the equation y = kx, k is called the **constant of variation**. To find the constant of variation, divide each side by x.

$$\frac{y}{x} = k$$

Example 1

Teaching Tip ❸

The weight of an object on the moon varies directly as its weight on Earth. With all his gear on, Neil Armstrong weighed 360 pounds on Earth, but when he stepped on the moon on July 20, 1969, he weighed 60 pounds. Kristina weighs 108 pounds on Earth. What would she weigh on the moon?

Let x = weight on Earth, and let y = weight on the moon. Find the value of k in the equation y = kx.

$$k = \frac{y}{x}$$

$$k = \frac{60}{360} \quad \text{Substitute the astronaut's weights for x and y.}$$

$$k = \frac{1}{6}$$

Next find Kristina's weight on the moon. Find y when x is 108.

$$y = kx$$

$$y = \frac{1}{6}(108) \quad \text{Substitute 108 for x and } \tfrac{1}{6} \text{ for k.}$$

$$y = 18 \quad \text{Thus, Kristina would weigh 18 pounds on the moon.}$$

ALTERNATE TEACHING STRATEGIES

Using Connections

Have students draw a triangle with the following sides: 2 cm, 3 cm, and 4 cm. Challenge students to draw another triangle that is directly proportional to the first. Encourage students to describe the methods used to determine appropriate side lengths of the second triangle.

Direct variations are also related to proportions. From the table on Yana's income, many proportions can be formed. Two examples are shown.

number of hours

$$\frac{5}{2975} = \frac{15}{8925}$$

income

number of hours $\frac{10}{25} = \frac{5950}{14,875}$ *income*

x_1 is read "x sub 1."

Two general forms for proportions like these can be derived from the equation $y = kx$. Let (x_1, y_1) be a solution for $y = kx$. Let a second solution be (x_2, y_2). Then $y_1 = kx_1$ and $y_2 = kx_2$.

$y_1 = kx_1$ *This equation describes a direct variation.*

$\dfrac{y_1}{y_2} = \dfrac{kx_1}{kx_2}$ *Use the division property of equality. Since y_2 and kx_2 are equivalent, you can divide the left side by y_2 and the right side by kx_2.*

$\dfrac{y_1}{y_2} = \dfrac{x_1}{x_2}$ *Simplify.*

Let's see how another proportion can be derived from this proportion.

$x_2y_1 = x_1y_2$ *Find the cross products of the proportion above.*

$\dfrac{x_2y_1}{y_1y_2} = \dfrac{x_1y_2}{y_1y_2}$ *Divide each side by y_1y_2.*

$\dfrac{x_2}{y_2} = \dfrac{x_1}{y_1}$ *Simplify.*

Example 2

If y varies directly as x, and $y = 27$ when $x = 6$, find x when $y = 45$.

Use $\dfrac{y_1}{y_2} = \dfrac{x_1}{x_2}$ to solve the problem.

$\dfrac{27}{45} = \dfrac{6}{x_2}$ *Let $y_1 = 27$, $x_1 = 6$, and $y_2 = 45$.*

$27x_2 = 45(6)$ *Find the cross products.*

$27x_2 = 270$

$x_2 = 10$

Thus, $x = 10$ when $y = 45$.

Example 3

APPLICATION
Electronics

In an electrical transformer, voltage is directly proportional to the number of turns on the coil. If 110 volts comes from 55 turns, what would be the voltage produced by 66 turns?

Write an equation of the form $y = kx$ for the variation.

$110 = 55k$

$2 = k$

The equation is $y = 2x$. Thus, the voltage produced by 66 turns would be $2(66)$ or 132 volts.

LESSON 4-8 DIRECT VARIATION 163

RETEACHING THE LESSON

For each exercise, write a proportion to solve the problem. Do *not* solve the problem.

1. A car used 6 gallons of gasoline in 150 miles. At this rate, how much gasoline would the car use in 475 miles? $\dfrac{6}{150} = \dfrac{x}{475}$

2. There are 35 calories in a teaspoon of sugar. How many calories are there in 4 teaspoons of sugar? $\dfrac{35}{1} = \dfrac{x}{4}$

Chalkboard Examples

For Example 1

A car uses 8 gallons of gasoline to travel 290 miles. How much gasoline will the car use to travel 400 miles?   **11.034 gallons**

For Example 2

Solve each problem. Assume that y varies directly as x.

a. If $y = 6$ when $x = 8$, find y when $x = 12$.   **9**

b. If $y = 8$ when $x = 20$, find x when $y = 6$.   **15**

c. If $y = 3$ when $x = 9$, find y when $x = 40.5$.   **13.5**

d. If $x = -5$ when $y = 6$, find y when $x = -8$.   **9.6**

For Example 3

If 4 pounds of peanuts cost $7.50, how much will 2.5 pounds cost?   **$4.69**

Teaching Tip ① Point out that the phrase *y varies directly as x* can also be phrased *y is directly proportional to x*. Both phrases mean that as *y* increases or decreases in value, *x* respectively increases or decreases in value.

Reteaching Masters Booklet, p. 28

NAME _____ DATE _____

4-8   **Reteaching Worksheet**

Direct Variation

If two variables x and y are related by the equation $y = kx$, where k is a nonzero constant, then the equation is called a **direct variation**. The constant k is the **constant of variation**. Any problem that can be solved using direction variation can also be solved using a proportion. For any such problems, any of the following three formulas may be used.

$$y = kx \qquad \frac{x_1}{x_2} = \frac{y_1}{y_2} \qquad \frac{x_1}{y_1} = \frac{x_2}{y_2}$$

Example 1: If y varies directly as x, and $y = 12$ when $x = 4$, find y when $x = 7$.

$k = \dfrac{y}{x}$ (another form of $y = kx$)

$k = \dfrac{12}{4}$

$k = 3$

$y = kx$

$y = 3(7)$

$y = 21$

Example 2: On the map of Alicia's property, 1 cm represents 80 m. Find the distance represented by 3.5 cm.

$\dfrac{y_1}{y_2} = \dfrac{x_1}{x_2}$

$\dfrac{80}{y_2} = \dfrac{1}{3.5}$

$1y_2 = 80(3.5)$

$y_2 = 280$

The actual distance is 280 m.

Solve. Assume that y varies directly as x.

1. If $y = 4$ when $x = 2$, find y when $x = 16$.   32

2. If $y = 9$ when $x = -3$, find x when $y = 6$. -2

3. If $y = \dfrac{2}{5}$ when $x = \dfrac{1}{3}$, find y when $x = \dfrac{1}{10}$. $\dfrac{3}{10}$

4. If $y = \dfrac{1}{4}$ when $x = \dfrac{1}{8}$, find x when $y = \dfrac{3}{16}$. $\dfrac{3}{32}$

Solve.

5. John's wages vary directly as the number of hours that he works. If his wages for 5 days are $260, how much will they be for 20 days? $1040

6. A truck uses 20 gallons of diesel fuel to travel 325 miles. How much diesel fuel will the truck use to travel 1000 miles? About 61.5 gal.

CHECKING FOR UNDERSTANDING

Communicating Mathematics

Read and study the lesson to answer each question. **1. See margin.**

1. How do you find the constant of variation in a direct variation?

2. *True* or *false:* A person's height varies directly as his or her age. Why or why not? **False, because growth rates vary widely.**

Guided Practice

Find the constant of variation for each direct variation.

3. $y = 3x$ **3**   4. $-3a = b$ **−3**   5. $d = 7t$ **7**   6. $n = \frac{1}{3}m$ **$\frac{1}{3}$**

Solve. Assume that y varies directly as x.

7. If $y = 12$ when $x = 3$, find y when $x = 7$. **28**

8. If $y = -8$ when $x = 2$, find y when $x = 10$. **−40**

EXERCISES

Practice

Solve. Assume that y varies directly as x.

9. If $y = 3$ when $x = 15$, find y when $x = -25$. **−5**

10. If $y = -7$ when $x = -14$, find y when $x = 20$. **10**

11. If $y = -6$ when $x = 9$, find x when $y = -4$. **6**

12. If $y = -8$ when $x = -3$, find x when $y = 6$. **$2\frac{1}{4}$**

13. If $y = 12$ when $x = 15$, find x when $y = 21$. **$26\frac{1}{4}$**

14. If $y = 2\frac{2}{3}$ when $x = \frac{1}{4}$, find y when $x = 1\frac{1}{8}$. **12**

15-20. For Exercises 9-14, find the constant of variation. Then write an equation of the form $y = kx$ for each variation. **See margin.**

21. y varies directly as the square of x. If $y = 14$ when $x = 4$, find y when $x = 9$. **$\frac{567}{8}$**

22. y varies directly as $x - 10$. If $y = -12$ when $x = -3$, find x when $y = 7$. **$\frac{211}{12}$**

Critical Thinking

23. Look back at the proportions on page 163. Does it follow that $\frac{y_1}{x_2} = \frac{x_1}{y_2}$? Why or why not? **No; there is no divisor of $x_2 y_1 = x_1 y_2$ that would produce this result.**

Applications

24. **Electronics** If 2.5 m of copper wire weighs 0.325 kg, how much will 75 m of wire weigh? **9.75 kg**

25. **Consumerism** Six pounds of sugar costs $2.00. At that rate, how much will 40 pounds of sugar cost? **$13.33**

26. **Travel** A car uses 5 gallons of gasoline to travel 143 miles. At that rate, how much gasoline will the car use to travel 200 miles? **6.993 gallons**

27. **Chemistry** Charles' Law says that the volume of a gas is directly proportional to its temperature. If the volume of a gas is 2.5 cubic feet at 150° (absolute temperature), what is the volume of the same gas at 200° (absolute temperature)? **$3\frac{1}{3}$ ft³**

164 CHAPTER 4 APPLICATIONS OF RATIONAL NUMBERS

Additional Answers

1. **Divide each side of the equation $y = kx$ by x.**

15. $\frac{1}{5}$; $y = \frac{1}{5}x$

16. $\frac{1}{2}$; $y = \frac{1}{2}x$

17. $-\frac{2}{3}$; $y = -\frac{2}{3}x$

18. $\frac{8}{3}$; $y = \frac{8}{3}x$

19. $\frac{4}{5}$; $y = \frac{4}{5}x$

20. $\frac{32}{3}$; $y = \frac{32}{3}x$

28. Solve $5n + 3 = 9$.   (Lesson 3-5) $\frac{6}{5}$

29. Sales tax of 6% is added to a purchase of $11. Find the total price.   (Lesson 4-4) $11.66

30. Make a table to solve the following problem.   (Lesson 4-5)

    Mei tore a sheet of paper in half. Then she tore each of the resulting pieces in half. If she continued this process 15 more times, how many pieces of paper would she end up with? 2^{17} or 131,072

31. **Sales** How much coffee that costs $3 a pound should be mixed with 5 pounds of coffee that costs $3.50 a pound to obtain a mixture that costs $3.25 a pound?   (Lesson 4-6) 5 pounds

32. **Travel** Brad and Scott leave home at the same time, riding on their bicycles in opposite directions. Scott rides at 10 kilometers per hour and Brad rides at 12 kilometers per hour. In how many hours will they be 110 kilometers apart?   (Lesson 4-7) 5 hours

HISTORY CONNECTION

A'h-Mose

A'h-mose (more commonly referred to as Ahmes) was an Egyptian scribe who copied an earlier mathematics text on papyrus in 1650 B.C. Papyrus was a writing material made from the papyrus plant that was used by the ancient Egyptians. A'h-mose's papyrus was purchased by the English Egyptologist A. Henry Rhind. As a result, it has come to be called the *Rhind Papyrus*.

A'h-mose began his text with a table of fractions and an explanation of the Egyptian method of using fractions. The ancient Egyptians defined all fractions, with the single exception of the fraction $\frac{2}{3}$, in terms of *unit fractions*. That is, they only used fractions with a numerator of one. For example, instead of writing $\frac{3}{4}$, they wrote $\frac{1}{2} + \frac{1}{4}$. Instead of writing $\frac{5}{6}$, they wrote $\frac{1}{2} + \frac{1}{3}$.

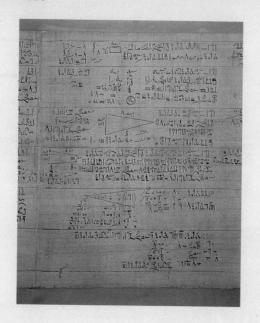

Write each fraction in terms of unit fractions only.

1. $\frac{2}{5}$ $\frac{1}{3} + \frac{1}{15}$

2. $\frac{3}{8}$ $\frac{1}{4} + \frac{1}{8}$

3. $\frac{5}{12}$ $\frac{1}{4} + \frac{1}{6}$

4. $\frac{7}{24}$ $\frac{1}{6} + \frac{1}{8}$

LESSON 4-8   DIRECT VARIATION   165

EXTENDING THE LESSON

Math Power: Problem Solving

Six feet of steel wire weighs 0.7 kilograms. How much does 100 feet of steel wire weigh?

$11\frac{2}{3}$ kg or $11.\overline{6}$ kg

History Connection

The History Connection features introduce students to persons or cultures who were involved in the development of mathematics. You may want students to further research A'h-mose or to research the invention of fractions.

INTRODUCING THE LESSON

 5-Minute Check

(over Lesson 4-8)

Tell whether the equation shows direct variation. If so, state the constant of variation.

1. $y = 4x$ yes, 4
2. $7 \times 2 = 10y$ no

Solve. Assume that y varies directly as x.

3. If $y = 15$ when $x = 3$, find y when $x = 4$. 20
4. If $y = 10$ when $x = 20$, find y when $x = 11$. 5.5
5. If 6 pounds of sugar cost $2.00, how much will 40 pounds cost? $13.33

Motivating the Lesson

Discuss the meaning of the terms "directly" and "inversely" with the class. Have a volunteer mime a series of five actions. Ask other volunteers to mime the five actions directly and then inversely.

TEACHING THE LESSON

Teaching Tip ❶ Emphasize that any of the length/width combinations give a product of 4. Therefore, in order to always obtain that same product, as one increases, the other must decrease.

4-9 Inverse Variation

Objective
4-9

After studying this lesson, you should be able to:
■ solve problems involving inverse variations.

Connection

The three rectangles at the right have the same area, 4 square units. Notice that as the length increases, the width decreases. As the length decreases, the width increases. However, their product stays the same.

ℓ	2	4	8
w	2	1	$\frac{1}{2}$
A	4	4	4

Teaching Tip ❶

This is an example of an **inverse variation**. We say that ℓ *varies inversely as* w.

Definition of Inverse Variation	An inverse variation is described by an equation of the form $xy = k$, where $k \neq 0$.

Sometimes inverse variations are written in the form $y = \frac{k}{x}$.

Example 1

APPLICATION
Music

The pitch of a musical tone varies inversely as its wavelength. If one tone has a pitch of 440 vibrations per second and a wavelength of 2.4 feet, find the wavelength of a tone that has a pitch of 660 vibrations per second.

Let p = pitch and w = wavelength. Find the value of k.

$pw = k$
$(440)(2.4) = k$ *Substitute 440 for p and 2.4 for w.*
$1056 = k$ *The constant of variation is 1056.*

Next, find the wavelength of the second tone.

$w = \dfrac{k}{p}$ *Divide each side of pw = k by p.*

$w = \dfrac{1056}{660}$ *Substitute 1056 for k and 660 for p.*

$w = 1.6$ The wavelength is 1.6 feet.

Let (x_1, y_1) be a solution of an inverse variation, $xy = k$. Let (x_2, y_2) be a second solution. Then $x_1y_1 = k$ and $x_2y_2 = k$.

$x_1y_1 = k$
$x_1y_1 = x_2y_2$ *You can substitute x_2y_2 for k because $x_2y_2 = k$.*

166 CHAPTER 4 APPLICATIONS OF RATIONAL NUMBERS

ALTERNATE TEACHING STRATEGIES

Using Models

In sound and harmonics, the frequency of a vibrating string is inversely proportional to its length. Demonstrate this principle using a violin, guitar, or other stringed instrument to show that the length of a string determines the type of sound produced.

Using Logical Reasoning

Does the percent grade on a test vary directly or inversely as the number of correct answers? directly

The equation $x_1y_1 = x_2y_2$ is called the *product rule for inverse variations*. Study how it can be used to form a proportion.

$$x_1y_1 = x_2y_2$$
$$\frac{x_1y_1}{x_2y_1} = \frac{x_2y_2}{x_2y_1} \qquad \textit{Divide each side by } x_2y_1.$$
$$\frac{x_1}{x_2} = \frac{y_2}{y_1} \qquad \textit{Notice that this proportion is different from}$$
the proportions for direct variation on page 163. **Teaching Tip ②**

Example 2

If y varies inversely as x, and $y = 3$ when $x = 12$, find x when $y = 4$.

Let $x_1 = 12$, $y_1 = 3$, and $y_2 = 4$. Solve for x_2.

Method 1	**Method 2**
Use the product rule.	Use the proportion.
$x_1y_1 = x_2y_2$	$\frac{x_1}{x_2} = \frac{y_2}{y_1}$
$12 \cdot 3 = x_2 \cdot 4$	$\frac{12}{x_2} = \frac{4}{3}$
$\frac{36}{4} = x_2$	$36 = 4x_2$
$9 = x_2$	$9 = x_2$

Thus, $x = 9$ when $y = 4$.

If you have observed people on a seesaw, you may have noticed that the heavier person must sit closer to the fulcrum (pivot point) to balance the seesaw. A seesaw is a type of *lever*, and all lever problems involve inverse variation.

Property of Levers

Suppose weights w_1 and w_2 are placed on a lever at distances d_1 and d_2, respectively, from the fulcrum. The lever is balanced when $w_1d_1 = w_2d_2$.

The property of levers is illustrated at the right.

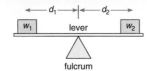

Example 3

APPLICATION
Physics

An 8-ounce weight is placed at one end of a yardstick. A 10-ounce weight is placed at the other end. Where should the fulcrum be placed to balance the yardstick?

Let d = distance from fulcrum to 8-ounce weight, in inches.
Then $36 - d$ = distance from fulcrum to 10-ounce weight, in inches.

$$w_1d_1 = w_2d_2$$
$$8d = 10(36 - d)$$
$$8d = 360 - 10d \qquad \textit{Distributive property}$$
$$18d = 360$$
$$d = 20$$

The fulcrum should be placed 20 inches from the 8-ounce weight.

RETEACHING THE LESSON

With a set number of pizza pieces, the number of people and the number of pizza pieces per person vary inversely. With 3 people, there are 10 pizza pieces per person. How many pieces of pizza would each person get if there are 4 people?   **7.5**
5 people?   **6** 6 people?   **5**

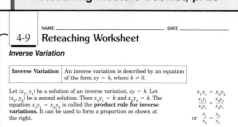

Teaching Tip ③ In this example, two persons are seated on the same side of a seesaw, and a third person is seated on the other side. Point out that the formula to use in this case is $w_1d_1 + w_2d_2 = w_3d_3$. In general, when two or more weights are placed on the same side of a lever, find the product of w and d for each weight, then add.

EVALUATING THE LESSON

Checking for Understanding

Exercises 1-14 are designed to help you assess understanding through reading, writing, and speaking. You should work through Exercises 1-3 with your students, and then monitor their work on Exercises 4-14.

Practice Masters Booklet, p. 32

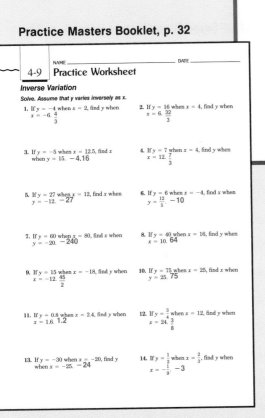

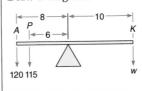

Example 4

APPLICATION

Physics

Pat and Ann are seated on the same side of a seesaw. Pat is 6 feet from the fulcrum and weighs 115 pounds. Ann is 8 feet from the fulcrum and weighs 120 pounds. Kai is seated on the other side of the seesaw, 10 feet from the fulcrum. If the seesaw is balanced, how much does Kai weigh?

Draw a diagram.

Let w = Kai's weight.

$$120(8) + 115(6) = 10w$$
$$960 + 690 = 10w$$
$$1650 = 10w$$
$$165 = w$$

Thus, Kai weighs 165 pounds.

CHECKING FOR UNDERSTANDING

Communicating Mathematics

Read and study the lesson to fill in the blanks.

1. A(n) __?__ variation is described by an equation of the form $xy = k$, where $k \neq 0$. **inverse**

2. A(n) __?__ variation is described by an equation of the form $y = kx$, where $k \neq 0$. **direct**

3. The equation $x_1y_1 = x_2y_2$ is called the __?__. **product rule**

Guided Practice

Determine which equations are inverse variations and which are direct variations. Then find the constant of variation.

4. $ab = 6$ **I, 6**

5. $c = 3.14d$ **D, 3.14**

6. $\frac{50}{y} = x$ **I, 50**

7. $\frac{1}{5}a = d$ **D, $\frac{1}{5}$**

8. $s = 3t$ **D, 3**

9. $14 = ab$ **I, 14**

10. $xy = 1$ **I, 1**

11. $a = \frac{7}{b}$ **I, 7**

12. $2x = y$ **D, 2**

Suppose two people are on a seesaw. For the seesaw to balance, which person must sit closer to the fulcrum?

13. Jorge, 168 pounds
Emilio, 220 pounds **Emilio**

14. Shawn, 114 pounds
Shannon, 97 pounds **Shawn**

EXERCISES

Practice

Solve. Assume that y varies inversely as x.

A

15. If $y = 24$ when $x = 8$, find y when $x = 4$. **48**

16. If $y = -6$ when $x = -2$, find y when $x = 5$. $\frac{12}{5}$

17. If $y = 99$ when $x = 11$, find x when $y = 11$. **99**

18. If $y = 7$ when $x = \frac{2}{3}$, find y when $x = 7$. $\frac{2}{3}$

B

19. If $x = 2.7$ when $y = 8.1$, find y when $x = 3.6$. **6.075**

20. If $x = 6.1$ when $y = 4.4$, find x when $y = 3.2$. **8.3875**

Critical Thinking

21. Assume y varies inversely as x. If the value of x is doubled, what happens to the value of y? If the value of y is tripled, what happens to the value of x? **It is halved; it is divided by 3.**

Applications

Chemistry: Boyle's Law states that the volume of a gas (V) varies inversely with applied pressure (P). This is shown by the formula $P_1V_1 = P_2V_2$. Use the formula to solve Exercises 22 and 23.

22. Pressure on 60 m³ of a gas is raised from 1 atmosphere to 2 atmospheres. What new volume does the gas occupy? **30 m³**

23. A helium-filled balloon has a volume of 16 m³ at sea level. The pressure at sea level is 1 atmosphere. The balloon rises to a point in the air where the pressure is 0.75 atmosphere. What is its volume? **$21\frac{1}{3}$ m³**

Harmonics: The frequency of a vibrating string is inversely proportional to its length. Use this information to solve Exercises 24 and 25.

24. A violin string 10 inches long vibrates at a frequency of 512 cycles per second. Find the frequency of an 8-inch string. **640 cycles per second**

25. A piano string 36 inches long vibrates at a frequency of 480 cycles per second. Find the frequency of the string if it were shortened to 24 inches. **720 cycles per second**

Physics: Use the property of levers to solve Exercises 26-28.

26. Grant, who weighs 150 pounds, is seated 8 feet from the fulcrum of a seesaw. Mariel is seated 10 feet from the fulcrum. If the seesaw is balanced, how much does Mariel weigh? **120 pounds**

27. Weights of 100 pounds and 115 pounds are placed on a lever. The two weights are 15 feet apart, and the lever is balanced. How far from the fulcrum is the 100-pound weight? **$8\frac{1}{43}$ feet; about 8 ft $\frac{1}{4}$ in.**

28. Macawi, who weighs 108 pounds, is seated 5 feet from the fulcrum of a seesaw. Barbara is seated on the same side of the seesaw, two feet farther from the fulcrum than Macawi. Barbara weighs 96 pounds. The seesaw is balanced when Sue, who weighs 101 pounds, sits on the other side. How far is Sue from the fulcrum? **12 feet**

Mixed Review

29. Evaluate $5 - y$, if $y = 20$. **(Lesson 2-2)** -15

30. Solve $\frac{x-7}{5} = 12$. **(Lesson 3-7) 67**

31. Use $I = prt$ to find r if $I = \$3487.50$, $p = \$6000$, and $t = 3\frac{1}{2}$ years. **(Lesson 4-3) 16.6%**

32. **Chemistry** A chemist has 2.5 liters of a solution that is 70% acid. How much water should be added to obtain a 50% acid solution? **(Lesson 4-6) 1 liter**

33. **Employment** Hugo's wages vary directly as the time he works. If his wages for 4 days are $110, how much will they be for 17 days? **(Lesson 4-8) $467.50**

EXTENDING THE LESSON

Math Power: Reasoning

In a closed room, the number of hours at a safe oxygen level varies inversely as the number of people in the room. If there are 2 hours of oxygen available for 100 people, how many hours of oxygen are there for 600 people? **$\frac{1}{3}$ hour or 20 minutes**

Closing the Lesson
Modeling Activity Have students create a diagram that illustrates how a lever works.

APPLYING THE LESSON

Homework Exercises

Assignment Guide
Basic: 15-24, 29-33
Average: 17-33
Enriched: 19-33

Chapter 4, Quiz D, (Lessons 4-8 through 4-9), is available in the Evaluation Masters Booklet, p. 52.

Enrichment Masters Booklet, p. 29

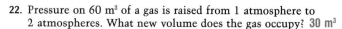

NAME _____ DATE _____

4-9 Enrichment Worksheet

Analyzing Data

Fill in each table below. Then write *inversely*, or *directly* to complete each conclusion.

1.

I	2	4	8	16	32
w	4	4	4	4	4
A	8	16	32	64	128

For a set of rectangles with a width of 4, the area varies **directly** as the length.

2.

Hours	3	4	5	6
Speed	55	55	55	55
Distance	165	220	275	330

For a car traveling at 55 mi/h, the distance covered varies **directly** as the hours driven.

3.

Oat bran	$\frac{1}{3}$ cup	$\frac{2}{3}$ cup	1 cup
Water	1 cup	2 cup	3 cup
Servings	1	2	3

The number of servings of oat bran varies **directly** as the number of cups of oat bran.

4.

Hours of Work	128	128	128
People Working	2	4	8
Hours per Person	64	32	16

A job requires 128 hours of work. The number of hours each person works varies **inversely** as the number of people working.

5.

Miles	100	100	100	100
Rate	20	25	50	100
Hours	5	4	2	1

For a 100-mile car trip, the time the trip takes varies **inversely** as the average rate of speed the car travels.

6.

b	3	4	5	6
h	10	10	10	10
A	15	20	25	30

For a set of right triangles with a height of 10, the area varies **directly** as the base.

Use the table at the right.

7. x varies **directly** as y.

8. z varies **inversely** as y.

9. x varies **inversely** as z.

x	1	1.5	2	2.5	3
y	2	3	4	5	6
z	60	40	30	24	20

SUMMARY AND REVIEW

VOCABULARY

Upon completing this chapter, you should be
familiar with the following terms:

base	138	146	percent of decrease
constant of variation	162	146	percent of increase
direct variation	162	134	proportion
extremes	134	136, 138	rate
inverse variation	166	134	ratio
means	134	142	simple interest
percent	138	158	uniform motion
percentage	138		

SKILLS AND CONCEPTS

OBJECTIVES AND EXAMPLES	REVIEW EXERCISES

Upon completing this chapter, you should be able to:

Use these exercises to review and prepare for the chapter test.

- solve proportions **(Lesson 4-1)**

$$\frac{x}{3} = \frac{x + 1}{2}$$
$$2(x) = 3(x + 1)$$
$$2x = 3x + 3$$
$$-x = 3$$
$$x = -3$$

Solve each proportion.

1. $\frac{6}{15} = \frac{n}{45}$ 18

2. $\frac{4}{8} = \frac{11}{t}$ 22

3. $\frac{x}{11} = \frac{35}{55}$ 7

4. $\frac{5}{6} = \frac{a - 2}{4}$ $\frac{32}{6}$, $5.\overline{3}$

5. $\frac{y + 4}{y - 1} = \frac{4}{3}$ 16

6. $\frac{z - 7}{6} = \frac{z + 3}{7}$ 67

- solve percent problems **(Lesson 4-2)**

Nine is what percent of 15?

$$\frac{9}{15} = \frac{r}{100}$$
$$9(100) = 15r$$
$$\frac{900}{15} = \frac{15r}{15}$$
$$60 = r$$

Solve.

7. What number is 60% of 80? 48

8. Twenty-one is 35% of what number? 60

9. Eighty-four is what percent of 96? 87.5%

10. What percent of 17 is 34? 200%

11. What number is 0.3% of 62.7? 0.1881

- solve problems involving simple interest **(Lesson 4-3)**

Use the formula $I = prt$, where $I =$ interest, $p =$ principal, $r =$ annual interest rate, and $t =$ time in years.

Solve. $5400 at 8%, $2600 at 12%

12. Maria Cruz invested $8000 for one year, part at 8% and the rest at 12%. Her total interest for the year was $744. How much money did Maria invest at each rate?

Using the Chapter Summary and Review

The Chapter Summary and Review begins with an alphabetical listing of the new terms that were presented in the chapter. Have students define each term and provide an example of it, if appropriate.

The Skills and Concepts presented in the chapter are reviewed using a side-by-side format. Encourage students to refer to the Objectives and Examples on the left as they complete the Review Exercises on the right.

The Chapter Summary and Review ends with exercises that review Applications and Connections.

OBJECTIVES AND EXAMPLES	REVIEW EXERCISES

■ solve problems involving percent of increase or decrease **(Lesson 4-4)**

$$\frac{\text{amount of decrease}}{\text{original price}} = \frac{r}{100}$$

$$\frac{\text{amount of increase}}{\text{original price}} = \frac{r}{100}$$

Solve.

13. A price decreased from $40 to $35. Find the percent of decrease. **12.5%**

14. A price increased from $35 to $37.10. Find the percent of increase. **6%**

■ solve problems involving discount or sales tax **(Lesson 4-4)**

At Debbie's Dresses, a dress priced at $45 has a 5% discount. Find the discount price before sales tax.

$$5\% \text{ of } \$45 = 0.05(45)$$
$$= 2.25$$

$$\$45 - \$2.25 = \$42.75$$

Solve.

15. Inez Alonso made purchases at Martin's Department Store totaling $179.96. If she has to pay 5.5% sales tax, what should be the dollar amount she writes on her check? **$189.86**

16. Larry is buying a stereo that costs $399. Since he is an employee of the store, he receives a 15% discount. He also has to pay 6% sales tax. If the discount is computed first, what is the total cost of Larry's stereo? **$359.50**

■ solve mixture problems **(Lesson 4-6)**

Juana bought 16 used paperback books for $10.95. Some cost 60¢ and the rest cost 75¢ each. How many of each did she buy?

	Number	Total Price
60¢ books	x	$0.60x$
75¢ books	$16 - x$	$0.75(16 - x)$

$$0.60x + 0.75(16 - x) = 10.95$$

7 at 60¢ and $16 - 7$ or 9 at 75¢

Copy and complete the chart. Then write an equation and use it to solve the problem.

17. How much whipping cream (9% butterfat) should be added to 1 gallon of milk (4% butterfat) to obtain a 6% butterfat mixture? **0.67 gal**

	Gallons	Amt. of Butterfat
9% butterfat	x	$0.09x$
4% butterfat	1	$0.04(1)$
6% butterfat	$x + 1$	$0.06(x + 1)$

$$0.09x + 0.04 = 0.06(x + 1)$$

■ solve problems involving uniform motion by using the formula $d = rt$ **(Lesson 4-7)**

d = distance

r = rate

t = time

Use $d = rt$ to answer each question.

18. Pat is driving at 80 kilometers per hour. How far will she travel:
   a. in 2 hours?   b. in 6 hours?
   c. in h hours? **160 km, 480 km, 80h km**

19. Marilyn traveled 240 miles. What was her rate if she made the trip:
   a. in 6 hours?   b. in t hours?
   40 mph, $\frac{240}{t}$ mph

Alternate Review Strategy

To provide a brief in-class review, you may wish to read the following questions to the class and require a verbal response.

1. Solve $\frac{7}{9} = \frac{x}{108}$.   **x = 84**

2. What number is 55% of 180? **99**

3. Leslie Wright invested $1200 for one year, part at 7% and the rest at 12%. Her total interest for the year was $99. How much money did Leslie invest at each rate?   **$900 at 7% and $300 at 12%**

4. A price decreased from $105 to $70. What was the percent of decrease?   **$33\frac{1}{3}$%**

5. Ted wants to purchase a suitcase that sells for $129. Since it is a sale day, the suitcase has been reduced by 15%. Ted will have to pay 6% sales tax on his purchase. If the discount is computed first, what will be the total cost of the purchase? **$116.23**

6. Judy bought five cassettes for $30.75. Some cost $4.95 each and others cost $6.95 each. How many of each did she buy?   **2 cassettes at $4.95 and 3 cassettes at $6.95**

7. Joan is driving at 80 kilometers per hour. How far will she travel in 8 hours? **640 km**

8. If x varies directly as y and $y = 25$ when $x = 5$, find y when $x = 9$.   **45**

9. If y varies inversely as x and $y = 32$ when $x = 10$, find x when $y = 80$.   **4**

The Cumulative Review shown below can be used to review skills and concepts presented thus far in the text. Standardized Test Practice Questions are also provided in the Evaluation Masters Booklet.

Evaluation Masters Booklet, pp. 53-54

OBJECTIVES AND EXAMPLES	REVIEW EXERCISES

■ solve problems involving direct variation (Lesson 4-8)

If x varies directly as y, and $x = 15$ when $y = 1.5$, find x when $y = 9$.
$$\frac{1.5}{9} = \frac{15}{x}$$
$$\frac{1.5x}{1.5} = \frac{135}{1.5}$$
$$x = 90$$

Solve. Assume that y varies directly as x.

20. If $y = 15$ when $x = 5$, find y when $x = 7$. **21**

21. If $y = 35$ when $x = 175$, find y when $x = 75$. **15**

22. If $y = 3$ when $x = 99.9$, find y when $x = 522.81$. **15.7**

■ solve problems involving inverse variation (Lesson 4-9)

If y varies inversely as x, and $y = 24$ when $x = 30$, find x when $y = 10$.
$$\frac{30}{x} = \frac{10}{24}$$
$$\frac{10x}{10} = \frac{720}{10}$$
$$x = 72$$

Solve. Assume that y varies inversely as x.

23. If $y = 15$ when $x = 5$, find y when $x = 7$. $\frac{75}{7}$; **10.714**

24. If $y = 35$ when $x = 175$, find y when $x = 75$. $\frac{245}{3}$; **81.$\overline{6}$**

25. If $y = 28$ when $x = 42$, find y when $x = 56$. **21**

APPLICATIONS AND CONNECTIONS

26. **Entertainment** The television series with the largest audience to date was the final episode of M*A*S*H. 77% of the 162 million people watching TV that night saw the program. How many people were watching? **(Lesson 4-2)** 124.74 million

27. **Cooking** George is in charge of preparing Thanksgiving dinner. The menu is shown below, along with the preparation time and cooking time for each dish. Dinner must be ready by 5:00 P.M. Make a timetable to determine when George should begin preparing each dish. **(Lesson 4-5)** See margin.

Thanksgiving Dinner Menu

Item	Preparation Time	Cooking Time
15-pound turkey		4 hours (plus 30 minutes to cool)
Mashed potatoes	30 minutes to peel, mash	45 minutes to boil
Candied yams	1 hour to boil and prepare	30 minutes to bake
Green beans	30 minutes to cut and wash	20 minutes to cook
Hot cranberry sauce		5 minutes to heat
Gravy		10 minutes to cook
Dinner rolls		15 minutes to bake
Jello mold	15 minutes to make	4 hours to set

28. **Physics** Lee and Rena sit on opposite ends of a 12-foot teetertotter. Lee weighs 180 pounds and Rena weighs 108 pounds. Where should the fulcrum be placed in order for the teetertotter to be balanced? **(Lesson 4-9)** $4\frac{1}{2}$ feet from the end where Lee is seated

Additional Answers

27. turkey-12:30;
    potatoes-3:45;
    yams-3:30;
    green beans-4:10;
    cranberry sauce-4:45;
    gravy-4:50;
    rolls-4:45;
    jello-12:45

Solve each proportion.

1. $\frac{7}{8} = \frac{5}{t}$ $\frac{40}{7}$; 5.714

2. $\frac{n}{4} = \frac{3.25}{52}$ 0.25

3. $\frac{y+2}{8} = \frac{7}{5}$ $\frac{46}{5}$; 9.2

4. $\frac{2}{5} = \frac{x-3}{-2}$ $\frac{11}{5}$; 2.2

5. $\frac{9}{11} = \frac{x-3}{x+5}$ 39

6. $\frac{x+1}{-3} = \frac{x-4}{5}$ $\frac{7}{8}$; 0.875

Solve.

7. Find 6.5% of 80. **5.2**

8. Forty-two is what percent of 126? **33.3̄%**

9. Eighty-four is 60% of what number? **140**

10. What number decreased by 20% is 16? **20**

11. What is 50% of 17? **8.5**

12. Twenty-four is what percent of 8? **300%**

13. What number increased by $33\frac{1}{3}$% is 52? **39**

14. 54 is 20% more than what number? **45**

15. A price decreased from $60 to $45. Find the percent of decrease. **25%**

16. The price in dollars (p) minus a 15% discount is $3.40. Find p. **$4.00**

17. The price in dollars (p) plus 5.75% sales tax is $10.52. Find p. **$9.95**

18. **Sales** Jason paid $21.96 for a new shirt that was marked 20% off. What was the price before the discount? **$27.45**

19. **Employment** Ahmed's wages vary directly as the days he works. If his wages for 5 days are $26, how much would they be for 12 days? **$62.40**

20. **Chemistry** How many ounces of a 6% iodine solution needs to be added to 12 ounces of a 10% iodine solution to create a 7% iodine solution? **36 ounces**

21. **Cartography** The scale on a map is 2 centimeters to 5 kilometers. Doe Creek and Kent are 15.75 kilometers apart. How far apart are they on the map? **6.3 cm**

22. **Travel** Susan drove 3.25 hours at a rate of 50 miles per hour. To the nearest tenth, how long would it take her to drive the same distance at 45 miles per hour? **3.6 hours**

23. **Physics** A person weighs 0.5% less at the Equator than at the North or South Poles. How much would a person weigh at the Equator if the person weighed 148 pounds at the North Pole? **147 lb 4 oz**

24. **Finance** Gladys deposited an amount of money in the bank at 6.5% annual interest. After 6 months, she received $7.80 interest. How much money had Gladys deposited in the bank? **$240**

25. **Physics** Marcie weighs 133 pounds and sits 6 feet from the fulcrum of a seesaw. She balances with Rosalinda if Rosalinda sits 7 feet from the fulcrum. How much does Rosalinda weigh? **114 lb**

Bonus

Travel Ben, who is bicycling at the rate of x miles per hour, has a head start of 2 miles on Rachel, who is bicycling at the rate of y miles per hour (y > x). In how many hours will Rachel overtake Ben? $\left(\frac{2}{y-x}\right)$ **hours**

5 Inequalities

PREVIEWING THE CHAPTER

This chapter develops the properties for solving inequalities. Students will find using the addition and subtraction properties to be fairly straightforward, but will have to pay particular attention when using the multiplication and division properties where the inequality symbol must be reversed when multiplying or dividing each side of an inequality by the same negative number. The chapter concludes with lessons on solving compound inequalities and open sentences involving absolute value where students show the solutions two ways, by description using set notation and by drawing a geometric model to graph the solutions on a number line.

Problem-Solving Strategy Students learn that many problems can be solved more easily if they draw a picture or diagram to represent the situation.

Lesson Objective Chart

Lesson (Pages)	Lesson Objectives	State/Local Objectives
5-1 (176-180)	**5-1:** Solve inequalities by using addition and subtraction.	
5-2 (181-185)	**5-2:** Solve inequalities by using multiplication and division.	
5-3 (186-190)	**5-3:** Solve inequalities involving more than one operation.	
5-4 (192-193)	**5-4:** Solve problems by making a diagram.	
5-5 (194-198)	**5-5A:** Solve compound inequalities and graph their solution sets.	
	5-5B: Solve problems that involve compound inequalities.	
5-6 (199-203)	**5-6:** Solve open sentences involving absolute values and graph the solutions.	

ORGANIZING THE CHAPTER

You may want to refer to the **Course Planning Calendar** on page T36.

Lesson (Pages)	Pacing Chart (days) Course I	II	III	Reteaching	Practice	Enrichment	Evaluation	Technology	Lab Manual	Mixed Problem Solving	Applications	Cooperative Learning Activity	Multicultural	Transparencies
5-1 (176-180)	1.5	1.5	1.5	p. 30	p. 33	p. 30		p. 5				p. 35		5-1
5-2 (181-185)	1.5	1	1	p. 31	p. 34	p. 31	Quiz A, p. 65							5-2
5-3 (186-190)	1	1	1	p. 32	p. 35	p. 32	Quiz B, p. 65 Mid-Chapter Test, p. 69				p. 20		p. 50	5-3
5-4 (192-193)	1	0.5	0.5		p. 36									5-4
5-5 (194-198)	1.5	1.5	1.5	p. 33	p. 37	p. 33	Quiz C, p.66	p. 20	pp. 25-26	p.5				5-5
5-6 (199-203)	1.5	1.5	1.5	p. 34	p. 38	p. 34	Quiz D, p. 66							5-6
Review (204-206)	1	1	1	Multiple Choice Tests, Forms 1A and 1B, pp. 57-60 Free Response Tests, Forms 2A and 2B, pp. 61-64										
Test (207)	1	1	1	Cumulative Review, pp. 67-68 Standardized Test Practice Questions, p. 70										

Lesson Planning Guide / **Blackline Masters Booklets** / **Activities**

Course I: Chapters 1-13; Course II: Chapters 1-14; Course III: Chapters 1-15

Other Chapter Resources

Student Edition

History Connection, p. 180
Reading Algebra, p. 185
Mid-Chapter Review, p. 190
Technology, p. 191
Cooperative Learning Activity, p. 193
Algebraic Skills Review, p. 656

Teacher Resource Package

Activity Masters Booklet
   Mixed Problem Solving, p. 5
   Applications, p. 20
   Cooperative Leaning Activity, p. 35
   Multicultural Activity, p. 50
Technology Masters Booklet
   Scientific Calculator Activity, p. 5
   Graphing Calculator Activity, p. 20
Lab Manual
   Lab Activity, pp. 25-26

Other Supplements

Transparency for Chapter Opener
Problem-of-the-Week Activity
   Cards, 11-12
Video Algebra, 12-13

Software

Algebra 1 Test and Review
   Generator Software
   Available for Apple and IBM.

ENHANCING THE CHAPTER

Cooperative Learning

Assigning Students to Groups

There are many ways to assign students to groups. Research indicates that a heterogeneous group will allow for a more effective learning situation than will a homogeneous group. Therefore, letting students choose who they want to work with is probably the least desirable way to form groups. A more desirable way would be to randomly assign students by having them count off and placing the 1s in one group, the 2s in another, and so on. An even better way is to form groups so that each group has members of varying levels of ability. Keep in mind that students do not need to remain members of the same group for the entire year. In fact, it may be desirable if membership is changed periodically, giving students the opportunity and experience of working with most of their classmates at one time or another.

Technology

The Technology Feature after Lesson 5-5 employs the *Mathematical Exploration Toolkit* (MET). MET provides an effective way for students to focus on the decisions required to solve inequalities. Since the computer performs the calculating and simplifying steps, students can concentrate on choosing the appropriate operations. Remind them that HELP screens are available by pressing the F1 key.

The Guided Exploration titled "Linear Equations and Inequalities" is provided with MET. You may want to preview this MET lesson for use now or in conjunction with Chapters 9 and 10. The lesson ties linear equations and inequalities to graphical representations.

Critical Thinking

Students who correctly answer the practice exercises, for the most part, are demonstrating only their knowledge and comprehension of the content presented in the lesson. They are not necessarily exhibiting any ability to utilize the higher-level thinking skills that would be required in real life where conditions do not always remain stable. One way to help accustom students to sudden or unexpected changes in the rules that often occur in real life is to ask What-if questions. For example, after students demonstrate their ability to solve one or more inequalities, say, "What if the only acceptable answers are even numbers (or numbers divisible by 3, or numbers greater than 10, etc.)? Now what is the solution?"

Cooperative Learning, p. 35

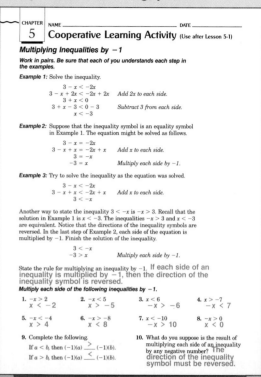

Technology, p. 5

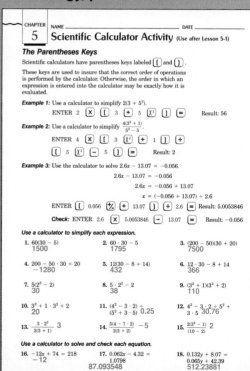

The card shown below is one of two available for this chapter. It can be used as a class or small group activity.

Activity Card

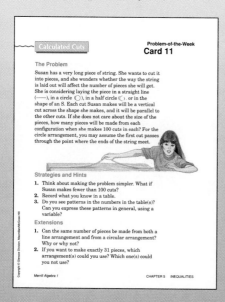

Calculated Cuts

Problem-of-the-Week
Card 11

The Problem

Susan has a very long piece of string. She wants to cut it into pieces, and she wonders whether the way the string is laid out will affect the number of pieces she will get. She is considering laying the piece in a straight line (———), in a circle (◯), in a half circle (◡), or in the shape of an S. Each cut Susan makes will be a vertical cut across the shape she makes, and it will be parallel to the other cuts. If she does not care about the size of the pieces, how many pieces will be made from each configuration when she makes 100 cuts in each? For the circle arrangement, you may assume the first cut passes through the point where the ends of the string meet.

Strategies and Hints

1. Think about making the problem simpler. What if Susan makes fewer than 100 cuts?
2. Record what you know in a table.
3. Do you see patterns in the numbers in the table(s)? Can you express these patterns in general, using a variable?

Extensions

1. Can the same number of pieces be made from both a line arrangement and from a circular arrangement? Why or why not?
2. If you want to make exactly 31 pieces, which arrangement(s) could you use? Which one(s) could you not use?

Merrill Algebra 1   CHAPTER 5 INEQUALITIES

Manipulatives and Models

The following materials may be used as models or manipulatives in Chapter 5.

- ruler (Lesson 5-1)
- two-pan balance (Lessons 5-1, 5-2, 5-3)
- newspapers and/or magazines (Lesson 5-4)
- posterboard (Lesson 5-4)

Outside Resources

Books/Periodicals

Hartkopf, Roy. *Math Without Tears*. Emerson Book, Inc. 1980

Mitchell, Robert. *Number Power 3 - Algebra*. Contemporary Books, Inc., 1988.

Films/Videotapes/Videodiscs

Donald in Mathmagic Land, Disney Educational Productions

Mathematics - Life's Number Game, Coronet Film and Video

Software

Algebra Shop, Math Shop Series, Scholastic

Mission: Algebra, Designware

Mathematical Exploration Toolkit, IBM

Multicultural

Multicultural Activity, p. 50

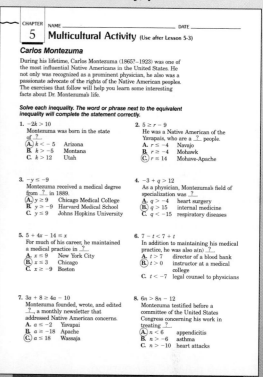

CHAPTER **5** Multicultural Activity (Use after Lesson 5-3)

NAME _____ DATE _____

Carlos Montezuma

During his lifetime, Carlos Montezuma (1865?–1923) was one of the most influential Native Americans in the United States. He not only was recognized as a prominent physician, he also was a passionate advocate of the rights of the Native American peoples. The exercises that follow will help you learn some interesting facts about Dr. Montezuma's life.

Solve each inequality. The word or phrase next to the equivalent inequality will complete the statement correctly.

1. $-2k > 10$
   Montezuma was born in the state of ? .
   A. $k < -5$ Arizona
   B. $k > -5$ Montana
   C. $k > 12$ Utah

2. $5 \geq r - 9$
   He was a Native American of the Yavapais, who are a ? people.
   A. $r \leq -4$ Navajo
   B. $r \geq -4$ Mohawk
   C. $r \leq 14$ Mohave-Apache

3. $-y \leq -9$
   Montezuma received a medical degree from ? in 1889.
   A. $y \geq 9$ Chicago Medical College
   B. $y \geq -9$ Harvard Medical School
   C. $y \leq 9$ Johns Hopkins University

4. $-3 + q > 12$
   As a physician, Montezuma's field of specialization was ? .
   A. $q > -4$ heart surgery
   B. $q > 15$ internal medicine
   C. $q < -15$ respiratory diseases

5. $5 + 4x - 14 \leq x$
   For much of his career, he maintained a medical practice in ? .
   A. $x \leq 9$ New York City
   B. $x \leq 3$ Chicago
   C. $x \geq -9$ Boston

6. $7 - t < 7 + t$
   In addition to maintaining his medical practice, he was also a(n) ? .
   A. $t > 7$ director of a blood bank
   B. $t > 0$ instructor at a medical college
   C. $t < -7$ legal counsel to physicians

7. $3a + 8 \geq 4a - 10$
   Montezuma founded, wrote, and edited ? , a monthly newsletter that addressed Native American concerns.
   A. $a \leq -2$ Yavapai
   B. $a \geq -18$ Apache
   C. $a \leq 18$ Wassaja

8. $6n > 8n - 12$
   Montezuma testified before a committee of the United States Congress concerning his work in treating ? .
   A. $n < 6$ appendicitis
   B. $n > -6$ asthma
   C. $n > -10$ heart attacks

Lab Manual

Lab Activity, pp. 25-26

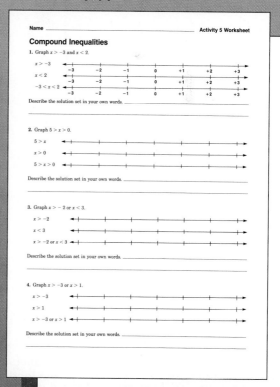

Name _____   Activity 5 Worksheet

Compound Inequalities

1. Graph $x > -3$ and $x < 2$.

   $x > -3$
   $x < 2$
   $-3 < x < 2$

   Describe the solution set in your own words. _____

2. Graph $5 > x > 0$.

   $5 > x$
   $x > 0$
   $5 > x > 0$

   Describe the solution set in your own words. _____

3. Graph $x > -2$ or $x < 3$.

   $x > -2$
   $x < 3$
   $x > -2$ or $x < 3$

   Describe the solution set in your own words. _____

4. Graph $x > -3$ or $x > 1$.

   $x > -3$
   $x > 1$
   $x > -3$ or $x > 1$

   Describe the solution set in your own words. _____

Using the Chapter Opener

Transparency 5-0 is available in the Transparency Package. It provides a full-color visual and motivational activity that you can use to engage students in the mathematical content of the chapter.

Background Information

Structural engineers calculate load limits of buildings and bridges by measuring stress versus strain. Stress = $\frac{load}{area}$, and might be measured in pounds of force per square inch. Strain = $\frac{increase\ in\ length\ under\ a\ load}{original\ length}$, and is measured in units of length. By the strength of a material, we usually mean the stress which is needed to break it. Maximum elevator capacities, for example, are based on allowing each person 1.5 square feet of area, and are calculated using a range of 125 to 150 pounds per person.

CHAPTER OBJECTIVES

In this chapter, you will:
- Solve inequalities.
- Solve compound inequalities.
- Graph solutions of open sentences that involve absolute value.
- Solve problems that can be represented by inequalities.
- Solve problems by making a diagram.

Chapter Project

Materials: graph paper, pencil

Organize students into cooperative groups of technicians. Assign each group the task of selecting an area of study within which it will measure and establish ranges of activity or capacity. The following is a partial list of possible choices from which each group might choose.

A. Health Measure and determine ranges of body activities within the group such as body temperature, pulse rate, breathing rate, and so on.

B. Load Capacity Construct bridges and other structures from popsicle sticks, or other building material, and determine the load capacity of each.

C. Room Temperatures Measure and determine ranges of thermostat settings in classrooms, corridors, gym, and so on around the school.

Instruct each group to graph its findings, establish ranges, and present results to class.

Inequalities

APPLICATION IN STATISTICS

During election campaigns, candidates need to know how people in their area will vote. Since it is not possible to question all of the voters, candidates use *polls* to find this information. In a poll, a sampling of voters is asked how they will vote in the election. Then, based on the results, a projection is made on how the actual vote will turn out.

Since the results of a poll are based on projections, their accuracy in predicting the actual election results depend greatly on the number of people used in the sampling. One measure of the accuracy of a poll is its *tolerance*. Tolerance is based in part on the size of the poll's sampling. The tolerance, along with the poll's results, define a range of values within which the actual election results should fall. This range of values can be described using a *compound inequality*.

Suppose that a poll projects that a candidate will receive 48% of the votes for mayor, and that the poll's results are accurate to within ±4%. This means the poll has a 4% tolerance and in the actual election, the candidate should receive somewhere between 44% (48% − 4%) and 52% (48% + 4%) of the votes. If x represents the percent of the vote received by this candidate, then we write $44 \leq x \leq 52$.

ALGEBRA IN ACTION

The chart below shows the results of polls taken to determine the voters' preference for governor. The results of the poll are accurate to within ±3%. During what months do the results indicate that *either* of the candidates could win the election?
April, October

Candidate	April	June	August	October
Alvarez	44%	48%	49%	49%
Taylor	40%	41%	42%	44%
Undecided	16%	11%	9%	7%

According to the latest poll on Issue 3, 51% of the voters plan to vote yes, 42% plan to vote no, and 7% are undecided. If these results are off by as much as 3%, could Issue 3 lose? what about 5%?

POLLS OPEN 7 A.M.   CLOSE 8 P.M.

POLLING PLACE
VOTE HERE

Lesson	Connections (C) and Applications (A)	Examples	Exercises
5-1	A: Budgeting	3	
	Sports	4	51
	School		49
	Banking		50
	Sales		56
5-2	C: Geometry	3	33-36
	A: Sales	5	50
	Business		49
	Finance		51
	Consumerism		53
5-3	C: Statistics	4	43
	A: Sales		44
	Sports		46
	Employment		45, 48
5-5	C: Probability		45
	A: Sales	7	
	Consumerism		46
	Career		47
	Running		48
	Entertainment		51
5-6	C: Geometry		57
	Statistics		58
	A: Machinery	4	
	Chemistry		49
	Travel		50
	Manufacturing		51
	Shipping		52
	Finance		55

175

Lesson Resources

- Reteaching Master 5-1
- Practice Master 5-1
- Enrichment Master 5-1
- Technology Master, p. 5
- Activity Master, p. 35
- Video Algebra, 12

 Transparency 5-1 contains the 5-Minute Check and a teaching aid for this lesson.

INTRODUCING THE LESSON

5-Minute Check
(over Chapter 4)

Solve. Assume y varies inversely as x.

1. If $y = 10$ when $x = 5$, find y when $x = 4$.   **12.5**
2. If $y = 2.5$ when $x = 4$, find y when $x = 2$.   **5**
3. If $y = 14$ when $x = 3$, find y when $x = 7$.   **6**
4. If $y = -13$ when $x = -6$, find y when $x = 3$.   **26**
5. Sam drove 3 hours at a rate of 45 mph. How long would it take to travel the same distance if Sam's rate was 50 mph?   **2.7 hours**

Motivating the Lesson

Open this lesson on inequalities by having students name some values for *a* and *b* that make all three of the following inequalities true.

$$a < 0, b < 0, a - b < 0$$

Then ask them to describe the relationship between *a* and *b* for the above inequalities to be true. $a < b$

TEACHING THE LESSON

Teaching Tip ❶ Emphasize that solutions of open sentences are sets.

5-1 Solving Inequalities Using Addition and Subtraction

Objective
5-1
After studying this lesson, you should be able to:
- solve inequalities by using addition and subtraction.

Application

Eric Stevens had bowling scores of 183 and 164 for the first two games of a three-game series. What is the lowest score he can bowl in his third game and have a three-game total that is more than 500?

Let t = Eric's score for the third game. Write an inequality to represent the situation.

The sum of the scores   *is more than*   *500.*

$$183 + 164 + t \qquad > \qquad 500$$
$$347 + t > 500$$

If we were solving an equation instead of an inequality, at this point we would subtract 347 from each side, or add -347 to each side. Can these same procedures be applied to inequalities? Consider an inequality, such as $5 > -2$, that we know is true. If 3 is added to each side of $5 > -2$, the resulting inequality is $8 > 1$, which is also true. If 4 is subtracted from each side of $5 > -2$, the resulting inequality is $1 > -6$, which is also true.

These examples illustrate the following properties.

Addition and Subtraction Properties for Inequalities	For all numbers *a, b,* and *c,* 1. if $a > b$, then $a + c > b + c$ and $a - c > b - c$, and 2. if $a < b$, then $a + c < b + c$ and $a - c < b - c$.

These properties are also true when $<$ and $>$ are replaced by $\leq$ and $\geq$.

Example 1

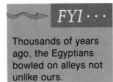

FYI···

Thousands of years ago, the Egyptians bowled on alleys not unlike ours.

Solve $347 + t > 500$ to answer the bowling problem presented above.

$$347 + t > 500$$
$$347 - 347 + t > 500 - 347 \qquad \textit{Subtract 347 from each side.}$$
$$t > 153$$

The solution set is {all numbers greater than 153}. **Teaching Tip ❶**

To check this solution, substitute a number greater than 153 and a number less than 153 in the original inequality. The inequality should be true only for whole numbers greater than 153 and less than or equal to 300, the highest score in bowling.

Check: $347 + t \overset{?}{>} 500$ $347 + t \overset{?}{>} 500$
     $347 + 155 \overset{?}{>} 500$ *Try 155.* $347 + 150 \overset{?}{>} 500$ *Try 150.*
         $502 > 500$ *True* $497 > 500$ *False*

ALTERNATE TEACHING STRATEGIES

Using Models

Use the concept of an unbalanced scale to help students solve inequalities using addition and subtraction. Use a ruler, white squares for positive numbers, red squares for negative numbers, and a triangular piece of cardboard. Place the ruler on the triangle so that the side corresponding to the open end of the inequality is up.

The representation of $x - 5 > -3$ is shown below.

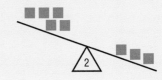

Since the solution set for $347 + t > 500$ is {all whole numbers greater than 153 and less than or equal to 300}, the lowest score Eric can bowl in his third game and have a three-game total that is more than 500 is 154.

The solution to the inequality in Example 1 was expressed as a set. A more concise way of writing this set is to use **set-builder notation**. The solution in set-builder notation is $\{t \mid t$ is a whole number and $153 < t \le 300\}$. This is read *the set of all whole numbers t such that t is greater than 153 and less than or equal to 300*.

Example 2

Solve $8y + 3 > 9y - 14$.

$$8y + 3 > 9y - 14$$
$$8y - 8y + 3 > 9y - 8y - 14 \quad \text{Subtract 8y from each side.}$$
$$3 > y - 14$$
$$3 + 14 > y - 14 + 14 \quad \text{Add 14 to each side.}$$
$$17 > y$$

Since $17 > y$ is the same as $y < 17$, the solution set is usually written $\{y \mid y < 17\}$. **Teaching Tip** ②

Verbal problems containing phrases like *greater than* or *less than* can often be solved by using inequalities. The following chart shows some other phrases that indicate inequalities.

Inequalities

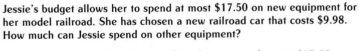

<	>	≤	≥

■ less than
■ fewer than
	■ greater than
	■ more than
		■ at most
		■ no more than
		■ less than or
		  equal to
			■ at least
			■ no less than
			■ greater than or
			  equal to

Example 3

APPLICATION

Budgeting

Jessie's budget allows her to spend at most $17.50 on new equipment for her model railroad. She has chosen a new railroad car that costs $9.98. How much can Jessie spend on other equipment?

EXPLORE   At most $17.50 means less than or equal to (≤) $17.50.
Let x = the amount that Jessie can spend on other equipment.

PLAN   Total to spend is at most $17.50.

$$9.98 + x \quad \le \quad 17.50$$

SOLVE $9.98 - 9.98 + x \le 17.50 - 9.98$ *Subtract 9.98 from each side.*
Jessie can spend $7.52 or less on other equipment.

EXAMINE   Since $9.98 + $7.52 = $17.50, Jessie can spend $7.52 or less on other equipment.

LESSON 5-1 SOLVING INEQUALITIES USING ADDITION AND SUBTRACTION 177

Chalkboard Examples

For Example 1
Solve.

a. $x + (-14) < 16$ $x < 30$

b. $y + (-21) > 7$ $y > 28$

c. $(-11) + t > 5$ $t > 16$

For Example 2
Solve.

a. $3r - 17 > 2r + 14$ $r > 31$

b. $9t + 5 < 10t - 3$ $t > 8$

c. $12p - 24 > 10p + 16$
$p > 20$

For Example 3
A stove and a freezer together weigh at least 260 kg. The stove weighs 115 kg. What is the weight of the freezer?   **at least 145 kg**

Teaching Tip ②   Make sure students understand that $17 > y$ and $y < 17$ are equivalent inequalities. Students may find it easier to determine the solution set by writing the inequality with the variable on the left side.

ALTERNATE TEACHING STRATEGIES (continued)

The 2 in the triangle indicates the difference of the absolute values of the numbers represented on each side of the "scale." This difference needs to stay the same throughout. To solve, place 5 white squares on each side of the scale. Thus, the solution is $x > 2$.

EVALUATING THE LESSON

Checking for Understanding

Exercises 1-16 are designed to help you assess understanding through reading, writing, and speaking. You should work through Exercises 1-4 with your students, and then monitor their work on Exercises 5-16.

Error Analysis

Students may assume they have solved an inequality correctly by substituting representative values into the original inequality. For example, suppose they solve $x + 3 < 7$ incorrectly as $x < 1$. Substituting 3 into the original inequality makes it true $3 + 3 < 7$. However, substituting 3 into the inequality given as the solution is false: $3 \not< 1$.

Reteaching Masters Booklet, p. 30

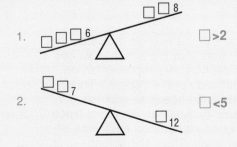

178   Chapter 5

Example 4

APPLICATION

Sports

Roberto has scores of 63.2, 59.8, 61.5, and 71.1 for his first four dives in a springboard diving competition. He has one more dive remaining. If Roberto's total score must be greater than 322.7 to win the competition, what score must he receive on his fifth dive?

EXPLORE   You want to find the score for Roberto's fifth dive that will make his total score, which is the sum of his scores on the five dives, greater than 322.7. Let s = the score on Roberto's fifth dive.

PLAN

Roberto's total score	is greater than	322.7
$63.2 + 59.8 + 61.5 + 71.1 + s$	$>$	322.7

SOLVE
$$255.6 + s > 322.7$$
$$255.6 - 255.6 + s > 322.7 - 255.6$$
$$s > 67.1$$

Roberto will win if the score on his fifth dive is greater than 67.1.

EXAMINE   Since $63.2 + 59.8 + 61.5 + 71.1 + 67.1 = 322.7$, if Roberto scores more than 67.1 on his fifth dive, his total score will be more than 322.7.

CHECKING FOR UNDERSTANDING

Communicating Mathematics

Read and study the lesson to answer each question. 2-3. See margin.

1. Explain why it was not really necessary to state the subtraction property for inequalities. **Subtraction is the inverse of addition.**
2. Write three inequalities that are equivalent to $x < 5$.
3. Write two inequalities that each have $\{y \mid y > -4\}$ as their solution set.
4. Refer to the situation at the beginning of the lesson. If Eric wanted to have a three-game total that was greater than 525, what is the lowest score he could bowl in his third game? **179**

Guided Practice

State the number you would add to each side to solve each inequality.

5. $x - 17 > 43$ **17**
6. $-8 + a \geq -7$ **8**
7. $11 \leq m - 14.5$ **14.5**
8. $y + 4 < -4$ **−4**

State the number you would subtract from each side to solve each inequality.

9. $z + 1 \leq 5$ **1**
10. $-3 \geq b + 11$ **11**
11. $n + (-8) > 22$ **−8**
12. $9x < 8x - 2$ **8x**

Solve each inequality. Check the solution.

13. $r + 11 < 6$ $\{r \mid r < -5\}$
14. $y - 18 > -3$ $\{y \mid y > 15\}$
15. $10 \geq -3 + x$ $\{x \mid x \leq 13\}$
16. $4a - 3 \leq 5a$ $\{a \mid a \geq -3\}$

178   CHAPTER 5   INEQUALITIES

RETEACHING THE LESSON

Use a two-pan balance to demonstrate how to solve inequalities. If no balance is handy, draw a large balance on the chalkboard. Boxes have identical weights. What can be concluded about the weight of one box? Explain.

1.   □ □ □ 6   □ 8   □ >2

2.   □ □ 7   □ 12   □ <5

EXERCISES

Closing the Lesson

Writing Activity Without solving, rewrite each inequality in a form that has the same meaning.
1. $17 < x + 4$ $x + 4 > 17$
2. $-3 + x > 2x - 4$
   $2x - 4 < -3 + x$
3. $4 + x < 8$ $8 > 4 + x$

Practice

Solve each inequality. Check the solution.

17. $a + 4 < 13$ $\{a|a < 9\}$
18. $x - 3 < -17$ $\{x|x < -14\}$
19. $r - 19 \geq 23$ $\{r|r \geq 42\}$
20. $y + 15 \geq -2$ $\{y|y \geq -17\}$
21. $9 + w \leq 9$ $\{w|w \leq 0\}$
22. $-9 + c > 9$ $\{c|c > 18\}$
23. $-11 > d - 4$ $\{d|d < -7\}$
24. $-11 \leq k - (-4)$ $\{k|k \geq -15\}$
25. $2x > x - 3$ $\{x|x > -3\}$
26. $5y + 4 < 6y$ $\{y|y > 4\}$
27. $-7 < 16 - z$ $\{z|z < 23\}$
28. $-p - 11 \geq 23$ $\{p|p \leq -34\}$
29. $2x - 3 \geq x$ $\{x|x \geq 3\}$
30. $7h - 1 \leq 6h$ $\{h|h \leq 1\}$
31. $-5 + 14b \leq -4 + 15b$ $\{b|b \geq -1\}$
32. $6r + 4 \geq 5r + 4$ $\{r|r \geq 0\}$
33. $2s - 6.5 < -11.4 + s$ $\{s|s < -4.9\}$
34. $1.1v - 1 > 2.1v - 3$ $\{v|v < 2\}$
35. $3x + \frac{4}{5} \leq 4x + \frac{3}{5}$ $\{x|x \geq \frac{1}{5}\}$
36. $\frac{1}{2}t + \frac{1}{4} \geq \frac{3}{2}t - \frac{2}{3}$ $\{t|t \leq \frac{11}{12}\}$
37. $17.42 - 7.029z \geq 15.766 - 8.029z$ $\{z|z \geq -1.654\}$

38–43. See margin for inequalities.

Write an inequality and solve. Then check each solution.

38. A number decreased by 17 is less than -13. $\{x|x < 4\}$

39. A number increased by 4 is at least 3. $\{x|x \geq -1\}$

40. A number subtracted from 21 is no less than -2. $\{x|x \leq 23\}$

41. Twice a number added to 8 is more than three times the number. $\{x|x < 8\}$

42. Four more than 6 times a number is at most 5 times the number decreased by 3. $\{x|x \leq -7\}$

43. The sum of two numbers is less than 25. One of the numbers is 18. What is the other number? **The other number is less than 7.**

If $2x \geq x - 5$, then complete each inequality.

44. $2x + 3 \geq x - \underline{?}$ **2**
45. $2x - 7 \geq x - \underline{?}$ **12**
46. $2x + \underline{?} \geq x + 3$ **8**
47. $\underline{?} \leq x$ **−5**

Critical Thinking

48. Is it possible for the solution set of an inequality to be the empty set (Ø)? If so, name an example. **Yes; examples are $x > x$ and $2x + 1 \leq 2x$.**

Applications

Define a variable, write an inequality, and solve each problem.

49. **School** Eva has earned 453 points prior to the 200-point semester test in her biology class. To get an A for the semester, she must earn at least 630 points. What is the minimum number of points she can score on the test and still get an A? **177 points**

50. **Banking** City Bank requires a minimum balance of $1200 for free checking. If Mr. Findlay still has free checking after making withdrawals of $2000 and $1454, how much was in his account before the withdrawals? **at least $4654**

APPLYING THE LESSON

Homework Exercises

Assignment Guide

Basic: 17-37, 48-50, 53-57
Average: 22-42, 48-57
Enriched: 27-57

Practice Masters Booklet, p. 33

NAME _____ DATE _____

5-1   **Practice Worksheet**

Solving Inequalities Using Addition and Subtraction

Solve and check each solution.

1. $n + 5 \geq 32$
  $n \geq 27$
2. $v - 8 \leq 35$
  $v \leq 43$
3. $r - 6 < -15$
  $r < -9$

4. $-81 > 16 + q$
  $q < -97$
5. $-51 \leq x - (-38)$
  $x \geq -89$
6. $m - (-3.4) \geq 12.7$
  $m \geq 9.3$

7. $4.2 > -11 + t$
  $t < 15.2$
8. $2l < l - 6$
  $l < -6$
9. $16w \geq 15w - 8$
  $w \geq -8$

10. $6p > 5p + 19$
  $p > 19$
11. $u - 12 < 2u$
  $u > -12$
12. $2y - 17 + y - 6$
  $y \geq 11$

13. $3e - 0.2 \geq 4e + 0.5$
  $e \leq -0.7$
14. $-3 + 12a < -4 + 11a$
  $a < -1$
15. $-11.4 + s > 2s - 6.5$
  $s < -4.9$

16. $2.1k - 4 \geq 3.1k + 4$
  $k \leq -8$
17. $-\frac{3}{10} + d < \frac{9}{10}$
  $d < \frac{6}{5}$
18. $\frac{3}{4}c \leq \frac{7}{4}c - 1$
  $c \geq 1$

Write an inequality and solve. Then check each solution.

19. A number decreased by 10 is greater than -5.
  $n - 10 > -5; n > 5$
20. A number increased by 2 is at most 6.
  $n + 2 \leq 6; n \leq 4$

21. A number increased by -1 is less than 10.
  $n - 1 < 10; n < 11$
22. A number decreased by -4 is at least 9.
  $n - (-4) \geq 9; n \geq 5$

Additional Answers

2. Answers will vary; typical answers are $x - 1 < 4$ and $-2x > -10$.
3. Answers will vary; typical answers are $y > -4$ and $y + 4 > 0$.

38. $x - 17 < -13$
39. $x + 4 \geq 3$
40. $21 - x \geq -2$
41. $2x + 8 > 3x$
42. $6x + 4 \leq 5x - 3$
43. $x + 18 < 25$

51. Sports Janine has a total score of 39.35 in the four events of a gymnastics competition. Her closest competitor, Nyoko, has scores of 9.8, 9.75, and 9.9 for three events and has one event left. What must Nyoko's score be in the last event for Janine to win the competition? **any score less than 9.9**

52. This BASIC program compares two rational numbers. The IF-THEN statements direct the flow of the program. When the condition following IF is true, the program goes to the line number after THEN. When the condition is false, the program goes to the next line. By the comparison property, either $\frac{A}{B} = \frac{C}{D}$ or $\frac{A}{B} > \frac{C}{D}$ or $\frac{A}{B} < \frac{C}{D}$.

```
10 PRINT "ENTER THE FIRST
   NUMERATOR AND DENOMINATOR."
20 INPUT A , B
30 PRINT "ENTER THE SECOND
   NUMERATOR AND DENOMINATOR."
40 INPUT C , D
50 IF A/B > C/D THEN 90
60 IF A/B < C/D THEN 110
70 PRINT A;"/";B;" = ";C;"/";D
80 GOTO 120
90 PRINT A;"/";B;" > ";C;"/";D
100 GOTO 120
110 PRINT A;"/";B;" < ";C;"/";D
120 END
```

Compare each pair of rational numbers. If a number is negative, enter the negative sign with the numerator. **a. > b. > c. < d. < e. =**

a. $\frac{9}{11}, \frac{15}{19}$ b. $\frac{7}{8}, \frac{13}{15}$ c. $-\frac{7}{8}, -\frac{13}{15}$ d. $\frac{16}{17}, \frac{17}{18}$ e. $-\frac{7}{6}, -\frac{21}{18}$

Mixed Review

53. Simplify $0.3(0.2 + 3y) + 0.21y$. **(Lesson 1-6)** $1.11y + 0.6$

54. Graph the solution set of $n \leq -2$. **(Lesson 2-3)** **See margin.**

55. Solve $\frac{4}{9}x = -9$. **(Lesson 3-3)** $-\frac{81}{4}$

56. Sales Denise bought a new dress for $32.86. This included 6% sales tax. What was the cost of the dress before tax? **(Lesson 4-4)** **$31.00**

57. If y varies inversely as x, and $y = 8$ when $x = 24$, find y when $x = 6$. **(Lesson 4-8)** **32**

HISTORY CONNECTION

Recorde, Harriot, and Oughtred

Three British mathematicians had a great impact on the way mathematics is written today. In 1557, in his *The Whetstone of Witte*, Robert Recorde (1510–1558) introduced the modern equals sign (=). He used a pair of equal parallel line segments for the symbol "bicause noe 2 thynges can be moare equalle." Thomas Harriot (1560–1621), in his *Artis analyticae praxis*, introduced the inequality signs, > and <. William Oughtred (1574–1660) placed great emphasis on mathematical symbols. It was he who introduced the cross (×) for multiplication.

EXTENDING THE LESSON

Math Power: Problem Solving

Find the least prime number greater than 80. **83**

History Connection

The History Connection features introduce students to persons or cultures who were involved in the development of mathematics.
You may want students to further research these historians or to research the introduction of other mathematical symbols.

Solving Inequalities Using Multiplication and Division

Objective
5-2

After studying this lesson, you should be able to:
- solve inequalities by using multiplication and division.

Application

Jerry Hamilton is an architect for a commercial architecture firm. He needs to design a roof that has a span of 32 feet and a pitch that is at most $\frac{3}{8}$. What is the largest possible rise the roof can have?

Let r = the rise of the roof. In Lesson 3-3, you learned that the pitch of a roof is equal to its rise divided by its span. Thus, the inequality to be solved is $\frac{r}{32} \le \frac{3}{8}$.

If you were solving an equation instead of an inequality, at this point you would multiply each side by 32. Can the same procedure be applied to inequalities? Consider an inequality, such as $5 > -2$, that we know is true.

If each side of $5 > -2$ is multiplied by 3, the resulting inequality is $15 > -6$, which is also true.

If each side of $5 > -2$ is multiplied by -4, the resulting inequality is $-20 > 8$, which is *false*. To be true, the resulting inequality would need to be $-20 < 8$.

The results of these examples can be summarized as follows.

If each side of a true inequality is multiplied by the same positive number, the resulting inequality is also true.

If each side of a true inequality is multiplied by the same negative number, the direction of the inequality symbol must be *reversed* so that the resulting inequality is also true.

Teaching Tip ❶
Multiplication Property for Inequalities

For all numbers a, b, and c,
1. if c is positive and $a < b$, then $ac < bc$, and
   if c is positive and $a > b$, then $ac > bc$.
2. If c is negative and $a < b$, then $ac > bc$, and
   if c is negative and $a > b$, then $ac < bc$.

Example 1

FYI···

There is a house in Rockport, Massachusetts, made entirely of newspaper.

Solve $\frac{r}{32} \le \frac{3}{8}$ to answer the roofing problem presented above.

$$\frac{r}{32} \le \frac{3}{8}$$
$$32\left(\frac{r}{32}\right) \le 32\left(\frac{3}{8}\right) \qquad \textit{Multiply each side by 32.} \textbf{ Teaching Tip ❷}$$
$$r \le 12 \qquad\qquad\qquad\qquad\qquad\qquad\qquad \textbf{Teaching Tip ❸}$$

The solution is $\{r | r \le 12\}$. The largest rise the roof can have is 12 feet.

LESSON 5-2 SOLVING INEQUALITIES USING MULTIPLICATION AND DIVISION 181

5-2 Lesson Notes

Lesson Resources

- Reteaching Master 5-2
- Practice Master 5-2
- Enrichment Master 5-2
- Video Algebra, 12

  Transparency 5-2 contains the 5-Minute Check and a teaching aid for this lesson.

INTRODUCING THE LESSON

🕐 5-Minute Check
(over Lesson 5-1)

Solve each inequality.

1. $y + 3 > 11$ $y > 8$
2. $t - 9 < 6$ $t < 15$
3. $3t + 11 < 4$ $t < -\frac{7}{3}$
4. $2y - 10 < y + 6$ $y < 16$
5. $0.9 - p < -3.4$ $p > 4.3$

Motivating the Lesson

Have students draw a number line and graph the following points: $A = 0.5$, $B = -1.5$. Then have students consider the following.

1. If the coordinates of A and B are multiplied by 2, where are the corresponding points located on the number line?
   $A = 1$, $B = -3$
2. If the coordinates of A and B are multiplied by -2, where are the corresponding points located on the number line?
   $A = -1$, $B = 3$

TEACHING THE LESSON

Teaching Tip ❶ Additional numerical examples may be used to reinforce the multiplication property for inequalities.

Teaching Tip ❷ Remind students that $\frac{r}{32}$ is equal to $\frac{1}{32}r$. The reciprocal of $\frac{1}{32}$ is $\frac{32}{1}$, or 32.

Teaching Tip ❸ Suggest to students that they check several numbers in the solution set to determine whether true statements result.

ALTERNATE TEACHING STRATEGIES

Using Discussion

The sentence $4 > -2$ is clearly true. Discuss what occurs when you do the following.

1. Multiply each side by 3. What is the resulting inequality? $12 > -6$
2. Multiply each side by -2. What is the resulting inequality? $-8 < 4$
3. Divide each side by 2. What is the resulting inequality? $2 > -1$
4. Divide each side by -2. What is the resulting inequality? $-2 < 1$

Teaching Tip 4

Teaching Tip 5

Example 2   a. Solve $-\frac{a}{7} > 2$.   b. Solve $\frac{4x}{3} \leq -12$.

$-\frac{a}{7} > 2$

$-7\left(\frac{-a}{7}\right) < -7(2)$ *Multiply each side by -7 and change $>$ to $<$.*

$a < -14$

The solution set is $\{a | a < -14\}$.

$\frac{4x}{3} \leq -12$

$\frac{4}{3}x \leq -12$ *The reciprocal of $\frac{4}{3}$ is $\frac{3}{4}$.*

$\frac{3}{4}\left(\frac{4}{3}x\right) \leq \frac{3}{4}(-12)$ *Multiply each side by $\frac{3}{4}$.*

$x \leq -9$

The solution set is $\{x | x \leq -9\}$.

Example 3

CONNECTION
Geometry

For what values of d is an angle with measure $(5d)°$ an acute angle?

The measure of an acute angle is less than $90°$. Since the measure of an angle must be positive, d must also be greater than zero.

$5d < 90$

$5d\left(\frac{1}{5}\right) < 90\left(\frac{1}{5}\right)$ *The reciprocal of 5 is $\frac{1}{5}$. Multiply each side by $\frac{1}{5}$.*

$d < 18$

The angle is acute when d is a number less than 18 but greater than 0.

The inequality $5d < 90$ was solved by multiplying each side by $\frac{1}{5}$. The same result could have been obtained by *dividing* each side by 5. This method uses the **division property for inequalities**.

Division Property for Inequalities

For all numbers a, b, and c, with $c \neq 0$,
1. if c is positive and $a < b$, then $\frac{a}{c} < \frac{b}{c}$, and
   if c is positive and $a > b$, then $\frac{a}{c} > \frac{b}{c}$.
2. If c is negative and $a < b$, then $\frac{a}{c} > \frac{b}{c}$, and
   if c is negative and $a > b$, then $\frac{a}{c} < \frac{b}{c}$.

Example 4   Solve $-72 \geq -6n$.

The inequality can be solved using either the multiplication or division properties for inequalities. *Choose the method that is easier for you.*

Teaching Tip 6

a. $-72 \geq -6n$

$\left(-\frac{1}{6}\right)(-72) \leq \left(-\frac{1}{6}\right)(-6n)$ *Multiply each side by $-\frac{1}{6}$ and change $\geq$ to $\leq$.*

$12 \leq n$

b. $-72 \geq -6n$

$\frac{-72}{-6} \leq \frac{-6n}{-6}$ *Divide each side by -6 and change $\geq$ to $\leq$.*

$12 \leq n$

The solution set is $\{n | 12 \leq n\}$.   *This can also be written $\{n | n \geq 12\}$.*

Example 5

APPLICATION
Sales

Readalot Bookstore makes a profit of $4.48 on the sale of each two-volume set of the book *Modern Astronomy*. How many sets must be sold for Readalot Bookstore to make a profit of at least $175?

EXPLORE   Let s = the number of two-volume sets sold.
At least $175 means greater than or equal to $175.

PLAN   The profit on the sales of *Modern Astronomy* is the profit per set sold times the number of sets sold.

Profit per set sold	times	number of sets sold	is at least	$175.
4.48	×	s	≥	175

SOLVE $\frac{4.48s}{4.48} \geq \frac{175}{4.48}$ *Divide each side by 4.48.*

$s \geq 39.0625$

Since the number of two-volume sets sold must be a whole number, Readalot Bookstore must sell 40 or more sets to make a profit of at least $175.

EXAMINE   The profit on sales of 39 two-volume sets is ($4.48)(39) or $174.72. The profit on sales of 40 two-volume sets is ($4.48)(40) or $179.20. Thus, the solution is correct.

CHECKING FOR UNDERSTANDING

Communicating Mathematics

Complete.

1. Explain why it was not really necessary to state the division property for inequalities. **Division is the inverse of multiplication.**

2. If each side of a true inequality is multiplied by the same ___?___ number, the direction of the inequality symbol must be reversed so that the resulting inequality is also true. **negative**

3. Multiplying by ___?___ is the same as dividing by −6. $-\frac{1}{6}$

4. The measure of an ___?___ angle is less than 90°. **acute**

Guided Practice

State the number by which you multiply each side to solve each inequality. Then indicate if the direction of the inequality symbol reverses.

5. $\frac{x}{4} < -5$ **4; no**   6. $\frac{-2z}{7} \geq -12$ $-\frac{7}{2}$; **yes**   7. $10x > 20$ $\frac{1}{10}$; **no**

State the number by which you divide each side to solve the inequality. Then indicate if the direction of the inequality symbol reverses.

8. $-6y \geq -24$ **−6; yes**   9. $-10a > 13$ **−10; yes**   10. $3.3m < -33$
3.3; no

Solve and check each inequality.

11. $8x < -48$ $\{x|x < -6\}$ 12. $-10a < -30$ $\{a|a > 3\}$
13. $-12d \leq 30$ $\left\{d|d \geq -\frac{5}{2}\right\}$ 14. $0.1t \geq 3$ $\{t|t \geq 30\}$

LESSON 5-2   SOLVING INEQUALITIES USING MULTIPLICATION AND DIVISION   183

RETEACHING THE LESSON

Use a two-pan balance to demonstrate how to solve these inequalities.

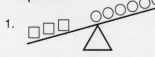

1.   ÷3☐=○○

2.   ×2☐=✶✶✶✶6

Teaching Tip ④ Stress the various ways a negative fraction can be written.

$$\frac{-2}{3} = \frac{2}{-3} = -\frac{2}{3}$$

Teaching Tip ⑤ You may wish to show an alternate solution.

$$\frac{4x}{3} \leq -12$$
$$3\left(\frac{4x}{3}\right) \leq 3(-12)$$
$$4x \leq -36$$
$$\frac{4x}{4} \leq \frac{-36}{4}$$
$$x \leq -9$$

Teaching Tip ⑥ Emphasize that when multiplying or dividing an inequality by a negative number, the inequality sign is reversed when the negative factor first appears.

EVALUATING THE LESSON

Checking for Understanding

Exercises 1-14 are designed to help you assess understanding through reading, writing, and speaking. You should work through Exercises 1-4 with your students, and then monitor their work on Exercises 5-14.

Reteaching Masters Booklet, p. 31

NAME _____ DATE _____

5-2 **Reteaching Worksheet**

Solving Inequalities Using Multiplication and Division

You can solve inequalities by using the same methods you have already used to solve equations. However, when solving inequalities, if you multiply or divide each side by the same negative number, you must *reverse* the direction of the inequality symbol. The following chart shows the multiplication and division properties for solving inequalities.

Multiplication Property for Inequalities	Division Property for Inequalities

For all numbers a, b, and c,
1. If c is positive and $a < b$, then $ac < bc$.
 	
   If c is positive and $a > b$, then $ac > bc$.
 	
2. If c is negative and $a < b$, then $ac > bc$.
 	
   If c is negative and $a > b$, then $ac < bc$.
	For all numbers a, b, and c,
	1. If c is positive and $a < b$, then $\frac{a}{c} < \frac{b}{c}$.
	
	   If c is positive and $a > b$, then $\frac{a}{c} > \frac{b}{c}$.
	
	2. If c is negative and $a < b$, then $\frac{a}{c} > \frac{b}{c}$.
	
	   If c is negative and $a > b$, then $\frac{a}{c} < \frac{b}{c}$.

State the number by which you multiply each side to solve each inequality. Then indicate if the direction of the inequality symbol reverses.

1. $4s < 24$ 2. $-9k > 2$ 3. $-5\frac{1}{3} > 2n$ 4. $\frac{7}{3} < -\frac{1}{9}n$
$\frac{1}{4}$; no $-\frac{1}{9}$; yes $\frac{1}{2}$; no   −9; yes

Solve and check each solution.

5. $77 < 12r$ 6. $-5c > 2$ 7. $25g \geq -100$ 8. $\frac{n}{-50} > 22$
$\left\{r|r > 6\frac{5}{12}\right\}$ $\left\{c|c < -\frac{2}{5}\right\}$ $\{g|g \geq -4\}$ $\{n|n < -1100\}$

9. $0.24 < 0.6w$ 10. $-2.51 \leq \frac{2h}{-4}$ 11. $\frac{2a}{7} \geq -6$ 12. $-\frac{1}{3} < \frac{2p}{9}$
$\{w|w > 0.4\}$ $\{h|h \leq 5.02\}$ $\{a|a \geq -21\}$ $\left\{p|p > -\frac{3}{2}\right\}$

Write an inequality and solve. Then check each solution.

13. Four times a number is no more than 108.
$4n \leq 108$; $\{n|n \leq 27\}$

14. A number divided by 5 is at least −10.
$\frac{n}{5} \geq -10$; $\{n|n \geq -50\}$

EXERCISES 18. $\{r|r < -6\}$ 19. $\{t|t > -36\}$ 20. $\left\{a|a > \frac{28}{15}\right\}$ 23. $\{x|x > 0.6\}$

Error Analysis

Some students may add an extra step when solving inequalities that involve dividing or multiplying. Example:

$-3x \leq 12$

$x \leq -4$ Divide by -3.

$x \geq -4$ Reverse the sign.

Remind students that the sign must be reversed in the same step as the multiplying or dividing.

Closing the Lesson

Speaking Activity   Discuss the following: If $-2a < b$, is it possible that

1. a and b are both positive? **yes**

2. a is positive and b is negative? **yes**

3. a is negative and b is positive? **yes**

4. a and b are both negative? **no**

Practice Masters Booklet, p. 34

Practice

Solve and check each inequality.

$\{z|z \leq 9\}$

A

15. $16x < 96$ $\{x|x < 6\}$ **16.** $-y \leq 44$ $\{y|y \geq -44\}$ **17.** $-8z \geq -72$

18. $-102 > 17r$ **19.** $396 > -11t$ **20.** $-15a < -28$

21. $4c \geq -6$ $\left\{c|c \geq \frac{-3}{2}\right\}$ **22.** $6 \leq 0.8n$ $\{n|n \geq 7.5\}$ **23.** $-4.3x < -2.58$

24. $\frac{b}{-12} \leq 3$ $\{b|b \geq -36\}$ **25.** $-25 > \frac{a}{-6}$ $\{a|a > 150\}$ **26.** $13 \geq \frac{t}{13}$ $\{t|t \leq 169\}$

              $\{m|m \geq -33\}$

B

27. $\frac{2}{3}m \geq -22$ **28.** $-\frac{7}{9}x < 42$ $\{x|x > -54\}$ **29.** $\frac{3y}{8} \leq 32$ $\left\{y|y \leq \frac{256}{3}\right\}$

30. $\frac{-5x}{6} < \frac{2}{9}$ $\left\{x|x > -\frac{4}{15}\right\}$ **31.** $-\frac{2}{5} > \frac{4z}{7}$ $\left\{z|z < -\frac{7}{10}\right\}$ **32.** $\frac{3b}{4} \leq \frac{2}{3}$ $\left\{b|b \leq \frac{8}{9}\right\}$

CONNECTION

Geometry

For what values of d is an angle with the given measure an acute angle? Assume that d is greater than zero. Teaching Tip ⑦

33. $(6d)°$ $d < 15$ **34.** $(24d)°$ $d < 3.75$ **35.** $\left(\frac{5d}{8}\right)°$ $d < 144$ **36.** $(3.6d)°$ $d < 25$

Write an inequality and solve. Then check each solution.

See margin for inequalities.

37. Six times a number is less than 216. $\{x|x < 36\}$

38. Negative eight times a number is at most 112. $\{x|x \geq -14\}$

39. A number divided by negative 4 is no less than -2. $\{x| x \leq 8\}$

40. Five thirds of a number is no more than -15. $\{x|x \leq -9\}$

C

41. Eighty percent of a number is greater than 24. $\{x|x > 30\}$

42. The product of two numbers is no less than 144. One of the numbers is -18. What is the other number? **-8 or less**

Complete.

43. If $5x < 12$, then $20x < \underline{?}$. **48**   **44.** If $24k \geq 16$, then $\underline{?} \geq 12$. **18k**

45. If $-10a > 21$, then $30a \underline{?} -63$. **<** **46.** If $-9 \leq 15t$, then $25t \underline{?} -15$. **≥**

Critical Thinking

Determine the conditions under which each sentence is true.

47. If $\frac{2}{x} < 5$, then $2 < 5x$. **$x > 0$**   **48.** If $x > y$, then $x^2 > y^2$.

                                             $x > 0$ and $x > |y|$

Applications

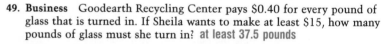

Define a variable, write an inequality, and solve each problem.

49. Business   Goodearth Recycling Center pays $0.40 for every pound of glass that is turned in. If Sheila wants to make at least $15, how many pounds of glass must she turn in? **at least 37.5 pounds**

50. Sales   Julio's budget allows him to spend at most $17 on gasoline for his car this week. If gasoline sells for $1.36 a gallon, how many gallons can he buy for his car this week? **12.5 gallons or less**

51. Finance   Michael uses at least 60% of his annual Merricoe stock dividend to purchase more shares of Merricoe stock. If his dividend last year was $885 and Merricoe stock is selling for $14 a share, what is the greatest number of shares he can purchase? **37 shares**

Additional Answers

37. $6x < 216$

38. $-8x \leq 112$

39. $\frac{x}{-4} \geq -2$

40. $\frac{5}{3}x \leq -15$

41. $0.8x > 24$

42. $-18x \geq 144$

Computer

52. For three line segments to form a triangle, the sum of the lengths of any two sides must exceed the length of the third side. Let the lengths be represented by a, b, and c. Then these three inequalities must be true: $a + b > c$, $a + c > b$, and $b + c > a$. Lines 30 through 50 of the BASIC program determine if the segments form a triangle.

```
10 PRINT "ENTER THREE LENGTHS."
20 INPUT A,B,C
30 IF C >= A + B THEN 80
40 IF B >= A + C THEN 80
50 IF A >= B + C THEN 80
60 PRINT "THIS IS A TRIANGLE."
70 GOTO 90
80 PRINT "NOT A TRIANGLE."
90 END
```

Use the program to determine whether the segments with the given lengths form a triangle.

a. 11 in., 14 in., 26 in. no   **b.** 5 ft, 12 ft, 13 ft yes

c. 75 cm, 87 cm, 110 cm yes   **d.** 1.5 m, 2.0 m, 2.5 m yes

Mixed Review

53. Consumerism Which is a better buy: 12 ounces of orange juice at $1.69 or 16 ounces at $2.29? **(Lesson 2-4)**

Solve each equation or inequality.

54. $5 - 3x = 32$ **(Lesson 3-5)** -9 **55.** $6 - 9y < -10y$ **(Lesson 5-1)** $\{y|y < -6\}$

56. $\frac{4r + 8}{16} = 7$ **(Lesson 3-5)** 26 **57.** $\frac{12 - x}{6} = \frac{x + 7}{4}$ **(Lesson 4-1)** $\frac{3}{5}$

58. $3(4a - 9) = -7(2a - 3)$ **(Lesson 3-6)** $1\frac{11}{13}$

READING ALGEBRA

The two sentences below are examples of **compound sentences**.

A square has 4 sides *and* 3 < 3.   A square has 4 sides *or* 3 < 3.

A compound sentence consists of two statements that are connected by the words *and* or *or*. A **conjunction** is a compound statement where the statements are connected using *and*. A **disjunction** is a compound sentence where the statements are connected using *or*. Thus, the sentence at the left above is a conjunction, while the sentence on the right is a disjunction.

To determine if a compound sentence is true, determine whether the two statements are true or false. A conjunction is true only if *both* statements are true. A disjunction is true if *one* or *both* statements are true.

Determine whether each compound sentence is *true* or *false*.

1. A square has 4 sides and 3 < 3. false   **2.** A square has 4 sides or 3 < 3. true

3. 0.2 is an integer or September has 31 days. false   **4.** Chicago is in Illinois and every whole number is a rational number. true

LESSON 5-2 SOLVING INEQUALITIES USING MULTIPLICATION AND DIVISION   **185**

EXTENDING THE LESSON

Math Power: Problem Solving

A plumber charges $36 for the first half hour of work and $16 for every half hour or any part of a half hour thereafter. Find the longest amount of time this plumber can work without having the bill exceed $150. **4 hours**

Reading Algebra

You may want to present this feature prior to discussing Lesson 5-5 as it is intended to prepare students for working with conjunctions and disjunctions.

Enrichment Masters Booklet, p. 31

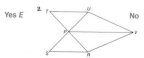

NAME _____ DATE _____

5-2   **Enrichment Worksheet**

Traceable Figures

Try to trace over each of the figures below without tracing the same segment twice.

The figure at the left cannot be traced, but the one at the right can. The rule is that a figure is traceable if it has no points, or exactly two points where an odd number of segments meet. The figure at the left has three segments meeting at each of the four corners. However, the figure at the right has exactly two points, L and Q, where an odd number of segments meet.

Determine whether each figure can be traced. If it can, then name the starting point and number the sides in the order in which they should be traced.

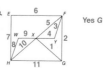

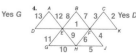

INTRODUCING THE LESSON

⏱ 5-Minute Check
(over Lesson 5-2)

Solve each inequality.

1. $\frac{a}{4} > 16$ $a > 64$
2. $15 < \frac{x}{3}$ $x > 45$
3. $\frac{5}{7}p > -20$ $p > -28$
4. $-9v \le -108$ $v \ge 12$
5. $-13x \ge 208$ $x \le -16$

Motivating the Lesson

Write the following equations on the chalkboard:
$$-3x + 5 = -10$$
$$-3(a + 2) = 8(a - 4)$$
Ask students to identify the steps needed to solve each equation. Then replace each = with >. Challenge students to compare the steps needed to solve the inequalities with those for equations.

TEACHING THE LESSON

Teaching Tip ①   You may wish to review the properties of inequalities before solving the application problem.

Teaching Tip ②   Suggest to students that they check several numbers in the solution set to determine whether true statements result.

| 5-3 | **Inequalities with More Than One Operation** |

Objective **5-3**

After studying this lesson, you should be able to:
- solve inequalities involving more than one operation.

Application **Teaching Tip ①**

Manuel has to choose between two after-school job offers at local video stores. The job at Videotyme pays a weekly salary of $90. The job at Videobarn pays a weekly salary of $70 *plus* a 10% commission on his weekly sales of videotapes. To help him choose the better job, Manuel needs to know how many dollars worth of videotapes he must sell in order to earn more per week at Videobarn.

You can write and solve an inequality to determine how much Manuel needs to sell. Let s = Manuel's weekly sales of videotapes.

Weekly salary	plus	10% of weekly sales	is more than	$90.
70	+	0.10s	>	90

This inequality involves more than one operation. It can be solved by undoing the operations in reverse of the order of operations.

$70 + 0.10s > 90$	*Undo the addition first. Use the*
$70 - 70 + 0.10s > 90 - 70$	*subtraction property for inequalities.*
$0.10s > 20$	
$10(0.10s) > 10(20)$	*Then undo the multiplication. Use the*
	multiplication property for inequalities.
$s > 200$	*You could also divide each side by 0.10.*

Manuel must sell more than $200 worth of videotapes each week to earn more money per week at Videobarn. Since Manuel considers himself a good salesperson, he takes the job at Videobarn.

Inequalities involving more than one operation can be solved by applying methods similar to those used for solving equations involving more than one operation.

186   CHAPTER 5   INEQUALITIES

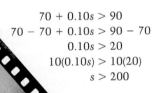

ALTERNATE TEACHING STRATEGIES

Using Cooperative Groups

Divide the class into four or five small groups. Have each group create 5 word problems similar to that of Example 4. Have groups switch and solve each other's problems. Answers are verified by the group that originally created the problems.

Using Logical Reasoning

Have students solve and graph the solution set of $-3x + 5 = -10$. Challenge students to write two new inequalities whose solutions would be graphed as the remaining portions of the number line.
$$-3x + 5 > -10, \quad -3x + 5 < -10$$

Example 1

Solve $16 - 5b \geq 29$.

$$16 - 5b \geq 29$$
$$16 - 16 - 5b \geq 29 - 16 \qquad \textit{Subtract 16 from each side.}$$
$$-5b \geq 13$$
$$\frac{-5b}{-5} \leq \frac{13}{-5} \qquad \textit{Divide each side by } -5 \textit{ and change } \geq \textit{ to } \leq.$$
$$b \leq -\frac{13}{5}$$

The solution set is $\left\{ b \mid b \leq \frac{-13}{5} \right\}$.

Example 2

Solve $9x + 4 < 7 - 13x$.

$$9x + 4 < 7 - 13x$$
$$9x + 13x + 4 < 7 - 13x + 13x \qquad \textit{Add 13x to each side.}$$
$$22x + 4 < 7$$
$$22x + 4 - 4 < 7 - 4 \qquad \textit{Subtract 4 from each side.}$$
$$22x < 3$$
$$\frac{22x}{22} < \frac{3}{22} \qquad \textit{Divide each side by 22.}$$
$$x < \frac{3}{22}$$

The solution set is $\left\{ x \mid x < \frac{3}{22} \right\}$. **Teaching Tip ❷**

When solving some inequalities that contain grouping symbols, remember to first use the distributive property to remove the grouping symbols.

Example 3

Solve $0.7(n - 3) \leq n - 0.6(n + 5)$.

$$0.7(n - 3) \leq n - 0.6(n + 5)$$
$$0.7n - 2.1 \leq n - 0.6n - 3.0 \qquad \textit{Use the distributive property.}$$
$$0.7n - 2.1 \leq 0.4n - 3.0$$
$$0.7n - 0.4n - 2.1 \leq 0.4n - 0.4n - 3.0 \qquad \textit{Subtract 0.4n from each side.}$$
$$0.3n - 2.1 \leq -3.0$$
$$0.3n - 2.1 + 2.1 \leq -3.0 + 2.1 \qquad \textit{Add 2.1 to each side.}$$
$$0.3n \leq -0.9$$
$$\frac{0.3n}{0.3} \leq \frac{-0.9}{0.3} \qquad \textit{Divide each side by 0.3.}$$
$$n \leq -3$$

The solution set is $\{ n \mid n \leq -3 \}$.

LESSON 5-3 INEQUALITIES WITH MORE THAN ONE OPERATION 187

Example 4

CONNECTION

Statistics

Owen's scores on the first three of four 100-point tests were 89, 92, and 82. What score must he receive on the fourth test to have an average (mean) of at least 90 for all the tests?

EXPLORE   Let s = Owen's score on the fourth test.

PLAN   The sum of Owen's scores on the four tests, divided by 4, must be at least 90.

$$\frac{89 + 92 + 82 + s}{4} \geq 90$$

SOLVE
$$4\left(\frac{89 + 92 + 82 + s}{4}\right) \geq 4(90) \quad \textit{Multiply each side by 4.}$$
$$89 + 92 + 82 + s \geq 360$$
$$263 + s \geq 360$$
$$263 - 263 + s \geq 360 - 263 \quad \textit{Subtract 263 from each side.}$$
$$s \geq 97$$

Owen's score on the fourth test must be at least 97.

EXAMINE   Here's another way to solve the problem. Look at Owen's scores on the first three tests. 89 is 1 less than 90, 92 is 2 more than 90, and 82 is 8 less than 90. Since the sum $-1 + 2 + (-8)$ is -7, it follows that Owen needs a score at least 7 more points than 90, or 97, on the fourth test to have an average of 90 on all the tests.

CHECKING FOR UNDERSTANDING

Communicating Mathematics

Read and study the lesson to answer each question.

1. Write an example of an inequality requiring more than one operation to solve. **Answers will vary; an example is $2x > 5x - 1$.**

2. How could you solve $16 - 5b > 29$ *without* dividing by -5? **See margin.**

3. Refer to the situation at the beginning of the lesson. If the commission on videotape sales at Videobarn is 16% instead of 10%, how much does Manuel need to sell to earn more per week at Videobarn? **more than $125 worth of videotapes each week**

4. In Example 4, can Owen have an average of at least 91 points on all four 100-point tests? Explain.   **No, since he would need to score 101 on the fourth test.**

Guided Practice

Explain how to solve each inequality. Then solve. **See margin.**

5. $3x - 1 > 14$ $\{x \mid x > 5\}$

6. $-20 \geq 8 + 7a$ $\{a \mid a \leq -4\}$

7. $\frac{n - 11}{-2} \leq -6$ $\{n \mid n \geq 23\}$

8. $12 - \frac{5z}{4} < 37$ $\{z \mid z > -20\}$

9. $y + 1 \geq 5y + 5$ $\{y \mid y \leq -1\}$

10. $2k + 7 > 11 - k$ $\left\{k \mid k > \frac{4}{3}\right\}$

RETEACHING THE LESSON

Use a two-pan balance to demonstrate how to solve these inequalities. □ □ 3 represents 2 identical objects of unknown weight and a weight of 3 units.

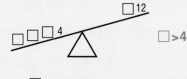

EXERCISES

Practice

Solve each inequality. Check the solution. **11-22. See margin.**

11. $9x + 2 > 20$
12. $4y - 7 < 21$
13. $-7a + 6 \le 48$
14. $-5 - 8b \ge 59$
15. $-12 + 11m \le 54$
16. $5 - 6n > -19$
17. $\frac{z}{4} + 7 \ge -5$
18. $\frac{2x}{3} - 3 \le 7$
19. $-2 - \frac{d}{5} < 23$
20. $\frac{2t + 5}{3} < -9$
21. $\frac{11 - 6w}{5} > 10$
22. $7y - 27 \ge 4y$

B

Teaching Tip ③

23. $13r - 11 > 7r + 37$ $\{r|r > 8\}$
24. $6a + 9 < -4a + 29$ $\{a|a < 2\}$
25. $0.1y - 2 \le 0.3y - 5$ $\{y|y \ge 15\}$
26. $1.3x + 6.7 \ge 3.1x - 1.4$ $\{x|x \le 4.5\}$
27. $7(g + 8) < 3(g + 12)$ $\{g|g < -5\}$
28. $-5(k + 4) \ge 3(k - 4)$ $\{k|k \le -1\}$
29. $8c - (c - 5) > c + 17$ $\{c|c > 2\}$
30. $3d - 2(8d - 9) < 3 - (2d + 7)$ $\{d|d > 2\}$

Write an inequality and solve. Then check each solution.
See margin for inequalities.

31. The sum of twice a number and 17 is no greater than 41. $\{x|x \le 12\}$
32. Two-thirds of a number decreased by 27 is at least 9. $\{x|x \ge 54\}$
33. Three times the sum of a number and 7 is greater than five times the number less 13. $\{x|x < 17\}$
34. Twice a number increased by 32 is no less than three times the number subtracted from 2. $\{x|x \ge -6\}$

Define a variable, write an inequality, and solve each problem.

35. The sum of two consecutive even integers is greater than 75. Find the pair with the least sum. **38 and 40**
36. The sum of two consecutive odd integers is at most 123. Find the pair with the greatest sum. **59 and 61**

C

37. Find all sets of two consecutive positive odd integers whose sum is no greater than 18. **7 and 9, 5 and 7, 3 and 5, 1 and 3**
38. Find all sets of three consecutive positive even integers whose sum is less than 30. **2, 4, and 6; 4, 6, and 8; 6, 8, and 10**

Solve each inequality. Check the solution. **40.** $n \ge \frac{23}{3}$ **41.** $c \le -4$

39. $\frac{5y - 4}{3} > \frac{y + 5}{3}$ $y > \frac{9}{4}$
40. $\frac{2n + 1}{7} \ge \frac{n + 4}{5}$
41. $\frac{c + 8}{4} \le \frac{5 - c}{9}$

Critical Thinking

42. Write an inequality that has no solution.
Answers will vary; an example is $x + 1 < x - 1$.

Applications

Define a variable, write an inequality, and solve each problem.

43. **Statistics** Abeytu's scores on the first four of five 100-point tests were 85, 89, 90, and 81. What score must she receive on the fifth test to have an average of at least 87 points for all the tests?
at least 90 points

LESSON 5-3 INEQUALITIES WITH MORE THAN ONE OPERATION **189**

Additional Answers

2. Add $5b$ to each side. Subtract 29 from each side. Divide each side by 5.
5. Add 1 to each side. Then divide each side by 3.
6. Subtract 8 from each side. Divide each side by 7. Rewrite as $a \le -4$.
7. Multiply each side by -2 and reverse the inequality symbol. Add 11 to each side.
8. Subtract 12 from each side. Multiply each side by $-\frac{4}{5}$ and reverse the inequality symbol.
9. Subtract $5y$ and 1 from each side. Divide each side by -4 and reverse the inequality symbol.
10. Add k to each side. Subtract 7 from each side. Divide each side by 3.
11. $\{x|x > 2\}$
12. $\{y|y < 7\}$

APPLYING THE LESSON

Homework Exercises

Assignment Guide

Basic: 11-36, 42-44, 46-49
Average: 17-39, 42-49
Enriched: 19-49

Chapter 5, Quiz B, (Lesson 5-3), is available in the Evaluation Masters Booklet, p. 65.

Teaching Tip ③ Before students solve Exercises 25-26, remind them that multiplying each side of an inequality by 10 will eliminate the decimals.

Additional Answers

13. $\{a|a \ge -6\}$
14. $\{b|b \le -8\}$
15. $\{m|m \le 6\}$
16. $\{n|n < 4\}$
17. $\{z|z \ge -48\}$
18. $\{x|x \le 15\}$
19. $\{d|d > -125\}$
20. $\{t|t < -16\}$
21. $\{w|w < -6.5\}$
22. $\{y|y \ge 9\}$
31. $2x + 17 \le 41$
32. $\frac{2}{3}x - 27 \ge 9$
33. $3(x + 7) > 5x - 13$
34. $2x + 32 \ge 2 - 3x$

Practice Masters Booklet, p. 35

NAME _____ DATE _____

5-3 Practice Worksheet

Inequalities with More Than One Operation

Solve and check each solution.

1. $7a - 5 < 9$
   $a < 2$
2. $6 - 11b \le -3$
   $b \ge \frac{9}{11}$
3. $15 < 5 - 8c$
   $c < -\frac{5}{4}$
4. $\frac{d}{6} - 16 < -9$
   $d < 42$
5. $\frac{e}{-4} + 8 \le 1$
   $e \ge 28$
6. $-12 \ge \frac{r}{8} - 5$
   $r \le -56$
7. $\frac{5s}{6} + 7 > -3$
   $s > -12$
8. $5 \ge \frac{3x}{4} + 12$
   $x \le -\frac{28}{3}$
9. $-3 - \frac{k}{5} \ge -10$
   $k \le 35$
10. $15 > \frac{2m}{3} - 1$
    $m < 24$
11. $\frac{t + 3}{2} < -8$
    $t < -19$
12. $\frac{3x - 1}{6} < 2$
    $x > \frac{13}{3}$
13. $4n - 6 > 6n - 20$
    $n < 7$
14. $2.4x + 13 \le 5x$
    $x \ge 5$
15. $5p - 3(p - 6) \le 0$
    $p \le -9$

Write an inequality and solve. Then check each solution.

16. The sum of a number and 81 is greater than the product of -3 and that number.
    $n + 81 > -3n; n > -\frac{81}{4}$
17. Four more than the quotient of a number and 3 is at least that number.
    $\frac{n}{3} + 4 \ge n; n \le 6$

44. **Sales** Don earns $24,000 per year in salary and 8% commission on his sales. If he must have a total annual income of at least $30,000 to pay all of his expenses, how much sales per year must he have? **at least $75,000**

45. **Employment** Maria earns $4.76 an hour at the local supermarket. Each week, 25% of her total pay is deducted for taxes. In addition, she pays $25 a week, after taxes, for union dues. If she wants her take-home pay to be at least $100 a week, how many hours must she work? **more than 35 hours**

Mixed Review

46. Define the variable, then write an equation. **Sports** Megan scored 12 points in a basketball game. This was 4 points less than the previous game. How many points did Megan score in both games? **(Lesson 2-8)** **See margin.**

47. Solve $\frac{2}{5}x - 1 = \frac{1}{4}x + 2$. **(Lesson 3-6)** **20**

48. **Employment** Deidre's wages vary directly as the time she works. If her wages for 6 days are $121, what are her wages for 20 days? **(Lesson 4-7)** **$403.33**

49. Solve $-13z > -1.04$. **(Lesson 5-2)** $\{z|z < 0.08\}$

MID-CHAPTER REVIEW

Solve and check each inequality. **(Lessons 4-1, 4-2, and 4-3)** 3. $\{z|z < -3\}$ 9. $\left\{n|n > -\frac{5}{12}\right\}$

1. $a + 2 < 10$ $\{a|a < 8\}$
2. $-12 \leq s - (-3)$ $\{s|s \geq -15\}$
3. $-3 + 13z > 14z$
4. $23b \geq 276$ $\{b|b \geq 12\}$
5. $-\frac{1}{3}k > \frac{6}{7}$ $\left\{k|k < -\frac{18}{7}\right\}$
6. $\frac{4a}{5} \leq -\frac{13}{8}$ $\left\{a|a \leq -\frac{65}{32}\right\}$
7. $-6x + 9 < 4x + 29$ $\{x|x > -2\}$
8. $9d - 5 \geq 8 - d$ $\left\{d|d \geq \frac{13}{10}\right\}$
9. $3(7 - 2n) < 2(3n + 13)$

Write an inequality and solve. Then check each solution. **See margin for inequalities.**

10. The sum of a number and 11 is at least 23. **(Lesson 4-1)** $\{n|n \geq 12\}$
11. Three fourths of a number is less than 90. **(Lesson 4-2)** $\{n|n < 120\}$
12. Twice a number less 9 is no more than 75. **(Lesson 4-3)** $\{n|n \leq 42\}$
13. Three times a number subtracted from 10 is at least 6 more than the number. **(Lesson 4-3)** $\{n|n \leq 1\}$

14. **Business** The Gahanna Tribune pays its carriers 8¢ for each newspaper delivered. How many newspapers must a newspaper carrier deliver to earn at least $5.00 a day? **(Lesson 4-2)** **63 newspapers or more**

15. **Communications** City Phone charges $13 a month plus $0.21 per call for local phone service. If Jay can spend no more than $20 a month on this service, how many calls can he make? **(Lesson 4-3)** **33 or less**

EXTENDING THE LESSON

Math Power: Reasoning

Give an example of an inequality involving more than one operation for which the solution set is the empty set. **Possible answers include** $3x - 6 > 3(x + 2)$.

Mid-Chapter Review

The Mid-Chapter Review provides students with a brief review of the concepts and skills in Lessons 5-1 through 5-3. Lesson numbers are given at the end of problems or instruction lines so students may review concepts not yet mastered.

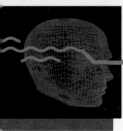

Technology

Solving Inequalities

BASIC
Graphing Calculators
▶ Graphing Software
Spreadsheets

The examples below show how to use the *Mathematics Exploration Toolkit* to practice the steps for solving inequalities. You will use the same CALC commands that were used in Chapter 3. Remember that you may enter the abbreviations shown instead of typing the entire command.

ADD (add)	SUBTRACT (sub)	MULTIPLY (mult)
DIVIDE (div)	SIMPLIFY (simp) or [F5]	

To enter the symbol $\leq$ type the left brace, {. To enter the symbol $\geq$ type the right brace, }.

Example 1

Solve $3x - 4 < 7x + 20$.

Enter	Result
$3x - 4 < 7x + 20$	$3x - 4 < 7x + 20$
sub 7x	$3x - 4 - 7x < 7x + 20 - 7x$
simp	$-4x - 4 < 20$
add 4	$-4x - 4 + 4 < 20 + 4$
simp	$-4x < 24$
div -4	$\frac{-4x}{-4} > \frac{24}{-4}$
simp	$x > -6$

Example 2

Solve $\left(\frac{x-2}{3}\right) \geq 6$.

Enter	Result
(x−2)/3}6	$\frac{x-2}{3} \geq 6$
mult 3	$3\left(\frac{x-2}{3}\right) \geq 3(6)$
simp	$x - 2 \geq 18$
add 2	$x - 2 + 2 \geq 18 + 2$
simp	$x \geq 20$

EXERCISES

See students' work.

Use CALC to solve each inequality. Record each step and solution.

1. $2x + 8 < 5x + 11$ $x > -1$
2. $5 - x > x - 7$ $x < 6$
3. $6(x + 4) \geq 5x - 3 - 2x$ $x \geq -9$
4. $8.6x - (6.4 + 4.2x) \leq 0.2$ $x \leq 1.5$
5. $\frac{2x - 6}{5} > \frac{3x + 2}{5}$ $x < -8$
6. $\frac{x}{3} \leq \frac{x + 1}{4}$ $x \leq 3$

TECHNOLOGY: SOLVING INEQUALITIES 191

Using Technology

Objective This optional page shows how the BASIC programming language can be used to perform mathematical computations and to enhance and extend mathematical concepts.

Teaching Suggestions

The command SOLVEFOR will not solve inequalities automatically as it does equations. Encourage students to record the steps they used for review and comparison. Direct them to compare the steps they chose to those chosen by other students. Focus their attention on steps which involve multiplying or dividing by a negative number. You may want to have students check their solutions. The MET command SUBSTITUTE (subs) allows replacing a variable with a value. Have the students enter the original inequality then substitute various values in the solution set. If the resulting statement is true, that value checked.

Lesson Resources

- Practice Master 5-4
- Transparency 5-4 contains the 5-Minute Check and a teaching aid for this lesson.

INTRODUCING THE LESSON

🕐 5-Minute Check

(over Lesson 5-3)

Solve.

1. $3x - 15 < 45$ $\;\;$ $x < 20$
2. $2p - 22 \geq 4p + 14$ $\;\;$ $p \leq -18$
3. $7y + 12 > 46 - 10y$ $\;\;$ $y > 2$
4. $3(m + 2) \leq 6(2m - 5)$ $\;\;$ $m \geq 4$
5. $5(r + 3) > 2(4r - 6)$ $\;\;$ $r < 9$

Motivating the Lesson

Present the following problem to the class: Meg left her home and walked 3 blocks north and 4 blocks east to the school. After school, she walked 1 block south and 1 block west to visit her friend. Meg then walked to the library which was 2 blocks north and 3 blocks west of her friend's house. If Meg goes directly home from the library, how many blocks will she walk? Encourage students to draw a map to solve the problem. **4 blocks south**

TEACHING THE LESSON

Teaching Tip ① Challenge students to identify other types of diagrams that could be used to solve the problem.

Chalkboard Example

For the Example

Five people come together for a meeting. If each person shakes each other person's hand once, what is the total number of handshakes that will occur? **10**

5-4 Problem-Solving Strategy: Make a Diagram

Objective 5-4

After studying this lesson, you should be able to:
- solve problems by making a diagram.

You can solve many problems more easily if you draw a picture or diagram. Sometimes a picture will help you decide how to work the problem. At other times the picture will show the answer to the problem.

Application

Let's listen in on a meeting of the Brookhaven High School Chess Club.

"Mei, would you please read the minutes of the last meeting?"

"Sure, John. At the last meeting it was decided that each member should play each of the other nine members so we can figure out who are the five best players. These five players will then play in interschool competitions. Then the meeting was adjourned."

How many games must be played to determine the five best players?

> **FYI···**
>
> Chess originated in ancient India. It was originally called *Chaturanga*.

Since each member plays every other member, you might think that there would be a total of 90 games (9 games × 10 members). But let's try looking at this problem another way. Draw a diagram to represent the 10 players. An easy way is to use dots.

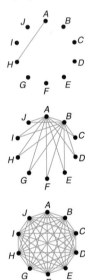

Label the points from *A* to *J*. Each point represents a player. Use a line segment joining two points to represent a game between two players. How many line segments are required to join the ten dots?

Teaching Tip ①

First, draw all possible segments from *A*. There are nine. Then draw all possible segments from *B*. There are eight new segments.

To check this solution, solve the problem using a different strategy.

Continue until all of the dots are connected. If you keep careful count, you will find that there are $9 + 8 + 7 + 6 + 5 + 4 + 3 + 2 + 1$, or 45 segments. Thus, 45 games would be played.

CHECKING FOR UNDERSTANDING

Communicating Mathematics

Read and study the lesson to answer each question.

1. Name two ways a picture or diagram can help you solve a problem more easily. **Helps you plan the solution; provides the solution.**

2. Suppose two students join the chess club. How many games will have to be played now? **66 games**

RETEACHING THE LESSON

Tell students to look for examples of charts and diagrams in newspapers and magazines. Then have the students cut the visuals from the periodicals and mount them on a sheet of poster board. Underneath each visual, students should identify the type of information being presented and how the visual helps the reader comprehend the information.

Additional Answer

8. Luis won the race. If Luis started two miles behind Kevin, they were even after Luis ran the length of the first race. Then, because Luis ran faster, he won the race.

Solve by making a drawing or diagram.

25 thumbtacks

3. Kathy Velasquez is a geography teacher. She wants to put 16 rectangular pictures of "Countries Around the World" on the wall of her classroom, but she only has a few thumbtacks. What is the least number of thumbtacks that she can use to tack up these pictures so they can all be seen? (Assume that each corner of each picture must be tacked and that the pictures are the same size.)

4. You can cut a pizza into 7 pieces with only 3 straight cuts. What is the greatest number of pieces you can make with 5 straight cuts? **16 pieces**

5. There are eight houses on Elm Street, all in a row. These houses are numbered from 1 to 8. Allison, whose house number is greater than 2, lives next door to her best friend, Adrienne. Belinda, whose house number is greater than 5, lives two doors away from her boyfriend, Benito. Chumani, whose house number is greater than Benito's, lives three doors away from her piano teacher, Mr. Crawford. Darryl, whose house number is less than 4, lives four doors away from his teammate, Don. Who lives in each house? **1-Darryl, 2-Adrienne, 3-Allison, 4-Mr. Crawford, 5-Don, 6-Benito, 7-Chumani, 8-Belinda**

EXERCISES

Practice

Solve. Use any strategy. 7. $1^2 = 1$, $(25)^2 = 625$, or $(76)^2 = 5776$

Strategies
Look for a pattern.
Solve a simpler problem.
Act it out.
Guess and check.
Draw a diagram.
Make a chart.
Work backwards.

6. What is the next letter in the sequence below? **E for eighth**

F, S, T, F, F, S, S, __?__

7. **Number Theory** *Automorphic numbers* are whole numbers whose square ends in the same number. Two examples are $5^2 = 25$ and $6^2 = 36$. 10 is not an automorphic number, since the last two digits of 10^2 are not 1 and 0. Find another automorphic number.

8. On Saturday, Kevin challenged Luis to a 10-mile bicycle race. When Luis reached the finish line, Kevin was two miles behind him. On Sunday, Kevin challenged Luis to another race. To even up the contest, Luis started two miles behind Kevin. Assuming they cycled the same distance at the same speeds as before, which cyclist won the race? **See margin.**

COOPERATIVE LEARNING ACTIVITY

Work in groups of three. Each person in the group must understand the solution and be able to explain it to any person in the class.

When changing a dollar bill, you can give one coin (silver dollar), two coins (2 half-dollars), three coins (2 quarters and 1 half-dollar), and so forth. What is the least positive number of coins that is *impossible* to give as change for a dollar bill? **77 coins**

LESSON 5-4 PROBLEM-SOLVING STRATEGY: MAKE A DIAGRAM 193

EXTENDING THE LESSON

Math Power: Connections

A staircase with 3 steps was built with 6 blocks. Can a staircase be built with 28 blocks? If so, how many steps would it have? **yes; 7 steps**

Cooperative Learning Activity

This activity provides students with an opportunity to *learn* things together, not just do things together. You may wish to refer to pages T6 - T8 and page 6C for the various elements of cooperative groups and specific goals and strategies for using them.

INTRODUCING THE LESSON

 5-Minute Check

(over Lesson 5-3)

Solve.

1. $-2 + 9n \le 10n$ $n \ge -2$
2. $-5e + 9 > 24$ $e < -3$
3. $3y - 4 > -37$ $y > -11$
4. $-2k + 12 < 30$ $k > -9$
5. $-6v - 3 \ge -33$ $v \le 5$

Motivating the Lesson

Ask students to list any integers that are less than 7 and greater than 2.   **3, 4, 5, 6**
Then have them list any integers that are greater than 2 or less than 7.   **all integers**
Challenge students to identify how the use of the words "and" or "or" changes the way a solution set is determined.
"and" requires the intersection of sets; "or" requires the union

TEACHING THE LESSON

Chalkboard Examples

For Example 1
Write the compound sentence $m \ge 6$ and $m < 12$ without using the word "and". $6 \le m < 12$

For Example 2
Write y is positive and y is less than 5 as a compound inequality without using "and".
$0 < y < 5$

Objectives
5-5A
5-5B

After studying this lesson, you should be able to:
- solve compound inequalities and graph their solution sets, and
- solve problems that involve compound inequalities.

Application

FYI · · ·

In 1914, only 1% of Americans paid income tax, at an average of 41¢ each.

Melody Harrison works part-time while attending college. Last year she paid $629 in federal income tax. The tax table that she used is shown at the right. Since she is single, her taxable income must have been at least $4650 but less than $4700.

Let I = her taxable income. Then the two inequalities below describe her income.

$$I \ge 4650 \text{ and } I < 4700$$

When considered together, these two inequalities form a **compound inequality.** The compound inequality $I \ge 4650$ and $I < 4700$ can also be written without using *and* in either of the following ways.

$$4650 \le I < 4700 \text{ or } 4700 > I \ge 4650$$

The statement $4650 \le I < 4700$ can be read *4650 is less than or equal to I, which is less than 4700.* The statement $4700 > I \ge 4650$ can be read *4700 is greater than I, which is greater than or equal to 4650.*

If 1040A, line 17, OR 1040EZ, line 7 is—		And you are—			
At least	But less than	Single (and 1040EZ filers)	Married filing jointly	Married filing separately	Head of a household
			Your tax is—		
4,000	4,050	532	484	544	504
4,050	4,100	539	491	551	511
4,100	4,150	547	499	559	519
4,150	4,200	554	506	566	526
4,200	4,250	562	514	574	534
4,250	4,300	569	521	581	541
4,300	4,350	577	529	589	549
4,350	4,400	584	536	596	556
4,400	4,450	592	544	604	564
4,450	4,500	599	551	611	571
4,500	4,550	607	559	619	579
4,550	4,600	614	566	626	586
4,600	4,650	622	574	634	594
4,650	4,700	629	581	641	601
4,700	4,750	637	589	649	609
4,750	4,800	644	596	656	616
4,800	4,850	652	604	664	624
4,850	4,900	659	611	671	631
4,900	4,950	667	619	679	639
4,950	5,000	674	626	686	646

Example 1

Write $x > -5$ and $x \le 1$ as a compound inequality without using *and*.

$x > -5$ and $x \le 1$ can be written as $-5 < x \le 1$ or $1 \ge x > -5$.

Example 2

Write y is positive and y is less than 10 as a compound inequality without using *and*.

y is positive means $y > 0$. *y is less than 10* means $y < 10$. Thus, the compound inequality can be written as $0 < y < 10$ or $10 > y > 0$.

Recall that the graph of an inequality is the graph of its solution set.

A compound inequality containing *and* is true only if *both* inequalities are true. Thus, the graph of a compound inequality containing *and* is the *intersection* of the graphs of the two inequalities. The intersection can be found by graphing the two inequalities and then determining where these graphs overlap. In other words, make a diagram.

ALTERNATE TEACHING STRATEGIES

Using Critical Thinking

What is the relationship between set intersections and unions and the solutions of compound sentences using the words "and" and "or"?

Using Connections

Consider the sets $A = \{1, 2, 3, 4, 5, 6, 7, 8\}$ and $B = \{6, 7, 8, 9, 10\}$.
Find the intersection of sets A and B.
$\{6, 7, 8\}$
Describe this set in an inequality.
$\{x \mid 6 \le x \le 8\}$
Find the union of sets A and B.
$\{1, 2, 3, 4, 5, 6, 7, 8, 9, 10\}$
Describe this set in an inequality.
$\{x \mid 1 \le x \le 10\}$

Example 3
Teaching Tip ❶

Graph the solution set of $x > -5$ and $x \le 1$.

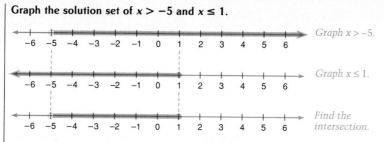

Graph $x > -5$.

Graph $x \le 1$.

Find the intersection.

The solution set, shown in the bottom graph, is $\{x \mid -5 < x \le 1\}$.

Example 4

Solve $x - 4 < -1$ and $x - 4 > 1$. Then graph the solution set.

$$x - 4 < -1 \qquad \text{and} \qquad x - 4 > 1$$
$$x - 4 + 4 < -1 + 4 \qquad\qquad x - 4 + 4 > 1 + 4$$
$$x < 3 \qquad\qquad\qquad x > 5$$

Graph $x < 3$.

Graph $x > 5$.

There is no intersection.

There are *no* points in the intersection of the graphs. That is, there are no numbers that are *both* less than 3 and greater than 5. Therefore, the solution set, shown in the bottom graph, is the empty set (∅).

Another type of compound inequality contains *or* instead of *and*. A compound inequality containing *or* is true if *either* of the inequalities or *both* of the inequalities are true. The graph of a compound inequality containing *or* is the *union* of the graphs of the two inequalities.

Example 5

Graph the solution set of $x \ge 3$ or $x < -2$.

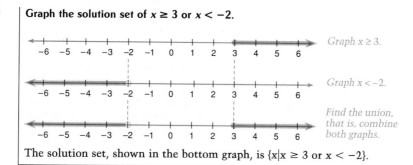

Graph $x \ge 3$.

Graph $x < -2$.

Find the union, that is, combine both graphs.

The solution set, shown in the bottom graph, is $\{x \mid x \ge 3 \text{ or } x < -2\}$.

For Example 3
Graph the solution set of $x < 10$ and $x < 5$.

For Example 4
Graph the solution set of $m < 8$ and $m > 10$.

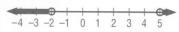

∅

For Example 5
Graph the solution set of $x < -2$ or $x > 5$.

Teaching Tip ❶ Before introducing Example 3, discuss possible solutions to the compound sentence in the example, $x > -5$ and $x \le 1$. Have students choose a number and substitute it for *x*. Then have them determine whether the number is a solution to the compound sentence. For example, try 5. Is 5 greater than −5 and less than 1? Note that 5 is greater than −5, but it is not less than 1. Therefore, the number 5 is not a solution to the compound sentence. Other numbers that students could try are −6, 1, −2, and −5.

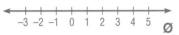
Example 6

Solve $2y > y - 3$ or $3y < y + 6$. Then graph the solution set.

$$2y > y - 3 \qquad \text{or} \qquad 3y < y + 6$$
$$2y - y > y - y - 3 \qquad\qquad 3y - y < y - y + 6$$
$$y > -3 \qquad\qquad\qquad 2y < 6$$
$$\frac{2y}{2} < \frac{6}{2}$$
$$y < 3$$

Graph the solution sets for $y > -3$ and $y < 3$. **Teaching Tip ②**

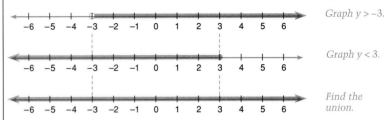

Graph $y > -3$.

Graph $y < 3$.

Find the union.

The solution set, shown in the bottom graph, is {all numbers}.

Example 7

Dwayne earns $15,600 per year in salary and 6% commission on his sales at Stride City Shoes. What would his sales have to be if his total income falls between $21,000 and $25,500?

EXPLORE   Dwayne's total income is $15,600 plus 6% of his sales. Let s = Dwayne's sales. Then $15,600 + 0.06s$ = his total income.

PLAN   If Dwayne's total income falls between $21,000 and $25,500, then it was greater than $21,000 and it was less than $25,500.

$$21,000 < 15,600 + 0.06s \quad \text{and} \quad 15,600 + 0.06s < 25,500$$

SOLVE

$$21,000 < 15,600 + 0.06s \qquad \text{and} \qquad 15,600 + 0.06s < 25,500$$
$$5400 < 0.06s \qquad\qquad\qquad 0.06s < 9900$$
$$\frac{5400}{0.06} < \frac{0.06s}{0.06} \qquad\qquad\qquad \frac{0.06s}{0.06} < \frac{9900}{0.06}$$
$$90,000 < s \qquad\qquad\qquad\qquad s < 165,000$$

Dwayne's sales are between $90,000 and $165,000.

EXAMINE   If Dwayne's sales are $90,000, then his total income would be $15,600 + 0.06($90,000) or $21,000. If his sales are $165,000, then his total income would be $15,600 + 0.06($165,000) or $25,500. Any amount of sales between $90,000 and $165,000 would make his total income fall between $21,000 and $25,500. Thus, the solution is correct.

RETEACHING THE LESSON

Graph sets A, B, and C.
$A = \{x \mid x > 3\}$ $B = \{x \mid x \leq 1\}$
$C = \{x \mid x < 6\}$
Use these graphs to graph the intersections and unions.

1. $A \cap C$

2. $A \cup C$

all numbers

3. $B \cap C$

4. $B \cup C$

5. $A \cup B$

CHECKING FOR UNDERSTANDING

Communicating Mathematics

Read and study the lesson to answer each question. 3. See margin.

1. What is a compound inequality? Two inequalities connected by *and* or *or*.

2. Refer to the application at the beginning of the lesson. If Melody had paid $607 in federal income tax last year, what would be the range of her taxable income, I? $4500 \leq I < $4550

3. What is the difference between a compound inequality containing *and* and a compound inequality containing *or*?

4. Can you write a compound inequality containing *or* without using *or*? Why or why not? See margin.

Guided Practice

Write each compound inequality without using *and*.

5. $0 \leq m$ and $m < 9$ $0 \leq m < 9$

6. $0 < y$ and $y \leq 12$ $0 < y \leq 12$

7. $z > -\frac{4}{5}$ and $z < \frac{2}{3}$ $-\frac{4}{5} < z < \frac{2}{3}$

8. $r \geq -\frac{3}{4}$ and $r \leq \frac{1}{10}$ $-\frac{3}{4} \leq r \leq \frac{1}{10}$

Graph the solution set of each compound inequality. See margin.

9. $m < -7$ or $m \geq 0$ 10. $x \geq -2$ and $x \leq 5$ 11. $y > -5$ and $y < 0$

12. $r > 2$ or $r \leq -2$ 13. $w > -3$ or $w < 1$ 14. $n \leq -5$ and $n \geq -1$

EXERCISES

Practice

Graph the solution set of each compound inequality. See Solutions Manual.

A

15. $b > 5$ or $b \leq 0$ 16. $d > 0$ or $d < 4$ 17. $d \geq -6$ and $d \leq -3$

18. $1 > q \geq -5$ 19. $s \geq 8$ or $s < 5$ 20. $-1 < p \leq 6$

21. $t < -3$ and $t > 3$ 22. $a \leq 8$ or $a \geq 3$ 23. $r > -4$ or $r \leq 0$

B

Solve each compound inequality and graph the solution set. See margin.

24. $3 + x < -4$ or $3 + x > 4$

25. $-1 + d > -4$ or $-1 + d < 3$

26. $5n < 2n + 9$ and $9 - 2n > 11$

27. $2 > 3z + 2 > 14$

28. $-2 \leq x + 3 < 4$

29. $8 + 3t < 2$ or $-12 < 11t - 1$

30. $a \neq 6$ and $3a + 1 > 10$

31. $3x + 11 \leq 13$ or $2x \geq 5x - 12$

32. $5(x - 3) + 2 < 7$ and $5x > 4(2x - 3)$

33. $2 - 5(2x - 3) > 2$ or $3x < 2(x - 8)$

Write a compound inequality for each solution set shown below.

34.
$-2 < x \leq 3$

35.
$x < -3$ or $x > 3$

36.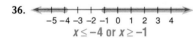
$x \leq -4$ or $x \geq -1$

37.
$-3 \leq x < 5$

Checking for Understanding

Exercises 1-14 are designed to help you assess understanding through reading, writing, and speaking. You should work through Exercises 1-4 with your students, and then monitor their work on Exercises 5-14.

Assignment Guide

Basic: 15-37, 44-46, 49-53
Average: 20-40, 44-53
Enriched: 24-53

Additional Answers

13.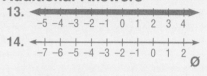

14.
-7 -6 -5 -4 -3 -2 -1 0 1 2   ∅

24. $\{x \mid x < -7 \text{ or } x > 1\}$
25. $\{\text{all numbers}\}$
26. $\{n \mid n < -1\}$
27. $\varnothing$
28. $\{x \mid x < 1 \text{ and } x \geq -5\}$
29. $\{t \mid t < -2 \text{ or } t > -1\}$
30. $\{a \mid a > 3 \text{ and } a \neq 6\}$
31. $\{x \mid x \leq 4\}$
32. $\{x \mid x < 4\}$
33. $\left\{x \mid x < \frac{3}{2}\right\}$

Practice Masters Booklet, p. 37

NAME _____ DATE _____

5-5   **Practice Worksheet**

Compound Sentences

Graph the solution of each compound inequality.

1. $b > 3$ or $b \leq 0$ 2. $x > 0$ or $x < 3$

3. $y < -2$ or $y \geq 2$ 4. $0 < k < 4$

5. $-1 \leq z \leq 5$ 6. $e \geq -4$ and $e \leq 0$

Solve each compound inequality and graph the solution set.

7. $c + 2 \leq 3$ and $4 - c > 2$ $c \leq 1$

8. $-n < 2$ or $2n - 3 > 5$ $n > -2$ or $n > 4$

9. $2x - 1 < -1$ or $2x - 1 > 1$ $x < 0$ or $x > 1$

10. $0 \geq -1 - z$ and $-3 < -2z - 1$ $-1 \leq z < 1$

Write a compound inequality whose solution set is graphed.

11. $x < -2$ or $x \geq 1$ 12. $-3 < x \leq 3$

Additional Answers

3. One containing *and* is true when both inequalities are true; one containing *or* is true if either inequality is true.

4. No; for $a < b$, $a > x > b$ implies that $x < a$ and $x > b$ are true; however, this is not possible.

9.
-8 -7 -6 -5 -4 -3 -2 -1 0 1

10.
-3 -2 -1 0 1 2 3 4 5 6

11.
-7 -6 -5 -4 -3 -2 -1 0 1 2

12.
-4 -3 -2 -1 0 1 2 3 4 5

Write a compound inequality and solve. Then check each solution.

C 38. The sum of a number and 2 is no more than 6 or no less than 10. $n \leq 4$ or $n \geq 8$

39. The sum of twice a number and 5 lies between 7 and 11. $1 < n < 3$

40. Five less than 6 times a number is at most 37 and at least 31.
    $6 \leq n \leq 7$

Solve each inequality and graph the solution set.

41. $\frac{5}{x} + 3 > 0$ 42. $-3 - x < 2x < 3 + x$ 43. $x - 5 < 2x - 1 < x$
    $x < -\frac{5}{3}$ or $x > 0$ $-1 < x < 3$ $-4 < x < 1$

Critical Thinking 44. Under what conditions will the compound sentence $x < a$ and $-a < x$ have no solutions? when a is negative or 0

45. **Probability** A certain event has a probability of 1. An impossible event has a probability of 0. Write a compound inequality about possible probabilities. $0 \leq p \leq 1$, where p is a possible probability.

Applications   **Define a variable, write a compound inequality, and solve each problem.**

46. **Consumerism** Consuela estimates that between 14 and 18 gallons of paint are needed to paint her house. The paint costs \$9.75 per gallon. What will the total cost of the paint be? between \$136.50 and \$175.50

47. between \$131,250 and \$181,250

47. **Career** Wanita earns \$17,500 per year in salary and 8% commission on her sales at Fitright Shoes. What would her sales have to be if her total income falls between \$28,000 and \$32,000?

48. **Running** One member of a cross-country team placed first in a meet. The next four finishers on the team placed in consecutive order. To find the team score, the finishing places of team members are added. If the team score was between 35 and 45, in what places did the other members finish? 8th, 9th, 10th, 11th or 9th, 10th, 11th, 12th

Mixed Review   Solve. **(Lessons 3-6 and 3-7)**

49. $4(1 - 2x) = 10(x + 13)$ -7 50. $5.1n + 8.6 = 9.5n - 2.4$ 2.5

51. **Entertainment** At Backintime Cinema, tickets for adults cost \$5.75 and tickets for children cost \$3.75. How many of each kind of ticket were purchased if 16 tickets were bought for \$68? **(Lesson 4-5)**
    4 adult, 12 children

Solve each inequality. (Lessons 5-2 and 5-3)

52. $2r - 2.1 < -8.7 + r$ $\{r \mid r < -6.6\}$ 53. $10x - 2 \geq 4(x - 2)$ $\{x \mid x \geq -1\}$

EXTENDING THE LESSON

Math Power: Reasoning

Points A, B, C, and D are located on the same number line. If A is to the left of B, A is to the right of C, and C is to the right of D, what is the order of the points from left to right? D, C, A, B

5-6 Open Sentences Involving Absolute Value

Objective
5-6

After studying this lesson, you should be able to:

■ solve open sentences involving absolute value and graph the solutions.

Application

Suppose you have a container full of water at 50°C. If the temperature of the water is raised to 100°C, it boils and becomes a gas (steam). If the temperature of the water drops to 0°C, it freezes and becomes a solid (ice). Thus, the water changes to a gas or a solid if its temperature is raised or lowered by 50°C.

Let T represent the temperature (°C) of water at the point that it turns into a gas or a solid. Recall that the absolute value of a number is the number of units it is from 0 on the number line. So, the solution of the open sentence below represents the point at which water at 50°C changes from a liquid to a gas or a solid.

$$|T - 50| = 50$$ *The difference between the water's temperature and 50°C is 50°C.*

Open sentences that involve absolute value must be interpreted carefully. There are 3 cases: $|x| = n$, $|x| < n$, and $|x| > n$. **Teaching Tip**

$$|x| = 2$$

The distance from 0 to x is 2 units.

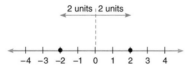

The solution set is $\{-2, 2\}$. This can also be written as $\{x \mid x = -2 \text{ or } x = 2\}$.

Therefore, x = −2 or x = 2.

Equations involving absolute value can be solved by graphing them on a number line or by writing them as a compound sentence and solving it.

Example 1

Solve $|x - 2| = 4$ in two ways.

Graphing: $|x - 2| = 4$ means the distance between x and 2 is 4 units. So to find x on the number line, start at 2 and move 4 units in either direction.

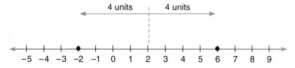

The solution set is $\{-2, 6\}$.   *This can be written $\{x \mid x = -2 \text{ or } x = 6\}$.*

Compound Sentence: $|x - 2| = 4$ also means x − 2 = 4 or x − 2 = −4.

x − 2 = 4	or	x − 2 = −4	**Teaching Tip** ②
x = 6		x = −2	This verifies the solution set.

LESSON 5-6   OPEN SENTENCES INVOLVING ABSOLUTE VALUE   **199**

ALTERNATE TEACHING STRATEGIES

Using Cooperative Groups

Divide the class into four or five small groups. Have each group member create an inequality and then graph its solution set. Have groups switch graphs and identify the inequality that each solution set solves. Have groups return papers and verify each other's answers.

Using Discussion

If there are no values of *m* for which $|m| < b$, then what must be true of *b*? $b \leq 0$

Lesson Resources

• Reteaching Master 5-6
• Practice Master 5-6
• Enrichment Master 5-6

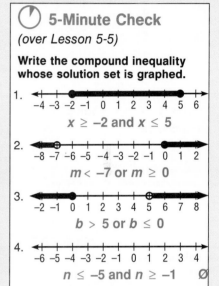

Transparency 5-6 contains the 5-Minute Check and a teaching aid for this lesson.

INTRODUCING THE LESSON

🕐 **5-Minute Check**
(over Lesson 5-5)

Write the compound inequality whose solution set is graphed.

1. [number line graph]
   x ≥ −2 and x ≤ 5

2. [number line graph]
   m < −7 or m ≥ 0

3. [number line graph]
   b > 5 or b ≤ 0

4. [number line graph]
   n ≤ −5 and n ≥ −1   ∅

5. [number line graph]
   t ≤ 8 or t ≥ 3

Motivating the Lesson

Jim's average is less than 5 points from Sam's. Sam's average is 74. What conclusion can be drawn about Jim's average?   **His average is less than 79 (74 + 5) and greater than 69 (74 − 5).**

TEACHING THE LESSON

Teaching Tip ①   Open sentences involving absolute values with = or > are rewritten with *or* and those with < are rewritten with *and*.

Chalkboard Examples

For Example 1
Solve.

a. $|4p - 3| = 7$ $\left\{p \mid p = \frac{5}{2} \text{ or } p = -1\right\}$

b. $|4k + 6| = 5$ $\left\{k \mid k = -\frac{1}{4} \text{ or } k = -\frac{11}{4}\right\}$

For Example 2
Solve $|2x + 1| < 8$ and graph the solution set. $\left\{x \mid x > -\frac{9}{2} \text{ and } x < \frac{7}{2}\right\}$

For Example 3
Solve $|4x - 5| > 3$ and graph the solution set. $\left\{x \mid x < \frac{1}{2} \text{ or } x > 2\right\}$

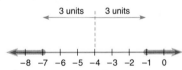

Inequalities involving absolute value can also be represented on a number line or as compound inequalities.

$$|x| < 2$$
The distance from 0 to x is less than 2 units.

The solution set is $\{x \mid -2 < x < 2\}$.

Therefore, $x > -2$ and $x < 2$.

$$|x| > 2$$
The distance from 0 to x is more than 2 units.

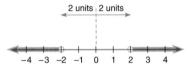

The solution set is $\{x \mid x < -2 \text{ or } x > 2\}$.

Therefore, $x < -2$ or $x > 2$.

Example 2 **Solve $|3x + 4| < 8$ and graph the solution set. Teaching Tip ❸**

$|3x + 4| < 8$ means $3x + 4 > -8$ and $3x + 4 < 8$.

$3x + 4 > -8$	and	$3x + 4 < 8$	
$3x > -12$		$3x < 4$	*Subtract 4 from each side.*
$\dfrac{3x}{3} > \dfrac{-12}{3}$		$\dfrac{3x}{3} < \dfrac{4}{3}$	*Divide each side by 3.*
$x > -4$		$x < \dfrac{4}{3}$	

The solution set is $\left\{x \mid x > -4 \text{ and } x < \frac{4}{3}\right\}$ or $\left\{x \mid -4 < x < \frac{4}{3}\right\}$.

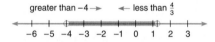

Example 3 **Solve $|t + 4| \geq 3$ in two ways.**

Graphing: $|t + 4| \geq 3$ means the distance between t and -4 is greater than or equal to 3 units. So to find t on the number line, start at -4 and move 3 units in either direction.

The solution set is $\{t \mid t \leq -7 \text{ or } t \geq -1\}$.

Compound Inequality: $|t + 4| \geq 3$ also means $t + 4 \leq -3$ or $t + 4 \geq 3$.

$$t + 4 \leq -3 \quad \text{or} \quad t + 4 \geq 3$$
$$t \leq -7 \qquad\qquad t \geq -1 \quad \textit{Subtract 4 from each side.}$$

This verifies the solution set found graphically.

Example 4

APPLICATION

Machinery

Ball bearings are used to connect moving parts in such a way that friction between the parts is minimized. A certain ball bearing used in automobiles will work properly only if its diameter differs from 1 cm by no more than 0.001 cm. Write an open sentence involving absolute value to represent the range of acceptable diameters for this ball bearing. Then find and graph the corresponding compound sentence.

Let $d =$ the acceptable diameter for this type of ball bearing. Then d can differ from 1 cm by no more than 0.001 cm. Write an open sentence to represents the range of acceptable diameters.

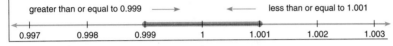

<u>d differs from 1</u>	<u>by no more than</u>	<u>0.001.</u>	"d differs from 1" can be
$|d - 1|$	$\leq$	0.001	interpreted as the distance from 1 to d.

Now, solve $|d - 1| \leq 0.001$ to find the corresponding compound sentence.

$$d - 1 \geq -0.001 \quad \text{and} \quad d - 1 \leq 0.001$$
$$d \geq 0.999 \qquad\qquad d \leq 1.001 \quad \textit{Add 1 to each side.}$$

The corresponding compound sentence is $0.999 \leq d \leq 1.001$.

greater than or equal to 0.999 ⟶   ⟵ less than or equal to 1.001

0.997   0.998   0.999   1   1.001   1.002   1.003

CHECKING FOR UNDERSTANDING

Communicating Mathematics

State which graph below matches each open sentence in Exercises 1–4.

1. $|x| = 4$ **c**
2. $|x| < 4$ **a**
3. $|x| > 4$ **d**
4. $|x| \leq 4$ **b**

a. –8 –4 0 4 8

b. –8 –4 0 4 8

c. –8 –4 0 4 8

d. –8 –4 0 4 8

5. When Michael weighed himself, the scale read 122 pounds. However, the scale may have been off by as much as 3 pounds. Suppose that w represents Michael's actual weight in pounds.

a. Graph the possible values of w on a number line. See margin.

b. Write an open sentence involving absolute value for the variation between w and the reading on the scale. $|w - 122| < 3$

c. Use the open sentence in part b to write a compound inequality for the possible values of Michael's weight. $119 < w < 125$

LESSON 5-6 OPEN SENTENCES INVOLVING ABSOLUTE VALUE **201**

RETEACHING THE LESSON

Graph each open sentence.

1. $|x - 2| = 4$

    –3 –2 –1 0 1 2 3 4 5 6

2. $|x - 2| < 4$
   x is within 4 units of 2.

    –3 –2 –1 0 1 2 3 4 5 6

3. $|x - 2| > 4$
   x is more than 4 units from 2.

    –3 –2 –1 0 1 2 3 4 5 6

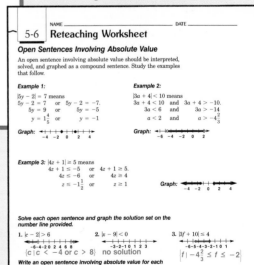

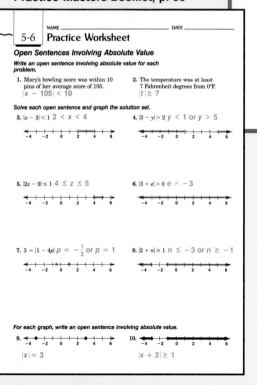
Guided Practice   Complete.

6. If the distance from 0 to x is less than 3 units, then $|x|$ ______ 3. $<$

7. $|2x - 5| = 7$ has ___?___ solution(s). two

8. $|2x - 5| = -1$ has ___?___ solution(s). no

9. $|7 - 3y| < 10$ means $7 - 3y < 10$ ___?___ $7 - 3y > -10$. and

Describe what each open sentence means in terms of distance on the number line. Then write the sentence as a compound sentence and solve. See margin.

10. $|x| = 4$ 11. $|y| > 3$ 12. $|t - 1| \leq 5$

13. $|x - 12| < 9$ 14. $|x + 2| \geq 9$ 15. $|7 - r| = 4$

EXERCISES

Practice   **Write an open sentence involving absolute value for each problem.**

A
16. The temperature was more than 5°F from 0°F. $|T| > 5$

17. Karen's golf score was within 6 strokes of her average score of 90. $|s - 90| < 6$

18. The board needs to be 1.5 meters long, plus or minus 0.005 meters. $|b - 1.5| \leq 0.005$

Solve each open sentence and graph the solution set. See margin.

19. $|x - 1| < 4$ 20. $|y - 7| < 2$ 21. $|a + 8| \geq 1$

22. $|2 - t| \leq 1$ 23. $|9 - y| \geq 13$ 24. $|3 - 3x| = 0$

25. $|14 - 2z| = 16$ 26. $|2b - 11| \geq 7$ 27. $|3x - 12| < 12$

B
28. $|4k + 2| \leq 14$ 29. $|10w + 10| > 90$ 30. $|x + 1| > -2$

31. $|2y - 7| \geq -6$ 32. $|a - 5| = -3$ 33. $|5b + 6| < 0$

34. $|13 - 5y| = 8$ 35. $\left|3t - \frac{1}{2}\right| \geq \frac{11}{2}$ 36. $\left|\frac{1}{2} - 3n\right| < \frac{7}{2}$

For each graph, write an open sentence involving absolute value.

37.
-5 -4 -3 -2 -1 0 1 2 3 4
$|x| = 1$

38.
-5 -4 -3 -2 -1 0 1 2 3 4
$|x| < 3$

C
39.
-5 -4 -3 -2 -1 0 1 2 3 4
$|x| \geq 2$

40.
-5 -4 -3 -2 -1 0 1 2 3 4
$|x + 1| = 3$

41.
-5 -4 -3 -2 -1 0 1 2 3 4
$|x + 1| < 3$

42.
-5 -4 -3 -2 -1 0 1 2 3 4
$|x - 1| \geq 1$

Solve each problem.

43. Find all integer solutions of $|x| \leq 2$. $\{-2, -1, 0, 1, 2\}$

44. Find all integer solutions of $|x| < 4$. $\{-3, -2, -1, 0, 1, 2, 3\}$

45. If $a \geq 0$, how many integer solutions exist for $|x| \leq a$? **$2a + 1$**

46. If $a \geq 0$, how many integer solutions exist for $|x| < a$? **$2a - 1$**

Critical Thinking

47. $|x| = |y|$

47. Suppose $x < 0$, $y > 0$, and $x + y = 0$. Is $|x| > |y|$, $|x| = |y|$, or $|x| < |y|$?

48. Under what conditions is $-|a|$ negative? positive? **when $a \neq 0$; never**

Applications

Define a variable, write a open sentence involving absolute value, and solve each problem.

49. Chemistry For hydrogen to be a liquid, its temperature must be within 2°C of −257°C. What is the range of temperatures for this substance to remain a liquid? **between −259°C and −255°C**

50. Travel Ben's car gets between 18 and 21 miles per gallon of gasoline. If his car's tank holds 15 gallons, what is the range of distance that Ben can drive his car on one tank of gasoline? **270 miles to 315 miles**

51. Manufacturing A certain bolt used in lawn mowers will work properly only if its diameter differs from 2 cm by no more than 0.04 cm. What is the range of acceptable diameters for this bolt? **1.96 cm to 2.04 cm, inclusive**

52. Shipping A crate weighs 6 kg when empty. The weight of a certain book is about 0.8 kg. For shipping, a crate of books must weigh between 40 and 50 kg. What is an acceptable number of books that can be packed in the crate? **between 43 and 54 books**

Mixed Review

53. Solve $3(2n - x) = 1 - n$ for x. **(Lesson 3-7)** $\frac{7n - 1}{3}$

54. Twelve is 15% of what number? **(Lesson 4-2) 80**

55. Finance Marco Flores invested $10,000 for one year, part at 8% annual interest and the balance at 10% annual interest. His total interest for the year was $873. How much did he invest at each rate? **(Lesson 4-3) $6350 at 8% and $3650 at 10%**

56. What percent of 87 is 290? **(Lesson 4-4)** $333\frac{1}{3}\%$

57. Geometry There are seven points in a plane such that no three of the points lie on the same line. How many line segments are needed to connect each pair of points? **(Lesson 5-4) 21 line segments**

58. Statistics Darlene's scores on the first three of four 100-point biology tests were 88, 90, and 91. To get an A− in the class, she must have an average between 88 and 92, inclusive, on all tests. What score must she receive on the fourth test to get an A− in biology? **(Lesson 5-5) between 83 and 99, inclusive**

LESSON 5-6   OPEN SENTENCES INVOLVING ABSOLUTE VALUE   203

Chapter 5, Quiz D, (Lesson 5-6), is available in the Evaluation Masters Booklet, p. 66.

Additional Answers

34. $\left\{y | y = 1 \text{ or } y = \frac{21}{5}\right\}$

35. $\left\{t | t \leq -\frac{5}{3} \text{ or } t \geq 2\right\}$

36. $\left\{n | -1 < n < \frac{4}{3}\right\}$

Enrichment Masters Booklet, p. 34

NAME _____ DATE _____

5-6   Enrichment Worksheet

Consecutive Integer Problems

Many types of problems and puzzles involve the idea of consecutive integers. Here is an example.

Find four consecutive odd integers whose sum is −80.

An odd integer can be written as $2n + 1$, where n is any of the numbers 0, 1, 2, 3, and so on. Then, the equation for the problem is

$$(2n + 1) + (2n + 3) + (2n + 5) + (2n + 7) = -80$$

Solve these problems. Write an equation or inequality for each.

1. Complete the solution to the problem in the example.
$n = -12$; The integers are −23, −21, −19, −17.

2. Find three consecutive even integers whose sum is 132.
$2n + (2n + 2) + (2n + 4) = 132$; $n = 21$; Integers are 42, 44, 46.

3. Find the two least consecutive integers whose sum is greater than 20.
$n + (n + 1) > 20$; $n > 9.5$; integers are 10 and 11.

4. Find the two greatest consecutive integers whose sum is less than 100.
$n + (n + 1) < 100$; $n < 49.5$; Integers are 49 and 50.

5. The lesser of two consecutive even integers is 10 more than one-half the greater. Find the integers.
$2n = 10 + \frac{1}{2}(2n + 2)$; $n = 11$; Integers are 22 and 24.

6. The greater of two consecutive even integers is 6 less than three times the lesser. Find the integers.
$2n + 2 = 3(2n) - 6$; $n = 2$; Integers are 4 and 6.

7. Find four consecutive integers such that twice the sum of the two greater integers exceeds three times the first by 91.
$2[(n + 2) + (n + 3)] = 3n + 91$; $n = 81$; Integers are 81, 82, 83, 84.

8. Find all sets of four consecutive positive integers such that the greatest integer in the set is greater than twice the least integer in the set.
$n + 3 > 2n$; $n < 3$; The two sets are {1, 2, 3, 4} and {2, 3, 4, 5}.

EXTENDING THE LESSON

Math Power: Problem Solving

Find all integer values of x for which $|x - 2| < x$.   **$x > 1$**

Additional Answers

24. $\{x | x = 1\}$

25. $\{z | z = -1 \text{ or } z = 15\}$

26. $\{b | b \leq 2 \text{ or } b \geq 9\}$

27. $\{x | 0 < x < 8\}$

28. $\{k | k - 4 \leq k \leq 3\}$

29. $\{w | w > 8 \text{ or } w < -10\}$

30. {all numbers}

31. {all numbers}

32. $\varnothing$

33. $\varnothing$

Additional Answers

1. $\{n|n < 13\}$
2. $\{r|r \le -11\}$
3. $\{a|a \ge -5.5\}$
4. $\{z|z > 6\}$
5. $\{x|x > 7\}$
6. $\left\{y|y > -\frac{1}{6}\right\}$
9. $\{x|x \le 4\}$
10. $\{y|y \le -13\}$
11. $\{t|t > 1.2\}$
12. $\{m|m > 12\}$
13. $\left\{k|k \ge \frac{1}{5}\right\}$
14. $\left\{z|z \le -\frac{7}{10}\right\}$
17. $\{x|x < 6\}$
18. $\{r|r > 1.8\}$
19. $\left\{y|y \le -\frac{9}{2}\right\}$
20. $\{m|m > -4\}$
21. $\{z|z \le 20\}$

VOCABULARY

Upon completing this chapter, you should be
familiar with the following terms:

compound inequality	**194**	**185**	disjunction
compound sentence	**185**	**177**	set-builder notation
conjunction	**185**		

SKILLS AND CONCEPTS

OBJECTIVES AND EXAMPLES	REVIEW EXERCISES

Upon completing this chapter, you should
be able to:

■ solve inequalities by using addition and
subtraction **(Lesson 5-1)**

$$3x - 2 < 4x$$
$$3x - 3x - 2 < 4x - 3x$$
$$-2 < x$$
$$\{x|x > -2\}$$

Use these exercises to review and prepare
for the chapter test.

See margin.
Solve each inequality. Check the solution.

1. $n - 4 < 9$ 2. $r + 8 \le -3$
3. $a - 2.3 \ge -7.8$ 4. $5z - 6 > 4z$
5. $2x + 7 < 3x$ 6. $y + \frac{5}{8} > \frac{11}{24}$

**Write an inequality and solve. Then check
each solution.**

7. A number added to 7 is at least 12. $\{n|n \ge 5\}$

8. Three times a number is greater than
four times the number less 8. $\{n|n < 8\}$

■ solve inequalities by using multiplication and division **(Lesson 5-2)**

$$-\frac{2}{3}m \le 10$$

$$-\frac{3}{2}\left(-\frac{2}{3}m\right) \ge -\frac{3}{2}(10)$$

$$m \ge -15$$

$$\{m \mid m \ge -15\}$$

See margin.
Solve each inequality. Check the solution.

9. $6x \le -24$ 10. $-7y \ge 91$

11. $0.8t > 0.96$ 12. $-\frac{4}{3}m < -16$

13. $\frac{2}{3}k \ge \frac{2}{15}$ 14. $\frac{4}{7}z \le -\frac{2}{5}$

Write an inequality and solve. Then check each solution. 15. $\{n \mid n < -22\}$

15. Seven times a number is less than -154.

16. Negative three fourths of a number is no more than 30. $\{n \mid n \ge -40\}$

■ solve inequalities involving more than one operation   **(Lesson 5-3)**

$$14c - 11 \ge 6c + 37$$
$$14c - 6c - 11 \ge 6c - 6c + 37$$
$$8c - 11 \ge 37$$
$$8c - 11 + 11 \ge 37 + 11$$
$$8c \ge 48$$
$$\frac{8c}{8} \ge \frac{48}{8}$$
$$c \ge 6$$

$$\{c \mid c \ge 6\}$$

See margin.
Solve each inequality. Check the solution.

17. $7x - 12 < 30$ 18. $2r - 3.1 > 0.5$
19. $4y - 11 \ge 8y + 7$ 20. $4(n - 1) < 7n + 8$
21. $0.3(z - 4) \le 0.8(0.2z + 2)$

Write an inequality and solve. Then check each solution.

22. The sum of three times a number and 11 is at most 47. $\{n \mid n \le 12\}$

23. Twice a number subtracted from 12 is no less than the number increased by 27. $\{n \mid n \le -5\}$

■ solve compound inequalities and graph the solution sets   **(Lesson 5-5)**

$$2a > a - 3 \quad \text{and} \quad 3a < a + 6$$
$$2a - a > a - a - 3 \qquad 3a - a < a - a + 6$$
$$a > -3 \qquad\qquad 2a < 6$$
$$\frac{2a}{2} < \frac{6}{2}$$
$$a < 3$$

$$\{a \mid -3 < a < 3\}$$

Graph the solution set of each compound inequality. **See margin.**

24. $x > -1$ and $x \le 3$ 25. $y \le -3$ or $y > 0$
26. $2a + 5 \le 7$ or $2a \ge a - 3$
27. $4r \ge 3r + 7$ and $3r + 7 < r + 29$

Write the compound inequality whose solution set is graphed.

28.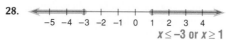
$x \le -3$ or $x \ge 1$

29.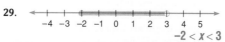
$-2 < x < 3$

To provide a brief in-class review, you may wish to read the following questions to the class and require a verbal or written response.

1. A number added to 5 is at least 8. $\{n \mid n \ge 3\}$
2. Six times a number is less than eighty-four. $\{n \mid n < 14\}$
3. The sum of four times a number and 13 is at most seventy-three. $\{n \mid n \le 15\}$
4. Graph the solution set of $t > 5$ and $t < 8$.

5. Graph the solution set of $|m + 1| > 4$.

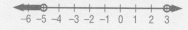

Additional Answers

24.

25.

26.

27.

The Cumulative Review shown below can be used to review skills and concepts presented thus far in the text. Standardized Test Practice Questions are also provided in the Evaluation Masters Booklet.

Evaluation Masters Booklet, pp. 67-68

■ solve open sentences involving absolute value and graph the solution sets (Lesson 5-6)

$$|2x+1|>1$$

$$2x+1>1 \quad\text{or}\quad 2x+1<-1$$
$$2x+1-1>1-1 \qquad 2x+1-1<-1-1$$
$$\frac{2x}{2}>\frac{0}{2} \qquad\qquad \frac{2x}{2}<\frac{-2}{2}$$
$$x>0 \qquad\qquad x<-1$$

$$\{x\mid x>0 \text{ or } x<-1\}$$

(number line -4 to 4)

Solve each open sentence and graph the solution set. See margin.

30. $|y-2|>0$

31. $|1-n|\leq5$

32. $|7x-10|<0$

33. $\left|2p-\frac{1}{2}\right|>\frac{9}{2}$

APPLICATIONS AND CONNECTIONS

34. **Geometry** For what values of d is an angle with measure $(3.6d)°$ an acute angle? (Lesson 5-2) $0<d<25$

35. **Number Theory** The sum of three consecutive integers is less than 100. Find the three integers with the greatest sum. (Lesson 5-3) 32, 33, 34

Solve by drawing a diagram. (Lesson 5-4)

36. Six softball teams qualified for the city softball playoffs. To determine the two representatives to the state playoffs, each team plays every other team exactly once. How many playoff games will be played? 15 games

37. A spider begins climbing a 10-foot tree on Monday. Each day it climbs 4 feet. Each night it slips back 1 foot. On which day will the spider reach the top of the tree? Wednesday

Solve.

38. **Sales** Linda plans to spend at most $85 on jeans and shirts. She bought 2 shirts for $15.30 each. How much can she spend on jeans? (Lesson 5-3) $54.40 or less

39. **Work** At most, Sung and Jill can earn a total of $312 in a week. If Jill earns twice as much as Sung, what is the greatest amount each one can earn? (Lesson 5-3) Jill: $208, Sung: $104

40. **Banking** Sean budgets between $3 and $4 a month to spend on bank checking charges. His bank charges $1.75 a month plus $0.08 per check. How many checks can Sean write each month and still meet his budget? (Lesson 5-5) between 15 and 29 checks

41. **Shipping** An empty book crate weighs 30 pounds. The weight of a book is 1.5 pounds. For shipping, the crate can weight between 55 and 60 pounds. What is the acceptable number of books that can be packed in the crate? (Lesson 5-5) 17 to 19 books

Additional Answers

30. $\{y\mid y\neq2\}$

31. $\{n\mid-4\leq n\leq6\}$

32. $\varnothing$

33. $\left\{p\mid p<-2 \text{ or } p>\frac{5}{2}\right\}$

Solve each inequality.

1. $a - 2 > 11$ $\{a|a > 13\}$

2. $-12 \leq d + 7$ $\{d|d \geq -19\}$

3. $7x < 6x - 11$ $\{x|x < -11\}$

4. $z - 1 \geq 2z - 3$ $\{z|z \leq 2\}$

5. $3y > 63$ $\{y|y > 21\}$

6. $-\frac{2}{3}r \leq \frac{7}{12}$ $\{r|r \geq -\frac{7}{8}\}$

7. $3x + 1 \geq 16$ $\{x|x \geq 5\}$

8. $5 - 4b > -23$ $\{b|b < 7\}$

9. $\frac{2n - 3}{-7} \leq 5$ $\{n|n \geq -16\}$

10. $8y + 3 < 13y - 9$ $\{y|y > \frac{12}{5}\}$

11. $8(1 - 2z) \leq 25 + z$ $\{z|z \geq -1\}$

12. $0.3(m + 4) > 0.5(m - 4)$ $\{m|m < 16\}$

Solve each inequality and graph the solution set. **See Solutions Manual for graphs.**

13. $x + 1 > -2$ and $3x < 6$ $\{x| -3 < x < 2\}$

14. $2n + 1 \geq 15$ or $2n + 1 \leq -1$ $\{n|n \geq 7$ or $n \leq -1\}$

15. $8 + 3t > 2$ and $-12 > 11t - 1$ $\{t| -2 < t < -1\}$

16. $|n| > 3$ $\{n|n > 3$ or $n < -3\}$

17. $|2x - 1| < 5$ $\{x| -2 < x < 3\}$

18. $|5 - 3b| \geq 1$ $\left\{b|b \geq 2$ or $b \leq \frac{4}{3}\right\}$

Write an inequality and solve.

19. Four times a number less 8 is at least five times the number. $\{n|n \leq -8\}$

20. Seven less than twice a number is between 71 and 83. $\{n|39 < n < 45\}$

21. The product of two integers is no less than 30. One of the integers is 6. What is the other integer? **5 or more**

22. The average of four consecutive odd integers is less than 20. What are the greatest integers that satisfy this condition? **15, 17, 19, 21**

Solve.

23. **Gymnastics** Montega has scores of 9.1, 9.3, 9.6, and 8.7 in a pommel horse competition. He has one more trial. If Montega's total score must be greater than 46.1 points to win the competition, what score must he receive on his final trial? **greater than 9.4 points**

24. **Statistics** Jean's scores on the first three of four 100-point tests were 82, 86, and 91. What score must she receive on the fourth test to have an average of at least 87 points for all the tests? **at least 89 points**

25. **Sales** Kathy earns $18,000 per year in salary and 5% commission on her sales at Autorama Motors. What would her sales have to be if her total income falls between $37,000 and $40,000? **between $380,000 and $440,000**

Bonus For what values of d is an angle with measure $\left(30 - \frac{1}{2}d\right)^{\circ}$ an acute angle? **$60 > d > -120$**

NAME _____ DATE _____

Chapter 5 Test, Form 1A

Write the letter for the correct answer in the blank at the right of each problem.

1. Solve $n - 6 < -5$.
   A. $\{n|n < -11\}$ B. $\{n|n > 1\}$ C. $\{n|n < 1\}$ D. $\{n|n > -11\}$ 1. __C__

2. Solve $2x - 7 \geq 3x$.
   A. $\{x|x \leq \frac{5}{7}\}$ B. $\{x|x \leq -7\}$ C. $\{x|x \geq 7\}$ D. $\{x|x \geq -7\}$ 2. __B__

3. Solve $-13 > w - (-12)$.
   A. $\{w|w < -25\}$ B. $\{w|w > -25\}$ C. $\{w|w > -1\}$ D. $\{w|w < -1\}$ 3. __A__

4. Solve $\frac{m}{5} < -3$.
   A. $\{m|m > -15\}$ B. $\{m|m < -15\}$ C. $\{m|m < 15\}$ D. $\{m|m > 15\}$ 4. __B__

5. Solve $-21 \leq 3n$.
   A. $\{n|n \geq 7\}$ B. $\{n|n \geq -7\}$ C. $\{n|n \leq 7\}$ D. $\{n|n \leq -7\}$ 5. __B__

6. Solve $-\frac{2}{3}s > 6$.
   A. $\{s|s > -9\}$ B. $\{s|s > 9\}$ C. $\{s|s < 9\}$ D. $\{s|s < -9\}$ 6. __D__

7. Solve $-1.1t \leq 4.62$.
   A. $\{t|t \leq -5.06\}$ B. $\{t|t \geq -5.06\}$ C. $\{t|t \leq -4.2\}$ D. $\{t|t \geq -4.2\}$ 7. __D__

8. Solve $6d + 10 < 46$.
   A. $\{d|d < 6\}$ B. $\{d|d > 6\}$ C. $\{d|d < -6\}$ D. $\{d|d > -6\}$ 8. __A__

9. Solve $5z - 4 > 2z + 8$.
   A. $\{z|z > 4\}$ B. $\{z|z < 1\}$ C. $\{z|z < 4\}$ D. $\{z|z > 1\}$ 9. __A__

10. Solve $5w - (w - 8) > 9 + 3(2w - 3)$.
    A. $\{w|w < \frac{11}{5}\}$ B. $\{w|w < -\frac{11}{5}\}$ C. $\{w|w < -4\}$ D. $\{w|w < 4\}$ 10. __D__

11. Solve $4m - 6 - 2m > 8$.
    A. $\{m|m < 1\}$ B. $\{m|m < 7\}$ C. $\{m|m > 7\}$ D. $\{m|m > 1\}$ 11. __C__

12. Solve $(0.5)(r + 1) \leq (0.6)(r - 2)$.
    A. $\{r|r \leq 30\}$ B. $\{r|r \geq 17\}$ C. $\{r|r \geq 30\}$ D. $\{r|r \leq 17\}$ 12. __B__

13. The sum of two consecutive positive integers is at most 3. What is the greater integer?
    A. 5 B. 1 C. 3 D. 2 13. __D__

NAME _____ DATE _____

Chapter Test, Form 1A (continued)

14. Three times a number decreased by 6 is at least 3. What is the number?
    A. -1 or greater B. 6 or less
    C. 3 or greater D. -3 or less 14. __C__

15. The books in Charlotte's library are between 2 cm and 6 cm wide. How many books can Charlotte put on a shelf that is 1 m long?
    A. 50 or more B. 16 or less
    C. between 16 and 50 D. less than 50 15. __C__

16. What compound sentence is graphed below?
    ```
    ←+++●━━━━━━●+++→
    -5-4-3-2-1 0 1 2 3 4 5
    ```
    A. $-2 < y < 3$ B. $-2 < y \leq 3$
    B. $y \geq -2$ or $y < 3$ D. $-2 \leq y < 3$ 16. __D__

17. Which of the following is a graph of the solution set of the compound sentence $x > 0$ or $x < -4$?
    A. ```←━━━●++++●━━━→
       -5-4-3-2-1 0 1 2 3 4 5```
    B. ```←━━●++++++●+→
       -5-4-3-2-1 0 1 2 3 4 5```
    C. ```←+++●++++●━━→
       -5-4-3-2-1 0 1 2 3 4 5```
    D. ```←●++++●━━━━→
       -5-4-3-2-1 0 1 2 3 4 5``` 17. __B__

18. Which of the following is the graph of the solution set of $-3 < 2x + 7 \leq 13$?
    A. ```←++●━━━━━●++→
       -7-6-5-4-3-2-1 0 1 2 3```
    B. ```←++++●━━━●+→
       -7-6-5-4-3-2-1 0 1 2 3```
    C. ```←━━●+++++●━→
       -7-6-5-4-3-2-1 0 1 2 3```
    D. ```←+++●━━━●++→
       -7-6-5-4-3-2-1 0 1 2 3``` 18. __A__

19. Which of the following is the solution set of $|x - 3| = 6$?
    A. $\{9\}$ B. $\{-3\}$ C. $\{-3, 9\}$ D. $\{-9, 3\}$ 19. __C__

20. Which of the following is a graph of the solution set of $|4x - 8| \leq 16$?
    A. ```←━━━━●++++++++→
       -7-6-5-4-3-2-1 0 1 2 3 4 5 6 7```
    B. ```←+++++++++●━━━→
       -7-6-5-4-3-2-1 0 1 2 3 4 5 6 7```
    C. ```←+++++●━━━━●++→
       -7-6-5-4-3-2-1 0 1 2 3 4 5 6 7```
    D. ```←+++●━━━━━━●+→
       -7-6-5-4-3-2-1 0 1 2 3 4 5 6 7``` 20. __B__

Bonus Find all sets of three consecutive positive odd integers whose sum if at most 24.   Bonus: $\{1, 3, 5\}$; $\{3, 5, 7\}$ $\{5, 7, 9\}$

6

Polynomials

PREVIEWING THE CHAPTER

This chapter provides activities to help students master the concepts and skills required to operate with monomials and polynomials. Multiplication and division of monomials is developed first by having students make the mathematical connection between their familiarity with powers of whole numbers and a new understanding of monomials that contain variables with exponents. Polynomials are defined and students learn to add, subtract, and multiply polynomials. (Division of polynomials is developed in Chapter 8.) The chapter concludes with a look at some special products.

Problem-Solving Strategy   The opening lesson focuses on *looking for a pattern,* one of the most-used strategies in solving problems whether such problems be from the real-world or from within mathematics itself.

Lesson Objective Chart

Lesson (Pages)	Lesson Objectives	State/Local Objectives
6-1 (210-212)	**6-1:** Solve problems by looking for a pattern.	
6-2 (213-216)	**6-2A:** Multiply monomials.	
	6-2B: Simplify expressions involving powers of monomials.	
6-3 (217-220)	**6-3A:** Simplify expressions involving quotients of monomials.	
	6-3B: Simplify expressions containing negative exponents.	
6-4 (221-225)	**6-4A:** Express numbers in scientific and decimal notation.	
	6-4B: Find products and quotients of numbers expressed in scientific notation.	
6-5 (226-229)	**6-5A:** Find the degree of a polynomial.	
	6-5B: Arrange the terms of a polynomial so that the powers of a certain variable are in ascending or descending order.	
6-6 (230-233)	**6-6:** Add and subtract polynomials.	
6-7 (234-237)	**6-7A:** Multiply a polynomial by a monomial.	
	6-7B: Simplify expressions involving polynomials.	
6-8 (238-242)	**6-8A:** Use the FOIL method to multiply two binomials.	
	6-8B: Multiply any two polynomials by using the distributive property.	
6-9 (243-246)	**6-9:** Use the patterns for $(a + b)^2$, $(a - b)^2$, and $(a + b)(a - b)$.	

ORGANIZING THE CHAPTER

You may want to refer to the **Course Planning Calendar** on page T36.

Lesson (Pages)	Course I	Course II	Course III	Reteaching	Practice	Enrichment	Evaluation	Technology	Lab Manual	Mixed Problem Solving	Applications	Cooperative Learning Activity	Multicultural	Transparencies
6-1 (210-212)	1	1	1		p. 39									6-1
6-2 (213-216)	1	1	1	p. 35	p. 40	p. 35	Quiz A, p. 79	p. 21						6-2
6-3 (217-220)	1	1	1	p. 36	p. 41	p. 36								6-3
6-4 (221-225)	1.5	1	1	p. 37	p. 42	p. 37	Quiz B, p. 79 Mid-Chapter Test, p.83	p. 6			p. 21			6-4
6-5 (226-229)	1	1	1	p. 38	p. 43	p. 38							p. 51	6-5
6-6 (230-233)	1	1	1	p. 39	p. 44	p. 39	Quiz C, p. 80							6-6
6-7 (234-237)	1	1	1	p. 40	p. 45	p. 40						p. 36		6-7
6-8 (238-242)	1.5	1	1	p. 41	p. 46	p. 41			pp. 27-28	p. 6				6-8
6-9 (243-246)	1	1	1	p. 42	p. 47	p. 42	Quiz D, p. 80							6-9
Review (248-250)	1	1	1	Multiple Choice Tests, Forms 1A and 1B, pp. 71-74 Free Response Tests, Forms 2A and 2B, pp. 75-78										
Test (251)	1	1	1	Cumulative Review, pp. 81-82 Standardized Test Practice Questions, p. 84										

Lesson Planning Guide — Pacing Chart (days) — **Blackline Masters Booklets** — Activities

Course I: Chapters 1-13; Course II: Chapters 1-14; Course III: Chapters 1-15

Other Chapter Resources

Student Edition
Cooperative Learning Activity, p. 212
Reading Algebra, p. 220
Application, p. 225
Mid-Chapter Review, p. 229
History Connection, p. 233
Extra, p. 242
Application, p. 246
Technology, p. 247
Algebraic Skills Review, pp. 657, 658

Teacher Resource Package
Activity Masters Booklet
Mixed Problem Solving, p. 6
Applications, p. 21
Cooperative Learning Activity, p. 36
Multicultural Activity, p. 51
Technology Masters Booklet
Scientific Calculator Activity, p. 6
Graphing Calculator Activity, p. 21
Lab Manual
Lab Activity, pp. 27-28

Other Supplements
Transparency for Chapter Opener
Problem-of-the-Week Activity
Cards, 13-15
Video Algebra, 14-16

Software
Algebra 1 Test and Review
Generator Software
Available for Apple and IBM.

ENHANCING THE CHAPTER

Cooperative Learning

Planning Teaching Materials

When groups have had considerable experience and exhibit reasonable competence in cooperative-learning skills, you may not have to give much special care to how you arrange materials. However, until this situation exists you should consider how to distribute materials in order to communicate that the activity is to be a group and not an individual activity. One way to do this is to provide only one set of materials or one copy of the worksheet to the group. The members of the group will quickly realize that they have to work together if they are to be successful in achieving the objective and receiving your recognition. A variation on this method is to provide each member of the group with a worksheet but tell the group that you will collect only one of them. This method also encourages the members to help one another and make sure that each member has and understands the correct answer. A third method, appropriate in some activities, is to give each member only part of the materials or resources required to complete the task. This method requires that every member participate in order for the group to be successful.

Technology

The Technology Feature after Lesson 6-9 investigates the use of a spreadsheet program. Students will learn how the spreadsheet program uses formulas to compute values by using a spreadsheet to investigate volumes and surface areas. If a computer spreadsheet program is available, you may wish to have students enter the program provided and find the volumes and surface areas of various rectangular solids.

Critical Thinking

All students should be encouraged to examine numerical patterns that result from manipulation, make conjectures about general algebraic properties based on their observations, and verify their conjectures with numerical substitutions. Powers provide one such opportunity to do this. Beginning with numerical expressions such as $7^2 \cdot 7^3$, they rewrite it as $(7 \cdot 7) \cdot (7 \cdot 7 \cdot 7)$ and then as 7^5. Looking for a pattern as they work with other powers of 7, they can generalize that $7^a \cdot 7^b = 7^{a+b}$. Next, they can conjecture about the pattern being true for all numbers; that is, $x^a \cdot x^b = x^{a+b}$, and verify this conjecture by replacing the variables with various numbers.

Cooperative Learning, p. 36

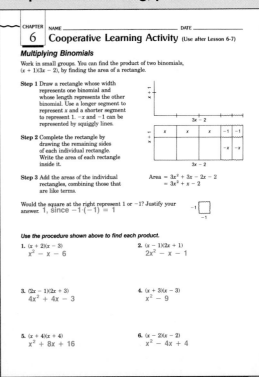

Technology, p. 21

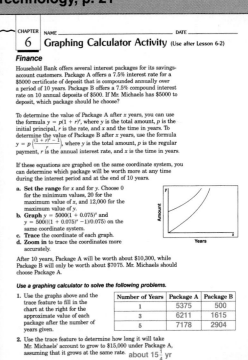

Problem of the Week Activity

The card shown below is one of three available for this chapter. It can be used as a class or small group activity.

Activity Card

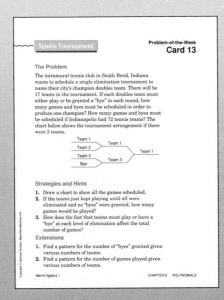

Manipulatives and Models

The following materials may be used as models or manipulatives in Chapter 6.

- grid paper (Lessons 6-1, 6-2, 6-7)
- circle markers (Lesson 6-2)
- index cards (Lesson 6-5)
- scientific calculator (Lesson 6-5)

Outside Resources

Books/Periodicals

Olney, Ross & Pat. *Pocket Calculator Fun & Games.* Franklin Watts, 1977.

Tamarkin, Kenneth. *Number Power 6 - Word Problems.* Contemporary Books, Inc. 1983.

Films/Videotapes/Videodiscs

Word Problems, Video Tutor, Inc.

For All Practical Purposes III - Social Choice, Consortium for Mathematics and Its Applications

Software

The Problem Solving Tutor, R.G. Computer Workshops

Practical Algebra Series I - Algebra Word Problems, IS, Intellectual Software

Multicultural

Multicultural Activity, p. 51

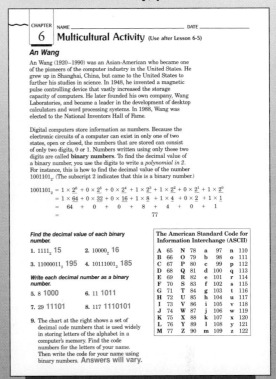

Lab Manual

Lab Activity, pp. 27-28

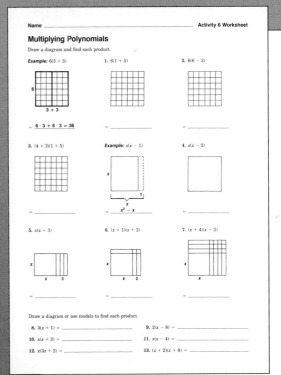

Using the Chapter Opener

Transparency 6-0 is available in the Transparency Package. It provides a full-color visual and motivational activity that you can use to engage students in the mathematical content of the chapter.

Background Information

Predator-prey relationships control the population of both predator and prey. Consider the arctic fox and its prey, the arctic lemming. When the fox population is small, the lemmings increase because fewer are eaten. As the lemmings increase, there is less competition among foxes for food. More food available for the foxes results in an increase in their population. When the fox population increases, more lemmings are eaten. Thus, the population of lemmings decreases. As a result, there is not as much food for the foxes and the fox population becomes smaller.

In this chapter, you will:
- Arrange the terms of a polynomial in order.
- Add, subtract, and multiply polynomials.
- Solve polynomial equations.
- Solve problems by looking for a pattern.

Chapter Project

Materials: ruler, paper, pencil, library resources

Organize students into cooperative groups of student ecologists. Instruct each group to adopt two or more endangered species of animals on which to (1) conduct research and (2) generate population polynomials. Assign each to conduct historical research to find how and why the population of each of its endangered species has come to be endangered. In addition, have each group prepare a chart, similar to the sample provided, for each of its species. Then, assuming each species can be protected, have each group use its charts to generate a population polynomial for each species. First, each group is to find the average number of offspring per litter for each animal. Then, instruct them to estimate the number of females per litter; for example, 50%. This figure will serve as *x*. Finally, groups are to find the number of animals that can be expected after at least four generations by completing each chart.

6

Polynomials

APPLICATION IN BIOLOGY

These days, many cities support herds of deer in their metropolitan parks, supplying them with food, medical care, shelter in winter, and protection from predators.

But uncontrolled, an animal population develops *polynomially.* That is, if one animal has x offspring, then it will have an average of x^2 grandoffspring, x^3 great-grandoffspring, x^4 great-great-grandoffspring, and so on, assuming that each animal has an average of x babies in its lifetime. We can represent the number of descendants of one animal with the polynomial expression $x + x^2 + x^3 + x^4 + \ldots$, continuing for any number of generations, assuming that none of the animals dies early. So, if an animal has an average of 13 offspring in its lifetime, then it will probably have 30,940 descendants in four generations.

So this is the problem caused by cities' support of deer in parks. Any natural ecosystem has a delicate balance. In the wild, deer populations are controlled naturally—by predators, disease, starvation, and other forms of natural competition. Since we have eliminated nearly all of the population controls for the deer living in city parks, we now have a responsibility to provide them with new ones or face the consequences of an uncontrolled population.

Population control for deer? This might seem like an unwarranted interference with nature, but this problem is much more complex.

ALGEBRA IN ACTION

A deer has an average of 4 offspring during its lifetime. Complete the chart below to determine the probable number of deer descendants in five generations.

Generation	Polynomial	Number of Deer Descendants
1	x	4
2	$x + x^2$	4 + 16 = 20
3	$x + x^2 + x^3$	4 + 16 + 64 = _?_
4	$x + x^2 + x^3 + x^4$	4 + 16 + 64 + _?_ = _?_
5	$x + x^2 + x^3 + x^4 + $ _?_	4 + 16 + 64 + _?_ + _?_ = _?_

x^5 84; 256, 340; 256, 1024, 1364

209

Connections and Applications

Lesson	Connections (C) and Applications (A)		Examples	Exercises
6-2	C:	Geometry	1, 3	11-16
	A:	Finance		50-51
6-3	A:	Finance		51-52
		Consumerism		53
		Government		55
6-4	A:	Biology	3	49
		Economics	5	
		Health		43
		Census		44
		Government		45
		Space		46
		Biology		49
6-5	A:	Finance	2	45-46, 50
		Biology		47
6-6	C:	Geometry	3	31-33
	A:	Travel		38
		Basketball		39
		Sports		41
		Bicycling		42
6-7	C:	Geometry	4	33-35, 53
	A:	Sports		54
		Construction		55
		Finance		59
6-8	A:	Gardening	6	45
		Construction		46
		Sales		48
6-9	C:	Geometry		3, 36
	A:	City Planning		37
		Photography		38
		Sales		40

Animal: _____Cat_____
Average number of offspring per litter: _____5-9_____
Estimated number of females per litter: _____5_____

First generation female (1)	Second generation females (x)	Third generation females (x^2)	Fourth generation females (x^3)	Total ($1 + x + x^2 + x^3$)
1	5	25	125	156

6-1 Problem-Solving Strategy: Look for a Pattern

Lesson Resources

• Practice Master 6-1

 Transparency 6-1 contains the 5-Minute Check and a teaching aid for this lesson.

INTRODUCING THE LESSON

 5-Minute Check

(over Chapter 5)

Solve.

1. $6 + n > 40$ $n > 34$
2. $14p < 84$ $p < 6$
3. $12 + 4x < 20$ $x < 2$
4. $13r - 11 > 7r + 37$ $r > 8$
5. $3 + x < -4$ or $3 + x > 4$
   $x < -7$ or $x > 1$

Motivating the Lesson

Write the following sequence of numbers on the chalkboard: 5, 3, 6, 2, 7, 1, 8, 0. Ask students to identify the relationship between the first two numbers. **Subtract 2.** Then have them identify the relationship between the second and third numbers. **Add 3.** Challenge students to identify the general pattern of the numbers. **Subtract, then add consecutive whole numbers.**

TEACHING THE LESSON

Teaching Tip ❶ Reinforce student understanding of perfect squares by having them identify all the perfect squares less than 100.

Objective
6-1

After studying this lesson, you should be able to:

■ solve problems by looking for a pattern.

One of the most-used strategies in problem solving is *look for a pattern*. When using this strategy, you will often need to make a table to organize the information.

Example

How many squares are there on a checkerboard?

FYI ···

The ancient Chinese used checkerboards as counting boards for solving equations.

Teaching Tip ❶

You might say that there are 64 squares on an 8×8 checkerboard. But the problem does not ask for only 1×1 squares. There are also 2×2 squares, 3×3 squares, and so on. Since the checkerboard is 8×8, you know that there are 64 of the 1×1 squares. Count the number of 2×2 squares. There are seven 2×2 squares on each row, and 7 rows, so there are 49 of the 2×2 squares. Then count the number of 3×3 squares. There are 36. Do you notice a pattern in the number of squares of each size?

$$64 = 8 \cdot 8 \qquad 49 = 7 \cdot 7 \qquad 36 = 6 \cdot 6$$

The number of squares of a given size will always be a perfect square.

Make a table to see the pattern more clearly.

Square Size	1×1	2×2	3×3	4×4	5×5	6×6	7×7	8×8
Number of Squares	64	49	36	25	16	9	4	1

The total number of squares on an 8×8 checkerboard is $64 + 49 + 36 + 25 + 16 + 9 + 4 + 1$ or 204 squares.

Another strategy you could use to solve this problem is to solve a simpler problem and then look for the pattern. Think about the number of squares on a 1×1 checkerboard, a 2×2 checkerboard, a 3×3 checkerboard, and so on. Make a table to see the pattern more clearly.

Checkerboard Size	1×1	2×2	3×3	4×4	5×5	6×6	7×7	8×8
Number of Squares	1	5	14	30	55	?	?	?

ALTERNATE TEACHING STRATEGIES

Using Manipulatives

Have students use grid paper to model a 10 by 10 square. Then ask them to identify the number of square grids contained on the paper.

Using Logical Reasoning

Magic squares are unique squares in which the sum of each column, row, or diagonal is the same. Have students create their own 3×3 magic square on a piece of grid paper. Then have them make a copy of the magic square, leaving out some numbers. Students should switch papers and complete each other's magic squares.

Can you see a pattern in the total number of squares? Try finding the difference between each pair of numbers.

Now do you see the pattern? The numbers 4, 9, 16, and 25 are all perfect squares. If you continued adding squares to each entry, you would eventually verify that there are 204 squares on an 8 × 8 checkerboard.

CHECKING FOR UNDERSTANDING

Communicating Mathematics

Read and study the lesson to answer each question.

1. How many squares are there on a 10 × 10 checkerboard? **385**

2. Look at the first table on the previous page. If $n \times n$ represents the size of the squares on the checkerboard, write an expression to represent the total number of squares of that size. $(9 - n)^2$

Guided Practice

Solve by extending the pattern.

3. $4 \times 6 = 24$
   $14 \times 16 = 224$
   $24 \times 26 = 624$
   $34 \times 36 = 1224$
   $124 \times 126 = ?$ **15,624**

4. $1 \times \frac{1}{2} = 1 - \frac{1}{2}$
   $2 \times \frac{2}{3} = 2 - \frac{2}{3}$
   $3 \times \frac{3}{4} = 3 - \frac{3}{4}$
   $4 \times \frac{4}{5} = 4 - \frac{4}{5}$
   $12 \times \frac{?}{?} = 12 - \frac{?}{?}$ **$\frac{12}{13}$**

5. $1^3 = 1^2 - 0^2$
   $2^3 = 3^2 - 1^2$
   $3^3 = 6^2 - 3^2$
   $4^3 = 10^2 - 6^2$
   $6^3 = ? - ?$ **$21^2; 15^2$**

Solve by looking for a pattern.

6. How many triangles are shown at the right? Count only the triangles pointing upward. **120**

7. At the City Center Mall, there are 25 lockers. Suppose a shopper opens every locker. Then a second shopper closes every second locker. Next a third shopper changes the state of every third locker. (If it's open, the shopper closes it. If it's closed, the shopper opens it.) Suppose this process continues until the 25th person changes the state of the 25th locker. Which lockers will still be open? **1, 4, 9, 16, 25**

LESSON 6-1 PROBLEM-SOLVING STRATEGY: LOOK FOR A PATTERN 211

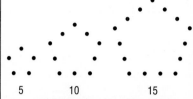

Homework Exercises

Assignment Guide

Basic: 9-12
Average: 9-12
Enriched: 9-12

Additional Answer

11. You could never say this for the first time. The first time you say it, you would be lying; therefore, only a Falsite could say it.

---

8. Number Theory The sequence 1, 1, 2, 3, 5, 8, . . . is called the *Fibonacci sequence*. The terms of this sequence are called *Fibonacci numbers.*

   a. List the first 10 Fibonacci numbers. **1, 1, 2, 3, 5, 8, 13, 21, 34, 55**

   b. Find the following quotients: $\frac{2\text{nd term}}{1\text{st term}}, \frac{3\text{rd term}}{2\text{nd term}}, \frac{4\text{th term}}{3\text{rd term}}, \cdots, \frac{10\text{th term}}{9\text{th term}}$. What do you notice? **They approach 1.618.**

EXERCISES

Practice   **Solve. Use any strategy.**

Strategies

Look for a pattern.
Solve a simpler problem.
Act it out.
Guess and check.
Draw a diagram.
Make a chart.
Work backwards.

9. Fred the frog loves to sit on lily pads and sun himself. When Fred came to his newest spot, there was only one lily pad on the surface of the pond. However, the number of lily pads doubled each day. After 30 days, the lily pads completely covered the surface of the pond. How long did it take for the pond to be half-covered? **29 days**

10. At Chicken Little's, you can order Little Bits in boxes of 6, 9, or 20. If you order two boxes of 6, you can get 12 bits. But you cannot order 13, since no combination of 6, 9, and 20 adds up to 13. What is the greatest number of Little Bits that you *cannot* order? **43 Little Bits**

11. In the town of Verityville, there are two types of residents. The Factites make only true statements, and the Falsites make only false statements. On a visit to Verityville, you meet a resident who says, "This is not the first time I have said what I am now saying." Is this a Factite or a Falsite? How do you know? **A Falsite; see margin.**

12. The symbol used for a U.S. dollar is a capital S with a vertical line through it. The line separates the S into 4 parts, as shown at the right. How many parts would there be if the S had 100 vertical lines through it? **301 parts**

~ COOPERATIVE LEARNING ACTIVITY ~

Work in groups of three. Each person must understand the solution and be able to explain it to any person in the class.

Place a digit from 0 to 9 in each box below. The digit you place in Box #0 should indicate the number of 0s in all of the boxes. The digit you place in Box #1 should indicate the number of 1s in all of the boxes. Continue this process until Box #9 indicates the number of 9s in all of the boxes. (*Hint:* You may use a digit more than once, and you may not need to use every digit.) Good luck!

0	1	2	3	4	5	6	7	8	9
?	?	?	?	?	?	?	?	?	?
6	2	1	0	0	0	1	0	0	0

EXTENDING THE LESSON

Math Power: Connections

What pattern exists in the following sequence of geometric figures: triangle, quadrilateral, pentagon, hexagon? **Each figure has one more side than the previous figure.**

Cooperative Learning Activity

This activity provides students with an opportunity to *learn* things together, not just do things together. You may wish to refer to pages T6 - T8 and page 6C for the various elements of cooperative groups and specific goals and strategies for using them.

Practice Masters Booklet, p. 39

NAME _____ DATE _____

6-1 Practice Worksheet

Problem-Solving: Look for a Pattern

Solve by looking for a pattern.

1. The symbol used for a cent is lower-case c with a vertical line through it. The line separates the c into 3 parts, as shown at the right. How many parts would there be if the c had 101 lines through it?
203 parts

2. How many different squares are there on the board below?

91 squares

3. How many different squares are there on the board below?

140 squares

4. How many different squares are there on the board below?

385 squares

5. A basketball team scored 31 points. The points were made up of three-pointers (3 points), field goals (2 points), and foul shots (1 point). How many different ways could the team have scored 31 points?
111 ways

6-2 Multiplying Monomials

Objectives
6-2A
6-2B

After studying this lesson, you should be able to:
- multiply monomials, and
- simplify expressions involving powers of monomials.

Teaching Tip ①

A **monomial** is a number, a variable, or a product of a number and one or more variables. Monomials that are real numbers are called **constants**.

These are monomials. **Teaching Tip ②**

$$-9 \qquad y \qquad 7a \qquad 3y^3 \qquad \frac{1}{2}abc^5$$

These are not monomials. *Why not?* **Teaching Tip ③**

$$m + n \qquad \frac{x}{y} \qquad 3 - 4ab \qquad \frac{1}{x^2} \qquad \frac{7y}{9z}$$

Recall that an expression of the form x^n is a power. The base is x and the exponent is n. A table of powers of 2 is shown below.

2^1	2^2	2^3	2^4	2^5	2^6	2^7	2^8	2^9	2^{10}
2	4	8	16	32	64	128	256	512	1024

Notice that each of the following is true.

$$4 \cdot 16 = 64 \qquad 8 \cdot 16 = 128 \qquad 8 \cdot 32 = 256$$

$$\downarrow \qquad\qquad \downarrow \qquad\qquad \downarrow$$

$$2^2 \cdot 2^4 = 2^6 \qquad 2^3 \cdot 2^4 = 2^7 \qquad 2^3 \cdot 2^5 = 2^8$$

Look for a pattern in the products shown. If you consider only the exponents, you will find that $2 + 4 = 6$, $3 + 4 = 7$, and $3 + 5 = 8$.

These examples suggest that you can multiply powers that have the same base by adding exponents.

Product of Powers	**For any number a and all integers m and n,** $a^m \cdot a^n = a^{m+n}$.

Teaching Tip ④

Example 1

CONNECTION
Geometry

Find the measure of the area of the rectangle.

$A = \ell w$
$= x^3 \cdot x^4$
$= x^{3+4}$
$= x^7$

Since $x^3 > x^4$, what can you say about the value of x?

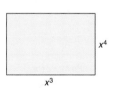
x^4
x^3

ALTERNATE TEACHING STRATEGIES

Using Connections

Have each student draw a square and a rectangular solid on a piece of grid paper. Tell students to label the measure of one side of the square and two sides of the rectangular solid using monomials. Have students switch papers and find the area of each square and volume of each rectangular solid.

INTRODUCING THE LESSON

⏱ 5-Minute Check
(over Lesson 6-1)

Continue the pattern in each of the following sequences.

1. a, c, e, ___, ___   g, i
2. −10, −5, 0, ___, ___   5, 10
3. 1, 4, 9, ___, ___   16, 25
4. −6, −5, −3, 0, ___, ___   4, 9
5. 3, 6, 12, 24, ___, ___   48, 96

Motivating the Lesson

A certain number is multiplied by itself four times. The sum of the digits in the product is equal to the number. What is the number?   7

TEACHING THE LESSON

Teaching Tip ① Monomial is pronounced mah-NOH-mee-ul.

Teaching Tip ② Explain that $\frac{1}{2} + \frac{1}{4}$ and $3a + 5a$ are monomials when they are expressed in simplest form.

Teaching Tip ③ Emphasize the difference between term and monomial. A term may represent division of variables, but a monomial may not. The expressions in the text are not monomials for these reasons.

$m + n$ shows addition not multiplication.

$\frac{x}{y}, \frac{1}{x^2}$, and $\frac{7y}{9z}$ show division, not multiplication.

$3 - 4ab$ shows subtraction, not multiplication.

Example 2 | Simplify $(-5x^2)(3x^3y^2)\left(\frac{2}{5}xy^4\right)$.

$(-5x^2)(3x^3y^2)\left(\frac{2}{5}xy^4\right) = \left(-5 \cdot 3 \cdot \frac{2}{5}\right)(x^2 \cdot x^3 \cdot x)(y^2 \cdot y^4)$ *Commutative and associative properties*

$= -6x^{2+3+1}y^{2+4}$ *Product of powers property*

$= -6x^6y^6$

Take a look at the examples below.

$(5^2)^4 = (5^2)(5^2)(5^2)(5^2)$ $(x^6)^2 = (x^6)(x^6)$

$= 5^{2+2+2+2}$ $= x^{6+6}$

$= 5^8$ $= x^{12}$

Since $(5^2)^4 = 5^8$ and $(x^6)^2 = x^{12}$, these examples suggest that you can find the power of a power by multiplying exponents. **Teaching Tip** ⑤

Power of a Power	For any number a and all integers m and n, $(a^m)^n = a^{mn}$.

Here are a few more examples.

$(xy)^3 = (xy)(xy)(xy)$ $(4ab)^4 = (4ab)(4ab)(4ab)(4ab)$

$= (x \cdot x \cdot x)(y \cdot y \cdot y)$ $= (4 \cdot 4 \cdot 4 \cdot 4)(a \cdot a \cdot a \cdot a)(b \cdot b \cdot b \cdot b)$

$= x^3y^3$ $= 4^4a^4b^4$ or $256a^4b^4$

These examples suggest that the power of a product is the product of the powers.

Power of a Product	For all numbers a and b and any integer m, $(ab)^m = a^m b^m$.

Example 3

CONNECTION

Geometry

Find the measure of the volume of the cube.

$V = s^3$

$= (x^2y^4)^3$

$= (x^2)^3 \cdot (y^4)^3$

$= x^{2 \cdot 3}y^{4 \cdot 3}$

$= x^6y^{12}$

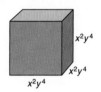

x^2y^4

x^2y^4

x^2y^4

In Example 4, the two power properties on this page are used together. This can be stated as follows.

Power of a Monomial	For all numbers a and b and any integers m, n, and p, $(a^m b^n)^p = a^{mp} b^{np}$.

RETEACHING THE LESSON

Use circular markers or chips to illustrate the difference between the product of powers and a power of a power. For example, consider $2^3 \times 2^2$ and $(2^3)^2$. Let each marker represent the base 2. For the first example, lay out a group of 3 markers and a group of 2 markers. This is a total of 5 markers. Thus, $2^3 \times 2^2 = 2^5$. For the second example, lay out 2 groups of 3 markers. This is a total of 6. Thus, $(2^3)^2 = 2^6$. This model can be used with any examples in which the bases are the same.

Example 4

Simplify $(9b^4y)^2[(-b)^2]^3$. Teaching Tips **6** **7**

$$(9b^4y)^2[(-b)^2]^3 = 9^2(b^4)^2y^2(b^2)^3 \qquad (-b)^2 = b^2$$
$$= 81b^8y^2b^6$$
$$= 81b^{14}y^2 \qquad \text{The variables in a monomial are usually arranged in alphabetical order.}$$

Some calculators have a *power key* labeled y^x. You can use it to find powers of numbers.

Example 5

Evaluate $(0.14)^3$ to the nearest thousandth.

Enter: 0.14 $\boxed{y^x}$ 3 $\boxed{=}$ Teaching Tip **8**

Display: `0.002744`   So, $(0.14)^3$ is about 0.003.

CHECKING FOR UNDERSTANDING

Communicating Mathematics

Read and study the lesson to answer each question. 2–4. See students' work.

1. Why does the product of powers property *not* apply to the expression $x^3 \cdot y^7$? **x^3 and y^7 have different bases.**

2. Write the product of powers property in your own words.

3. Write the power of a power property in your own words.

4. Write the power of a product property in your own words.

Guided Practice

Are the expressions equivalent? Write *yes* or *no*.

5. $(4y)^2$ and $4y^2$ **no**

6. $3xy^5$ and $3(xy)^5$ **no**

7. $(2a)^3$ and $8a^3$ **yes**

8. $(ab)^2$ and $a^2 \cdot b^2$ **yes**

9. xy^3 and x^3y^3 **no**

10. $4(x^3)^2$ and $16x^6$ **no**

EXERCISES

Practice

Find the measure of the area of each rectangle and the measure of the volume of each rectangular solid.

 A CONNECTION Geometry

11. p^7 p^{14} p^7

12. 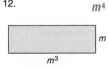 m^4 m m^3

13. 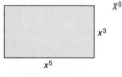 x^8 x^3 x^5

14. 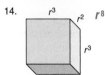 r^3 r^2 r^8 r^3

15. a^2 a^6 a^2 a^2

16. yz^4 y^3z^{12} yz^4 yz^4

Teaching Tip **6** Look for error patterns such as $9^2 = 18$ and miscalculations with powers involving negative products. Advise students to carefully analyze what monomial goes with each exponent.

Teaching Tip **7** Be sure students understand that $\frac{(-b)^2}{-b^2} = -1$. $(-b)^2$ means $(-b)(-b)$, or b^2. $-b^2$ means $-(b)(b)$, or $-(b^2)$.

Teaching Tip **8** Some calculators without an x^2 key will find the square of a number as follows. Enter the number, then $\boxed{\times}$ $\boxed{=}$. To cube a number, enter the number, then $\boxed{\times}$ $\boxed{=}$ $\boxed{=}$, and so on for other powers.

Practice Masters Booklet, p. 40

6-2 **Practice Worksheet**

NAME _____ DATE _____

Multiplying Monomials

Find the measure of the area of each rectangle and the measure of the volume of the rectangular solid.

1. e^7 e^2 e^5

2. x^3y^3 xy xy xy

3. a^2b^4 ab^2 ab^2

Simplify.

4. $a^2(a^3)(a^6)$
a^{11}

5. $(cd^2)(c^3d^2)$
c^4d^4

6. $(e^2f^4)(ef)^2$
e^4f^6

7. $x(x^2)(x^7)$
x^{10}

8. $(y^2z)(yz^2)$
y^3z^3

9. $(l^2k^2)(l^3k)$
l^5k^3

10. $(10^2)^3$
10^6 or 1,000,000

11. $[(-3)^2]^2$
81

12. $[(4^2)^2]^2$
4^8 or 65,536

13. $(t^3s^5)(t^2s)$
t^5s^6

14. $(2x^3)(3x^5)$
$6x^7$

15. $(-5a^2b)(3a^4)$
$-15a^6b$

16. $(3cd^4)(-2c^5)$
$-6c^3d^4$

17. $(-3l)^3$
$-27l^3$

18. $(-6p)^2$
$36p^2$

19. $\left(\frac{2e}{3}\right)^2$ $\frac{4e^2}{9}$

20. $(4g^3h)(-2g)^5$
$-128g^8h$

21. $r^3(r^2s^4)$
r^5s^4

22. $(2ab^2c^3)(4a^3b^2c^3)$
$8a^4b^4c^4$

23. $(0.5t)^2$
$0.25t^2$

24. $-6(x^2y^3)^4$
$-6x^8y^{12}$

25. $(3pq^2)^2$
$9p^2q^4$

26. $(ef)(eg)(fg)$
$e^2f^2g^2$

27. $(-xy)^3(xz)$
$-x^4y^3z$

28. $-\frac{3r}{5}(15r^2)$
$-9r^3$

29. $(-18mn^4)\left(-\frac{1}{6}mn^2\right)$
$3m^2n^6$

30. $\left(\frac{1}{4}cd^3\right)^2 \frac{1}{16}c^2d^6$

31. $-4(cs^2t)^2$
$-4c^2s^4t^2$

32. $(-15ap^4)\left(-\frac{1}{3}ap^3\right)$
$5a^2p^7$

33. $(0.2a^2b^3)^2$
$0.04a^4b^6$

17. $a^5(a)(a^7)$ a^{13}

18. $(a^2b)(ab^4)$ a^3b^5

19. $(m^3n)(mn^2)$ m^4n^3

20. $(10^2)^2$ 10^4 or 10,000

21. $[(-4)^2]^2$ $(-4)^4$ or 256

22. $[(3^2)^4]^2$

B

23. $(r^3t^4)(r^4t^4)$ r^7t^8

24. $(3a^2)(4a^3)$ $12a^5$

25. $(-10x^3y)(2x^2)$ $-20x^5y$

26. $(m^2)^5$ m^{10}

27. $(-7z)^3$ $-343z^3$

28. $\left(\frac{2}{5}d\right)^2$ $\frac{4}{25}d^2$

29. $(3y^3z)(7y^4)$ $21y^7z$

30. $m^4(m^3b^2)$ m^7b^2

31. $(3x^2y^2z)(2x^9y^2z^3)$

32. $(0.6d)^3$ $0.216d^3$

33. $(a^3x^2)^4$ $a^{12}x^8$

34. $(2a^2b)^2$ $4a^4b^2$

35. $(ab)(ac)(bc)$ $a^2b^2c^2$

36. $-\frac{5}{6}c(12a^3)$ $-10a^3c$

37. $(-27ay^3)\left(-\frac{1}{3}ay^3\right)$

38. $-3(ax^3y)^2$ $-3a^2x^6y^2$

39. $\left(\frac{1}{2}xy^2\right)^3$ $\frac{1}{8}x^3y^6$

40. $(0.3x^3y^2)^2$ $0.09x^6y^4$

C

41. $(-3ab)^3(2b^3)$ $-54a^3b^6$

42. $(2x^2)^2\left(\frac{1}{2}y^2\right)^2$ x^4y^4

43. $\left(\frac{3}{10}y^2\right)^2(10y^2)^3$ $90y^{10}$

44. $\left(-\frac{1}{8}a\right)\left(-\frac{1}{6}\right)(b)(48c)$ abc

45. $\left(-\frac{1}{3}c^2b^3a\right)(18a^2b^2c^3)$ $-6a^3b^5c^5$

46. $(3a^2)^3 + (5a^2)^3$ $152a^6$

47. $(-3x^3y)^3 - 3(x^2y)^2(x^5y)$ $-30x^9y^3$

Critical Thinking   Answer each question. **You may wish to substitute numbers and evaluate.**

48. For all numbers a and b and any integer m, is $(a + b)^m = a^m + b^m$ a true sentence? no

49. For all numbers a and b and any integer m, is $\left(\frac{a}{b}\right)^m = \frac{a^m}{b^m}$ a true sentence? No, $b \neq 0$.

Applications

50. **Finance**   To determine how your money will grow in an account that is compounded annually, you can use the formula $T = p(1 + r)^t$, where T is the total amount, p is the principal (amount invested), r is the annual interest rate, and t is the time in years. Use a calculator to find the final amount if you invest \$5000 at 7% for 10 years. \$9835.76

51. **Finance**   To determine how your money will grow if you make regular deposits to an account that is compounded annually, you can use the formula $T = P\left[\frac{(1 + r)^t - 1}{r}\right]$, where T is the total amount, P is the regular payment, r is the annual interest rate, and t is the time in years. Will you have more money if you deposit \$500 per year for 10 years at 7% than you would if you invested \$5000, as in Exercise 50? No, you will have \$6908.22.

Mixed Review

52. Find the next three numbers in each pattern: $-8, -4, -2, \underline{\ ?\ }, \underline{\ ?\ }, \underline{\ ?\ }$. **(Lesson 2-1)** $-1, -\frac{1}{2}, -\frac{1}{4}$

53. Mrs. Lazo has 5 times as many sons as daughters. She has 6 children altogether. How many daughters does she have? **(Lesson 3-5)** 1 daughter

54. Solve: $2x + 4 \leq 6$ or $x \geq 2x - 4$. **(Lesson 5-5)** $\{x|x \leq 4\}$

55. Solve $|6 - x| \leq x$. Then graph the solution set. **(Lesson 5-6)** $\{x|x \geq 3\}$

56. How many rectangles are shown at the right? **(Lesson 6-1)**
15 rectangles

EXTENDING THE LESSON

Math Power:
Problem Solving
Find a if $(3^{a+2})^2 \times 3^{3a-10} = 81$.
(Hint: Write 81 as a power of 3.)
$a = 2$

Checking for Understanding
Exercises 1-10 are designed to help you assess understanding through reading, writing, and speaking. You should work through Exercises 1-4 with your students, and then monitor their work on Exercises 5-10.

Closing the Lesson
Writing Activity   Have students write a summary of each property of monomials described in this lesson. Tell them to make up examples to illustrate each property.

APPLYING THE LESSON

Homework Exercises
See assignment guide on page 215.

Chapter 6, Quiz A, (Lessons 6-1 through 6-2), is available in the Evaluation Masters Booklet, p. 79.

Enrichment Masters Booklet, p. 35

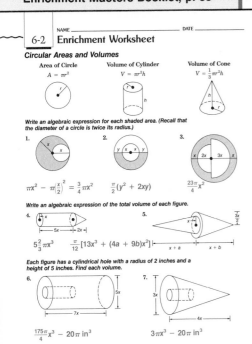

6-3 Dividing Monomials

Objectives
6-3A
6-3B

After studying this lesson, you should be able to:
- simplify expressions involving quotients of monomials, and
- simplify expressions containing negative exponents.

Consider each of the following quotients. Each number can be expressed as a power of 3.

$$\frac{81}{27} = 3 \qquad\qquad \frac{27}{3} = 9 \qquad\qquad \frac{243}{9} = 27$$

$$\downarrow \qquad\qquad\qquad \downarrow \qquad\qquad\qquad \downarrow$$

$$\frac{3^4}{3^3} = 3^1 \qquad\qquad \frac{3^3}{3^1} = 3^2 \qquad\qquad \frac{3^5}{3^2} = 3^3$$

Once again, look for a pattern in the quotients shown. If you consider only the exponents, you may notice that $4 - 3 = 1$, $3 - 1 = 2$, and $5 - 2 = 3$.

Now simplify $\frac{b^5}{b^2}$, $b \neq 0$.

$$\frac{b^5}{b^2} = \frac{\cancel{b} \cdot \cancel{b} \cdot b \cdot b \cdot b}{\cancel{b} \cdot \cancel{b}} \qquad \textit{Notice that } \frac{b \cdot b}{b \cdot b} \textit{ is equal to 1.}$$
$$= b \cdot b \cdot b \qquad\qquad \textit{The quotient has b as a factor } 5 - 2 \textit{ or 3 times.}$$
$$= b^3$$

These examples suggest that to divide powers with the same base, you can subtract the exponents.

Quotient of Powers	For all integers m and n, and any nonzero number a, $\dfrac{a^m}{a^n} = a^{m-n}$.

Example 1

Simplify $\dfrac{a^4 b^3}{ab^2}$.

$$\frac{a^4 b^3}{ab^2} = \left(\frac{a^4}{a^1}\right)\left(\frac{b^3}{b^2}\right) \qquad \textit{Group the powers that have the same base.}$$
$$= a^{4-1} b^{3-2} \qquad\qquad \textit{Subtract the exponents by the quotient of powers property.}$$
$$= a^3 b \qquad\qquad\qquad \textit{Recall that } b^1 = b.$$

Study the two ways shown below to simplify $\dfrac{a^3}{a^3}$, $a \neq 0$.

$$\frac{a^3}{a^3} = \frac{a \cdot a \cdot a}{a \cdot a \cdot a} \qquad\qquad \frac{a^3}{a^3} = a^{3-3}$$
$$= 1 \qquad\qquad\qquad\qquad\quad = a^0$$

ALTERNATE TEACHING STRATEGIES

Using Discussion

Ask students to explain why 0^0 is undefined. 0^0 is derived from an expression such as $0^{x-x} = \frac{0^x}{0^x}$ which is not defined.

Lesson Resources

- Reteaching Master 6-3
- Practice Master 6-3
- Enrichment Master 6-3
- Video Algebra, 15
- Transparency 6-3 contains the 5-Minute Check and a teaching aid for this lesson.

INTRODUCING THE LESSON

🕐 5-Minute Check
(over Lesson 6-2)

Simplify.

1. $a^4 \times a^7$ a^{11}
2. $(2p^3)(5p)$ $10p^4$
3. $(x^4 y^5)^2$ $x^8 y^{10}$
4. $(2x^3 y^4)^2$ $4x^6 y^8$
5. $-3(ax^3 y)^2$ $-3a^2 x^6 y^2$

Motivating the Lesson

A number multiplied by itself five times divided by the number multiplied by itself twice is the number multiplied by itself three times. What is the number? **any positive whole number**

TEACHING THE LESSON

Chalkboard Example

For Example 1
Simplify.

a. $\dfrac{m^7 n^5}{mn^2}$ $m^6 n^3$

b. $\dfrac{x^3 y^7}{x^2 y^6}$ xy

c. $\dfrac{3^4 a^8 b^3}{3^2 a^5 b}$ $9a^3 b^2$

Teaching Tip 1 Have students find several numbers to the zero power on their calculators, using the y^x key. For example, find 2^0, 5^0, 16^0, and 2472^0. Have students conjecture as to the value of a^0.

Teaching Tip 2 Reinforce the zero exponent concept with numerical examples, such as the one below.
$\frac{2^5}{2^5} = 1$ and $2^{5-5} = 2^0$, so $2^0 = 1$

Teaching Tip 3 Reinforce the negative exponent concept with numerical examples, such as the one below.
$\frac{5^2}{5^4} = 5^{-2}$ and $\frac{5^2}{5^4} = \frac{1}{5^2}$, so $5^{-2} = \frac{1}{5^2}$

Teaching Tip 4 You may wish to point out that $\frac{r^3}{r^{-7}} = r^{3-(-7)}$ or r^{10}. Also, point out that

$$\frac{1}{t^{-2}} = \frac{1}{\frac{1}{t^2}} = 1 \times t^2 = t^2.$$

0^0 is not defined.

Since $\frac{a^3}{a^3}$ cannot have two different values, we can conclude that $a^0 = 1$. In general, any nonzero number raised to the zero power is equal to 1.

Teaching Tip 1

Zero Exponent Teaching Tip 2	**For any nonzero number a, $a^0 = 1$.**

Study the two ways shown below to simplify $\frac{k^2}{k^7}$, $k \neq 0$.

$$\frac{k^2}{k^7} = \frac{\cancel{k} \cdot \cancel{k}}{\cancel{k} \cdot \cancel{k} \cdot k \cdot k \cdot k \cdot k \cdot k} = \frac{1}{k \cdot k \cdot k \cdot k \cdot k} = \frac{1}{k^5}$$

$$\frac{k^2}{k^7} = k^{2-7} = k^{-5}$$

Since $\frac{k^2}{k^7}$ cannot have two different values, we can conclude that $k^{-5} = \frac{1}{k^5}$. This example suggests the following definition.

Negative Exponents	**For any nonzero number a and any integer n, $a^{-n} = \frac{1}{a^n}$.**

Teaching Tip 3

To **simplify** an expression involving monomials, write an equivalent expression that has positive exponents and no powers of powers. Also, each base should appear only once and all fractions should be in simplest form.

Example 2 Simplify $\frac{-6r^3s^5}{18r^{-7}s^5t^{-2}}$.

$$\frac{-6r^3s^5}{18r^{-7}s^5t^{-2}} = \left(\frac{-6}{18}\right)\left(\frac{r^3}{r^{-7}}\right)\left(\frac{s^5}{s^5}\right)\left(\frac{1}{t^{-2}}\right)$$

$= -\frac{1}{3}r^{3-(-7)}s^{5-5}t^2$ *$\frac{1}{t^{-2}} = t^2$*

$= -\frac{1}{3}r^{10}s^0t^2$ *Subtract the exponents.*

$= -\frac{r^{10}t^2}{3}$ *Remember that $s^0 = 1$.*

Teaching Tip 4

Example 3 Simplify $\frac{(4a^{-1})^{-2}}{(2a^4)^2}$.

$\frac{(4a^{-1})^{-2}}{(2a^4)^2} = \frac{4^{-2}a^2}{2^2a^8}$ *Power of a product property*

$= \frac{4^{-2}a^2}{4a^8}$

$= (4^{-2-1})(a^{2-8})$ *Subtract the exponents.*

$= 4^{-3}a^{-6}$

$= \frac{1}{4^3a^6}$ *Definition of negative exponents*

$= \frac{1}{64a^6}$

Reteaching Masters Booklet, p. 36

NAME ______ DATE ______

6-3 Reteaching Worksheet

Dividing Monomials

Study the following exponent rules.

	Rule	Example
Quotient of Powers	For all integers m and n, and any nonzero number a, $\frac{a^m}{a^n} = a^{m-n}$.	$q^9 \div q^4 = q^{9-4} = q^5$
Zero Exponent	For any nonzero number a, $a^0 = 1$.	$4^0 = 1$ $6^0 = 1$
Negative Exponents	For any nonzero number a, and any integer n, $a^{-n} = \frac{1}{a^n}$.	$\frac{r^3}{r^6} = \frac{r \cdot r \cdot r}{r \cdot r \cdot r \cdot r \cdot r \cdot r} = \frac{1}{r^3}$ or $\frac{r^3}{r^6} = r^{3-6} = r^{-3}$

Simplify. Assume no denominator is equal to zero.

1. $\frac{a^2}{a}$ a
2. $\frac{x^5y^3}{x^5y^2}$ y
3. $\frac{15a^3}{45a^2}$ $\frac{a}{3}$
4. $\frac{s^{-3}t^{-5}}{(s^2t^3)^{-1}}$ $\frac{1}{st^2}$
5. $\frac{a^5b^3}{a^2b^2}$ a^3b
6. $\frac{k^0}{k^7}$ $\frac{1}{k^7}$
7. $\frac{(6a^{-1}b)^2}{(b^2)^4}$ $\frac{36}{a^2b^6}$
8. $\frac{66w^3x^6y^9}{-22wxy^7}$ $-3w^2x^5y^2$
9. $\left(\frac{4m^2n^2}{8m^{-1}l}\right)^0$ 1
10. $\frac{15x^3}{5x^0}$ $3x^3$
11. $\frac{x^2}{x^3}$ $\frac{1}{x}$
12. $\frac{(3st)^2u^{-4}}{s^{-1}t^2u^7}$ $\frac{9s^3}{u^{11}}$
13. $\frac{b^5}{b^6}$ $\frac{1}{b}$
14. $\frac{x^9}{x^2}$ x^7
15. $\frac{24w^7t^4}{6w^3t^2}$ $4w^4t^2$
16. $\frac{9x^2z^5}{-3xz^3}$ $-3xz^2$
17. $\frac{(-x^{-1}y)^0}{4w^{-1}y^2}$ $\frac{w}{4y^2}$
18. $\frac{wt^3x}{wx}$ t^3
19. $\frac{w^2}{w}$ w
20. $\frac{(a^2b^3)^2}{(ab)^{-2}}$ a^6b^8

RETEACHING THE LESSON

What numbers are needed to continue the patterns?

$2^4 = 16$	$3^4 = 81$
$2^3 = 8$	$3^3 = 27$
$2^2 = 4$	$3^2 = 9$
$2^1 = 2$	$3^1 = 3$
$2^0 = \underline{1}$	$3^0 = \underline{1}$
$2^{-1} = \underline{\frac{1}{2}}$	$3^{-1} = \underline{\frac{1}{3}}$
$2^{-2} = \underline{\frac{1}{4}}$	$3^{-2} = \underline{\frac{1}{9}}$
$2^{-3} = \underline{\frac{1}{8}}$	$3^{-3} = \underline{\frac{1}{27}}$

CHECKING FOR UNDERSTANDING

Communicating Mathematics

Read and study the lesson to answer each question. See margin.

1. In the quotient of powers property, why must a be nonzero?

2. Use the fact that $2^4 = 16$, $2^3 = 8$, $2^2 = 4$, and $2^1 = 2$ to make a convincing argument that $2^0 = 1$.

3. Why is 0^0 undefined?

Guided Practice

Evaluate.

4. 5^0 1

5. $(-8)^{-1}$ $-\frac{1}{8}$

6. 10^{-2} $\frac{1}{100}$

7. $(-2)^{-3}$ $-\frac{1}{8}$

8. $(5^{-1})^2$ $\frac{1}{25}$

9. $\frac{4^{-2}}{4}$ $\frac{1}{64}$

10. $\left(\frac{1}{3} \cdot \frac{1}{6}\right)^{-1}$ 18

11. $(2^0 3^{-2})^{-2}$ 81

Simplify. Assume no denominator is equal to zero. (Remember to express the results with positive exponents.)

12. $m^{-5}n^0$ $\frac{1}{m^5}$

13. $a^0 b^{-2} c^{-1}$ $\frac{1}{b^2 c}$

14. $x^5 y^0 z^{-5}$ $\frac{x^5}{z^5}$

15. $\frac{5n^5}{n^8}$ $\frac{5}{n^3}$

16. $\frac{b^9}{b^4 c^3}$ $\frac{b^5}{c^3}$

17. $\frac{1}{r^{-4}}$ r^4

18. $\frac{a^{-4}}{b^{-3}}$ $\frac{b^3}{a^4}$

19. $\frac{an^6}{n^5}$ an

EXERCISES

Practice

Simplify. Assume no denominator is equal to zero.

20. $\frac{a^0}{a^{-2}}$ a^2

21. $\frac{1}{r^{-3}}$ r^3

22. $\frac{k^{-2}}{k^4}$ $\frac{1}{k^6}$

23. $\frac{m^2}{m^{-4}}$ m^6

24. $\frac{b^6 c^5}{b^3 c^2}$ $b^3 c^3$

25. $\frac{(-a)^4 b^8}{a^4 b^7}$ b

26. $\frac{(-x)^3 y^3}{x^3 y^6}$ $-\frac{1}{y^3}$

27. $\frac{12b^5}{4b^4}$ $3b$

28. $\frac{10m^4}{30m}$ $\frac{m^3}{3}$

29. $\frac{x^3 y^6}{x^3 y^3}$ y^3

30. $\frac{b^6 c^5}{b^{14} c^2}$ $\frac{c^3}{b^8}$

31. $\frac{(-r)^5 s^8}{r^5 s^2}$ $-s^6$

32. $\frac{30x^4 y^7}{-6x^{13} y^2}$ $-\frac{5y^5}{x^9}$

33. $\frac{16b^4 c}{-4bc^3}$ $-\frac{4b^3}{c^2}$

34. $\frac{22a^2 b^5 c^7}{-11abc^2}$ $-2ab^4 c^5$

35. $\frac{24x^2 y^2 z^3}{-6x^2 y^3 z}$ $-4y^4 z^2$

36. $\frac{7x^3 z^5}{4z^{15}}$ $\frac{7x^3}{4z^{10}}$

37. $\frac{27a^4 b^6 c^9}{15a^3 c^{15}}$ $\frac{9ab^6}{5c^6}$

38. $\frac{(a^7 b^2)^2}{(a^{-2} b)^{-2}}$ $a^{10} b^6$

39. $\frac{r^{-5} s^{-2}}{(r^2 s^5)^{-1}}$ $\frac{s^3}{r^3}$

40. $\frac{(r^{-4} k^2)^2}{(5k^2)^2}$ $\frac{1}{25r^8}$

41. $\left(\frac{3m^2 n^2}{6m^{-1} k}\right)^0$ 1

42. $\frac{(-b^{-1}c)^0}{4a^{-1}c^2}$ $\frac{a}{4c^2}$

43. $\left(\frac{7m^{-1} n^3}{n^2 r^{-2}}\right)^{-1}$ $\frac{m}{7nr^2}$

44. $\left(\frac{2xy^{-2} z^4}{3xyz^{-1}}\right)^{-2}$ $\frac{9y^6}{4z^{10}}$

Critical Thinking

Simplify.

45. $y^2 \cdot y^b$ y^{2+b}

46. $x^{2a} \cdot x^{4a}$ x^{6a}

47. $(2^{7x+6})(2^{3x-4})$ 2^{10x+2}

48. $\frac{x^{y+2}}{x^{y-3}}$ x^5

49. $\frac{(a^{x+2})^2}{(a^{x-3})^2}$ a^{10}

50. $\frac{a^b}{a^{a-b}}$ a^{2b-a}

LESSON 6-3 DIVIDING MONOMIALS 219

Additional Answers

1. Because division by 0 is undefined.
2. Look for a pattern:
   $16 \div 2 = 8$, $8 \div 2 = 4$,
   $4 \div 2 = 2$, and $2 \div 2 = 1$.
3. *(See "Using Discussion", p. 217.)
   $0^0 = 0^{x-x} = \frac{0^x}{0^x}$ and division by
   0 is undefined.

Applications

51. **Finance** To determine what is still owed on a car loan, you can use the formula $B = P\left[\dfrac{1 - (1 + i)^{k-n}}{i}\right]$, where B is the balance due (or payoff), P is the current monthly payment, i is the monthly interest rate (or the annual rate $\div$ 12), k is the number of payments already made, and n is the total number of monthly payments. Use a calculator to find the payoff on a 48-month loan, after 24 payments of $213.87 have been made, at an annual interest rate of 10.8%. **$4597.87**

52. **Finance** To determine the monthly payment on a home, you can use the formula $P = A\left[\dfrac{i}{1 - (1 + i)^{-n}}\right]$, where P is the monthly payment, A is the price of the home less down payment, i is the *monthly* interest rate (or the annual rate $\div$ 12), and n is the total number of monthly payments. Use a calculator to find the monthly payment on an $80,000 home, with 5% down, over 30 years at an *annual* interest rate of 12%. **$781.75**

Mixed Review

53. **Consumerism** Which is the better buy: 12 extra-large eggs weighing 27 ounces for $1.09, or 12 large eggs weighing 24 ounces for 99¢? **(Lesson 2-4)**

54. Solve $-\frac{7}{6} + k = \frac{5}{6}$. **(Lesson 3-1)** 2

55. **Government** The shape of the U.S. flag is determined by federal standards set by Executive Order of President Eisenhower in 1959. The width-to-length ratio must be 1:1.9. How long would a U.S. flag be that is 3 feet wide? **(Lesson 4-1)** $5\frac{7}{10}$ feet or 5 feet $8\frac{2}{5}$ in.

56. Three spiders are on a 9-foot-high wall. Susie is 4 feet from the top. Sam is 7 feet from the bottom. Shirley is 3 feet below Sam. Which spider is nearest the top of the wall? **(Lesson 5-4) Sam**

57. Simplify $a^2(a^5)$. **(Lesson 6-2)** a^7

READING ALGEBRA

You can read powers containing the exponent 2 or 3 in two ways.

x^2 is read "x squared" or "x to the second power."
x^3 is read "x cubed" or "x to the third power."

Powers containing other numerical exponents are usually read as follows.

x^6 is read "x to the sixth power."

The phrase *the quantity* is used to indicate parentheses when reading expressions.

$3x^2$ is read "three x squared."
$(3x)^2$ is read "three x *the quantity* squared."
$(2a + b)^4$ is often read "*the quantity* 2a plus b all to the fourth power."

Read each expression to a classmate while they write the expression in words. See margin.
1. 4^2 2. 3^3 3. a^5 4. $5b^2$ 5. $(12r)^5$
6. $9x^3y$ 7. $(x + 2y)^2$ 8. $4m^2n^4$ 9. $(6a^2b)^4$ 10. $a - b^3$

EXTENDING THE LESSON

Math Power: Problem Solving

Simplify $\dfrac{a^0(a)(a^2)^2(a^3)^3}{(a^{-1})^{-1}(a^{-2})^{-2}(a^{-3})^{-3}}$. 1

Reading Algebra Answers

1. four squared
2. three cubed
3. *a* to the fifth power
4. five times *b* squared
5. twelve times *r* the quantity to the fifth power
6. nine times *x* cubed times *y*
7. *x* plus two times *y* the quantity squared
8. four times *m* squared times *n* to the fourth power
9. six *a* squared times *b* the quantity to the fourth power
10. *a* minus *b* cubed

Scientific Notation

Objectives
6-4A
6-4B

After studying this lesson, you should be able to:
- express numbers in scientific and decimal notation, and
- find products and quotients of numbers expressed in scientific notation.

Application

What can fly through hundreds of thousands of miles of space in a single day? What can photograph objects billions of miles from Earth? What can send messages at the speed of light—186,282 miles per second? A space probe! Space probes allow scientists to explore other planets without ever leaving Earth.

The chart at the right shows how far nine space probes have traveled. These distances are NASA estimates for travel as of late 1989 and have been rounded to the nearest million miles.

Space Probe	Miles Traveled
Magellan	40,000,000
Pioneer 6	62,000,000
Pioneer 7	78,000,000
Pioneer 8	142,000,000
Pioneer 10	4,382,000,000
Pioneer 11	2,705,000,000
Pioneer 12	100,000,000
Voyager 1	3,641,000,000
Voyager 2	2,793,000,000

FYI · · ·

Our universe is estimated to be 2.1×10^{23} miles wide.

Astronomers use large numbers like these all of the time when measuring distances in space. Sometimes it is not desirable to express these numbers in **decimal notation**, as they are shown in the chart. So scientists use **scientific notation** to express very large numbers.

Teaching Tip ①

Definition of Scientific Notation	A number is expressed in scientific notation when it is in the form $a \times 10^n$, where $1 \le a < 10$ and n is an integer.

For example, the average distance between the sun and Earth is about 93,000,000 miles. To write this number in scientific notation, express it as the product of a number greater than or equal to 1, but less than 10, and a power of 10.

$93,000,000 = 9.3 \times 10,000,000$ *Move the decimal point 7 places to the left.*
$\qquad\qquad = 9.3 \times 10^7$ *The exponent is 7.*

Example 1

Express 5093.4 in scientific notation.

$5093.4 = 5.0934 \times 1000$ *Move the decimal point 3 places to the left.*
$\qquad\quad = 5.0934 \times 10^3$ *The exponent is 3.*

ALTERNATE TEACHING STRATEGIES

Using Applications

Have students research the mass of five elements on the Periodic Table. Then have students use this information to write three word problems about the elements that require an answer expressed in scientific notation. Have students switch problems and solve each other's creations.

Using Problem Solving

Space Travel, Inc. wants to establish round trip rocket flights from Earth to Mars. Mars is 2.28×10^8 km from the sun and Earth is 1.50×10^8 km from the sun. If Earth is aligned between the sun and Mars, how long would the round trip take if the rocket travels 30,000 km per hour? **about 5200 hours or 217 days**

Lesson Resources

- Reteaching Master 6-4
- Practice Master 6-4
- Enrichment Master 6-4
- Technology Master, p. 6
- Activity Master, p. 21

 Transparency 6-4 contains the 5-Minute Check and a teaching aid for this lesson.

INTRODUCING THE LESSON

🕐 5-Minute Check
(over Lesson 6-3)

Simplify.

1. $\dfrac{n^6}{n^2}$ n^4
2. $\dfrac{b^5}{b^7}$ $\dfrac{1}{b^2}$
3. $\dfrac{ab^2}{a^2b}$ $\dfrac{b}{a}$
4. $\dfrac{36x^4y^2}{12x^6y}$ $\dfrac{3y}{x^2}$
5. $\dfrac{10t^6r}{40t^3r^5}$ $\dfrac{t^3}{4r^4}$

Motivating the Lesson

Begin the lesson by having students examine large numbers such as the distance between Earth and the sun or the population of China. Ask students to describe problems that could arise when working with such large numbers.

TEACHING THE LESSON

Teaching Tip ① Emphasize the difference between scientific notation and decimal notation. Students should feel comfortable with the terminology.

Chalkboard Example

For Example 1
Express 381,677 in scientific notation. 3.81677×10^5

Example 2

Express 2.6 × 10⁵ in decimal notation.

$2.6 \times 10^{5} = 2.6 \times 100{,}000$
$= 260{,}000$ *Because the exponent on 10 was 5, the decimal point was moved 5 places to the right.*

Scientific notation is also used to express very small numbers. When numbers between zero and one are written in scientific notation, the exponent of 10 is negative.

Example 3

APPLICATION

Biology

An organism called the *Mycoplasma laidlawii* has a diameter of only 100 millimicrons, or 0.000004 inches, during the early part of its life. Write this number in scientific notation.

$0.000004 = 4 \times 0.000001$ *Move the decimal point 6 places to the right.*
$= 4 \times \dfrac{1}{1{,}000{,}000}$
$= 4 \times \dfrac{1}{10^{6}}$ *The exponent is 6.*
$= 4 \times 10^{-6}$ *Remember that $\dfrac{1}{a^{n}} = a^{-n}$.*

So the Mycoplasma laidlawii has a diameter of 4×10^{-6} inches.

Example 4

Express 3.2 × 10⁻⁷ in decimal notation.

$3.2 \times 10^{-7} = 3.2 \times 0.0000001$
$= 0.00000032$ *Because the exponent on 10 was −7, the decimal point was moved 7 places to the left.*

You can find products or quotients of numbers that are expressed in scientific notation.

Example 5

APPLICATION

Economics

FYI · · ·

Earth's population increases by 155 people every minute.

Suppose you have to feed all of the people on Earth using the 4.325 × 10¹¹ kilograms of food produced by the United States and Canada each year. You need to divide this food among the world population so that each person receives the same amount of food each day. How would you do this, if Earth has about 4.8 × 10⁹ inhabitants?

If the food is to be equally divided among all inhabitants, each person would receive $(4.325 \times 10^{11}) \div (4.8 \times 10^{9})$ kilograms of food.

$\dfrac{4.325 \times 10^{11}}{4.8 \times 10^{9}} = \dfrac{4.325}{4.8} \times \dfrac{10^{11}}{10^{9}}$
$\approx 0.9 \times 10^{2}$
≈ 90

Thus, each person would receive about 90 kilograms of food each year, or about 90 ÷ 365 or 0.25 kilograms of food each day.

RETEACHING THE LESSON

1. Use a calculator to find each product.
   a. 4,000,000 × 20,000,000
      8   13
   b. 0.000003 × 0.0000002
      6   13
   Interpret the answers displayed.

2. Complete the table.

decimal	scientific	EE	
5,000,000	5×10^{6}	5	06
24,100	2.41×10^{4}	2.41	04
0.000036	3.6×10^{-5}	3.6	−05
0.00073	7.3×10^{-4}	7.3	−0.4

Example 6

Use scientific notation to find the product of 0.000008 and 3,500,000,000. Express the result in scientific notation and decimal notation. **Teaching Tip ❷**

$$(0.000008)(3,500,000,000) = (8 \times 10^{-6})(3.5 \times 10^9) \quad \text{Express in scientific notation.}$$
$$= (8 \times 3.5)(10^{-6} \times 10^9) \quad \text{Use the commutative and associative properties.}$$
$$\quad\quad\quad\quad\quad\quad\quad\quad\quad\quad\quad \text{Recall that } 1 \le a < 10.$$
$$= 28 \times 10^3$$
$$= 2.8 \times 10^4 \text{ or } 28,000$$

Many calculators use scientific notation to display answers that are either too large or too small to display on the calculator screen in decimal notation. You can enter numbers in scientific notation using keys often labeled ⌨EE or ⌨EXP.

Example 7

Use a calculator to express 230×10^{15} in scientific notation.

Enter: 230 ⌨EE 15 ⌨= $2.3 \; 17$

The calculator has expressed 230×10^{15} as 2.3 17. That means 2.3×10^{17}.

CHECKING FOR UNDERSTANDING

Communicating Mathematics

Read and study the lesson to answer each question. See margin.

1. When do you use positive exponents in scientific notation?
2. When do you use negative exponents in scientific notation?

Complete.

3. The number 876,200 is written in ___?___ notation. **decimal**
4. The number 8.762×10^5 is written in ___?___ notation. **scientific**

Guided Practice

Teaching Tip ❸

Express each number in the second column in decimal notation. Express each number in the third column in scientific notation. See margin.

	Planet	Diameter (km)	Distance From Sun (km)
5.	Mercury	5.0×10^3	57,900,000
6.	Venus	1.208×10^4	108,230,000
7.	Earth	1.276×10^4	149,590,000
8.	Mars	6.79×10^3	227,920,000
9.	Jupiter	1.432×10^5	778,320,000
10.	Saturn	1.21×10^5	1,427,000,000
11.	Uranus	5.18×10^4	2,870,000,000
12.	Neptune	4.95×10^4	4,497,000,000
13.	Pluto	3×10^3	5,900,000,000

Additional Answers

1. when the number is greater than or equal to 10
2. when the number is less than 1
5. 5000; 5.79×10^7
6. 12,080; 1.0823×10^8
7. 12,760; 1.4959×10^8
8. 6790; 2.2792×10^8
9. 143,200; 7.7832×10^8
10. 121,000; 1.427×10^9

11. 51,800; 2.87×10^9
12. 49,500; 4.497×10^9
13. 3000; 5.9×10^9

Teaching Tip ❷ When expressing 0.000008 and 3,500,000,000 in scientific notation, help students derive a method to recognize when base 10 will have a negative or a positive exponent.

Teaching Tip ❸ The distances given in the chart are average distances. They vary considerably due to the elliptical orbits of the planets.

EVALUATING THE LESSON

Checking for Understanding
Exercises 1-13 are designed to help you assess understanding through reading, writing, and speaking. You should work through Exercises 1-4 with your students, and then monitor their work on Exercises 5-13.

Closing the Lesson
Modeling Activity Have students identify three very large or very small numbers in the real world, such as the population of India or the mass of an element. Tell students to express each number in scientific and decimal notation. Extend the activity by compiling a class list that ranks numbers from greatest to least.

Reteaching Masters Booklet, p. 37

6-4 NAME _____ DATE _____
Reteaching Worksheet

Scientific Notation

Scientists use scientific notation to express very large or very small numbers. A number is expressed in scientific notation when it is expressed as the product of a number between one and ten, and a power of ten.

Example 1: $37,000 = 3.7 \times 10^4$ **Example 2:** $0.00391 = 3.91 \times 10^{-3}$

You can find products or quotients of numbers that are expressed in scientific notation by following the rules for multiplying and dividing monomials and powers.

Example 3: $\frac{8.4 \times 10^8}{4.2 \times 10^5} = \frac{8.4}{4.2} \times \frac{10^8}{10^5}$ **Example 4:** $(6700)(0.00002)$
$= 2 \times 10^3$, or 2000
$\quad = (6.7 \times 10^3)(2 \times 10^{-5})$
$\quad = (6.7 \times 2)(10^3 \times 10^{-5})$
$\quad = 13.4 \times 10^{-2}$
$\quad = 1.34 \times 10^{-1}$, or 0.134

Express each number in scientific notation.

1. 0.0000456   2. 0.01   3. 590,000,000   4. 640×10^5
4.56×10^{-4} 10^{-2} 5.9×10^8 6.4×10^7

Evaluate. Express each result in scientific and decimal notation.

5. $\frac{1.4 \times 10^4}{0.2 \times 10^2}$ 6. $\frac{3.3 \times 10^{-12}}{1.1 \times 10^{-14}}$ 7. $\frac{0.000042}{600}$
7×10^2; 700 3×10^2; 300 7×10^{-8}; 0.00000007

8. $(2 \times 10^4)(4 \times 10^{-5})$ 9. $(77 \times 10^4)(0.02 \times 10^3)$ 10. $(3.2 \times 10^{-2})(2.0 \times 10^2)$
8×10^{-1}; 0.8 1.54×10^7; 15,400,000 6.4×10^0; 6.4

11. $250,000 \div 0.0005$ 12. $(0.00004)(20,000)$ 13. $(1.5 \times 10^5)(3.3 \times 10^{-4})$
5×10^8; 500,000,000 8×10^{-1}; 0.8 4.95×10^1; 49.5

Homework Exercises

Assignment Guide

Basic: 14-34, 39-44, 48-53
Average: 20-36, 39-53
Enriched: 23-53

Chapter 6, Quiz B, (Lessons 6-3 through 6-4), is available in the Evaluation Masters Booklet, p. 79.

Additional Answers

14. 4.293×10^3
15. 2.4×10^5
16. 3.19×10^{-4}
17. 4.296×10^{-3}
18. 9.2×10^{-8}
19. 3.17×10^{-9}
20. 3.2×10^6
21. 2.84×10^5
22. 3.1×10^0 or 3.1

Practice Masters Booklet, p. 42

NAME _____ DATE _____
6-4 **Practice Worksheet**

Scientific Notation

Express each number in scientific notation.

1. 6387
6.387×10^3
2. 560,000
5.6×10^5
3. 41,000,000
4.1×10^7

4. 0.003157
3.157×10^{-3}
5. 0.00009621
9.621×10^{-5}
6. 0.0000000814
8.14×10^{-9}

7. 4740×10^5
4.74×10^8
8. 56×10^7
5.6×10^8
9. 0.0057×10^3
5.7×10^0

10. 0.076×10^{-3}
7.6×10^{-5}
11. 915,600,000,000
9.156×10^{11}
12. 0.0000000000112
1.12×10^{-11}

Evaluate. Express each result in scientific and decimal notation.

13. $\frac{5.1 \times 10^8}{1.5 \times 10^5}$
3.4×10^4; 34,000
14. $\frac{3 \times 10^{-3}}{1.2 \times 10^2}$
2.5×10^{-5}; 0.000025
15. $\frac{7.2 \times 10^{-5}}{4 \times 10^{-3}}$
1.8×10^{-2}; 0.018

16. $\frac{1.17 \times 10^2}{5 \times 10^{-1}}$
2.34×10^2; 234
17. $\frac{1.82 \times 10^5}{9.1 \times 10^7}$
2.0×10^{-3}; 0.002
18. $\frac{1.68 \times 10^4}{8.4 \times 10^{-4}}$
2.0×10^7; 20,000,000

19. $\frac{1.2 \times 10^7}{6.0 \times 10^3}$
2.0×10^3; 2000
20. $\frac{6.72 \times 10^3}{4.2 \times 10^8}$
1.6×10^{-5}; 0.000016
21. $\frac{9.6 \times 10^{-4}}{1.6 \times 10^{-5}}$
6.0×10; 60

22. $(3.1 \times 10^5)(2 \times 10^{-5})$
6.2×10^2; 620
23. $(5 \times 10^{-2})(1.4 \times 10^{-4})$
7.0×10^{-6}; 0.000007

24. $(8.3 \times 10^3)(9.1 \times 10^{-7})$
7.553×10^{-4}; 0.0007553
25. $(9.72 \times 10^7)(4.8 \times 10^{-10})$
4.6656×10^{-2}; 0.046656

26. $(1.39 \times 10^{-3})(5.82 \times 10^{-6})$
8.0898×10^{-9};
0.0000000080898
27. $(2.5 \times 10^5)(3.62 \times 10^{-5})$
9.05×10^0; 9.05

28. $(9.8 \times 10^6)(1.12 \times 10^2)$
1.0976×10^9; 1,097,600,000
29. $(7.8 \times 10^5)(3.45 \times 10^{-6})$
2.691×10^0; 2.691

EXERCISES

Practice

A

Express each number in scientific notation. **See margin.**

14. 4293
15. 240,000
16. 0.000319
17. 0.004296
18. 0.000000092
19. 0.00000000317
20. 32×10^5
21. 284×10^3
22. 0.0031×10^8

B

Evaluate. Express each result in scientific and decimal notation. **See margin.**

23. $\frac{4.8 \times 10^9}{1.6 \times 10^1}$
24. $\frac{5.2 \times 10^5}{1.3 \times 10^2}$
25. $\frac{7.8 \times 10^{-5}}{1.3 \times 10^{-7}}$

26. $\frac{8.1 \times 10^2}{2.7 \times 10^{-3}}$
27. $\frac{1.32 \times 10^{-6}}{2.4 \times 10^2}$
28. $\frac{2.31 \times 10^{-2}}{3.3 \times 10^{-3}}$

29. $(2 \times 10^5)(3 \times 10^{-8})$
30. $(4 \times 10^2)(1.5 \times 10^6)$
31. $(3.1 \times 10^{-2})(2.1 \times 10^5)$
32. $(3.1 \times 10^4)(4.2 \times 10^{-3})$
33. $(78 \times 10^6)(0.01 \times 10^3)$
34. $(0.2 \times 10^5)(31 \times 10^{-6})$

C

Use a calculator to evaluate. Express each result in scientific and decimal notation. **See margin.**

35. $(0.000003)(70,000)$
36. $(86,000,000)(0.005)$
37. $24,000 \div 0.00006$
38. $0.0000039 \div 650,000$

Critical Thinking

Use a calculator to evaluate. Express each result in scientific and decimal notation. **See margin.**

39. $\frac{(35,987,000)(58 \times 10^3)}{42.5 \times 10^4}$
40. $\frac{(3 \times 10^8)(43 \times 10^{-4})}{23,000,000}$
41. $\frac{8.9 \times 10^5}{(98,000)(14 \times 10^3)}$
42. $\frac{57,800,000,000}{(2.3 \times 10^6)(38 \times 10^{-5})}$

Applications

Use scientific notation to solve each problem.

43. **Health** A radio station advertised the Columbus Marathon by saying that about 12,000,000 calories would be burned in one day. If there were 4000 runners, about how many calories did each runner burn? **3000 calories**

44. **Census** In 1990, the population of the United States was 248,200,000. The area of the United States is 3,540,000 square miles. If the population were equally spaced over the land, how many people would there be for each square mile? **70.113 people**

45. **Government** In 1990, the U.S. federal budget deficit was $220,000,000,000. Using the U.S. population figures given in Exercise 44, find how much each American would have had to pay in 1990 to erase the deficit. **$886.38**

46. **Space** We learned in the lesson introduction that one of the space probes to travel space was *Pioneer 10*.

   a. How long did it take *Pioneer 10*'s radio signals, traveling at the speed of light (about 1.86×10^5 miles per second), to reach Earth from a distance of 2.85×10^9 miles? **15,300 seconds or 4.25 hours**

   b. What was *Pioneer 10*'s average speed (in miles per hour) if it traveled about 2.85×10^9 miles in 4070 days? **2.92×10^4 mph**

Additional Answers

23. 3×10^2; 300
24. 4×10^3; 4000
25. 6×10^2; 600
26. 3×10^5; 300,000
27. 5.5×10^{-9}; 0.0000000055
28. 7×10^0; 7
29. 6×10^{-3}; 0.006
30. 6×10^8; 600,000,000
31. 6.51×10^3; 6510
32. 1.302×10^2; 130.2

33. 7.8×10^8; 780,000,000
34. 6.2×10^{-1}; 0.62
35. 2.1×10^{-1}; 0.21
36. 4.3×10^5; 430,000
37. 4×10^8; 400,000,000
38. 6×10^{-12}; 0.000000000006
39. 4.91116706×10^6; 4,911,167.06
40. 5.608696×10^{-2}; 0.05608696
41. 6.4868805×10^{-4}; 0.00064869
42. $6.6132723.1 \times 10^7$; 66,132,723.1

47. In the BASIC language, powers are written using the symbols ↑ or ^. The program at the right evaluates the expression $(2ab^2)^3$ when $a = 9$ and $b = 10$. Notice that the output for the program is in E notation. This is the computer equivalent of scientific notation. Thus, $5.832E + 09$ means 5.832×10^9. The computer used E notation because there were more than six significant digits in the output. See margin for programs.

```
10 READ A, B
20 DATA 9, 10
30 PRINT (2*A*B↑2)↑3
40 END

RUN
5.832E + 09
```

Teaching Tip ➍ Remind students that in BASIC, multiplication must be specified by the * symbol. Use the exercises to review the order of operations and to practice scientific notation.

Write a program that will evaluate each expression if $a = 4$, $b = 6$, and $c = 8$. Then use the program to evaluate each expression.

a. $a^2b^3c^4$
1.416E+7

b. $(-2a)^2(4b)^3$
884,736

c. $(4a^2b^4)^3$
5.706E+14

d. $(ac)^3 + (3b)^2$
33,092

Mixed Review

48. Simplify $\dfrac{60a - 30b}{-6}$. (Lesson 2-7) $-10a + 5b$

49. Biology A crab has 2 more legs than a scorpion. Together they have 18 legs. How many legs does a scorpion have? (Lesson 3-5) 8 legs

50. Thirty-five is 50% of what number? (Lesson 4-2) 70

51. Solve $-16q > -128$. (Lesson 5-2) $\{q \mid q < 8\}$

Simplify.

52. $4(a^2b^3)^3$ (Lesson 6-2) $4a^6b^9$

53. $\dfrac{48a^8}{12a}$ (Lesson 6-3) $4a^7$

APPLICATION

Black Holes

A *black hole* is a region in space where matter seems to disappear. Scientists believe that when a large star runs out of nuclear fuel, it begins to break down under the force of its own gravity. The gravity eventually becomes so intense that even light cannot escape, making the star look black.

How do we know when a star has become a black hole? A star is a black hole when the radius of the star reaches a certain critical value called the *Schwarzschild radius*. This value is given by the equation $R_s = \dfrac{2GM}{c^2}$, where R_s is the Schwarzschild radius in meters, M is the mass in kilograms, G is the gravitational constant (6.7×10^{-11}), and c is the speed of light $(3 \times 10^8$ meters per second).

Our sun is a star, but it is not large enough to become a black hole. However, we can use it as an example of how a black hole is formed. The mass of the sun is about 2×10^{30} kilograms.

$$R_s = \frac{2(6.7 \times 10^{-11})(2 \times 10^{30})}{(3 \times 10^8)^2} \approx 3000 \text{ meters}$$

The radius of the sun is about 700,000 kilometers. If the radius were reduced to about 3000 meters, in theory, it would become a black hole.

EXTENDING THE LESSON

Math Power: Problem Solving

Evaluate. Express the result in scientific notation.
$$\frac{(3.266 \times 10^3)^{-2}(0.815 \times 10^{-4})^{-2}}{(1.96 \times 10^{-5})^2}$$
3.674×10^{10}

Application

Black holes are one type of condensed object in space. Two other types are white dwarfs and neutron stars. Interested students may wish to do more research on these three types of condensed objects. They can investigate how the size (diameter) of each depends on its mass and how the size changes if mass is added.

Enrichment Masters Booklet, p. 37

NAME _____ DATE _____

6-4 **Enrichment Worksheet**

Converting Metric Units

Scientific notation is convenient to use for unit conversions in the metric system.

Example 1: How many kilometers are there in 4,300,000 meters?

Divide the measure by the number of meters (1000) in one kilometer. Express both numbers in scientific notation.
$\frac{4.3 \times 10^6}{1 \times 10^3} = 4.3 \times 10^3$ The answer is 4.3×10^3 km.

Example 2: Convert 3700 grams into milligrams.

Multiply by the number of milligrams (1000) in 1 gram.
$(3.7 \times 10^3)(1 \times 10^3) = 3.7 \times 10^6$ There are 3.7×10^6 mg in 3700 g.

Complete the following. Express each answer in scientific notation.

1. 250,000 m = 2.5×10^2 km
2. 375 km = 3.75×10^5 m
3. 247 m = 2.47×10^4 cm
4. 5000 m = 5.0×10^6 mm
5. 0.0004 km = 4.0×10^{-1} m
6. 0.01 mm = 1.0×10^{-5} m
7. 6000 m = 6×10^6 mm
8. 340 cm = 3.4×10^{-3} km
9. 52,000 mg = 5.2×10^1 g
10. 420 kL = 4.2×10^5 L

Solve.

11. The planet Mars has a diameter of 6.76×10^3 km. What is the diameter of Mars in meters? Express the answer in both scientific and decimal notation. 6,760,000 m; 6.76×10^6 m

12. The distance of the earth from the sun is 149,590,000 km. Light travels 3.0×10^8 meters per second. How long does it take light from the sun to reach the earth in minutes? 8.31 min

13. A light-year is the distance that light travels in one year. (See Exercise 12.) How far is a light year in kilometers? Express your answer in scientific notation. 9.46×10^{12} km

Lesson Resources

- Reteaching Master 6-5
- Practice Master 6-5
- Enrichment Master 6-5
- Activity Master, p. 51
- Video Algebra, 14

 Transparency 6-5 contains the 5-Minute Check and a teaching aid for this lesson.

INTRODUCING THE LESSON

5-Minute Check

(over Lesson 6-4)

Express in scientific notation.

1. 42,345 4.2345×10^4
2. 62,917.6 6.29176×10^4
3. 0.000567 5.67×10^{-4}

Express in decimal notation.

4. 3.7×10^5 370,000
5. 7.0×10^{-6} 0.000007

Motivating the Lesson

Introduce the lesson with a discussion of the prefixes "mono", "bi", "tri", and "poly". Ask students to give examples of common terms that contain these prefixes. Develop the idea that "mono" means one, "bi" means two, "tri" means three, and "poly" means more than one.

TEACHING THE LESSON

Chalkboard Example

For Example 1

State whether each expression is a polynomial. If it is a polynomial, identify it as either a monomial, binomial, or trinomial.

a. $7y^3 - 4y^2 + 2$ trinomial

b. $10x^3y^2z$ monomial

6-5 Polynomials

Objectives
6-5A
6-5B

After studying this lesson, you should be able to:
- find the degree of a polynomial, and
- arrange the terms of a polynomial so that the powers of a certain variable are in ascending or descending order.

Application

Polynomials with more than three terms have no special name.

Each summer, Li Chiang works at Burger World. She earns about $1600 and saves $1000, which she invests in a savings account at a local bank. If Li works at Burger World each summer that she is in high school, will she have enough money to pay for her first year of college, a cost of $6000?

Banks and savings institutions pay interest on savings account deposits. To calculate how Li's money will grow, use the formula for compound interest, $T = p(1 + r)^t$, where T is the total amount, p is the principal, r is the annual interest rate, and t is the time in years that the money has been in the account. To simplify the formula, let $x = 1 + r$. When Li goes to college three years later, the money she earned the first summer will be worth $1000x^3$. The money she earned the second summer will be worth $1000x^2$, and the money she earned the third summer will be worth $1000x$. The money she earns the last summer will not have a chance to earn interest, since Li will enter college at the end of that summer. The **polynomial** below represents the amount Li will have saved.

$$1000x^3 + 1000x^2 + 1000x + 1000$$

A polynomial is a monomial or a sum of monomials. Recall that a monomial is a number, a variable, or a product of numbers and variables. A monomial is one term with a positive exponent. A **binomial** is the sum of two monomials, and a **trinomial** is the sum of three monomials.

Monomial	Binomial	Trinomial
$5x^2$	$3x + 2$	$5x^2 - 2x + 7$
$4abc$	$4x + 5y$	$a^2 + 2ab + b^2$
-7	$3x^2 - 8xy$	$4a + 2b^2 - 3c$

Recall that $5x^2 - 2x + 7$ is equivalent to $5x^2 + (-2x) + 7$.

Example 1

State whether each expression is a polynomial. If the expression is a polynomial, identify it as either a monomial, binomial, or trinomial.

a. $8x^2 - 3xy$

The expression $8x^2 - 3xy$ can be written as $8x^2 + (-3xy)$. Therefore, $8x^2 - 3xy$ is a polynomial. Since $8x^2 - 3xy$ can be written as the sum of two monomials, $8x^2$ and $-3xy$, it is also a binomial.

b. $\frac{5}{2y^2} + 7y + 6$

The expression $\frac{5}{2y^2} + 7y + 6$ is not a polynomial because $\frac{5}{2y^2}$ is not a monomial. It is not the product of a number and a variable.

ALTERNATE TEACHING STRATEGIES

Using Calculators

When her daughter was born, Mary Evans placed $750 in a savings account that paid 9% interest annually. Use a calculator to determine how much the account will hold when her daughter enters college at the age of 18.   3537.84

Using Cooperative Groups

Have each group member write a polynomial on an index card. Collect the cards, shuffle them, and place in a pile. Students then take turns drawing a card and identifying the degree of each polynomial.

Example 2

APPLICATION

Finance

If Li's savings account pays 8% annually, will Li have enough money for her first year of college?

If $r = 8\%$, the polynomial below represents the amount Li will have saved after working for four summers.

$$1000(1.08)^3 + 1000(1.08)^2 + 1000(1.08) + 1000$$

Use a calculator to evaluate this sum.

Enter: 1.08 $\boxed{y^x}$ 3 $\boxed{\times}$ 1000 $\boxed{+}$ 1.08 $\boxed{y^x}$ 2 $\boxed{\times}$

1000 $\boxed{+}$ 1.08 $\boxed{\times}$ 1000 $\boxed{+}$ 1000 $\boxed{=}$

Display: 4506.112

So Li will have only $4506.11, not enough to pay for her first year.

The **degree** of a monomial is the sum of the exponents of its variables.

Monomial	Degree
$5x^2$	2
$4ab^3c^4$	$1 + 3 + 4 = 8$
-9	0

Teaching Tip ①

Remember that $a = a^1$, $x^0 = 1$, and $-9 = -9x^0$.

To find the degree of a polynomial, find the degree of each of its terms. The degree of the polynomial is the greatest of the degrees of its terms.

Example 3

Find the degree of each polynomial.

a. $8x^3 - 2x^2 + 7$

This polynomial has three terms, $8x^3$, $-2x^2$, and 7. Their degrees are 3, 2, and 0, respectively. The greatest degree is 3. Therefore, the degree of $8x^3 - 2x^2 + 7$ is 3.

b. $6x^2y + 5x^3y^2z - x + x^2y^2$

This polynomial has four terms, $6x^2y$, $5x^3y^2z$, $-x$, and x^2y^2. Their degrees are 3, 6, 1, and 4, respectively. Therefore, the degree of $6x^2y + 5x^3y^2z - x + x^2y^2$ is 6.

The terms of a polynomial are usually arranged so that the powers of one variable are in either ascending or descending order.

Ascending Order	Descending Order
$3 + 5a - 8a^2 + a^3$	$a^3 - 8a^2 + 5a + 3$
(in x) $5xy + x^3y^2 - x^4 + x^5y^2$	(in x) $x^5y^2 - x^4 + x^3y^2 + 5xy$
(in y) $x^3 - 3x^2y + 4x^2y^2 - y^3$	(in y) $-y^3 + 4x^2y^2 - 3x^2y + x^3$

Teaching Tip ②

RETEACHING THE LESSON

If the expression is a polynomial give the degree. If not, tell why.

1. $-3x + 7$ yes, 1

2. $3x^{-2} + 4x^{-1}$ no, not the sum of monomials

3. $4x^2y - 3xy^2$ yes, 3

4. $6x + 9 - 5x^2$ yes, 2

Checking for Understanding
Exercises 1-21 are designed to help you assess understanding through reading, writing, and speaking. You should work through Exercises 1-3 with your students, and then monitor their work on Exercises 4-21.

Closing the Lesson
Speaking Activity Ask students to explain the difference between a monomial and polynomial. Then have them give examples of a monomial, binomial, and trinomial.

APPLYING THE LESSON

Homework Exercises

Assignment Guide
Basic: 22-37, 44-45, 50-53
Average: 27-40, 44-53
Enriched: 32-53
All: Mid-Chapter Review, 1-14

Practice Masters Booklet, p. 43

CHECKING FOR UNDERSTANDING

Communicating Mathematics

Read and study the lesson to answer each question.

1. Why is $\frac{17}{5x}$ *not* a monomial? It is not the product of a number and a variable.

2. Why is $a + \frac{3}{b}$ *not* a binomial? Because $\frac{3}{b}$ involves division, not multiplication.

3. Why is the degree of 12 zero? Because $12 = 12x^0$.

Guided Practice

State whether each expression is a polynomial. If the expression is a polynomial, identify it as a monomial, binomial, or trinomial.

4. $5x^2y + 3xy + 7$ yes, trinomial

5. $\frac{5}{k} - k^2y$ not a polynomial

6. 0 yes, monomial

7. $\frac{a^3}{3}$ yes, monomial

8. $3a^2x - 5a$ yes, binomial

9. $x^2 - \frac{x}{2} + \frac{1}{3}$ yes, trinomial

Find the degree of each polynomial.

10. $100x$ 1

11. -18 0

12. $29xyz$ 3

13. $8x^2$ 2

14. $-14x^3z$ 4

15. 0 none

16. $12s + 21t$ 1

17. $22x + 5y^4$ 4

18. $-2a^2b^{10} + 3a^9b$ 12

19. $29x + x^{29}$ 29

20. $27x^4 - 3x^3yz$ 5

21. $17x^3y^4 - 11xy^5$ 7

EXERCISES

Practice

Find the degree of each polynomial.

22. $5x^2 - 2x^5$ 5

23. $11wxyz - 9w^4$ 4

24. $12x^4y^5 + xy^6$ 9

25. $7x^3 + 4xy + 3xz^3$ 4

26. $5r - 3s + 7t$ 1

27. $17r^2t + 3r + t^2$ 3

28. $13s^2t^2 + 4st^2 - 5s^5t$ 6

29. $32xyz + 11x^2y + 17xz^2$ 3

30. $2x^3yz - 5xy^3z + 11z^5$ 5

31. $-4yzw^4 + 10x^4z^2w - 2z^2w^3$ 7

Arrange the terms of each polynomial so that the powers of *x* are in ascending order. **See margin.**

32. $3 + x^4 + 2x^2$

33. $2x^2 + 5ax + a^3$

34. $1 + x^3 + x^5 + x^2$

35. $-2x^2y + 3xy^3 + x^3$

36. $17bx^2 + 11b^2x - x^3$

37. $5b + b^3x^2 + \frac{2}{3}bx$

Arrange the terms of each polynomial so that the powers of *x* are in descending order. **See margin.**

38. $-6x + x^5 + 4x^3 - 20$

39. $5x^2 - 3x^3 + 7 + 2x$

40. $4x^3y + 3xy^4 - x^2y^3 + y^4$

41. $11x^2 + 7ax^3 - 3x + 2a$

42. $\frac{3}{4}x^3y - x^2 + 4 + \frac{2}{3}x$

43. $7a^3x - 8a^3x^3 + \frac{1}{5}x^5 + \frac{2}{3}x^2$

Critical Thinking

44. A numeral in base ten can be written in polynomial form. For example, $2137 = 2(10)^3 + 1(10)^2 + 3(10) + 7$. Suppose 3254 is a numeral in base *b*. Write 3254 in polynomial form. **See margin.**

228 CHAPTER 6 POLYNOMIALS

Additional Answers

32. $3 + 2x^2 + x^4$

33. $a^3 + 5ax + 2x^2$

34. $1 + x^2 + x^3 + x^5$

35. $3xy^3 - 2x^2y + x^3$

36. $11b^2x + 17bx^2 - x^3$

37. $5b + \frac{2}{3}bx + b^3x^2$

38. $x^5 + 4x^3 - 6x - 20$

39. $-3x^3 + 5x^2 + 2x + 7$

40. $4x^3y - x^2y^3 + 3xy^4 + y^4$

41. $7ax^3 + 11x^2 - 3x + 2a$

42. $\frac{3}{4}x^3y - x^2 + \frac{2}{3}x + 4$

43. $\frac{1}{5}x^5 - 8a^3x^3 + \frac{2}{3}x^2 + 7a^3x$

44. $3254 = 3(b)^3 + 2(b)^2 + 5(b) + 4$

48.
```
  +--+--+--●--●--●--●--●
  2  3  4  5  6  7  8
```

Applications

45. **Finance** Look back at the application at the beginning of this lesson. Suppose that upon her graduation from high school, Li receives a $2000 inheritance from her grandfather. Would she then have enough money to finance her first year in college? **yes**

46. **Finance** Upon his graduation from college, Mark Price inherited $10,000. If he invests this money in an account with an annual interest rate of 6% and adds $1000 of his own money to the account at the end of each year, will his money have doubled after 5 years? If not, when? **No; after 6 years.**   **Teaching Tip ③**

47. **Biology** The average number of eggs carried by a certain type of female moth is given by the polynomial $14x^3 - 17x^2 - 16x + 34$, where x represents the width of the abdomen. About how many eggs should you expect this type of moth to produce if her abdomen measures 3 millimeters? **211 eggs**

Mixed Review

48. Graph {all integers greater than 3} on a number line.   **(Lesson 2-3)**
   See margin.

49. Solve $11y = -77$.   **(Lesson 3-3)** -7

50. **Finance** Delores Delgado invested some of $12,500 at 6.2% interest and the rest at 8.6% interest. How much did she invest at each rate if her total income from both investments is $967?   **(Lesson 4-5)**
   50. $4500 at 6.2%, $8000 at 8.6%

51. Solve $10p - 14 < 8p - 17$.   **(Lesson 5-3)** $\left\{p \mid p < -\frac{3}{2}\right\}$

Express each number in scientific notation. (Lesson 6-4)

52. 42,350 4.235×10^4

53. 0.00000628 6.28×10^{-6}

MID-CHAPTER REVIEW

1. Solve by looking for a pattern. What is the ones digit of 3^{999}?   **(Lesson 6-1)** 7

Simplify. Assume no denominator is equal to zero.   (Lessons 6-2, 6-3)

2. $(b^4)(b^4)b$ b^9

3. $(x^3y)(xy^3)$ x^4y^4

4. $(-2n^4y^3)(3ny^4)$ $-6n^5y^7$

5. $[(-5)^2]^3$ 15,625

6. $(4xy)^2(-3x)$ $-48x^3y^2$

7. $(-3a^2b^5)^2$ $9a^4b^{10}$

8. $\dfrac{n^8}{n^5}$ n^3

9. $\dfrac{24a^3b^6}{-2a^2b^2}$ $-12ab^4$

10. $\dfrac{(5r^{-1}s)^3}{(s^2)^3}$ $\dfrac{125}{r^3s^3}$

Express each number in scientific notation.   (Lesson 6-4)

11. 28.5×10^6 2.85×10^7

12. 0.005×10^{-3} 5×10^{-6}

Arrange the terms of each polynomial so that the powers of x are in ascending order. (Lesson 6-5)   See margin.

13. $\frac{1}{3}s^2x^3 + 4x^4 - \frac{2}{5}s^4x^2 + \frac{1}{4}x$

14. $21p^2x + 3px^3 + p^4$

EXTENDING THE LESSON

Math Power: Problem Solving

Arrange the terms of the following polynomial so that the powers of y are in descending order. Then find the degree of the polynomial.
$16xy^4 - 8y^7z^5 - 2.8xyz + 14x^2y^3 + 3.9y^9z - 10$ $3.9y^9z - 8y^7z^5 + 16xy^4 + 14x^2y^3 - 2.8xyz - 10; 12$

Mid-Chapter Review

The Mid-Chapter Review provides students with a brief review of the concepts and skills in Lessons 6-1 through 6-5. Lesson numbers are given at the end of problems or instruction lines so students may review concepts not yet mastered.

Teaching Tip ③   You may wish to extend Exercise 46 by having students investigate the average yearly costs of 3 colleges of their choice. Students should then determine how much money they would need to save each summer during their high school years to cover one year's costs at each school selected.

Additional Answers to Mid-Chapter Review

13. $\frac{1}{4}x - \frac{2}{5}s^4x^2 + \frac{1}{3}s^2x^3 + 4x^4$

14. $p^4 + 21p^2x + 3px^3$

Enrichment Masters Booklet, p. 38

NAME _____ DATE _____

6-5   Enrichment Worksheet

Reading Algebra: The Vocabulary of Polynomials

In the paragraphs below, use one word from the box to fill in each blank. Each word is used only once, but not all of the words will be used.

sum	coefficient	quotient	degree
power	trinomial	exponent	product
constant	term	polynomial	variable

1. A monomial is a number, a ___variable___, or a product of a number and one or more variables. For example, in $3x^5$, the letter x is the variable, 5 is the ___exponent___, and 3 is the ___coefficient___. A monomial that is a real number without any variable is called a ___constant___.

2. A polynomial is a monomial or a ___sum___ of monomials. Each of the monomials is called a ___term___ of the polynomial. A binomial has two terms and a ___trinomial___ has three terms.

3. The sum of the exponents of the variables of a monomial is the ___degree___ of the monomial. The degree of a ___polynomial___ is the greatest of the degrees of its terms.

Write a definition of each word.

4. monomial ___a number, a variable, or the product of one or more variables___

5. polynomial ___a monomial or a sum of monomials___

6. trinomial ___a polynomial with three terms___

Lesson Resources

- Reteaching Master 6-6
- Practice Master 6-6
- Enrichment Master 6-6
- Video Algebra, 14

 Transparency 6-6 contains the 5-Minute Check and a teaching aid for this lesson.

INTRODUCING THE LESSON

🕐 5-Minute Check
(over Lesson 6-5)

State whether each expression is a polynomial. If the expression is a polynomial, identify it as either a monomial, binomial, or trinomial and give its degree.

1. $8a^2 + 5ab$ **binomial, 2**
2. $3x^2 + 4x - \frac{7}{x}$ **not a polynomial**
3. $5x^2 + 7x + 2$ **trinomial, 2**
4. $6a^2b^2 + 7ab^5 - 6b^3$ **trinomial, 6**
5. $w^2x - \frac{7w}{3} + 6x$ **trinomial, 3**

Motivating the Lesson

Develop student understanding of polynomials through the following activity. The first student in a row identifies a monomial with a degree greater than 2. The next student adds a term to the monomial to create a binomial. The next student adds another term to create a trinomial. A fourth student then identifies the degree of the trinomial. Repeat the procedure until all class members have had a turn playing.

TEACHING THE LESSON

Teaching Tip ❶ Stress to students that sometimes they will have to rearrange terms of a polynomial in order to use the column method.

Teaching Tip ❷ There is less chance for error if students subtract by adding the additive inverse.

6-6 Adding and Subtracting Polynomials

Objective
6-6

After studying this lesson, you should be able to:
- add and subtract polynomials.

Application

FYI · · ·

The largest windows in the world are in the Palace of Industry and Technology in France. They measure 715.2 feet wide by 164 feet high.

The standard measurement for a window is the *united inch.* The united inch measurement of a window is equal to the sum of the length and the width of the window. If the length of the window at the right is $2x + 8$ inches and the width is $x - 3$ inches, what is the size of the window in united inches?

The size of the window is $(2x + 8) + (x - 3)$ inches. To add two polynomials, add the like terms.

$$(2x + 8) + (x - 3) = 2x + 8 + x - 3$$
$$= (2x + x) + (8 - 3) \quad \text{*Commutative and associative properties*}$$
$$= 3x + 5$$

The size of the window in united inches is $3x + 5$ inches.

You can add polynomials by grouping the like terms together and then finding the sum (as in the example above), or by writing them in column form.

Example 1

Find $(3y^2 + 5y - 6) + (7y^2 - 9)$.

Method 1   Group the like terms together.

$$(3y^2 + 5y - 6) + (7y^2 - 9) = (3y^2 + 7y^2) + 5y + [-6 + (-9)]$$
$$= (3 + 7)y^2 + 5y + (-15)$$
$$= 10y^2 + 5y - 15$$

Method 2   Add in column form. **Teaching Tip** ❶

$$
\begin{array}{r}
3y^2 + 5y - 6 \\
(+)\ 7y^2 - 9 \\
\hline
10y^2 + 5y - 15
\end{array}
$$

Notice that like terms are aligned.
There is no term in the y column.

Recall that you can subtract a rational number by adding its additive inverse or opposite. Similarly, you can subtract a polynomial by adding its additive inverse. **Teaching Tip** ❷

ALTERNATE TEACHING STRATEGIES

Using Problem Solving

Have each student write six terms on a piece of paper. Tell students to group the terms so that there are either two polynomials, three binomials, five monomials, one binomial and three monomials, and so on. Students then find the sum of the terms. On another sheet of paper, students write the original six terms and the final sum. Students then switch papers and identify how the original terms were grouped to total the sum indicated.

To find the additive inverse of a polynomial, replace each term with its additive inverse.

Polynomial	Additive Inverse
$x + 2y$	$-x - 2y$
$2x^2 - 3x + 5$	$-2x^2 + 3x - 5$
$-8x + 5y - 7z$	$8x - 5y + 7z$
$3x^3 - 2x^2 - 5x$	$-3x^3 + 2x^2 + 5x$

Teaching Tip

Example 2

Find $(4x^2 - 3y^2 + 5xy) - (8xy + 6x^2 + 3y^2)$.

Method 1 Group the like terms together.

$(4x^2 - 3y^2 + 5xy) - (8xy + 6x^2 + 3y^2)$
$= (4x^2 - 3y^2 + 5xy) + (-8xy - 6x^2 - 3y^2)$
$= 4x^2 - 3y^2 + 5xy - 8xy - 6x^2 - 3y^2$
$= (4x^2 - 6x^2) + (5xy - 8xy) + (-3y^2 - 3y^2)$
$= -2x^2 + (-3xy) + (-6y^2)$
$= -2x^2 - 3xy - 6y^2$

Method 2 Subtract in column form.

First, reorder the terms so that the powers of x are in descending order.

$$(4x^2 + 5xy - 3y^2) - (6x^2 + 8xy + 3y^2)$$

Then, subtract.

$$
\begin{array}{r}
4x^2 + 5xy - 3y^2 \\
(-)\ 6x^2 + 8xy + 3y^2 \\
\hline
\end{array}
$$

 Add the additive inverse.

$$
\begin{array}{r}
4x^2 + 5xy - 3y^2 \\
(+)\ -6x^2 - 8xy - 3y^2 \\
\hline
-2x^2 - 3xy - 6y^2
\end{array}
$$

To check this result, add $-2x^2 - 3xy - 6y^2$ and $6x^2 + 8xy + 3y^2$.

Example 3

CONNECTION

Geometry

Find the measure of the third side of the triangle at the right. P is the measure of the perimeter.

$3x^2 + 2x - 1$, s, $8x^2 - 8x + 5$, $P = 12x^2 - 7x + 9$

The perimeter is the sum of the measures of the three sides of the triangle. Let s represent the measure of the third side.

$(12x^2 - 7x + 9) = (3x^2 + 2x - 1) + (8x^2 - 8x + 5) + s$ *Substitution*
$12x^2 - 7x + 9 - (3x^2 + 2x - 1) - (8x^2 - 8x + 5) = s$ *Solve for s.*
$12x^2 - 7x + 9 - 3x^2 - 2x + 1 - 8x^2 + 8x - 5 = s$
$(12x^2 - 3x^2 - 8x^2) + (-7x - 2x + 8x) + (9 + 1 - 5) = s$ *Group the*
$x^2 - x + 5 = s$ *like terms.*

The measure of the third side is $x^2 - x + 5$.

RETEACHING THE LESSON

Make a model block out of cardboard. Identify the dimensions of the block to be x inches long and y inches high. Measure one wall of the classroom using the block. For example, $12x + 4$ would be a distance of 12 blocks long plus 4 inches. Find the polynomial perimeter and height of the room.

Teaching Tip ③ Emphasize that the additive inverse of every term must be found.

Chalkboard Examples

For Example 1
Add.

a. $(9y - 7x + 15a) + (-3y + 8x - 8a$
$6y + x + 7a$

b. $(3a^2 + 3ab - b^2) + (4ab + 6b^2)$
$3a^2 + 7ab + 5b^2$

For Example 2
Subtract.

a. $(7a - 10b) - (3a + 4b)$
$4a - 14b$

b. $(3y^2 + 7y + 8) - (2y^2 - 4y + 3)$
$y^2 + 11y + 5$

For Example 3

The perimeter of a triangle is $4x^2 + 5x + 5$. One side of the triangle is $x^2 + 3x - 5$ and the other side is $2x^2 + 3x + 6$. Find the measure of the third side.
$x^2 - x + 4$

Reteaching Masters Booklet, p. 39

Checking for Understanding

Exercises 1-12 are designed to help you assess understanding through reading, writing, and speaking. You should work through Exercises 1-2 with your students, and then monitor their work on Exercises 3-12.

Error Analysis

Students sometimes fail to "distribute" or apply the minus to individual terms of a polynomial that is being subtracted. For example, they may write $(5x^2 - 4x + 7) - (2x^2 - 3x + 3)$ as $5x^2 - 4x + 7 - 2x^2 - 3x + 3$. Point out that all terms of the second trinomial are to be subtracted.

Closing the Lesson

Writing Activity Have students write a paragraph summarizing the process of adding and subtracting polynomials.

Practice Masters Booklet, p. 44

NAME _____ DATE _____

6-6 Practice Worksheet

Adding and Subtracting Polynomials

Find each sum or difference.

1.
$$\begin{array}{r} a^2 + ab - 3b^2 \\ (+)\ 4a^2 - ab + b^2 \\ \hline 5a^2 \qquad - 2b^2 \end{array}$$

2.
$$\begin{array}{r} 6b^2z + 3b^2z - 8b^3 \\ (+)\ 3b^2z - 7b^2z - 3b^3 + 6 \\ \hline 9bz^2 - 4b^2z - 11b^3 + 6 \end{array}$$

3.
$$\begin{array}{r} 2x + 6y - 3z + 5 \\ 4x - 8y + 6z - 1 \\ (+)\ x - 3y \quad + 6 \\ \hline 7x - 5y + 3z + 10 \end{array}$$

4.
$$\begin{array}{r} 7m^2 - 3m + 3 \\ 3m^2 + 5m - 5 \\ (+)\ -11m^2 - 6m + 1 \\ \hline -m^2 - 4m - 1 \end{array}$$

5.
$$\begin{array}{r} 7a^2 - a + 4 \\ (-)\ 3a^2 - 4a - 3 \\ \hline 4a^2 + 3a + 7 \end{array}$$

6.
$$\begin{array}{r} 5c^2d^2 \qquad - 9 \\ (-)\ 2c^2d^2 + 3cd - 1 \\ \hline 3c^2d^2 - 3cd - 8 \end{array}$$

7.
$$\begin{array}{r} 5e^2 - e - 7 \\ (-)\ -2e^2 + 3e + 4 \\ \hline 7e^2 - 4e - 11 \end{array}$$

8.
$$\begin{array}{r} x^2 + xy - 3y^2 \\ (-)\ 4x^2 - xy + y^2 \\ \hline -3x^2 + 2xy - 4y^2 \end{array}$$

9. $(2x + 3y) + (4x + 9y)$
$6x + 12y$

10. $(5a + 9b) - (2a + 4b)$
$3a + 5b$

11. $(11m - 7n) - (2m + 6n)$
$9m - 13n$

12. $(6s + 5t) + (4t + 8s)$
$14s + 9t$

13. $(5x^2 - x - 7) + (2x^2 + 3x + 4)$
$7x^2 + 2x - 3$

14. $(7x^2 + x + 1) - (3x^2 - 4x - 3)$
$4x^2 + 5x + 4$

15. $(5x + 3z) + 9x$
$14x + 3z$

16. $(15c + 8d) - 13d$
$15c - 5d$

17. $(x^2 - 3x) - (2x^2 + 5x)$
$-x^2 - 8x$

18. $6p - (8q + 5p)$
$p - 8q$

19. $(2e^2 - 5e) + (7e - 3e^2)$
$-e^2 + 2e$

20. $(m^2 - m) + (2m + m^2)$
$2m^2 + m$

21. $(d^2 - d + 5) - (2d + 5)$
$d^2 - 3d$

22. $(l^2 - 5l - 6) + (2l^2 + l + 5)$
$3l^2 - 4l - 1$

CHECKING FOR UNDERSTANDING

Communicating Mathematics

Read and study the lesson to answer each question.

1. What is the first step when adding or subtracting in column form?

2. What is the best way to check the subtraction of two polynomials?
1. Make sure that the terms are in the same order.   2. by adding

Guided Practice

Find the additive inverse of each polynomial. 5-8. See margin.

3. $3x + 2y$ $-3x - 2y$ 4. $-8m + 7n$ $8m - 7n$ 5. $x^2 + 3x + 7$

6. $-4h^2 - 5hk - k^2$ 7. $-3ab^2 + 5a^2b - b^3$ 8. $x^3 + 5x^2 - 3x - 11$

Name the like terms in each group. See margin.

9. $5m, 4mn, -3m, 2n, -mn, 8n$ 10. $2x^3, 5xy, -x^2y, 14xy, 12xy$

11. $-7ab^2, 8a^2b, 11b^2, 16a^2b, -2b^2$ 12. $3p^3q, -2p, 10p^3q, 15pq, -p$

EXERCISES

Practice

Find each sum or difference. See margin.

A

13.
$$\begin{array}{r} 5ax^2 + 3a^2x - 7a^3 \\ (+)\ 2ax^2 - 8a^2x \qquad + 4 \\ \hline \end{array}$$

14.
$$\begin{array}{r} a^3 \qquad\qquad - b^3 \\ (+)\ 3a^3 + 2a^2b - b^2 + 2b^3 \\ \hline \end{array}$$

15.
$$\begin{array}{r} 4a + 5b - 6c + d \\ 3a - 7b + 2c + 8d \\ (+)\ 2a - b \qquad + 7d \\ \hline \end{array}$$

16.
$$\begin{array}{r} 2x^2 - 5x + 7 \\ 5x^2 + 7x - 3 \\ (+)\ x^2 - x + 11 \\ \hline \end{array}$$

17.
$$\begin{array}{r} 6x^2y^2 - 3xy - 7 \\ (-)\ 5x^2y^2 + 2xy + 3 \\ \hline \end{array}$$

18.
$$\begin{array}{r} 5x^2 \qquad - 4 \\ (-)\ 3x^2 + 8x + 4 \\ \hline \end{array}$$

19.
$$\begin{array}{r} 11m^2n^2 + 2mn - 11 \\ (-)\ 5m^2n^2 - 6mn + 17 \\ \hline \end{array}$$

20.
$$\begin{array}{r} 2a - 7 \\ (-)\ 5a^2 + 8a - 11 \\ \hline \end{array}$$

B

21. $(5x + 6y) + (2x + 8y)$

22. $(7n + 11m) - (4m + 2n)$

23. $(3x - 7y) + (3y + 4x)$

24. $(5a - 6m) - (2a + 5m)$

25. $(5m + 3n) + 8m$

26. $(13x + 9y) - 11y$

C

27. $(3 + 2a + a^2) - (5 + 8a + a^2)$

28. $(n^2 + 5n + 3) + (2n^2 + 8n + 8)$

29. $(5ax^2 + 3a^2x - 5x) + (2ax^2 - 5ax + 7x)$

30. $(x^3 - 3x^2y + 4xy^2 + y^3) - (7x^3 - 9xy^2 + x^2y + y^3)$

CONNECTION

Geometry

Find the measure of the third side of each triangle. **P** is the measure of the perimeter. 31. $x + y$ 32. $2x + 6y$ 33. $5x^2 - 23x - 23$

31. $P = 3x + 3y$ 32. $P = 7x + 2y$ 33. $P = 11x^2 - 29x + 10$

$x + y$ $x + y$

$2x + y$ $3x - 5y$

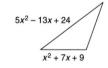
$5x^2 - 13x + 24$
$x^2 + 7x + 9$

Additional Answers

5. $-x^2 - 3x - 7$
6. $4h^2 + 5hk + k^2$
7. $3ab^2 - 5a^2b + b^3$
8. $-x^3 - 5x^2 + 3x + 11$
9. $5m$ and $-3m$; $4mn$ and $-mn$; $2n$ and $8n$
10. $5xy$, $14xy$, and $12xy$
11. $8a^2b$ and $16a^2b$; $11b^2$ and $-2b^2$

12. $3p^3q$ and $10p^3q$; $-2p$ and $-p$
13. $7ax^2 - 5a^2x - 7a^3 + 4$
14. $4a^3 + 2a^2b - b^2 + b^3$
15. $9a - 3b - 4c + 16d$
16. $8x^2 + x + 15$
17. $x^2y^2 - 5xy - 10$
18. $2x^2 - 8x - 8$
19. $6m^2n^2 + 8mn - 28$
20. $-5a^2 - 6a + 4$

Critical Thinking

The sum of the degree measures of the three angles of a triangle is 180. Find the degree measure of the third angle of each triangle given the degree measures of the other two angles. **35.** $-7x^2 - 2x + 184$

34. $5 - 2x$; $7 + 8x$ $168 - 6x$

35. $3x^2 - 5$; $4x^2 + 2x + 1$

36. $4 - 2x$; $x^2 - 1$ $-x^2 + 2x + 177$

37. $x^2 - 8x + 2$; $x^2 - 3x - 1$ $-2x^2 + 11x + 179$

Applications

38. Travel Joan Bedney travels from Cincinnati to Winston-Salem at an average rate of 40 miles per hour and returns at an average rate of 60 miles per hour. What is her average speed for the trip? (*Hint:* The average speed is *not* 50 miles per hour.) 48 mph

39. Basketball On December 13, 1983, the Denver Nuggets and the Detroit Pistons broke the record for the highest score in a basketball game. The two teams scored a total of 370 points. If the Nuggets scored 2 less points than the Pistons, what was the Nuggets' final score? 184

Mixed Review

40. Evaluate $|x|$ if $x = -2.1$. (**Lesson 2-2**) 2.1

41. Sports There were 3 times as many sports in the 1976 Summer Olympics as there were in the 1976 Winter Olympics. There were 14 more sports in the Summer Olympics than there were in the Winter Olympics. How many sports were there in the 1976 Summer Olympics? (**Lesson 3-6**) 21 sports

42. Bicycling Adita rode his bicycle 72 kilometers. How long did it take him if his rate was: **a.** 9 km/h? **b.** 18 km/h? (**Lesson 4-7**) 8 h, 4 h

43. Solve $3m < 2m - 7$. (**Lesson 5-1**) $\{m | m < -7\}$

44. Find the degree of $x + 2y^2 + 3z^3$. (**Lesson 6-5**) 3

HISTORY CONNECTION

Emmy Noether

Emmy Noether (1882–1935) was a German mathematician whose strength was in abstract algebra. In her hands the axiomatic method (using axioms or properties) became a powerful tool of mathematical research. Noether did much of her research while living in Göttingen, Germany, which was then the principal center for mathematics research in Europe. Because she was female, Noether was unable to secure a teaching position at the University of Göttingen. However, her influence there was vast. During World War II, Noether was forced to leave Germany. She became a professor at Bryn Mawr College, in the United States, where she remained until her death. Albert Einstein paid her a great tribute in 1935: "In the judgment of the most competent living mathematicians, (Emmy) Noether was the most significant creative mathematical genius thus far produced since the higher education of women began."

LESSON 6-6 ADDING AND SUBTRACTING POLYNOMIALS 233

EXTENDING THE LESSON

Math Power: Connections

A pentagon is a geometric figure with five sides. Find its perimeter if the lengths of its sides are $(x^2 + 2x)$ ft, $(2x^2 - 5x)$ ft, $(4x + 3x^2)$ ft, $(6x + 2)$ ft, and $(7x^2 + 3x + 4)$ ft.
$(13x^2 + 10x + 6)$ ft

History Connection

The History Connection features introduce students to persons or cultures who were involved in the development of mathematics. You may want students to further research Emmy Noether or to research the axiomatic method.

Chapter 6, Quiz C, (Lessons 6-5 through 6-6), is available in the Evaluation Masters Booklet, p. 80.

Additional Answers

21. $7x + 14y$

22. $7m + 5n$

23. $7x - 4y$

24. $3a - 11m$

25. $13m + 3n$

26. $13x - 2y$

27. $-2 - 6a$

28. $3n^2 + 13n + 11$

29. $7ax^2 + 3a^2x - 5ax + 2x$

30. $-6x^3 - 4x^2y + 13xy^2$

Enrichment Masters Booklet, p. 39

Lesson Resources

- Reteaching Master 6-7
- Practice Master 6-7
- Enrichment Master 6-7
- Activity Master, p. 36
- Video Algebra, 15, 16

 Transparency 6-7 contains the 5-Minute Check and a teaching aid for this lesson.

INTRODUCING THE LESSON

⏱ 5-Minute Check

(over Lesson 6-6)

Simplify.

1. $(6a + 7b) + (11a + 4b)$
   $17a + 11b$
2. $(5x^2 - 7x + 3) + (16x + 4x^2 - 9)$
   $9x^2 + 9x - 6$
3. $(3a^2 + 7ab - 9b^2) + (4a^2 + ab - 11b^2)$
   $7a^2 + 8ab - 20b^2$
4. $(2w^2 + 3w - 7) + (6w^2 + 4)$
   $8w^2 + 3w - 3$
5. $(6x^2 + 2x - 9) - (3x^2 - 8x + 11)$
   $3x^2 + 10x - 20$

Motivating the Lesson

This is an excellent opportunity to review the distributive property and its applications for students.

TEACHING THE LESSON

Chalkboard Examples

For Example 1
Multiply.

a. $5(7n - 2)$ $35n - 10$

b. $\frac{3}{4}a(8a + 12)$ $6a^2 + 9a$

For Example 2
Multiply.

a. $6rs(r^2s - 3)$ $6r^3s^2 - 18rs$

b. $4t^2(3t^2 + 2t - 5)$
   $12t^4 + 8t^3 - 20t^2$

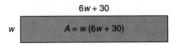

6-7   Multiplying a Polynomial by a Monomial

Objectives

After studying this lesson, you should be able to:

6-7A ■ multiply a polynomial by a monomial, and
6-7B ■ simplify expressions involving polynomials.

Application

The world's largest swimming pool is the Orthlieb Pool in Casablanca, Morocco. It is 30 meters longer than 6 times its width. Express the area of the swimming pool algebraically.

To find the area of the swimming pool, multiply the length by the width. Let w represent the width. Then $6w + 30$ represents the length.

> **FYI ···**
> The Orthlieb Pool is 480 meters long and 75 meters wide. Its area is 36,000 square meters.

This diagram of the swimming pool shows that the area is $w(6w + 30)$ square meters.

This diagram of the same swimming pool shows that the area is $(6w^2 + 30w)$ square meters.

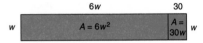

Since the areas are equal, $w(6w + 30) = 6w^2 + 30w$.

The application above shows how the distributive property can be used to multiply a polynomial by a monomial.

Example 1

Find $5a(3a^2 + 4)$.

You can multiply either horizontally or vertically.

a. Use the distributive property.

$$5a(3a^2 + 4) = 5a(3a^2) + 5a(4)$$
$$= 15a^3 + 20a$$

b. Multiply each term by $5a$.

$$\begin{array}{r} 3a^2 + 4 \\ (\times) \quad 5a \\ \hline 15a^3 + 20a \end{array}$$

Example 2

Find $2m^2(5m^2 - 7m + 8)$.

$$2m^2(5m^2 - 7m + 8) = 2m^2(5m^2) + 2m^2(-7m) + 2m^2(8)$$
$$= 10m^4 - 14m^3 + 16m^2 \quad \textit{Product of powers property}$$

In Example 3, you can simplify the expression by using the distributive property and then combining like terms.

ALTERNATE TEACHING STRATEGIES

Using Discussion

If a polynomial of degree n is combined with a polynomial of degree m and the result is a polynomial of degree $n + m$, what operation was used to combine the polynomials?
multiplication

Using Connections

Have students draw a figure such as a trapezoid or parallelogram on a piece of grid paper. Tell students to label an appropriate number of sides of the figure with either a binomial or trinomial measure. Students then switch papers to find the area of each other's figures.

Example 3

Find $-3xy(2x^2y + 3xy^2 - 7y^3)$.

$-3xy(2x^2y + 3xy^2 - 7y^3) = -3xy(2x^2y) + (-3xy)(3xy^2) + (-3xy)(-7y^3)$
$= -6x^3y^2 - 9x^2y^3 + 21xy^4$ **Teaching Tip ①**

Example 4

Find the measure of the area of the shaded region in simplest terms.

Subtract the measure of the area of the smaller rectangle from the measure of the area of the larger rectangle.

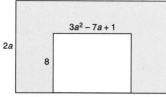

$5a^2 + 3a - 2$
$3a^2 - 7a + 1$
$2a$
8

$2a(5a^2 + 3a - 2) - 8(3a^2 - 7a + 1)$
$= 2a(5a^2) + 2a(3a) + 2a(-2) + (-8)(3a^2) + (-8)(-7a) + (-8)(1)$
$= 10a^3 + 6a^2 - 4a - 24a^2 + 56a - 8$
$= 10a^3 - 18a^2 + 52a - 8$ *Combine like terms.*

The measure of the area of the shaded region is $10a^3 - 18a^2 + 52a - 8$.

Many equations contain polynomials that must be added, subtracted, or multiplied before the equation can be solved.

Example 5

Solve $x(x - 3) + 4x - 3 = 8x + 4 + x(3 + x)$.

$x(x - 3) + 4x - 3 = 8x + 4 + x(3 + x)$
$x^2 - 3x + 4x - 3 = 8x + 4 + 3x + x^2$ *Multiply.*
$x^2 + x - 3 = x^2 + 11x + 4$ *Combine like terms.*
$x - 3 = 11x + 4$ *Subtract x^2 from each side.*
$-3 = 10x + 4$ *Subtract x from each side.*
$-7 = 10x$ *Subtract 4 from each side.*
$-\frac{7}{10} = x$ *Check this result.*

The solution is $-\frac{7}{10}$.

CHECKING FOR UNDERSTANDING

Communicating Mathematics

Read and study the lesson to answer each question.

1. When you simplify $4y(2y + 1)$, what property is used? **distributive**

2. Draw a model of a rectangular garden $5a + 6$ units long and $3a$ units wide. **See students' work.**

3. Write an expression for the area of the garden described in Exercise 2 in the following two ways.
   a. a product of a monomial and a polynomial $3a(5a + 6)$
   b. in simplified form $15a^2 + 18a$

RETEACHING THE LESSON

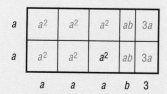

	a^2	a^2	a^2	ab	$3a$
a					
a	a^2	a^2	a^2	ab	$3a$
	a	a	a	b	3

1. What is the width? **2a**
2. What is the length?
   $3a + b + 3$
3. Find the area.
   $2a(3a + b + 3) = 6a^2 + 2ab + 6a$
4. Inside each small square or rectangle, write its area.
   See diagram.
5. Add the areas in 4. Compare with your answer in 3. **same**

Chalkboard Examples

For Example 3
Multiply.

a. $4m^2(3m + 2n - 4p)$
   $12m^3 + 8m^2n - 16m^2p$

b. $-\frac{x}{3}(27x^2 - 6x + 12)$
   $-9x^3 + 2x^2 - 4x$

For Example 4
Simplify $3r(9r^2 + 7r - 12) - 4(4r^2 - 3r + 7)$.
$27r^3 + 5r^2 - 24r - 28$

For Example 5
Solve $t(t - 5) + 2t - 1 = 7t + 3 + t(8 + t)$. $-\frac{2}{9}$

EVALUATING THE LESSON

Checking for Understanding

Exercises 1-13 are designed to help you assess understanding through reading, writing, and speaking. You should work through Exercises 1-3 with your students, and then monitor their work on Exercises 4-13.

Reteaching Masters Booklet, p. 40

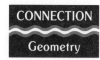

Closing the Lesson

Have students write a paragraph summarizing the process of multiplying a polynomial by a monomial.

APPLYING THE LESSON

Homework Exercises

Assignment Guide
Basic: 14-44, 53-54, 56-61
Average: 20-48, 53-61
Enriched: 25-61

Practice Masters Booklet, p. 45

236 Chapter 6

Guided Practice   **Find each product.** 5. $24m^2 + 21m$ 6. $-20m^5 - 8m^4$

4. $-5a(12a^2)$ $-60a^3$

5. $3m(8m + 7)$

6. $-4m^3(5m^2 + 2m)$

7. $\begin{array}{r} 5x - 3 \\ (\times) \quad 2 \\ \hline 10x - 6 \end{array}$

8. $\begin{array}{r} m - 7 \\ (\times) \quad 2mn \\ \hline 2m^2n - 14mn \end{array}$

9. $\begin{array}{r} 5ab^2 + b^2 \\ (\times) \quad 7ab \\ \hline 35a^2b^3 + 7ab^3 \end{array}$

Simplify.

10. $b(4b - 1) + 10b$
    $4b^2 + 9b$

11. $2a(a^3 - 2a^2 + 7) + 5(a^4 + 5a^3 - 3a + 5)$
    $7a^4 + 21a^3 - a + 25$

Solve.

12. $11(a - 3) + 5 = 2a + 44$ **8**

13. $x(x + 2) + 3x = x(x - 3)$ **0**

EXERCISES

Practice   **Find each product.** **See margin.**

A

14. $5(3a + 7)$

15. $-3(8x + 5)$

16. $\frac{1}{2}x(8x + 6)$

17. $3b(5b + 8)$

18. $-2x(5x + 11)$

19. $1.1a(2a + 7)$

20. $7a(3a^2 - 2a)$

21. $3st(5s^2 + 2st)$

22. $7xy(5x^2 - y^2)$

23. $2a(5a^3 - 7a^2 + 2)$

24. $7x^2y(5x^2 - 3xy + y)$

25. $5y(8y^3 + 7y^2 - 3y)$

26. $-4x(7x^2 - 4x + 3)$

27. $5x^2y(3x^2 - 7xy + y^2)$

28. $4m^2(9m^2n + mn - 5n^2)$

29. $-8xy(4xy + 7x - 14y^2)$

30. $-\frac{1}{3}x(9x^2 + x - 5)$

31. $-\frac{3}{4}ab^2\left(\frac{1}{3}b^2 - \frac{4}{9}b + 1\right)$

32. $-2mn(8m^2 - 3mn + n^2)$

B

Find the measure of the area of each shaded region in simplest terms.

CONNECTION
Geometry

33.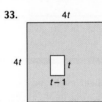

34.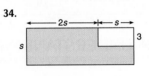

35.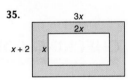

Simplify. 33. $15t^2 + t$ 34. $3s^2 - 3s$ 35. $x^2 + 6x$

36. $6m(m^2 - 11m + 4) - 7(m^3 + 8m - 11)$ $-m^3 - 66m^2 - 32m + 77$

37. $2.5t(8t - 12) + 5.1(6t^2 + 10t - 20)$ $50.6t^2 + 21t - 102$

38. $\frac{3}{4}m(8m^2 + 12m - 4) + \frac{3}{2}(8m^2 - 9m)$ $6m^3 + 21m^2 - \frac{33}{2}m$

236 CHAPTER 6 POLYNOMIALS

Additional Answers

14. $15a + 35$

15. $-24x - 15$

16. $4x^2 + 3x$

17. $15b^2 + 24b$

18. $-10x^2 - 22x$

19. $2.2a^2 + 7.7a$

20. $21a^3 - 14a^2$

21. $15s^3t + 6s^2t^2$

22. $35x^3y - 7xy^3$

23. $10a^4 - 14a^3 + 4a$

24. $35x^4y - 21x^3y^2 + 7x^2y^2$

25. $40y^4 + 35y^3 - 15y^2$

26. $-28x^3 + 16x^2 - 12x$

27. $15x^4y - 35x^3y^2 + 5x^2y^3$

28. $36m^4n + 4m^3n - 20m^2n^2$

29. $-32x^2y^2 - 56x^2y + 112xy^3$

30. $-3x^3 - \frac{1}{3}x^2 + \frac{5}{3}x$

31. $-\frac{1}{4}ab^4 + \frac{1}{3}ab^3 - \frac{3}{4}ab^2$

32. $-16m^3n + 6m^2n^2 - 2mn^3$

39. $5m^2(m + 7) - 2m(5m^2 - 3m + 7) + 2(m^3 - 8)$ $-3m^3 + 41m^2 - 14m - 16$

40. $6a^2(3a - 4) + 5a(7a^2 - 6a + 5) - 3(a^2 + 6a)$ $53a^3 - 57a^2 + 7a$

41. $3a^2(a - 4) + 6a(3a^2 + a - 7) - 4(a - 7)$ $21a^3 - 6a^2 - 46a + 28$

42. $8r^2(r + 8) - 3r(5r^2 - 11) - 9(3r^2 - 8r + 1)$ $-7r^3 + 37r^2 + 105r - 9$

Solve.

43. $-3(2a - 12) + 48 = 3a - 3$ $\frac{29}{3}$ **44.** $2(5w - 12) = 6(-2w + 3) + 2$ 2

C **45.** $-6(12 - 2w) = 7(-2 - 3w)$ $\frac{58}{33}$ **46.** $7(x - 12) = 13 + 5(3x - 4)$ $-\frac{77}{8}$

47. $\frac{1}{2}(2x - 34) = \frac{2}{3}(6x - 27)$ $\frac{1}{3}$ **48.** $w(w + 12) = w(w + 14) + 12$ -6

49. $a(a - 6) + 2a = 3 + a(a - 2)$ $-\frac{3}{2}$ **50.** $q(2q + 3) + 20 = 2q(q - 3)$ $-\frac{20}{9}$

51. $x(x + 8) - x(x + 3) - 23 = 3x + 11$ 17

52. $y(y - 12) + y(y + 2) + 25 = 2y(y + 5) - 15$ 2

Critical Thinking
Teaching Tip ②

53. Geometry A trapezoid has an area of 162 m² and a height of 12 m. The lower base is 6 m more than twice the upper base. Find the length of the upper base. Use $A = \frac{1}{2}h(a + b)$. **7 m**

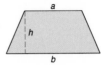

Applications

54. Sports The perimeter of a football field is 1040 feet. The length of the field is 120 feet less than 3 times the width. What are the dimensions of the field? **160 ft by 360 ft**

55. Construction Mr. Herrera had a concrete sidewalk built on three sides of his yard as shown at the right. The yard measures 24 feet by 42 feet. The longer walk is 3 feet wide. The price of the concrete was $22 per square yard, and the total bill was $902. What is the width of the walk on the remaining two sides? **4.5 ft**

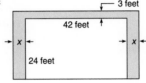

Mixed Review

56. Find $-7.9 + 3.5 + 2.4$. **(Lesson 2-5)** -2

57. Find $\left(-\frac{1}{3}\right)\left(-\frac{3}{4}\right)\left(-\frac{4}{5}\right)$. **(Lesson 2-6)** $-\frac{1}{5}$

58. Solve $x + \frac{4}{9} = -\frac{2}{27}$. **(Lesson 3-2)** $-\frac{14}{27}$

59. Finance Patricia invested $5000 for one year. Martin also invested $5000 for one year. Martin's account earned interest at a rate of 10% per year. At the end of the year, Martin's account earned $125 more than Patricia's account. What was the annual interest rate on Patricia's account? **(Lesson 4-3)** $7\frac{1}{2}\%$

60. Solve $|7 - x| \geq 4$. Then graph the solution set. **(Lesson 5-6)** $\{x | x \leq 3 \text{ or } x \geq 11\}$

61. Find $(4a + 6b) + (2a + 3b)$. **(Lesson 6-6)** $6a + 9b$

EXTENDING THE LESSON

Math Power: Connections

The perimeter of a square can be found by using the formula $P = 4s$ where s represents the length of a side. Find the perimeter of a square if its side is $(3x^2 + 2)$ cm. $(12x^2 + 8)$ cm

---

Enrichment Masters Booklet, p. 40

NAME _____ DATE _____

6-7 | **Enrichment Worksheet**

Geometric Series

The terms of this polynomial form a geometric series.
$$a + ar + ar^2 + ar^3 + ar^4$$
The first term is the constant a. Then each term after that is found by multiplying by a constant multiplier r.

Use the equation $S = a + ar + ar^2 + ar^3 + ar^4$ *for these problems.*

1. Multiply each side of the equation by r.
   $rS = ar + ar^2 + ar^3 + ar^4 + ar^5$

2. Subtract the original equation from your result in Exercise 1.
   $rS - S = ar^5 - a$

3. Solve the result from Exercise 2 for the variable S. $S = \frac{a(r^5 - 1)}{r - 1}$

Use the polynomial $a + ar + ar^2 + ar^3 + ar^4 + ... + ar^{n-1}$ *for these problems.*

4. Write the 10th term of the polynomial. ar^9

5. If $a = 5$ and $r = 2$, what is the 8th term? $ar^7 = 640$

6. Follow the steps in Exercises 1–3 to write a formula for the sum of this polynomial. $S = \frac{a(r^n - 1)}{r - 1}$

7. If the 3rd term is 20 and the 6th term is 160, solve for r^3 and then find r. Then solve $ar^2 = 20$ for a and find the value of the first six terms of the polynomial.
   $\frac{ar^5}{ar^2} = \frac{160}{20}, r^3 = 8, r = 2; ar^2 = 20; a = 5; 5, 10, 20, 40, 80, 160$

8. Find the sum of the first six terms of the geometric series that begins 3, 6, 12, 24, ... First write the values for a and r.
   $a = 3, r = 2$
   $S = \frac{3(2^6 - 1)}{2 - 1} = 3 \times 63 = 189$

INTRODUCING THE LESSON

 5-Minute Check

(over Lesson 6-7)

Simplify.

1. $3x(2x^2 - 7)$ $6x^3 - 21x$
2. $3c^2(4c^2 + 3c - 9)$
   $12c^4 + 9c^3 - 27c^2$
3. $5ab(4a^2b - 7ab^2 - 6b^3)$
   $20a^3b^2 - 35a^2b^3 - 30ab^4$
4. $2x(3x^2 - 4x + 7) -$
   $5(4x^2 + 3x - 9)$
   $6x^3 - 28x^2 - x + 45$
5. $3a(a + 2b) + 7b(a + 2b)$
   $3a^2 + 13ab + 14b^2$

Motivating the Lesson

Introduce the lesson by having students describe possible ways of finding the product of $(2a + y)$ and $(2a + 5t - 6y + 5r)$.

TEACHING THE LESSON

Teaching Tip **1** Remind students that FOIL is a memory device, not a mathematical theorem or rule. Stress that this works only with two binomials.

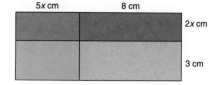

6-8 Multiplying Polynomials

Objectives

6-8A
6-8B

After studying this lesson, you should be able to:
- use the FOIL method to multiply two binomials, and
- multiply any two polynomials by using the distributive property.

Connection

You know that the area of a rectangle is the product of its length and width. You can multiply $2x + 3$ and $5x + 8$ to find the area of the large rectangle.

$$(2x + 3)(5x + 8) = 2x(5x + 8) + 3(5x + 8) \quad \textit{Distributive property}$$
$$= (2x)(5x) + (2x)(8) + (3)(5x) + (3)(8)$$
$$= 10x^2 + 16x + 15x + 24$$
$$= 10x^2 + 31x + 24$$

But you also know that the area of the large rectangle equals the sum of the areas of the four smaller rectangles.

$$(2x + 3)(5x + 8) = 2x \cdot 5x + 2x \cdot 8 + 3 \cdot 5x + 3 \cdot 8$$
$$= 10x^2 + 16x + 15x + 24$$
$$= 10x^2 + 31x + 24$$

This example illustrates a shortcut of the distributive property called the **FOIL method.**

$$(2x + 3)(5x + 8) = (2x)(5x) + (2x)(8) + (3)(5x) + (3)(8)$$

F	O	I	L
product of FIRST terms	product of OUTER terms	product of INNER terms	product of LAST terms

$$= 10x^2 + 16x + 15x + 24$$
$$= 10x^2 + 31x + 24$$

FOIL Method for Multiplying Two Binomials
Teaching Tip **1**

> **To multiply two binomials, find the sum of the products of**
> F   the first terms,
> O   the outer terms,
> I   the inner terms, and
> L   the last terms.

ALTERNATE TEACHING STRATEGIES

Using Communication

FOIL is an example of a pneumonic device. Pneumonic devices are nonsensical ways of remembering a series of steps. Discuss with the students other pneumonic devices they may have used to aid in memorizing a series of steps. Then have them create their own pneumonic device to help remember the steps to take when multiplying polynomials.

Example 1

Find $(y + 5)(y + 7)$.

$$\begin{array}{cccc} F & O & I & L \end{array}$$
$$(y + 5)(y + 7) = y \cdot y + y \cdot 7 + y \cdot 5 + 5 \cdot 7$$
$$= y^2 + 7y + 5y + 35$$
$$= y^2 + 12y + 35 \quad \textit{Combine like terms.}$$

Example 2

Find $(3x - 5)(5x + 2)$. **Teaching Tip** ②

$$\begin{array}{cccc} F & O & I & L \end{array}$$
$$(3x - 5)(5x + 2) = (3x)(5x) + (3x)(2) + (-5)(5x) + (-5)(2)$$
$$= 15x^2 + 6x - 25x - 10$$
$$= 15x^2 - 19x - 10$$

The distributive property can be used to multiply any two polynomials.

Example 3

Find $(2x - 5)(3x^2 - 5x + 4)$. **Teaching Tip** ③

$$(2x - 5)(3x^2 - 5x + 4)$$
$$= 2x(3x^2 - 5x + 4) - 5(3x^2 - 5x + 4) \qquad \textit{Distributive property}$$
$$= (6x^3 - 10x^2 + 8x) - (15x^2 - 25x + 20)$$
$$= 6x^3 - 10x^2 + 8x + (-15x^2 + 25x - 20) \qquad \textit{Additive inverse}$$
$$= 6x^3 + (-10x^2 - 15x^2) + (8x + 25x) - 20$$
$$= 6x^3 - 25x^2 + 33x - 20$$

Example 4

Find $(x^2 - 5x + 4)(2x^2 + x - 7)$.

$$(x^2 - 5x + 4)(2x^2 + x - 7)$$
$$= x^2(2x^2 + x - 7) - 5x(2x^2 + x - 7) + 4(2x^2 + x - 7)$$
$$= 2x^4 + x^3 - 7x^2 - 10x^3 - 5x^2 + 35x + 8x^2 + 4x - 28$$
$$= 2x^4 - 9x^3 - 4x^2 + 39x - 28$$

Polynomials can also be multiplied in column form. Be careful to align the like terms.

Example 5

Find $(x^3 + 5x - 6)(2x - 9)$ in column form.

Since there is no x^2 term in $x^3 + 5x - 6$, $0x^2$ is used as a placeholder.

$$\begin{array}{r} x^3 + 0x^2 + 5x - 6 \\ (\times) \qquad \qquad 2x - 9 \\ \hline -9x^3 - 0x^2 - 45x + 54 \\ 2x^4 + 0x^3 + 10x^2 - 12x \qquad \qquad \\ \hline 2x^4 - 9x^3 + 10x^2 - 57x + 54 \end{array}$$

This is the product of $x^3 + 5x - 6$ and -9.
This is the product of $x^3 + 5x - 6$ and $2x$.
This is the sum of the partial products.

Chalkboard Examples

For Example 1
Multiply.

a. $(m - 3)(m + 4)$
$m^2 + m - 12$

b. $(n + 6)(n + 1)$ $\quad n^2 + 7n + 6$

For Example 2
Multiply.

a. $(2m + 6)(m - 1)$
$2m^2 + 4m - 6$

b. $(5a - 1)(5a + 6)$
$25a^2 + 25a - 6$

For Example 3
Find $(2x + 3)(x^2 + 3x + 8)$.
$2x^3 + 9x^2 + 25x + 24$

For Example 4
Multiply.

a. $(b^2 + 7b - 2)(4b^2 - 2b + 6)$
$4b^4 + 26b^3 - 16b^2 + 46b - 12$

b. $(m^2 + 5m - 3)(m^2 + 7m + 4)$
$m^4 + 12m^3 + 36m^2 - m - 12$

For Example 5
Multiply in column form.

a. $(3x - 7)(2x^2 + x + 5)$
$6x^3 - 11x^2 + 8x - 35$

b. $(3x - 5)(x^3 - 2x^2 + 6)$
$3x^4 - 11x^3 + 10x^2 + 18x - 30$

Teaching Tip ② When finding the product $(3x - 5)(5x + 2)$, the -5 is distributed in the same way as a negative 5. You may want to rewrite $(3x - 5)(5x + 2)$ as $[3x + (-5)](5x + 2)$ and show how to find this product first.

Teaching Tip ③ Emphasize to students that they must multiply each term in the first polynomial by each term in the second polynomial.

EVALUATING THE LESSON

Checking for Understanding

Exercises 1-12 are designed to help you assess understanding through reading, writing, and speaking. You should work through Exercises 1-2 with your students, and then monitor their work on Exercises 3-12.

Closing the Lesson

Writing Activity   Have students write a paragraph summarizing the process of multiplying polynomials.

240   Chapter 6

Example 6

APPLICATION

Gardening

Maria Orozco has a rectangular garden that is 10 feet longer than it is wide. A brick path 3 feet in width surrounds the garden. The total area of the path is 396 square feet. What are the dimensions of the garden?

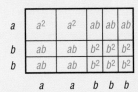

EXPLORE   Draw a diagram to represent the situation. Let w = the width of the garden, $w + 10$ = the length of the garden, $w + 6$ = the width of the garden and path, and $w + 16$ = the length of the garden and path.

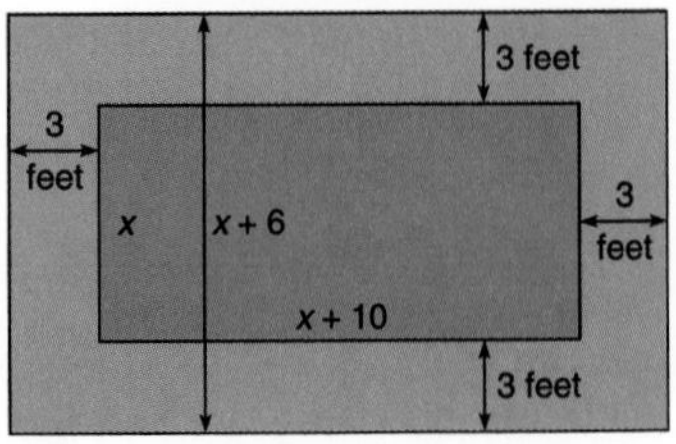

Then $w(w + 10)$ = the area of the garden, and $(w + 6)(w + 16)$ = the area of the garden and path.

PLAN
$$\underset{\text{and path}}{\underline{\text{area of garden}}} - \underset{\text{garden}}{\underline{\text{area of}}} = \underset{\text{path}}{\underline{\text{area of}}}$$

$$(w + 6)(w + 16) - w(w + 10) = 396$$

SOLVE
$$w^2 + 16w + 6w + 96 - w^2 - 10w = 396 \quad \textit{Use the FOIL method.}$$
$$(w^2 - w^2) + (16w + 6w - 10w) + 96 = 396$$
$$12w + 96 = 396 \quad \textit{Combine like terms.}$$
$$12w = 300$$
$$w = 25$$

The width is 25 feet and the length is $w + 10$ or 35 feet.

EXAMINE   To examine the solution, compute the total area of the garden and path in two ways and compare the results.

$$\underline{\text{area of garden}} + \underline{\text{area of path}} = \underline{\text{total area}}$$
$$25 \times 35 \quad + \quad 396 \quad = \quad 1271$$

$$\underline{\text{total length}} \times \underline{\text{total width}} = \underline{\text{total area}}$$
$$(35 + 6) \times (25 + 6) = 41 \times 31 \text{ or } 1271$$

Thus, the solution checks.

CHECKING FOR UNDERSTANDING

Communicating Mathematics

Read and study the lesson to answer each question.

1. In the FOIL method, what do the letters F, O, I, and L stand for?
   first, outer, inner, last

2. Use the FOIL method to evaluate $4\frac{1}{2} \cdot 6\frac{3}{4}$. (*Hint:* Rewrite as $\left(4 + \frac{1}{2}\right)\left(6 + \frac{3}{4}\right) \cdot$) $30\frac{3}{8}$

240   CHAPTER 6   POLYNOMIALS

RETEACHING THE LESSON

	a²	a²	ab	ab	ab
(a)					
(b)	ab	ab	b²	b²	b²
(b)	ab	ab	b²	b²	b²

(row labels: a, b, b on the left; column labels: a, a, b, b, b on the bottom)

1. What is the width? $a + 2b$
2. What is the length? $2a + 3b$
3. What is the area?
   $(a + 2b)(2a + 3b)$ or
   $2a^2 + 7ab + 6b^2$
4. Inside each small square or rectangle, write its area.
   See diagram.
5. Add the area in 4. Compare with your answer in 3.   same

Find the sum of the product of the inner terms and the product of the outer terms.

3. $(x + 5)(x + 3)$ $8x$

4. $(2a + 1)(a + 5)$ $11a$

5. $(x + 5)(5x - 3)$ $22x$

6. $(3x + 2)(2x + 3)$ $13x$

7. $(5b - 3)(2b + 1)$ $-b$

8. $(2m + 4)(m + 5)$ $14m$

Find each product.

9. $(a + 3)(a + 7)$ $a^2 + 10a + 21$

10. $(m - 5)(m - 11)$ $m^2 - 16m + 55$

11. $(x + 11)(x - 4)$ $x^2 + 7x - 44$

12. $(2x + 1)(x + 8)$ $2x^2 + 17x + 8$

EXERCISES

Practice

Find each product. **19–24, 27–40. See margin.**

13. $(c + 2)(c + 8)$ $c^2 + 10c + 16$

14. $(x - 4)(x - 8)$ $x^2 - 12x + 32$

15. $(y + 3)(y - 7)$ $y^2 - 4y - 21$

16. $(5y - 3)(y + 2)$ $5y^2 + 7y - 6$

17. $(4a + 3)(2a - 1)$ $8a^2 + 2a - 3$

18. $(7y - 1)(2y - 3)$ $14y^2 - 23y + 3$

19. $(2x + 3y)(5x + 2y)$

20. $(2a + 3b)(5a - 2b)$

21. $(5q + 2r)(8q - 3r)$

22. $(5r - 7s)(4r + 3s)$

23. $(2r + 0.1)(5r - 0.3)$

24. $(0.7x + 2y)(0.9x + 3y)$

25. $\left(3x + \frac{1}{4}\right)\left(6x - \frac{1}{2}\right)$ $18x^2 - \frac{1}{8}$

26. $(x - 2)(x^2 + 2x + 4)$ $x^3 - 8$

27. $x^2 + 7x - 9$
     $(\times)$ $2x + 1$

28. $a^2 - 3a + 11$
     $(\times)$ $5a + 2$

29. $3x^2 + 5xy + y^2$
     $(\times)$ $4x - 3y$

30. $6x^2 - 5xy + 9y^2$
     $(\times)$ $5x - 2y$

31. $(3x + 5)(2x^2 - 5x + 11)$

32. $(4s + 5)(3s^2 + 8s - 9)$

33. $(3a + 5)(2a - 8a^2 + 3)$

34. $(5x - 2)(7 - 5x^2 + 2x)$

35. $5x^2 - 6x + 9$
     $(\times) \, 4x^2 + 3x + 11$

36. $5x^4 + 0x^3 - 2x^2 + 1$
     $(\times)$ $x^2 - 5x + 3$

37. $(x^2 - 7x + 4)(2x^2 - 3x - 6)$

38. $(a^2 + 2a + 5)(a^2 - 3a - 7)$

39. $(-2x^2 + 3x - 8)(3x^2 + 7x - 5)$

40. $(-7b^3 + 2b - 3)(5b^2 - 2b + 4)$

41–44. See margin.

Critical Thinking

If $R = 2x - 1$, $S = 3x + 2$, and $T = -3x^2$, find each of the following.

41. $R \cdot S$ **42.** $TS - R$ **43.** $R(S + T)$ **44.** $3R(2S + 5T)$

Applications

45. Gardening A rectangular garden is 5 feet longer than twice its width. It has a sidewalk 3 feet wide on two of its sides, as shown at the right. The area of the sidewalk is 213 square feet. Find the dimensions of the garden.
21 ft by 47 ft

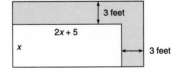

LESSON 6-8 MULTIPLYING POLYNOMIALS **241**

Additional Answers

19. $10x^2 + 19xy + 6y^2$

20. $10a^2 + 11ab - 6b^2$

21. $40q^2 + qr - 6r^2$

22. $20r^2 - 13rs - 21s^2$

23. $10r^2 - 0.1r - 0.03$

24. $0.63x^2 + 3.9xy + 6y^2$

27. $2x^3 + 15x^2 - 11x - 9$

28. $5a^3 - 13a^2 + 49a + 22$

29. $12x^3 + 11x^2y - 11xy^2 - 3y^3$

30. $30x^3 - 37x^2y + 55xy^2 - 18y^3$

31. $6x^3 - 5x^2 + 8x + 55$

32. $12s^3 + 47s^2 + 4s - 45$

33. $-24a^3 - 34a^2 + 19a + 15$

34. $-25x^3 + 20x^2 + 31x - 14$

35. $20x^4 - 9x^3 + 73x^2 - 39x + 99$

36. $5x^6 - 25x^5 + 13x^4 + 10x^3 - 5x^2 - 5x + 3$

37. $2x^4 - 17x^3 + 23x^2 + 30x - 24$

38. $a^4 - a^3 - 8a^2 - 29a - 35$

39. $-6x^4 - 5x^3 + 7x^2 - 71x + 40$

APPLYING THE LESSON

Homework Exercises

Assignment Guide
Basic: 13-34, 41-45, 47-51
Average: 19-37, 41-51
Enriched: 27-51

Teaching Tip ④ Encourage students to work out each multiplication step by step until they have gained some mastery. Then they should gradually be able to do the problems mentally.

Additional Answers

40. $-35b^5 + 14b^4 - 18b^3 - 19b^2 + 14b - 12$

41. $6x^2 + x - 2$

42. $-9x^3 - 6x^2 - 2x + 1$

43. $-6x^3 + 9x^2 + x - 2$

44. $-90x^3 + 81x^2 + 6x - 12$

Practice Masters Booklet, p. 46

NAME _____ DATE _____
6-8 **Practice Worksheet**

Multiplying Polynomials
Find each product.

1. $(x + 2)(x + 7)$
$x^2 + 9x + 14$

2. $(y + 6)(y + 3)$
$y^2 + 9y + 18$

3. $(a - 3)(a - 8)$
$a^2 - 11a + 24$

4. $(r - 5)(r - 1)$
$r^2 - 6r + 5$

5. $(x - 10)(x + 2)$
$x^2 - 8x - 20$

6. $(3t + 2q)(7t - 9q)$
$21t^2 - 13qt - 18q^2$

7. $(7y - 4t)(2y + 5t)$
$14y^2 + 27ty - 20t^2$

8. $(5w - 3y)(w - 2y)$
$5w^2 - 13yw + 6y^2$

9. $(a + b)(2a - 3b)$
$2a^2 - ab - 3b^2$

10. $(0.3n + 5)(0.4n - 11)$
$0.12n^2 - 1.3n - 55$

11. $(1.3g + 3)(0.4g + 5)$
$0.52g^2 + 7.7g + 15$

12. $(x + y)(x + y)$
$x^2 + 2xy + y^2$

13. $(z - 2x)(z - 2x)$
$z^2 - 4xz + 4x^2$

14. $(3x + 2y)(2y + 3x)$
$4y^2 + 12xy + 9x^2$

15. $y^2 + 3y - 6$
     $\times \quad 2y + 3$
     $2y^3 + 9y^2 - 3y - 18$

16. $a^2 + 2a - 9$
     $\times \quad a + 3$
     $a^3 + 5a^2 - 3a - 27$

17. $e^2 - 2ef + f^2$
     $\times \quad e - f$
     $e^3 - 3e^2f + 3ef^2 - f^3$

18. $9m^2 - 12m + 4$
     $\times \quad 3m + 2$
     $27m^3 - 18m^2 - 12m + 8$

19. $(2a - 1)(a^2 + 3a + 5)$
$2a^3 + 5a^2 + 7a - 5$

20. $(2 + 3c)(4 + 6c + 9c^2)$
$8 + 24c + 36c^2 + 27c^3$

46. **Construction** The length of a rectangular lot is 7 yards less than twice its width. If the length was increased by 11 yards and the width decreased by 6 yards, the area would be decreased by 40 square yards. Find the original dimensions of the lot. **16 yd by 25 yd**

Mixed Review

47. Solve by working backwards. **(Lesson 3-4)**

Jack, Jared, and Jason are playing a game in which two of them win and one of them loses on each play. The one who loses takes some of his own points and gives them to each winner so that their points are doubled. The boys play the game three times; each wins twice and loses once. At the end of three plays, each boy has 40 points. How many points did each player have at the beginning of the game? **20, 35, 65**

48. **Sales** Sales tax of 6% is added to a purchase of $11. Find the total price. **(Lesson 4-4)** **$11.66**

49. Solve $14 + 7x > 8x$. **(Lesson 5-1)** $x < 14$

50. Simplify $\dfrac{ab^5c}{ac}$. Assume that the denominator is not equal to zero. **(Lesson 6-3)** b^5

51. Multiply $\dfrac{2}{3}a(6a + 15)$. **(Lesson 6-7)** $4a^2 + 10a$

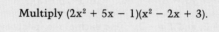

EXTRA

Another way to multiply two polynomials is to use an array. Write the coefficients of the first polynomial from left to right as the headings of the columns. Then write the coefficients of the second polynomial as the headings of the rows. Next fill in the array with the products of the column headings and the row headings. Finally, add diagonally as shown. These sums will be the coefficients of the product. Study the example below.

Multiply $(2x^2 + 5x - 1)(x^2 - 2x + 3)$.

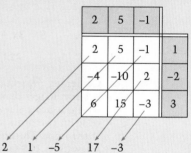

So, $(2x^2 + 5x - 1)(x^2 - 2x + 3) =$
$2x^4 + x^3 - 5x^2 + 17x - 3$.

EXTENDING THE LESSON

Math Power: Problem Solving

Find the product of $(4m^2 - m + 8)$ and $(m^3 + 2m^2 + 3m + 4)$.
$4m^5 + 7m^4 + 18m^3 + 29m^2 + 20m + 32$

Extra

Students may wish to use this method to check their answers to Exercises 27-40.

6-9 Some Special Products

Objective
6-9

After studying this lesson, you should be able to:
- use the patterns for $(a + b)^2$, $(a - b)^2$, and $(a + b)(a - b)$.

Connection

Study the diagram below. There are two ways to find the area of the large square.

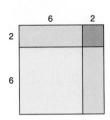

Method 1: The length of each side is $6 + 2$ units. The area is the product of $(6 + 2)$ and $(6 + 2)$ or $(6 + 2)^2$.

$$(6 + 2)^2 = 8^2$$
$$= 64$$

Method 2: The area of the large square is the sum of the areas of the four smaller rectangles.

$$6^2 + 6 \cdot 2 + 6 \cdot 2 + 2^2 = 36 + 12 + 12 + 4$$
$$= 64$$

Thus, $(6 + 2)^2 = 6^2 + 6 \cdot 2 + 6 \cdot 2 + 2^2$.

Using a procedure similar to the one described above, we can derive a general form for the expression $(a + b)^2$.

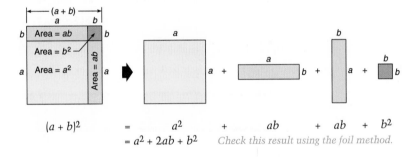

$$(a + b)^2 = a^2 + ab + ab + b^2$$
$$= a^2 + 2ab + b^2 \quad \textit{Check this result using the foil method.}$$

Square of a Sum	$(a + b)^2 = (a + b)(a + b) = a^2 + 2ab + b^2$

Example 1

Find $(x + 3)^2$.

$(x + 3)^2 = x^2 + 2(x)(3) + 3^2$ *Replace a with x and b with 3.*
$\qquad\qquad = x^2 + 6x + 9$

LESSON 6-9 SOME SPECIAL PRODUCTS **243**

ALTERNATE TEACHING STRATEGIES

Using Problem Solving

Pete has a rectangular garden 15 feet longer than it is wide. A cement divider that is 4 feet wide surrounds the garden. The total area of the divider is 632 square feet. What are the dimensions of the garden? Draw a diagram of the garden on a piece of paper to illustrate its dimensions.
28 feet by 43 feet

Lesson Resources

- Reteaching Master 6-9
- Practice Master 6-9
- Enrichment Master 6-9

 Transparency 6-9 contains the 5-Minute Check and a teaching aid for this lesson.

INTRODUCING THE LESSON

5-Minute Check
(over Lesson 6-8)

Multiply.

1. $(3w + 7)(2w + 5)$
   $6w^2 + 29w + 35$
2. $(a + 6)(a - 3)$
   $a^2 + 3a - 18$
3. $(3m - 4)(5m + 6)$
   $15m^2 - 2m - 24$
4. $(2b - 5)(5b + 3)$
   $10b^2 - 19b - 15$
5. $(8j - 2)(2j + 8)$
   $16j^2 + 60j - 16$

Motivating the Lesson

Introduce the lesson by having students identify all the perfect squares less than 100.   **1, 4, 9, 16, 25, 36, 49, 64, 81**

TEACHING THE LESSON

Chalkboard Example

For Example 1
Multiply.

a. $(3a + 2)^2$ $9a^2 + 12a + 4$

b. $(5b + 7)^2$
   $25b^2 + 70b + 49$

---

244 Chapter 6

Example 2 Find $(5m + 3n)^2$.

$(5m + 3n)^2 = (5m)^2 + 2(5m)(3n) + (3n)^2$ *Replace a with 5m and b with 3n.*
$= 25m^2 + 30mn + 9n^2$

To find $(a - b)^2$, express $(a - b)$ as $[a + (-b)]$ and square it.

$(a - b)^2 = [a + (-b)]^2$
$= a^2 + (2)(a)(-b) + (-b)^2$
$= a^2 - 2ab + b^2$

Square of a Difference	$(a - b)^2 = (a - b)(a - b) = a^2 - 2ab + b^2$ Teaching Tip ❶

Example 3 Find $(c - 2)^2$.

$(c - 2)^2 = c^2 - 2(c)(2) + (2)^2$ *Replace a with c and b with 2.*
$= c^2 - 4c + 4$

Example 4 Find $(3x - 2y)^2$.

$(3x - 2y)^2 = (3x)^2 - 2(3x)(2y) + (2y)^2$ *Replace a with 3x and b with 2y.*
$= 9x^2 - 12xy + 4y^2$

You can use the FOIL method to find the product of a sum and a difference of the same two numbers.

$(a + b)(a - b) = (a)(a) + (a)(-b) + (a)(b) + (b)(-b)$
$= a^2 - ab + ab - b^2$
$= a^2 - b^2$

This product is called the **difference of squares.**

Product of a Sum and a Difference	$(a + b)(a - b) = (a - b)(a + b) = a^2 - b^2$

Example 5 Find $(x + 5)(x - 5)$.

$(x + 5)(x - 5) = x^2 - 5^2$ *Replace a with x and b with 5.*
$= x^2 - 25$

Example 6 Find $(5a + 6b)(5a - 6b)$.

$(5a + 6b)(5a - 6b) = (5a)^2 - (6b)^2$ *Replace a with 5a and b with 6b.*
$= 25a^2 - 36b^2$

244 CHAPTER 6 POLYNOMIALS

RETEACHING THE LESSON

Use the pattern of the square of a sum, $(a + b)^2 = a^2 + 2ab + b^2$, to square numbers.

For example:
$(27)^2 = (20 + 7)^2 = 20^2 + 2 \cdot 140 + 49$ or 729

Additional Answers

2. The square of a difference is $(a - b)^2 = a^2 - 2ab + b^2$. The difference of two squares is $a^2 - b^2 = (a - b)(a + b)$.
10. $16x^2 + 8xy + y^2$
11. $4a^2 - 4ab + b^2$
12. $36m^2 + 24mn + 4n^2$
13. $16x^2 - 72xy + 81y^2$
14. $25a^2 - 120ab + 144b^2$
15. $25x^2 + 60xy + 36y^2$

CHECKING FOR UNDERSTANDING

Communicating Mathematics

Read and study the lesson to answer each question.

1. Compare the square of a sum and the square of a difference. How do they vary? **The middle terms have different signs.**

2. Compare the square of a difference and the difference of two squares. **See margin. Teaching Tip 2**

CONNECTION Geometry

3. What does the diagram at the right represent if the shading represents regions to be removed or subtracted? $(a - b)^2 = a^2 - 2ab + b^2$

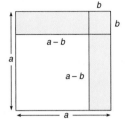

4. $a^2 + 4ab + 4b^2$ 5. $a^2 - 6ab + 9b^2$ 6. $4x^2 + 4xy + y^2$

Guided Practice **Find each product.**

4. $(a + 2b)^2$ 5. $(a - 3b)^2$ 6. $(2x + y)^2$

7. $(3x - 2y)^2$ 8. $(2a + 3)(2a - 3)$ 9. $(5a - 3b)(5a + 3b)$
   $9x^2 - 12xy + 4y^2$ $4a^2 - 9$ $25a^2 - 9b^2$

EXERCISES

Practice **Find each product. See margin.**

A
10. $(4x + y)^2$ 11. $(2a - b)^2$ 12. $(6m + 2n)^2$
13. $(4x - 9y)^2$ 14. $(5a - 12b)^2$ 15. $(5x + 6y)^2$
16. $\left(\frac{1}{2}a + b\right)^2$ 17. $(5 - x)^2$ 18. $(1 + x)^2$

B
19. $(1.1x + y)^2$ 20. $(a^2 - 3b^2)^2$ 21. $(x^3 - 5y^2)^2$
22. $(3x + 5)(3x - 5)$ 23. $(8a - 2b)(8a + 2b)$
24. $(7a^2 + b)(7a^2 - b)$ 25. $(8x^2 - 3y)(8x^2 + 3y)$
26. $\left(\frac{4}{3}x^2 - y\right)\left(\frac{4}{3}x^2 + y\right)$ 27. $(x + 2)(x - 2)(2x + 5)$

C
28. $(4x - 1)(4x + 1)(x - 4)$ 29. $(x - 3)(x + 4)(x + 3)(x - 4)$
30. $(x - 2y)^3$ 31. $(2x - 3y)^3$ 32. $(a + b)^4$
33. $(2x - y)^4$ 34. $(3m + 2n)^4$ 35. $(a - b)^5$

Critical Thinking
CONNECTION Geometry

36. The diagram at the right represents $(a + b + c)^2$. Use the diagram to write the measure of the area as a polynomial. $(a + b + c)^2 = a^2 + b^2 + c^2 + 2ab + 2ac + 2bc$

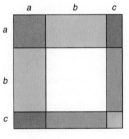

LESSON 6-9 SOME SPECIAL PRODUCTS 245

Additional Answers

16. $\frac{1}{4}a^2 + ab + b^2$
17. $25 - 10x + x^2$
18. $1 + 2x + x^2$
19. $1.21x^2 + 2.2xy + y^2$
20. $a^4 - 6a^2b^2 + 9b^4$
21. $x^6 - 10x^3y^2 + 25y^4$
22. $9x^2 - 25$
23. $64a^2 - 4b^2$
24. $49a^4 - b^2$
25. $64x^4 - 9y^2$
26. $\frac{16}{9}x^4 - y^2$

27. $2x^3 + 5x^2 - 8x - 20$
28. $16x^3 - 64x^2 - x + 4$
29. $x^4 - 25x^2 + 144$
30. $x^3 - 6x^2y + 12xy^2 - 8y^3$
31. $8x^3 - 36x^2y + 54xy^2 - 27y^3$
32. $a^4 + 4a^3b + 6a^2b^2 + 4ab^3 + b^4$
33. $16x^4 - 32x^3y + 24x^2y^2 - 8xy^3 + y^4$
34. $81m^4 + 216m^3n + 216m^2n^2 + 96mn^3 + 16n^4$
35. $a^5 - 5a^4b + 10a^3b^2 - 10a^2b^3 + 5ab^4 - b^5$

Teaching Tip 1 Emphasize to students that the square of a difference is another case of multiplying binomials by FOIL.
$(a - b)^2 = (a - 2ab)(2ba - b)$
     F   O   I   L
$= a^2 - ab - ba + b^2$
$= a^2 - 2ab + b^2$

Teaching Tip 2 Have students compare these expressions:
square of a difference
$(a - b)^2$
and
difference of two squares
$a^2 - b^2$.

Point out that the difference of two squares is the only time the product of two binomials is a binomial.

EVALUATING THE LESSON

Checking for Understanding
Exercises 1-9 are designed to help you assess understanding through reading, writing, and speaking. You should work through Exercises 1-3 with your students, and then monitor their work on Exercises 4-9.

Assignment Guide
Basic: 10-27, 36-37, 39-41
Average: 15-31, 36-41
Enriched: 19-41

Practice Masters Booklet, p. 47

NAME _____ DATE _____
6-9 Practice Worksheet

Some Special Products
Find each product.

1. $(z + 4)^2$ $z^2 + 8z + 16$
2. $(3p + 9)^2$ $9p^2 + 54p + 81$
3. $(4u - 5)^2$ $16u^2 - 40u + 25$
4. $(5v - 8)^2$ $25v^2 - 80v + 64$
5. $(10r - 3s)^2$ $100r^2 - 60rs + 9s^2$
6. $(6 - p)^2$ $36 - 12p + p^2$
7. $(3k + 2h)^2$ $9k^2 + 12kh + 4h^2$
8. $(y - 2z)^2$ $y^2 - 4yz + 4z^2$
9. $(11a^4 - p^3)^2$ $121a^8 - 22a^4p^3 + p^6$
10. $(3.1y + 0.4w)^2$ $9.61y^2 + 2.48wy + 0.16w^2$
11. $(0.4x - 3.2)^2$ $0.16x^2 - 2.56x + 10.24$
12. $(2.2c + d)^2$ $4.84c^2 + 4.4cd + d^2$
13. $(t^3 - 3r^5)^2$ $t^6 - 6r^2t^3 + 9r^4$
14. $(x^2 - 5y^2)^2$ $x^4 - 10x^2y^2 + 25y^4$
15. $(2x - 3)(2x + 3)$ $4x^2 - 9$
16. $(c - 8)(c + 8)$ $c^2 - 64$
17. $(2u + 1)(2u - 1)$ $4u^2 - 1$
18. $(7n - 9)(7n + 9)$ $49n^2 - 81$
19. $(3d + 8x)(3d - 8x)$ $9d^2 - 64x^2$
20. $(2x - 3y)(2x + 3y)$ $4x^2 - 9y^2$
21. $\left(\frac{4}{5}y + m\right)\left(\frac{4}{5}y - m\right)$ $\frac{16}{25}y^2 - m^2$
22. $\left(\frac{1}{3}x - \frac{2}{3}y\right)\left(\frac{1}{3}x + \frac{2}{3}y\right)$ $\frac{1}{9}x^2 - \frac{4}{9}y^2$
23. $(6x^2 - 5y^3)(6x^2 + 5y^3)$ $36x^4 - 25y^6$
24. $(2y^3 - 7z^2)(2y^3 + 7z^2)$ $4y^6 - 49z^4$
25. $(8 - n^3)(8 + n^3)$ $64 - n^6$
26. $(2a^2 + 3b^2)(2a^2 + 3b^2)$ $4a^4 + 12a^2b^2 + 9b^4$
27. $(x + 1)(x + 2)(x - 1)$ $x^3 + 2x^2 - x - 2$
28. $(2p - 1)(2p + 1)(2p - 1)$ $8p^3 - 4p^2 - 2p + 1$

Chapter 6 245

It is very common for students to assume that $(a + b)^2 = a^2 + b^2$. They reason that to square a quantity, it is acceptable to square its parts. Remind students to write out the multiplication. $(a + b)^2$ means $(a + b)(a + b)$ or $a^2 + 2ab + b^2$.

Closing the Lesson

Writing Activity Have students write a paragraph summarizing the steps to follow when squaring binomials.

APPLYING THE LESSON

Homework Exercises

See assignment guide on page 245.

Chapter 6, Quiz D, (Lessons 6-7 through 6-9), is available in the Evaluation Masters Booklet, p. 80.

Enrichment Masters Booklet, p. 42

6-9 | NAME _____ DATE _____
Enrichment Worksheet

Special Polynomial Products

Sometimes the product of two polynomials can be found readily with the use of one of the special products of binomials.

For example, you can find the square of a trinomial by recalling the square of a binomial.

Example 1: Find $(x + y + z)^2$.

$$(a + b)^2 = a^2 + 2 \cdot a \cdot b + b^2$$
$$[(x + y) + z]^2 = (x + y)^2 + 2(x + y)z + z^2$$
$$= x^2 + 2xy + y^2 + 2xz + 2yz + z^2$$

Example 2: Find $(3t + x + 1)(3t - x - 1)$.

Hint: $(3t + x + 1)(3t - x - 1)$ is the product of a sum $3t + (x + 1)$ and a difference $3t - (x + 1)$.

$$(3t + x + 1)(3t - x - 1) = [3t + (x + 1)][3t - (x + 1)]$$
$$= 9t^2 - (x + 1)^2$$
$$= 9t^2 - x^2 - 2x - 1$$

Use a special product of binomials to find each product.

1. $(x + y - z)^2$
   $x^2 + 2xy - 2xz + y^2 - 2yz + z^2$

2. $(r + s + 5)^2$
   $r^2 + 2rs + s^2 + 10r + 10s + 25$

3. $(b - 3 + d)^2$
   $b^2 - 6b + 2bd + 9 - 6d + d^2$

4. $(k - m - 2)^2$
   $k^2 - 2km + m^2 - 4k + 4m + 4$

5. $(x + 1 + 2b)(x + 1 - 2b)$
   $x^2 + 2x + 1 - 4b^2$

6. $(y - 2 + x)(y - 2 - x)$
   $y^2 - 4y + 4 - x^2$

7. $(5 + b - x)(5 + b + x)$
   $25 + 10b + b^2 - x^2$

8. $(j - 5 - f)(j + 5 + f)$
   $j^2 - f^2 - 10f - 25$

9. $[(x + y) + (z + w)][(x + y) - (z + w)]$
   $x^2 + 2xy + y^2 - z^2 - 2zw - w^2$

10. $(2a + 1 + 3b - c)(2a + 1 - 3b + c)$
    $4a^2 + 4a + 1 - 9b^2 + 6bc - c^2$

246   Chapter 6

---

37. City Planning A certain section of town is shaped like a trapezoid with an area of 81 square miles. The distance between Union St. and Lee St. is 9 miles. The length of Union St. is 14 miles less than 3 times the length of Lee St. Find the length of Lee St. Use $A = \frac{1}{2}h(a + b)$.
8 miles

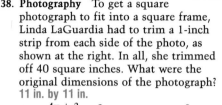

38. Photography To get a square photograph to fit into a square frame, Linda LaGuardia had to trim a 1-inch strip from each side of the photo, as shown at the right. In all, she trimmed off 40 square inches. What were the original dimensions of the photograph? **11 in. by 11 in.**

Mixed Review

39. Solve $\frac{4y + 3}{7} = \frac{9}{14}$. **(Lesson 3-7)** $\frac{3}{8}$

40. Sales On the first day of school, 264 school notebooks were sold. Some sold for 95¢ each and the rest sold for $1.25 each. How many of each were sold if the total sales were $297? **(Lesson 4-6)**
110 at 95¢, 154 at $1.25

41. Is the statement $3 - 1\frac{1}{2} = \frac{1}{2}$ true or false? **(Lesson 1-3)** *false*

~ APPLICATION ~

Punnett Squares

Punnett squares are used to show possible ways that genes can combine at fertilization. In a Punnett square, *dominant* genes are shown with capital letters. *Recessive* genes are shown with lowercase letters. Letters representing the parents' genes are placed on the outer sides of the Punnett square. Letters inside the boxes of the square show the possible gene combinations for their offspring.

The Punnett square at the right represents a cross between tall pea plants and short pea plants. Let T represent the dominant gene for tallness. Let t represent the recessive gene for shortness. Since the parents have one of each type of gene, they are called *hybrids*.

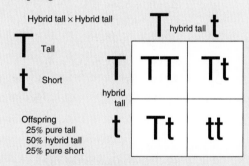

Because the parent plants have both a dominant tall gene and a recessive short gene, their offspring can be predicted as follows: 1 TT (tall), 2 Tt (tall with a recessive short gene), and 1 tt (short). Do you notice the similarity between this Punnett square and the square of a polynomial $(a + b)^2 = a \cdot a + 2ab + b \cdot b$?

EXTENDING THE LESSON

Math Power: Connections

The formula for the volume of a cube is $V = e^3$, where e represents the length of an edge. Find the volume of a cube if the length of its edge is $a + b$.
$a^3 + 3a^2b + 3ab^2 + b^3$

Application

Have students draw a Punnett square for the cross AaBb × AaBb to show all possible combinations of genes at fertilization, or genotypes. Students' Punnett squares should show that all the possible genotypes are AABB, AABb, AaBB, AaBb, AAbb, Aabb, aaBB, aaBb, and aabb.

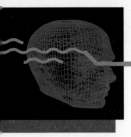

Technology
Volume and Surface Area

BASIC
Graphing calculator
Graphing software
▶ **Spreadsheets**

As you learned in Chapter 1, a spreadsheet is a computer program that allows the user to easily prepare tables and charts. You can use a spreadsheet to project results, make calculations, and print anything that can be organized in a table.

The spreadsheet below is set up to find the volume and surface area of a rectangular solid. To use the spreadsheet, you would enter the length, width, and height and the computer would find the volume and the surface area of the solid. The formula in cell B4 tells the computer to multiply the values in cells B1, B2, and B3 together.

```
======A========= B ======================= C
1: LENGTH        B1
2: WIDTH         B2
3: HEIGHT        B3
4: VOLUME        B1*B2*B3
5: SURFACE AREA  2B1*B2+2B1*B3+2B2*B3
```

A printout of the spreadsheet for finding the volume and surface area of a rectangular solid is shown at the right. The values 14.2, 7.5, and 9.7 have been entered for the length, width, and height. The computer has found that the volume of this solid is 1033.05 and the surface area is 633.98.

	VOLUME AND SURFACE AREA OF A RECTANGULAR SOLID	
	A	B
1	LENGTH	14.2
2	WIDTH	7.5
3	HEIGHT	9.7
4	VOLUME	1033.05
5	SURFACE AREA	633.98

EXERCISES

1. What does the formula in cell B5 tell the computer to do?
   Find the surface area.
2. Write the formula that you would enter to have the computer find the volume and the surface area of a cube if the length of a side is entered in cell B5.
   Volume: B5*B5*B5 or B5^3; surface area: 6*B5*B5 or 6*B5^2.
3. How could you modify the program to find the area and perimeter of a rectangle?
   A3: area; B3: B1*B2; A4: perimeter; B4: 2*B1+2*B2.

Using Technology

Objective This optional page shows how spreadsheets can be used to perform mathematical computations and to enhance and extend mathematical concepts.

Teaching Suggestions

If a computer spreadsheet program is available, have students enter the program for finding the volume and surface area of a rectangular solid. Have students enter various values for the length, width, and height of the rectangular solid and investigate the changes in volume and surface area. For example, what happens to the volume and surface area of a rectangular solid if you double the dimensions? The volume is eight times greater and the surface area is four times greater.

You may also have students modify the spreadsheet to find the perimeter and area of a circle, or the volume and surface area of a sphere.

Using the Chapter Summary and Review

The Chapter Summary and Review begins with an alphabetical listing of the new terms that were presented in the chapter. Have students define each term and provide an example of it, if appropriate.

The Skills and Concepts presented in the chapter are reviewed using a side-by-side format. Encourage students to refer to the Objectives and Examples on the left as they complete the Review Exercises on the right.

The Chapter Summary and Review ends with exercises that review Applications and Connections.

SUMMARY AND REVIEW

VOCABULARY

Upon completing this chapter, you should be familiar with the following terms:

binomial	**226**	**213**	monomial
constants	**213**	**226**	polynomial
decimal notation	**221**	**221**	scientific notation
degree	**227**	**218**	simplify
FOIL method	**238**	**226**	trinomial

SKILLS AND CONCEPTS

OBJECTIVES AND EXAMPLES	REVIEW EXERCISES

Upon completing this chapter, you should be able to:

■ multiply monomials and simplify expressions involving powers of monomials **(Lesson 6-2)**

$$(2ab^2)(3a^2b^3) = (2 \cdot 3)(a \cdot a^2)(b^2 \cdot b^3)$$
$$= 6a^3b^5$$

$$(2x^2y^3)^3 = 2^3(x^2)^3(y^3)^3$$
$$= 8x^6y^9$$

Use these exercises to review and prepare for the chapter test.

Simplify. See margin.

1. $y^3 \cdot y^3 \cdot y$ 2. $(3ab)(-4a^2b^3)$

3. $(-4a^2x)(-5a^3x^4)$ 4. $(4a^2b)^3$

5. $(-3xy)^2(4x)^3$ 6. $(-2c^2d)^4(-3c^2)^3$

7. $-\frac{1}{2}(m^2n^4)^2$ 8. $(5a^2)^3 + 7(a^6)$

■ simplify expressions involving quotients of monomials and simplify expressions containing negative exponents **(Lesson 6-3)**

$$\frac{2x^6y}{8x^2y^2} = \frac{2}{8} \cdot \frac{x^6}{x^2} \cdot \frac{y}{y^2} = \frac{x^4}{4y}$$

$$\frac{3a^{-2}}{4a^6} = \frac{3}{4}(a^{-2-6}) = \frac{3}{4a^8}$$

Simplify. Assume no denominator is equal to zero.

9. $\frac{y^{10}}{y^6}$ y^4 10. $\frac{(3y)^0}{6a}$ $\frac{1}{6a}$

11. $\frac{42b^7}{14b^4}$ $3b^3$ 12. $\frac{27b^{-2}}{14b^{-3}}$ $\frac{27b}{14}$

13. $\frac{(3a^3bc^2)^2}{18a^2b^3c^4}$ $\frac{a^4}{2b}$ 14. $\frac{-16a^3b^2x^4y}{-48a^4bxy^3}$ $\frac{bx^3}{3ay^2}$

OBJECTIVES AND EXAMPLES	REVIEW EXERCISES

■ express numbers in scientific and
decimal notation **(Lesson 6-4)**

$3,600,000 = 3.6 \times 10^6$

$0.0021 = 2.1 \times 10^{-3}$

Express each number in scientific notation.
See margin.

15. 240,000 16. 4,880,000,000

17. 0.000314 18. 0.00000187

■ find products and quotients of numbers
expressed in scientific notation
(Lesson 6-4)

$(2 \times 10^2)(5.2 \times 10^6)$
$= (2 \times 5.2)(10^2 \times 10^6)$
$= 10.4 \times 10^8$
$= 1.04 \times 10^9$

$\dfrac{1.2 \times 10^{-2}}{0.6 \times 10^3} = \dfrac{1.2}{0.6} \times \dfrac{10^{-2}}{10^3}$
$= 2 \times 10^{-5}$

Evaluate. Express each result in scientific notation.

19. $(2 \times 10^5)(3 \times 10^6)$ 6×10^{11}

20. $(3 \times 10^3)(1.5 \times 10^6)$ 4.5×10^9

21. $\dfrac{5.4 \times 10^3}{0.9 \times 10^4}$ 6×10^{-1}

22. $\dfrac{8.4 \times 10^{-6}}{1.4 \times 10^{-9}}$ 6×10^3

■ find the degree of a polynomial
(Lesson 6-5)

Find the degree of $2xy^3 + x^2y$.

degree of $2xy^3$: 1 + 3 or 4
degree of x^2y: 2 + 1 or 3
degree of $2xy^3 + x^2y$: 4

Find the degree of each polynomial.

23. $n - 2p^2$ 2

24. $29n^2 + 17n^2t^2$ 4

25. $4xy + 9xz^2 + 17rs^3$ 4

26. $-6y - 2y^4 + 4 - 8y^2$ 4

■ arrange the terms of a polynomial so
that the powers of a certain variable are
in ascending or descending order
(Lesson 6-5)

Arrange the terms of $4x^2 + 9x^3 - 2 - x$
in descending order.

$9x^3 + 4x^2 - x - 2$

Arrange the terms of each polynomial so that the powers of x are in descending order.

27. $3x^4 - x + x^2 - 5$ $3x^4 + x^2 - x - 5$

28. $ax^2 - 5x^3 + a^2x - a^3$
$-5x^3 + ax^2 + a^2x - a^3$

■ add and subtract polynomials **(Lesson 6-6)**

$\begin{array}{r} 4x^2 - 3x + 7 \\ (+)\ 2x^2 + 4x \quad\ \ \\ \hline 6x^2 +\ \ x + 7 \end{array}$

$(7r^2 + 9r) - (12r^2 - 4)$
$= 7r^2 + 9r - 12r^2 + 4$
$= (7r^2 - 12r^2) + 9r + 4$
$= -5r^2 + 9r + 4$

Find each sum or difference. 29–30. See margin.

29. $(2x^2 - 5x + 7) - (3x^3 + x^2 + 2)$

30. $(x^2 - 6xy + 7y^2) + (3x^2 + xy - y^2)$

31. $\begin{array}{r} 11m^2n^2 + 4mn -\ \ 6 \\ (+)\ \ 5m^2n^2 - 6mn + 17 \\ \hline \end{array}$ $16m^2n^2 - 2mn + 11$

32. $\begin{array}{r} 7z^2 \quad\quad + 4 \\ (-)\ 3z^2 + 2z - 6 \\ \hline \end{array}$ $4z^2 - 2z + 10$

Additional Answers

1. y^7
2. $-12a^3b^4$
3. $20a^5x^5$
4. $64a^6b^3$
5. $576x^5y^2$
6. $-432c^{14}d^4$
7. $-\frac{1}{2}m^4n^8$
8. $132a^6$
15. 2.4×10^5
16. 4.88×10^9

17. 3.14×10^{-4}
18. 1.87×10^{-6}
29. $-3x^3 + x^2 - 5x + 5$
30. $4x^2 - 5xy + 6y^2$

The Cumulative Review shown below can be used to review skills and concepts presented thus far in the text. Standardized Test Practice Questions are also provided in the Evaluation Masters Booklet.

Evaluation Masters Booklet, pp. 81-82

OBJECTIVES AND EXAMPLES	REVIEW EXERCISES

- multiply a polynomial by a monomial and simplify expressions involving polynomials **(Lesson 6-7)**

$$x^2(x + 2) + 3(x^3 + 4x^2)$$
$$= x^3 + 2x^2 + 3x^3 + 12x^2$$
$$= 4x^3 + 14x^2$$

Simplify. 34–36. See margin.

33. $4ab(3a^2 - 7b^2)$ $12a^3b - 28ab^3$

34. $7xy(x^2 + 4xy - 8y^2)$

35. $x(3x - 5) + 7(x^2 - 2x + 9)$

36. $4x^2(x + 8) - 3x(2x^2 - 8x + 3)$

- use the FOIL method to multiply two binomials and multiply any two polynomials by using the distributive property **(Lesson 6-8)**

$$(3x + 2)(x - 2)$$
$$= (3x)(x) + (3x)(-2) + 2(x) + 2(-2)$$
$$= 3x^2 - 6x + 2x - 4$$
$$= 3x^2 - 4x - 4$$

Find each product. See margin.

37. $(r - 3)(r + 7)$ 38. $(x + 5)(3x - 2)$

39. $(4x - 3)(x + 4)$ 40. $(2x + 5y)(3x - y)$

41. $(x - 4)(x^2 + 5x - 7)$

42. $(2a + b)(a^2 - 17ab - 3b^2)$

- use the patterns for $(a + b)^2$, $(a - b)^2$, and $(a + b)(a - b)$ **(Lesson 6-9)**

$$(x + 4)^2 = x^2 + 2(4x) + 4^2$$
$$= x^2 + 8x + 16$$

$$(r - 5)^2 = r^2 - 2(5r) + 5^2$$
$$= r^2 - 10r + 25$$

$$(b + 9)(b - 9) = b^2 - 9^2$$
$$= b^2 - 81$$

Find each product. See margin.

43. $(x - 6)(x + 6)$ 44. $(5x - 3y)(5x + 3y)$

45. $(4x + 7)^2$ 46. $(a^2 + b)^2$

47. $(8x - 5)^2$ 48. $(6a - 5b)^2$

APPLICATIONS AND CONNECTIONS

Solve by looking for a pattern. (Lesson 6-1) 49. Fibonacci sequence

49. Male bees have only one parent, a mother, while female bees have both a mother and a father. How many grandparents does a male bee have? How many great-grandparents? If you continue to look at the bee's ancestry, what pattern do you notice?

50. The night of Ann's party, her doorbell rang 10 times. The first time, one guest arrived. Then, each time the doorbell rang, two more guests arrived than had arrived on the previous ring. How many guests were at Ann's party? **100 guests**

51. **Geometry** Find the measure of the third side of the triangle below if $P = 3x^2 - 12$. **(Lesson 6-6)** $x^2 - 4$

$x^2 - 4$ /\ $x^2 - 4$

52. **Geometry** Find the measure of the area of the shaded region in the figure below. **(Lesson 6-7)** $x^2 + 4x$

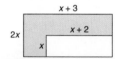

Additional Answers

34. $7x^3y + 28x^2y^2 - 56xy^3$

35. $10x^2 - 19x + 63$

36. $-2x^3 + 56x^2 - 9x$

37. $r^2 + 4r - 21$

38. $3x^2 + 13x - 10$

39. $4x^2 + 13x - 12$

40. $6x^2 + 13xy - 5y^2$

41. $x^3 + x^2 - 27x + 28$

42. $2a^3 - 33a^2b - 23ab^2 - 3b^3$

43. $x^2 - 36$

44. $25x^2 - 9y^2$

45. $16x^2 + 56x + 49$

46. $a^4 + 2a^2b + b^2$

47. $64x^2 - 80x + 25$

48. $36a^2 - 60ab + 25b^2$

6 TEST

Simplify. Assume no denominator is equal to zero.

1. $a^2 \cdot a^3 \cdot b^4 \cdot b^5$ a^5b^9

2. $(-12abc)(4a^2b^3)$ $-48a^3b^4c$

3. $(9a)^2$ $81a^2$

4. $(-3a)^4(a^5b)$ $81a^9b$

5. $(-5a^2)(-6b)^2$ $-180a^2b^2$

6. $(5a)^2b + 7a^2b$ $32a^2b$

7. $\dfrac{y^{11}}{y^6}$ y^5

8. $\dfrac{y^3x}{yx}$ y^2

9. $\dfrac{63a^2bc}{9abc}$ $7a$

10. $\dfrac{48a^2bc^5}{(3ab^3c^2)^2}$ $\dfrac{16c}{3b^5}$

11. $\dfrac{14ab^{-3}}{21a^2b^{-5}}$ $\dfrac{2b^2}{3a}$

12. $\dfrac{10a^2bc}{20a^{-1}b^{-1}c}$ $\dfrac{a^3b^2}{2}$

Express in scientific notation.

13. $52{,}800$ 5.28×10^4

14. 0.00378 3.78×10^{-3}

Evaluate. Express each result in scientific notation.

15. $(3 \times 10^3)(2 \times 10^4)$ 6×10^7

16. $(4 \times 10^{-3})(3 \times 10^{16})$ 1.2×10^{14}

17. $\dfrac{2.5 \times 10^3}{5 \times 10^{-3}}$ 5×10^5

18. $\dfrac{91 \times 10^{18}}{13 \times 10^{14}}$ 7×10^4

Arrange the terms of each polynomial so that the powers of *x* are in descending order.

19. $5x^2 - 3 + x^3 + 5x$ $x^3 + 5x^2 + 5x - 3$

20. $5 - xy^3 + x^3y^2 - x^2$ $x^3y^2 - x^2 - xy^3 + 5$

Simplify.   25. $-20x^3y + 24x^2y^4 - 8xy^3$ 27. $0.12b^3 - 0.21b^2 + 1.2b$

21. $(a + 5)^2$ $a^2 + 10a + 25$

22. $(2x - 5)(7x + 3)$ $14x^2 - 29x - 15$

23. $(3a^2 + 3)[2a - (-6)]$ $6a^3 + 18a^2 + 6a + 18$

24. $3x^2y^3(2x - xy^2)$ $6x^3y^3 - 3x^3y^5$

25. $-4xy(5x^2 - 6xy^3 + 2y^2)$

26. $(4x^2 - y^2)(4x^2 + y^2)$ $16x^4 - y^4$

27. $0.3b(0.4b^2 - 0.7b + 4)$

28. $(2a^2b + b^2)^2$ $4a^4b^2 + 4a^2b^3 + b^4$

29. $x^2(x - 8) - 3x(x^2 - 7x + 3) + 5(x^3 - 6x^2)$ $3x^3 - 17x^2 - 9x$

30. $a^2(a + 5) + 7a(a^2 + 8) - 7(a^3 - a + 2)$ $a^3 + 5a^2 + 63a - 14$

Solve each equation.

31. $5y - 8 - 13y = 12y + 6$ $-\dfrac{7}{10}$

32. $2(a + 2) + 3a = 13 - (2a + 2)$ 1

33. **Geometry** The length of a rectangle is eight times its width. If the length was decreased by 10 meters and the width was decreased by 2 meters, the area would be decreased by 162 square meters. Find the original dimensions.   7 m by 56 m

Bonus Find n if $2^{n+3} \cdot 2^{3n-2} \cdot 2^{5n+1} = 32$. (Hint: Write 32 as a power of 2.) $n = \dfrac{1}{3}$

Using the Chapter Test

This page may be used as a test or as a review. In addition, two multiple-choice tests and two free-response tests are provided in the Evaluation Masters Booklet. Chapter 6 Test, Form 1A is shown below.

Evaluation Masters Booklet, pp. 71-72

NAME _____ DATE _____

Chapter 6 Test, Form 1A

Write the letter for the correct answer in the blank at the right of each problem.

1. What is the simplest form of $m^4 \cdot m^2$?
   A. m^2 B. m^8 C. m^6 D. $2m^8$ 1. **C**

2. What is the simplest form of $(3w^2v)(-2w^5v^2)(4w^6v^5)$?
   A. $-24w^{13}v^8$ B. $5w^{40}v^{10}$ C. $-24w^{40}v^{10}$ D. $5w^{13}v^8$ 2. **A**

3. What is the simplest form of $(p^4q^5)^3$?
   A. p^7q^8 B. pq^2 C. $p^{12}q^{15}$ D. p^4q^{15} 3. **C**

4. What is the simplest form of $(y^2n^3)^4 + (3y^4n^6)^2$?
   A. $10y^5n^{12}$ B. $9y^{16}n^{27}$ C. $10y^8 + 2n^{12}$ D. $y^6n^7 + 9y^6n^8$ 4. **A**

5. What is the simplest form of $\dfrac{m^6n^2}{m^2n^5}$? Assume the denominator is not equal to zero.
   A. $\dfrac{m^4}{n^3}$ B. $-\dfrac{m^4}{n^3}$ C. $-\dfrac{m^8}{n^3}$ D. $\dfrac{m^4}{n^3}$ 5. **A**

6. What is the simplest form of $\dfrac{6n^{-3}yw^{-5}}{2n^{-1}y^{-3}w^2}$? Assume the denominator is not equal to zero.
   A. $\dfrac{4y^3}{n^4w^7}$ B. $\dfrac{3y^4}{n^2w^7}$ C. $\dfrac{3}{n^4w^3y^3}$ D. $\dfrac{3n^2}{y^4w^7}$ 6. **B**

7. What is 0.000543 expressed in scientific notation?
   A. 5.43×10^4 B. 5.43×10^{-3} C. 543×10^6 D. 5.43×10^{-4} 7. **D**

8. What is the value of $\dfrac{2.88 \times 10^3}{2.4 \times 10^{-7}}$?
   A. 0.48×10^{-4} B. 1.2×10^{-4} C. 1.2×10^{10} D. 0.48×10^{10} 8. **C**

9. What is the degree of $2x^3y - 4xy^2 + 9x^3y^9$?
   A. 4   B. 3   C. 12   D. 5   9. **D**

10. Which of the following shows the terms of $x^2y^3 + 4xy^2 - 3x^3y + 6$ arranged so that the powers of x are in ascending order?
    A. $6 + 4xy^2 + x^2y^3 - 3x^3y$ B. $x^2y^3 - 3x^3y + 4xy^2 + 6$
    C. $6 + 4xy^2 - 3x^3y + x^2y^3$ D. $6 + 4xy^2 + x^2y^3 + 4xy^2 + x^2y^3$ 10. **A**

11. What is the simplest form of $(6w^2 - 5wz - 3z^2) - (4w^2 + 6wz - 8z^2)$?
    A. $10w^2 + wz - 11z^2$ B. $2w^2 - 11wz + 5z^2$
    C. $2w^2 + wz - 11z^2$ D. $2w^2 - 11wz - 5z^2$ 11. **B**

12. What is the simplest form of $8a^2b(3a + 2ab^3)$?
    A. $24a^2b + 16a^2b^3$ B. $24a^3b + 2ab^3$
    C. $24a^3b + 16a^3b^4$ D. $11a^2b + 10a^2b^3$ 12. **C**

NAME _____ DATE _____

Chapter 6 Test, Form 1A (continued)

13. What is the simplest form of $(x + 2)(x + 4)$?
    A. $x^2 + 8$ B. $2x + 6$ C. $2x + 8$ D. $x^2 + 6x + 8$ 13. **D**

14. What is the simplest form of $(2n - 6)(4n + 2)$?
    A. $6n^2 + 28n - 12$ B. $8n^2 - 12$
    C. $8n^2 - 20n - 12$ D. $8n^2 + 20n - 12$ 14. **C**

15. Find a pattern in the sequences below. Then write the next three numbers in the sequence. 1, 7, 17, 31, 49, ...
    A. 71, 97, 127   B. 64, 81, 100   C. 67, 85, 103   D. none of these   15. **A**

16. What is the simplest form of $(x + 6)^2$?
    A. $x^2 + 36$ B. $x^2 + 12x + 36$ C. $x^2 + 12$ D. $2x + 12$ 16. **B**

17. What is the simplest form of $(3y + 4z)(3y - 4z)$?
    A. $9y^2 - 16z^2$ B. $9y^2 - 24yz - 16z^2$
    C. $9y^2 + 16z^2$ D. $9y^2 - 24yz + 16z^2$ 17. **A**

18. Find the solution of $-4(5 - 2n) = 8(-6 - 5n)$.
    A. $-\dfrac{1}{9}$ B. $-\dfrac{28}{3}$ C. $-\dfrac{7}{8}$ D. $-\dfrac{7}{12}$ 18. **D**

19. Find the solution of $8 - 3(2x - 4) = 8x - 6$.
    A. 7   B. -13 C. $\dfrac{1}{7}$ D. $\dfrac{13}{7}$ 19. **D**

20. A picture is 4 inches longer than it is wide. It is surrounded by a mat 2 inches wide. The total area of the mat is 112 square inches. If w is the width of the picture, which equation is true?
    A. $(w + 4)(w + 8) + w(w + 4) = 112$
    B. $(w + 2)(w + 6) - w(w + 4) = 112$
    C. $(w + 4)(w + 8) - w(w + 4) = 112$
    D. $(w + 2)(w + 6) + w(w + 4) = 112$ 20. **C**

Bonus: Solve $3^{2n-1} \cdot 3^{5n} = (3^4)^{a+2}$ for n.   Bonus: **3**

Test Generator Software is provided in both Apple and IBM versions. You may use this software to create your own tests, based on the needs of your students.

College Entrance Exam Preview

The test questions on these pages deal with fraction concepts, ratios, proportions, and percents.

Directions: Choose the best answer. Write A, B, C, or D.

1. In a class of 27 students, six are honor
B students. What part of the class is *not* honor students?

   (A) $\frac{7}{11}$ (B) $\frac{7}{9}$ (C) $\frac{2}{7}$ (D) $\frac{2}{9}$

2. The months from April to December,
B inclusive, are what fractional part of a year?

   (A) $\frac{7}{12}$ (B) $\frac{3}{4}$ (C) $\frac{5}{12}$ (D) $\frac{2}{3}$

3. What fractional part of a week is one
A sixth of a day?

   (A) $\frac{1}{42}$ (B) $\frac{1}{30}$ (C) $\frac{4}{7}$ (D) $\frac{7}{168}$

4. 0.7% is the ratio of 7 to
D

   (A) 100   (B) $\frac{1}{10}$

   (C) $\frac{1}{1000}$ (D) 1000

5. 37.5% of a pound is equivalent to what
B fractional part of a pound?

   (A) $\frac{37}{100}$ (B) $\frac{3}{8}$ (C) $\frac{37}{99}$ (D) $37\frac{1}{2}$

6. Five sixths is how many sevenths?
C
   (A) $5\frac{5}{7}$ (B) $8\frac{2}{5}$ (C) $5\frac{5}{6}$ (D) $4\frac{2}{7}$

7. How many elevenths is 75%?
A
   (A) $8\frac{1}{4}$ (B) $\frac{3}{4}$ (C) $6\frac{9}{11}$ (D) $\frac{12}{11}$

8. 90% of 270 is 2.7% of
D
   (A) 729   (B) 900
   (C) 2000   (D) 9000

9. A box contains 60 red, blue, and green
B pens. If 35% are red and 9 pens are blue, what percent are green?

   (A) 40%   (B) 50%   (C) 60%   (D) 65%

10. Doralina wishes to run a certain
C distance in 20% less time than she usually takes. By what percent must she increase her overall average speed?

    (A) 5%   (B) 20%   (C) 25%   (D) 50%

11. 150% of $5c$ is b. What percent of $2b$
B is c?

    (A) $5\frac{1}{2}$%   (B) $6\frac{2}{3}$%   (C) 15%   (D) 75%

12. Two fifths times five sevenths is equal
A to what number times six elevenths?

    (A) $\frac{11}{21}$ (B) $\frac{55}{63}$ (C) $\frac{20}{77}$ (D) $\frac{22}{43}$

13. A woman owns $\frac{3}{4}$ of a business. She
C sells half of her share for $30,000. What is the total value of the business?

    (A) $45,000   (B) $75,000
    (C) $80,000   (D) $112,000

14. On a map, a line segment 1.75 inches
B long represents 21 miles. What
distance in miles is represented by a
segment 0.6 inch long?

(A) 6   (B) 7.2

(C) 12.6   (D) 24.15

15. A cake recipe that serves 6 people
D calls for 2 cups of flour. How many
cups of flour would be needed to bake
a smaller cake that serves 4 people?

(A) $\frac{3}{4}$ (B) 1   (C) $1\frac{1}{4}$ (D) $1\frac{1}{3}$

16. The price of an item was reduced by
B 10%, then later reduced by 20%. The
two reductions were equivalent to a
single reduction of

(A) 15%   (B) 28%   (C) 30%   (D) 70%

17. The discount price for a $50 item is
D $40. What is the discount price for a
$160 item if the rate of discount is
$1\frac{1}{2}$ times the rate of the discount for
the $50 item?

(A) $20   (B) $48   (C) $96   (D) $112

18. A car was driven twice as many miles
B in July as in each of the other 11
months of the year. What fraction of
the total mileage for the year occurred
in July?

(A) $\frac{2}{11}$ (B) $\frac{2}{13}$ (C) $\frac{1}{6}$ (D) $\frac{1}{7}$

19. $\dfrac{68 + 68 + 68 + 68}{4} =$
B

(A) 17   (B) 68   (C) 136   (D) 272

20. The sum of twelve numbers is 4965.
B If each number is increased by 16,
what is the sum of the new numbers?

(A) 192   (B) 5157   (C) 4773   (D) 4981

TEST TAKING TIP

Most standardized tests have a time
limit, so you must budget your time
carefully. Some questions will be
much easier than others. If you cannot answer a question within a few
minutes, go on to the next one. If
there is still time left when you get
to the end of the test, go back to the
ones that you skipped.

21. Which of the following *cannot* be the
A average of 10, 7, 13, 2, and x if x > 4?

(A) 7   (B) 9   (C) 13   (D) 258

22. The average of eight integers *can* be
D

(A) 127.6   (B) 130.8

(C) 131.3   (D) 135.5

23. If the product of a number and b is
A increased by y, the result is t. Find the
number in terms of b, y, and t.

(A) $\dfrac{t - y}{b}$ (B) $\dfrac{y - t}{b}$

(C) $\dfrac{b + y}{t}$ (D) $t - by$

24. Mark can type 60 words per minute
C and there is an average of 360 words
per page. At this rate, how many
hours would it take him to type k
pages?

(A) $\dfrac{k}{6}$ (B) $\dfrac{k}{60}$ (C) $\dfrac{k}{10}$ (D) $\dfrac{10}{k}$

25. Eight people can sit at a square table.
B If three such tables are placed
end-to-end to form a rectangle, how
many people can be seated?

(A) 12   (B) 16   (C) 20   (D) 24

CHAPTER 7

Factoring

PREVIEWING THE CHAPTER

This chapter covers the important algebraic topic of factoring. Students begin by finding the greatest common factor for a set of monomials and then use the distributive property to factor polynomials. Then in a carefully developed sequence of lessons that includes the use of geometric models, students learn additional techniques to factor quadratic trinomials, the difference of squares, and perfect squares. The chapter concludes with activities that require students to apply what they have learned about factoring to solve quadratic equations.

Problem-Solving Strategy Students use the strategy of *guess and check* to solve problems. They guess the answer, check the guess, analyze the result, and continue to guess and check until they find the correct answer.

Lesson Objective Chart

Lesson (Pages)	Lesson Objectives		State/Local Objectives
7-1 (256-260)	**7-1A:**	Find the prime factorization of an integer.	
	7-1B:	Find the greatest common factor (GCF) for a set of monomials.	
7-2 (261-264)	**7-2:**	Use the GCF and the distributive property to factor polynomials.	
7-3 (265-268)	**7-3:**	Use grouping techniques to factor polynomials with four or more terms.	
7-4 (269-270)	**7-4:**	Solve problems by using guess and check.	
7-5 (271-275)	**7-5:**	Factor quadratic trinomials.	
7-6 (276-280)	**7-6:**	Identify and factor polynomials that are the differences of squares.	
7-7 (281-284)	**7-7:**	Identify and factor perfect square trinomials.	
7-8 (286-289)	**7-8:**	Factor polynomials by applying the various methods of factoring.	
7-9 (290-294)	**7-9:**	Use the zero product property to solve equations.	
7-10 (295-299)	**7-10:**	Solve equations by using various factoring methods and applying the zero product property.	

ORGANIZING THE CHAPTER

You may want to refer to the **Course Planning Calendar** on page T36.

Lesson Planning Guide

Lesson (Pages)	Pacing Chart (days) Course I	II	III	Reteaching	Practice	Enrichment	Evaluation	Technology	Lab Manual	Mixed Problem Solving	Applications	Cooperative Learning Activity	Multicultural	Transparencies
7-1 (256-260)	1.5	1	1	p. 43	p. 48	p. 43				p. 7				7-1
7-2 (261-264)	1.5	1	1	p. 44	p. 49	p. 44	Quiz A, p. 93							7-2
7-3 (265-268)	1	1	1	p. 45	p. 50	p. 45								7-3
7-4 (269-270)	1	0.5	0.5		p. 51			p. 7						7-4
7-5 (271-275)	1.5	1.5	1.5	p. 46	p. 52	p. 46	Quiz B, p. 93 Mid-Chapter Test, p. 97				p. 22			7-5
7-6 (276-280)	1.5	1	1	p. 47	p. 53	p. 47						p. 37		7-6
7-7 (281-284)	1	1	1	p. 48	p. 54	p. 48	Quiz C, p. 94		pp. 29-30					7-7
7-8 (286-289)	1	1	1	p. 49	p. 55	p. 49								7-8
7-9 (290-294)	1.5	1.5	1	p. 50	p. 56	p. 50							p. 52	7-9
7-10 (295-299)	1.5	1.5	1	p. 51	p. 57	p. 51	Quiz D, p 94	p. 22						7-10
Review (300-302)	1	1	1	Multiple Choice Tests, Forms 1A and 1B, pp. 85-88 Free Response Tests, Forms 2A and 2B, pp. 89-92										
Test (303)	1	1	1	Cumulative Review, pp. 95-96 Standardized Test Practice Questions, p. 98										

Course I: Chapters 1-13; Course II: Chapters 1-14; Course III: Chapters 1-15

Other Chapter Resources

Student Edition

History Connection, p. 260
Cooperative Learning Activity, p. 270
Mid-Chapter Review, p. 280
Technology, p. 285
Algebraic Skills Review, pp. 659, 661
(ex. 25-39)

Teacher Resource Package

Activity Masters Booklet
Mixed Problem Solving, p. 7
Applications, p. 22
Cooperative Learning Activity, p. 37
Multicultural Activity, p. 52
Technology Masters Booklet
Scientific Calculator Activity, p. 7
Graphing Calculator Activity, p. 22
Lab Manual
Lab Activity, pp. 29-30

Other Supplements

Transparency for Chapter Opener
Problem-of-the-Week Activity
Cards, 16-17
Video Algebra, 18-21, 23-26, 53

Software

Algebra 1 Test and Review
Generator Software
Available for Apple and IBM.

ENHANCING THE CHAPTER

Cooperative Learning

Describing the Student's Responsibilities to the Group

It is important for students to understand that they are expected not merely to work in a group but to work cooperatively in a group. Each member must understand that he or she is responsible for learning the assigned material *and* for making sure every other member of the group also learns the material; that is, as the saying goes, they all sink or swim together. One way to encourage such behavior is to have the group generate a single product, report, or set of answers that each member must sign to signify agreement with the responses and ability to justify or explain why the responses are appropriate. Be alert for other ways to encourage group members to count on each other and look for ways to help each other do better. For example, when you administer a quiz or test, inform the group that each member will earn an individual score and will also earn bonus points based on how much the group's average score exceeds a preset level of performance.

Technology

The Technology Feature after Lesson 7-7 employs the *Mathematical Exploration Toolkit* (MET). CALC can completely factor polynomials involving one variable. A command is available to display the steps used by the computer in finding the factors. Common monomial, linear, and quadratic factors are found. Integral powers and rational coefficients are supported. The commands for factoring will be used in Chapter 8 to simplify rational expressions. Encourage students to become competent with the factor commands introduced in this chapter.

Critical Thinking

The acquisition of critical-thinking skills involving analysis and synthesis are virtually indispensable for success in factoring. You can help students improve their facility with these requisite skills by taking advantage of problem-solving activities involving the strategy *guess and check*. During these activities, make students aware that you expect them to be able to explain, when their first guess is not the answer, how and why they chose each successive guess. Such analysis of the results of initial guesses to make more intelligent guesses can then be transferred to exercises involving the factoring of binomials and trinomials. Continue to require students to discuss and justify their choices.

Cooperative Learning, p. 37

CHAPTER 7 — Cooperative Learning Activity (Use after Lesson 7-6)

Factoring Trinomial Squares

Work in small groups.

Use x^2, x, and 1 to represent x^2, x, and 1, respectively.

Use the models to represent the trinomial $x^2 + 4x + 4$.

Arrange the models to form a rectangle.

1. What do you notice about the length and width of the final rectangle? **They are the same.**

2. Give the dimensions of the final rectangle. (The dimensions are the factors of the trinomial.) **$(x + 2)$ by $(x + 2)$**

Factor each of the following polynomials by forming rectangular regions with the models.

3. $x^2 + 6x + 9$ — $(x + 3)^2$

4. $4x^2 + 4x + 1$ — $(2x + 1)^2$

5. $x^2 + 4x + 3$ — $(x + 3)(x + 1)$

6. $x^2 + 2x + 1$ — $(x + 1)^2$

7. $x^2 + 8x + 16$ — $(x + 4)^2$

8. $3x^2 + 4x + 1$ — $(3x + 1)(x + 1)$

9. Which of the rectangles above are squares? **$x^2 + 6x + 9$, $4x^2 + 4x + 1$, $x^2 + 2x + 1$, $x^2 + 8x + 16$**

10. What do you call a trinomial whose representation is a square? **perfect square trinomial**

11. How can you tell whether a trinomial is a perfect square trinomial? **The first and third terms are squares and the middle term is twice the product of the square roots of the first and third terms.**

12. Factor $x^2 - 4$ by forming a rectangular region from two trapezoids. **$(x + 2)(x - 2)$**

Technology, p. 7

CHAPTER 7 — Scientific Calculator Activity (Use after Lesson 7-4)

Finding Factors Using the Store and Recall Keys

You can use a calculator to help you guess and then quickly check the factors of a number. One useful key is the *memory* or **storage** key. This is represented by an abbreviation such as M+ or STO. When you enter a number and then press STO (or M+), the number is stored in the memory of the calculator. To recall the number you have stored, press the **recall** key, which is abbreviated on some calculator as MR (recall memory) or as RCL.

Example: What are some factors of 26,496?
Guesses: 96 and 496

First, store 26,496.

ENTER 26496 [STO]

Then check each guess.

ENTER [RCL] [÷] 96 [=] Result: 276

Therefore, 96 is a factor of 26,496.

Now check 496.

ENTER [RCL] [÷] 496 [=] Result: 53.41935484

Therefore, 496 is not a factor of 26,496.

Guess three factors between 20 and 40 for each of the following numbers and then use a calculator to check them. List each guess and tell whether it is a factor. **Answers will vary.**

1. 1000
2. 432
3. 8756
4. 12,000
5. 5679
6. 20,757
7. 91,977
8. 765,049
9. 23,207,189

Problem of the Week Activity

The card shown below is one of two available for this chapter. It can be used as a class or small group activity.

Activity Card

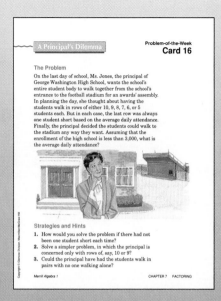

Manipulatives and Models

The following materials may be used as models or manipulatives in Chapter 7.

- index cards (Lessons 7-1 and 7-8)
- clear beaker (Lesson 7-4)
- paper clips (Lesson 7-4)
- centimeter blocks (Lesson 7-6)
- algebra tiles (Lesson 7-7)
- grid paper (Lesson 7-8)

Outside Resources

Books/Periodicals

Goldberg, Kenneth P. *Pushbutton Mathematics*. Prentice-Hall, Inc.

Kogelman, Dr. Stanley and Dr. Joseph Warren. *Mind Over Math*. McGraw Hill Book Company.

Films/Videotapes/Videodiscs

Algebra, TPC Training Systems

Two Laws of Algebra, Pyramid Films

Software

Algebra, True BASIC

Factoring Algebraic Expressions, Micro Computer Workshop

Mathematical Exploration Toolkit, IBM

Multicultural

Multicultural Activity, p. 52

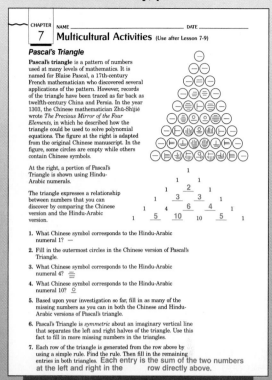

Lab Manual

Lab Activity, pp. 29-30

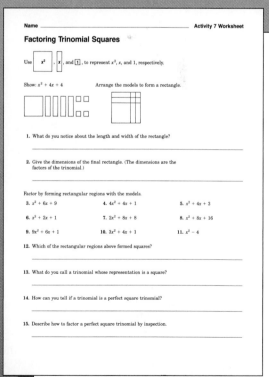

Using the Chapter Opener

Transparency 7-0 is available in the Transparency Package. It provides a full-color visual and motivational activity that you can use to engage students in the mathematical content of the chapter.

Background Information

The dolphin is the most elaborate creature in the sea. It probably communicates by a modulated (varied frequency, amplitude, or phase) language, but we don't know yet to what extent it can store and transmit information. If necessary, the dolphin can swim at a speed of 9 meters per second (20 mph) almost indefinitely. It can dive deeper than 90 meters (300 feet) and can remain underwater for more than five miutes. As a game, dolphins often ride the bow waves in front of a moving boat. They expend little or no energy, letting humans do the work.

In this chapter, you will:
- Find prime factorizations of integers.
- Factor polynomials.
- Solve quadratic equations using factoring and the zero product property.
- Solve problems that can be represented by quadratic equations.
- Guess and check to solve problems.

Chapter Project

Materials: paper, pencil, ball or other object, stopwatch

Organize students into cooperative groups. Tell them that the polynomial of the chapter opener is derived from the equation $d = v_i t - \frac{1}{2} g t^2$, where d is height, v_i is initial velocity, t is time, and g is the acceleration of an object as a result of the force of gravity. The value of g is more accurately represented as $9.8 \frac{m}{s^2}$. (This value is rounded to $10 \frac{m}{s^2}$ in the chapter opener.) First, have one member of each group drop a ball from a window or from the roof of the school, while another member uses a stopwatch to measure the time it takes to reach the ground. Since initial velocity when the ball is released is zero, v_i is zero. Have each group conduct several trials, record each on a chart, and use the average of all trials for t. Then, instruct each group to find the height (d) from which the ball was dropped using the above equation. A negative distance means the direction was downward.

Connections and Applications

Any trip to an aquatic park is just not complete until you have seen a dolphin leap high above the water to grab a fish or a whale splash the visitors who are brave enough to sit in the front row!

APPLICATION IN MARINE BIOLOGY

Have you ever wondered how long a dolphin can stay in the air after jumping out of the water? In a standard aquatic park pool, dolphins can reach speeds in excess of 24 mph just before breaking the surface of the water. If a dolphin leaves the water traveling at 24 mph, then its height h, in feet, above the water after t seconds is given by the formula $h = 24t - 16t^2$.

When the dolphin returns to the water, it is 0 feet above the water. Thus, the amount of time that the dolphin stays in the air can be found by solving $0 = 24t - 16t^2$ for t. An obvious solution of the equation is $t = 0$, since after 0 seconds, the dolphin has not jumped! But how do we find the real solution?

Notice that this is a polynomial equation. In this chapter, you will learn a technique called *factoring* that may be used to solve equations like the one above.

ALGEBRA IN ACTION

You can solve the problem by finding the height of the dolphin at various times using the formula $h = 24t - 16t^2$. Copy and complete the chart below. Does $h = 0$ for any value of t? If so, that value is the amount of time that our dolphin stays in the air. **yes; 1.5 seconds**

t	$24t - 16t^2$	h
0.25	$24(0.25) - 16(0.25)^2$	5
0.5	$24(0.5) - 16(0.5)^2$	8
0.75	$24(0.75) - 16(0.75)^2$	?9
1.0	$24(1.0) - 16(1.0)^2$	?8
1.25	?	?5
1.5	?	?0
1.75	?	?−7
2.0	?	?−16

255

Lesson	Connections (C) and Applications (A)	Examples	Exercises
7-1	C: Geometry		68-69
	A: Gardening		71
	Travel		72
	Sports		73
	Metallurgy		78
7-2	C: Geometry	4	36-39, 44-45
	A: Gardening		46
	Stocks		47
	Sales		49
7-3	C: Geometry		34-38, 43
	A: Conference		44
	Construction		45
	Sales		47
7-4	C: Number Theory		10
7-5	C: Geometry	2	44,55
	A: Shipping		56
	Agriculture		57
	Finance		58
7-6	C: Geometry	6	42-45, 52
	Number Theory		41
	A: Photography		57
	Finance		58
	Travel		60
7-7	C: Geometry	4	43-46, 59-60
	Number Theory		65
	A: Photography		61
	Construction		62
	Travel		64
7-8	C: Geometry	4	51,60
	A: Gardening		53
	Conferences		54
	Sales		56
7-9	A: Gardening		41
	Construction		42
	Physics		43-44
	Sales		45
7-10	C: Number Theory	3	33-37
	Geometry		32
	A: Gardening		45
	Photography		46
	Agriculture		47
	Physics		48-49, 56
	Basketball		50

INTRODUCING THE LESSON

🕐 5-Minute Check

(over Chapter 6)

Multiply.

1. $(a + 2b)^2$ $a^2 + 4ab + 4b^2$
2. $(x - 3r)^2$ $x^2 - 6rx + 9r^2$
3. $(5m^2 + 7n)^2$ $25m^4 + 70m^2n + 49n^2$
4. $(2x^2 - 3y^3)^2$ $4x^4 - 12x^2y^3 + 9y^6$
5. $(5a - 4b)(5a + 4b)$ $25a^2 - 16b^2$

Motivating the Lesson

Introduce the lesson by having students identify factors of numbers such as 12, 36, 64, and 100.

TEACHING THE LESSON

Teaching Tip ❶

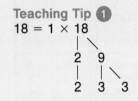

$18 = 1 \times 18$

7-1 Factors and Greatest Common Factors

Objectives

After studying this lesson, you should be able to:

7-1A ■ find the prime factorization of an integer, and

7-1B ■ find the greatest common factor (GCF) for a set of monomials.

Connection

In mathematics, there are many situations where there is more than one correct answer. Suppose three students are asked to draw and label a rectangle that has an area of 18 square inches. As shown below, each student can draw a different rectangle, and each drawing is correct.

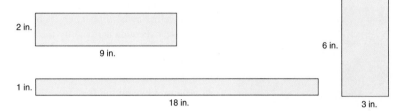

Since 2×9, 3×6, and 1×18 all equal 18, each rectangle above has an area of 18 square inches.

When two or more numbers are multiplied, each number is a **factor** of the product. In the example above, 18 is expressed as the product of different pairs of whole numbers.

$$18 = 2 \cdot 9 \qquad 18 = 3 \cdot 6 \qquad 18 = 1 \cdot 18$$

The whole numbers 1, 18, 2, 9, 3, and 6 are factors of 18. Some whole numbers have exactly two factors, the number itself and 1. These numbers are called **prime numbers**. Whole numbers that have more than two factors are called **composite numbers**.

Definition of Prime and Composite Numbers	A prime number is a whole number, greater than 1, whose only factors are 1 and itself. A composite number is a whole number, greater than 1, that is not prime.

0 and 1 are neither prime nor composite.

Teaching Tip ❶

The number 9 is a factor of 18, but not a **prime factor** of 18, since 9 is not a prime number. When a whole number is expressed as a product of factors that are all prime, the expression is called the **prime factorization** of the number. Thus, the prime factorization of 18 is $2 \cdot 3 \cdot 3$ or $2 \cdot 3^2$.

The prime factorization of every number is unique except for the order in which the factors are written. For example, $3 \cdot 2 \cdot 3$ is also a prime factorization of 18, but it is the same as $2 \cdot 3 \cdot 3$. This property of numbers is called the *Unique Factorization Theorem*.

256 CHAPTER 7 FACTORING

ALTERNATE TEACHING STRATEGIES

Using Manipulatives

Divide the class into pairs. Give each pair 20 index cards. Students should write two numbers on each of 10 cards and the GCF of the numbers on separate index cards. Students then exchange cards. Tell students to shuffle the cards and place them face down on a flat surface. Students take turns flipping over two cards to match numbers and their GCF. If a match is made, the student keeps the cards. The student holding the greatest number of cards once all the cards have been picked up is the winner.

Example 1

Find the prime factorization of 84.

You can begin by dividing 84 by its least prime factor. Continue dividing by least prime factors until all the factors are prime.

$84 = 2 \cdot 42$ *The least prime factor of 84 is 2.*

$= 2 \cdot 2 \cdot 21$ *The least prime factor of 42 is 2.*

$= 2 \cdot 2 \cdot 3 \cdot 7$ *The least prime factor of 21 is 3.*

All of the factors above are prime. Thus, the prime factorization of 84 is $2 \cdot 2 \cdot 3 \cdot 7$ or $2^2 \cdot 3 \cdot 7$. Teaching Tip 2

Example 2

Factor −525. Teaching Tip 3

To factor a negative integer, first express it as the product of a whole number and −1. Then find the prime factorization.

$$\begin{aligned} -525 &= -1 \cdot 525 \\ &= -1 \cdot 3 \cdot 175 \\ &= -1 \cdot 3 \cdot 5 \cdot 35 \\ &= -1 \cdot 3 \cdot 5 \cdot 5 \cdot 7 \text{ or } -1 \cdot 3 \cdot 5^2 \cdot 7 \end{aligned}$$

A monomial is written in *factored form* when it is expressed as the product of prime numbers and variables where no variable has an exponent greater than 1.

Example 3

Factor $20a^2b$.

$$\begin{aligned} 20a^2b &= 2 \cdot 10 \cdot a \cdot a \cdot b \\ &= 2 \cdot 2 \cdot 5 \cdot a \cdot a \cdot b \end{aligned}$$

Two or more numbers may have some common factors. Consider the prime factorizations of 90 and 105 shown below.

$90 = 2 \cdot 3 \cdot 3 \cdot 5$ $\qquad$ $105 = 3 \cdot 5 \cdot 7$

1 is always a common factor.

The integers 90 and 105 have 3 and 5 as common prime factors. The product of these prime factors, $3 \cdot 5$ or 15, is called the **greatest common factor (GCF)** of 90 and 105. Teaching Tip 4

Definition of Greatest Common Factor

The greatest common factor of two or more integers is the product of the prime factors common to each integer.

The GCF of two or more monomials is the product of their common factors, when each monomial is expressed as a product of prime factors.

Chalkboard Examples

For Example 1

Find the prime factorization of each number.

a. 200 $2 \times 2 \times 2 \times 5 \times 5$

b. 650 $2 \times 5 \times 5 \times 13$

c. 420 $2 \times 2 \times 3 \times 5 \times 7$

d. 168 $2 \times 2 \times 2 \times 3 \times 7$

For Example 2

Factor.

a. −210 $-1 \times 2 \times 3 \times 5 \times 7$

b. −448 $-1 \times 2 \times 2 \times 2 \times 2 \times 2 \times 2 \times 7$

For Example 3

Factor.

a. $45a^2b^2$ $3 \times 3 \times 5 \times a \times a \times b \times b$

b. $77ab^2$ $7 \times 11 \times a \times b \times b$

Teaching Tip 2 The order of prime factors in a prime factorization is not critical. Usually the factors are ordered from least prime factor to greatest.

Teaching Tip 3 −1 is factored out first so that the factoring will be consistent with prime factoring of positive numbers.

Teaching Tip 4 Emphasize that 15 is the greatest whole number that will divide 90 and 105 evenly.

Example 4 | **Find the GCF of 54, 63, and 180.**

$54 = 2 \cdot 3 \cdot 3 \cdot 3$ *Factor each number.*
$63 = 3 \cdot 3 \cdot 7$
$180 = 2 \cdot 2 \cdot 3 \cdot 3 \cdot 5$ *Then circle the common factors.*

The GCF of 54, 63, and 180 is $3 \cdot 3$ or 9.

Example 5 | **Find the GCF of $8a^2b$ and $18a^2b^2c$.**

$8a^2b = 2 \cdot 2 \cdot 2 \cdot a \cdot a \cdot b$
$18a^2b^2c = 2 \cdot 3 \cdot 3 \cdot a \cdot a \cdot b \cdot b \cdot c$

The GCF of $8a^2b$ and $18a^2b^2c$ is $2a^2b$.

CHECKING FOR UNDERSTANDING

Communicating Mathematics

Read and study the lesson to answer each question. 1, 4. See margin.

1. Draw and label as many rectangles as possible with sides of integral length that have an area of 50 square inches.
2. Name the first ten prime numbers. 2, 3, 5, 7, 11, 13, 17, 19, 23, 29
3. Is $2 \cdot 3^2 \cdot 4$ the prime factorization of 72? Why or why not? No; 4 is not prime.
4. What is the difference between a common factor of two numbers and a greatest common factor?

Guided Practice

State whether each number is prime or composite. If the number is composite, find its prime factorization.

5. 89 prime   6. 39 composite; $3 \cdot 13$ 7. 24 composite; $2^3 \cdot 3$ 8. 91 composite; $7 \cdot 13$

Find the GCF of each pair of numbers.

9. 4, 12 4   10. 9, 36 9   11. 15, 5 5   12. 11, 22 11
13. 10, 15 5   14. 20, 30 10   15. 18, 35 1   16. 16, 18 2

EXERCISES

Practice

A

Find the prime factorization of each number.

17. 21 $3 \cdot 7$ 18. 28 $2^2 \cdot 7$ 19. 60 $2^2 \cdot 3 \cdot 5$
20. 51 $3 \cdot 17$ 21. 63 $3^2 \cdot 7$ 22. 72 $2^3 \cdot 3^2$
23. 112 $2^4 \cdot 7$ 24. 150 $2 \cdot 3 \cdot 5^2$ 25. 304 $2^4 \cdot 19$
26. 216 $2^3 \cdot 3^3$ 27. 300 $2^2 \cdot 3 \cdot 5^2$ 28. 1540 $2^2 \cdot 5 \cdot 7 \cdot 11$

258   CHAPTER 7   FACTORING

RETEACHING THE LESSON

To find the prime factorization of an integer, use "factor stairs." Divide the integer by its least prime factor. Repeat for the quotient. When you reach 1, the factorization is complete. The answer is on the steps.
$252 = 2 \cdot 2 \cdot 3 \cdot 3 \cdot 7$

$$
\begin{array}{r|r}
 & 1 \\
7 & 7 \\
3 & 21 \\
3 & 63 \\
2 & 126 \\
2 & 252 \\
\end{array}
$$

Additional Answer

1.

Factor each expression. Do not use exponents. **See margin.**

29. -64 30. -26 31. -240 32. -231

33. $98a^2b$ 34. $44rs^2t^3$ 35. $756(mn)^3$ 36. $-102x^3y$

Find the GCF of the given monomials.

37. $16, 60$ **4**   38. $15, 50$ **5**   39. $-80, 45$ **5**

40. $29, -58$ **29**   41. $305, 55$ **5**   42. $252, 126$ **126**

43. $128, 245$ **1**   44. $95, 304$ **19**   45. $7y^2, 14y^2$ **$7y^2$**

46. $17a, 34a^2$ **$17a$**   47. $-12ab, 4a^2b^2$ **$4ab$**   48. $4xy, -6x$ **$2x$**

49. $50n^4, 40n^2p^2$ **$10n^2$**   50. $60x^2y^2, 35xz^3$ **$5x$**   51. $12an^2, 40a^4$ **$4a$**

52. $56x^3y, 49ax^2$ **$7x^2$**   53. $5, 15, 10$ **5**   54. $16, 24, 28$ **4**

55. $18, 30, 54$ **6**   56. $24, 84, 168$ **12**   57. $16, 24, 30$ **2**

58. $12mn, 10mn, 15mn$ **mn**   59. $6a^2, 18b^2, 9b^3$ **3**

60. $8b^4, 5c, 3a^2b$ **1**   61. $15abc, 35a^2c, 105a$ **$5a$**

62. $14a^2b^2, 18ab, 2a^3b^3$ **$2ab$**   63. $18x^2y^2, 6y^2, 42x^2y^3$ **$6y^2$**

Find the missing factor.

64. $48a^5b^4 = 3a^3b^2(\underline{\ ?\ })$ **$16a^2b^2$**   65. $-28x^4y^3 = 7x^2(\underline{\ ?\ })$ **$-4x^2y^3$**

66. $36m^5n^7 = 2m^3n(6n^5)(\underline{\ ?\ })$ **$3m^2n$**   67. $48a^5b^5 = 2ab^2(4ab)(\underline{\ ?\ })$ **$6a^3b^2$**

CONNECTION
Geometry

68. The area of a rectangle is 1363 square inches. If the measures of the length and width of this rectangle are both prime numbers, what are its dimensions? **29 in. by 47 in.**

Critical Thinking

69. **Geometry** Draw and label all the rectangles that satisfy the following conditions. The area of a rectangle is $8b^2$ square centimeters and the measure of each of its sides can be expressed as a monomial with integral coefficients. (*Hint:* There are 6.) **See margin.**

70. *Twin primes* are two consecutive odd prime numbers, such as 11 and 13. How many pairs of twin primes are there where both primes are less than 100? Find them. **8: 3, 5; 5, 7; 11, 13; 17, 19; 29, 31; 41, 43; 59, 61; 71, 73**

5 rows of 20 plants; 10 rows of 10 plants; 20 rows of 5 plants

Applications

71. **Gardening** Anita is planning to have 100 tomato plants in her garden. In what ways can she arrange them so that she has the same number of plants in each row and at least 5 rows of plants?

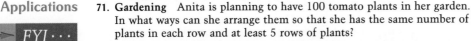
FYI · · ·

A 7 lb 12 oz tomato was grown by Gordon Graham of Oklahoma in 1986.

72. **Travel** Jackie and Jaime left at the same time on a 300-mile trip. Jaime's average speed for the trip was 10 miles per hour slower than Jackie's. If it took Jaime one hour longer than Jackie to complete the trip, what was his average speed for the trip? **50 mph**

73. **Sports** A new athletic field is being sodded at Beck High School using 2-yard-by-2-yard squares of sod. If the width of the field is 70 yards less than its length and its area is 6000 square yards, how many squares of sod will be needed? **60×25 or 1500 squares of sod**

Additional Answers

4. **A common factor is any number that is a factor of both numbers. The greatest common factor is the largest of all the common factors.**

29. $-1 \cdot 2 \cdot 2 \cdot 2 \cdot 2 \cdot 2 \cdot 2$

30. $-1 \cdot 2 \cdot 13$

31. $-1 \cdot 2 \cdot 2 \cdot 2 \cdot 2 \cdot 3 \cdot 5$

32. $-1 \cdot 3 \cdot 7 \cdot 11$

33. $2 \cdot 7 \cdot 7 \cdot a \cdot a \cdot b$

34. $2 \cdot 2 \cdot 11 \cdot r \cdot s \cdot s \cdot t \cdot t \cdot t$

35. $2 \cdot 2 \cdot 3 \cdot 3 \cdot 3 \cdot 7 \cdot m \cdot m \cdot m \cdot n \cdot n \cdot n$

36. $-1 \cdot 2 \cdot 3 \cdot 17 \cdot x \cdot x \cdot x \cdot y$

APPLYING THE LESSON

Homework Exercises

Assignment Guide

Basic: 17-57, 69-72, 76-82
Average: 25-57, 60-62, 69-82
Enriched: 33-82

Additional Answer

69.

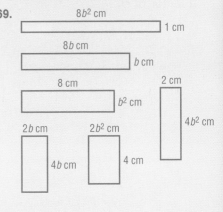

Practice Masters Booklet, p. 48

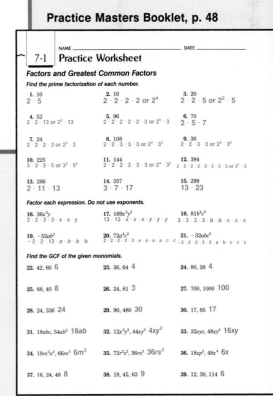

7-1 **Practice Worksheet**

Factors and Greatest Common Factors

Find the prime factorization of each number.

1. 10 $2 \cdot 5$ 2. 16 $2 \cdot 2 \cdot 2 \cdot 2$ or 2^4 3. 20 $2 \cdot 2 \cdot 5$ or $2^2 \cdot 5$

4. 52 $2 \cdot 2 \cdot 13$ or $2^2 \cdot 13$ 5. 96 $2 \cdot 2 \cdot 2 \cdot 2 \cdot 2 \cdot 3$ or $2^5 \cdot 3$ 6. 70 $2 \cdot 5 \cdot 7$

7. 24 $2 \cdot 2 \cdot 2 \cdot 3$ or $2^3 \cdot 3$ 8. 108 $2 \cdot 2 \cdot 3 \cdot 3 \cdot 3$ or $2^2 \cdot 3^3$ 9. 36 $2 \cdot 2 \cdot 3 \cdot 3$ or $2^2 \cdot 3^2$

10. 225 $3 \cdot 3 \cdot 5 \cdot 5$ or $3^2 \cdot 5^2$ 11. 144 $2 \cdot 2 \cdot 2 \cdot 2 \cdot 3 \cdot 3$ or $2^4 \cdot 3^2$ 12. 384 $2 \cdot 2 \cdot 2 \cdot 2 \cdot 2 \cdot 2 \cdot 2 \cdot 3$ or $2^7 \cdot 3$

13. 286 $2 \cdot 11 \cdot 13$ 14. 357 $3 \cdot 7 \cdot 17$ 15. 299 $13 \cdot 23$

Factor each expression. Do not use exponents.

16. $36x^2y$ $2 \cdot 2 \cdot 3 \cdot 3 \cdot x \cdot x \cdot y$ 17. $169x^3y^3$ $13 \cdot 13 \cdot x \cdot x \cdot x \cdot y \cdot y \cdot y$ 18. $81b^2c^3$ $3 \cdot 3 \cdot 3 \cdot 3 \cdot b \cdot b \cdot c \cdot c \cdot c$

19. $-52ab^3$ $-2 \cdot 2 \cdot 13 \cdot a \cdot b \cdot b \cdot b$ 20. $72a^4c^2$ $2 \cdot 2 \cdot 2 \cdot 3 \cdot 3 \cdot a \cdot a \cdot a \cdot a \cdot c \cdot c$ 21. $-32abc^3$ $-2 \cdot 2 \cdot 2 \cdot 2 \cdot 2 \cdot a \cdot b \cdot c \cdot c \cdot c$

Find the GCF of the given monomials.

22. $42, 60$ 6   23. $36, 64$ 4   24. $80, 28$ 4

25. $88, 40$ 8   26. $24, 81$ 3   27. $700, 1000$ 100

28. $24, 336$ 24   29. $90, 480$ 30   30. $17, 85$ 17

31. $18abc, 54ab^2$ $18ab$ 32. $12x^3y^2, 44xy^3$ $4xy^2$ 33. $32xyz, 48x^4y^4$ $16xy$

34. $18m^3n^2, 66m^3$ $6m^2$ 35. $72r^4s^2, 36rs^3$ $36rs^2$ 36. $18xp^2, 48x^4$ $6x$

37. $16, 24, 48$ 8   38. $18, 45, 63$ 9   39. $12, 30, 114$ 6

Computer Teaching Tip ⑤

The program at the right finds the GCF of two numbers. The INT or greatest integer function is used to determine factors. Line 40 determines if F is a factor of the first number. Line 60 determines if F is a common factor. Since values for F are checked from greatest to least, the first common factor found is the GCF.

```
10  PRINT "ENTER TWO
    NUMBERS,"
20  INPUT A, B
30  FOR F = A TO 1 STEP -1
40  IF INT(A/F) = A/F THEN 60
50  NEXT F
60  IF INT(B/F) = B/F THEN 80
70  NEXT F
80  PRINT "THE GCF OF ";A;
90  PRINT " AND ";B;" IS ";F
100 END
```

74. Use the program to find the GCF of each pair of numbers.
 a. 30, 42 **6**   b. 27, 81 **27**   c. 76, 133 **19**   d. 29, 37 **1**

75. See margin for program.

75. Change the program so it will find the GCF of three numbers. Use the new program to find the GCF of each set of numbers below.
 a. 16, 48, 128 **16**   b. 27, 32, 42 **1**   c. 60, 84, 132 **12**

Mixed Review

76. Solve $6(x - 2) = 5(x - 11) - 21$. (Lesson 3-6) **−64**

77. Solve $x + r = 2d$ for x. (Lesson 3-7) $x = 2d - r$

78. **Metallurgy** An aluminum alloy that is 48% aluminum is to be made by combining 30% and 60% alloys. How many pounds of 60% alloy must be added to 24 pounds of 30% alloy to produce the alloy? (Lesson 4-6) **36 pounds**

Solve each inequality. Check the solution. (Lessons 5-3, 5-6)

79. $5x \le 10(3x + 4)$ $\left\{x \mid x \ge -\frac{8}{5}\right\}$ 80. $|2y - 5| \ge 4$ $\left\{y \mid y \ge \frac{9}{2} \text{ or } y \le \frac{1}{2}\right\}$

Simplify. (Lessons 6-7, 6-9) 81. $-40a^3 - 64a^2 + 24a$

81. $-8a(5a^2 + 8a - 3)$ 82. $(5r - 7s)^2$ $25r^2 - 70rs + 49s^2$

HISTORY CONNECTION

Eratosthenes

Eratosthenes was a Greek astronomer and poet (c. 200 B.C.). He is known for the "sieve of Eratosthenes," a method for finding prime numbers. To use this method, first list the positive integers beginning with 2. Then cross out each multiple of a prime number. For example, cross out every second number after 2, every third number after 3, every fifth number after 5, and so on. When the process is completed, the numbers *not* crossed out are prime.

Copy and complete the sieve of Eratosthenes below to find all of the prime numbers from 2 to 100. *The multiples of 2 have been crossed out for you.*

```
 2   3   4   5   6   7   8   9  10  11  12  13  14  15  16
17  18  19  20  21  22  23  24  25  26  27  28  29  30  31
32  33  34  35  36  37  38  39  40  41  42  43  44  45  46
47  48  49  50  51  52  53  54  55  56  57  58  59  60  61
62  63  64  65  66  67  68  69  70  71  72  73  74  75  76
77  78  79  80  81  82  83  84  85  86  87  88  89  90  91
92  93  94  95  96  97  98  99 100
```
Underlined numbers are prime.

EXTENDING THE LESSON

Math Power: Problem Solving

Find the GCF of the given monomials so the second factor has integral coefficients.
$\frac{3}{8}a^3b^3c^7$, $\frac{7}{20}a^2b^2c^6$, $\frac{1}{12}ab^6c^4$

$\frac{1}{120}ab^2c^4$

History Connection

The History Connection features introduce students to persons or cultures who were involved in the development of mathematics. You may want students to further research Eratosthenes.

7-2 Factoring Using the Distributive Property

Objective

7-2

After studying this lesson, you should be able to:

■ use the GCF and the distributive property to factor polynomials.

Connection

Since $A = \ell w$, $w = \frac{A}{\ell}$.

To find the width of the rectangle at the right, divide the area by the length.

$$w = \frac{3x^2 - 8x}{x}$$
$$= \frac{3x^2}{x} - \frac{8x}{x}$$
$$= 3x - 8$$

[Rectangle diagram: top labeled x, inside labeled $A = 3x^2 - 8x$, right side labeled $w = ?$]

Since the area of the rectangle is the product of its length and width, $3x^2 - 8x = x(3x - 8)$. The expression $x(3x - 8)$ is called the *factored form* of $3x^2 - 8x$. A polynomial is in factored form, or *factored*, when it is expressed as the product of monomials and polynomials.

In Chapter 6, you multiplied a polynomial by a monomial by using the distributive property. You can also reverse this process and express a polynomial in factored form by using the distributive property.

Multiplying Polynomials	Factoring Polynomials
$3(a + b) = 3a + 3b$	$3a + 3b = 3(a + b)$
$x(y - z) = xy - xz$	$xy - xz = x(y - z)$
$3y(4x + 2) = 3y(4x) + 3y(2)$ $= 12xy + 6y$	$12xy + 6y = 3y(4x) + 3y(2)$ $= 3y(4x + 2)$

The expression $3y(4x + 2)$ at the right above is not considered completely factored since the polynomial $4x + 2$ can be factored as $2(2x + 1)$. The completely factored form of $12xy + 6y$ is $6y(2x + 1)$. Factoring a polynomial or finding the factored form of a polynomial means to find its *completely* factored form.

Example 1

Use the distributive property to factor $10y^2 + 15y$.

First, find the greatest common factor for $10y^2$ and $15y$.

$10y^2 = 2 \cdot \boxed{5} \cdot \boxed{y} \cdot y$

$15y = 3 \cdot \boxed{5} \cdot \boxed{y}$ *The GCF is 5y.*

Then, express each term as the product of the GCF and its remaining factors. **Teaching Tip ①**

$10y^2 + 15y = 5y(2y) + 5y(3)$
$= 5y(2y + 3)$ *Distributive property* **Teaching Tip ②**

LESSON 7-2 FACTORING USING THE DISTRIBUTIVE PROPERTY 261

ALTERNATE TEACHING STRATEGIES

Using Logical Reasoning

Some simple rules can help you determine if a number is divisible by 2, 3, or 5. If the ones digit is 0, 2, 4, 6, or 8, the number is divisible by 2. If the ones digit is 0 or 5, the number is divisible by 5. If the sum of the digits is divisible by 3, the number is divisible by 3. Use these rules to determine divisibility rules for 4, 6, and 9.

Using Discussion

If the greatest common factor of x^n and x^m is x^m, what can you say about *n* and *m*? $m \leq n$

7-2 Lesson Notes

Lesson Resources

• Reteaching Master 7-2
• Practice Master 7-2
• Enrichment Master 7-2
• Video Algebra, 18

 Transparency 7-2 contains the 5-Minute Check and a teaching aid for this lesson.

INTRODUCING THE LESSON

 5-Minute Check

(over Lesson 7-1)

Find the prime factorization of each number.

1. 86 2×43
2. 168 $2 \times 2 \times 2 \times 3 \times 7$

Find the GCF.

3. 49 and 77   7
4. 24 and 104   8
5. $40xy^2$ and $64yz^2$ $8y$

Motivating the Lesson

Show that 2(3) can be solved by distribution using only 1s. For example:

$2(3) = (1 + 1)(1 + 1 + 1)$
$= (1 + 1)(1) + (1 + 1)(1) +$
$(1 + 1)(1)$
$= 1 + 1 + 1 + 1 + 1 + 1$
$= 6$

Have students solve 3(5) using only 1s and 2s.

TEACHING THE LESSON

Teaching Tip ①   After the GCF is determined, the remaining factors may be found by dividing each term in the expression by the GCF. For example, in $10y^2 + 15y$, the GCF is $5y$. The remaining factors are found as follows: $\frac{10y^2}{5y} = 2y$ and $\frac{15y}{5y} = 3$. So $10y^2 + 15y = 5y(2y) + 5y(3)$
$= 5y(2y + 3)$

Teaching Tip ②   Encourage students to check the factoring process by multiplying the factors.

Example 2
Factor $21ab^2 - 33a^2bc$.

$$21ab^2 = ③ \cdot 7 \cdot ⓐ \cdot ⓑ \cdot b$$
$$33a^2bc = ③ \cdot 11 \cdot ⓐ \cdot a \cdot ⓑ \cdot c \qquad \text{The GCF is } 3ab.$$
$$21ab^2 - 33a^2bc = 3ab(7b) - 3ab(11ac)$$
$$= 3ab(7b - 11ac) \qquad \textit{Distributive property}$$

Example 3
Factor $6x^3y^2 + 14x^2y + 2x^2$.   **Teaching Tip ③**

$$6x^3y^2 = ② \cdot 3 \cdot ⓧ \cdot ⓧ \cdot x \cdot y \cdot y$$
$$14x^2y = ② \cdot 7 \cdot ⓧ \cdot ⓧ \cdot y$$
$$2x^2 = ② \cdot ⓧ \cdot ⓧ \qquad \textit{The GCF is } 2x^2.$$
$$6x^3y^2 + 14x^2y + 2x^2 = 2x^2(3xy^2) + 2x^2(7y) + 2x^2(1)$$
$$= 2x^2(3xy^2 + 7y + 1)$$

Example 4

CONNECTION
Geometry

FYI ···
The first indoor swimming pool was installed in 1742 in London, England.

A deck 3 meters wide is to be built around a swimming pool like the one shown in the figure below. In order to determine the amount of material that is needed to build the deck, a carpenter needs to calculate the area of the deck. Write an equation that represents this area.

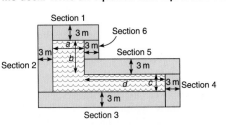

You can find the area of the deck by finding the sum of the areas of the 6 rectangular sections shown in the figure. The resulting expression can be simplified by first using the distributive property and then factoring.

Section 1   Section 2   Section 3   Section 4   Section 5   Section 6

$$A = 3(a + 3) + 3(b + c + 3) + 3(a + d + 3) + 3(c + 3) + 3(d + 3) + 3(b - 3)$$
$$= 3a + 9 + 3b + 3c + 9 + 3a + 3d + 9 + 3c + 9 + 3d + 9 + 3b - 9$$
$$= 6a + 6b + 6c + 6d + 36 \qquad \textit{Combine like terms.}$$
$$= 6(a + b + c + d + 6) \qquad \textit{The GCF is 6.}$$

The area of the deck is $6(a + b + c + d + 6)$ square units.

2. $3(5a + 4a^2)$, $a(15 + 12a)$, $3a(5 + 4a)$

CHECKING FOR UNDERSTANDING

Communicating Mathematics

Read and study the lesson to answer each question.

1. When you factor $15a + 12a^2$, what property do you use? **distributive**

2. Express $15a + 12a^2$ as a product in three different ways.

3. Which of the three answers in Exercise 2 is the completely factored form of $15a + 12a^2$? Why? $3a(5 + 4a)$; $3a$ is the GCF of $15a + 12a^2$.

RETEACHING THE LESSON

Find the GCF of the terms in each expression.

4. $3y^2 + 12$ **3**   5. $4a + 2b$ **2**   6. $5y - 9y^2$ **y**

7. $9b + 5c$ **1**   8. $9a^2 + 3a$ **3a**   9. $7mn - 21m^3$ **7m**

Complete.

10. $6x + 3y = 3(\underline{\ ?\ } + y)$ **2x**   11. $8x^2 - 4x = 4x(2x - \underline{\ ?\ })$ **1**

12. $12a^2b + 6a = 6a(\underline{\ ?\ } + 1)$ **2ab** 13. $14r^2t - 42t = 14t(\underline{\ ?\ } - 3)$ **r^2**

Factor each expression.

14. $29xy - 3x$ **$x(29y - 3)$**   15. $x^5y - x$ **$x(x^4y - 1)$**

16. $27a^2b + 9b^3$ **$9b(3a^2 + b^2)$**   17. $3c^2d - 6c^2d^2$ **$3c^2d(1 - 2d)$**

EXERCISES

Practice

A

Complete.

18. $16x + 4y = 4(4x + \underline{\ ?\ })$ **y**   19. $24x^2 + 12y^2 = 12(\underline{\ ?\ } + y^2)$ **$2x^2$**

20. $12xy + 12x^2 = \underline{\ ?\ }(y + x)$ **12x**   21. $5a^2b + 10ab = \underline{\ ?\ }(a + 2)$ **5ab**

Factor each expression. 31-35. See margin.

22. $11x + 44x^2y$ **$11x(1 + 4xy)$**   23. $16y^2 + 8y$ **$8y(2y + 1)$**

24. $14xz - 18xz^2$ **$2xz(7 - 9z)$**   25. $14mn^2 + 2mn$ **$2mn(7n + 1)$**

B

26. $18xy^2 - 24x^2y$ **$6xy(3y - 4x)$**   27. $15xy^3 + y^4$ **$y^3(15x + y)$**

28. $25a^2b^2 + 30ab^3$ **$5ab^2(5a + 6b)$** 29. $36p^2q^2 - 12pq$ **$12pq(3pq - 1)$**

30. $17a - 41a^3b$ **$a(17 - 41a^2b)$**   31. $2m^3n^2 - 16m^2n^3 + 8mn$

32. $3x^3y + 9xy^2 + 36xy$ 33. $28a^2b^2c^2 + 21a^2bc^2 - 14abc$

34. $12ax + 20bx + 32cx$ 35. $a + a^2b + a^3b^3$

Write an equation that represents the measure of the area of the shaded region in factored form.

36.

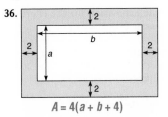

$A = 4(a + b + 4)$

37.

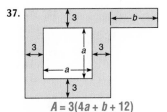

$A = 3(4a + b + 12)$

38.

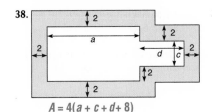

$A = 4(a + c + d + 8)$

39.

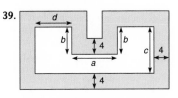

$A = 8(a + b + c + 2d + 8)$

Additional Answers

31. $2mn(m^2n - 8mn^2 + 4)$
32. $3xy(x^2 + 3y + 12)$
33. $7abc(4abc + 3ac - 2)$
34. $4x(3a + 5b + 8c)$
35. $a(1 + ab + a^2b^3)$

Factor each expression. See margin.

40. $ax^3 + 5bx^3 + 9cx^3$

41. $y^5 + 5y^4 + 3y^2 + 2y$

Teaching Tip 4 42. $\frac{2}{3}x + \frac{1}{3}x^2 - \frac{4}{3}xy^2$

43. $\frac{4}{5}a^2b - \frac{3}{5}ab^2 - \frac{1}{5}ab$

CONNECTION
Geometry

44. The measure of the perimeter of a square is $16a + 20b$. Find the measure of the area of the square. $16a^2 + 40ab + 25b^2$

Critical Thinking

45. **Geometry** The measures of the length and width of a rectangle are $(2x + 3)$ and $(9 - 4x)$. If x must be an integer, what are the possible measures for the area of this rectangle? 7, 13, 25, and 27

Applications

46. **Gardening** The length of Jeremy's garden is 5 feet more than twice its width, w. This year, Jeremy decided to make the garden 4 feet longer and double its width. How much additional area did Jeremy add to his garden? $w(2w + 13)$ square feet

47. **Stocks** During the first hour of trading, Sheila sold x shares of a stock that cost $4 per share. During the next hour, she sold stock that cost $8 per share. She sold 5 more shares during the first hour than the second hour. If she had sold only the $4-per-share stock during the first two hours, how many shares would she have needed to sell to have the same amount of total sales? $(3x - 10)$ shares

Mixed Review

48. Write an algebraic expression for the expression x *is no more than negative 3*. **(Lesson 2-3)** $x \le -3$

49. **Sales** Jerome bought a used computer for $8 less than one-third its original price. Jerome paid $525 for the computer. What was the original price? **(Lesson 3-5)** $1599

50. Solve $\frac{2}{11} = \frac{x - 5}{x + 3}$. **(Lesson 4-1)** $\frac{61}{9}$

51. Evaluate $\frac{7.8 \times 10^4}{2.6 \times 10^2}$. Express the result in scientific notation and decimal notation. **(Lesson 6-4)** 3×10^2, 300

52. Arrange the terms of $2mx^4 - 3x^5 + 4m^5 + 6x^3$ so that the powers of x are in descending order. **(Lesson 6-5)** $-3x^5 + 2mx^4 + 6x^3 + 4m^5$

53. Find the GCF of $38ab^3$ and $-74a^3b$. **(Lesson 7-1)** $2ab$

EXTENDING THE LESSON

Math Power: Connections

The area of a triangle is represented by $7a^3 - 28a^2b$. What could be the measures of its base and altitude? $14a^2$, $a - 4b$

Additional Answers

40. $x^3(a + 5b + 9c)$

41. $y(y^4 + 5y^3 + 3y + 2)$

42. $\frac{1}{3}x(2 + x - 4y^2)$

43. $\frac{1}{5}ab(4a - 3b - 1)$

7-3 Factoring by Grouping

Objective

7-3

After studying this lesson, you should be able to:

■ use grouping techniques to factor polynomials with four or more terms.

Connection

Suppose you know that the area of a certain rectangle is $3xy - 21y + 5x - 35$ square feet. Is it possible for this rectangle to have dimensions that can be represented by binomials with integral coefficients? If so, what are these dimensions?

Since the area of a rectangle is the product of its length and width, you can determine an answer to the questions above if you can find two binomials with integral coefficients whose product is $3xy - 21y + 5x - 35$. You can do this by factoring.

Polynomials with four or more terms, like $3xy - 21y + 5x - 35$, can sometimes be factored by grouping terms of the polynomials. One method is to group the terms into binomials that can each be factored using the distributive property. Then use the distributive property again with a binomial as the common factor.

Example 1

Factor $3xy - 21y + 5x - 35$ to answer the questions presented above.

$3xy - 21y + 5x - 35 = (3xy - 21y) + (5x - 35)$ *Group terms that have a common monomial factor.*
$= 3y(x - 7) + 5(x - 7)$ *Factor. Notice that $(x - 7)$ is a common factor.*
$= (3y + 5)(x - 7)$ *Distributive property*

Check by using FOIL.

$$FOIL$$
$(3y + 5)(x - 7) = 3y(x) + 3y(-7) + 5(x) + 5(-7)$
$= 3xy - 21y + 5x - 35$ ✔

Thus, the dimensions of this rectangle can be represented by binomials with integral coefficients. These dimensions would be $3y + 5$ feet and $x - 7$ feet.

Example 2

Factor $8m^2n - 5m - 24mn + 15$.

Teaching Tip ❶

$8m^2n - 5m - 24mn + 15 = (8m^2n - 5m) + (-24mn + 15)$
$= m(8mn - 5) + (-3)(8mn - 5)$
$= (m - 3)(8mn - 5)$

Check: $(m - 3)(8mn - 5) = m(8mn) + m(-5) + (-3)(8mn) + (-3)(-5)$
$= 8m^2n - 5m - 24mn + 15$ ✔

LESSON 7-3   FACTORING BY GROUPING   265

ALTERNATE TEACHING STRATEGIES

Using Problem Solving

The area of a rectangle is represented by $6x^3 - 10x^2 + 21x - 35$. What could its dimensions be?
$2x^2 + 7$ by $3x - 5$

Using Connections

One side of a rectangle is represented by $3a^2 - 8$. If the area is given as $12a^3 - 3a^2 - 32a + 8$, find the perimeter of the rectangle.
$6a^2 + 8a - 18$

Lesson Resources

- Reteaching Master 7-3
- Practice Master 7-3
- Enrichment Master 7-3
- Video Algebra, 21

 Transparency 7-3 contains the 5-Minute Check and a teaching aid for this lesson.

INTRODUCING THE LESSON

⏱ 5-Minute Check
(over Lesson 7-2)

Use the distributive property to factor.

1. $32x^3 - 28x^2$ $4x^2(8x - 7)$
2. $42a^3b^2 + 56a^2b$
   $14a^2b(3ab + 4)$
3. $18m^3n^2 + 12mn^2 - 36n^2$
   $6n^2(3m^3 + 2m - 6)$
4. $45a^2b^3 - 9ab - 36a^2b$
   $9ab(5ab^2 - 1 - 4a)$

5. The area of a rectangle is represented by $35a^3b - 30a^2b^3$. Find its dimensions.
   $5ab(7a^2 - 6ab^2)$

Motivating the Lesson

On a large table are 40 apples, 55 grapefruit, 66 bananas, and 48 pears. You wish to place 5 of one kind of fruit and 6 of another into bags. How can you divide the fruit to do this? How many bags can you fill?   19 bags if the fruit is distributed as $8(5a + 6p) + 11(5g + 6b)$

TEACHING THE LESSON

Chalkboard Examples

For Example 1
Factor using grouping.

a. $15ab - 3a + 10b - 2$
   $(3a + 2)(5b - 1)$

b. $6xy + 8x - 21y - 28$
   $(2x - 7)(3y + 4)$

Teaching Tip ❶   The terms with a common monomial factor should be grouped in pairs.

Sometimes you can group the terms in more than one way when factoring a polynomial. For example, the polynomial in Example 2 could have been factored in the following way.

$$8m^2n - 5m - 24mn + 15 = (8m^2n - 24mn) + (-5m + 15)$$
$$= 8mn(m - 3) + (-5)(m - 3)$$
$$= (8mn - 5)(m - 3) \quad \text{The result is the same as in Example 2.}$$

Example 3

Factor $2a^2 + 2bc + ab + 4ac$ in two different ways.

Method 1: $2a^2 + 2bc + ab + 4ac = (2a^2 + ab) + (4ac + 2bc)$
$= a(2a + b) + 2c(2a + b)$
$= (a + 2c)(2a + b)$

Method 2: $2a^2 + 2bc + ab + 4ac = (2a^2 + 4ac) + (ab + 2bc)$
$= 2a(a + 2c) + b(a + 2c)$
$= (2a + b)(a + 2c)$ *The result is the same.*

Check: $(2a + b)(a + 2c) = 2a(a) + 2a(2c) + b(a) + b(2c)$
$= 2a^2 + 4ac + ba + 2bc$
$= 2a^2 + 2bc + ab + 4ac$ ✔

Recognizing binomials that are additive inverses is often helpful in factoring. For example, the binomials $3 - a$ and $a - 3$ are additive inverses since the sum of $3 - a$ and $a - 3$ is 0. Thus, $3 - a$ and $-a + 3$ are equivalent. What is the additive inverse of $5 - y$?

$-1(a - 3) = -a + 3$
$= 3 - a$

Example 4

Factor $15x - 3xy + 4y - 20$.

$15x - 3xy + 4y - 20 = (15x - 3xy) + (4y - 20)$
$= 3x(5 - y) + 4(y - 5)$ *$(5 - y)$ and $(y - 5)$ are additive inverses.*
$= -3x(y - 5) + 4(y - 5)$ *$(5 - y) = -1(y - 5)$*
$= (-3x + 4)(y - 5)$

Check: $(-3x + 4)(y - 5) = (-3x)(y) + (-3x)(-5) + 4(y) + 4(-5)$
$= -3xy + 15x + 4y - 20$
$= 15x - 3xy + 4y - 20$ ✔

CHECKING FOR UNDERSTANDING

Communicating Mathematics

Read and study the lesson to answer each question.

1. When you factor $7mn + 14n + 5m + 10$ by grouping, what properties do you use? **distributive, associative, commutative**

2. Group the terms of $7mn + 14n + 5m + 10$ in pairs in two different ways so that the pairs of terms have a common monomial factor.

3. What is the additive inverse of $3a^2 - b$? $b - 3a^2$

2. $(7mn + 14n) + (5m + 10)$; $(7mn + 5m) + (14n + 10)$

Express each polynomial in factored form. See margin.

4. $k(r + s) - m(r + s)$

5. $t(t - s) + s(t - s)$

6. $3ab(a - 4) - 8(a - 4)$

7. $8m(x + y) + (x + y)$

Complete. In each exercise, both 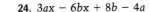**s represent the same expression.**

8. $(bx + by) + (3ax + 3ay) = b(\underline{\quad?\quad}) + 3a(\underline{\quad?\quad})$ $x + y$

9. $(3mx + 2my) + (3kx + 2ky) = m(\underline{\quad?\quad}) + k(\underline{\quad?\quad})$ $3x + 2y$

10. $(a^2 + 3ab) + (2ac + 6bc) = a(\underline{\quad?\quad}) + 2c(\underline{\quad?\quad})$ $a + 3b$

11. $(6xy - 15x) + (-8y + 20) = 3x(\underline{\quad?\quad}) - 4(\underline{\quad?\quad})$ $2y - 5$

Factor each polynomial. Check by using FOIL. See margin.

12. $rx + 2ry + kx + 2ky$

13. $ay - ab + cb - cy$

14. $a^2 - 4ac + ab - 4bc$

15. $5a + 10a^2 + 2b + 4ab$

EXERCISES

 Practice

Complete. In each exercise, both 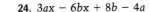**s represent the same expression.**

16. $(10x^2 - 6xy) + (15x - 9y) = 2x(\underline{\quad?\quad}) + 3(\underline{\quad?\quad})$ $5x - 3y$

17. $(6x^3 + 6x) + (7x^2y + 7y) = 6x(\underline{\quad?\quad}) + 7y(\underline{\quad?\quad})$ $x^2 + 1$

18. $(4m^2 - 3mp) + (6p - 8m) = m(\underline{\quad?\quad}) - 2(\underline{\quad?\quad})$ $4m - 3p$

19. $(20k^2 - 28kp) + (7p^2 - 5kp) = 4k(\underline{\quad?\quad}) - p(\underline{\quad?\quad})$ $5k - 7p$

Factor each polynomial. Check by using FOIL. See margin.

20. $2ax + 6xc + ba + 3bc$

21. $6mx - 4m + 3rx - 2r$

22. $2my + 7x + 7m + 2xy$

23. $3my - ab + am - 3by$

 24. $3ax - 6bx + 8b - 4a$

25. $a^2 - 2ab + a - 2b$

26. $2ab + 2am - b - m$

27. $3m^2 - 5m^2p + 3p^2 - 5p^3$

28. $5a^2 - 4ab + 12b^3 - 15ab^2$

29. $4ax - 14bx + 35by - 10ay$

30. $6a^2 - 6ab + 3cb - 3ca$

31. $ax + a^2x - a - 2a^2$

32. $a^3 - a^2b + ab^2 - b^3$

33. $2x^3 - 5xy^2 - 2x^2y + 5y^3$

CONNECTION
Geometry

Find the dimensions of a rectangle having the given area if its dimensions can be represented by binomials with integral coefficients.

34. $5xy + 15x - 6y - 18$ cm²
$5x - 6$ cm by $y + 3$ cm

35. $4z^2 - 24z - 18m + 3mz$ ft²
$4z + 3m$ ft by $z - 6$ ft

Additional Answers

22. $(m + x)(2y + 7)$

23. $(m - b)(3y + a)$

24. $(a - 2b)(3x - 4)$

25. $(a + 1)(a - 2b)$

26. $(2a - 1)(b + m)$

27. $(m^2 + p^2)(3 - 5p)$

28. $(a - 3b^2)(5a - 4b)$

29. $(2x - 5y)(2a - 7b)$

30. $3(2a - c)(a - b)$

31. $a(x + ax - 1 - 2a)$

32. $(a^2 + b^2)(a - b)$

33. $(2x^2 - 5y^2)(x - y)$

CONNECTION
Geometry

Write an expression in factored form for the measure of the perimeter of each quadrilateral shown below. Teaching Tip ❷

36.

rz
6q
6z
rq
$(r + 6)(z + q)$

37.

3by
4ax
4bx
3ay
$(4x + 3y)(a + b)$

38.
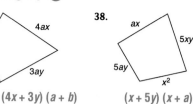
ax
5xy
5ay
x^2
$(x + 5y)(x + a)$

C ▷ **Factor each polynomial. Check by using FOIL.** See margin.

39. $7xa + 7xb + 3ma + 3mb - 4b - 4a$ 40. $ax - ay - 4yb + 4xb + 5x - 5y$

41. $2ax + bx - 6ay - 3by - bz - 2az$ 42. $ar - 3ya + br - 3by + 3cy - rc$

Critical Thinking

43. **Geometry** The measure of the perimeter of a rectangle is $2x + 4y + 8xy + 2$. Find all the possible expressions, in factored form, for the measure of its area. (*Hint:* There are three.) $(x + 2y)(4xy + 1)$, $(x + 4xy)(2y + 1)$, $2(x + 1)(2xy + y)$

Applications

44. **Conference** A North American fellowship conference is being attended by 96 students from the United States, 56 from Mexico, and 72 from Canada. **a. 8 groups**

   a. What is the greatest number of activity groups that can be formed so that students from each country are distributed equally among all the groups?

   b. How many students are in each activity group? **28 students**

45. **Construction** A 4-foot wide stone path is to be built along each of the longer sides of a rectangular flower garden. The length of the longer side of the garden is 3 feet less than twice the length of the shorter side, *s*. Write an expression, in factored form, to represent the total area of the garden and path. $(s + 8)(2s - 3)$

Mixed Review

46. Find the solution set for $5 - 2n < 3n$ if the replacement set is $\{-1, 0, 1, 2, 3\}$. **(Lesson 1-3)** $\{2, 3\}$

47. **Sales** Blaine bought a stereo for $476.79. This price was 20% less than the original price. What was the original price? **(Lesson 4-4)** $595.99

48. What is the next number in the sequence below? **(Lesson 6-1)**
    $-2, -1, 1, 5, 13, 29, \ldots$ **61**

49. Multiply $(2x + 5)(3x - 8)$. **(Lesson 6-8)** $6x^2 - x - 40$

50. Factor $10x^4 - 6x^3y - 8x^2y^2$. **(Lesson 7-2)** $2x^2(5x^2 - 3xy - 4y^2)$

EXTENDING THE LESSON

Math Power: Connections

The length of a rectangle is greater than its width and both are whole numbers. Find the minimum numerical area if the area is represented by $10xy + 6x - 45y - 27$. **The minimum area is 3 square units.**

Additional Answers

39. $(7x + 3m - 4)(a + b)$
40. $(a + 4b + 5)(x - y)$
41. $(x - 3y - z)(2a + b)$
42. $(a + b - c)(r - 3y)$

7-4 Problem-Solving Strategy: Guess and Check

Objective
7-4

After studying this lesson, you should be able to:

■ solve problems by using guess and check.

An important problem-solving strategy is guess and check, or trial and error. To use this strategy, guess the answer to the problem, then check whether the guess is correct. If the first guess is incorrect, guess and check again until you find the right answer. Often, the results of one guess can help you make a better guess. Always keep an organized record of your guesses so you don't make the same guess twice.

Example

Insert one set of parentheses so that a true equation results.
$$10 - 4 \cdot 2 - 1 = 3$$

$10 - 4 \cdot (2 - 1) = 6$	*Try again since the value does not equal 3.*
$(10 - 4) \cdot 2 - 1 = 11$	*Try again.*
$10 - (4 \cdot 2 - 1) = 3$	*Correct!*

CHECKING FOR UNDERSTANDING

Communicating Mathematics

Read and study the lesson to answer each question.

1. What is another name for the guess-and-check strategy? **trial and error**

2. Why should you keep a record of your guesses? **So you do not waste time by making the same guess twice. Also, so you can see patterns developing.**

Guided Practice

Insert one set of parentheses so that a true equation results.

3. $4 \cdot (5 - 2) + 7 = 19$

4. $25 - 4 \cdot (2 + 3) = 5$

Strategies

Look for a pattern.
Solve a simpler problem.
Act it out.
Guess and check.
Draw a diagram.
Make a chart.
Work backwards.

Solve by using guess and check.

5. Place the digits 1, 2, 3, 4, 5, 6, 8, 9, 10, and 12 at the dots at the right so that the sum of the integers on any line equals the sum on any other line.

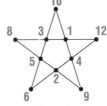

6. Numero Uno says, "I am thinking of a three-digit number. If you multiply the digits together and then multiply the result by 4, the answer is the number I'm thinking of. What is my number?" **384**

7. Using the digits 1, 2, 3, 4, 5, and 6 only once, find two whole numbers whose product is as large as possible. **631, 542**

LESSON 7-4 PROBLEM-SOLVING STRATEGY: GUESS AND CHECK 269

RETEACHING THE LESSON

Have students work in small groups to solve the following problem using the guess-and-check strategy. Encourage them to use wrong answers to make better guesses.

Pins are 5 for $1, bows are $2 each, and combs are $3 each. If $100 buys 100 items, what are possible combinations of items?
One possible answer is 60 pins, 32 bows, and 8 combs.

INTRODUCING THE LESSON

Lesson Resources

• Practice Master 7-4
• Technology Master, p. 7

Transparency 7-4 contains the 5-Minute Check and a teaching aid for this lesson.

5-Minute Check
(over Lesson 7-3)

Factor.

1. $a(x + y) + b(x + y)$
   $(a + b)(x + y)$
2. $7mn + 14n + 5m + 10$
   $(7n + 5)(m + 2)$
3. $49c - 7cd - 21 + 3d$
   $(7c - 3)(7 - d)$
4. $6rt - 4r + 3st - 2s$
   $(2r + s)(3t - 2)$

Motivating the Lesson

Fill a clear beaker with small objects. Have each student guess as to the number of objects the beaker holds. Have the student with the correct (or closest) guess explain how he or she arrived at the number.

TEACHING THE LESSON

Chalkboard Example

For the Example

Insert one set of parentheses so that a true equation results.

$9 \times 5 + 4 - 2 = 79$
$9 \times (5 + 4) - 2 = 79$

EVALUATING THE LESSON

Checking for Understanding

Exercises 1-7 are designed to help you assess understanding through reading, writing, and speaking. You should work through Exercises 1-2 with your students, and then monitor their work on Exercises 3-7.

Speaking Activity Have students identify types of problems in which the guess-and-check strategy is appropriate and instances in which it is an inappropriate way of finding a solution.

APPLYING THE LESSON

Homework Exercises

Assignment Guide
Basic: 8-11
Average: 8-11
Enriched: 8-11

Teaching Tip ❶ After students work through Exercises 8-11, have them identify the problem-solving strategy used for each problem.

Additional Answer to Cooperative Learning Activity

3. The numbers in each column increase by the triangular number in the column directly to the left.

Practice Masters Booklet, p. 51

EXERCISES

Practice   Solve. Use any strategy.   Teaching Tip ❶

8. On a recent safari, a group of people and elephants contained 100 knees and 100 trunks. If each person took 3 trunks, how many people and elephants went on safari? **30 people and 10 elephants**

9. Fill in each box at the right with a digit from 1 to 6 to make this multiplication work. Use each digit exactly once.

```
        3
  ×  5  4
  1  6  2
```

10. **Number Theory** The *word* "six" has three letters. Since the *number* 6 is divisible by 3, we say that 6 is *word-factorable*. In the same way, 36 is word-factorable because "thirty-six" has 9 letters and 36 is divisible by 9. Find five other word-factorable numbers less than 100.

11. The Canadian Can Company sent a bill to the American Aluminum Association. The payment deadline on the bill was given in the form day/month/year. AAA read this as month/day/year and paid the bill *exactly* 60 days after the due date. What two dates were involved?

10. 12, 30, 33, 40, 45, 50, 54, 56, 60, 70, 81, 88, 90
11. July 9 and September 7

∿ COOPERATIVE LEARNING ACTIVITY ∿

Work in groups of three. Each person in the group must understand the solution and be able to explain it to any person in the class. 1. See Solutions Manual.

In Lesson 4-5, you learned about figurate numbers. The table below shows several figurate number patterns. The letter *n* refers to the number of dots on each side.

Figurate Number	Shape of Figure	*n*									
		1	2	3	4	5	6	7	8	9	10
triangular	3-sided	1	3	6	10	15	21	28	36	45	55
square	4-sided	1	4	9	16	25	36	49	64	81	100
pentagonal	5-sided	1	5	12	22	35	51	70	92	117	145
hexagonal	6-sided	1	6	15	28	45	66	91	120	153	190
heptagonal	7-sided	1	7	18	34	55	81	112	148	189	235
octagonal	8-sided	1	8	21	40	65	96	133	176	225	280

1. Draw an example of each type of figurate number, with 3 on each side.
2. Copy and complete the table. **See above.**
3. Describe how the numbers increase in each column of the table. **See margin.**
4. Write an expression to describe the number of dots in a square number. n^2

EXTENDING THE LESSON

Math Power: Reasoning

At Madison High School, there are 3500 students. One-tenth of the students ride bicycles to school. Of the balance of students, one-fifth walk less than 0.2 km to school. How many students do not ride bicycles or walk less than 0.2 km to the school? **2520 students**

Cooperative Learning Activity

This activity provides students with an opportunity to *learn* things together, not just do things together. You may wish to refer to pages T6 - T8 and page 6C for the various elements of cooperative groups and specific goals and strategies for using them.

Factoring Trinomials

Objective
7-5

After studying this lesson, you should be able to:
- factor quadratic trinomials.

In Lesson 7-1, you learned that when two numbers are multiplied, each number is a *factor* of the product. Similarly, if two binomials are multiplied, each binomial is a *factor* of the product.

Consider the binomials $5x + 2$ and $3x + 7$. You can use the FOIL method to find their product.

$$\begin{array}{cccc} F & O & I & L \end{array}$$

$$(5x + 2)(3x + 7) = (5x)(3x) + (5x)(7) + (2)(3x) + (2)(7)$$
$$= 15x^2 + 35x + 6x + 14$$
$$= 15x^2 + (35 + 6)x + 14 \qquad \textit{Notice that } 15 \cdot 14 = 210$$
$$\textit{and } 35 \cdot 6 = 210.$$
$$= 15x^2 + 41x + 14$$

The binomials $5x + 2$ and $3x + 7$ are factors of $15x^2 + 41x + 14$.

Teaching Tip ❶
When using the FOIL method above, look at the product of the coefficients of the first and last terms, 15 and 14. Notice that it is the same as the product of the two terms, 35 and 6, whose sum is the coefficient of the middle term. You can use this pattern to factor quadratic trinomials, such as $2y^2 + 7y + 6$.

$$\overset{\downarrow \qquad \downarrow}{2y^2 + 7y + 6} \qquad \text{The product of 2 and 6 is 12.}$$

$$2y^2 + (\underline{} + \underline{})y + 6 \qquad \text{You need to find two integers whose } \textit{product is 12} \text{ and whose } \textit{sum is 7.}$$

You can use the guess-and-check strategy to find these numbers.

Factors of 12	Sum of Factors	
1, 12	$1 + 12 = 13$	*no*
2, 6	$2 + 6 = 8$	*no*
3, 4	$3 + 4 = 7$	*yes*

Teaching Tip ❷

$2y^2 + (3 + 4)y + 6$ *Select the factors 3 and 4.*

$2y^2 + 3y + 4y + 6$

$(2y^2 + 3y) + (4y + 6)$ *Group terms that have a common monomial factor.*

$y(2y + 3) + 2(2y + 3)$ *Factor.*   **Teaching Tip ❸**

$(y + 2)(2y + 3)$ *Use the distributive property.*

Therefore, $2y^2 + 7y + 6 = (y + 2)(2y + 3)$.   *Check this by using FOIL.*

LESSON 7-5 FACTORING TRINOMIALS 271

ALTERNATE TEACHING STRATEGIES

Using Discussion

Can you find a trinomial in the form $ax^2 + bx + c$ in which a, b, and c are all prime numbers, but the trinomial itself is not prime (that is, can be factored)? **Answers will vary. A typical answer is $2x^2 + 11x + 5$.**

Lesson Resources

- Reteaching Master 7-5
- Practice Master 7-5
- Enrichment Master 7-5
- Activity Master, p. 22
- Video Algebra, 23

 Transparency 7-5 contains the 5-Minute Check and a teaching aid for this lesson.

INTRODUCING THE LESSON

🕐 **5-Minute Check**
(over Lesson 7-3)

Factor by grouping.

1. $10xy + 25x - 14y - 35$
   $(5x - 7)(2y + 5)$
2. $18x^2y^2 + 21x^3y - 30y - 35x$ $(3x^2y - 5)(6y + 7x)$

3. **The area of a rectangle is represented by $12ab + 30a - 14b^2 - 35b$. What could its dimensions be?**
   $6a - 7b$ by $2b + 5$

Motivating the Lesson

Have students use FOIL and write out all four terms for the following products:
$(3x + 2)(5x + 3)$ $(t + 7)(3t - 5)$
$(2a - 5)(3a - 4)$
In groups, ask the students to list all the relationships they notice relative to the coefficients. This can be used as a springboard to the sum-product method of factoring the general trinomial.

TEACHING THE LESSON

Teaching Tip ❶ Remind students that coefficient means numerical coefficient as defined in Chapter 1.

Teaching Tip ❷ Point out that only positive factors of 12 need to be considered because the sum of the factors is positive.

Teaching Tip ❸ Point out that the same factors are obtained if $2y^2 + 3y + 4y + 6$ is grouped as $(2y^2 + 4y) + (3y + 6)$.

Chalkboard Examples

For Example 1
Factor.

a. $2x^2 + 9x + 10$
$(x + 2)(2x + 5)$

b. $3a^2 + 13a + 4$
$(3a + 1)(a + 4)$

c. $6t^2 + 25t + 14$
$(2t + 7)(3t + 2)$

d. $15y^2 + 34y + 15$
$(3y + 5)(5y + 3)$

For Example 2
Factor.

a. $15x^2 - 13x + 2$
$(5x - 1)(3x - 2)$

b. $14a^2 - 43a + 20$
$(7a - 4)(2a - 5)$

c. $8a^2 - 14a + 3$
$(4a - 1)(2a - 3)$

d. $35r^2 - 88r + 45$
$(7r - 5)(5r - 9)$

Teaching Tip ④ Remind students to check for a GCF first.

Example 1

Factor $5x^2 - 17x + 14$. Teaching Tip ④

$$5x^2 - 17x + 14$$

$$5x^2 + (\underline{\ ?\ } + \underline{\ ?\ })x + 14$$

The product of 5 and 14 is 70. Since the product is positive and the sum is negative, both factors of 70 must be negative. *Why?*

Factors of 70	Sum of Factors	
$-1, -70$	$-1 + (-70) = -71$	no
$-2, -35$	$-2 + (-35) = -37$	no
$-5, -14$	$-5 + (-14) = -19$	no
$-7, -10$	$-7 + (-10) = -17$	yes

You can stop listing factors when you find a pair that works.

$$5x^2 + [-10 + (-7)]x + 14$$
$$5x^2 - 10x - 7x + 14$$
$$(5x^2 - 10x) + (-7x + 14)$$
$$5x(x - 2) + (-7)(x - 2) \quad \text{Factor the GCF from each group.}$$
$$(5x - 7)(x - 2) \quad \text{Use the distributive property.}$$

Therefore, $5x^2 - 17x + 14 = (5x - 7)(x - 2)$.   *Check this by using FOIL.*

Example 2

CONNECTION

Geometry

The area of a rectangle is $a^2 - 9a - 36$ square centimeters. This area is increased by increasing both the length and width by 4 centimeters. If the dimensions of the original rectangle are represented by binomials with integral coefficients, find the area of the new rectangle.

To determine the area of the new rectangle, you must first find the dimensions of the original rectangle by factoring $a^2 - 9a - 36$. The coefficient of a^2 is 1. Thus, you must find two numbers whose product is $1 \cdot -36$ or -36 and whose sum is -9.

Factors of -36	Sum of Factors	
$1, -36$	$1 + (-36) = -35$	no
$2, -18$	$2 + (-18) = -16$	no
$3, -12$	$3 + (-12) = -9$	yes

The factors of -36 should be chosen so that exactly one factor in each pair is negative and that factor has the greater absolute value. Why?

$$\begin{aligned}
a^2 - 9a - 36 &= a^2 + [3 + (-12)]a - 36 \\
&= a^2 + 3a - 12a - 36 \\
&= (a^2 + 3a) + (-12a - 36) \\
&= a(a + 3) + (-12)(a + 3) \\
&= (a - 12)(a + 3) \quad \text{Check this by using FOIL.}
\end{aligned}$$

The dimensions of the original rectangle are $a - 12$ cm and $a + 3$ cm. Therefore, the dimensions of the new rectangle are $(a - 12) + 4$ or $a - 8$ cm and $(a + 3) + 4$ or $a + 7$ cm. Now, find an expression for the area of the new rectangle.

$$(a - 8)(a + 7) = a^2 + 7a - 8a - 56 \text{ or } a^2 - a - 56$$

The area of the new rectangle is $a^2 - a - 56$ cm².

Let us study the factorization of $a^2 - 9a - 36$ from Example 2 more closely.

$$a^2 - 9a - 36 = (a - 12)(a + 3)$$

Notice that the sum of the constant terms -12 and 3 is equal to 9, the coefficient of a in the trinomial. Also, the product of these terms is equal to 36, the constant term of the trinomial. This pattern holds for all trinomials whose quadratic term has a coefficient of 1.

Example 3 | **Factor $5x - 6 + x^2$.**

The trinomial $5x - 6 + x^2$ can be written as $x^2 + 5x - 6$. For this trinomial, the constant term is -6 and the coefficient of x is 5. Thus, we need to find two factors of -6 whose sum is 5.

Factors of -6	Sum of Factors	
$1, -6$	$1 + (-6) = -5$	*no*
$-1, 6$	$-1 + 6 = 5$	*yes*

Select the factors -1 and 6.   *Check by using FOIL and the*
Therefore, $x^2 + 5x - 6 = (x - 1)(x + 6)$.   *method in Examples 1 and 2.*

Example 4 | **Factor $2n^2 - 11n + 7$.**

You must find two numbers whose product is $2 \cdot 7$ or 14 whose sum is -11.

Factors of 14	Sum of Factors	
$-1, -14$	$-1 + (-14) = -15$	*Why should you test only*
$-2, -7$	$-2 + (-7) = -9$	*negative factors of 14?*

There are no factors of 14 whose sum is -11.
Therefore, $2n^2 - 11n + 7$ cannot be factored using integers.

A polynomial that *cannot* be written as a product of two polynomials with integral coefficients is called a **prime polynomial**. Thus, the trinomial $2n^2 - 11n + 7$ from Example 4 is a prime polynomial.

Example 5 | **Find all values of k so that the trinomial $x^2 + kx + 8$ can be factored using integers.**

For $x^2 + kx + 8$, the value of k is the sum of the factors of $1 \cdot 8$ or 8.

Factors of 8	Sum of Factors
$1, 8$	$1 + 8 = 9$
$-1, -8$	$-1 + (-8) = -9$
$2, 4$	$2 + 4 = 6$
$-2, -4$	$-2 + (-4) = -6$

Therefore, the values of k are 9, -9, 6, and -6.

RETEACHING THE LESSON

What values of b will make these trinomials factorable by unFOILing?

1. $x^2 + bx + 12$ $\{\pm7, \pm8, \pm13\}$
2. $x^2 + bx - 20$ $\{\pm19, \pm8, \pm1\}$
3. $x^2 + bx - 8$ $\{\pm7, \pm2\}$
4. $2x^2 + bx + 15$
   $\{\pm11, \pm13, \pm17, \pm31\}$
5. $3x^2 + bx - 8$
   $\{\pm2, \pm5, \pm10, \pm23\}$
6. $6x^2 + bx + 7$
   $\{\pm13, \pm17, \pm23, \pm43\}$

For Example 3
Factor.

a. $6y^2 - 13y - 5$
   $(2y - 5)(3y + 1)$

b. $8t^2 - 6t - 9$
   $(4t + 3)(2t - 3)$

c. $20a^2 - 21a - 5$
   $(5a + 1)(4a - 5)$

d. $12x^2 + 11x - 5$
   $(4x + 5)(3x - 1)$

For Example 4
Factor.

a. $x^2 - 2x - 63$ $(x + 7)(x - 9)$

b. $a^2 - 9a + 20$ $(a - 4)(a - 5)$

c. $t^2 + 14t + 45$ $(t + 9)(t + 5)$

d. $r^2 + 4r - 21$ $(r - 3)(r + 7)$

For Example 5
Find all values of k that make each trinomial factorable using integers.

a. $x^2 + kx + 9$ $6, -6, 10, -10$

b. $y^2 + ky + 6$ $5, -5, 7, -7$

c. $b^2 + kb + 10$
   $7, -7, 11, -11$

d. $z^2 + kz + 12$
   $7, -7, 8, -8, 13, -13$

Reteaching Masters Booklet, p. 46

CHECKING FOR UNDERSTANDING

Communicating Mathematics

Complete.

1. You factor a trinomial by writing it as the __?__ of two binomials. **product**

2. When you factor $3x^2 + 11x + 6$, you want to find two numbers whose product is __?__ and whose sum is 11. **18**

3. When you factor $a^2 - 24a + 12$, you know that both factors of 12 must be __?__. **negative**

4. A polynomial that *cannot* be written as the product of two polynomials is called a __?__ polynomial. **prime**

Guided Practice

For each trinomial of the form $ax^2 + bx + c$, find two integers whose product is equal to ac and whose sum is equal to b.

5. $3x^2 + 11x + 6$ **2, 9**   6. $3x^2 + 14x + 8$ **2, 12**   7. $x^2 + 9x + 14$ **2, 7**

8. $x^2 + 5x - 36$ **9, −4**   9. $4x^2 - 8x + 3$ **−2, −6**   10. $5x^2 - 13x - 6$ **−15, 2**

Complete.

11. $p^2 + 9p - 10 = (p + \underline{?})(p - 1)$ **10**   12. $y^2 - 2y - 35 = (y + 5)(y - \underline{?})$ **7**

13. $4a^2 + 4a - 63 = (2a - 7)(2a + \underline{?})$ **9**

14. $4r^2 - 25r + 6 = (r - 6)(\underline{?}\ \underline{?}\ 1)$ **4r −**

Factor each trinomial.

15. $x^2 + 2x - 15$ **$(x + 5)(x - 3)$**   16. $n^2 - 8n + 15$ **$(n - 3)(n - 5)$**

17. $b^2 + 12b + 35$ **$(b + 5)(b + 7)$**   18. $2x^2 + x - 21$ **$(2x + 7)(x - 3)$**

EXERCISES

Practice

A

Complete.

19. $3a^2 - 2a - 21 = (a\ \underline{?}\ \underline{?})(3a + 7)$ **− 3**

20. $4y^2 + 11y + 6 = (\underline{?}\ \underline{?}\ 3)(y + 2)$ **4y +**

21. $2z^2 - 11z + 15 = (\underline{?} - 5)(z - \underline{?})$ **2z, 3**

22. $6n^2 + 7n - 3 = (2n + \underline{?})(\underline{?} - 1)$ **3, 3n**

Factor each trinomial, if possible. If the trinomial cannot be factored using integers, write *prime*. **See margin.**

B

23. $y^2 + 12y + 27$ 24. $a^2 + 22a + 21$ 25. $c^2 + 2c - 3$

26. $h^2 + 5h - 8$ 27. $x^2 - 5x - 24$ 28. $3y^2 + 8y + 5$

29. $7a^2 + 22a + 3$ 30. $8m^2 - 10m + 3$ 31. $6y^2 - 11y + 4$

32. $2r^2 + 3r - 14$ 33. $2x^2 - 5x - 12$ 34. $2q^2 - 9q - 18$

35. $12r^2 - 11r + 3$ 36. $10 + 19m + 6m^2$ 37. $36 - 13y + y^2$

38. $x^2 - 4xy - 5y^2$ 39. $a^2 + 2ab - 3b^2$ 40. $15x^2 - 13xy + 2y^2$

41. $3s^2 - 10st - 8t^2$ 42. $9k^2 + 30km + 25m^2$ 43. $10a^2 - 34ab + 27b^2$

274   CHAPTER 7   FACTORING

Additional Answers

23. $(y + 3)(y + 9)$
24. $(a + 21)(a + 1)$
25. $(c + 3)(c - 1)$
26. prime
27. $(x - 8)(x + 3)$
28. $(3y + 5)(y + 1)$
29. $(7a + 1)(a + 3)$
30. $(4m - 3)(2m - 1)$
31. $(3y - 4)(2y - 1)$
32. $(2r + 7)(r - 2)$

33. $(2x + 3)(x - 4)$
34. $(2q + 3)(q - 6)$
35. prime
36. $(2 + 3m)(5 + 2m)$
37. $(9 - y)(4 - y)$
38. $(x - 5y)(x + y)$
39. $(a + 3b)(a - b)$
40. $(5x - y)(3x - 2y)$
41. $(3s + 2t)(s - 4t)$
42. $(3k + 5m)(3k + 5m)$

44. The area of a rectangle is $3x^2 + 14x + 15$ square meters. This area is reduced by decreasing both the length and width by 3 meters. If the dimensions of the original rectangle are represented by binomials with integral coefficients, find the area of the new rectangle. $3x^2 + 2x$ m²

See margin.

Find all values of k so that each trinomial can be factored using integers.

45. $x^2 + kx + 10$ 46. $m^2 + km + 6$ 47. $r^2 + kr - 13$

48. $2c^2 + kc + 12$ 49. $3s^2 + ks - 14$ 50. $4y^2 + ky - 15$

Factor. See margin.

51. $40x^4 - 116x^3 + 84x^2$ 52. $20a^4b - 59a^3b^2 + 42a^2b^3$

53. $2a^2x + 3a^2y - 14ax - 21ay + 24x + 36y$

54. $4ax^2 - 12bx^2 - ax + 3bx - 18a + 54b$

Critical Thinking

55. **Geometry** The measure of the area of a triangle is $7.5x^2 + 15.5x - 12$ where x is a positive integer. If the measure of the height of the triangle is $3x + 8$, what is the least possible measure of its base? **2**

Applications

56. **Shipping** A shipping crate is to be built in the shape of a rectangular solid. The volume of the crate is $45x^2 - 174x + 144$ cubic feet where x is a positive integer. If the height of the crate is 3 feet, what is the minimum possible volume for this crate? **27 ft³**

57. **Agriculture** The length of a rectangular vineyard is 20 meters greater than its width. Due to land rezoning, the length of the vineyard was increased by 16 meters and the width was decreased by 10 meters. If the area remained the same, find the original dimensions of the vineyard. **60 m by 80 m**

Mixed Review

58. **Finance** Hiroko invested $11,700, part at 5% interest and the balance at 7% interest. If her annual earnings from both investments is $733, how much is invested at each rate? **(Lesson 4-3)** **$4300 at 5%, $7400 at 7%**

59. Solve $2n - 6 > n + 8.2$. **(Lesson 5-1)** **{n|n > 14.2}**

60. Simplify $(-2x^2y)(-6x^4y^7)$. **(Lesson 6-2)** **$12x^6y^8$**

61. Subtract $(3x^2 - 7x + 4) - (2x^2 + 8x - 6)$. **(Lesson 6-6)** **$x^2 - 15x + 10$**

62. Factor $15a + 6b + 10a^2 + 4ab$. **(Lesson 7-3)** **$(5a + 2b)(3 + 2a)$**

63. Solve by using guess and check. **(Lesson 7-4)**

At a banquet, every 3 guests shared a dish of rice, every 2 guests shared a dish of fish, and every 4 guests shared a dish of corn. There were 65 dishes in all. How many guests attended the banquet? **60 guests**

LESSON 7-5 FACTORING TRINOMIALS **275**

Chapter 7, Quiz B, (Lessons 7-3 through 7-5), is available in the Evaluation Masters Booklet, p. 93.

Additional Answers

51. $4x^2(5x - 7)(2x - 3)$
52. $a^2b(4a - 7b)(5a - 6b)$
53. $(a - 3)(a - 4)(2x + 3y)$
54. $(4x - 9)(x + 2)(a - 3b)$

Enrichment Masters Booklet, p. 46

EXTENDING THE LESSON

Math Power: Problem Solving

Factor $24x^6 - 114x^4 - 225x^2$.
$3x^2(2x - 5)(2x + 5)(2x^2 + 3)$

Additional Answers

43. prime
45. 7, −7, 11, −11
46. 5, −5, 7, −7
47. 12, −12
48. 10, −10, 11, −11, 14, −14, 25, −25
49. 1, −1, 11, −11, 19, −19, 41, −41
50. 4, −4, 7, −7, 11, −11, 17, −17, 28, −28, 59, −59

NAME _____   DATE _____

7-5 Enrichment Worksheet

Area Models for Quadratic Trinomials

After you have factored a quadratic trinomial, you can use the factors to draw geometric models of the trinomial.

$x^2 + 5x - 6 = (x - 1)(x + 6)$

To draw a rectangular model, the value 2 was used for x so that the shorter side would have a length of 1. Then the drawing was done in centimeters. So, the area of the rectangle is $x^2 + 5x - 6$.

To draw a right triangle model, recall that the area of a triangle is one-half the base times the height. So, one of the sides must be twice as long as the shorter side of the rectangular model.

$x^2 + 5x - 6 = (x - 1)(x + 6)$
$= \frac{1}{2}(2x - 2)(x + 6)$

The area of the right triangle is also $x^2 + 5x - 6$.

Factor each trinomial. Then follow the directions to draw each model of the trinomial.

1. $x^2 + 2x - 3$ Use x = 2. Draw a rectangle in centimeters. $(x + 3)(x - 1)$

2. $3x^2 + 5x - 2$ Use x = 1. Draw a rectangle in centimeters. $(x + 2)(3x - 1)$

3. $x^2 - 4x + 3$ Use x = 4. Draw two different right triangles in centimeters. $(x - 1)(x - 3)$

4. $9x^2 - 9x + 2$ Use x = 2. Draw two different right triangles. Use 0.5 centimeter for each unit. $(3x - 2)(3x - 1)$

Lesson Resources
- Reteaching Master 7-6
- Practice Master 7-6
- Enrichment Master 7-6
- Activity Master, p. 37
- Video Algebra, 19

 Transparency 7-6 contains the 5-Minute Check and a teaching aid for this lesson.

INTRODUCING THE LESSON

 5-Minute Check

(over Lesson 7-5)

Factor each trinomial.

1. $10x^2 + 9x - 9$
   $(5x - 3)(2x + 3)$
2. $y^2 - 15y + 56$
   $(y - 7)(y - 8)$
3. $12t^2 + 35t + 8$
   $(4t + 1)(3t + 8)$
4. $p^2 + 6p - 27$
   $(p + 9)(p - 3)$
5. $6n^2 - 25n + 14$
   $(2n - 7)(3n - 2)$

Motivating the Lesson

Cut out pieces of paper as shown in the lesson to show how they fit to form a rectangle after a square has been removed from a larger square. This can be illustrated very well on an overhead projector. Students may want to cut out a square of any size and discover the remaining "L" can always be cut to form a rectangle.

TEACHING THE LESSON

Teaching Tip 1 A physical model of this relationship may help clarify the concept $a^2 - b^2 = (a - b)(a + b)$.

7-6 Factoring Differences of Squares

Objective
7-6

After studying this lesson, you should be able to:
- identify and factor polynomials that are the differences of squares.

Application

You can refer to Lesson 6-9 to review the rule for the product of a sum and a difference.

Every Friday in Ms. Leshlock's algebra class, each student is given a problem that must be solved without using paper and pencil. This week, Justin's problem was to find the product $93 \cdot 87$. How did he determine that the answer was 8091 without doing the multiplication on paper?

Justin noticed that this product could be written as the product of a sum and a difference.

$$93 \cdot 87 = (90 + 3)(90 - 3)$$

He then did the calculation mentally using the rule for this special product.

$$(90 + 3)(90 - 3) = 90^2 - 3^2$$
$$= 8100 - 9$$
$$= 8091$$

The product of a sum and a difference is called the *difference of squares*. The process for finding this product can be reversed in order to factor the difference of squares. Factoring the difference of squares can also be modeled geometrically. Consider the two squares shown below. The area of the larger square is a^2 and the area of the smaller square is b^2.

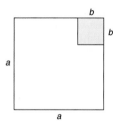

Teaching Tip 1

The area $a^2 - b^2$ can be found by subtracting the area of the smaller square from the area of the larger square.

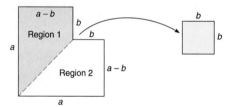

Notice that the square with area b^2 has been removed.

ALTERNATE TEACHING STRATEGIES

Using Logical Reasoning

If $x^n - y^m$ is the difference of two squares, what are some possible values of n and m?   **any two positive even integers**

By rearranging these regions as shown below, you can see that $a^2 - b^2$ is equal to the product of $(a - b)$ and $(a + b)$.

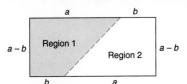

The area of the rectangle is $(a - b)(a + b)$. This is the same as $a^2 - b^2$.

Both the geometric model and the rule for the product of a sum and a difference lead us to the following rule for factoring the difference of squares.

Difference of Squares	$a^2 - b^2 = (a - b)(a + b) = (a + b)(a - b)$

Teaching Tip ②

You can use this rule to factor binomials that can be written in the form $a^2 - b^2$.

Example 1

Factor $a^2 - 64$.

$$a^2 - 64 = (a)^2 - (8)^2 \qquad \textit{a · a = a}^2 \textit{ and 8 · 8 = 64}$$
$$= (a - 8)(a + 8) \qquad \textit{Use the difference of squares.}$$

Example 2

Factor $9x^2 - 100y^2$.

$$9x^2 - 100y^2 = (3x)^2 - (10y)^2 \qquad \textit{3x · 3x = 9x}^2 \textit{ and 10y · 10y = 100y}^2$$
$$= (3x - 10y)(3x + 10y) \qquad \textit{Use the difference of squares.}$$

Example 3

Factor $\frac{1}{4}t^2 - \frac{4}{9}p^2$.

$$\frac{1}{4}t^2 - \frac{4}{9}p^2 = \left(\frac{1}{2}t\right)^2 - \left(\frac{2}{3}p\right)^2 \qquad \textit{Why?}$$
$$= \left(\frac{1}{2}t - \frac{2}{3}p\right)\left(\frac{1}{2}t + \frac{2}{3}p\right) \qquad \textit{Check this result by using FOIL.}$$

Teaching Tip ③

Teaching Tip ④ Sometimes the terms of a binomial have common factors. If so, the GCF should always be factored out first. Occasionally, the difference of squares needs to be applied more than once or along with grouping in order to completely factor a polynomial.

Example 4

Factor $12x^3 - 27xy^2$.

$$12x^3 - 27xy^2 = 3x(4x^2 - 9y^2) \qquad \textit{The GCF of 12x}^3 \textit{ and 27xy}^2 \textit{ is 3x.}$$
$$= 3x(2x - 3y)(2x + 3y) \qquad \textit{2x · 2x = 4x}^2 \textit{ and 3y · 3y = 9y}^2$$

LESSON 7-6 FACTORING DIFFERENCES OF SQUARES 277

278 Chapter 7

Chalkboard Examples

For Example 5

Factor.

a. $16x^4 - z^4$
$(4x^2 + z^2)(2x - z)(2x + z)$

b. $a^4 - 81b^8$
$(a^2 + 9b^4)(a - 3b^2)(a + 3b^2)$

For Example 6

Factor.

a. $3a^3 - 3ab^2 + 2a^2b - 2b^3$
$(3a + 2b)(a - b)(a + b)$

b. $4x^3 - 9xy^2 + 12x^2y - 27y^3$
$(x + 3y)(2x - 3y)(2x + 3y)$

EVALUATING THE LESSON

Checking for Understanding

Exercises 1-13 are designed to help you assess understanding through reading, writing, and speaking. You should work through Exercises 1-3 with your students, and then monitor their work on Exercises 4-13.

Assignment Guide

Basic: 14-43, 53-54, 58-64
Average: 23-48, 55-64
Enriched: 29-64
All: Mid-Chapter Review, 1-15

Reteaching Masters Booklet, p. 47

7-6 | Reteaching Worksheet

NAME _____ DATE _____

Factoring Difference of Squares

Use the difference of two squares to factor polynomials.

| Difference of Two Squares | $a^2 - b^2 = (a - b)(a + b) = (a + b)(a - b)$ |

Example 1: Factor $4y^2 - 81z^2$.
$4y^2 - 81z^2 = (2y)^2 - (9z)^2$ $2y \cdot 2y = 4y^2$ and $9z \cdot 9z = 81z^2$
$= (2y - 9z)(2y + 9z)$ *Use the difference of squares.*

In some binomials you have to factor a GCF before you can factor the difference of two squares.

Example 2: Factor $50a^2 - 72$.
$50a^2 - 72 = 2(25a^2 - 36)$ *The GCF is 2.*
$= 2(5a - 6)(5a + 6)$ *Use the difference of squares.*

State whether each binomial can be factored as a difference of squares.

1. $a^2 - b^2$ yes   2. $x^2 + y^2$ no   3. $a^2 - 36$ yes   4. $2p - \frac{1}{9}$ no
5. $\frac{1}{2}m^2 + \frac{1}{4}n^2$ no   6. $\frac{49}{289}x^3 - 1$ no   7. $0.16m^2 + 0.25n^2$ no   8. $225b^2 - a^2$ yes
9. $a - 16$ no   10. $15x^2 + 5$ no   11. $9y^2 - 4x^2$ yes   12. $\frac{1}{2}p^2 + 9q^2$ yes

Factor each polynomial, if possible. If the polynomial cannot be factored using integers, write *prime*.

13. $m^2 - 16n^2$ 14. $4a^2 - 9b^2$ 15. $x^2 - 64$
$(m - 4n)(m + 4n)$ $(2a + 3b)(2a - 3b)$ $(x - 8)(x + 8)$

16. $-81 + a^4$ 17. $m^6 - 16n^4$ 18. $-2 + 2y^2$
$(a - 3)(a + 3)(a^2 + 9)$ $(m^3 - 4n^2)(m^3 + 4n^2)$ $2(y - 1)(y + 1)$

19. $p^2q^2 - \frac{1}{16}$ 20. $\frac{1}{4}z^4 - 25$ 21. $\frac{2}{3}x^2 - 9$ prime
$\left(pq - \frac{1}{4}\right)\left(pq + \frac{1}{4}\right)$ $\left(\frac{1}{2}z^2 - 5\right)\left(\frac{1}{2}z^2 + 5\right)$

22. $12x^2 - 27y^2$ 23. $6 - 54z^2$ 24. $(x + y)^2 - w^2$
$3(2x - 3y)(2x + 3y)$ $6(1 + 3z)(1 - 3z)$ $(x + y - w)(x + y + w)$

25. $3x^4 - 75$ 26. $(n + 7)^2 - 1$ 27. $2p^4 - 32q^4$
$3(x^2 - 5)(x^2 + 5)$ $(n + 6)(n + 8)$ $2(p - 2q)(p + 2q)(p^2 + 4q^2)$

Example 5

Factor $162m^4 - 32n^8$.

$162m^4 - 32n^8 = 2(81m^4 - 16n^8)$ *Why?*
$= 2(9m^2 - 4n^4)(9m^2 + 4n^4)$
$= 2(3m - 2n^2)(3m - 2n^2)(9m^2 + 4n^4)$ *$9m^2 + 4n^4$ cannot be factored. Why not?*

Example 6

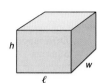

CONNECTION
Geometry

The measure of the volume of a rectangular solid is $5x^3 - 20x + 2x^2 - 8$. Find the measures of the dimensions of the solid if each one can be written as a binomial with integral coefficients.

The volume of a rectangular solid is the product of its length, width, and height. To find these dimensions, you must factor $5x^3 - 20x + 2x^2 - 8$ as the product of three binomials.

$5x^3 - 20x + 4x^2 - 8 = (5x^3 - 20x) + (2x^2 - 8)$
$= 5x(x^2 - 4) + 2(x^2 - 4)$
$= (5x + 2)(x^2 - 4)$
$= (5x + 2)(x - 2)(x + 2)$

The measures of the dimensions are $(5x + 2)$, $(x - 2)$, and $(x + 2)$.

CHECKING FOR UNDERSTANDING

Communicating Mathematics

Read and study the lesson to answer each question.

1. Under what conditions can a binomial be classified as the difference of two squares? **See margin.**

2. Can a difference of squares be factored using the method for factoring trinomials presented in Lesson 7-5? Explain. **See margin.**

3. Use the difference of squares to evaluate $\frac{15}{16} \cdot \frac{17}{16}$. $\frac{255}{256}$

Guided Practice

State whether each binomial can be factored as a difference of squares.

4. $x^2 - y^2$ yes   5. $a^2 - b^2$ yes   6. $4c^2 - 7$ no

7. $a^2 - 4b^2$ yes   8. $a - 9$ no   9. $0.04m^2 - 0.09n^2$ yes

Match each binomial with its factored form.

10. $4x^2 - 25$ c   a. $25(x - 1)(x + 1)$

11. $16x^2 - 4$ d   b. $(5x - 2)(5x + 2)$

12. $25x^2 - 4$ b   c. $(2x - 5)(2x + 5)$

13. $25x^2 - 25$ a   d. $4(2x - 1)(2x + 1)$

RETEACHING THE LESSON

The difference of two squares can be used to find the product of two numbers that are the same difference from a multiple of ten. For example,
$(17)(23) = (20 - 3)(20 + 3)$
$= 20^2 - 3^2$
$= 400 - 9$
$= 391.$

Additional Answers

1. Each term of the binomial is a perfect square, and the binomial can be written as a difference of terms.

2. Yes; write the binomial as a trinomial where the coefficient of the middle term is 0, and then factor this trinomial.

EXERCISES

Practice

Factor each polynomial, if possible. If the polynomial cannot be factored using integers, write *prime*. **See margin.**

14. $a^2 - 9$ **15.** $x^2 - 49$ **16.** $4x^2 - 9y^2$

17. $x^2 - 36y^2$ **18.** $1 - 9y^2$ **19.** $16a^2 - 9b^2$

20. $49 - a^2b^2$ **21.** $2a^2 - 25$ **prime** **22.** $8x^2 - 12y^2$

23. $2z^2 - 98$ **24.** $12a^2 - 48$ **25.** $8x^2 - 18$

26. $45x^2 - 20y^2z^2$ **27.** $25y^2 - 49z^4$ **28.** $17 - 68a^2$

29. $0.01n^2 - 1.69r^2$ **30.** $a^2x^2 - 0.64y^2$ **31.** $36x^2 - 125y^2$ **prime**

32. $9x^4 - 16y^2$ **33.** $-16 + 49x^2$ **34.** $-9x^2 + 81$

35. $\frac{1}{16}x^2 - 25z^2$ **36.** $\frac{9}{2}a^2 - \frac{49}{2}b^2$ **37.** $\frac{1}{4}n^2 - 16$

38. $(a + b)^2 - m^2$ **39.** $(r - t)^2 + t^2$ **40.** $(x - y)^2 - y^2$

CONNECTION
Number Theory

41. The difference of two numbers is 3. If the difference of their squares is 15, what is the sum of the numbers? **5**

CONNECTION
Geometry

Find the dimensions of each rectangular solid having the given volume measure if each dimension can be written as a binomial with integral coefficients. **42.** $x - 1, x + 1, x + 1$ **43.** $3a - 2, 3a + 2, a + 2$

42. $x^3 + x^2 - x - 1$ **43.** $9a^3 + 18a^2 - 4a - 8$

44. $7mp^2 + 2np^2 - 7mr^2 - 2nr^2$ $p - r, p + r, 7m + 2n$ **45.** $5a^3 - 125ab^2 - 75b^3 + 3a^2b$ $a - 5b, a + 5b, 5a + 3b$

Factor each polynomial. **See margin.**

46. $x^4 - y^4$ **47.** $16 - a^4$ **48.** $9x^4 - 25y^4$

49. $48x^5 - 3xy^4$ **50.** $48s^5t - 243st^5$ **51.** $x^8 - 1$

CONNECTION
Geometry

52. The side of a square is x centimeters long. The length of a rectangle is 5 centimeters longer than a side of this square and the width is 5 centimeters shorter.

  a. Which has the greater area, the square or the rectangle? **square**

  b. How much greater is that area? **25 cm²**

Critical Thinking

Find positive integers m and n such that $m^2 - n^2$ has each value. **See margin.**

53. 11 **54.** 15 **55.** 45 **56.** 105

Applications

57. Photography To get a square photograph to fit into a rectangular frame, Li-Chih had to trim a 1-inch strip from one pair of opposite sides of the photo and a 2-inch strip from the other two sides. In all, he trimmed off 64 square inches. What were the original dimensions of the photograph? **12 in. by 12 in.**

Additional Answers

14. $(a - 3)(a + 3)$
15. $(x - 7)(x + 7)$
16. $(2x - 3y)(2x + 3y)$
17. $(x - 6y)(x + 6y)$
18. $(1 - 3y)(1 + 3y)$
19. $(4a - 3b)(4a + 3b)$
20. $(7 - ab)(7 + ab)$
22. $4(2x^2 - 3y^2)$
23. $2(z - 7)(z + 7)$
24. $12(a - 2)(a + 2)$

25. $2(2x - 3)(2x + 3)$
26. $5(3x - 2yz)(3x + 2yz)$
27. $(5y - 7z^2)(5y + 7z^2)$
28. $17(1 - 2a)(1 + 2a)$
29. $(0.1n - 1.3r)(0.1n + 1.3r)$
30. $(ax - 0.8y)(ax + 0.8y)$
32. $(3x^2 - 4y)(3x^2 + 4y)$
33. $(7x - 4)(7x + 4)$
34. $9(3 - x)(3 + x)$

Error Analysis

Here are two common errors in factoring.
1. $5a^2 - 20 = 5(a^2 - 4)$
           $= (a + 2)(a - 2)$
The factor of 5 was ommitted.
2. $16x^2 - 36 = (4x + 6)(4x - 6)$
This was not factored completely. The GCF should be removed first.

Additional Answers

35. $\left(\frac{1}{4}x - 5z\right)\left(\frac{1}{4}x + 5z\right)$
36. $\frac{1}{2}(3a - 7b)(3a + 7b)$
37. $\left(\frac{1}{2}n - 4\right)\left(\frac{1}{2}n + 4\right)$
38. $(a + b + m)(a + b - m)$
39. prime
40. $x(x - 2y)$
46. $(x - y)(x + y)(x^2 + y^2)$
47. $(2 - a)(2 + a)(4 + a^2)$
48. $(3x^2 - 5y^2)(3x^2 + 5y^2)$
49. $3x(2x - y)(2x + y)(4x^2 + y^2)$
50. $3st(2s - 3t)(2s + 3t) \cdot$
    $(4s^2 + 9t^2)$
51. $(x - 1)(x + 1)(x^2 + 1)(x^4 + 1)$
53. $m = 6, n = 5$
54. $m = 4, n = 1; m = 8, n = 7$
55. $m = 7, n = 2; m = 9, n = 6;$
    $m = 23, n = 22$
56. $m = 11, n = 4; m = 13,$
    $n = 8; m = 19, n = 16;$
    $m = 53, n = 52$

Practice Masters Booklet, p. 53

NAME _____ DATE _____
7-6 | **Practice Worksheet**

Factoring Differences of Squares

Factoring each polynomial, if possible. If the polynomial cannot be factored, write *prime*.

1. $a^2 - 4$ $(a - 2)(a + 2)$ **2.** $y^2 - 1$ $(y - 1)(y + 1)$ **3.** $x^2 - 64$ $(x - 8)(x + 8)$

4. $1 - 49c^2$ $(1 - 7c)(1 + 7c)$ **5.** $-16 + p^2$ $(p - 4)(p + 4)$ **6.** $100r^2 - 9$ $(10r - 3)(10r + 3)$

7. $36 - n^2$ $(6 - n)(6 + n)$ **8.** $144 - 9f^2$ $(12 - 3f)(12 + 3f)$ **9.** $-r^2s^2 + 81$ $(9 - rs)(9 + rs)$

10. $5c^2 - 4d^2$ prime **11.** $4g^2 - 81h^2$ $(2g - 9h)(2g + 9h)$ **12.** $36j^2 - 49m^2$ $(6j - 7m)(6j + 7m)$

13. $8n^2 - 72p^2$ $8(n - 3p)(n + 3p)$ **14.** $20q^2 - 5r^2$ $5(2q - r)(2q + r)$ **15.** $s^4t^2 - 4t^2$ $t^2(s^2 - 2)(s^2 + 2)$

16. $36n^2 - 25$ $(6n - 5)(6n + 5)$ **17.** $49 - 100k^2$ $(7 - 10k)(7 + 10k)$ **18.** $32 - 8n^2$ $8(2 - n)(2 + n)$

19. $t^2 - 64u^2$ $(t - 8u)(t + 8u)$ **20.** $121r^2 - 1$ $(11r - 1)(11r + 1)$ **21.** $2yz^4 - 50yz^2$ $2yz^2(z - 5)(z + 5)$

22. $25v^5x - 9v^3x$ $v^3x(5v - 3)(5v + 3)$ **23.** $4t^2 - s^4t^2$ $t^2(2 - s^2)(2 + s^2)$ **24.** $200y^2z^5 - 242y^4z^3$ $2y^2z^3(10z - 11y)(10z + 11y)$

25. $75x^2 - 147y^2$ $3(5x - 7y)(5x + 7y)$ **26.** $32h^3 - 18j^2$ $2(4h - 3/)(4y + 3/)$ **27.** $x^2 + y^2$ prime

28. $x^2y^2 - z^2$ $(xy - z)(xy + z)$ **29.** $-4c^2 + 25$ $(5 - 2c)(5 + 2c)$ **30.** $j^2 - 33k^2$ prime

31. $100b^4 - 169$ $(10b^2 - 13)(10b^2 + 13)$ **32.** $24e^2 - 54f^4$ $6(2e - 3f^2)(2e + 3f^2)$ **33.** $32a^2 - 50b^2$ $2(4a - 5b)(4a + 5b)$

34. $-98r^2 + 8t^2$ $2(2t - 7r)(2t + 7r)$ **35.** $x^{12} - 4x^2$ $x^2(x^5 - 2)(x^5 + 2)$ **36.** $3/^2 - \frac{1}{3}$ $3(/ - \frac{1}{3})(/ + \frac{1}{3})$

37. $\frac{1}{4}u^2 - \frac{9}{4}$ $\frac{1}{4}(u - 3)(u + 3)$ **38.** $9t^6m^4 - 196t^6m^4$ $t^6m^4(3 - 14t)(3 + 14t)$ **39.** $5v^2 - \frac{5}{4}$ $5(v - \frac{1}{2})(v + \frac{1}{2})$

40. $64v^7x^3 - 121vx^7$ $vx^3(8v^3 - 11x^2)(8v^3 + 11x^2)$ **41.** $2z^2 - 196c^2$ $2(z^2 - 98c^2)$ **42.** $85p^2 - 17q^2$ $17(5p^2 - q^2)$

58. **Finance** Maria invested some money at 8.5% annual interest. Juanita invested $800 more than Maria at 7.5% annual interest. If Maria and Juanita received the same amount of interest after one year, how much money did each invest? **Maria, $6000; Juanita, $6800**

Mixed Review

59. Solve $\frac{8}{3}x = \frac{4}{9}$. **(Lesson 3-3)** $\frac{1}{6}$

60. **Travel** Bob and Vicki took a trip to Zuma Beach. On the way there, their average speed was 42 miles per hour. On the way home, their average speed was 56 miles per hour. If their total travel time was 7 hours, find the distance to the beach. **(Lesson 4-7)** **168 miles**

61. Solve $|2x + 7| < 11$. **(Lesson 5-6)** $\{x | -9 < x < 2\}$

62. Simplify $\frac{-8a^3b^7}{a^2b^6}$. **(Lesson 6-3)** $-8ab$

63. Find the degree of $6mn^4t - 3m^4nt^2 + mn^6$. **(Lesson 6-5)** **7**

64. Factor $16x^2 + 14x - 15$. **(Lesson 7-5)** $(8x - 5)(2x + 3)$

MID-CHAPTER REVIEW

Find the GCF of the given monomials.   (Lesson 7-1)

1. $39a^2$, $13a^3$ $13a^2$
2. $64a^2c^2$, $4ab^2c^4$ $4ac^2$
3. $55m^3n$, $275m^5n^2$, $165m^2n^3$ $55m^2n$

Factor each polynomial, if possible. If the polynomial cannot be factored using integers, write *prime*.   (Lessons 7-2, 7-3, 7-5, and 7-6) 11. $7ab^2(-a - 11a^2 + 11b)$

4. $y^2 - 8y + 7$ $(y - 1)(y - 7)$
5. $25m^3n + 15m^2n^2$ $5m^2n(5m + 3n)$
6. $r^2 + 3r - 18$ $(r + 6)(r - 3)$
7. $3a^2b - 8a - 12ab - 32$ prime
8. $5a^3 + 45a^2 - 15a$ $5a(a^2 + 9a - 3)$
9. $6p^2 + 7p - 3$ $(2p + 3)(3p - 1)$
10. $8k^2 - 72z^2$ $8(k + 3z)(k - 3z)$
11. $-7a^2b^2 - 77a^3b^2 + 77ab^3$
12. $5x^2 - 19x + 14$ $(5x - 14)(x - 1)$
13. $y^2m + y^2n - 4m - 4n$
    $(y + 2)(y - 2)(m + n)$

14. Solve by using guess and check.   **(Lesson 7-4)**
    Write an eight-digit number using the digits 1, 2, 3, and 4 each twice so that the 1s are separated by 1 digit, the 2s are separated by 2 digits, the 3s are separated by 3 digits, and the 4s are separated by 4 digits. **41,312,432 or 23,421,314**

15. **Geometry** The area of a rectangle is $4x^2 - 196$ square meters. This area was increased by increasing both the length and width by 9 meters. If the dimensions of the original rectangle are binomials with integral coefficients, find the area of the new rectangle.   **(Lesson 7-6)** $4x^2 + 36x - 115$ m²

7-7 Perfect Squares and Factoring

Objective
7-7

After studying this lesson, you should be able to:
- identify and factor perfect square trinomials.

Numbers such as 1, 4, 9, and 16 are called *perfect squares* since they can be expressed as the square of an integer. Products of the form $(a + b)^2$ and $(a - b)^2$ are also called perfect squares, and the expansions of these products are called **perfect square trinomials**.

Perfect Square Trinomials	$(a + b)^2 = a^2 + 2ab + b^2$ $(a - b)^2 = a^2 - 2ab + b^2$

Teaching Tip 1

These patterns can be used to help you factor trinomials.

Finding a Product

$$(y + 8)^2 = y^2 + 2(y)(8) + 8^2$$
$$= y^2 + 16y + 64$$

$$(2x - 5z)^2$$
$$= (2x)^2 - 2(2x)(5z) + (5z)^2$$
$$= 4x^2 - 20xz + 25z^2$$

Factoring

$$y^2 + 16y + 64 = (y)^2 + 2(y)(8) + (8)^2$$
$$= (y + 8)^2$$

$$4x^2 - 20xz + 25z^2$$
$$= (2x)^2 - 2(2x)(5z) + (5z)^2$$
$$= (2x - 5z)^2$$

To determine whether a trinomial can be factored by using these patterns, you must first decide if it is a perfect square trinomial. In other words, you must determine if it can be written in the form $a^2 + 2ab + b^2$ or in the form $a^2 - 2ab + b^2$.

Example 1

Determine whether $x^2 + 22x + 121$ is a perfect square trinomial. If so, factor it. **Teaching Tip 2**

To determine whether $x^2 + 22x + 121$ is a perfect square trinomial, answer each question. **Teaching Tip 3**

a. Is the first term a perfect square? $x^2 \stackrel{?}{=} (x)^2$ *yes*

b. Is the last term a perfect square? $121 \stackrel{?}{=} (11)^2$ *yes*

c. Is the middle term twice the product of x and 11? $22x \stackrel{?}{=} 2(x)(11)$ *yes*

So, $x^2 + 22x + 121$ is a perfect square trinomial. It can be factored as follows.

$$x^2 + 22x + 121 = (x)^2 + 2(x)(11) + (11)^2$$
$$= (x + 11)^2$$

LESSON 7-7 PERFECT SQUARES AND FACTORING 281

ALTERNATE TEACHING STRATEGIES

Using Discussion
Find two numbers a^2 and b^2 so that $2ab$ is a perfect square number. Let a or b equal a perfect square and the other equal twice or half a perfect square. For example, let $a = 9(3^2)$ and $b = 8(2 \times 4$ or $2 \times 2^2)$. Then $2(9)(8) = 144$, which is a perfect square number.

Using Problem Solving
Explore informally how to complete the square for any missing term. Find c if:
a. $cx^2 - 40x + 25$. 16
b. $49t^2 + ct + 16$. 56, −56
c. $81n^2 - 108n + c$. 36

Lesson Resources
- Reteaching Master 7-7
- Practice Master 7-7
- Enrichment Master 7-7
- Lab Manual, pp. 29-30
- Video Algebra, 20

 Transparency 7-7 contains the 5-Minute Check and a teaching aid for this lesson.

INTRODUCING THE LESSON

5-Minute Check
(over Lesson 7-6)

Factor.

1. $n^2 - 81$ $(n - 9)(n + 9)$
2. $64p^2 - 25g^2$
   $(8p - 5g)(8p + 5g)$
3. $2a^5 - 162a$
   $2a(a^2 + 9)(a - 3)(a + 3)$
4. $75a^4 - 12a^2$
   $3a^2(5a - 2)(5a + 2)$

Motivating the Lesson
Nancy said, "31^2 equals $30^2 + 1^2$". Do you agree or disagree? Emphasize the value of and need for the middle term of a binomial square.

TEACHING THE LESSON

Teaching Tip 1   Caution students against confusing the difference of squares with the square of a difference.
$(a + b)(a - b) = a^2 - b^2$
$(a - b)^2 \neq a^2 - b^2$

Teaching Tip 2   Point out that before factoring a polynomial its terms should be arranged so that the powers of x are in descending or ascending order. For example, $8x + x^2 + 16$ should be written as $x^2 + 8x + 16$ or $16 + 8x + x^2$.

Teaching Tip 3   Steps **a, b,** and **c** give students a system for determining perfect square trinomials.

Example 2 | **Determine whether $16a^2 + 81 - 72a$ is a perfect square trinomial. If so, factor it.** **Teaching Tip** ④

First arrange the terms of $16a^2 + 81 - 72a$ so that the powers of a are in descending order.

$16a^2 + 81 - 72a = 16a^2 - 72a + 81$

a. Is the first term a perfect square? $16a^2 \stackrel{?}{=} (4a)^2$ *yes*

b. Is the last term a perfect square? $81 \stackrel{?}{=} (9)^2$ *yes*

c. Is the middle term twice the product of $4a$ and 9? $72a \stackrel{?}{=} 2(4a)(9)$ *yes*

$16a^2 - 72a + 81$ is a perfect square trinomial.
$16a^2 - 72a + 81 = (4a)^2 - 2(4a)(9) + (9)^2$
$= (4a - 9)^2$

Example 3 | **Determine whether $9p^2 - 56p + 49$ is a perfect square trinomial. If so, factor it.**

a. Is the first term a perfect square? $9p^2 \stackrel{?}{=} (3p)^2$ *yes*

b. Is the last term a perfect square? $49 \stackrel{?}{=} (7)^2$ *yes*

c. Is the middle term twice the product of $3p$ and 7? $56p \stackrel{?}{=} 2(3p)(7)$ *no*

$9p^2 - 56p + 49$ is *not* a perfect square trinomial.

Example 4

CONNECTION

Geometry

Is it possible for $9x^2 + 12xy + 4y^2$ to be the measure of the area of a square? If so, what is the measure of each side of the square?

For $9x^2 + 12xy + 4y^2$ to be the measure of the area of a square, it must be a perfect square trinomial.   *Why?*

Since $9x^2 = (3x)^2$, $4y^2 = (2y)^2$, and $12xy = 2(3x)(2y)$, the trinomial $9x^2 + 12xy + 4y^2$ is a perfect square trinomial.

$9x^2 + 12xy + 4y^2 = (3x)^2 + 2(3x)(2y) + (2y)^2$
$= (3x + 2y)^2$

Thus, $9x^2 + 12xy + 4y^2$ can be the measure of the area of a square. The measure of each side of this square is $3x + 2y$.

RETEACHING THE LESSON

Have students use algebra tiles to model the trinomials in Exercises 16-21. Point out that if the tiles form a square that the trinomial is a perfect square. The length of each side represents each factor of the trinomial.

CHECKING FOR UNDERSTANDING

Communicating Mathematics

Read and study the lesson to answer each question.

1. If an integer is a perfect square, what are the possible values for its units digit? **0, 1, 4, 5, 6, 9**

2. In a perfect square trinomial, can the constant term ever be a negative integer? Why or why not? **No; a negative integer can never be a perfect square.**

3. *True* or *False:* The middle term of a perfect square trinomial is twice the product of the first and last term of the trinomial. **false**

Guided Practice

Complete.

4. $b^2 + 10b + 25 = (b + \underline{\ ?\ })^2$ **5**   5. $y^2 + 14y + 49 = (y + \underline{\ ?\ })^2$ **7**

6. $m^2 - 24m + 144 = (m - \underline{\ ?\ })^2$ **12**   7. $64b^2 - 16b + 1 = (\underline{\ ?\ } - 1)^2$ **8b**

8. $81n^2 + 36n + 4 = (\underline{\ ?\ } + 2)^2$ **9n**   9. $1 - 12x + 36x^2 = (1 - \underline{\ ?\ })^2$ **6x**

Determine whether each trinomial is a perfect square trinomial. If so, factor it. **See margin for factorizations.**

10. $a^2 + 4a + 4$ **yes**   11. $x^2 + 20x - 100$ **no**   12. $y^2 - 10y + 100$ **no**

13. $b^2 - 14b + 49$ **yes**   14. $4x^2 + 4x + 1$ **yes**   15. $2n^2 + 17n + 21$ **no**

EXERCISES

Practice

Determine whether each trinomial is a perfect square trinomial. If so, factor it. **See margin for factorizations.**

16. $n^2 - 13n + 36$ **no**   17. $p^2 + 12p + 36$ **yes**   18. $9b^2 - 6b + 1$ **yes**

19. $9y^2 + 8y - 16$ **no**   20. $9x^2 - 10x + 4$ **no**   21. $4a^2 - 20a + 25$ **yes**

40. $(4m^2 - 9n^2)^2$ or $(2m - 3n)^2(2m + 3n)^2$

Factor each trinomial, if possible. If the trinomial cannot be factored using integers, write *prime*. 22. $(x + 8)^2$ 23. $(n - 4)^2$ 24. $(a + 11)^2$

22. $x^2 + 16x + 64$ 23. $n^2 - 8n + 16$ 24. $a^2 + 22a + 121$

25. $4k^2 - 4k + 1$ $(2k - 1)^2$ 26. $100x^2 + 20x + 1$ $(10x + 1)^2$

27. $x^2 + 6x - 9$ **prime**   28. $9a^2 + 12a - 4$ **prime**

29. $1 - 10z + 25z^2$ $(1 - 5z)^2$ 30. $4 - 28r + 49r^2$ $(2 - 7r)^2$

31. $50x^2 + 40x + 8$ $2(5x + 2)^2$ 32. $18a^2 - 48a + 32$ $2(3a - 4)^2$

33. $49m^2 - 126m + 81$ $(7m - 9)^2$ 34. $64b^2 - 72b + 81$ **prime**

35. $25x^2 - 120x + 144$ $(5x - 12)^2$ 36. $9x^2 + 24xy + 16y^2$ $(3x + 4y)^2$

37. $m^2 + 16mn + 64n^2$ $(m + 8n)^2$ 38. $16p^2 - 40pr + 25r^2$ $(4p - 5r)^2$

39. $4x^2 + 4xz^2 + z^4$ $(2x + z^2)^2$ 40. $16m^4 - 72m^2n^2 + 81n^4$

41. $\frac{1}{4}a^2 + 3a + 9$ $\left(\frac{1}{2}a + 3\right)^2$ 42. $\frac{4}{9}x^2 - \frac{16}{3}x + 16$ $\left(\frac{2}{3}x - 4\right)^2$

Additional Answers

10. $(a + 2)^2$
13. $(b - 7)^2$
14. $(2x + 1)^2$
17. $(p + 6)^2$
18. $(3b - 1)^2$
21. $(2a - 5)^2$

Checking for Understanding

Exercises 1-15 are designed to help you assess understanding through reading, writing, and speaking. You should work through Exercises 1-3 with your students, and then monitor their work on Exercises 4-15.

Error Analysis

Students may overlook the sign of the constant term of a trinomial when factoring. For example, students might factor $x^2 - 12x - 36$ into $(x - 6)(x - 6)$. You may wish to review the difference between -6^2 and $(-6)^2$ again.

$$-6^2 = -36 \text{ and } (-6)^2 = 36$$

Assignment Guide

Basic: 16-49, 60-61, 63-69
Average: 22-54, 60-69
Enriched: 28-69

Practice Masters Booklet, p. 54

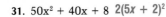

NAME _____ DATE _____

7-7   **Practice Worksheet**

Perfect Squares and Factoring

Determine whether each trinomial is a perfect square trinomial. If so, factor it.

1. $a^2 + 2a + 1$
$(a + 1)^2$

2. $2c^2 - 4c + 9$
no

3. $4d^2 - 4d + 1$
$(2d - 1)^2$

4. $r^2 + 4r + 4$
$(r + 2)^2$

Factor each trinomial, if possible. If the trinomial cannot be factored using integers, write *prime*.

5. $x^2 - 6x + 9$
$(x - 3)^2$

6. $m^2 + 16m + 64$
$(m + 8)^2$

7. $s^2 - 14s + 49$
$(s - 7)^2$

8. $a^2 - 14 + 36$
prime

9. $c^2 + 24c + 144$
$(c + 12)^2$

10. $49z^2 - 56z + 16$
$(7z - 4)^2$

11. $25v^2 + 30v + 9$
$(5v + 3)^2$

12. $36s^2 - 24s + 4$
$4(3s - 1)^2$

13. $4 - 28t + 49t^2$
$(2 - 7t)^2$

14. $9p^2 + 12pq + 4q^2$
$(3p + 2q)^2$

15. $16m^2 - 24mn + 9n^2$
$(4m - 3n)^2$

16. $9r^2 + 48rt + 64t^2$
$(3r + 8t)^2$

17. $28m^2 - 28mp + 7p^2$
$7(2m - p)^2$

18. $16s^2 + 56s + 49$
$(4s + 7)^2$

19. $16c^2 + 72cd + 81d^2$
$(4c + 9d)^2$

20. $9k^2 - 30k - 25$
prime

21. $\frac{1}{9}h^2 - 4hj + 36j^2$
$\left(\frac{1}{3}h - 6j\right)^2$

22. $\frac{1}{4}x^2 - 5xz + 25z^2$
$\left(\frac{1}{2}x - 5z\right)^2$

23. $4e^2 - 44ef + 121f^2$
$(2e - 11f)^2$

24. $16a^4 - 40a^2b^3 + 25b^6$
$(4a^2 - 5b^3)^2$

25. $c^2d^2 - 2cde + e^2$
$(cd - e)^2$

26. $\frac{1}{16}m^2 - \frac{1}{4}mn + \frac{1}{4}n^2$
$\left(\frac{1}{4}m - n\right)^2$

284 Chapter 7

Closing the Lesson

Writing Activity Bernie said, "For a quadratic trinomial of the form $ax^2 + bx + c$, give me two of the constants a, b, or c and I can find the missing constant to make the trinomial a perfect square". Do you agree or disagree with him? Write a paragraph to support your opinion.

APPLYING THE LESSON

Homework Exercises

See assignment guide on page 283.

Chapter 7, Quiz C, (Lessons 7-6 through 7-7), is available in the Evaluation Masters Booklet, p. 94.

Enrichment Masters Booklet, p. 48

| NAME _____ DATE _____
7-7 | Enrichment Worksheet

Factoring Trinomials of Fourth Degree

Some trinomials of the form $a^4 + a^2b^2 + b^4$ can be written as the difference of two squares and then factored.

Example: Factor $4x^4 - 37x^2y^2 + 9y^4$.

Step 1: Find the square roots of the first and last terms.
$\sqrt{4x^4} = 2x^2 \qquad \sqrt{9y^4} = 3y^2$

Step 2: Find twice the product of the square roots.
$2(2x^2)(3y^2) = 12x^2y^2$

Step 3: Separate the middle term into two parts. One part is either your answer to Step 2 or its opposite. The other part should be the opposite of a perfect square.
$-37x^2y^2 = -12x^2y^2 - 25x^2y^2$

Step 4: Rewrite the trinomial as the difference of two squares and then factor.
$4x^4 - 37x^2y^2 + 9y^4 = (4x^4 - 12x^2y^2 + 9y^4) - 25x^2y^2$
$= (2x^2 - 3y^2)^2 - 25x^2y^2$
$= [(2x^2 - 3y^2) + 5xy][(2x^2 - 3y^2) - 5xy]$
$= (2x^2 + 5xy - 3y^2)(2x^2 - 5xy - 3y^2)$

Factor each trinomial.

1. $x^4 + x^2y^2 + y^4$
$(x^2 + xy + y^2)(x^2 - xy + y^2)$

2. $x^4 + x^2 + 1$
$(x^2 + x + 1)(x^2 - x + 1)$

3. $9a^4 - 15a^2 + 1$
$(3a^2 + 3a - 1)(3a^2 - 3a - 1)$

4. $16a^4 - 17a^2 + 1$
$(4a - 1)(a + 1)(4a + 1)(a - 1)$

5. $4a^4 - 13a^2 + 1$
$(2a^2 + 3a - 1)(2a^2 - 3a - 1)$

6. $9a^4 + 26a^2b^2 + 25b^4$
$(3a^2 + 2ab + 5b^2)(3a^2 - 2ab + 5b^2)$

7. $4x^4 - 21x^2y^2 + 9y^4$
$(2x^2 + 3xy - 3y^2)(2x^2 - 3xy - 3y^2)$

8. $4a^4 - 29a^2c^2 + 25c^4$
$(2a + 5c)(a - c)(2a - 5c)(a + c)$

CONNECTION Geometry

Determine whether each trinomial could be the measure of the area of a square. If so, find the measure of the side of the square.

43. $121y^2 + 22y + 1$ yes; $11y + 1$

44. $64x^2 - 80x + 25$ yes; $8x - 5$

45. $49m^2 + 150m + 100$ no

46. $4b^2 - 24bc + 36c^2$ yes; $2(b - 3c)$

Find all values of c so that each trinomial is a perfect square.

47. $cx^2 + 28x + 49$ 4

48. $cn^2 - 220n + 121$ 100

49. $9a^2 - 12ab + c$ $4b^2$

50. $9x^2 + cxy + 49y^2$ 42 or -42

51. $16m^2 + cmp + 25p^2$ 40 or -40

52. $64x^2 - 16xy + c$ y^2

Factor each polynomial. 53-56. See margin.

53. $a^2 + 4a + 4 - 9b^2$

54. $x^2 + 2xy + y^2 - r^2$

55. $m^2 - k^2 + 6k - 9$

56. $16 - 9x^2 - 12xz - 4z^2$

57. $a^2m - 2a^2 + 6am - 12a + 9m - 18$ $(m - 2)(a + 3)^2$

58. $8ay^2 + 12y^2 + 40ay + 60y + 50a + 75$ $(2a + 3)(2y + 5)^2$

CONNECTION Geometry

59. The measure of the area of a circle is $(9y^2 + 78y + 169)\pi$. What is the measure of its diameter? $6y + 26$

Critical Thinking

60. **Geometry** The measure of the area of a square is $81 - 90x + 25x^2$, where x is a positive integer. What is the smallest possible perimeter measure for this square? 4

Applications

61. **Photography** A square photograph is placed in a frame that is 2 inches wide on all sides. If the measure of the area of the frame is 184 square inches, what are the dimensions of the photograph? 21 in. by 21 in.

62. **Construction** The length of a rectangular lot is 60 yards greater than its width, w. To change the lot into a square lot, 900 square yards were added. Find the length of a side of this square lot. $(w + 30)$ yards

Mixed Review

63. Fifteen is 40% of what number? **(Lesson 4-2)** 37.5

64. **Travel** A car uses 8 gallons of gasoline to travel 264 miles. How much gasoline will the car use to travel 500 miles? **(Lesson 4-8)** 15.152 gallons

65. **Number Theory** If 6.5 times an integer is increased by 11, the result is between 55 and 75. What is the integer? **(Lesson 5-5)** 7, 8, or 9

Simplify. (Lessons 6-8, 6-9)

66. $(3x - 2)(3x + 2)$ $9x^2 - 4$

67. $(8t - 3)(2t + 5)$ $16t^2 + 34t - 15$

Factor each polynomial. (Lessons 7-2, 7-6)

68. $5x^2 - 80y^4$ $5(x - 4y^2)(x + 4y^2)$

69. $15x^3y^4 - 30x^2yz$ $15x^2y(xy^3 - 2z)$

EXTENDING THE LESSON

Math Power: Problem Solving

Factor each trinomial.

a. $6.25a^2 + 7.5a + 2.25$
$(2.5a + 1.5)^2$

b. $0.01c^2 + 1.69a^2b^2 - 0.26abc$
$(1.3ab - 0.1c)^2$

Additional Answers

53. $(a + 2 - 3b)(a + 2 + 3b)$
54. $(x + y - r)(x + y + r)$
55. $(m - k + 3)(m + k - 3)$
56. $(4 - 3x - 2z)(4 + 3x + 2z)$

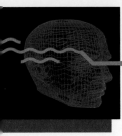

Technology
Factoring

BASIC
Graphing calculators
▶ Graphing software
Spreadsheets

The examples below show how to use the *Mathematics Exploration Toolkit* to factor polynomials. You will need the following CALC commands.

FACTOR (fac)   FSTEPS (fst)   GFACTOR (gcf)   SIMPLIFY (simp)

GFACTOR factors out the greatest common monomial factor of a polynomial. If the polynomial has no common monomial factors, the original polynomial will be displayed again. Sometimes SIMPLIFY must be used first, as in Example 1.

Example 1

Factor $2a(3b + 6) + 3ab(4a - 2)$.	
Enter	**Result**
$2a(3b + 6) + 3ab(4a - 2)$	$2a(3b + 6) + 3ab(4a - 2)$
simp	$12a^2b + 12a$
gcf	$12a(ab + 1)$

FACTOR finds the factors of polynomials with one variable. FSTEPS displays the steps used to execute the FACTOR command.

Example 2

Factor $x^5 - 16x$.	
Enter	**Result**
x^5 - 16x	$x^5 - 16x$
gcf	$x(x^4 - 16)$
fac	$x((x - 2)(x + 2)(x^2 + 4))$
fst	$x^4 - 16$
	$(x^2 - 4)(x^2 + 4)$
	$((x - 2)(x + 2))(x^2 + 4)$
	$x((x - 2)(x + 2)(x^2 + 4))$

EXERCISES

Use GFACTOR to find the greatest common factor of each polynomial.

1. $96x^3y^3 - 80x^2y + 64xy^2$ $16xy$

2. $5x(y^2 + 10y) - 20x^2$ $5x$

Use FACTOR and FSTEPS to factor each polynomial. Record each step.
See students' work for steps.

3. $36x^2 - 64$ $4(3x - 4)(3x + 4)$

4. $25y^2 + 10y + 1$ $(5y + 1)(5y + 1)$

5. $81z^4 - 625$
$(3z^2 - 5)(3z + 5)(9z^2 + 25)$

6. $36a^3 - 5a^2 - a$ $a(4a - 1)(9a + 1)$

TECHNOLOGY: FACTORING 285

Using Technology
Objective This optional page shows how graphing software can be used to perform mathematical computations and to enhance and extend mathematical concepts.

Teaching Suggestions
The FACTOR and GCFACTOR commands will not factor terms within a polynomial, but will only find factors common to all terms. FACTOR uses division to find quadratic and linear factors one at a time. Therefore the order of steps displayed by FSTEPS will be different than the order usually taught. As shown in Example 2, have students use the GCFACTOR command before the FACTOR command to display steps in the usual order.

Encourage students to record the steps shown by FSTEPS. You may want to have them use SIMPLIFY to check factors. Challenge them to attempt to stump the computer by multiplying factors of their choice and entering the product into CALC.

Lesson Resources

- Reteaching Master 7-8
- Practice Master 7-8
- Enrichment Master 7-8
- Video Algebra, 24

 Transparency 7-8 contains the 5-Minute Check and a teaching aid for this lesson.

INTRODUCING THE LESSON

 5-Minute Check

(over Lesson 7-7)

Determine whether each of the following is a perfect square. If it is, factor it.

1. $n^2 - 14n + 49$ $(n - 7)^2$
2. $t^2 - 6t - 9$ no
3. $9t^2 - 42tv + 49v^2$
   $(3t - 7v)^2$
4. $16 + 49t^2 - 56t$
   $(7t - 4)^2$
5. $25n^2 + 64p^2$ no

Motivating the Lesson

Ask students whether each of the following can be a perfect square.
monomial   **yes**
binomial   **no**
trinomial   **yes**
Have students give examples to support each answer.

TEACHING THE LESSON

Teaching Tip ❶   The chart shows a practical set of guidelines that students can refer to when factoring.

Teaching Tip ❷   You may wish to show that the difference of squares method can be used to factor a polynomial with six terms as follows.
$$x^2 + 6x + 9 - a^2 - 4a - 4$$
$$= (x^2 + 6x + 9) - (a^2 + 4a + 4)$$
$$= (x + 3)^2 - (a + 2)^2$$
$$= [(x + 3) + (a + 2)] \cdot$$
$$\quad [(x + 3) - (a + 2)]$$
$$= (x + 3 + a + 2) \cdot$$
$$\quad (x + 3 - a - 2)$$
$$= (x + a + 5)(x - a + 1)$$

7-8 Summary of Factoring

Objective
7-8

After studying this lesson, you should be able to:
- factor polynomials by applying the various methods of factoring.

In this chapter, you have used various methods to factor different types of polynomials. The following chart summarizes these methods and can help you decide when to use a specific method.   **Teaching Tip ❶**

Teaching Tip ❷

Check for:	Number of Terms		
	Two	Three	Four or More
greatest common factor	✔	✔	✔
difference of squares	✔		✔
perfect square trinomial		✔	
trinomial that has two binomial factors		✔	
pairs of terms that have a common monomial factor			✔

Whenever there is a GCF other than 1, always factor it out first. Then, check the appropriate factoring methods in the order shown in the table. Use these methods to factor until all of the factors are prime.

Example 1

Factor $3x^2 - 27$.

First check for a GCF. Then, since there are two terms, check for the difference of squares.

$$3x^2 - 27 = 3(x^2 - 9) \qquad \text{\textit{3 is the GCF.}}$$
$$= 3(x - 3)(x + 3) \qquad \text{\textit{x}}^2 - 9 \text{ \textit{is the difference of squares}}$$
$$\text{\textit{since } x \cdot x = x}^2 \text{ \textit{and } 3 \cdot 3 = 9.}$$

Thus, $3x^2 - 27$ is completely factored as $3(x - 3)(x + 3)$.   **Teaching Tip ❸**

Example 2

Factor $9y^2 - 58y + 49$.

The polynomial has three terms. So, check for the following.

GCF	The GCF is 1.
Perfect square trinomial	Although $9y^2 = (3y)^2$ and $49 = (7)^2$, $58y \neq 2(3y)(7)$.
Trinomial with two binomial factors	Are there two numbers whose product is $9 \cdot 49$ or 441 and whose sum is -58? Yes, the product of -9 and -49 is 441 and their sum is -58.

ALTERNATE TEACHING STRATEGIES

Using Models

Have students draw models of two rectangular solids on a piece of grid paper. Tell them to identify the binomial dimensions of one model and the total volume of the other model. Then have students exchange papers to find the total volume of their classmate's first model and the dimensions of the second model.

Using Connections

The area of a rectangle is represented by $18x^2 + 9x - 20$. What could its dimensions be? $6x - 5$ and $3x + 4$

$$9y^2 - 58y + 49 = 9y^2 + [-9 + (-49)]y + 49$$
$$= (9y^2 - 9y) + (-49y + 49)$$
$$= 9y(y - 1) + (-49)(y - 1)$$
$$= (9y - 49)(y - 1) \qquad \text{\textit{Check this by using FOIL.}}$$

Thus, $9y^2 - 58y + 49$ is completely factored as $(9y - 49)(y - 1)$.

Example 3

Factor $4m^4n + 6m^3n^2 - 16m^2n - 24mn^2$.

Since $4m^4n + 6m^3n^2 - 16m^2n - 24mn^2$ has four terms, first check for the GCF. Then, check for pairs of terms that have a common monomial factor.

$$4m^4n + 6m^3n^2 - 16m^2n - 24mn^2 = 2mn(2m^3 + 3m^2n - 8m - 12n)$$
$$= 2mn[(2m^3 + 3m^2n) + (-8m - 12n)]$$
$$= 2mn[m^2(2m + 3n) + (-4)(2m + 3n)]$$
$$= 2mn[(m^2 - 4)(2m + 3n)]$$
$$= 2mn(m - 2)(m + 2)(2m + 3n)$$

Thus, $4m^4n + 6m^3n^2 - 16m^2n - 24mn^2$ is completely factored as $2mn(m - 2)(m + 2)(2m + 3n)$. *Check this by multiplying the factors.*

Example 4

CONNECTION

Geometry

The length of a rectangle is 3 centimeters more than the length of the side of a square. The width of this rectangle is one-half the length of the side of the square. If the area of the square is $4x^2 + 12x + 9$ square centimeters, what is the area of the rectangle?

You need to factor $4x^2 + 12x + 9$ in order to determine the length of the side of the square. $4x^2 + 12x + 9$ is a perfect square trinomial. *Why?*

$$4x^2 + 12x + 9 = (2x)^2 + 2(2x)(3) + (3)^2$$
$$= (2x + 3)^2$$

The length of the side of the square is $2x + 3$ cm. Thus, the length of the rectangle is $(2x + 3) + 3$ or $2x + 6$ cm and the width is $\frac{1}{2}(2x + 3)$ cm. Now multiply to determine the area of the rectangle.

$$(2x + 6)\left[\frac{1}{2}(2x + 3)\right] = \frac{1}{2}[2x(2x) + (2x)(3) + 6(2x) + 6(3)] \quad \text{\textit{Use FOIL.}}$$
$$= \frac{1}{2}(4x^2 + 18x + 18)$$
$$= 2x^2 + 9x + 9$$

The area of the rectangle is $2x^2 + 9x + 9$ cm^2.

RETEACHING THE LESSON

Play Algebraic Jeopardy. Have each student write only the product of two binomials on a card such as $x^2 - 2x - 15$. Collect the cards. Show students a card. For the example given, students should respond by saying, "What is the product of $(x + 3)$ and $(x - 5)$?

Teaching Tip ③ Emphasize checking factorization by FOIL or the distributive property.

Chalkboard Examples

For Example 1
Factor.

a. $5ax^2 - 45a$
$5a(x - 3)(x + 3)$

b. $32x^3 - 50x$
$2x(4x - 5)(4x + 5)$

For Example 2
Factor.

a. $x^4 + x^3 - 12x^2$
$x^2(x - 3)(x + 4)$

b. $12a^3 - 16a^2 - 16a$
$4a(a - 2)(3a + 2)$

For Example 3
Factor.

a. $12ab - 15a + 28b - 35$
$(3a + 7)(4b - 5)$

b. $3x^3 - 4x^2 - 12x + 16$
$(3x - 4)(x - 2)(x + 2)$

For Example 4
The area of a rectangle is represented by $10a^2 - 29a - 21$. What are its dimensions?
$5a + 3$ and $2a - 7$

Reteaching Masters Booklet, p. 49

7-8 | NAME _____ DATE _____
Reteaching Worksheet

Summary of Factoring

The following table can help you decide which method to use to factor polynomials.

	Number of Terms		
Check for:	**Two**	**Three**	**Four or More**
greatest common factor	✔	✔	✔
difference of squares	✔		✔
perfect square trinomial		✔	
trinomial that has two binomial factors		✔	
pairs of terms that have a common monomial factor			✔

If there is a GCF, factor that out first. Then, check the appropriate factoring methods in the order shown in the table. Using these methods, factor until each of the remaining factors is prime.

Factor. Check by using FOIL or the distributive property.

1. $5a^2b + 10acd - abcd - 2c^2d^2$
$(ab + 2cd)(5a - cd)$

2. $3y^2 - 39$
$3(y^2 - 13)$

3. $2x^4 + 5x^3 - 3x^2$
$x^2(x^2 + 5x - 3)$

4. $3m^4 - m^2q - 2q^2$
$(3m^2 + 2q)(m^2 - q)$

5. $17b^2 - 34b + 17$
$17(b - 1)^2$

6. $-45a^4 - 135a^2d - 40d^2$
$-5(3a^2 + 8d)(3a^2 + d)$

7. $y^3 - 8y + 2y^2 - 16$
$(y^2 - 8)(y + 2)$

8. $6r^3m^3 - 42r^3m^2 + 54rm - 378$
$6(r^2m^2 + 9)(rm - 7)$

9. $8x^2 + 64x + 128$
$8(x + 4)^2$

10. $6d^2 + 48cd + 32c^2$
$2(3d^2 + 24cd + 16c^2)$

11. $7a^2 - 252$
$7(a - 6)(a + 6)$

12. $5x^2 - 5y^2 + mx^2 - my^2$
$(5 + m)(x + y)(x - y)$

Checking for Understanding

Exercises 1-16 are designed to help you assess understanding through reading, writing, and speaking. You should work through Exercises 1-4 with your students, and then monitor their work on Exercises 5-16.

Closing the Lesson

Writing Activity   Summarize the procedure to follow when factoring a binomial and a trinomial. Give an example of each procedure.

APPLYING THE LESSON

Homework Exercises

Assignment Guide
Basic: 17-44, 52-53, 55-60
Average: 22-47, 52-60
Enriched: 26-60

Teaching Tip ④   Remind students to always look for a GCF in any expression before factoring it.

Practice Masters Booklet, p. 55

7-8   **Practice Worksheet**

NAME _____ DATE _____

Summary of Factoring

Factor. Check by using FOIL or the distributive property.

1. $6x^2 + x - 15$
$(3x + 5)(2x - 3)$

2. $m^2 - 12m + 36$
$(m - 6)^2$

3. $2p^2 - 18$
$2(p - 3)(p + 3)$

4. $12w^2 + 28w + 15$
$(6w + 5)(2w + 3)$

5. $28z^2 - 65z + 28$
$(7z - 4)(4z - 7)$

6. $42x^2 - xy - 30y^2$
$(7x - 6y)(6x + 5y)$

7. $15y^2 - y - 2$
$(5y - 2)(3y + 1)$

8. $a^2 - b^2$
$(a - b)(a + b)$

9. $21x^3 - 35xy^2$
$7x(3x^2 - 5y^2)$

10. $6ax^2 + 11ax - 10a$
$a(3x - 2)(2x + 5)$

11. $45 + 2f^2$
prime

12. $6c^2 - 10c - 4$
$2(3c + 1)(c - 2)$

13. $18z^2 + 9z + 1$
$(6z + 1)(3z + 1)$

14. $3s^2 - 12$
$3(s - 2)(s + 2)$

15. $15r^2 - 16rt + 4t^2$
$(5r - 2t)(3r - 2t)$

16. $4y^3 + 12y^2 - y - 3$
$(2y - 1)(2y + 1)(y + 3)$

17. $10k^2 + 105km + 270m^2$
$5(2k + 9m)(k + 6m)$

18. $3w^3 - w^2 - 12w + 4$
$(w - 2)(w + 2)(3w - 1)$

19. $102 - 23c + c^2$
$(6 - c)(17 - c)$

20. $6a^2 + 2a + 6am + 2m$
$2(a + m)(3a + 1)$

21. $u^4 - 7u^3 - 18u^2$
$u^2(u - 9)(u + 2)$

22. $2n^3 - 12n^2y + 18ny^2$
$2n(n - 3y)^2$

23. $p^4 + 5p^2 + 6$
$(p^2 + 3)(p^2 + 2)$

24. $7j^3 - 112j$
$7j(j - 16)$

25. $3ar - 6yr + 9am - 18ym$
$3(r + 3m)(a - 2y)$

26. $0.36x + 0.6x + 0.25$
$(0.6x + 0.5)^2$

27. $15 + 78v - 72v^2$
$3(5 - 4v)(1 + 6v)$

28. $36d^3e + de^3 - 12d^2e^2$
$de(6d - e)^2$

CHECKING FOR UNDERSTANDING

Communicating Mathematics

Complete.

1. When factoring, the ___?___ of the terms of a polynomial should always be factored out first. **GCF**

2. To factor a ___?___, you check for the GCF, for a perfect square, and for two binomial factors. **trinomial**

3. You should check for pairs of terms that have a common monomial factor when you factor a polynomial with ___?___ terms. **four or more**

4. A polynomial is factored completely when each of its factors is ___?___. **prime**

Guided Practice
See margin.

Indicate which method of factoring you would apply first to each polynomial.

5. $x^2 - 5x$

6. $64c^2 - 25p^2$

7. $9x^2 - 12xy + 4y^2$

8. $16m^2 - 64n^2$

9. $35z^2 + 13z - 12$

10. $2x^2 + 4xy - x - 2y$

Factor. Check by using FOIL or the distributive property. See margin.

11. $3x^2 + 15$

12. $8mn^2 - 13m^2n$

13. $a^2 - 9b^2$

14. $x^2 - 5x + 6$

15. $a^2 + 8a + 16$

16. $3a^2b + 6ab + 9ab^2$

EXERCISES

Teaching Practice Tip ④

Factor. Check by using FOIL or the distributive property. See margin.

17. $12a^2 + 18ay^2$

18. $2a^2 - 72$

19. $3y^2 - 147$

20. $2k^2 + 3k + 1$

21. $m^3 + 6m^2 + 9m$

22. $18y + 12y^2 + 2y^3$

23. $6r^2 + 13r + 6$

24. $4x^3 - 3x^2 - 12x + 9$

25. $m^4 - p^2$

26. $4a^3 - 36a$

27. $3x^3 - 27x$

28. $3y^2 + 21y - 24$

29. $20n^2 + 34n + 6$

30. $m^2 + 8mn + 16n^2$

31. $4a^2 + 12ab + 9b^2$

32. $4y^3 - 12y^2 + 8y$

33. $9t^3 + 66t^2 - 48t$

34. $a^2b^3 - 25b$

35. $m^3n^2 - 49m$

36. $0.4r^2 + 1.6r + 1.6$

37. $0.7y^2 - 3.5y + 4.2$

38. $\frac{1}{3}b^2 + 2b + 3$

39. $m^2 + \frac{5}{12}m - \frac{1}{6}$

40. $\frac{1}{4}x^2 + \frac{3}{2}x + 2$

41. $x^3y + 2x^2 + 8xy + 16$

42. $4a^3 + 3a^2b^2 + 8a + 6b^2$

43. $x^2y^2 - z^2 - y^2 + x^2z^2$

44. $20a^2x - 4a^2y - 45xb^2 + 9yb^2$

45. $(x + y)^2 - (a - b)^2$

46. $x^2 + 6x + 9 - y^2$

47. $(x + 1)^2 - 3(x + 1) + 2$

48. $(2x - 3)^2 - 4(2x - 3) - 5$

49. $x^4 + 6x^3 + 9x^2 - 3x^2y - 18xy - 27y$

50. $12mp^2 - 15np^2 - 16m + 20np - 16mp + 20n$

Additional Answers

5. greatest common factor

6. difference of squares

7. perfect square trinomial

8. greatest common factor

9. trinomial that has two binomial factors

10. pairs of terms that have a common monomial factor

11. $3(x^2 + 5)$

12. $mn(8n - 13m)$

13. $(a - 3b)(a + 3b)$

14. $(x - 2)(x - 3)$

15. $(a + 4)^2$

16. $3ab(a + 2 + 3b)$

17. $6a(2a + 3y^2)$

18. $2(a - 6)(a + 6)$

19. $3(y - 7)(y + 7)$

20. $(2k + 1)(k + 1)$

21. $m(m + 3)^2$

22. $2y(3 + y)^2$

51. The measure of the volume of a rectangular solid is $x^3y - 63y^2 + 7x^2 - 9xy^3$. What are the measures of its dimensions?

$x - 3y, x + 3y, xy + 7$

Critical Thinking

52. A *nasty* number is a positive integer with at least four different factors such that the difference between the numbers in one pair of factors equals the sum of the numbers in another pair. The first nasty number is 6 since $6 = 6 \cdot 1 = 2 \cdot 3$ and $6 - 1 = 2 + 3$. Find the next five nasty numbers. (*Hint:* They are all multiples of 6.) **24, 30, 54, 60, and 84**

Applications

53. **Gardening** The length of Jillian's rectangular garden is 12 feet greater than its width. Because she wants to plant some flowers next to the garden, she decreased its length by 5 feet and increased its width by 2 feet. If the area of the garden was decreased by 55 square feet, what were its original dimensions?

23 feet by 35 feet

54. **Conferences** A one-day Pacific Coast Land Usage Conference is being attended by 32 delegates from California, 24 from Washington, and 20 from Oregon.

a. What is the greatest number of meetings that can be held so that the delegates from each state are distributed equally among all the meetings? **4 meetings**

b. If each meeting room can seat 20 people, how many extra seats will there be at each meeting? **1 seat**

Mixed Review

55. A price was increased from $85 to $110. Find the percent of increase, to the nearest tenth of a percent. **(Lesson 4-4) 29.4%**

56. **Sales** Carita plans to spend at most $50 on shorts and blouses. She bought 2 pair of shorts for $14.20 each. How much can she spend on blouses? **(Lesson 5-1) $21.60 or less**

57. Solve by drawing a diagram. **(Lesson 5-4)**

Eight soccer teams play in the Central League. Each team is required to play every other team exactly once. How many games will be played in this league? **28 games**

58. Simplify $(-0.2x^3y)^3$. **(Lesson 6-2)** $-0.008x^9y^3$

59. Simplify $\frac{(2a^{-1}b^2)^2}{4a^{-3}b}$. **(Lesson 6-3)** ab^3

60. **Geometry** The measure of the area of a square is $9s^2 - 42s + 49$. What is the measure of its perimeter? **(Lesson 7-7)** $12s - 28$

LESSON 7-8 SUMMARY OF FACTORING **289**

EXTENDING THE LESSON

Math Power: Connections

The measure of the area of a trapezoid is $\frac{15}{2}x^2 + \frac{45}{2}y^2 + 15$.

Use the formula $A = \frac{1}{2}h(a + b)$ to find a possible measure of the height of the trapezoid.

15 or $x^2 + 3y^2 + 2$

Additional Answers

23. $(3r + 2)(2r + 3)$
24. $(x^2 - 3)(4x - 3)$
25. $(m^2 - p)(m^2 + p)$
26. $4a(a - 3)(a + 3)$
27. $3x(x - 3)(x + 3)$
28. $3(y + 8)(y - 1)$
29. $2(5n + 1)(2n + 3)$
30. $(m + 4n)^2$
31. $(2a + 3b)^2$
32. $4y(y - 2)(y - 1)$

Additional Answers

33. $3t(3t - 2)(t + 8)$
34. $b(ab + 5)(ab - 5)$
35. $m(mn + 7)(mn - 7)$
36. $0.4(r + 2)^2$
37. $0.7(y - 2)(y - 3)$
38. $\frac{1}{3}(b + 3)^2$
39. $\frac{1}{12}(4m - 1)(3m + 2)$
40. $\frac{1}{4}(x + 4)(x + 2)$
41. $(x^2 + 8)(xy + 2)$
42. $(a^2 + 2)(4a + 3b^2)$
43. $(y^2 + z^2)(x + 1)(x - 1)$
44. $(2a + 3b)(2a - 3b)(5x - y)$
45. $(x + y + a - b)(x + y - a + b)$
46. $(x + 3 - y)(x + 3 + y)$
47. $x(x - 1)$
48. $4(x - 1)(x - 4)$
49. $(x^2 - 3y)(x + 3)^2$
50. $(4m - 5n)(3p + 2)(p - 2)$

Enrichment Masters Booklet, p. 49

Lesson Resources

- Reteaching Master 7-9
- Practice Master 7-9
- Enrichment Master 7-9
- Activity Master, p. 52
- Video Algebra, 25, 53

 Transparency 7-9 contains the 5-Minute Check and a teaching aid for this lesson.

INTRODUCING THE LESSON

⏱ 5-Minute Check
(over Lesson 7-8)

Factor completely.

1. $16x^4 - 36x^2y^2$
   $4x^2(2x - 3y)(2x + 3y)$
2. $20a^2 - 7a - 6$
   $(4a - 3)(5a + 2)$
3. $6t^3 - 21t^2 - 45t$
   $3t(t - 5)(2t + 3)$
4. $4n^3 - 20n^2 - 9n + 45$
   $(n - 5)(2n - 3)(2n + 3)$

5. The area of a rectangle is represented by $20a^2 + 13a - 15$. Find its dimensions.
   $5a - 3$ and $4a + 5$

Motivating the Lesson

Ask students, "About how large would you expect the product of all integers −100 to 100, inclusive, to be? Take a few minutes to discuss it with your neighbor". The answer is zero since zero is one of the factors. This is a good way to introduce students to the zero product property.

TEACHING THE LESSON

Chalkboard Example

For Example 1
Solve each equation.

a. $5a(a + 4) = 0$ $\{0, -4\}$

b. $2x(x - 4) = 0$ $\{0, 4\}$

c. $-4(5 - t) = 0$ $\{5\}$

7-9 Solving Equations by Factoring

Objective
7-9

After studying this lesson, you should be able to:
- use the zero product property to solve equations.

Application

FYI ⋯

The Assyrians first used life rafts made of inflated goat skins in 880 B.C.

A flare is launched from a life raft with an initial upward velocity of 144 feet per second. How many seconds will it take for the flare to return to the sea?

If an object is launched from ground level, it reaches its maximum height in the air at a time halfway between the launch and impact times. Its height above the ground after t seconds is given by the formula $h = vt - 16t^2$. In this formula, h represents the height of the object in feet, and v represents the object's initial velocity in feet per second.

Since the flare's height when it returns to the sea is 0 feet, $h = 0$. Since the flare's initial velocity is 144 feet per second, $v = 144$. Thus, this problem can be represented by the equation $0 = 144t - 16t^2$.

$$0 = 144t - 16t^2 \quad \text{The GCF is } 16t.$$
$$0 = 16t(9 - t)$$

To solve this equation, you need to find the values of t that make the product $16t(9 - t)$ equal to 0. Consider the following products.

$$3(0) = 0 \qquad 0(-8) = 0 \qquad \left(\frac{1}{2} - \frac{1}{2}\right)(0) = 0 \qquad 0(x + 2) = 0$$

Notice that in each case, *at least one* of the factors is zero. These examples illustrate the **zero product property.**

Zero Product Property	For all numbers a and b, if $ab = 0$, then $a = 0$, $b = 0$, or both a and b equal 0.

Thus, if an equation can be written in the form $ab = 0$, then the zero product property can be applied to solve that equation.

Example 1

Solve $16t(9 - t) = 0$ to find how long it took the flare to return to the sea.

If $16t(9 - t) = 0$, then $16t = 0$ or $9 - t = 0$.   *Zero product property*

$$16t = 0 \quad \text{or} \quad 9 - t = 0 \quad \text{Solve each equation.}$$
$$t = 0 \qquad\qquad 9 = t$$

ALTERNATE TEACHING STRATEGIES

Using Logical Reasoning

Duane, Doug, and Dugan have jobs as a farmer, florist, and forester (but not necessarily in that order). Duane lives 10 miles from the farmer. Doug and the forester both enjoy playing golf. Dugan is older than both the florist and the forester. What is the job of each individual?   **Duane - forester, Doug - florist, Dugan - farmer**

Check: Substitute 0 and 9 for t in the original equation.

$$16t(9 - t) = 0$$

$$16(0)(9 - 0) \stackrel{?}{=} 0 \qquad \text{or} \quad 16(9)(9 - 9) \stackrel{?}{=} 0$$

$$0(9) \stackrel{?}{=} 0 \qquad\qquad\qquad 144(0) \stackrel{?}{=} 0$$

$$0 = 0 \quad \text{✓} \qquad\qquad\qquad 0 = 0 \quad \text{✓}$$

The solutions of $16t(9 - t) = 0$ are 0 and 9. So, the flare returns to the sea in 9 seconds. The answer 0 seconds is not reasonable since it represents the time when the flare was launched from the life raft.

Teaching Tip **1**

Example 2

Solve $(y + 2)(3y + 5) = 0$. Then check the solution.

If $(y + 2)(3y + 5) = 0$, then $y + 2 = 0$ or $3y + 5 = 0$. *Zero product property*

$$y + 2 = 0 \quad \text{or} \quad 3y + 5 = 0$$

$$y = -2 \qquad\qquad 3y = -5$$

$$y = -\frac{5}{3}$$

Check: $\qquad\qquad (y + 2)(3y + 5) = 0$

$$(-2 + 2)[3(-2) + 5] \stackrel{?}{=} 0 \qquad \text{or} \quad \left(-\frac{5}{3} + 2\right)\left[3\left(-\frac{5}{3}\right) + 5\right] \stackrel{?}{=} 0$$

$$0(-1) \stackrel{?}{=} 0 \qquad\qquad\qquad\qquad \frac{1}{3}(0) \stackrel{?}{=} 0$$

$$0 = 0 \quad \text{✓} \qquad\qquad\qquad\qquad\qquad 0 = 0 \quad \text{✓}$$

The solution set is $\left\{-2, -\frac{5}{3}\right\}$.

Example 3

Solve $x^2 = 7x$. Then check the solution.

To use the zero product property, the equation must be written in the form $ab = 0$.

$$x^2 = 7x$$

$$x^2 - 7x = 0$$

$$x(x - 7) = 0 \qquad \textit{Factor out the GCF, x.}$$

$$x = 0 \quad \text{or} \quad x - 7 = 0 \qquad \textit{Zero product property}$$

$$x = 7$$

Check: $\qquad\qquad x^2 = 7x$

$$(0)^2 \stackrel{?}{=} 7(0) \qquad \text{or} \quad (7)^2 \stackrel{?}{=} 7(7)$$

$$0 = 0 \quad \text{✓} \qquad\qquad 49 = 49 \quad \text{✓}$$

The solution set is $\{0, 7\}$.

Teaching Tip 1   Have students consider the equation $3(x + 7) = 0$. Since $3 \neq 0$, it is reasonable to set only the factor with the variable equal to zero. Therefore, $3(x + 7) = 0$ can be solved as follows.

$$3(x + 7) = 0$$

$$\frac{3(x + 7)}{3} = \frac{0}{3}$$

$$x + 7 = 0$$

$$x = -7$$

Chalkboard Examples

For Example 4

Jules said, "The product of three more than twice the number of nickels I have and half the number of nickels decreased by three is zero". How much money does he have in nickels?
30 cents

For Example 5

The product of twice a number and three less than the number is 0. Find the number.   **0 or 3**

Reteaching Masters Booklet, p. 50

292 Chapter 7

Example 4

Maria told this puzzle to her friends. "The product of four times my age and 45 less than three times my age is zero. How old am I?" Find Maria's age now.

EXPLORE Let m = Maria's age now.

PLAN $\underbrace{\text{Four times her age}}$ times $\underbrace{\text{45 less than three times her age}}$ is $\underbrace{0.}$

$$4m \qquad\qquad (3m - 45) \qquad\qquad = 0$$

SOLVE $4m(3m - 45) = 0$

$4m = 0 \quad \text{or} \quad 3m - 45 = 0$ *Zero product property*
$m = 0 \qquad\qquad 3m = 45$
$\qquad\qquad\qquad m = 15$

Maria is 15 years old now. The solution 0 is not reasonable since Maria cannot be 0 years old.

EXAMINE If $m = 15$, then $3m - 45$ is 0, and the product will be 0. Thus, the answer is correct.

Example 5

The product of twice a number increased by five and three times the number decreased by two is zero. Find the number.

EXPLORE Let n = the number.

PLAN $\underbrace{\text{Twice a number increased by 5}}$ times $\underbrace{\text{three times the number decreased by 2}}$ is $\underbrace{0.}$

$$(2n + 5) \qquad\qquad (3n - 2) \qquad\qquad = 0$$

SOLVE $(2n + 5)(3n - 2) = 0$

$2n + 5 = 0 \quad \text{or} \quad 3n - 2 = 0$ *Zero product property*
$2n = -5 \qquad\qquad 3n = 2$
$n = -\frac{5}{2} \qquad\qquad n = \frac{2}{3}$

The number is either $-\frac{5}{2}$ or $\frac{2}{3}$.

EXAMINE If n is $-\frac{5}{2}$, then $2n + 5$ is 0, and the product will be 0. If n is $\frac{2}{3}$, then $3n - 2$ is 0 and the product will be 0. Thus, the answer is correct.

292 CHAPTER 7 FACTORING

RETEACHING THE LESSON

Abe adds up the number of runs that the Reds score in each game for the season. Bob multiplies together the number of runs that the Mets score in each game. Who will probably have the larger number at the end of the season? Why? **Abe. Think of the effects of a shutout.**

1. If the product of two numbers is 0, then at least one of the numbers is 0.

CHECKING FOR UNDERSTANDING

Communicating Mathematics

Read and study the lesson to answer each question.

1. Write the zero product property in your own words.
2. If a product of more than two factors is equal to 0, what must be true of the factors? **At least one of the factors is 0.**
3. Can you solve $(x + 3)(x + 1) = 0$ by dividing each side of the equation by $x + 3$? Why or why not? **No, since -3 is a solution, and $-3 + 3 = 0$, you would be dividing by 0.**

Guided Practice

State the conditions under which each equation will be true. **See margin.**
Example: $x(x + 7) = 0$ will be true if $x = 0$ or $x + 7 = 0$.

4. $x(x + 3) = 0$
5. $3r(r - 4) = 0$
6. $3t(4t - 32) = 0$
7. $(x - 6)(x + 4) = 0$
8. $(2y + 8)(3y + 24) = 0$
9. $(4x - 7)(3x + 5) = 0$

Solve. Check each solution. **See margin.**

10. $n(n - 3) = 0$
11. $8c(c + 4) = 0$
12. $3x^2 - \frac{3}{4}x = 0$
13. $7y^2 = 14y$
14. $8a^2 = -4a$
15. $-13x = -26x^2$

Practice

Solve. Check each solution.

A
16. $y(y - 12) = 0$ $\{0, 12\}$
17. $7a(a + 6) = 0$ $\{0, -6\}$
18. $2x(5x - 10) = 0$ $\{0, 2\}$
19. $(b - 3)(b - 5) = 0$ $\{3, 5\}$
20. $(t - 5)(t + 5) = 0$ $\{5, -5\}$
21. $(4x + 4)(2x + 6) = 0$ $\{-1, -3\}$
22. $(p - 8)(2p + 7) = 0$ $\left\{8, -\frac{7}{2}\right\}$
23. $(3x - 5)^2 = 0$ $\left\{\frac{5}{3}\right\}$
24. $x^2 - 6x = 0$ $\{0, 6\}$
25. $m^2 + 36m = 0$ $\{0, -36\}$

B
26. $2x^2 + 4x = 0$ $\{0, -2\}$
27. $4s^2 = -36s$ $\{0, -9\}$
28. $y^2 - 3y = 4y$ $\{0, 7\}$
29. $2x^2 = x^2 - 8x$ $\{0, -8\}$
30. $7y - 1 = -3y^2 + y - 1$ $\{0, -2\}$
31. $z^2 - 8z + 2 = 2 - 13z$ $\{0, -5\}$
32. $\frac{1}{2}y^2 - \frac{1}{4}y = 0$ $\left\{0, \frac{1}{2}\right\}$
33. $\frac{2}{3}x = \frac{1}{3}x^2$ $\{0, 2\}$
34. $\frac{5}{6}x^2 - \frac{1}{3}x = \frac{1}{3}x$ $\left\{0, \frac{4}{5}\right\}$
35. $\frac{3}{4}a^2 + \frac{7}{8}a = a$ $\left\{0, \frac{1}{6}\right\}$

For each problem, define a variable. Then use an equation to solve the problem. Disregard any unreasonable solutions. **37. 16 years old**

36. The product of a certain negative number decreased by 5 and the same number increased by 7 is 0. What is the number? **-7**

37. Randy told Honovi, "The product of twice my age decreased by 32 and 5 times my age increased by 6 is 0. How old am I?" Find Randy's age.

LESSON 7-9 SOLVING EQUATIONS BY FACTORING **293**

Additional Answers

4. $x = 0$ or $x + 3 = 0$
5. $3r = 0$ or $r - 4 = 0$
6. $3t = 0$ or $4t - 32 = 0$
7. $x - 6 = 0$ or $x + 4 = 0$
8. $2y + 8 = 0$ or $3y + 24 = 0$
9. $4x - 7 = 0$ or $3x + 5 = 0$
10. $\{0, 3\}$

11. $\{0, -4\}$
12. $\left\{0, \frac{1}{4}\right\}$
13. $\{0, 2\}$
14. $\left\{0, -\frac{1}{2}\right\}$
15. $\left\{0, \frac{1}{2}\right\}$

Practice Masters Booklet, p. 56

Speaking Activity If
$(a + b)(a - b) = 0$, what can be
concluded about a and b?
$a = b$ or $a = -b$

APPLYING THE LESSON

Homework Exercises
See assignment guide on
page 293.

Teaching Tip ② Before
students work on Exercise 39,
review with them how to
represent consecutive integers
and consecutive even or
consecutive odd integers.

Enrichment Masters Booklet, p. 50

For each problem, define a variable. Then use an equation to solve the
problem. Disregard any unreasonable solutions.

Teaching Tip ②

38. The square of a number subtracted from 8 times the number is equal
    to twice the number. Find the number. **0 or 6**

39. When one integer is added to the square of the next consecutive
    integer, the sum is 1. Find the integers. **0, 1; -3, -2**

Critical Thinking

40. Write an equation with integral coefficients that has $\{0, 7, -3\}$ as its
    solution set. $x^3 - 4x^2 - 21x = 0$

Applications

41. **Gardening** Mr. Steinborn tripled
    the area of his square garden by
    increasing its length by 18 feet.
    What were the dimensions of his
    original garden? **9 feet by 9 feet**

42. **Construction** The length of a
    rectangular playground is 10 yards
    less than 3 times its width. In order
    to add a baseball diamond next to
    it, the width of the playground is
    decreased by 15 yards and the
    length is decreased by 35 yards. The
    area of this reduced playground is
    675 square yards. What are the
    dimensions of the original
    playground? **30 yards by 80 yards**

Use the formula $h = vt - 16t^2$ to solve each problem.

43. **Physics** A flare is launched from a life raft with an initial upward
    velocity of 192 feet per second. How many seconds will it take for the
    flare to return to the sea? **12 seconds**

44. **Physics** A ball is tossed directly upward with an initial velocity of
    120 feet per second. How many seconds will it take for the ball to hit
    the ground? **7.5 seconds**

Mixed Review

45. **Sales** During a special promotion, Southern Air issued round-trip
    first-class tickets from Orlando to Dallas at $255 and round-trip coach
    tickets at $198. If 167 tickets were purchased for a total price of
    $40,191, how many first-class tickets were sold? **(Lesson 4-6) 125 tickets**

46. Solve $-\frac{5s}{8} \geq \frac{15}{4}$. **(Lesson 5-2)** $\{s \mid s \leq -6\}$

47. Find $(3mn^2 + 3mn - n^3) + (5mn^2 - n - 2n^3)$. **(Lesson 6-6)** $8mn^2 + 3mn - n - 3n^3$

48. Find the prime factorization of 2700. **(Lesson 7-1)** $2^2 \cdot 3^3 \cdot 5^2$

49. Find all values of k so that $4y^2 + ky - 4$ can be factored using integers.
    (Lesson 7-5) 15, -15, 6, -6, 0

50. Factor $12c^2 + 10cd - 42d^2$. **(Lesson 7-8)** $2(3c + 7d)(2c - 3d)$

EXTENDING THE LESSON

Math Power: Connections

Two circles have radii that are
consecutive numbers. Find their
radii if their areas differ by 37π
square feet. **18 and 19 feet**

7-10 More Solving Equations by Factoring

Objective
7-10

After studying this lesson, you should be able to:
- solve equations by using various factoring methods and applying the zero product property.

Application

As a professional photographer, Patricia Newman often needs to make prints of her photographs to show to clients. Usually, she is asked to make different-sized prints of the same photograph. She has just finished making a print that is 8 centimeters long by 6 centimeters wide. Now, Patricia wants to reduce the length and width of the print by the same amount so that the area of the new print is one-half the area of the original print. By what amount should she reduce the length and width of the original print? What are the length and width of the new print?

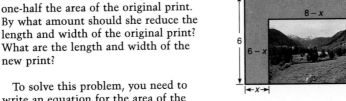

To solve this problem, you need to write an equation for the area of the new print. Let x = the amount by which the length and width should be reduced. Then, the new print is 8 − x cm long and 6 − x cm wide. Since the area of the original print is 8 · 6 or 48 cm², the area of the new print should be $\frac{1}{2}$(48) or 24 cm².

Therefore, the area of the new print of the photograph can be represented by the following equation.

$$24 = (8 - x)(6 - x) \quad \textit{area = length · width}$$

You can solve equations like this one by first writing them as a product of factors equal to zero and then applying the zero product property.

$$24 = (8 - x)(6 - x)$$
$$24 = 48 - 8x - 6x + x^2$$
$$x^2 - 14x + 24 = 0 \quad \textit{Rewrite the equation.}$$
$$(x - 12)(x - 2) = 0 \quad \textit{Factor } x^2 - 14x + 24.$$
$$x - 12 = 0 \quad \text{or} \quad x - 2 = 0 \quad \textit{Zero product property}$$
$$x = 12 \qquad x = 2$$

The solution set is {2, 12}.

Lesson Resources

- Reteaching Master 7-10
- Practice Master 7-10
- Enrichment Master 7-10
- Technology Master, p. 22
- Video Algebra, 25, 26, 53
- Transparency 7-10 contains the 5-Minute Check and a teaching aid for this lesson.

INTRODUCING THE LESSON

5-Minute Check
(over Lesson 7-9)

Solve.

1. $3x(x + 11) = 0$ {0, −11}
2. $(4t − 3)(t + 2) = 0$ $\left\{\frac{3}{4}, -2\right\}$
3. $5a^2 = 13a$ $\left\{0, \frac{13}{5}\right\}$
4. The product of 3 times a number and twice the number decreased by 7 is 0. What is the number? 0 or $\frac{7}{2}$
5. One square has a side 3 cm greater than a second square. What are the lengths of the sides if the sum of their areas is 1017 square centimeters? 21 and 24 cm

Motivating the Lesson
Discuss the following with the class.
1. If $(a + b)^2 = 0$, what must be true of a and b? $a = -b$
2. If $(a - b)^2 = 0$, what must be true of a and b? $a = b$

ALTERNATE TEACHING STRATEGIES

Using Applications
Cosetta built a square pen in the corner of her square backyard. The side of her backyard is 24 ft longer than the side of the pen. Find the dimensions of the pen and Cosetta's backyard if the difference of their areas is 1152 square feet. pen - 12 ft by 12 ft; backyard - 36 ft by 36 ft

Therefore, Patricia should reduce the length and width by 2 cm each. The length of the new print will be $8 - 2$ or 6 cm and the width will be $6 - 2$ or 4 cm.

$$\begin{aligned}
\text{Check:} \quad (8 - x)(6 - x) &= 24 \\
(8 - 2)(6 - 2) &\stackrel{?}{=} 24 \\
6(4) &\stackrel{?}{=} 24 \\
24 &= 24 \quad \checkmark
\end{aligned}$$

Some equations have two solutions that are equal.

Chalkboard Examples

For Example 1
Solve.

a. $a^2 - 24a = -144$ {12}

b. $4m^2 - 25 = -20m$ $\left\{\frac{5}{2}\right\}$

For Example 2
Solve.

a. $x^3 + 2x^2 = 15x$ $\{0, -5, 3\}$

b. $a^3 - 13a^2 + 42a = 0$
$\{0, 6, 7\}$

c. $4r^3 - 9r = 0$ $\left\{0, \frac{3}{2}, -\frac{3}{2}\right\}$

d. $6t^3 + t^2 - 5t = 0$
$\left\{0, \frac{5}{6}, -1\right\}$

Teaching Tip ❶   Point out that the zero product property can be extended to more than two factors.

Example 1

Solve $a^2 + 64 = -16a$.

$$\begin{aligned}
a^2 + 64 &= -16a \\
a^2 + 16a + 64 &= 0 \qquad &\textit{Rewrite the equation.} \\
(a + 8)^2 &= 0 \qquad &\textit{Factor } a^2 + 16a + 64 \textit{ as a perfect} \\
(a + 8)(a + 8) &= 0 \qquad &\textit{square trinomial.}
\end{aligned}$$

$a + 8 = 0$ or $a + 8 = 0$ *Zero product property*
$\qquad a = -8 \qquad\qquad\quad a = -8$

$$\begin{aligned}
\text{Check:} \quad a^2 + 64 &= -16a \\
(-8)^2 + 64 &\stackrel{?}{=} -16(-8) \\
64 + 64 &= 128 \quad \checkmark
\end{aligned}$$

The solution set is $\{-8\}$.

You can apply the zero product property to an equation that is written as the product of *any* number of factors equal to zero.

Example 2

Solve $2y^3 - 24y = 13y^2$.   **Teaching Tip ❶**

$$\begin{aligned}
2y^3 - 24y &= 13y^2 \\
2y^3 - 13y^2 - 24y &= 0 \qquad &\textit{Arrange the terms so that the powers of } y \\
y(2y^2 - 13y - 24) &= 0 \qquad &\textit{are in descending order.} \\
y(y - 8)(2y + 3) &= 0 \qquad &\textit{Factor out the GCF, } y. \\
&\qquad &\textit{Factor } 2y^2 - 13y - 24.
\end{aligned}$$

$y = 0$ or $y - 8 = 0$ or $2y + 3 = 0$
$\qquad\qquad\qquad\quad y = 8 \qquad\qquad\quad 2y = -3$
$\qquad\qquad\qquad\qquad\qquad\qquad\qquad\quad y = -\frac{3}{2}$

The solution set is $\left\{0, 8, -\frac{3}{2}\right\}$. *Check this result.*

RETEACHING THE LESSON

Have each student pick two numbers and write an equation that has those two numbers in its solution set. For example, pick answers 5 and -3.

$x = 5$ or $x = -3$
$x - 5 = 0$ or $x + 3 = 0$
$(x - 5)(x + 3) = 0$
equation: $x^2 - 2x - 15 = 0$

Example 3

CONNECTION

Number Theory

Find two consecutive integers whose product is 72.

Let n = the least integer.
Then, $n + 1$ = the next greater integer.

$$n(n + 1) = 72$$
$$n^2 + n = 72$$
$$n^2 + n - 72 = 0$$
$$(n + 9)(n - 8) = 0$$

$n + 9 = 0$ or $n - 8 = 0$
$n = -9$ $\quad\quad\quad n = 8$

If $n = -9$, then $n + 1 = -8$. $\quad$ **Check:** $\quad (-9)(-8) = 72$ ✓
If $n = 8$, then $n + 1 = 9$. $\quad\quad\quad\quad\quad\quad\quad\quad 8(9) = 72$ ✓

Therefore, the two consecutive integers are -9 and -8 or 8 and 9.

1. When the equation can be written as a product of factors equal to 0.

CHECKING FOR UNDERSTANDING

Communicating Mathematics

Read and study the lesson to answer each question. 2. See margin.

1. When can the zero product property be used to solve an equation?

2. When solving a problem by using an equation, why must you check each solution with the original problem and not the equation?

3. Refer to the photography problem at the beginning of the lesson. If Patricia wants the new photo to have an area of 35 square centimeters, by what amount should she reduce the length and width of the original photo? **1 cm**

Guided Practice

Solve. Check each solution.

4. $a^2 + 4a - 21 = 0$ $\{3, -7\}$

5. $2y^2 + 5y + 2 = 0$ $\left\{-2, -\frac{1}{2}\right\}$

6. $10m^2 + m - 3 = 0$ $\left\{-\frac{3}{5}, \frac{1}{2}\right\}$

7. $y^2 - 16 = 0$ $\{4, -4\}$

8. $7x^2 = 70x - 175$ $\{5\}$

9. $x^3 + 29x^2 = -28x$ $\{0, -1, -28\}$

Define a variable and write an equation for each problem. See margin.

10. The product of two consecutive integers is 110.

11. The sum of two integers is 15 and their product is 44.

12. The area of a living room is 40 square meters. The length of the room is 3 meters more than its width.

13. A rectangle is 4 inches wide and 7 inches long. When the length and width are increased by the same amount, the area is increased by 26 square inches.

Additional Answers

2. A solution to the equation may not be a reasonable answer to the original problem. Also, you may have written an incorrect equation.

10. Let x = the smaller integer; $x(x + 1) = 110$.

11. Let x = one of the integers; $x(15 - x) = 44$.

12. Let w = the width of the room; $w(w + 3) = 40$.

13. Let x = the amount the length and width should be increased; $(7 + x)(4 + x) = 28 + 26$.

EXERCISES

Practice Solve. Check each solution.

14. $x^2 + 13x + 36 = 0$ $\{-4, -9\}$
15. $a^2 + a - 56 = 0$ $\{-8, 7\}$
16. $b^2 - 8b - 33 = 0$ $\{-3, 11\}$
17. $y^2 - 64 = 0$ $\{8, -8\}$
18. $c^2 - 17c + 60 = 0$ $\{5, 12\}$
19. $m^2 - 24m + 144 = 0$ $\{12\}$
20. $p^2 = 5p + 24$ $\{8, -3\}$
21. $r^2 = 18 + 7r$ $\{9, -2\}$

22. $6z^2 + 5 = -17z$ $\{-\frac{1}{3}, -\frac{5}{2}\}$
23. $3y^2 + 16y = 35$ $\{\frac{5}{3}, -7\}$
24. $\frac{x^2}{12} - \frac{2x}{3} - 4 = 0$ $\{12, -4\}$
25. $x^2 - \frac{x}{6} - \frac{35}{6} = 0$ $\{\frac{5}{2}, -\frac{7}{3}\}$
26. $m^3 - 81m = 0$ $\{0, 9, -9\}$
27. $5b^3 + 34b^2 = 7b$ $\{0, \frac{1}{5}, -7\}$

Teaching Tip

28. $81n^3 + 36n^2 = -4n$ $\{0, -\frac{2}{9}\}$
29. $(x + 8)(x + 1) = -12$ $\{-4, -5\}$
30. $(r - 1)(r - 1) = 36$ $\{-5, 7\}$
31. $(3y + 2)(y + 3) = y + 14$ $\{-4, \frac{2}{3}\}$

32. The area of a square is $4s^2 + 28s + 49$ square inches. Find the value of s if the perimeter of the square is 60 inches. **4**

For each problem, define a variable. Then use an equation to solve the problem.

33. Find two consecutive even integers whose product is 120.
$10, 12; -12, -10$
34. Find two integers whose sum is 11 and whose product is 24. **3, 8**
35. Find two integers whose difference is 3 and whose product is 88.
$8, 11; -8, -11$

36. The sum of the squares of two consecutive positive odd integers is 202. Find the integers. **9, 11**

37. When the square of the second of two consecutive even integers is added to twice the first integer, the sum is 76. Find the integers.
$6, 8; -12, -10$

Solve. Check each solution. 39. $\{2, -\frac{1}{3}, \frac{1}{3}\}$

38. $h^3 + h^2 - 4h - 4 = 0$ $\{-2, 2, -1\}$
39. $9m^3 - 18m^2 - m + 2 = 0$

40. $xy + 4x - 3y - 12 = 0$
$\{(x, y) | x = 3 \text{ or } y = -4\}$
41. $4pz - z + 12p - 3 = 0$
$\{(p, z) | p = \frac{1}{4} \text{ or } z = -3\}$

Critical Thinking Write an equation with integral coefficients that has the given solutions.

42. $\{-3, 5\}$
$x^2 - 2x - 15 = 0$

43. $\{\frac{2}{3}, -1\}$
$3x^2 + x - 2 = 0$

44. $\{-2, 2, 5\}$
$x^3 - 5x^2 - 4x + 20 = 0$

Applications

45. **Gardening** The length of Rachel's rectangular garden is 5 yards more than its width. The area of the garden is 234 square yards. What are its dimensions? **18 yd by 13 yd**

46. **Photography** A rectangular photograph is 8 centimeters wide and 12 centimeters long. The photograph is enlarged by increasing the length and the width by an equal amount. If the area of the new photograph is 69 square centimeters greater than the area of the original photograph, what are the dimensions of the new photograph? **11 cm by 15 cm**

47. **Agriculture** A strip of uniform width is plowed along all four sides of a 12-kilometer by 9-kilometer rectangular cornfield. How wide is the strip if the cornfield is half plowed? **1.5 km**

Use the formula $h = vt - 16t^2$ to solve each problem.

48. **Physics** A certain fireworks rocket is set off at an initial upward velocity of 440 feet per second. This type of fireworks is designed to explode at a height of 3000 feet. How many seconds after it is set off will the rocket reach 3000 feet and explode? **12.5 seconds**

49. **Physics** A missile is fired with an initial upward velocity of 2320 feet per second. When will it reach an altitude of 40,000 feet? **20 seconds**

Mixed Review

50. **Basketball** In 1962, Wilt Chamberlain set an NBA record by averaging 50.4 points per game. If he maintained this average over an 82-game season, how many total points would he score? Round to the nearest whole number. **(Lesson 2-7)** **4133 points**

51. Solve $\frac{x + 2}{x - 3} = \frac{4}{9}$. **(Lesson 4-1)** **−6**

52. If y varies inversely as x, and $y = 24$ when $x = 20$, find y when $x = 30$. **(Lesson 4-9)** **16**

53. Solve $5t - (t - 3) < 6t + 7$. **(Lesson 5-3)** $\{t | t > -2\}$

54. Multiply $8cd^2(7c^2d - cd + d^2)$. **(Lesson 6-7)** $56c^3d^3 - 8c^2d^3 + 8cd^4$

55. Find the value of c that would make $25x^2 + 5cxy + 64y^2$ a perfect square trinomial. **(Lesson 7-7)** **16 or −16**

56. **Physics** A flare is launched with an initial upward velocity of 128 feet per second. Use the formula $h = vt - 16t^2$ to determine how long it will take for the flare to hit the ground. **(Lesson 7-9)** **8 seconds**

EXTENDING THE LESSON

Math Power: Connections

The side of one square is 4 inches longer than the side of another square. Find the lengths of the sides of the two squares if the sum of their areas is 250 square inches. **9 in. and 13 in.**

Enrichment Masters Booklet, p. 51

NAME _____ DATE _____

7-10 **Enrichment Worksheet**

Find the Error

Computational errors can easily occur with variables unless the properties of numbers and of operations are kept in mind.

Suppose $a = b$.

$a = b$	Given
$a^2 = ab$	Multiplication property of equality
$a^2 - b^2 = ab - b^2$	Subtraction property of inequality
$(a - b)(a + b) = b(a - b)$	Factoring
$\frac{(a - b)(a + b)}{a - b} = \frac{b(a - b)}{a - b}$	Division property of equality
$a + b = b$	
$b + b = b$	Substitution property of equality
$2b = b$	
$2 = 1$	Division property of equality

You cannot divide by $a - b$ because $a - b = 0$. You cannot divide by 0.

Whoops!! Where's the error?

Now let us solve the following equation:

$\sqrt{5x - 4} + 8 = 2$
$\sqrt{5x - 4} = -6$ Subtraction property of equality
$(\sqrt{5x - 4})^2 = (-6)^2$ Square each side.
$5x - 4 = 36$
$5x = 40$ Addition property of equality
$x = 8$ Division property of equality

Check: $\sqrt{5(8) - 4} + 8 = 2$
$\sqrt{36} + 8 = 2$
$6 + 8 = 2$
$14 = 2$

Does not check!! Where's the error?
$\sqrt{5x - 4}$ is the positive square root of $5x - 4$. So, step 2 of the equation is false for all values of x, as then must also be step 1. You can sometimes square both sides of a false equation and obtain a true one. For example, $-1 = 1$ is false but $(-1)^2 = 1^2$ is true.

Using the Chapter Summary and Review

The Chapter Summary and Review begins with an alphabetical listing of the new terms that were presented in the chapter. Have students define each term and provide an example of it, if appropriate.

The Skills and Concepts presented in the chapter are reviewed using a side-by-side format. Encourage students to refer to the Objectives and Examples on the left as they complete the Review Exercises on the right.

The Chapter Summary and Review ends with exercises that review Applications and Connections.

CHAPTER

7 SUMMARY AND REVIEW

VOCABULARY

Upon completing this chapter, you should be familiar with the following terms:

composite number	256	256	prime factor
factor	256	256	prime factorization
greatest common factor, GCF	257	256	prime number
perfect square trinomial	281	273	prime polynomial

SKILLS AND CONCEPTS

OBJECTIVES AND EXAMPLES	REVIEW EXERCISES

Upon completing this chapter, you should be able to:

- find the greatest common factor (GCF) for a set of monomials **(Lesson 7-1)**

  Find the GCF of $15x^2y$ and $45xy^2$.
  $15x^2y = ③ \cdot ⑤ \cdot x \cdot ⓧ \cdot ⓨ$
  $45xy^2 = ③ \cdot 3 \cdot ⑤ \cdot ⓧ \cdot ⓨ \cdot y$
  The GCF is $3 \cdot 5 \cdot x \cdot y$ or $15xy$.

Use these exercises to review and prepare for the chapter test.

Find the GCF of the given monomials.

1. $35, 30$ **5**   2. $12ab, -4a^2b^2$ **4ab**

3. $12, 18, 40$ **2**   4. $16mrt, 30m^2r$ **2mr**

5. $20n^2, 24np^5$ **4n**   6. $60x^2y^2, 35xz^3$ **5x**

7. $2m^2n^3p, 8mn^2p^3, 5m^2np^3$ **mnp**

- use the GCF and the distributive property to factor polynomials **(Lesson 7-2)**

  Factor $12a^2 - 8ab$.
  $12a^2 - 8ab = 4a(3a - 2b)$

Factor each polynomial. See margin.

8. $13x + 26y$ 9. $6x^2y + 12xy + 6$

10. $24a^2b^2 - 18ab$ 11. $26ab + 18ac + 32a^2$

12. $m + m^2n + m^3n^3$ 13. $\frac{3}{5}a - \frac{3}{5}b + \frac{6}{5}c$

- use grouping techniques to factor polynomials with four or more terms **(Lesson 7-3)**

  Factor $2x^2 - 3xz - 2xy + 3yz$.
  $2x^2 - 3xz - 2xy + 3yz$
  $= x(2x - 3z) - y(2x - 3z)$
  $= (x - y)(2x - 3z)$

Factor each polynomial. Check with FOIL.

14. $a^2 - 4ac + ab - 4bc$ $(a + b)(a - 4c)$

15. $24am - 9an + 40bm - 15bn$

16. $2rs + 6ps + mr + 3mp$ $(2s + m)(r + 3p)$

17. $16k^3 - 4k^2p^2 - 28kp + 7p^3$

18. $dm + 7r + mr + 7d$ $(m + 7)(d + r)$

15. $(3a + 5b)(8m - 3n)$ 17. $(4k - p^2)(4k^2 - 7p)$

Additional Answers

8. $13(x + 2y)$
9. $6(x^2y + 2xy + 1)$
10. $6ab(4ab - 3)$
11. $2a(13b + 9c + 16a)$
12. $m(1 + mn + m^2n^3)$
13. $\frac{3}{5}(a - b + 2c)$

- factor quadratic trinomials (Lesson 7-5)

$a^2 - 3a - 4 = (a + 1)(a - 4)$

$4x^2 - 4xy - 15y^2$
$= 4x^2 + (-10 + 6)xy - 15y^2$
$= (4x^2 - 10xy) + (6xy - 15y^2)$
$= 2x(2x - 5y) + 3y(2x - 5y)$
$= (2x + 3y)(2x - 5y)$

- identify and factor polynomials that are the differences of squares (Lesson 7-6)

$a^2 - 9 = (a)^2 - (3)^2 = (a - 3)(a + 3)$

$3x^3 - 75x = 3x(x^2 - 25)$
$= 3x(x - 5)(x + 5)$

- identify and factor perfect square trinomials (Lesson 7-7)

$16z^2 - 8z + 1$
$= (4z)^2 - 2(4z)(1) + (1)^2$
$= (4z - 1)^2$

- factor polynomials by applying the various methods of factoring
(Lesson 7-8)

Check for:	Number of Terms		
	2	3	4+
greatest common factor	✔	✔	✔
difference of squares	✔		✔
perfect square trinomial		✔	
trinomial with two binomial factors		✔	
pairs of terms with a common monomial factor			✔

Factor each trinomial, if possible. If the trinomial cannot be factored using integers, write *prime*. 19–26. See margin.

19. $y^2 + 7y + 12$ 20. $x^2 - 9x - 36$
21. $b^2 + 5b - 6$ 22. $2r^2 - 3r - 20$
23. $3a^2 - 13a + 14$ 24. $6z^2 + 7z + 3$
25. $a^2 - 10ab + 9b^2$ 26. $r^2 - 8rs - 65s^2$
27. $56m^2 - 93mn + 27n^2$ $(8m - 3n)(7m - 9n)$

Factor each binomial, if possible. If the binomial cannot be factored using integers, write *prime*. See margin.

28. $b^2 - 16$ 29. $25 - 9y^2$
30. $16a^2 - 81b^4$ 31. $2y^3 - 128y$
32. $\frac{1}{4}n^2 - \frac{9}{16}r^2$ 33. $81x^4 - 16$

Factor each trinomial. 34–37. See margin.

34. $a^2 + 18a + 81$ 35. $16x^2 - 8x + 1$
36. $9k^2 - 12k + 4$ 37. $32n^2 - 80n + 50$
38. $6b^3 - 24b^2g + 24bg^2$ $6b(b - 2g)^2$
39. $y^2 - \frac{3}{2}yz^2 + \frac{9}{16}z^4$ $\left(y - \frac{3}{4}z^2\right)^2$

Factor each polynomial.

40. $3x^2 - 12$ $3(x - 2)(x + 2)$
41. $28y^2 - 13y - 6$ $(7y + 2)(4y - 3)$
42. $56a^2 - 93a + 27$ $(8a - 3)(7a - 9)$
43. $6m^3 + m^2 - 15m$ $m(3m + 5)(2m - 3)$
44. $15ay^2 + 37ay + 20a$ $a(5y + 4)(3y + 5)$
45. $2r^3 - 18r^2 + 30r$ $2r(r^2 - 9r + 15)$
46. $12mx + 3xb + 4my + by$ $(3x + y)(4m + b)$
47. $mx^2 + bx^2 - 49m - 49b$
$(x + 7)(x - 7)(m + b)$

Alternate Review Strategy
To provide a brief in-class review, you may wish to read the following questions to the class and require a verbal response.
1. Find the GCF of $56x^3y$ and $49ax^2$. $7x^2$
2. Factor $36abc - 9a^2b + 15ab^3c^2$.
   $3ab(12c - 3a + 5bc^2)$
3. Factor $10x^2 - 14xy + 5xy - 7y^2$. $(5x - 7y)(2x + y)$
4. Factor $a^2 - 4a - 21$.
   $(a + 3)(a - 7)$
5. Factor $x^2 - 36y^2$.
   $(x + 6y)(x - 6y)$
6. Factor $a^2 + 12a + 36$.
   $(a + 6)^2$
7. Factor $m^3 + 6m^2 + 9m$.
   $m(m + 3)^2$
8. Solve $7a(a + 6) = 0$. $\{0, -6\}$
9. The square of an integer increased by six times the integer is 567. Find the integer.   21 or -27

The Cumulative Review shown below can be used to review skills and concepts presented thus far in the text. Standardized Test Practice Questions are also provided in the Evaluation Masters Booklet.

Evaluation Masters Booklet, pp. 95-96

- use the zero product property to solve equations **(Lesson 7-9)**

$$x^2 = -4x$$
$$x^2 + 4x = -4x + 4x$$
$$x(x + 4) = 0$$
$$x = 0 \quad \text{or} \quad x + 4 = 0$$
$$x = -4$$

The solution set is $\{0, -4\}$.

- solve equations by using various factoring methods and applying the zero product property **(Lesson 7-10)**

$$m^2 - m = 2$$
$$m^2 - m - 2 = 2 - 2$$
$$(m + 1)(m - 2) = 0$$
$$m + 1 = 0 \quad \text{or} \quad m - 2 = 0$$
$$m = -1 \qquad m = 2$$

Solve. Check each solution.

48. $y(y + 11) = 0$ $\{0, -11\}$
49. $4t(2t - 10) = 0$ $\{0, 5\}$
50. $(3x - 2)(4x + 7) = 0$ $\left\{\frac{2}{3}, -\frac{7}{4}\right\}$
51. $2a^2 - 9a = 0$ $\left\{0, \frac{9}{2}\right\}$
52. $n^2 = -17n$ $\{0, -17\}$
53. $\frac{3}{4}y = \frac{1}{2}y^2$ $\left\{0, \frac{3}{2}\right\}$

Solve. Check each solution.

54. $y^2 + 13y + 40 = 0$ $\{-5, -8\}$
55. $2a^2 - 98 = 0$ $\{7, -7\}$
56. $2m^2 + 13m = 24$ $\left\{\frac{3}{2}, -8\right\}$
57. $25r^2 + 4 = -20r$ $\left\{-\frac{2}{5}\right\}$
58. $(x + 6)(x - 1) = 78$ $\{7, -12\}$
59. $6x^3 + 29x^2 + 28x = 0$ $\left\{0, -\frac{4}{3}, -\frac{7}{2}\right\}$

APPLICATIONS AND CONNECTIONS

Solve by using guess and check.   (Lesson 7-4)

60. Teresa wants to give $250 to each of her favorite charities, but she needs another $187 to be able to do so. If she gives each charity $180, she will have $163 left over. How much money does Teresa have? **$1063**

61. Richard needs 228 balloons to use for games at his party. Balloons came in packages of 24 or 36. If Richard bought 8 packages of balloons, how many of each size did he buy? **5 of the 24, 3 of the 36**

62. **Geometry** The measure of the perimeter of a square is $20m + 32p$. Find the measure of its area. **(Lesson 7-2)** $25m^2 + 80mp + 64p^2$

63. **Geometry** The measure of the area of a rectangle is $16x^2 - 9$. Find the measure of its perimeter. **(Lesson 7-6)** $16x$

64. **Geometry** The measure of the area of a square is $4m^2 - 3mp + 3p - 4m$. What are its dimensions? **(Lesson 7-8)** $4m - 3p, m - 1$

65. **Number Theory** The product of two consecutive odd integers is 99. Find the integers. **(Lesson 7-10)** 9, 11; -11, -9

66. **Construction** A tinsmith has a rectangular piece of tin with a 3-inch square cut from each corner so that the sides can be folded up to form a box. She has designed the box so that it is twice as long as it is wide. What are the dimensions of the box if it has a volume of 1350 cubic inches? **(Lesson 7-10)** 66. 3 in. by 30 in. by 15 in.

NAME _____ DATE _____

~~Cumulative Review (Chapters 1–7)~~

1. Evaluate $(2x + 5y)^2$ if x 0 and $y = -\frac{4}{3}$. 1. $44\frac{4}{9}$
2. State the property shown in $8 \cdot 1 = 8$. 2. Mult. Ident.

Simplify.
3. $7(5c + 2c + 6)$ 3. $49c + 42$
4. $4r + 3t + 2t + 6r$ 4. $10r + 5t$

Find each sum or difference.
5. $-25 + 9$ 5. -16
6. $-36wz + 14x + (-10wz) + (-12x)$ 6. $-46wx + 2x$
7. $-42 - 17$ 7. -59
8. Solve $y + \frac{2}{3} = \frac{5}{3}$. 8. 1

Simplify.
9. $\left(-\frac{3}{4}\right)\left(-\frac{4}{5}\right)\left(-\frac{5}{6}\right)$ 9. $-\frac{1}{2}$
10. $\frac{54}{-6}$ 10. -9
11. Solve $\frac{a}{6} - 5 = 12$. 11. 102
12. Twenty-eight is 40% of what number? 12. 70
13. Graph the solution set of $y \le -4$ on a number line. 13. [number line -7 to 1]

Solve each inequality.
14. $\frac{m}{-8} < -4$ 14. $m > 32$
15. $9 - 4x \le 21$ 15. $x \ge -3$
16. Which is a better buy, a 15-ounce can of soup for 98¢ or a 10-ounce can of soup for 55¢? 16. 10-oz can
17. Solve the open sentence $|3m + 1| < 7$. Then graph its solution set. 17. $-2\frac{2}{3} < m < 2$ [number line -4 to 4]

NAME _____ DATE _____

Cumulative Review (Chapters 1–7)

Simplify.
18. $(-4x^3y^3)(2xy^2)$ 18. $-8x^6y^5$
19. $\left(\frac{2}{3}c^2d^3\right)^4$ 19. $\frac{16}{81}c^8d^{12}$
20. $\frac{21hk^3j}{-14h^6kj^8}$ 20. $-\frac{3k^2}{2h^5j^7}$
21. Elisabeth is 6 years older than her sister Elisa. Their mother's age is twice the sum of their ages. How old are they if their mother is 40? 21. Elisabeth: 13, Elisa: 7
22. How many pounds of peanuts costing $2.00 a pound should be mixed with 4 pounds of cashews costing $4.50 a pound to obtain a mixture costing $3.00 a pound? 22. 6 pounds
23. Arrange the terms of $4x - 3 + 2x^2 + 3x^3$ so that the powers of x are in descending order. 23. $3x^3 + 2x^2 + 4x - 3$
24. Find $(4xy + 3x^2y - 5y^2) - (3y^2 - 5xy + 7x^2y)$. 24. $-4x^2y + 9xy - 8y^2$
25. Simplify $(a^2 - 2)(3a^2 + 3)$. 25. $3a^4 - 3a^2 - 6$
26. Solve $3(m - 1) + 3m = 4(8 - m)$. 26. $3\frac{1}{2}$
27. Sara leaves home at 7 A.M. traveling at a rate of 45 mi/h. Her son discovers that she has forgotten her briefcase and starts out to overtake her. Her son leaves at 7:30 A.M. traveling at a rate of 55 mi/h. At what time will he overtake his mother? 27. 9:45 A.M.

Factor, if possible.
28. $27f^2g^2 + 18f^2g^3 - 3f^2g$ 28. $3f^2g(9g + 6g^2 - 1)$
29. $x^2 - 9$ 29. $(x - 3)(x + 3)$
30. $a^2 + a - 12$ 30. $(a + 4)(a - 3)$
31. $mn + 2an + 3m + 6a$ 31. $(n + 3)(m + 2a)$
32. $3r^2 - r - 10$ 32. $(3r + 5)(r - 2)$
33. The square of a number added to three times the number is zero. What is the number? 33. 0 or -3

CHAPTER **7** **TEST**

Find the GCF of the given monomials.

1. $18a^2b, 28a^3b^2$ **$2a^2b$**

2. $6x^2y^3, 12x^2y^2z, 15x^2y$ **$3x^2y$**

Factor each polynomial, if possible. If the polynomial cannot be factored using integers, write *prime*.

3. $25y^2 - 49w^2$ **$(5y + 7w)(5y - 7w)$**

4. $t^2 - 16t + 64$ **$(t - 8)^2$**

5. $x^2 + 14x + 24$ **$(x + 2)(x + 12)$**

6. $28m^2 + 18m$ **$2m(14m + 9)$**

7. $12x^2 + 23x - 24$ **$(4x - 3)(3x + 8)$**

8. $a^2 - 11ab + 18b^2$ **$(a - 2b)(a - 9b)$**

9. $2h^2 - 3h - 18$ **prime**

10. $6x^3 + 15x^2 - 9x$ **$3x(2x - 1)(x + 3)$**

11. $36m^2 + 60mn + 25n^2$ **$(6m + 5n)^2$**

12. $36a^2b^3 - 45ab^4$ **$9ab^3(4a - 5b)$**

13. $4my - 20m + 15p - 3py$ **$(4m - 3p)(y - 5)$**

14. $x^3 - 5x^2 - 9x + 45$ **$(x - 3)(x + 3)(x - 5)$**

15. **Geometry** The measure of the area of a rectangle is $2x^2 + 3x - 20$. What is the measure of its perimeter? **$6x - 2$**

Solve. Check each solution.

16. $18s^2 + 72s = 0$ **$\{0, -4\}$**

17. $4x^2 = 36$ **$\{3, -3\}$**

18. $t^2 + 25 = 10t$ **$\{5\}$**

19. $a^2 - 9a - 52 = 0$ **$\{-4, 13\}$**

20. $x + 6 = 12x^2$ **$\{\frac{3}{4}, -\frac{2}{3}\}$**

21. $x^3 - 5x^2 - 66x = 0$ **$\{0, -6, 11\}$**

For each problem, define a variable. Then use an equation to solve the problem.

22. **Number Theory** Find two integers whose sum is 21 and whose product is 104. **8, 13**

23. **Geometry** A rectangle is 4 inches wide by 7 inches long. When the length and width are increased by the same amount, the area is increased by 26 square inches. What are the dimensions of the new rectangle? **23. 9 in. by 6 in.**

24. **Physics** A rocket is fired upward at an initial velocity of 2240 feet per second. Use the formula $h = vt - 16t^2$ to determine when the rocket will have an altitude of 78,400 feet. **70 seconds**

25. **Construction** A rectangular lawn is 24 feet wide by 32 feet long. A sidewalk will be built along the inside edges of all four sides. The remaining lawn will have an area of 425 square feet. How wide will the walk be? **3.5 ft**

Bonus The measure of the area of a rectangle is $12x^2 + x - 20$ where x is a positive integer. What is the smallest possible perimeter measure for this rectangle? **26**

CHAPTER 7 303

NAME _____ DATE _____

Chapter 7 Test, Form 1A

Write the letter for the correct answer in the blank at the right of each problem.

1. What is the prime factorization of 342?
   A. $2 \cdot 3 \cdot 57$ B. $1 \cdot 2 \cdot 3 \cdot 57$ C. $2 \cdot 3 \cdot 3 \cdot 19$ D. none of these **1. C**

2. Find the GCF of $18n^3y^4w$ and $24n^5y$.
   A. $6n^5y^4w$ B. $6n^3y$ C. $243n^5 6y^4w$ D. $243n^3y$ **2. B**

3. Factor $14xy^2 - 2xy$.
   A. $2xy(7y - 1)$ B. $2x(7y^2 - y)$ C. $-2xy(-7y)$ D. prime **3. A**

4. Factor $16 - n^4$.
   A. $(4 - n^2)(4 + n^2)$ B. $(n + 2)(n - 2)(4 + n^2)$ C. $(2 - n)(2 + n)(n^2 + 4)$ D. $(2 - n)(2 + n)(2 - n)(2 + n)$ **4. C**

5. If $8x^2 - 72y^2$ is factored completely, one of the factors is:
   A. $2x^2 - 18y^2$ B. $x + 3$ C. $x - 9y^2$ D. $x - 3y$ **5. D**

6. If $6x^2 + 48x + 96$ is factored completely, one of the factors is:
   A. $x + 4$ B. $3x + 8$ C. $3x + 12$ D. $6x + 16$ **6. A**

7. How many values of k can be found so that $m^2 + km + 9$ can be factored using integers?
   A. 2 B. 4 C. 3 D. 6 **7. B**

8. Factor $6y(y^2 - 6) + 5(6 - y^2)$.
   A. $(6y - 5)(y^2 - 6)$ B. $(6y + 5)(6 - y^2)$ C. $(6y + 5)(y^2 - 6)$ D. none of these **8. A**

9. If the polynomial $3a^2 - 3an^2 - 2an + 2n^3$ is to be factored by grouping pairs of terms, which grouping is *not* helpful?
   A. $3a^2$ paired with $-3an^2$ and $-2an$ paired with $2n^3$ B. $3a^2$ paired with $-2an$ and $-3an^2$ paired with $2n^3$ C. $3a^2$ paired with $2n^3$ and $-3an^2$ paired with $-2an$ D. All the above pairings are helpful. **9. C**

10. Factor $5x^2 - 13x + 6$.
    A. $(x + 3)(5x - 2)$ B. $(x - 3)(5x + 2)$ C. $(x + 2)(5x + 3)$ D. $(x - 2)(5x - 3)$ **10. D**

11. If $14a^2 - 15a + 4$ is factored completely, one of the factors is:
    A. $7a + 2$ B. $7a - 4$ C. $7a - 1$ D. $14a - 1$ **11. B**

12. If $6x^2 + 11x - 2$ is factored completely, one of the factors is:
    A. $3x - 1$ B. $6x - 1$ C. $2x + 1$ D. $3x - 2$ **12. B**

NAME _____ DATE _____

Chapter 7 Test, Form 1A (continued)

13. Which polynomial is prime?
    A. $2x^2 - 5x + 3$ B. $10x^2 - 11xw + 6w^2$ C. $9y^2 + 29yn + 6n^2$ D. none of the above **13. B**

14. What is the solution set of the equation $(3w + 4)(2w - 7) = 0$?
    A. $\left[-\frac{3}{4}, \frac{7}{2}\right]$ B. $\left[\frac{3}{4}, -\frac{2}{7}\right]$ C. $\left[-\frac{4}{3}, \frac{7}{2}\right]$ D. $\left[\frac{4}{3}, -\frac{7}{2}\right]$ **14. C**

15. What is the solution set of the equation $\frac{2}{5}x = \frac{7}{10}x^2$?
    A. $\left[0, \frac{4}{7}\right]$ B. $\left[0, \frac{2}{7}\right]$ C. $\{0\}$ D. $\left[\frac{7}{2}\right]$ **15. A**

16. What is the solution of the equation $4x^2 = 20x - 25$?
    A. $\left[0, \frac{5}{4}\right]$ B. $\left[0, -\frac{2}{5}\right]$ C. $\left[-\frac{4}{5}\right]$ D. $\left[\frac{5}{2}\right]$ **16. D**

17. What is the solution set of the equation $x^2 - 16x = 0$?
    A. $\{4, -4\}$ B. $\{0, 4, -4\}$ C. $\{0, 16\}$ D. $\{16\}$ **17. C**

18. The product of two consecutive odd integers is 255. If the lesser of the two integers is x, which equation must be true?
    A. $x(x + 1) = 255$ B. $x(x + 2) = 255$ C. $x(x + 3) = 255$ D. $(x + 1)(x + 3) = 255$ **18. B**

19. A rectangle is 6 centimeters wide and 12 centimeters long. If a strip of uniform width is added to each of the four sides, the area is increased by 88 square centimeters. If x is the width of the strip in centimeters, which equation must be true?
    A. $(6 + 2x)(12 + 2x) = 88$ B. $(6 + x)(12 + x) = 88$ C. $(6 + 2x)(12 + 2x) = 160$ D. $(6 + x)(12 + x) = 160$ **19. C**

20. When all possible numbers are put in place of m, the expression $m^2 - 10m + 25$ will
    A. always be positive. B. never be positive. C. sometimes be negative and sometimes be positive. D. never be negative. **20. D**

Bonus: Find the least integer greater than 1 that is a perfect square, a perfect cube and a perfect fourth power. **Bonus: 4096**

Chapter 7 303

CHAPTER 8

Rational Expressions

PREVIEWING THE CHAPTER

This chapter develops the concepts and skills required for working with
rational expressions. Students build on their understanding of fractions to
learn how to simplify, add, subtract, multiply, and divide rational expressions.
Continuing to connect the familiar with the new, students utilize their
knowledge of mixed numbers, improper and complex fractions to understand
and work with mixed expressions, rational expressions and complex fractions
containing variables. The chapter concludes by having students apply their
new knowledge to solve rational equations.

Problem-Solving Strategy   Students learn to solve problems by making an
organized list of the possible solutions and using a systematic approach to
determine which of these possibilities are the solutions.

Lesson Objective Chart

Lesson (Pages)	Lesson Objectives	State/Local Objectives
8-1 (306-310)	**8-1:** Simplify rational expressions.	
8-2 (311-314)	**8-2:** Multiply rational expressions.	
8-3 (316-318)	**8-3:** Divide rational expressions.	
8-4 (319-321)	**8-4:** Divide polynomials by binomials.	
8-5 (322-325)	**8-5:** Add and subtract rational expressions with like denominators.	
8-6 (326-328)	**8-6:** Solve problems by making an organized list of the possibilities.	
8-7 (329-333)	**8-7:** Add or subtract rational expressions with unlike denominators.	
8-8 (334-337)	**8-8:** Simplify mixed expressions and complex fractions.	
8-9 (338-342)	**8-9A:** Solve rational equations.	
	8-9B: Solve problems involving work and uniform motion.	
8-10 (343-347)	**8-10A:** Solve formulas for a specified variable.	
	8-10B: Use formulas that involve rational expressions.	

ORGANIZING THE CHAPTER

You may want to refer to the **Course Planning Calendar** on page T36.

Lesson Planning Guide

Lesson (Pages)	Pacing Chart (days) Course I	II	III	Reteaching	Practice	Enrichment	Evaluation	Technology	Lab Manual	Mixed Problem Solving	Applications	Cooperative Learning Activity	Multicultural	Transparencies
8-1 (306-310)	1.5	1	1	p. 52	p. 58	p. 52				p. 8				8-1
8-2 (311-314)	1	1	1	p. 53	p. 59	p. 53								8-2
8-3 (316-318)	1	1	1	p. 54	p. 60	p. 54	Quiz A, p. 107							8-3
8-4 (319-321)	1	1	1	p. 55	p. 61	p. 55		p. 8						8-4
8-5 (322-325)	1	1	1	p. 56	p. 62	p. 56	Quiz B, p. 107 Mid-Chapter Test, p. 11							8-5
8-6 (326-328)	1	1	1		p. 63								p. 53	8-6
8-7 (329-333)	1.5	1.5	1	p. 57	p. 64	p. 57								8-7
8-8 (334-337)	1	1	1	p. 58	p. 65	p. 58	Quiz C, p. 108				p. 23			8-8
8-9 (338-342)	1.5	1.5	1	p. 59	p. 66	p. 59		p. 23				p. 38		8-9
8-10 (343-347)	1.5	1	1	p. 60	p. 67	p. 60	Quiz D, p. 108							8-10
Review (348-350)	1	1	1	Multiple Choice Tests, Forms 1A and 1B, pp. 99-102 Free Response Tests, Forms 2A and 2B, pp. 103-106										
Test (351)	1	1	1	Cumulative Review, pp. 109-110 Standardized Test Practice Questions, p. 112										

Course I: Chapters 1-13; Course II: Chapters 1-14; Course III: 1-15.

Other Chapter Resources

Student Edition
History Connection, p. 310
Technology, p. 315
Extra, p. 318
Mid-Chapter Review, p. 325
Cooperative Learning Activity, p. 328
Algebraic Skills Review, pp. 660, 661(ex. 40-58)

Teacher Resource Package
Activity Masters Booklet
Mixed Problem Solving, p. 8
Applications, p. 23
Cooperative Learning Activity, p. 38
Multicultural Activity, p. 53
Technology Masters Booklet
Scientific Calculator Activity, p. 8
Graphing Calculator Activity, p. 23

Other Supplements
Transparency for Chapter Opener
Problem-of-the-Week Activity
  Cards, 18-20
Video Algebra, 27-30

Software
Algebra 1 Test and Review
  Generator Software
  Available for Apple and IBM.

ENHANCING THE CHAPTER

Cooperative Learning

Assigning Roles to Students

It is important to keep in mind that the past experiences of most students involve competitive rather than cooperative activities. Therefore, you should remember to be patient as well as persistent in your efforts to develop cooperative interdependence. One way to enhance these skills is to assign each student in the group a specific role. Examples of such roles include a *checker*, who makes sure all members know and can explain the responses, an *encourager*, who motivates silent or reluctant members to participate, a *praiser*, who commends members for good ideas or contributions, a *prober*, who asks questions about or calls for further clarifications of ideas that have been proposed, a *materials handler*, who obtains the necessary items for the activity and then returns them to their proper place, a *recorder*, who writes the group's ideas or answers on paper, a *help asker*, who requests assistance from the teacher when the group needs it, and so on. Other roles may suggest themselves to you to meet certain needs of a particular activity or student. For example, a group member who has difficulty remaining quiet can be assigned the role of *noise monitor*, who uses a non-verbal signal to remind the members to quiet down.

Technology

The Technology Feature after Lesson 8-2 employs the *Mathematical Exploration Toolkit* to simplify rational expressions. MET requires using the FACTOR command before a REDUCE command. Therefore, students will gain practice making the same decisions used when simplifying rational expressions by hand.

You may want to extend the use of MET in Lesson 8-9 for solving equations involving rational expressions. Once again, students will need to choose the appropriate steps. Solutions must be checked in the original equation by means of the SUBSTITUTE command. Extraneous solutions will cause a division by zero error.

Critical Thinking

Higher-level thinking skills involved in analysis and synthesis can be thought of as examining a large number of elements or examples to detect patterns or ideas and then the putting together of these specific elements or examples to make conjectures or generalizations. The activities with rational expressions provide many opportunities for students to utilize and improve these critical-thinking skills. For example, each and every one of the operations can be introduced by having students use whole numbers to write numerical expressions, examine the expressions for ideas, infer a generalization that can be stated with variables, and then test the conjecture by replacing the variables with other numbers of all types.

Cooperative Learning, p. 38

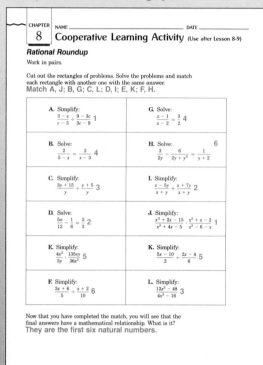

Technology, p. 23

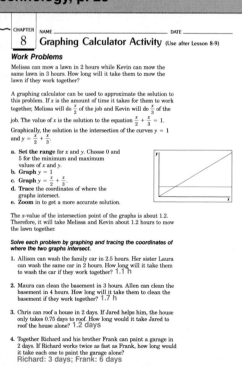

Problem of the Week Activity

The card shown below is one of three available for this chapter. It can be used as a class or small group activity.

Activity Card

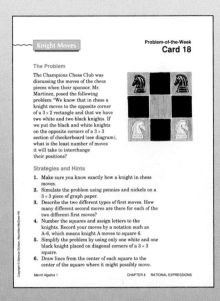

Manipulatives and Models

The following materials may be used as models of manipulatives in Chapter 8.

- paper bag (Lesson 8-6)
- coins (Lesson 8-7)

Outside Resources

Books/Periodicals

Ogilvy, C. Stanley. *Tomorrow's Math*. Oxford University Press.

Trigg, Charles W. *Mathematical Quickies*. Dover Publications, Inc.

Films/Videotapes/Videodiscs

The Fundamental Theorem of Algebra, Media Guild

Inequalities, Media Guild

Software

Mathematical Exploration Toolkit, IBM

The Function Analyzer, Sunburst Communications, Inc.

Multicultural

Multicultural Activity, p.53

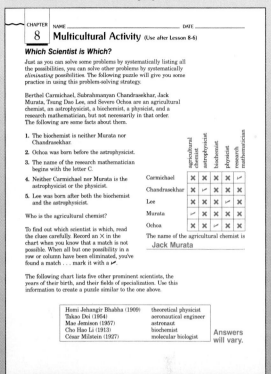

Applications

Application, p. 23

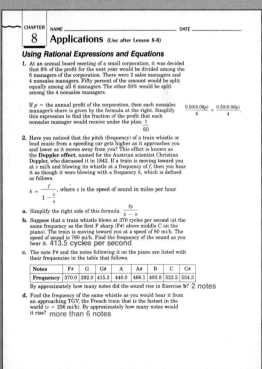

Using the Chapter Opener

Transparency 8-0 is available in the Transparency Package. It provides a full-color visual and motivational activity that you can use to engage students in the mathematical content of the chapter.

Background Information

Silvering glass to make mirrors was developed by Jean Fourcault in 1857. The earliest eye-glasses were made of thick convex lenses. These lenses reminded their makers of lentils. Hence, the term *lens,* from the Latin for "lentil beans."

In a convex mirror, the image is smaller than it would be in a plane, flat mirror. Our brain, seeing the smaller image, assumes a greater distance, as would be the case in a plane mirror. Hence, the need to remind the brain with a warning statement.

In this chapter, you will:
- Simplify rational expressions.
- Add, subtract, multiply, and divide rational expressions.
- Solve rational equations.
- Solve problems involving formulas that contain rational expressions.
- Solve problems by listing possibilities.

Chapter Project

Materials: convex lenses, like a magnifying glass or eyeglasses, metersticks, white posterboard, light source (lamp or sun from windows)

Organize students into cooperative groups of researchers. Instruct each group to cut a screen of white posterboard, 10 cm × 10 cm. Have each group tape its screen to one end of a meterstick. Direct groups to point their metersticks at, and several meters away from, a central light source or sunny windows. Then instruct one member of each group to move a convex lens along the meterstick, between the screen and the light source, until a clear image of the light source or windows appears up-side-down on the screen. Have another group member find d_i by measuring the distance between the screen and the lens. Have still another member find d_o by measuring the distance between the light source and the lens. Finally, have each group use the rational expression $f = \dfrac{d_i d_o}{(d_o + d_i)}$ to find and report the focal length of its lens.

8 Rational Expressions

THE FAR SIDE   By GARY LARSON

The Far Side ©1985 Universal Press Syndicate. Reprinted with permission. All rights reserved.

Why do some rearview and sideview mirrors on cars and trucks carry the warning OBJECTS IN MIRROR ARE CLOSER THAN THEY APPEAR?

APPLICATION IN PHYSICS

Most of the mirrors that you see each day are flat mirrors, which simply means that the surface of the mirror is flat. Some mirrors, like the ones found in fun houses, have curved surfaces. A mirror whose surface curves inward is called a *concave mirror* while one whose surface curves outward is called a *convex mirror*. Convex mirrors are often used in sideview and rearview mirrors for cars and trucks since they provide a wider field of vision than a flat mirror. The problem is that objects that are the same distance away from a convex mirror and a flat mirror appear smaller in the convex mirror.

Suppose you are driving on a highway and want to change lanes. If you see a car in your sideview mirror, then you can use its size to estimate how far away it is from your car. At this point, it is important that you know whether the sideview mirror is convex or flat. If the mirror is convex, then the car you see is actually closer to your car than one with the same size in a flat mirror. Thus, if you think your sideview mirror is flat when it is really convex, you might believe there is enough room to change lanes when there actually is not! It is for this reason that manufacturers place a warning on convex mirrors stating that objects in the mirror are closer than they appear.

ALGEBRA IN ACTION

Is the actual size of the object shown in the mirror at the left smaller or larger than the image shown in the mirror? **larger!!**

305

Connections and Applications

Lesson	Connections (C) and Applications (A)	Examples	Exercises
8-1	C: Statistics		54
	A: Motion		51
	Physics		52
	Chemistry		53
	Government		56
8-2	C: Geometry	6	35–37
	A: Consumer Awareness		46
	Construction		47
	Car Racing		48
8-3	C: Geometry		34
	A: Personal Finance		35
	Work		36
	Oceanography		37
	Travel		38
	Finance		39
8-4	C: Statistics		36
	A: Sports		35
	Physics		38
8-5	C: Geometry	5	42–44
	A: Entertainment		46
	History		47
	Travel		48
8-6	C: Probability		8
	Number Theory		13
8-7	A: Astronomy		40
	Agriculture		41
	Parades		42
	Work		43
	Travel		44
	Ping-pong		46
8-8	C: Statistics		32
	A: History		31
	Sales		33
8-9	A: Work	1	40–42
	Fishing	3	
	Physics		43–46, 48
	World Records		47
8-10	C: Geometry	1	
	Mathematics		29–34
	A: Photography	2	
	Electronics	3, 4, 5	23–28, 35–43
	Physics		11–16
	Business		17–22
	Temperature		44
	Finance		46
	Astronomy		47
	Work		49

INTRODUCING THE LESSON

🕐 5-Minute Check

(over Chapter 7)

Solve.

1. $x^3 + 2x^2 = 15x$ $\{0, -5, 3\}$
2. $a^3 - 13a^2 + 42a = 0$
   $\{0, 6, 7\}$
3. $4r^3 - 9r = 0$
   $\left\{0, \frac{3}{2}, \frac{-3}{2}\right\}$
4. The sum of the squares of two consecutive odd integers is 802. Find the integers. -21 and -19 or 19 and 21
5. Find two consecutive odd integers such that the square of the larger decreased by the smaller is 274. **15 and 17**

Motivating the Lesson

Review simplifying basic fractions. Have students simplify each fraction.

1. $\frac{2}{20}$ $\frac{1}{10}$ 2. $\frac{4}{14}$ $\frac{2}{7}$
3. $\frac{8}{-6}$ $\frac{-4}{3}$ 4. $\frac{-10}{25}$ $\frac{-2}{5}$
5. $\frac{-12}{-36}$ $\frac{1}{3}$ 6. $\frac{-15}{-12}$ $\frac{5}{4}$

TEACHING THE LESSON

Teaching Tip ① Emphasize that $x \neq -4$ because $-4 + 4 = 0$.

Teaching Tip ② $x^2 - 5x + 6$ factored is $(x - 2)(x - 3)$. Apply the zero product property to show that $x \neq 2$ or $x \neq 3$.

Simplifying Rational Expressions

Objective
8-1

After studying this lesson, you should be able to:
- simplify rational expressions.

A **rational expression** is an algebraic fraction whose numerator and denominator are polynomials. The expressions $\frac{36a^2bc}{24z^2}$, $\frac{2x}{x-5}$, and $\frac{p^2 + 25}{p^2 + 4p + 1}$ are examples of rational expressions.

Recall that division by zero is undefined.

Because algebraic fractions indicate division, zero cannot be used as a denominator. Therefore, any value assigned to a variable that results in a denominator of zero must be excluded from the domain of the variable. These are called **excluded values**.

For $\frac{5}{x}$, exclude $x = 0$.

For $\frac{6b - 3}{b + 4}$, exclude $b = -4$. *$-4 + 4 = 0$* **Teaching Tip ①**

For $\frac{y^2 - 5}{x^2 - 5x + 6}$, exclude $x = 2$ and $x = 3$. *Factor $x^2 - 5x + 6$ to see why.* **Teaching Tip ②**

Example 1

> For each fraction, state the values of the variable that must be excluded.
>
> a. $\dfrac{6n}{n + 7}$
>
> Exclude the values for which $n + 7 = 0$.
>
> $n + 7 = 0$
> $\quad n = -7$
>
> Therefore, n cannot equal -7.
>
> b. $\dfrac{2a - 3}{a^2 - a - 12}$
>
> Exclude the values for which $a^2 - a - 12 = 0$.
>
> $a^2 - a - 12 = 0$
> $(a - 4)(a + 3) = 0$ *Factor $a^2 - a - 12$.*
>
> $a = 4$ or $a = -3$ *Zero product property*
>
> Therefore, a cannot equal 4 or -3.

ALTERNATE TEACHING STRATEGIES

Using Discussion

Ask students if there is any difference between the expressions $\frac{x^2 - 4}{x + 2}$ and $x - 2$.
(Hint: Try substituting $x = -2$ into both expressions.) **The first expression is undefined. The second expression is equal to 0.**

Using Connections

The measure of the area of a rectangle is $3a^2 - 4a + 1$. If the length of the rectangle is $4a^2 - 8a + 4$, find the width. Express in simplest form. $\dfrac{3a - 1}{4a - 4}$

To simplify a rational expression such as $\frac{14a^2bc}{42abc^2}$, first factor the numerator and denominator. Then divide each by the greatest common factor. **Teaching Tip ③**

$$\frac{14a^2bc}{42abc^2} = \frac{2 \cdot 7 \cdot a \cdot a \cdot b \cdot c}{2 \cdot 3 \cdot 7 \cdot a \cdot b \cdot c \cdot c} \qquad \textit{Notice that } a \neq 0, b \neq 0, \text{ and } c \neq 0.$$

$$\frac{\overset{1}{\cancel{2}} \cdot \overset{1}{\cancel{7}} \cdot \overset{1}{\cancel{a}} \cdot a \cdot \overset{1}{\cancel{b}} \cdot \overset{1}{\cancel{c}}}{\underset{1}{\cancel{2}} \cdot 3 \cdot \underset{1}{\cancel{7}} \cdot \underset{1}{\cancel{a}} \cdot \underset{1}{\cancel{b}} \cdot \underset{1}{\cancel{c}} \cdot c} \quad \text{or} \quad \frac{a}{3c} \qquad \textit{The GCF is } 14abc.$$

You can use the same procedure to simplify rational expressions that have polynomials in the numerator and denominator.

Example 2

Simplify $\frac{x+2}{x^2-4}$. State the excluded values of x.

$$\frac{x+2}{x^2-4} = \frac{x+2}{(x+2)(x-2)} \qquad \textit{Factor the denominator.}$$

$$= \frac{\overset{1}{\cancel{(x+2)}}}{\underset{1}{\cancel{(x+2)}}(x-2)} \qquad \textit{The GCF is } x+2.$$

$$= \frac{1}{x-2}$$

The excluded values of x are any values for which $x^2 - 4 = 0$.

$$x^2 - 4 = 0$$
$$(x+2)(x-2) = 0$$
$$x + 2 = 0 \quad \text{or} \quad x - 2 = 0 \qquad \textit{Zero product property}$$
$$x = -2 \qquad\qquad x = 2$$

Therefore, x cannot equal 2 or −2.

Example 3

Simplify $\frac{3a^2 + a - 2}{a^2 + 7a + 6}$. State the excluded values of a. **Teaching Tip ④**

$$\frac{3a^2 + a - 2}{a^2 + 7a + 6} = \frac{(a+1)(3a-2)}{(a+6)(a+1)} \qquad \begin{array}{l}\textit{Factor } 3a^2 + a - 2.\\ \textit{Factor } a^2 + 7a + 6.\end{array}$$

$$= \frac{\overset{1}{\cancel{(a+1)}}(3a-2)}{(a+6)\underset{1}{\cancel{(a+1)}}} \qquad \textit{The GCF is } a+1.$$

$$= \frac{3a-2}{a+6}$$

The excluded values of a are any values for which $a^2 + 7a + 6 = 0$.

$$a^2 + 7a + 6 = 0$$
$$(a+6)(a+1) = 0$$
$$a = -6 \text{ or } a = -1 \qquad \textit{Zero product property}$$

Therefore, a cannot equal −6 or −1.

LESSON 8-1   SIMPLIFYING RATIONAL EXPRESSIONS   307

Teaching Tip ⑤ Another way to state the excluded values is x cannot equal y or $-y$.

Teaching Tip ⑥ Remind students that they must first factor the numerator and denominator in order to find the GCF.

EVALUATING THE LESSON

Checking for Understanding

Exercises 1-10 are designed to help you assess understanding through reading, writing, and speaking. You should work through Exercises 1-4 with your students, and then monitor their work on Exercises 5-10.

Reteaching Masters Booklet, p. 52

308 Chapter 8

Example 4 | Simplify $\dfrac{2x - 2y}{y^2 - x^2}$. State the excluded values of x and y.

$\dfrac{2x - 2y}{y^2 - x^2} = \dfrac{2(x - y)}{(y - x)(y + x)}$ *Distributive property*
Factor $y^2 - x^2$.

$= \dfrac{2(-1)(y - x)}{(y - x)(y + x)}$ *$x - y = -1(y - x)$*

$= \dfrac{-2\cancel{(y - x)}}{\cancel{(y - x)}(y + x)}$ *The GCF is $(y - x)$.*

$= \dfrac{-2}{y + x}$ or $-\dfrac{2}{y + x}$

The excluded values of x and y are any values for which $y^2 - x^2 = 0$.

$y^2 - x^2 = 0$

$(y - x)(y + x) = 0$ *Zero product property*

$y = x$ or $y = -x$

Therefore, y cannot equal x or $-x$. **Teaching Tip ⑤**

---

1. Factor the numerator and denominator.

CHECKING FOR UNDERSTANDING

Communicating Mathematics

Read and study the lesson to answer each question.

1. What is the first step when trying to find the GCF for a rational expression? **See margin.**

2. How would you determine the values to be excluded from $\dfrac{x + 1}{x^2 + 5x + 4}$?

3. Tell simply by looking at the denominator what values should be excluded in the expression $\dfrac{(a - 9)}{(a + 4)(a - 9)}$. **−4 and 9**

4. Write a rational expression that has -2, 3, and 7 as excluded values.
Answers may vary; a typical answer is $\dfrac{1}{(x + 2)(x - 3)(x - 7)}$.

Guided Practice

For each expression, find the greatest common factor (GCF) of the numerator and denominator. Then simplify and state the excluded values of the variables.

5. $\dfrac{42y}{18xy}$ $6y$; $x \neq 0$, $y \neq 0$

6. $\dfrac{-3x^2y^5}{18x^5y^2}$ $3x^2y^2$; $x \neq 0$, $y \neq 0$

7. $\dfrac{x(y + 1)}{x(y - 2)}$ x; $x \neq 0$, $y \neq 2$

8. $\dfrac{4a}{a(a + 7)}$ a; $a \neq 0$, -7

9. $\dfrac{(a + b)(a - b)}{(a - b)(a - b)}$ $a - b$; $a \neq b$

10. $\dfrac{y - 4}{y^2 - 16}$ $y - 4$; $y \neq 4$, -4

Exercises

11-49. See margin for excluded values. **17-19. See margin for answers.**

Practice

Ⓐ

Simplify. State the excluded values of the variables.

11. $\dfrac{13x}{39x^2}$ $\dfrac{1}{3x}$

12. $\dfrac{14y^2z}{49yz^3}$ $\dfrac{2y}{7z^2}$

13. $\dfrac{38a^2}{42ab}$ $\dfrac{19a}{21b}$

Teaching Tip ⑥ 14. $\dfrac{79a^2b}{158a^3bc}$ $\dfrac{1}{2ac}$

15. $\dfrac{m + 5}{2(m + 5)}$ $\dfrac{1}{2}$

16. $\dfrac{-3z^2}{z(z^2 - 5)}$ $\dfrac{-3z}{z^2 - 5}$

17. $\dfrac{y + 4}{(y - 4)(y + 4)}$

18. $\dfrac{(a - 4)(a + 4)}{(a - 2)(a - 4)}$

19. $\dfrac{-1(3w - 2)}{(3w - 2)(w + 4)}$

308 CHAPTER 8 RATIONAL EXPRESSIONS

RETEACHING THE LESSON

Write a rational expression with one variable and simplify it. Pick values for the variable and complete a table with headings "variable," "value of rational expression," and "value of simplified form." Write the table on the chalkboard. This may help students see how the rational expression is equivalent to its simplified form.

Additional Answers

2. Factor the denominator. Then use the zero product property to find the excluded values.

11. $x \neq 0$

12. $y, z \neq 0$

13. $a, b \neq 0$

14. $a, b, c \neq 0$

15. $m \neq -5$

16. $z \neq 0, \pm\sqrt{5}$

17. $\dfrac{1}{y - 4}$; $y \neq 4, -4$

18. $\dfrac{a + 4}{a - 2}$; $a \neq 2, 4$

B

20. $\dfrac{a+b}{a^2-b^2} \cdot \dfrac{1}{a-b}$

21. $\dfrac{c^2-4}{(c+2)^2} \cdot \dfrac{c-2}{c+2}$

22. $\dfrac{a^2-a}{a-1} \cdot a$

23. $\dfrac{m^2-2m}{m-2} \cdot m$

24. $\dfrac{x^2+4}{x^4-16} \cdot \dfrac{1}{x^2-4}$

25. $\dfrac{r^3-r^2}{r-1} \cdot r^2$

26. $\dfrac{4n^2-8}{4n-4} \cdot \dfrac{n^2-2}{n-1}$

27. $\dfrac{3m^3}{6m^2-3m} \cdot \dfrac{m^2}{2m-1}$

28. $\dfrac{6y^3-12y^2}{12y^2-18} \cdot \dfrac{y^2(y-2)}{2y^2-3}$

29. $\dfrac{-4y^2}{2y^2-4y^3} \cdot \dfrac{-2}{1-2y}$

30. $\dfrac{3a^3}{3a^3+6a^2b} \cdot \dfrac{a}{a+2b}$

31. $\dfrac{7a^3b^2}{21a^2b+49ab^3} \cdot \dfrac{a^2b}{3a+7b^2}$

32. $\dfrac{s+6}{s^2-36} \cdot \dfrac{1}{s-6}$

33. $\dfrac{x+y}{x^2+2xy+y^2} \cdot \dfrac{1}{x+y}$

34. $\dfrac{x-3}{x^2+x-12} \cdot \dfrac{1}{x+4}$

35. $\dfrac{6x^2+24x}{x^2+8x+16} \cdot \dfrac{6x}{x+4}$

36. $\dfrac{3-x}{6-17x+5x^2} \cdot \dfrac{1}{2-5x}$

37. $\dfrac{2x-14}{x^2-4x-21} \cdot \dfrac{2}{x+3}$

38. $\dfrac{x^2-x^2y}{x^3-x^3y} \cdot \dfrac{1}{x}$

39. $\dfrac{5x^2+10x+5}{3x^2+6x+3} \cdot \dfrac{5}{3}$

40. $\dfrac{x^2-x-20}{x^2+7x+12} \cdot \dfrac{x-5}{x+3}$

41. $\dfrac{4k^2-25}{4k^2-20k+25} \cdot \dfrac{2k+5}{2k-5}$

42. $\dfrac{2x^2-5x+3}{3x^2-5x+2} \cdot \dfrac{2x-3}{3x-2}$

43. $\dfrac{b^2-5b+6}{b^4-13b^2+36} \cdot \dfrac{1}{(b+3)(b+2)}$

C

44. $\dfrac{25-x^2}{x^2+x-30} \cdot \dfrac{-x+5}{x+6}$

45. $\dfrac{n^2-8n+12}{n^3-12n^2+36n} \cdot \dfrac{n-2}{n(n-6)}$

46. $\dfrac{16a^3-24a^2-160a}{8a^4-36a^3+16a^2} \cdot \dfrac{2(2a+5)}{a(2a-1)}$

47. $\dfrac{-x^2+6x-9}{x^2-6x+9} \cdot -1$

48. $\dfrac{y^4-13y^2+36}{y^2+5y+6} \cdot (y-2)(y-3)$

49. $\dfrac{x^4-16}{x^4-8x^2+16} \cdot \dfrac{x^2+4}{x^2-4}$

Critical Thinking

50. Explain why $\dfrac{x^2-4}{x+2}$ is not the same as $x-2$. In $\dfrac{x^2-4}{x+2}$, $x \ne -2$.

Applications

51. Motion If it takes 90 seconds to walk up a broken escalator and 60 seconds to ride up the same escalator (without walking) when it is moving, how long would it take to walk up the moving escalator?

36 seconds

52. Physics Chico needs to move a rock that weighs 1050 pounds. If he has a 6-foot long pinchbar and uses a fulcrum placed one foot from the rock, will he be able to lift the rock if he weighs 205 pounds? **no**

53. Chemistry At sea level, water boils at 212° F. At the top of Mt. Everest, water boils at 159.8° F. If Mt. Everest is 29,002 *feet* above sea level, how many degrees does the boiling point drop for every *mile* up from sea level? **about 9.5° F**

54. Statistics A crowd watching the Blueberry Festival Parade fills the sidewalks along Elm Street for about 1 mile on each side. If the sidewalks are 10 feet wide and an average person uses 4 square feet of sidewalk, about how many people are watching the parade?
26,400 people

LESSON 8-1 SIMPLIFYING RATIONAL EXPRESSIONS **309**

Error Analysis

Students sometimes simplify a rational expression and then find excluded values of the variable from this simplified form. This "loses" some excluded values of the variable. Excluded values of the variable must include all values that make any denominator zero at any step.

Closing the Lesson

Writing Activity At the end of class, have students write down the key points to consider in simplifying rational expressions.

APPLYING THE LESSON

Homework Exercises

Assignment Guide

Basic: 11-43, 50-52, 55-61
Average: 16-46, 50-61
Enriched: 20-61

Additional Answers

43. $b \ne 2, 3, -2, -3$
44. $x \ne -6, 5$
45. $n \ne 0, 6$
46. $a \ne 0, 4, \dfrac{1}{2}$
47. $x \ne 3$
48. $y \ne -2, -3$
49. $x \ne 2, -2$

Practice Masters Booklet, p. 58

NAME _____ DATE _____

8-1 | **Practice Worksheet**

Simplifying Rational Expressions

Simplify. State the excluded values of the variables.

1. $\dfrac{12a}{48a^3}$ $\dfrac{1}{4a^2}$; $a \ne 0$
2. $\dfrac{4x^2y^2}{16yx^3}$ $\dfrac{y}{4x}$; $x \ne 0$, $y \ne 0$
3. $\dfrac{6abc^3}{3a^2b^2}$ $\dfrac{2c^3}{ab}$; $a \ne 0$, $b \ne 0$
4. $\dfrac{n+6}{3(n+6)}$ $\dfrac{1}{3}$; $n \ne -6$
5. $\dfrac{-2w^3}{w(x^2+4)}$ $\dfrac{-2w^2}{w^2+4}$; $w \ne 0$
6. $\dfrac{z+1}{(z+1)(z-1)}$ $\dfrac{1}{z-1}$; $z \ne 1$, $z \ne -1$
7. $\dfrac{(c+5)(c-5)}{(c-5)(c+2)}$ $\dfrac{c+5}{c+2}$; $c \ne 5$, $c \ne -2$
8. $\dfrac{-1(2r-3)}{(r+3)(2r-3)}$ $\dfrac{-1}{r+3}$; $r \ne -3$, $r \ne \dfrac{3}{2}$
9. $\dfrac{a^2-b^2}{a-b}$ $a+b$; $a \ne b$
10. $\dfrac{4x-4}{4x+4}$ $\dfrac{x-1}{x+1}$; $x \ne -1$
11. $\dfrac{3a+15}{a^2-25}$ $\dfrac{3}{a-5}$; $a \ne 5$, $a \ne -5$
12. $\dfrac{t^2+5t+6}{t^2+6t+8}$ $\dfrac{t+3}{t+4}$; $t \ne -2$, $t \ne -4$
13. $\dfrac{3s^2-27}{s^2+7s+12}$ $\dfrac{3(s-3)}{s+4}$; $s \ne -3$, $s \ne -4$
14. $\dfrac{7k^4}{5k^3-2k^2}$ $\dfrac{7k^2}{5k-2}$; $k \ne 0$, $k \ne \dfrac{2}{5}$
15. $\dfrac{m^2-4m-12}{m-6}$ $m+2$; $m \ne 6$
16. $\dfrac{v^2+3v-4}{v^2+2v-8}$ $\dfrac{v-1}{v-2}$; $v \ne 2$, $v = -4$
17. $\dfrac{5z^2+5z-30}{7z^2+7z-42}$ $\dfrac{5}{7}$; $z \ne -3$, $z \ne 2$
18. $\dfrac{p^2+p-2}{p^4-5p^3+4}$ $\dfrac{1}{(p-2)(p+1)}$ $p \ne 2$, $p \ne -2$, $p \ne 1$, $p \ne -1$

Additional Answers

19. $\dfrac{-1}{w+4}$; $w \ne \dfrac{2}{3}$, -4

20. $a \ne \pm b$

21. $c \ne -2$

22. $a \ne 1$

23. $m \ne 2$

24. $x \ne \pm 2$

25. $r \ne 1$

26. $n \ne 1$

27. $m \ne 0, \dfrac{1}{2}$

28. $y \ne \pm \dfrac{\sqrt{6}}{2}$

29. $y \ne 0, \dfrac{1}{2}$

30. $a \ne 0, -2b$

31. $a \ne 0, -\dfrac{7}{3}b^2, b \ne 0$

32. $s \ne \pm 6$

33. $x \ne -y$

34. $x \ne -4, 3$

35. $x \ne -4$

36. $x \ne 3, \dfrac{2}{5}$

37. $x \ne 7, -3$

38. $x \ne 0, y \ne 1$

39. $x \ne -1$

40. $x \ne -3, -4$

41. $k \ne \dfrac{5}{2}$

42. $x \ne 1, \dfrac{2}{3}$

Chapter 8 309

55. Solve $\frac{5}{12} = \frac{2-x}{3+x}$. **(Lesson 4-1)** $\frac{9}{17}$

56. **Government** The term of office for a United States Senator is 150% as long as the term of office for the President. How long is the term of office for a U.S. Senator? **(Lesson 4-2)** 6 years

57. Solve $9q + 2 \le 7q - 25$. Express the solution in set-builder notation. **(Lesson 5-3)** $\left\{ q|q \le -\frac{27}{2} \right\}$

58. Evaluate $a^3 + b^2 - (c^2 + abcde) - a \div b + d \div e + c$ if $a = 2$, $b = \frac{1}{3}$, $c = 2.2$, $d = 4$, and $e = \frac{2}{5}$. **(Lesson 1-2)** 7.124

59. Simplify $(-5x^3)(4x^4)$. **(Lesson 6-2)** $-20x^7$

60. Find the common factor: $(3a^2b + 2ab^3) + (6ab + 4b^3)$. **(Lesson 7-3)** $3a + 2b^2$

61. Solve $x^2 + 22 = 58$. **(Lesson 7-9)** $\{6, -6\}$

HISTORY CONNECTION

Fractions

The Romans used a somewhat cumbersome system of fractions based on the number twelve, even though their counting system was based on the number ten. They used a unit of measure called the *as*, one-twelfth of which was called the *uncia*. All of the fractions that the Romans needed could be expressed in terms of uncia. Notice from the table that uncia could also be divided, allowing the Romans a fraction as small as $\frac{1}{2304}$.

In seventh-century India, people began writing fractions as we write them today, but without the fraction bar. Arab mathematicians later added the bar. However, it presented such a problem to the printers of the day that the use of the fraction bar did not become common practice until the sixteenth century.

Roman Fractions		
	As = 1	Uncia = 1
As	1	12
Deunx	$\frac{11}{12}$	11
Dextans	$\frac{5}{6}$	10
Dodrans	$\frac{3}{4}$	9
Bes	$\frac{2}{3}$	8
Septunx	$\frac{7}{12}$	7
Semis	$\frac{1}{2}$	6
Quincunx	$\frac{5}{12}$	5
Triens	$\frac{1}{3}$	4
Quadrans	$\frac{1}{4}$	3
Sextans	$\frac{1}{6}$	2
Sescuncia	$\frac{1}{8}$	$1\frac{1}{2}$
Uncia	$\frac{1}{12}$	1
Semuncia	$\frac{1}{24}$	$\frac{1}{2}$
Duella	$\frac{1}{36}$	$\frac{1}{3}$
Sicilicus	$\frac{1}{48}$	$\frac{1}{4}$
Sextula	$\frac{1}{72}$	$\frac{1}{6}$
Drachma	$\frac{1}{96}$	$\frac{1}{8}$
Dimidio sextula	$\frac{1}{144}$	$\frac{1}{12}$

310 CHAPTER 8 RATIONAL EXPRESSIONS

EXTENDING THE LESSON

Math Power: Connections

The measure of the area of a rectangle is $6x^2 - 7x - 20$, and the measure of one side is $2x - 5$. Find the measure of the other side of the rectangle.
$3x + 4$

History Connection

The History Connection features introduce students to persons or cultures who were involved in the development of mathematics. You may want students to further research why the fraction bar came into use again in the sixteenth century.

Enrichment Masters Booklet, p. 52

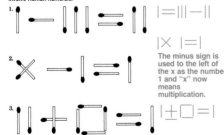

NAME _____ DATE _____

8-1 Enrichment Worksheet

Puzzles with Matchsticks

There are many puzzles and games that use only a box of wooden matches. The first four puzzles on this page also involve Roman numerals. In puzzle 3, the square shape is meant to stand for zero.

Each equation is false. Create a true equation by changing the position of just one matchstick. The new equation need not involve Roman numerals.

1. $|=|||-||$

2. The minus sign is used to the left of the x as the number 1 and "x" now means multiplication. $|X|=|$

3. $|+\square=|$

4. The square root sign is created. $\sqrt{|}=|$

5. In the figure, 13 matchsticks are used to create six rectangles of equal area. Remove one matchstick and then rearrange the remaining matchsticks to form a new figure that still has six sections of equal area.

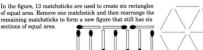

8-2 Multiplying Rational Expressions

Objective
8-2

After studying this lesson, you should be able to:
- multiply rational expressions.

To multiply fractions, you multiply the numerators and multiply the denominators.

$$\frac{3}{5} \cdot \frac{4}{7} = \frac{3 \cdot 4}{5 \cdot 7}$$
$$= \frac{12}{35}$$

You can use this same method to multiply rational expressions.

Example 1

Find $\frac{5}{a} \cdot \frac{b}{7}$. State any excluded values.

$$\frac{5}{a} \cdot \frac{b}{7} = \frac{5 \cdot b}{a \cdot 7} \qquad \textit{Multiply the numerators.}$$
$$\textit{Multiply the denominators.}$$
$$= \frac{5b}{7a}$$

Since $7a$ cannot equal 0, $a \neq 0$.

Example 2

Find $\frac{2a^2d}{3bc} \cdot \frac{9b^2c}{16ad^2}$. State any excluded values.

$$\frac{2a^2d}{3bc} \cdot \frac{9b^2c}{16ad^2} = \frac{18a^2b^2cd}{48abcd^2} \qquad \textit{Divide the numerator and denominator}$$
$$\textit{by the GCF, 6abcd.}$$
$$= \frac{3ab}{8d} \qquad \textit{Write the fraction in simplest form.} \textbf{ Teaching Tip } \textbf{1}$$

Since neither bc nor ad^2 can equal 0, $a \neq 0$, $b \neq 0$, $c \neq 0$, and $d \neq 0$.

From this point on, it will be assumed that all replacements for variables in rational expressions that result in denominators equal to zero will be excluded.

You may find it easier to use a shortcut before multiplying fractions, as shown below.

$$\frac{3}{4} \cdot \frac{16}{21} = \frac{\overset{1}{\cancel{3}}}{\underset{1}{\cancel{4}}} \cdot \frac{\overset{4}{\cancel{16}}}{\underset{7}{\cancel{21}}} = \frac{4}{7}$$

You can use the same shortcut when multiplying rational expressions.

LESSON 8-2 MULTIPLYING RATIONAL EXPRESSIONS 311

ALTERNATE TEACHING STRATEGIES

Using Discussion

Find a value for b so that $\frac{a+b}{b+c} = \frac{a}{c}$.

$b = 0$

Find values for b so that $\frac{ab}{bc} = \frac{a}{c}$.

b = any real number except 0

8-2 Lesson Notes

Lesson Resources
- Reteaching Master 8-2
- Practice Master 8-2
- Enrichment Master 8-2
- Video Algebra, 27
- Transparency 8-2 contains the 5-Minute Check and a teaching aid for this lesson.

INTRODUCING THE LESSON

 5-Minute Check
(over Lesson 8-1)

For each fraction, state the values of the variable that must be excluded.

1. $\frac{(y+4)}{(y-4)(y+4)}$ $y \neq 4, -4$
2. $\frac{4n^2 - 8}{4n - 4}$ $n \neq 1$
3. $\frac{x^2 - 49}{x^2 - 2x - 35}$ $x \neq -5, 7$
4. $\frac{m(m-1)}{m-1}$ $m \neq 1$
5. $\frac{y-3}{y^2-9}$ $y \neq -3, 3$

Motivating the Lesson

Before beginning the lesson, review the multiplication of arithmetic fractions. Have students find the following products expressed in simplest form.

1. $\frac{1}{2} \times \frac{4}{5}$ $\frac{2}{5}$
2. $\frac{2}{7} \times \frac{49}{50}$ $\frac{7}{25}$
3. $\frac{3}{8} \times \frac{20}{12}$ $\frac{5}{8}$
4. $\frac{12}{15} \times \frac{25}{16}$ $\frac{5}{4}$
5. $\frac{10}{18} \times \frac{27}{30}$ $\frac{1}{2}$

TEACHING THE LESSON

Teaching Tip 1 Remind students to express all fractions in simplest form.

Teaching Tip 2 Stress that each polynomial must be written in factored form and then simplified.

Chapter 8 311

Reteaching Masters Booklet, p. 53

Example 3

Find $\frac{x+5}{3x} \cdot \frac{12x^2}{x^2+7x+10}$.

$\frac{x+5}{3x} \cdot \frac{12x^2}{x^2+7x+10} = \frac{x+5}{3 \cdot x} \cdot \frac{2 \cdot 2 \cdot 3 \cdot x \cdot x}{(x+5)(x+2)}$ $x \neq 0$, $x \neq -5$, or $x \neq -2$ **Teaching Tip ②**

$= \frac{x+5}{3 \cdot x} \cdot \frac{2 \cdot 2 \cdot 3 \cdot x \cdot x}{(x+5)(x+2)}$ *Simplify.*

$= \frac{4x}{x+2}$

Example 4

Find $\frac{4a+8}{a^2-25} \cdot \frac{a-5}{5a+10}$.

$\frac{4a+8}{a^2-25} \cdot \frac{a-5}{5a+10} = \frac{4(a+2)}{(a-5)(a+5)} \cdot \frac{a-5}{5(a+2)}$ $a \neq 5$, $a \neq -5$, or $a \neq -2$

$= \frac{4(a+2)}{(a-5)(a+5)} \cdot \frac{a-5}{5(a+2)}$ *Simplify.*

$= \frac{4}{5(a+5)}$

$= \frac{4}{5a+25}$

Example 5

Find $\frac{x^2-x-6}{9-x^2} \cdot \frac{x^2+7x+12}{x^2+4x+4}$.

$\frac{x^2-x-6}{9-x^2} \cdot \frac{x^2+7x+12}{x^2+4x+4} = \frac{(x-3)(x+2)}{(3-x)(3+x)} \cdot \frac{(x+3)(x+4)}{(x+2)(x+2)}$ $x \neq 3$, $x \neq -3$, or $x \neq -2$

$= \frac{(x-3)(x+2)}{-1(x-3)(x+3)} \cdot \frac{(x+3)(x+4)}{(x+2)(x+2)}$ *Notice that* $3-x = -1(x-3)$

$= \frac{(x-3)(x+2)}{-1(x-3)(x+3)} \cdot \frac{(x+3)(x+4)}{(x+2)(x+2)}$ *Simplify.*

$= \frac{x+4}{-1(x+2)}$

$= -\frac{x+4}{x+2}$ **Teaching Tip ③**

Example 6

Find the measure of the area of the rectangle in simplest form.

$A = \ell w$

$= \frac{2x+4}{x} \cdot \frac{x^3-4x}{x^2+4x+4}$

$= \frac{2(x+2)(x)(x+2)(x-2)}{x(x+2)(x+2)}$

$= 2(x-2)$

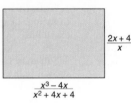

$\frac{2x+4}{x}$

$\frac{x^3-4x}{x^2+4x+4}$

The measure of the area of the rectangle is $2(x-2)$.

RETEACHING THE LESSON

Have students pick values for a and b and complete the table below. The ratio of opposites simplifies to -1.

a	b	$a-b$	$b-a$	$\frac{a-b}{b-a}$
1	4	-3	3	-1
3	-2	5	-5	-1

Pick $a = b$ to see excluded values.

Additional Answers

1. b = any number except 0
2. Only *factors* can be cancelled, not terms.

CHECKING FOR UNDERSTANDING

Communicating Mathematics

Read and study the lesson to answer each question. See margin.

1. Describe the value(s) for b such that $\frac{ab}{bc} = \frac{a}{c}$.

2. Find the error: $\frac{4\overset{2}{\cancel{x}}}{x + \underset{1}{\cancel{2}}} = \frac{2}{2} = 1$.

Guided Practice

Find each product. Assume that no denominator is equal to zero.

3. $\frac{3}{a} \cdot \frac{b}{4}$ $\frac{3b}{4a}$

4. $\frac{3a}{5} \cdot \frac{2x}{y}$ $\frac{6ax}{5y}$

5. $\frac{ab}{ac} \cdot \frac{c}{d}$ $\frac{b}{d}$

6. $\frac{6a^2n}{8n^2} \cdot \frac{12n}{9a}$ a

7. $\frac{y-3}{7} \cdot \frac{14}{y-3}$ 2

8. $\frac{9}{m-3} \cdot \frac{m^2-9}{12}$ $\frac{3m+9}{4}$

EXERCISES

15-34. See margin.

Practice

Find each product. Assume that no denominator is equal to zero.

 A

9. $\frac{a^2b}{b^2c} \cdot \frac{c}{d}$ $\frac{a^2}{bd}$

10. $\frac{10n^3}{6x^3} \cdot \frac{12n^2x^4}{25n^2x^2}$ $\frac{4n^3}{5x}$

11. $\left(\frac{2a}{b}\right)^2 \frac{5c}{6a}$ $\frac{10ac}{3b^2}$

12. $\frac{8}{m^2}\left(\frac{m^2}{2c}\right)^2$ $\frac{2m^2}{c^2}$

13. $\frac{6m^3n}{10a^2} \cdot \frac{4a^2m}{9n^3}$ $\frac{4m^4}{15n^2}$

14. $\frac{7xy^3}{11z^2} \cdot \frac{44z^3}{21x^2y}$ $\frac{4y^2z}{3x}$

B

15. $\frac{5n-5}{3} \cdot \frac{9}{n-1}$

16. $\frac{3a-3b}{a} \cdot \frac{a^2}{a-b}$

17. $\frac{-(2a+7c)}{6} \cdot \frac{36}{-7c-2a}$

18. $\frac{2a+4b}{5} \cdot \frac{25}{6a+8b}$

19. $\frac{3x+30}{2x} \cdot \frac{4x}{4x+40}$

20. $\frac{3}{x-y} \cdot \frac{(x-y)^2}{6}$

21. $\frac{a^2-b^2}{4} \cdot \frac{16}{a+b}$

22. $\frac{r^2}{r-s} \cdot \frac{r^2-s^2}{s^2}$

23. $\frac{a^2-b^2}{a-b} \cdot \frac{7}{a+b}$

24. $\frac{x^2-16}{9} \cdot \frac{x+4}{x-4}$

25. $\frac{x^2-y^2}{x^2-1} \cdot \frac{x-1}{x-y}$

26. $\frac{r^2+s^2}{r^2-s^2} \cdot \frac{r-s}{r+s}$

27. $\frac{3k+9}{k} \cdot \frac{k^2}{k^2-9}$

28. $\frac{3a-6}{a^2-9} \cdot \frac{a+3}{a^2-2a}$

29. $\frac{y^2-x^2}{y} \cdot \frac{x}{x-y}$

30. $\frac{b+a}{b-a} \cdot \frac{a^2-b^2}{a}$

31. $\frac{3mn^2-3m}{n} \cdot \frac{3m}{n^2-1}$

32. $\frac{x}{x^2+8x+15} \cdot \frac{2x+10}{x^2}$

33. $\frac{x-5}{x^2-7x+10} \cdot \frac{x-2}{3}$

34. $\frac{b^2+20b+99}{b+9} \cdot \frac{b+7}{b^2+12b+11}$

CONNECTION
Geometry

Find the measure of the area of each rectangle in simplest form.

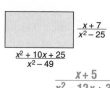

35.

$\frac{x+7}{x^2-25}$

$\frac{x^2+10x+25}{x^2-49}$

$\frac{x+5}{x^2-12x+35}$

36.

$\frac{2x+3}{x^2}$

$\frac{2x+3}{x^2}$

$\frac{4x^2+12x+9}{x^4}$

37.

$\frac{x^2y-x^2}{x^3-x^3y}$

$\frac{-x}{xy^2-y}$

$\frac{x^2}{xy^2-y}$

 C

Find each product. Assume that no denominator is equal to zero.

38. $\frac{z^2-15z+50}{z^2-9z+20} \cdot \frac{z^2-11z+24}{z^2-18z+80}$ $\frac{z-3}{z-4}$

39. $\frac{y^2+3y^3}{y^2-4} \cdot \frac{2y+y^2}{y+4y^2+3y^3}$ $\frac{y^2}{y^2-y-2}$

LESSON 8-2 MULTIPLYING RATIONAL EXPRESSIONS 313

Additional Answers

15. 15

16. $3a$

17. 6

18. $\frac{5a+10b}{3a+4b}$

19. $\frac{3}{2}$

20. $\frac{x-y}{2}$

21. $4a - 4b$

22. $\frac{r^3+r^2s}{s^2}$

23. 7

24. $\frac{x^2+8x+16}{9}$

25. $\frac{x+y}{x+1}$

26. $\frac{r^2+s^2}{r^2+2rs+s^2}$

27. $\frac{3k}{k-3}$

28. $\frac{3}{a^2-3a}$

29. $\frac{-xy-x^2}{y}$

30. $\frac{-a^2-2ab-b^2}{a}$

31. $\frac{9m^2}{n}$

32. $\frac{2}{x^2+3x}$

33. $\frac{1}{3}$

34. $\frac{b+7}{b+1}$

Chalkboard Example

For Example 6

The length of a rectangle is $\frac{x+7}{x^2-25}$, and its width is $\frac{x^2+10x+25}{x^2-49}$. Use the formula $A = \ell w$ to find the area of the rectangle.

Area = $\frac{x+5}{x^2-12x+35}$.

Teaching Tip ③ Caution students to write the negative sign before the fraction bar and not with the numerator. For example, $-\frac{x+4}{x+2}$ is not the same as $\frac{-x+4}{x+2}$.

EVALUATING THE LESSON

Checking for Understanding

Exercises 1-8 are designed to help you assess understanding through reading, writing, and speaking. You should work through Exercises 1-2 with your students, and then monitor their work on Exercises 3-8.

Assignment Guide

Basic: 9-37, 45-47, 49-54
Average: 12-40, 45-54
Enriched: 15-54

Practice Masters Booklet, p. 59

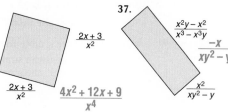

8-2 Practice Worksheet

NAME _____ DATE _____

Multiplying Rational Expressions

Find each product. Assume that no denominator is equal to zero.

1. $\frac{2a^2b}{b^2c} \cdot \frac{2a}{c}$

2. $\frac{18x^2}{10y^3} \cdot \frac{15y^2}{24x} \cdot \frac{9xy}{8}$

3. $\frac{24st^2}{8s^4t^3} \cdot \frac{12s^3t^2}{36c^2t} \cdot \frac{1}{s^2}$

4. $\frac{12a^2b}{4} \cdot \frac{4a+8b}{20a^2b^3} \cdot \frac{3(a+2b)}{5b^2}$

5. $\frac{12m-18}{18n} \cdot \frac{9n^2}{8m-12} \cdot \frac{3n}{4}$

6. $\frac{y^2-9}{4} \cdot \frac{8}{y+3} \cdot 2y-6$

7. $\frac{(x+2)^2}{8} \cdot \frac{72}{x^2-4} \cdot \frac{9x+18}{x-2}$

8. $\frac{2a^2+a}{4a^2-1} \cdot \frac{6a-3}{4a} \cdot \frac{3}{4}$

9. $\frac{5n+15}{8n+4} \cdot \frac{4n+2}{3n+9} \cdot \frac{5}{6}$

10. $\frac{e^2-1}{2e-6} \cdot \frac{e^2-9}{3e-3} \cdot \frac{e^2+4e+3}{6}$

11. $\frac{k^2-4}{8k^3+3k} \cdot \frac{16k+6}{k-2} \cdot \frac{2k+4}{k}$

12. $\frac{4r+r^2}{8+2r} \cdot \frac{4}{2r^3} \cdot \frac{1}{r^2}$

13. $\frac{25-c^2}{12} \cdot \frac{4}{5-c} \cdot \frac{5+c}{3}$

14. $\frac{xy}{3x-3y} \cdot \frac{x^2-xy}{xy} \cdot \frac{x}{3}$

15. $\frac{2c^2-5c-3}{c^2+d} \cdot \frac{c^3-d^2}{2c+1}$ $\frac{c^2-cd-3c+3d}{}$

16. $\frac{t^2+6t+9}{t^2-10t+25} \cdot \frac{t^2-t-20}{t^2+7t+12} \cdot \frac{t+3}{t-5}$

Error Analysis

When all the factors in the numerator or denominator cancel out, students may indicate its value as 0, rather than 1. For example, $\frac{4x(x-3)}{8x^2(x-3)} = \frac{0}{2x}$ rather than $\frac{1}{2x}$. Remind students to use small numbers when cancelling to show that $\frac{a}{a} = 1$.

Closing the Lesson

Writing Activity At the end of class, have students write down the key points to consider in multiplying rational expressions.

APPLYING THE LESSON

Homework Exercises

See assignment guide on page 313.

Additional Answer

45. Answers will vary. A typical answer is $\frac{6x-18}{x+7} \cdot \frac{x+2}{x-4}$.

Enrichment Masters Booklet, p. 53

NAME _____ DATE _____

8-2 Enrichment Worksheet

Continued Fractions

The following is an example of a continued fraction. By starting at the bottom you can simplify the expression to a rational number.

$$3 + \frac{4}{1 + \frac{6}{7}} = 3 + \frac{4}{\frac{13}{7}}$$

$$= 3 + \frac{28}{13}, \text{ or } \frac{67}{13}$$

Example: Express $\frac{48}{19}$ as a continued fraction.

$$\frac{48}{19} = 2 + \frac{10}{19}$$
Notice that the numerator of the last fraction must be equal to 1 before the process stops.

$$= 2 + \frac{1}{\frac{19}{10}}$$

$$= 2 + \frac{1}{1 + \frac{9}{10}}$$

$$= 2 + \frac{1}{1 + \frac{1}{\frac{10}{9}}}$$

$$= 2 + \frac{1}{1 + \frac{1}{1 + \frac{1}{9}}}$$

Write each continued fraction as a rational number.

1. $6 + \cfrac{1}{1 + \cfrac{1}{3 + \frac{1}{3}}}$ $\frac{88}{13}$

2. $5 + \cfrac{7}{2 + \cfrac{3}{4 + \frac{2}{3}}}$ $\frac{283}{37}$

Write each rational number as a continued fraction.

3. $\frac{97}{17}$ $5 + \cfrac{1}{1 + \cfrac{1}{2 + \frac{1}{2}}}$

4. $\frac{22}{65}$ $2 + \cfrac{1}{1 + \frac{1}{21}}$

Find each product. Assume that no denominator is equal to zero.

40. $\frac{3t^3 - 14t^2 + 8t}{2t^2 - 3t - 20} \cdot \frac{16t^2 + 34t - 15}{24t^2 - 25t + 6}$ t

41. $\frac{6y^2 - 5y - 6}{3y^2 - 20y - 7} \cdot \frac{y^2 - 49}{12y^3 + 23y^2 + 10y}$ $\frac{2y^2 + 11y - 21}{12y^3 + 19y^2 + 5y}$

42. $\frac{2m^2 - 9m + 9}{3m^2 + 19m - 14} \cdot \frac{m^2 + 14m + 49}{9 - 6m + m^2}$ $\frac{2m^2 + 11m - 21}{3m^2 - 11m + 6}$

43. $\frac{a^2x - b^2x}{y} \cdot \frac{y^2 + y}{a - 2} \cdot \frac{4 - 2a}{axy - bxy}$ $\frac{-2(a+b)(y+1)}{y}$

44. $\frac{x^2y}{x^2 + 4xy + 4y^2} \cdot \frac{x^2 + 2xy}{xy} \cdot \frac{y}{x^4 - 9x^2}$ $\frac{x^2y}{x^5 + 2x^4y - 9x^3 - 18x^2y}$

Critical Thinking

45. Find two different pairs of rational expressions whose product is $\frac{6x^2 - 6x - 36}{x^2 + 3x - 28}$. **See margin.**

Applications

46. **Consumer Awareness** The price of eggs goes up 10% the first month, goes down 10% the second month, and then goes up 10% again the third month. By what percentage did the price of eggs go up from the initial price? **8.9%**

47. **Construction** A construction supervisor needs to determine how many truckloads of earth will have to be removed from a site before the foundation can be poured. The bed of the truck has the shape shown at the right. Use the formula $V = \frac{d(a+b)}{2} \times \ell$ to find the volume of the truck bed if $d = 5$ ft, $a = 18$ ft, $b = 15$ ft, and $\ell = 9$ ft. **742.5 ft³**

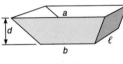

$V = \frac{d(a+b)}{2} \times \ell$

48. **Car Racing** The Indianapolis 500 is a 500-mile automobile race. If each lap is $2\frac{1}{2}$ miles long, how many laps does each driver complete to finish the race? **200**

Mixed Review

49. Make a table to solve the problem. **(Lesson 4-5)**
What is the sum of the first three consecutive odd whole numbers?
What is the sum of the first five consecutive odd whole numbers?
What is the sum of the first fifty consecutive odd whole numbers?
9, 25, 2500

50. Solve $\frac{h}{-18} > -25$. **(Lesson 5-2)** $h < 450$

51. Express 0.76×10^7 in scientific notation. **(Lesson 6-4)** 7.6×10^6

52. Simplify $(3x + 7)(5x - 1)$. **(Lesson 6-8)** $15x^2 + 32x - 7$

53. Factor $6y^2 - 24x^2$. **(Lesson 7-10)** $6(y + 2x)(y - 2x)$

54. Simplify $\frac{2x^3}{2x^2(x^2 - 4)}$. **(Lesson 8-1)** $\frac{x}{x^2 - 4}$

EXTENDING THE LESSON

Math Power: Problem Solving

Use the formula $V = \ell wh$ to represent the volume of a rectangular solid. Write the expression in simplest form.

$\frac{x^2 + 9x + 14}{2x^2 + x}$

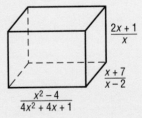

$2x + 1$ over x

$\frac{x + 7}{x - 2}$

$\frac{x^2 - 4}{4x^2 + 4x + 1}$

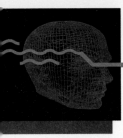

Technology
Rational Expressions

BASIC
Graphing calculators
► Graphing software
Spreadsheets

Using Technology

Objective This optional page shows how graphing software can be used to perform mathematical computations and to enhance and extend mathematical concepts.

Teaching Suggestions

Encourage students to experiment with the commands SIMPLIFY, FACTOR, and REDUCE. SIMPLIFY will reduce expressions in which the denominator is a factor of the numerator even if the FACTOR command is not used first. Answers to the exercises are left in factored form. You may want students to use the SIMPLIFY command to multiply the factors. Remind students that the command FSTEPS is available to reveal the steps used by the computer to factor.

The examples below show how to use the *Mathematics Exploration Toolkit* to simplify rational expressions. The following CALC commands will be used.

FACTOR (fac)   REDUCE (red)   SIMPLIFY (simp)

First, use the FACTOR command to factor the numerator and denominator. Then, use the REDUCE command to divide the numerator and denominator by the greatest common factor. Use the SIMPLIFY command to express monomials with exponents.

Example 1 Simplify $\dfrac{30a^2bc^4}{25a^3b^2c}$. *Exponents are entered with the ^ symbol.*

Enter	Result
$(30a\char`\^2bc\char`\^4)/(25a\char`\^3b\char`\^2c)$	$\dfrac{30a^2bc^4}{25a^3b^2c}$
fac	$\dfrac{5 \cdot 3 \cdot 2(aa)b(cccc)}{5 \cdot 5(aaa)(bb)c}$
red	$\dfrac{ccc \cdot 2 \cdot 3}{ba \cdot 5}$
simp	$\dfrac{6c^3}{5ab}$

Example 2 Simplify $\dfrac{3x^2 - 4x + 1}{9x^2 - 1}$.

Enter	Result
$(3x\char`\^2 - 4x + 1)/(9x\char`\^2 - 1)$	$\dfrac{3x^2 - 4x + 1}{9x^2 - 1}$
fac	$\dfrac{(x - 1)(3x - 1)}{(3x - 1)(3x + 1)}$
red	$\dfrac{x - 1}{3x + 1}$

EXERCISES

Use CALC to simplify each rational expression.

1. $\dfrac{12p^3q^5}{18p^2q^7} \cdot \dfrac{2p}{3q^2}$

2. $\dfrac{y^2 - 9}{y^2 - 6y + 9} \cdot \dfrac{y + 3}{y - 3}$

3. $\dfrac{x^3 - 2x^2}{x^4 - x^2} \cdot \dfrac{x - 2}{(x + 1)(x - 1)}$

4. $\dfrac{2y^2 - y - 1}{2y^2 + y} \cdot \dfrac{y - 1}{y}$

5. $\dfrac{x^2 + 19x + 60}{x^2 - 225} \cdot \dfrac{x + 4}{x - 15}$

TECHNOLOGY: RATIONAL EXPRESSIONS 315

Lesson Resources

- Reteaching Master 8-3
- Practice Master 8-3
- Enrichment Master 8-3
- Video Algebra, 27

 Transparency 8-3 contains the 5-Minute Check and a teaching aid for this lesson.

INTRODUCING THE LESSON

 5-Minute Check

(over Lesson 8-2)

Find each product and simplify.

1. $\frac{3}{5} \cdot \frac{35}{99}$ $\frac{7}{33}$ 2. $\frac{7a}{9a} \cdot \frac{3a^2}{6b^2}$ $\frac{7a^2}{18b^2}$

3. $\frac{a^2b}{b^3c} \cdot \frac{ac}{a^3}$ $\frac{1}{b^2}$

4. $\frac{5x-5}{4} \cdot \frac{12}{x-1}$ 15

5. $\frac{w-5}{w^2-7w+10} \cdot \frac{w-2}{12}$ $\frac{1}{12}$

Motivating the Lesson

Introduce the lesson with a review of division of fractions. Ask students to find each quotient in simplest form.

1. $\frac{2}{3} \div \frac{8}{9}$ $\frac{3}{4}$ 2. $\frac{3}{4} \div \frac{5}{6}$ $\frac{9}{10}$

3. $\frac{10}{21} \div \frac{25}{42}$ $\frac{4}{5}$ 4. $\frac{5}{8} \div \frac{1}{60}$ $\frac{75}{2}$

Reteaching Masters Booklet, p. 54

NAME _____ DATE _____

8-3 **Reteaching Worksheet**

Dividing Rational Expressions

You should recall that two numbers whose product is 1 are called **multiplicative inverses** or **reciprocals**. To find the quotient of two rational expressions, you multiply the first rational expression by the reciprocal of the second rational expression.

Dividing Rational Expressions
For all rational numbers $\frac{a}{b}$ and $\frac{c}{d}$, where $b \neq 0$, $c \neq 0$ and $d \neq 0$, $\frac{a}{b} \div \frac{c}{d} = \frac{a}{b} \cdot \frac{d}{c}$.

Example 1: Find $\frac{2}{x} \div \frac{y}{z}$.

$\frac{2}{x} \div \frac{y}{z} = \frac{2}{x} \cdot \frac{y}{z}$

$= \frac{2y}{xz}$

Example 2: Find $\frac{x^2+6x-27}{x^2+11x+18} \div \frac{x-3}{x^2+x-2}$.

$\frac{x^2+6x-27}{x^2+11x+18} \div \frac{x-3}{x^2+x-2} = \frac{x^2+6x-27}{x^2+11x+18} \cdot \frac{x^2+x-2}{x-3}$

$= \frac{(x+9)(x-3)}{(x+9)(x+2)} \cdot \frac{(x+2)(x-1)}{x-3}$

$= x-1$

Find each quotient. Assume that no denominator is equal to zero.

1. $\frac{5}{6} \div 5$ $\frac{1}{6}$ 2. $1 \div \frac{1}{3}$ 3   3. $\frac{n}{4} \div \frac{n}{m}$ $\frac{m}{4}$

4. $\frac{6}{11} \div \frac{12}{7x}$ $\frac{7x}{22}$ 5. $\frac{x}{y} \div \frac{2}{y}$ $\frac{x}{2}$ 6. $\frac{a+b}{a-b} \div (a^2+2ab+b^2)$ $\frac{1}{a^2-b^2}$

7. $\frac{3x^2y}{8} \div 6xy$ $\frac{x}{16}$ 8. $\frac{y^2-36}{y^2-49} \div \frac{y+6}{y+7}$ $\frac{y-6}{y-7}$ 9. $\frac{x^2-5x+6}{5} \div \frac{x-3}{15}$ $3(x-2)$

10. $\frac{49-m^2}{m} \div \frac{m^2-13m+42}{3m^2}$ $\frac{-3m(m+7)}{m-6}$, or $\frac{-3m^2-21m}{m-6}$ 11. $\frac{3a^3-27a}{2a^2+13a-7} \div \frac{9a^2}{4a^2-1}$ $\frac{(a^2-9)(2a+1)}{3a(a+7)}$, or $\frac{2a^3+a^2-18a-9}{3a^3+21a}$ 12. $\frac{p^2-5p+6}{p^2+3p} \div \frac{3-p}{4p+12}$ $\frac{4(2-p)}{p}$, or $\frac{8-4p}{p}$

Dividing Rational Expressions

Objective

8-3

After studying this lesson, you should be able to:
- divide rational expressions.

You should recall that two numbers whose product is 1 are called **multiplicative inverses** or **reciprocals.**

To find the quotient of two fractions, you multiply by the reciprocal of the divisor.

$$\frac{2}{3} \div \frac{3}{4} = \frac{2}{3} \cdot \frac{4}{3} \qquad \text{The reciprocal of } \frac{3}{4} \text{ is } \frac{4}{3}.$$
$$= \frac{8}{9}$$

You can use this same method to divide rational expressions.

Example 1 | Find $\frac{5}{x} \div \frac{y}{z}$.

$\frac{5}{x} \div \frac{y}{z} = \frac{5}{x} \cdot \frac{z}{y}$ *The reciprocal of $\frac{y}{z}$ is $\frac{z}{y}$.*

$= \frac{5z}{xy}$

Example 2 | Find $\frac{2x}{x+1} \div (x-1)$.

$\frac{2x}{x+1} \div (x-1) = \frac{2x}{x+1} \cdot \frac{1}{x-1}$ *The reciprocal of $x-1$ is $\frac{1}{x-1}$. Why?*

$= \frac{2x}{(x+1)(x-1)}$

$= \frac{2x}{x^2-1}$

Example 3 | Find $\frac{x-y}{x^2-y^2} \div \frac{x+y}{x^2+2xy+y^2}$.

$\frac{x-y}{x^2-y^2} \div \frac{x+y}{x^2+2xy+y^2} = \frac{x-y}{x^2-y^2} \cdot \frac{x^2+2xy+y^2}{x+y}$ *Multiply by the reciprocal.*

$= \frac{x-y}{(x+y)(x-y)} \cdot \frac{(x+y)(x+y)}{x+y}$ *Factor x^2-y^2 and $x^2+2xy+y^2$.*

$= \frac{x-y}{(x+y)(x-y)} \cdot \frac{(x+y)(x+y)}{x+y}$

$= 1$

RETEACHING THE LESSON

Have each student create a division problem that has binomial factors that cancel. Take four arbitrary binomials (A, B, C, and D). The division problem is $\frac{E}{F} \div \frac{A}{C}$ where $AB = E$ and $CD = F$. The quotient is $\frac{B}{D}$. Have students exchange problems with a neighbor to check.

CHECKING FOR UNDERSTANDING

Communicating Mathematics

Read and study the lesson to answer each question.

1. *True* or *false:* Every real number other than zero has a reciprocal. **true**

2. Why does zero *not* have a reciprocal? **See margin.**

Guided Practice

Find the reciprocal of each expression.

3. $\frac{m}{2}$ $\frac{2}{m}$

4. $\frac{x^2}{4}$ $\frac{4}{x^2}$

5. $\frac{-8}{3n}$ $-\frac{3n}{8}$

6. x $\frac{1}{x}$

7. $\frac{2m^2}{5}$ $\frac{5}{2m^2}$

8. $2bc$ $\frac{1}{2bc}$

9. $\frac{x+y}{x-y}$ $\frac{x-y}{x+y}$

10. $x-2$ $\frac{1}{x-2}$

Find each quotient. Assume that no denominator is equal to zero.

11. $\frac{y}{5} \div \frac{y^2-25}{5-y}$ $\frac{-y}{5y+25}$

12. $\frac{m^2+2m+1}{2} \div \frac{m+1}{m-1}$ $\frac{m^2-1}{2}$

26, 28. See margin.

EXERCISES

Practice

Find each quotient. Assume that no denominator is equal to zero.

13. $\frac{a^2}{b^2} \div \frac{b^2}{a^2}$ $\frac{a^4}{b^4}$

14. $\frac{a^2}{b} \div \frac{a^2}{b^2}$ b

15. $\frac{(-a)^2}{b} \div \frac{a}{b}$ a

16. $\frac{3m}{m+1} \div (m-2)$ $\frac{3m}{m^2-m-2}$

17. $\frac{b^2-9}{4b} \div (b-3)$ $\frac{b+3}{4b}$

18. $\frac{y^2+8y+16}{y^2} \div (y+4)$ $\frac{y+4}{y^2}$

19. $\frac{2a^3}{a+1} \div \frac{a^2}{a+1}$ $2a$

20. $\frac{p^2}{y^2-4} \div \frac{p}{2-y}$ $\frac{-p}{y+2}$

21. $\frac{x^2-16}{16-x^2} \div \frac{7}{x}$ $-\frac{x}{7}$

22. $\frac{x^2-4x+4}{3} \div \frac{x^2-4}{2x}$ $\frac{2x^2-4x}{3x+6}$

23. $\frac{a^2+2ab+b^2}{2x} \div \frac{a+b}{x^2}$ $\frac{ax+bx}{2}$

24. $\frac{k^2-81}{k^2-36} \div \frac{k-9}{k+6}$ $\frac{k+9}{k-6}$

25. $\frac{t^2+8t+16}{w^2-6w+9} \div \frac{2t+8}{3w-9}$ $\frac{3t+12}{2w-6}$

26. $\frac{k+2}{m^2+4m+4} \div \frac{4k+8}{m+4}$

27. $\frac{x}{x+2} \div \frac{x^2}{x^2+5x+6}$ $\frac{x+3}{x}$

28. $\frac{x^2+x-2}{x^2+5x+6} \div \frac{x^2+2x-3}{x^2+7x+12}$

29. $\frac{2m^2+7m-15}{m+5} \div \frac{9m^2-4}{3m+2}$ $\frac{2m-3}{3m-2}$

30. $\frac{2x^2-x-15}{x^2-2x-3} \div \frac{2x^2+3x-5}{1-x^2}$ -1

31. $\frac{x^2+5x+6}{x^2-x-12} \cdot \frac{x-4}{x^2+11x+18} \div \frac{x+7}{x^2+14x+45}$ $\frac{x+5}{x+7}$

32. $\frac{2x-3}{2x^2-7x+6} \cdot \frac{x^2+3x-10}{5x+1} \div \frac{3x^2+14x-5}{3x^2+2x-1}$ $\frac{x+1}{5x+1}$

33. $\frac{x^2-1}{2x^2+14x+12} \div \frac{2x^2-3x+1}{8x^2+36x-72} \cdot \frac{x^2+3x-4}{x^2+5x-6}$ $\frac{4x^2+10x-24}{2x^2+11x-6}$

Critical Thinking

34. **Geometry** The measure of the area of a rectangle is $\frac{x^2-y^2}{2}$. If the measure of the length is $2x+2y$, find the measure of the width. $\frac{x-y}{4}$

Applications

35. **Personal Finance** Brice had his allowance doubled. Next, he received a $3 increase. Then his allowance was cut in half. If Brice's allowance is now $10 per week, what was his original allowance? **$8.50**

LESSON 8-3 DIVIDING RATIONAL EXPRESSIONS   317

Additional Answers

2. Zero can be represented as $\frac{0}{1}$. The reciprocal of $\frac{0}{1}$ is $\frac{1}{0}$, which is not defined.

26. $\frac{m+4}{4m^2+16m+16}$

28. $\frac{x+4}{x+3}$

TEACHING THE LESSON

Chalkboard Examples

For Example 1

Find $\frac{5}{a} \div \frac{3}{a}$. $\frac{5}{3}$

For Example 2

Find $\frac{3a}{a+2} \div (a-2)$. $\frac{3a}{a^2-4}$

For Example 3

Find $\frac{y+5}{y^2-4y-5} \div \frac{y^2+4y-5}{y+1}$. $\frac{1}{y^2-6y+5}$

EVALUATING THE LESSON

Checking for Understanding

Exercises 1-12 are designed to help you assess understanding through reading, writing, and speaking. You should work through Exercises 1-2 with your students, and then monitor their work on Exercises 3-12.

Assignment Guide

Basic: 13-29, 34-36, 39-43
Average: 16-31, 34-43
Enriched: 18-43

Practice Masters Booklet, p. 60

8-3   **Practice Worksheet**

NAME _____ DATE _____

Dividing Rational Expressions

Find each quotient. Assume that no denominator is equal to zero.

1. $\frac{c^5}{d^3} \div \frac{d^4}{c^3} \cdot \frac{c^6}{d^6}$

2. $\frac{x^2}{y^2} \div \frac{x^3}{y} \cdot \frac{1}{y}$

3. $\frac{(-e)^3}{f^2} \div \frac{e^3}{f^2} \cdot -e$

4. $\frac{2x}{x-1} \div (x+1) \cdot \frac{2x}{x^2-1}$

5. $\frac{z^2-16}{3z} \div (z-4) \cdot \frac{z+4}{3z}$

6. $\frac{a^2-a-12}{a^2} \div (a+3) \cdot \frac{a-4}{a^2}$

7. $\frac{5m}{m+1} \div \frac{25m^2}{m^2+2m+1} \cdot \frac{m+1}{5m}$

8. $\frac{f^2-49}{f^2-36} \div \frac{f+7}{f-6} \cdot \frac{f-7}{f+6}$

9. $\frac{15b^2}{b^2-c^2} \div \frac{5b}{b^2-25} \cdot \frac{3b^3-75b}{b^2-c^2}$

10. $(6x-24) \div \frac{x^2-16}{6x} \cdot \frac{36x}{x+4}$

11. $\frac{z^2-1}{6z-10} \div \frac{2z-2}{9z^2-25} \cdot \frac{3z^2+8z+5}{4}$

12. $\frac{x^2-x-6}{x^2+2x-15} \div \frac{x^2-4x-5}{x^2-25} \cdot \frac{x+2}{x+1}$

13. $\frac{m^2+2m+1}{10m-10} \div \frac{m+1}{20} \cdot \frac{2m+2}{m-1}$

14. $\frac{a^2+10a+25}{a^2-9} \div \frac{a+5}{a^2-3a} \cdot \frac{a^2+5a}{a+3}$

15. $\frac{2y-6}{4y+28} \div \frac{y-3}{2y+14} \cdot 1$

16. $\frac{x^2-1}{x^2-3x-10} \div \frac{x^2+3x+2}{x^2+4x+4} \cdot \frac{x-1}{x-5}$

17. $\frac{6a}{a-4} \div \frac{a^2-7a}{a^2-11a+28} \cdot 6$

Closing the Lesson

Writing Activity At the end of the lesson, have students write down the key points to consider in dividing rational expressions.

APPLYING THE LESSON

Homework Exercises

See assignment guide on page 317.

Chapter 8, Quiz A, (Lessons 8-1 through 8-3), is available in the Evaluation Masters Booklet, p. 107.

36. **Work** JoAnn Young made $40,000 last year. In recognition of her good performance, JoAnn's boss offered her a 15% raise, to be taken in one of two ways: either she can take the 15% raise this year and receive no raise next year, or she can take a 7.5% raise this year and another 7.5% raise next year. Which option should JoAnn choose? **15%**

37. **Oceanography** The part of an iceberg that is below water is about seven times the size of the part that is above water. What percent of the iceberg is above water? **12.5%**

38. **Travel** A one-mile-long train is traveling at 60 miles per hour. If the train enters a one-mile-long tunnel, how long does it take the train to go completely through? **2 minutes**

Mixed Review

39. **Finance** Luis invested $5000 for one year at 9% interest. Marta invested some money at the same time at 8% interest. At the end of the year, Luis and Marta together had earned $810 in interest. How much money did Marta invest? **(Lesson 4-3)** $4500

40. Solve $x + 3 < -17$. **(Lesson 5-1)** $x < -20$

41. Find $(3m^2 + 2n)^2$. **(Lesson 6-9)** $9m^4 + 12m^2n + 4n^2$

42. Factor $\frac{1}{2}x^2 - \frac{1}{4}ax$. **(Lesson 7-2)** $\frac{1}{4}x(2x - a)$

43. Find $\frac{m^2 - 4}{2} \cdot \frac{4}{m - 2}$. **(Lesson 8-2)** $2m + 4$

~ EXTRA ~

Does 2 = 1?

Find the fallacy in the following "proof" of "2 = 1."

$$a = b$$
$$a \cdot a = b \cdot a \qquad \textit{Multiply each side by } a.$$
$$a^2 = ab$$
$$a^2 - b^2 = ab - b^2 \qquad \textit{Subtract } b^2 \textit{ from each side.}$$
$$(a - b)(a + b) = b(a - b) \qquad \textit{Factor.}$$
$$\frac{(a - b)(a + b)}{(a - b)} = \frac{b(a - b)}{(a - b)} \qquad \textit{Divide each side by } (a - b). \; (a - b) = 0$$
$$a + b = b$$
$$b + b = b \qquad \textit{Substitute } b \textit{ for } a.$$
$$2b = b$$
$$\frac{2b}{b} = \frac{b}{b} \qquad \textit{Divide each side by } b.$$
$$2 = 1$$

318 CHAPTER 8 RATIONAL EXPRESSIONS

NAME _____ DATE _____

8-3 Enrichment Worksheet

Reading Algebra

The French mathematician Fermat (1601–1665) studied the properties of prime numbers. In fact, prime numbers of a certain form are called *Fermat numbers* in his honor. To understand what Fermat numbers are, read the paragraph below. The questions that follow will help you understand the reading.

Numbers of the form $2^m + 1$ cannot be prime when m has an odd factor. That is, the following equation is true for certain whole-number values of k and d.

$2^{(2k+1)d} + 1 = (2^d + 1)[(2^d)^{2k} - (2^d)^{2k-1} + (2^d)^{2k-2} - \ldots - 2^d + 1]$

Fermat conjectured that if m has no odd factor, that is, if m is itself a power of 2, then $2^m + 1$ is a prime number. Numbers of this form, $F_n = 2^{2^n} + 1$, are called **Fermat numbers.** (Fermat's belief that F_n was a formula that produces *only* prime numbers was later shown to be incorrect.)

Answer each question.

1. The phrase "when m has an odd factor" is translated into algebraic symbols. The expression 2^m in the first line of the paragraph is rewritten as $2^{(2k+1)d}$ in the equation. Show that $m = (2k + 1)d$ means that m has an odd factor.
For $k = 1, 2, 3, 4, \ldots, (2k + 1) = 3, 5, 7, 9, \ldots$. So, $2k + 1$ is an odd number. One factor of m is $2k + 1$. The other factor is d.

2. In the equation, the expression $2^{(2k+1)d} + 1$ has been factored into two parts. Write the first factor.
$2^d + 1$

3. Give five examples to show that these phrases mean the same thing.
"m has no odd factor"   "m is itself a power of 2"
Possible examples are 2, 4, 8, 16, and 32.

4. Show that $2^m + 1$ is not a prime number for $m = 3, 5,$ and 7.
$9 = 3 \times 3; 33 = 3 \times 11; 129 = 3 \times 43$

5. Find F_n for $n = 0, 1, 2, 3,$ and 4. Recall that any number to a power of zero equals 1. So, $2^n = 1$ for $n = 0$.
3; 5; 17; 257; 65,537

6. Write the equation in the paragraph using $k = 3$ and $d = 1$. Then verify that it is true.
$2^7 + 1 = (2 + 1)[2^6 - 2^5 + 2^4 - 2^3 + 2^2 - 2^1 + 1]$
$129 = (3)[43]$

EXTENDING THE LESSON

Math Power:
Problem Solving

Perform the indicated operation and simplify.
$$\frac{2y}{y^2 - 4} \div \frac{3}{y^2 - 4y + 4} \cdot \frac{y^2 + 4y + 4}{y^2 - y - 2}.$$
$$\frac{2y^2 + 4y}{3y + 3}$$

Extra

Ask students who have difficulty finding the fallacy what $a - b$ is equal to. If they continue to experience difficulty, ask them what happens when each side of an equation is divided by zero.

Dividing Polynomials

Objective
8-4

After studying this lesson, you should be able to:
- divide polynomials by binomials.

To divide a polynomial by a polynomial, you can use a long division process similar to that used in arithmetic. For example, you can divide $x^2 + 8x + 15$ by $x + 5$ as shown below.

Step 1

To find the first term of the quotient, divide the first term of the dividend (x^2) by the first term of the divisor (x).

$$\begin{array}{r} x \\ x + 5 \overline{)\, x^2 + 8x + 15} \\ \underline{x^2 + 5x } \\ 3x \end{array}$$

Teaching Tip ①

When dividing x^2 by x, the result is x.
Multiply $x(x + 5)$.
Subtract.

Step 2

To find the next term of the quotient, divide the first term of the partial dividend ($3x$) by the first term of the divisor (x).

$$\begin{array}{r} x + 3 \\ x + 5 \overline{)\, x^2 + 8x + 15} \\ \underline{x^2 + 5x } \\ 3x + 15 \\ \underline{3x + 15} \\ 0 \end{array}$$

Teaching Tip ②

When dividing $3x$ by x, the result is 3.

Multiply $3(x + 5)$.
Subtract.

Therefore, $x^2 + 8x + 15$ divided by $x + 5$ is $x + 3$. Since the remainder is 0, the divisor is a factor of the dividend. This means that $(x + 5)(x + 3) = x^2 + 8x + 15$.

If the divisor is *not* a factor of the dividend, there will be a nonzero remainder. The quotient can be expressed as follows.

$$\text{quotient} = \text{partial quotient} + \frac{\text{remainder}}{\text{divisor}}$$

Example 1

Find $(2x^2 - 11x - 20) \div (2x + 3)$.

$$\begin{array}{r} x - 7 \\ 2x + 3 \overline{)\, 2x^2 - 11x - 20} \\ \underline{2x^2 + 3x } \\ -14x - 20 \\ \underline{-14x - 21} \\ 1 \end{array}$$

← *Multiply $x(2x + 3)$.*
← *Subtract, then bring down -20.*
← *Multiply $-7(2x + 3)$.*
← *Subtract. The remainder is 1.*

The quotient is $x - 7$ with remainder 1.

Thus, $(2x^2 - 11x - 20) \div (2x + 3) = x - 7 + \dfrac{1}{2x + 3}$.   ← *remainder*
   ← *divisor*

In an expression like $s^3 + 9$, there is no s^2 term and no s term. In such situations, rename the expression using 0 as the coefficient of these terms.

$$s^3 + 9 = s^3 + 0s^2 + 0s + 9$$

RETEACHING THE LESSON

Assign a division problem from the text to each student. After completing the division problem, have each student write the divisor and quotient with any remainder and exchange it with a neighbor. The neighbor computes the divisor times the quotient plus the remainder. Check this against the dividend.

Lesson Resources

- Reteaching Master 8-4
- Practice Master 8-4
- Enrichment Master 8-4
- Technology Master, p. 8
- Video Algebra, 27, 29

 Transparency 8-4 contains the 5-Minute Check and a teaching aid for this lesson.

INTRODUCING THE LESSON

🕐 **5-Minute Check**
(over Lesson 8-3)

Divide and simplify.

1. $\dfrac{5}{8} \div \dfrac{3}{4}$ $\dfrac{5}{6}$

2. $\dfrac{36}{64} \div \dfrac{27}{32}$ $\dfrac{2}{3}$

3. $\dfrac{5a}{6b} \div \dfrac{10d}{6c}$ $\dfrac{ac}{2bd}$

4. $\dfrac{a^2}{b} \div \dfrac{a^2}{b^2}$ b

Motivating the Lesson

Give each pair of students a worksheet containing 10 long division problems to solve. Ask the first student to solve problem 1 and the other student to solve problem 2. Students should verify each other's answers and follow the same procedure to solve the remaining problems.

Reteaching Masters Booklet, p. 55

Teaching Tip ❶ While presenting the technique of long division of polynomials, it may be helpful to present a parallel example of whole numbers to show the similarity of steps.

Teaching Tip ❷ You may want students to keep like terms in vertical columns as shown below.

$$\begin{array}{r} x + 3 \\ x + 5 \overline{)\, x^2 + 8x + 15} \\ \underline{x^2 + 5x} \\ 3x + 15 \\ \underline{3x + 15} \\ 0 \end{array}$$

Chalkboard Examples

For Example 1
Find $(x^2 + 12x + 36) \div (x + 6)$.
$x + 6$

For Example 2
Find $\dfrac{m^3 + 2m - 7}{m + 3}$.
$m^2 - 3m + 11 - \dfrac{40}{m + 3}$

Assignment Guide

Basic: 11-28, 32-35, 38-42
Average: 14-29, 32-42
Enriched: 17-42

Practice Masters Booklet, p. 61

Example 2 | Find $\dfrac{s^3 + 9}{s - 3}$.

$$\begin{array}{r} s^2 + 3s + 9 \\ s - 3 \overline{)\, s^3 + 0s^2 + 0s + 9} \\ \underline{s^3 - 3s^2} \\ 3s^2 + 0s \\ \underline{3s^2 - 9s} \\ 9s + 9 \\ \underline{9s - 27} \\ 36 \end{array}$$

Insert $0s^2$ and $0s$. Why?

Therefore, $\dfrac{s^3 + 9}{s - 3} = s^2 + 3s + 9 + \dfrac{36}{s - 3}$.

CHECKING FOR UNDERSTANDING

Communicating Mathematics

Read and study the lesson to answer each question. See margin.

1. What relationship is there between the degree of the divisor, the degree of the dividend, and the degree of the quotient?

2. What is a factor? Is 3 a factor of 7? Is $2x$ a factor of $4x^3$?

Guided Practice

State the first term of each quotient.

3. $\dfrac{a^2 + 3a + 2}{a + 1}$ a

4. $\dfrac{b^2 + 8b - 20}{b - 2}$ b

5. $\dfrac{8m^3 + 27}{2m + 3}$ $4m^2$

6. $\dfrac{2x^2 + 3x - 2}{2x - 1}$ x

7. $\dfrac{x^3 + 2x^2 - 5x + 12}{x + 4}$ x^2

8. $\dfrac{2x^3 - 5x^2 + 22x + 51}{2x + 3}$ x^2

Find each quotient.

9. $(x^2 + 7x + 12) \div (x + 3)$ $x + 4$

10. $(x^2 + 9x + 20) \div (x + 5)$ $x + 4$

EXERCISES

Practice

Find each quotient. 17-31. See margin.

11. $(a^2 - 2a - 35) \div (a - 7)$ $a + 5$

12. $(x^2 + 6x - 16) \div (x - 2)$ $x + 8$

13. $(c^2 + 12c + 36) \div (c + 9)$ $c + 3$ R9

14. $(y^2 - 2y - 30) \div (y + 7)$ $y - 9$ R33

15. $(2r^2 - 3r - 35) \div (2r + 7)$ $r - 5$

16. $(3t^2 - 14t - 24) \div (3t + 4)$ $t - 6$

17. $\dfrac{10x^2 + 29x + 21}{5x + 7}$

18. $\dfrac{12n^2 + 36n + 15}{6n + 3}$

19. $\dfrac{x^3 - 7x + 6}{x - 2}$

20. $\dfrac{4m^3 + 5m - 21}{2m - 3}$

21. $\dfrac{4t^3 + 17t^2 - 1}{4t + 1}$

22. $\dfrac{2a^3 + 9a^2 + 5a - 12}{a + 3}$

23. $\dfrac{27c^2 - 24c + 8}{9c - 2}$

24. $\dfrac{48b^2 + 8b + 7}{12b - 1}$

25. $\dfrac{6n^3 + 5n^2 + 12}{2n + 3}$

26. $\dfrac{t^3 - 19t + 9}{t - 4}$

27. $\dfrac{3s^3 + 8s^2 + s - 7}{s + 2}$

28. $\dfrac{9d^3 + 5d - 8}{3d - 2}$

29. $\dfrac{20t^3 - 27t^2 + t + 6}{4t - 3}$

30. $\dfrac{6x^3 - 9x^2 - 4x + 6}{2x - 3}$

31. $\dfrac{56x^3 + 32x^2 - 63x - 36}{7x + 4}$

Critical Thinking

32. Find the value of k if $(x + 2)$ is a factor of $x^3 + 7x^2 + 7x + k$. -6

33. Find the value of k if $(2m - 5)$ is a factor of $2m^3 - 5m^2 + 8m + k$. -20

34. Find the value of k if the remainder is 15 when $x^3 - 7x^2 + 4x + k$ is divided by $(x - 2)$. 27

320 CHAPTER 8 RATIONAL EXPRESSIONS

Additional Answers

1. degree of dividend − degree of divisor = degree of quotient
2. A factor is a number that is being multiplied; no, yes.
17. $2x + 3$
18. $2n + 5$
19. $x^2 + 2x - 3$
20. $2m^2 + 3m + 7$
21. $t^2 + 4t - 1$

22. $2a^2 + 3a - 4$
23. $3c - 2 + \dfrac{4}{9c - 2}$
24. $4b + 1 + \dfrac{8}{12b - 1}$
25. $3n^2 - 2n + 3 + \dfrac{3}{2n + 3}$
26. $t^2 + 4t - 3 - \dfrac{3}{t - 4}$
27. $3s^2 + 2s - 3 - \dfrac{1}{s + 2}$
28. $3d^2 + 2d + 3 - \dfrac{2}{3d - 2}$
29. $5t^2 - 3t - 2$
30. $3x^2 - 2$
31. $8x^2 - 9$

Applications

35. Sports A football field, not including endzones, is 160 feet wide by 100 yards long. A polo field is 160 yards wide and 300 yards long. How many football fields would it take to fill one polo field?

9 football fields

36. Statistics A recent survey found that American teenagers between the ages of 12 and 17 watch television an average of 22 hours per week.

    a. How much television does the average American teenager watch in one year? **1144 hours or 47 days 16 hours**

    b. If about 20% of all television time is for commercials, how much time does the average American teenager spend watching commercials each year?
    228 hours 48 minutes or 9 days 12 hours 48 minutes

Computer

37. The BASIC program at the right finds the quotient and the remainder when a polynomial is divided by a binomial of the form $(x - r)$. First, enter the degree of the polynomial. Next, enter the coefficients of the polynomial. Finally, enter the value of R in the divisor $(x - r)$. For example, in Exercise **c** below, enter 3 for the degree, 1, 2, −4, and −8 for the coefficients, and 2 for the value of r.

```
10 INPUT "DEGREE OF POLYNOMIAL:
   ";N
20 PRINT "ENTER COEFFICIENTS:"
30 FOR X = 1 TO N+1
40 INPUT A(X)
50 NEXT X
60 INPUT "CONSTANT R: ";R
70 LET B(1) = A(1)
80 PRINT "COEFFICIENTS OF
   QUOTIENT ARE:"
90 PRINT B(1);" ";
100 FOR X = 1 TO N-1
110 B(X+1)=A(X+1)+R*B(X)
120 PRINT B(X+1);" ";
130 NEXT X
140 PRINT
150 PRINT "REMAINDER: ";
    A(N+1)+R*B(N)
160 END
```

Use the program to find each quotient.

    a. $(3x^2 + 5x + 2) \div (x - 2)$ $3x + 11 + \dfrac{24}{(x-2)}$

    b. $(3x^2 + 7x + 2) \div (x + 2)$ $3x - 1 + \dfrac{4}{x+2}$

    c. $(x^3 + 2x^2 - 4x - 8) \div (x - 2)$ $x^2 + 4x + 4$

    d. $(x^3 + 2x^2 + 4x + 8) \div (x + 2)$ $x^2 + 4$

    e. $(2x^4 + x^3 - 2x^2 + 3x + 1) \div (x - 1)$ $2x^3 + 3x^2 + x + 4 + \dfrac{5}{(x-1)}$

Mixed Review

38. Physics Weights of 50 pounds and 75 pounds are placed on a lever. The two weights are 16 feet apart, and the lever is balanced. How far from the fulcrum is the 50-pound weight? **(Lesson 4-8)** $9\frac{3}{5}$ ft

39. Make a diagram to solve the problem. **(Lesson 5-4)**

An ant is climbing a 30-foot flagpole. Each day it climbs up 7 feet. Each night it slides back 4 feet. How many days will it take him to reach the top of the flagpole? **9 days**

40. Simplify $\dfrac{9xyz^5}{x^4}$. **(Lesson 6-3)** $\dfrac{9yz^5}{x^3}$

41. Factor $p^2 + 10p + 25$. **(Lesson 7-5)** $(p + 5)(p + 5)$

42. Find $\dfrac{y^2}{x^2} \div \dfrac{a^2}{x^2}$. **(Lesson 8-3)** $\dfrac{y^2}{a^2}$

LESSON 8-4 DIVIDING POLYNOMIALS   321

EXTENDING THE LESSON

Math Power: Problem Solving

Find the quotient.

$$\frac{2x^4 + 3x^3 - 6x^2 + 7x - 6}{x^2 + 2x - 3}$$

$2x^2 - x + 2$

EVALUATING THE LESSON

Checking for Understanding

Exercises 1-10 are designed to help you assess understanding through reading, writing, and speaking. You should work through Exercises 1-2 with your students, and then monitor their work on Exercises 3-10.

Error Analysis

Students sometimes make errors when subtracting binomials by subtracting only the first term. Find the error below.

$$\begin{array}{r} 4x + 1 \text{ R} -36 \\ 2x - 3 \overline{)8x^2 + 14x - 39} \\ \underline{-8x^2 - 12x} \\ 2x - 39 \end{array}$$

The result should be $26x - 39$ since $14x - (-12x) = 26x$.

Closing the Lesson

Speaking Activity Have students identify similarities in the procedures of long division and that of dividing polynomials.

APPLYING THE LESSON

Homework Exercises

See assignment guide on page 320.

Enrichment Masters Booklet, p. 55

NAME _____ DATE _____

8-4   **Enrichment Worksheet**

Synthetic Division

You can divide a polynomial such as $3x^3 - 4x^2 - 3x - 2$ by a binomial such as $x - 3$ by a process called **synthetic division**. Compare the process with long division in the following explanation.

Example: Divide using synthetic division: $(3x^3 - 4x^2 - 3x - 2) \div (x - 3)$

1. Show the coefficients of the terms in descending order.	3 −4 −3 −2
2. The divisor is $x - 3$. Since 3 is to be subtracted, write 3 in the corner ⌐.	
3. Bring down the first coefficient, 3.	
4. Multiply. $3 \cdot 3 = 9$	
5. Add. $-4 + 9 = 5$	
6. Multiply. $3 \cdot 5 = 15$	
7. Add. $-3 + 15 = 12$	
8. Multiply. $3 \cdot 12 = 36$	
9. Add. $-2 + 36 = 34$	

$$\begin{array}{r} 3 \quad -4 \quad -3 \quad -2 \\ 9 \quad 15 \quad 36 \\ \hline 3 \overline{\smash{)}3 \quad 5 \quad 12 \quad 34} \end{array}$$

$3x^2 + 5x + 12$, remainder 34

Check: Use long division.

$$\begin{array}{r} 3x^2 + 5x + 12 \\ x - 3 \overline{)3x^3 - 4x^2 - 3x - 2} \\ \underline{3x^3 - 9x^2} \\ 5x^2 - 3x \\ \underline{5x^2 - 15x} \\ 12x - 2 \\ \underline{12x - 36} \\ 34 \end{array}$$

The result is $3x^2 + 5x + 12 + \dfrac{34}{x - 3}$.

Divide using synthetic division. Check your result using long division.

1. $(x^3 + 6x^2 + 3x + 1) \div (x - 2)$
   $x^2 + 8x + 19 + \dfrac{39}{x - 2}$

2. $(x^3 - 3x^2 - 6x - 20) \div (x - 5)$
   $x^2 + 2x + 4$

3. $(2x^3 - 5x + 1) \div (x + 1)$
   $2x^2 - 2x - 3 + \dfrac{4}{x + 1}$

4. $(3x^3 - 7x^2 + 4) \div (x - 2)$
   $3x^2 - x - 2$

5. $(x^3 + 2x^2 - x + 4) \div (x + 3)$
   $x^2 - x + 2 - \dfrac{2}{x + 3}$

6. $(x^3 + 4x^2 - 3x - 11) \div (x - 4)$
   $x^2 + 8x + 29 + \dfrac{105}{x - 4}$

Chapter 8   321

INTRODUCING THE LESSON

 5-Minute Check

(over Lesson 8-4)

Divide.

1. $\dfrac{d^2 + 3d + 2}{d + 1}$ $d + 2$

2. $\dfrac{s^2 - 5s + 4}{s - 1}$ $s - 4$

3. $\dfrac{x^2 + 12x + 11}{x + 11}$ $x + 1$

4. $\dfrac{x^2 + 9x + 20}{x + 5}$ $x + 4$

5. $\dfrac{a^2 - 2a - 35}{a - 7}$ $a + 5$

TEACHING THE LESSON

Teaching Tip ① For the expression $-(a - 3)$, students may make the mistake of changing the sign of the first term only. Emphasize that $-(a - 3)$ means $-1 \times (a - 3)$ and -1 is distributed over the parentheses.

Chalkboard Examples

For Example 1
Find the sum.

a. $\dfrac{4}{y + 6} + \dfrac{y}{y + 6}$ $\dfrac{4 + y}{y + 6}$

b. $\dfrac{r}{r + s} + \dfrac{s}{r + s}$ 1

For Example 2
Find the difference.

a. $\dfrac{4}{b + 5} - \dfrac{b}{b + 5}$ $\dfrac{4 - b}{b + 5}$

b. $\dfrac{8}{m + 7} - \dfrac{m - 1}{m + 7}$ $\dfrac{9 - m}{m + 7}$

8-5 Rational Expressions with Like Denominators

Objective
8-5

After studying this lesson, you should be able to:
• add and subtract rational expressions with like denominators.

To add or subtract fractions with like denominators, you add or subtract the numerators. Then you can write the sum or difference over the common denominator.

$$\frac{3}{7} + \frac{2}{7} = \frac{5}{7} \qquad\qquad \frac{7}{9} - \frac{2}{9} = \frac{5}{9}$$

You can use these same methods to add or subtract rational expressions.

Example 1   Find $\dfrac{3}{x + 2} + \dfrac{1}{x + 2}$.

$$\frac{3}{x + 2} + \frac{1}{x + 2} = \frac{3 + 1}{x + 2}$$ *Since $x + 2$ is the common denominator, add the numerators.*

$$= \frac{4}{x + 2}$$

When subtracting rational expressions, remember to add the additive inverse of the second expression.

Example 2   Find $\dfrac{3a + 2}{a - 7} - \dfrac{a - 3}{a - 7}$.

$$\frac{3a + 2}{a - 7} - \frac{a - 3}{a - 7} = \frac{(3a + 2) + [-(a - 3)]}{a - 7}$$ *Add the additive inverse of $a - 3$.*
Teaching Tip ①

$$= \frac{3a + 2 - a + 3}{a - 7}$$ *Distributive property*

$$= \frac{2a + 5}{a - 7}$$

When adding or subtracting fractions, sometimes the result can be expressed in simplest form.

$$\frac{3}{8} + \frac{1}{8} = \frac{4}{8}$$ *The GCF of 4 and 8 is 4.* $$\frac{9}{16} - \frac{3}{16} = \frac{6}{16}$$ *The GCF of 6 and 16 is 2.*

$$= \frac{1}{2}$$ $$= \frac{3}{8}$$

ALTERNATE TEACHING STRATEGIES

Using Discussion
Find values for a, b, and c so that $\dfrac{a}{c} + \dfrac{b}{c} = 1$. What is the relationship among a, b, and c?   **Answers will vary. A sample answer is**
$\dfrac{2}{3} + \dfrac{1}{3} = \dfrac{3}{3} = 1$. $a + b = c$, $c \neq 0$

This process may also be used when adding or subtracting rational expressions.

Example 3

Find $\dfrac{8n + 3}{3n + 4} - \dfrac{2n - 5}{3n + 4}$.

$$\dfrac{8n + 3}{3n + 4} - \dfrac{2n - 5}{3n + 4} = \dfrac{(8n + 3) - (2n - 5)}{3n + 4} \qquad \textit{Since } 3n + 4 \textit{ is the common denominator, subtract the numerators.}$$

$$= \dfrac{8n + 3 - 2n + 5}{3n + 4}$$

$$= \dfrac{6n + 8}{3n + 4} \qquad \textit{Combine like terms.}$$

$$= \dfrac{2(\overset{1}{\cancel{3n + 4}})}{\underset{1}{\cancel{(3n + 4)}}} \qquad \textit{Factor and simplify.}$$

$$= 2$$

Example 4

Find $\dfrac{x}{x - 2} - \dfrac{x + 1}{2 - x}$.

$$\dfrac{x}{x - 2} - \dfrac{x + 1}{2 - x} = \dfrac{x}{x - 2} - \dfrac{x + 1}{-(x - 2)} \qquad \textit{Rewrite } 2 - x \textit{ as } -(x - 2) \text{ } \textbf{Teaching Tip ②}$$

$$= \dfrac{x}{x - 2} - \left(-\dfrac{x + 1}{x - 2}\right) \qquad \textit{Remember that } \dfrac{1}{-x} = -\dfrac{1}{x} \text{ } \textbf{Teaching Tip ③}$$

$$= \dfrac{x}{x - 2} + \dfrac{x + 1}{x - 2}$$

$$= \dfrac{2x + 1}{x - 2}$$

Example 5

CONNECTION
Geometry

Find the measure of the perimeter of the rectangle.

$$P = 2\ell + 2w$$

$$= 2\left(\dfrac{r}{r^2 - s^2}\right) + 2\left(\dfrac{s}{r^2 - s^2}\right)$$

$$= \dfrac{2r}{r^2 - s^2} + \dfrac{2s}{r^2 - s^2}$$

$$= \dfrac{2r + 2s}{r^2 - s^2}$$

$$= \dfrac{2(\overset{1}{\cancel{r + s}})}{\underset{1}{\cancel{(r + s)}}(r - s)} \qquad (r + s) \textit{ is the GCF.}$$

$$= \dfrac{2}{r - s}$$

The measure of the perimeter is $\dfrac{2}{r - s}$.

The rectangle has a top side labeled $\dfrac{r}{r^2 - s^2}$ and a right side labeled $\dfrac{s}{r^2 - s^2}$.

RETEACHING THE LESSON

When working with rational expressions, answers must be given in simplest form. Try these.

1. $\dfrac{7a}{a^2 - b^2} - \dfrac{5a + 4b}{a^2 - b^2} + \dfrac{2b}{a^2 - b^2}$

$\dfrac{2}{a + b}$

2. $\dfrac{3}{x^2 - 3x - 4} + \dfrac{x - 2}{x^2 - 3x - 4}$ $\dfrac{1}{x - 4}$

Checking for Understanding
Exercises 1-11 are designed to help you assess understanding through reading, writing, and speaking. You should work through Exercises 1-3 with your students, and then monitor their work on Exercises 4-11.

Closing the Lesson
Speaking Activity Have students identify ways in which addition and subtraction of fractions with like denominators is similar to addition and subtraction of rational expressions with like denominators.

Homework Exercises

Assignment Guide
Basic: 12-35, 45-46, 48-52
Average: 17-40, 45-52
Enriched: 21-52
All: Mid-Chapter Review, 1-11

Practice Masters Booklet, p. 62

8-5 **Practice Worksheet**

Adding and Subtracting Rational Expressions with Like Denominators

Find each sum or difference in simplest form.

1. $\frac{2x}{5} + \frac{4x}{5}$ $\frac{6x}{5}$ 2. $\frac{5a}{y} - \frac{a}{y}$ $\frac{4a}{y}$ 3. $\frac{3n}{10} - \frac{7n}{10}$ $-\frac{2n}{5}$

4. $\frac{3}{x} - \frac{9}{x}$ $-\frac{6}{x}$ 5. $\frac{m}{13} + \frac{3m}{13}$ $\frac{4m}{13}$ 6. $\frac{9z}{z} - \frac{8z}{z}$ 1

7. $\frac{t}{3} + \frac{t-5}{3}$ $\frac{2t-5}{3}$ 8. $\frac{b+3}{7} - \frac{b}{7}$ $\frac{3}{7}$

9. $\frac{w+9}{9} + \frac{w+4}{9}$ $\frac{2w+13}{9}$ 10. $\frac{6r-5}{8} + \frac{4r+2}{8}$ $\frac{10r-3}{8}$

11. $\frac{c+8}{4} - \frac{c+6}{4}$ $\frac{1}{2}$ 12. $\frac{3}{x+2} + \frac{2x}{x+2}$ $\frac{2x+3}{x+2}$

13. $\frac{s+14}{5} - \frac{s-14}{5}$ $\frac{28}{5}$ 14. $\frac{n-6}{4} - \frac{n+2}{4}$ -2

15. $\frac{w}{y-2} - \frac{w}{y-2}$ 0 16. $\frac{r}{r-5} - \frac{5}{r-5}$ 1

17. $\frac{u+t}{r-6} - \frac{u+t}{6-r}$ $\frac{2u+2t}{r-6}$ 18. $\frac{u+t}{r-6} + \frac{u+t}{6-r}$ 0

19. $\frac{r^2}{r+s} - \frac{s^2}{r+s}$ $r-s$ 20. $\frac{4n^2}{2n-3} + \frac{9}{3-2n}$ $2n+3$

21. $\frac{81}{9+e} - \frac{e^2}{9+e}$ $9-e$ 22. $\frac{3k}{k+h} + \frac{3h}{k+h}$ 3

23. $\frac{2x+3t}{4x-2t} - \frac{t-2x}{4x-2t}$ $\frac{2x+t}{2x-t}$ 24. $\frac{1}{c-d} + \frac{1}{d-c}$ 0

CHECKING FOR UNDERSTANDING

Communicating Mathematics

Read and study the lesson to answer each question.

1. If the sum of two fractions with the same denominator is zero, what can you say about the two fractions? **They are additive inverses.**
2. Can you find the sum of $\frac{1}{0}$ and $\frac{2}{0}$? Why or why not? **No; division by zero is undefined.**
3. Write two fractions with a denominator of 5 that have a sum of 1. **Answers may vary; a typical answer is $\frac{1}{5} + \frac{4}{5} = \frac{5}{5} = 1$.**

Guided Practice

Find each sum or difference in simplest form.

4. $\frac{5}{8} + \frac{2}{8}$ $\frac{7}{8}$ 5. $\frac{4}{a} + \frac{3}{a}$ $\frac{7}{a}$ 6. $\frac{b}{x} + \frac{2}{x}$ $\frac{b+2}{x}$ 7. $\frac{5}{2z} + \frac{-7}{2z}$ $-\frac{1}{z}$

8. $\frac{3}{11} - \frac{2}{11}$ $\frac{1}{11}$ 9. $\frac{14}{16} - \frac{15}{16}$ $-\frac{1}{16}$ 10. $\frac{a}{5} - \frac{b}{5}$ $\frac{a-b}{5}$ 11. $\frac{8k}{5m} - \frac{3k}{5m}$ $\frac{k}{m}$

12-41. For answers not shown with exercises, see margin.

EXERCISES

Practice

Find each sum or difference in simplest form. 26. $\frac{2a+2b}{x-3}$

A

12. $\frac{y}{2} + \frac{y}{2}$ y 13. $\frac{a}{12} + \frac{2a}{12}$ $\frac{a}{4}$ 14. $\frac{5x}{24} - \frac{3x}{24}$ $\frac{x}{12}$

15. $\frac{7t}{t} - \frac{8t}{t}$ -1 16. $\frac{y}{2} + \frac{y-6}{2}$ $y-3$ 17. $\frac{m+4}{5} + \frac{m-1}{5}$ $\frac{2m+3}{5}$

18. $\frac{a+2}{6} - \frac{a+3}{6}$ $-\frac{1}{6}$ 19. $\frac{x}{x+1} + \frac{1}{x+1}$ 1 20. $\frac{8}{y-2} - \frac{6}{y-2}$ $\frac{2}{y-2}$

B

21. $\frac{y}{b+6} - \frac{2y}{b+6}$ 22. $\frac{2n}{2n-5} + \frac{5}{5-2n}$ 1 23. $\frac{x+y}{y-2} + \frac{x-y}{2-y}$

24. $\frac{y}{a+1} - \frac{y}{a+1}$ 0 25. $\frac{a+b}{x-3} + \frac{a+b}{3-x}$ 0 26. $\frac{a+b}{x-3} - \frac{a+b}{3-x}$

27. $\frac{r^2}{r-s} + \frac{s^2}{r-s}$ 28. $\frac{x^2}{x-y} - \frac{y^2}{x-y}$ 29. $\frac{m^2}{m+n} + \frac{2mn+n^2}{m+n}$

30. $\frac{x^2}{x-y} - \frac{2xy+y^2}{x-y}$ 31. $\frac{12n}{3n+2} + \frac{8}{3n+2}$ 4 32. $\frac{6x}{x+y} + \frac{6y}{x+y}$ 6

33. $\frac{a^2}{a-b} + \frac{-b^2}{a-b}$ 34. $\frac{r^2}{r-3} + \frac{9}{3-r}$ 35. $\frac{x^2}{x^2-1} + \frac{2x+1}{x^2-1}$

C

36. $\frac{2x+1}{(x+1)^2} + \frac{x^2}{(x+1)^2}$ 1 37. $\frac{x-1}{(x+1)^2} - \frac{x-1}{(x+1)^2}$ 0

38. $\frac{25}{k+5} - \frac{k^2}{k+5}$ $5-k$ 39. $\frac{x}{x^2+2x+1} + \frac{1}{x^2+2x+1}$ $\frac{1}{x+1}$

40. $\frac{8y}{4y^2+12y+9} + \frac{12}{4y^2+12y+9}$ 41. $\frac{2}{t^2-t-2} - \frac{t}{t^2-t-2}$ $-\frac{1}{t+1}$

CONNECTION **Geometry**

Find the measure of the perimeter of each rectangle.

42. $\frac{t^2-2t}{t^2+t-6}$ $\frac{3t-6}{t^2+t-6}$ $P = 2$

43.  $\frac{x^2-5}{2-x}$ $\frac{-1}{x-2}$ $P = -2x-4$

44. 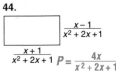 $\frac{x-1}{x^2+2x+1}$ $\frac{x+1}{x^2+2x+1}$ $P = \frac{4x}{x^2+2x+1}$

Critical Thinking

45. Is $\frac{-4}{9} = -\frac{4}{9}$? Is $\frac{4}{-9} = -\frac{4}{9}$? Is $\frac{-4}{-9} = -\frac{4}{9}$? **yes, yes, no**

324   CHAPTER 8   RATIONAL EXPRESSIONS

Additional Answers

21. $\frac{-y}{b+6}$

23. $\frac{2y}{y-2}$

27. $\frac{r^2+s^2}{r-s}$

28. $x+y$

29. $m+n$

30. $\frac{x^2-2xy-y^2}{x-y}$

33. $a+b$

34. $r+3$

35. $\frac{x+1}{x-1}$

40. $\frac{4}{2y+3}$

46. Entertainment The rock group MAXXX receives $12,500 for each concert performance. If there are five members who receive equal shares of the money and $\frac{1}{3}$ of the money goes to pay for other salaries and expenses, how much money does each member of MAXXX actually receive for a tour of 20 concert dates? **$33,333.33**

47. History In 1624, Peter Minuit paid 60 guilders, or about $24, to the Indians for Manhattan Island. What would be the value of that $24 in 1992 if it had been invested at 5% annual interest compounded annually since then? Use $T = p(1 + r)^t$. **$1,506,167,664**

Chapter 8, Quiz B, (Lessons 8-4 through 8-5), is available in the Evaluation Masters Booklet, p. 107.

Additional Answers to Mid-Chapter Review

5. $\dfrac{m^2 + 16}{m^2 + 8m + 16}$

6. $\dfrac{x}{x^2 + 8x + 16}$

9. $\dfrac{2m + 2n}{3m^2 - 3mn}$

11. $t^2 - 4t - 9 + \dfrac{16}{3t + 1}$

Mixed Review

48. Travel At 8:00 A.M., Alma drove west at 35 miles per hour. At 9:00 A.M., Reiko drove east from the same point at 42 miles per hour. When will they be 266 miles apart? **(Lesson 4-7)** 12:00 noon

49. Write $r > -\frac{1}{2}$ and $r < \frac{8}{3}$ without using *and*. **(Lesson 5-5)** $-\frac{1}{2} < r < \frac{8}{3}$

50. Multiply $8(7m + 2)$. **(Lesson 6-7)** $56m + 16$

51. Find the prime factorization of 1000. **(Lesson 7-1)** $2^3 \cdot 5^3$

52. Find $(m^3 - 6m^2 - m + 32) \div (m - 4)$. **(Lesson 8-4)** $m^2 - 2m - 9 + \frac{-4}{m - 4}$

MID-CHAPTER REVIEW

Simplify. State the excluded values of the variables. **(Lesson 8-1)**

1. $\dfrac{(a - 7)}{(a + 1)(a - 7)}$ $\frac{1}{a + 1}$

2. $\dfrac{y - 3}{y^2 - 9}$ $\frac{1}{y + 3}$

3. $\dfrac{4y^2 + 7y - 2}{8y^2 + 15y - 2}$ $\frac{4y - 1}{8y - 1}$

Find each product. Assume that no denominator is equal to zero. **(Lesson 8-2)**

4. $\dfrac{y^2 - 4}{y^2 - 1} \cdot \dfrac{y + 1}{y + 2}$ $\frac{y - 2}{y - 1}$

5. $\dfrac{m^2 + 16}{m^2 - 16} \cdot \dfrac{m - 4}{m + 4}$

6. $\dfrac{x + 3}{x + 4} \cdot \dfrac{x}{x^2 + 7x + 12}$

5, 6, 9, 11. See margin.

Find each quotient. Assume that no denominator is equal to zero. **(Lessons 8-3, 8-4)**

7. $\dfrac{a^2}{b} \div \dfrac{a^2}{b^2}$ b

8. $\dfrac{q}{y^2 - 4} \div \dfrac{q^2}{y + 2}$ $\frac{1}{q(y - 2)}$

9. $\dfrac{m^2 + 2mn + n^2}{3m} \div \dfrac{m^2 - n^2}{2}$

10. $(2m^2 + 5m - 3) \div (m + 3)$ $2m - 1$

11. $(3t^3 - 11t^2 - 31t + 7) \div (3t + 1)$

EXTENDING THE LESSON

Math Power: Connections

Find the perimeter of a rectangle with a width of $\frac{y}{2}$ and a length of $\frac{y - 6}{2}$. $2(y - 3)$

Mid-Chapter Review

The Mid-Chapter Review provides students with a brief review of the concepts and skills in Lessons 8-1 through 8-5. Lesson numbers are given at the end of problems or instruction lines so students may review concepts not yet mastered.

Enrichment Masters Booklet, p. 56

NAME _____ DATE _____

8-5 Enrichment Worksheet

Sum and Difference of Any Two Like Powers

The sum of any two like powers can be written $a^n + b^n$, where n is a positive integer. The difference of like powers is $a^n - b^n$. Under what conditions are these expressions exactly divisible by $(a + b)$ or $(a - b)$? The answer depends on whether n is an odd or even number.

Use long division to find the following quotients. (HINT: Write $a^3 + b^3$ as $a^3 + 0a^2 + 0a + b^3$.) **Is the numerator exactly divisible by the denominator? Write yes or no.**

1. $\frac{a^3 + b^3}{a + b}$ yes

2. $\frac{a^3 + b^3}{a - b}$ no

3. $\frac{a^3 - b^3}{a + b}$ no

4. $\frac{a^3 - b^3}{a - b}$ yes

5. $\frac{a^4 + b^4}{a + b}$ no

6. $\frac{a^4 + b^4}{a - b}$ no

7. $\frac{a^4 - b^4}{a + b}$ yes

8. $\frac{a^4 - b^4}{a - b}$ yes

9. $\frac{a^5 + b^5}{a + b}$ yes

10. $\frac{a^5 + b^5}{a - b}$ no

11. $\frac{a^5 - b^5}{a + b}$ no

12. $\frac{a^5 - b^5}{a - b}$ yes

13. Use the words odd and even to complete these two statements.
   a. $a^n + b^n$ is divisible by $a + b$ if n is odd, and by neither $a + b$ nor $a - b$ if n is even.
   b. $a^n - b^n$ is divisible by $a - b$ if n is odd, and by both $a + b$ and $a - b$ if n is even.

14. Describe the signs of the terms of the quotients when the divisor is $a - b$.
   The terms are all positive.

15. Describe the signs of the terms of the quotient when the divisor is $a + b$.
   The terms are alternately positive and negative.

Lesson Resources

- Practice Master 8-6
- Activity Master, p. 53

 Transparency 8-6 contains the 5-Minute Check and a teaching aid for this lesson.

INTRODUCING THE LESSON

5-Minute Check
(over Lesson 8-5)

Find the sum or difference.

1. $\dfrac{3a}{16} - \dfrac{2a}{16}$ $\dfrac{a}{16}$

2. $\dfrac{8}{x} + \dfrac{7}{x}$ $\dfrac{15}{x}$

3. $\dfrac{y}{x+4} - \dfrac{3y}{x+4}$ $\dfrac{-2y}{x+4}$

4. $\dfrac{11}{r} - \dfrac{5}{r}$ $\dfrac{6}{r}$

5. $\dfrac{x^2}{x-y} - \dfrac{y^2}{x-y}$ $x+y$

Motivating the Lesson

Have students work in small groups to solve the following problem. The first round in the NBA playoffs is won when a team wins three of five games. List all the possible outcomes for a playoff between the Mavericks and the Lakers.

TEACHING THE LESSON

Teaching Tip ❶ Develop the idea that Example 1 actually calls for common multiples of 3 and 4 that are less than 30. Have students identify the LCM of these numbers. LCM is 12.

Teaching Tip ❷ Develop the idea that the number of "branches" in a tree diagram is determined by the number of variables being considered. In Example 3, there are 3 general variables: type of topping, inclusion of whipped cream, and inclusion of nuts. Therefore, there are 3 branches in this tree. The number of ways a sundae can be served is the total number of lines in the last branch of the tree.

8-6 Problem-Solving Strategy: List Possibilities

Objective 8-6

After studying this lesson, you should be able to:
- solve problems by making an organized list of the possibilities.

You can solve problems by listing the possibilities in an organized way. Use a systematic approach so you do not omit any important items.

Example 1

Which whole numbers less than 30 are divisible by both 3 and 4?

List the numbers that are divisible by 3. **Teaching Tip ❶**
    0, 3, 6, 9, 12, 15, 18, 21, 24, 27

List the numbers that are divisible by 4.
    0, 4, 8, 12, 16, 20, 24, 28

Since 0, 12, and 24 are in both lists, they are divisible by both 3 and 4.

Example 2

Wacky Wheels carries bicycles, tricycles, and wagons. They have an equal number of tricycles and wagons in stock. If there are 60 pedals and 180 wheels, how many bicycles, tricycles, and wagons are there in stock?

Make a table to show the possibilities. *Recall that wagons do not have pedals and bicycles and tricycles each have 2 pedals.*

Bicycles (2 wheels)	10	20	18	10	8	6
Tricycles (3 wheels)	10	20	20	22	24	24
Wagons (4 wheels)	10	20	21	22	24	24
Total Wheels	90	180	180	174	184	180
Total Pedals	40	80	76	64	64	60
Solution?	no	no	no	no	no	yes

So there are 6 bicycles, 24 tricycles, and 24 wagons in stock.

A **tree diagram** is a special kind of organized list. Some people prefer to use tree diagrams because they show all of the possibilities.

Example 3

Ye Olde Ice Cream Shoppe makes chocolate, butterscotch, or strawberry sundaes. Any sundae can be served with whipped cream, nuts, neither or both. In how many ways can a sundae be served?

The tree diagram on the next page illustrates the various combinations.

ALTERNATE TEACHING STRATEGIES

Using Problem Solving

The school cafeteria offered three different lunches on Tuesday: pizza, chef salad, or a tuna sandwich. All three of the lunch selections came with a choice of juice or milk. Students had a choice of an apple, granola bar, or banana for desert. How many different lunch combinations were offered that day? **18**

Using Manipulatives

Place four common classroom objects such as a pencil, chalk, a paper clip, and an eraser in a bag. Ask students to predict in how many different orders the objects could be removed from the bag. Then have students remove the objects from the bag a number of times, noting the order. Have students use these results to check the accuracy of their predictions.

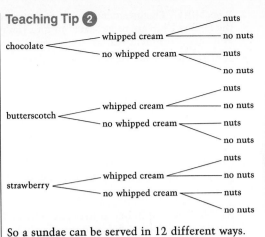

Teaching Tip ❷

chocolate
- whipped cream
  - nuts
  - no nuts
- no whipped cream
  - nuts
  - no nuts

butterscotch
- whipped cream
  - nuts
  - no nuts
- no whipped cream
  - nuts
  - no nuts

strawberry
- whipped cream
  - nuts
  - no nuts
- no whipped cream
  - nuts
  - no nuts

So a sundae can be served in 12 different ways.

CHECKING FOR UNDERSTANDING

Communicating Mathematics

Read and study the lesson to answer each question.

1. What do you notice about the numbers that are divisible by both 3 and 4? **They are all multiples of 12 and 12 = 3 · 4.**

2. Name another strategy that can be used with the strategy described in this lesson. **look for a pattern, make a table or chart, make a diagram, guess and check**

Guided Practice

Solve each problem by listing the possibilities. **3. 0, 24, 48**

3. Which whole numbers less than 50 are divisible by both 8 and 12?

4. Three darts are thrown at the target shown at the right. If we assume that each of the darts lands within one of the rings, how many different point totals are possible? **10**

5. How many different three-digit security codes can you make using the numbers 1, 2, and 3? You can use the numbers more than once. **27**

EXERCISES

Practice

Solve. Use any strategy.

6. In a twelve-hour period of time, how many times is the sum of the digits on a digital clock greater than 15? **120 times**

7. Frugal Fred Fudd left half of his estate to his wife, Flora; $50,000 to his daughter, Fawn; half of what remained to his butler, Franklin; half of the rest for the care and feeding of his dog, Fluffy; and the remaining $10,000 to his favorite charity. What was the value of Frugal Fred's estate? **$180,000**

LESSON 8-6   PROBLEM-SOLVING STRATEGY: LIST POSSIBILITIES   327

RETEACHING THE LESSON

Solve each problem by making an organized list of the possibilities.

1. How many four-digit numbers can be made using the digits 3, 3, 4, and 6?   **12**

2. How many five-digit numbers can be made using the digits 2, 2, 2, 5, and 9?   **20**

9. Since Ed was freshly shaved and neatly trimmed and there are only two barbers, we can assume that Floyd did it. Therefore, the visitor went to Floyd's.

13b. 1, 7, 10, 13, 19, 23, 28, 31, 32, 44, 49, 68, 70, 79, 82, 86, 91, 94, 97

Strategies

Look for a pattern.
Solve a simpler problem.
Act it out.
Guess and check.
Draw a diagram.
Make a chart.
Work backwards.

8. **Probability** The president, vice president, secretary, and treasurer of the Drama Club are to be seated in four chairs for a yearbook picture. How many different seating arrangements are possible? **24 arrangements**

9. A visitor to Nowheresville decided to get a haircut. The town had only two barbers, each with his own shop. The visitor glanced into Floyd's Barber Shop and saw that the shop was a mess and Floyd needed a shave and a haircut. When the visitor glanced into Ed's Hair Happening, he saw that Ed was freshly shaved and his hair neatly trimmed. The visitor went to Floyd's for his haircut. Why? **See margin.**

10. Can the design at the right be traced without going over any line segment more than once? **yes**

11. As Felicia waited in line at the ticket office, she noticed that two more people were ahead of her than were behind her. There were three times as many people in line as there were people behind Felicia. How many people are ahead of Felicia in line? **5 people**

12. A domino has two square spaces on its face. Each of the two spaces is marked with 1, 2, 3, 4, 5, or 6 dots, or it is blank. A complete set of dominoes includes one domino for each possible combination of dots. Doubles, such as 3 dots in each space, are included. How many dominoes are in a complete set? **28 dominoes**

13. **Number Theory** A positive integer is *happy* if the sum of the squares of its digits is 1, or if this process is continued, the result is 1.

$$23 \rightarrow 2^2 + 3^2 = 13$$
$$13 \rightarrow 1^2 + 3^2 = 10$$
$$10 \rightarrow 1^2 + 0^2 = 1 \qquad 23 \text{ is a happy number.}$$

a. If 23 is happy, what can you say about 32? **It is also happy.**

b. Find all happy numbers less than 100. **See margin.**

COOPERATIVE LEARNING ACTIVITY

Work in groups of four. Each person in the group should understand the solution and be able to explain it to any person in the class.

Throughout the text, you have learned about different types of numbers. This is part of the study of *number theory*. The Pythagoreans, a group of scholars in ancient Greece, studied the abstract relationships among numbers. They called some numbers *perfect*. A number is perfect if it is the sum of its *proper* divisors. The proper divisors of a number are all of its factors except itself. For example, 496 is a perfect number.

$$496 = 1 + 2 + 4 + 8 + 16 + 31 + 62 + 124 + 248$$

1. Find two other perfect numbers. **The first five are 6, 28, 496, 8128, and 33,550,336.**

2. *True* or *false:* If $2^n - 1$ is prime, then $(2^n - 1) \cdot 2^{n-1}$ is perfect. **true**

8-6 NAME _____ DATE _____

Practice Worksheet

Problem-Solving: List Possibilities

Solve each problem by listing the possibilities.

1. A president and secretary, are to be chosen for the Math Team. There are 5 members on the team. How many ways can these officers be chosen from the 5-member team?
Represent team as A, B, C, D, E:
AB, AC, AD, AE, BA, BC, BD,
BE, CA, CB, CD, CE, DA, DB,
DC, DE, EA, EB, EC, ED;
20 ways

2. How many different ways can nickels, dimes, and quarters be combined to total one dollar?
3Q, 2D, 1N   2Q, 1D, 8N
3Q, 1D, 3N   1Q, 7D, 1N
2Q, 4D, 2N   1Q, 6D, 3N
2Q, 3D, 4N   1Q, 5D, 5N
2Q, 2D, 6N   1Q, 4D, 7N
              1Q, 3D, 9N
              1Q, 2D, 11N
              1Q, 1D, 13N;
                    13 ways

3. In how many different orders can Juan, Kim, and Sean sit on a bench?
JKS   SJK
JSK   SKJ;
KJS   6 ways
KSJ

4. Four keys are on a key ring. How many different ways can these keys be arranged on this key ring?
Represent the keys as A, B, C, D:
  A   A   A
D   B   C   B   D   C   ;3 ways
  C   D   B
Note that on a key ring,
  A   A
D   B and B   D are the same.
  C   C

5. A business donated money to a high school library and media center for a 7-year period. The first year they gave $20,000. The second year they gave $40,000. The third year they gave $80,000, and so on. They continued giving money in this same pattern. How much money did they give for the 7 years? $2,540,000

6. Find the number of positive integers that are less than 100 and are divisible by 3.
3, 6, 9, 12, 15, 18, 21, 24, 27,
30, 33, 36, 39, 42, 45, 48, 51,
54, 57, 60, 63, 66, 69, 72, 75,
78, 81, 84, 87, 90, 93, 96, 99;
33

EXTENDING THE LESSON

Math Power: Problem Solving

In how many ways can you receive change for a quarter if at least one coin is a dime? **6 ways Use coins to model.**

Cooperative Learning Activity

This activity provides students with an opportunity to *learn* things together, not just do things together. You may wish to refer to pages T6 - T8 and page 6C for the various elements of cooperative groups and specific goals and strategies for using them.

Rational Expressions with Unlike Denominators

Objective
8-7

After studying this lesson, you should be able to:
- add or subtract rational expressions with unlike denominators.

Application

Judith Paulsen, the choreographer of a big Broadway musical, has requested that the producer of the show hire enough dancers so that they can be arranged in groups of 4, 6, or 9 with no one sitting out. What is the least number of dancers that can be hired?

If the choreographer wanted to arrange the dancers in groups of 6, then the producer should hire a number of dancers that is a multiple of 6. But since she wants to arrange the dancers in groups of 4, 6, or 9, the producer must be concerned with multiples of all three numbers. The least number of dancers is given by the **least common multiple (LCM)** of the three numbers. The least common multiple is the smallest number that is a common multiple of two or more numbers.

The multiples of 4, 6, and 9 can be found by multiplying 4, 6, and 9 by each whole number.

You can find the LCM by making an organized list.

multiples of 4: $4 \cdot 0, 4 \cdot 1, 4 \cdot 2, 4 \cdot 3, 4 \cdot 4, \ldots, 4 \cdot 9, \ldots$
     0,   4,   8,   12, 16,   36, ...

multiples of 6: $6 \cdot 0, 6 \cdot 1, 6 \cdot 2, 6 \cdot 3, 6 \cdot 4, 6 \cdot 5, 6 \cdot 6, \ldots$
     0,   6, 12, 18, 24, 30,   36, ...

multiples of 9: $9 \cdot 0, 9 \cdot 1, 9 \cdot 2, 9 \cdot 3, 9 \cdot 4, 9 \cdot 5, \ldots$
     0,   9, 18, 27, 36, 45, ...

Compare these multiples. Aside from 0, the least number that is common to all three sets of multiples is 36. Thus, the LCM of 4, 6, and 9 is 36, and the producer should hire 36 dancers.

You can also use prime factorization to find the LCM.

1. Find the prime factorization of each number.
    $4 = 2 \cdot 2$
    $6 = 2 \cdot 3$
    $9 = 3 \cdot 3$

LESSON 8-7 RATIONAL EXPRESSIONS WITH UNLIKE DENOMINATORS 329

ALTERNATE TEACHING STRATEGIES

Using Logical Reasoning

Can the LCD of two rational expressions be equal to the denominator of one of the rational expressions? Support your answer with an example. **Yes, if one denominator is a factor of the other.**

8-7 Lesson Notes

Lesson Resources
- Reteaching Master 8-7
- Practice Master 8-7
- Enrichment Master 8-7
- Video Algebra, 28

 Transparency 8-7 contains the 5-Minute Check and a teaching aid for this lesson.

INTRODUCING THE LESSON

5-Minute Check
(over Lesson 8-6)

Solve each problem by listing the possibilities.

1. There are 3 routes between Kelsey's house and the school. How many ways can Kelsey go from her house to the school and back home again? **9**
2. Phones come in 2 styles, wall and desk. They come in 5 colors, white, black, mauve, red, and beige. How many choices of phones are there? **10**

Motivating the Lesson
Have students find the LCD of several numbers such as 24, 48, 56, and 96.

TEACHING THE LESSON

Teaching Tip ❶ Emphasize that although 2 also appears as a factor in 6, it appears a greater number of times in 4.

Chalkboard Examples

For Example 1
Find the LCM.

a. $6x^2y$, $9xy^2$ $18x^2y^2$

b. $3a^2b$, $16ab^2$, $21ab$ $336a^2b^2$

For Example 2
Find the LCM.

a. $x^2 - 5x + 4$, $x^2 - 3x - 4$
$(x - 4)(x - 1)(x + 1)$

b. $x^2 - 9$, $x^2 + 6x + 9$
$(x - 3)(x + 3)^2$

For Example 3
Find each sum or difference. Simplify.

a. $\dfrac{2}{3y^2} - \dfrac{1}{12y^3}$ $\dfrac{8y - 1}{12y^3}$

b. $\dfrac{4a}{mn} + \dfrac{2a}{np}$ $\dfrac{4ap + 2am}{mnp}$

For Example 4
Find each sum or difference. Simplify.

a. $\dfrac{r}{r^2 - 16} - \dfrac{5}{r + 4}$ $\dfrac{-4r + 20}{r^2 - 16}$

b. $\dfrac{3}{y - 3} + \dfrac{2y}{y^2 - y - 6}$ $\dfrac{5y + 6}{y^2 - y - 6}$

---

2. Use each prime factor the greatest number of times it appears in any of the factorizations.

2 appears two times in 4.
3 appears two times in 9.

Thus, the LCM of 4, 6, and 9 is $2 \cdot 2 \cdot 3 \cdot 3$, or 36.

Example 1   **Find the LCM of $12x^2y$ and $15x^2y^2$.**

$12x^2y = 2 \cdot 2 \cdot 3 \cdot x \cdot x \cdot y$ *Factor each expression.*
$15x^2y^2 = 3 \cdot 5 \cdot x \cdot x \cdot y \cdot y$

$\text{LCM} = 2 \cdot 2 \cdot 3 \cdot 5 \cdot x \cdot x \cdot y \cdot y$ *Use each factor the greater number of*
$= 60x^2y^2$ *times it appears in either factorization.*

Example 2   **Find the LCM of $x^2 + x - 2$ and $x^2 + 5x - 6$.**

$x^2 + x - 2 = (x - 1)(x + 2)$ *Factor each expression.*
$x^2 + 5x - 6 = (x + 6)(x - 1)$

$\text{LCM} = (x - 1)(x + 2)(x + 6)$ *Use each factor the greater number of*
   times it appears in either factorization.

To add or subtract fractions with unlike denominators, first rename the fractions so the denominators are alike. Any common denominator could be used. However, the computation is usually easier if you use the **least common denominator (LCD)**. Recall that the least common denominator is the LCM of the denominators.

You will usually use the following steps to add or subtract rational expressions.

1. Find the LCD.
2. Change each rational expression into an equivalent expression with the LCD as the denominator.
3. Add or subtract as with rational expressions with like denominators.
4. Simplify if necessary.

Example 3   **Find $\dfrac{6}{5x} + \dfrac{7}{10x^2}$.**

$5x = 5 \cdot x$ *Use each factor the greater*
$10x^2 = 2 \cdot 5 \cdot x \cdot x$ *number of times it appears.*

The LCD for $\dfrac{6}{5x}$ and $\dfrac{7}{10x^2}$ is $2 \cdot 5 \cdot x \cdot x$ or $10x^2$. Since the denominator of $\dfrac{7}{10x^2}$ is already $10x^2$, only $\dfrac{6}{5x}$ needs to be renamed.

$\dfrac{6}{5x} + \dfrac{7}{10x^2} = \dfrac{6}{5x} \cdot \dfrac{2x}{2x} + \dfrac{7}{10x^2}$ *Why do you multiply $\dfrac{6}{5x}$ by $\dfrac{2x}{2x}$?*

$= \dfrac{12x}{10x^2} + \dfrac{7}{10x^2}$

$= \dfrac{12x + 7}{10x^2}$

Example 4

Find $\dfrac{a}{a^2-4}-\dfrac{4}{a+2}$.

Since $a^2-4=(a-2)(a+2)$, the LCD for $\dfrac{a}{a^2-4}$ and $\dfrac{4}{a+2}$ is $(a-2)(a+2)$, or a^2-4.

$$\dfrac{a}{a^2-4}-\dfrac{4}{a+2}=\dfrac{a}{(a-2)(a+2)}-\dfrac{4}{(a+2)}\cdot\dfrac{(a-2)}{(a-2)}$$
Multiply $\dfrac{4}{a+2}$ by $\dfrac{a-2}{a-2}$.

$$=\dfrac{a-4(a-2)}{(a-2)(a+2)}$$

$$=\dfrac{a-4a+8}{a^2-4}$$

$$=\dfrac{-3a+8}{a^2-4}$$

Example 5

Find $\dfrac{x+4}{(2-x)(x+3)}+\dfrac{x-5}{(x-2)^2}$.

Multiply the first fraction by $\dfrac{-1}{-1}$ to change $(2-x)$ to $(x-2)$.

$$\dfrac{x+4}{(2-x)(x+3)}+\dfrac{x-5}{(x-2)^2}=\dfrac{-1}{-1}\cdot\dfrac{(x+4)}{(2-x)(x+3)}+\dfrac{x-5}{(x-2)^2}$$

$$=\dfrac{-(x+4)}{(x-2)(x+3)}+\dfrac{x-5}{(x-2)^2}\quad -1(2-x)=x-2$$

The LCD for $(x-2)(x+3)$ and $(x-2)^2$ is $(x+3)(x-2)(x-2)$. *Why?*

$$\dfrac{-(x+4)}{(x-2)(x+3)}+\dfrac{x-5}{(x-2)^2}=\dfrac{-(x+4)}{(x-2)(x+3)}\cdot\dfrac{(x-2)}{(x-2)}+\dfrac{(x-5)}{(x-2)^2}\cdot\dfrac{(x+3)}{(x+3)}$$

$$=\dfrac{-x^2-2x+8+x^2-2x-15}{(x+3)(x-2)(x-2)}$$

$$=\dfrac{-4x-7}{(x+3)(x-2)^2}$$

Teaching Tip 2

1. Yes; when one denominator is a factor of the other.

CHECKING FOR UNDERSTANDING

Communicating Mathematics

Read and study the lesson to answer each question.

1. Can the LCD of two rational expressions be equal to the denominator of one of the rational expressions? When?

2. Why can't $\dfrac{4}{x-1}+\dfrac{5}{11}$ equal $\dfrac{9}{x+10}$? See margin.

Guided Practice

Find the LCD for each pair of rational expressions.

3. $\dfrac{4}{a^2},\dfrac{5}{a}$ a^2

4. $\dfrac{6}{b^3},\dfrac{7}{ab}$ ab^3

5. $\dfrac{3}{20a^2},\dfrac{1}{24ab^3}$ $120a^2b^3$

6. $\dfrac{1}{12an^2},\dfrac{3}{40a^4}$ $120a^4n^2$

7. $\dfrac{11}{56x^3y},\dfrac{10}{49ax^2}$ $392ax^3y$

8. $\dfrac{7}{a+5},\dfrac{a}{a-3}$ $(a+5)(a-3)$

9. $\dfrac{m}{m+n},\dfrac{6}{n}$ $n(m+n)$

10. $\dfrac{x+5}{3x-6},\dfrac{x-3}{x-2}$ $3(x-2)$

Find each sum or difference. 11-12. See margin.

11. $\dfrac{m-n}{m+n}-\dfrac{1}{m^2-n^2}$

12. $\dfrac{a}{a-b}+\dfrac{b}{2b+3a}$

LESSON 8-7 RATIONAL EXPRESSIONS WITH UNLIKE DENOMINATORS 331

Chalkboard Example

For Example 5

Find each sum or difference. Simplify.

a. $\dfrac{y}{(1-y)(y+1)}+\dfrac{y+2}{(y+1)^2}$
   $\dfrac{-2}{(y-1)(y+1)^2}$

b. $\dfrac{a-1}{(a+3)^2}-\dfrac{a+1}{(3-a)(a+3)}$
   $\dfrac{2a^2+6}{(a-3)(a+3)^2}$

Teaching Tip 2 Each student should be aware of how the LCD was determined. Remind them that each factor is used the greater number of times it appears in either factorization.

EVALUATING THE LESSON

Checking for Understanding

Exercises 1-12 are designed to help you assess understanding through reading, writing, and speaking. You should work through Exercises 1-2 with your students, and then monitor their work on Exercises 3-12.

Reteaching Masters Booklet, p. 57

reteaching worksheet image

NAME _____ DATE _____

8-7 Reteaching Worksheet

Adding and Subtracting Rational Expressions with Unlike Denominators

When you add or subtract rational expressions with *unlike* denominators, you must first rename the rational expressions so the denominators are alike. Any common denominator could be used. However, the computation is easier if the **least common denominator** (LCD) is used. The least common denominator is the **least common multiple** (LCM) of the denominators.

Example: Find $\dfrac{1}{2x^2+6x}+\dfrac{3}{x^2}$.

$$\dfrac{1}{2x^2+6x}+\dfrac{3}{x^2}=\dfrac{1}{2x(x+3)}+\dfrac{3}{x^2}$$

$$=\dfrac{1}{2x(x+3)}\cdot\dfrac{x}{x}+\dfrac{3}{x^2}\cdot\dfrac{2(x+3)}{2(x+3)}$$

$$=\dfrac{x+3(2)(x+3)}{2x^2(x+3)}$$

$$=\dfrac{x+6x+18}{2x^2(x+3)}$$

$$=\dfrac{7x+18}{2x^2(x+3)}$$

Find each sum or difference.

1. $\dfrac{1}{x}+\dfrac{7}{3x}$ $\dfrac{10}{3x}$

2. $\dfrac{1}{6x}+\dfrac{3}{8}$ $\dfrac{4+9x}{24x}$

3. $\dfrac{x}{x-3}-\dfrac{3}{x+3}$ $\dfrac{x^2+9}{x^2-9}$

4. $\dfrac{4}{h+1}+\dfrac{2}{h+2}$ $\dfrac{6h+10}{(h+1)(h+2)}$, or $\dfrac{6h+10}{h^2+3h+2}$

5. $\dfrac{x}{x-6}-\dfrac{1}{x+1}$ $\dfrac{x-6}{6(x+1)}$, or $\dfrac{x-6}{6x+6}$

6. $\dfrac{4x}{6x-2y}+\dfrac{3y}{9x-3y}$ $\dfrac{2x+y}{3x-y}$

7. $\dfrac{y+2}{y^2+5y+6}+\dfrac{2-y}{y^2+y-6}$ 0

8. $\dfrac{x}{x-7}-\dfrac{x+3}{x^2-4x-21}\cdot\dfrac{x-1}{x-7}$

9. $\dfrac{a-6b}{2a^2-5ab+2b^2}-\dfrac{7}{a-2b}$ $\dfrac{-13a+b}{(2a-b)(a-2b)}$, or $\dfrac{-13a+b}{2a^2-5ab+2b^2}$

10. $\dfrac{m}{1-2m}+\dfrac{4}{2m-1}\cdot\dfrac{4-m}{2m-1}$

11. $\dfrac{7d+4}{3d+9}-\dfrac{2d}{d+3}$ $\dfrac{d+4}{3(d+3)}$, or $\dfrac{d+4}{3d+9}$

12. $\dfrac{q}{q^3-16}+\dfrac{q+1}{q^2+5q+4}$ $\dfrac{2(q-2)}{(q-4)(q+4)}$, or $\dfrac{2q-4}{q^2-16}$

RETEACHING THE LESSON

When adding rational expressions, a common denominator is needed. The LCD provides the shortest solution but any common denominator will do. Work the problem below twice, once using a common denominator of $(2x-6)(x+3)$ and once using the LCD.

$$\dfrac{3x}{2x+6}-\dfrac{x-1}{x+3}\quad\dfrac{x+2}{2x+6}$$

Additional Answers

2. You cannot add fractions by adding numerators and adding denominators. To add, first write each term with the LCD, $11(x-1)$. Then add the numerators.

11. $\dfrac{m^2-2mn+n^2-1}{m^2-n^2}$

12. $\dfrac{3a^2+3ab-b^2}{3a^2-ab-2b^2}$

Chapter 8 331

Closing the Lesson

Speaking Activity Have students describe the similarities in addition or subtraction of fractions with unlike denominators and addition and subtraction of rational expressions with unlike denominators.

APPLYING THE LESSON

Homework Exercises

Assignment Guide

Basic: 13-32, 39-41, 45-50
Average: 18-35, 39-50
Enriched: 23-50

Practice Find each sum or difference. 25, 29-38. See margin.

A

13. $\frac{t}{3} + \frac{2t}{7}$ $\frac{13t}{21}$

14. $\frac{2n}{5} - \frac{3m}{4}$ $\frac{8n - 15m}{20}$

15. $\frac{5}{2a} + \frac{-3}{6a}$ $\frac{2}{a}$

16. $\frac{7}{3a} - \frac{3}{6a^2}$ $\frac{14a - 3}{6a^2}$

17. $\frac{5}{xy} + \frac{6}{yz}$ $\frac{5z + 6x}{xyz}$

18. $\frac{3z}{7w^2} - \frac{2z}{w}$ $\frac{3z - 14wz}{7w^2}$

19. $\frac{2}{t} + \frac{t + 3}{s}$ $\frac{2s + t^2 + 3t}{st}$

20. $\frac{m}{1(m - n)} - \frac{5}{m}$ $\frac{m^2 - 5m + 5n}{m(m - n)}$

21. $\frac{4a}{2a + 6} + \frac{3}{a + 3}$ $\frac{2a + 3}{a + 3}$

22. $\frac{-3}{a - 5} + \frac{-6}{a^2 - 5a}$ $\frac{-3a - 6}{a^2 - 5a}$

B

23. $\frac{2y}{y^2 - 25} + \frac{y + 5}{y - 5}$ $\frac{y^2 + 12y + 25}{y^2 - 25}$

24. $\frac{3a + 2}{3a - 6} - \frac{a + 2}{a^2 - 4}$ $\frac{3a - 1}{3a - 6}$

25. $\frac{x^2 - 1}{x + 1} + \frac{x^2 + 1}{x - 1}$

26. $\frac{k}{2k + 1} - \frac{2}{k + 2}$ $\frac{k^2 - 2k - 2}{(2k + 1)(k + 2)}$

27. $\frac{-18}{y^2 - 9} + \frac{7}{3 - y}$ $\frac{-7y - 39}{y^2 - 9}$

28. $\frac{a - 1}{4ab} + \frac{a^2 - a}{16b^2}$ $\frac{(4b + a^2)(a - 1)}{16ab^2}$

29. $\frac{x - 1}{3xy} - \frac{x^2 - x}{9y^2}$

30. $\frac{a - 2}{a^2 + 4a + 4} + \frac{a + 2}{a - 2}$

31. $\frac{x^2}{4x^2 - 9} + \frac{x}{(2x + 3)^2}$

32. $\frac{y}{y^2 - 2y + 1} - \frac{1}{y - 1}$

C

33. $\frac{x^2 + 4x - 5}{x^2 - 2x - 3} + \frac{2}{x + 1}$

34. $\frac{a + 2}{a^2 - 9} - \frac{2a}{6a^2 - 17a - 3}$

35. $\frac{3m}{m^2 + 3m + 2} - \frac{3m - 6}{m^2 + 4m + 4}$

36. $\frac{4a}{6a^2 - a - 2} - \frac{5a + 1}{2 - 3a}$

37. $\frac{2x + 1}{(x - 1)^2} + \frac{x - 2}{(1 - x)(x + 4)}$

38. $\frac{a + 3}{3a^2 - 10a - 8} + \frac{2a}{a^2 - 8a + 16}$

39c. The product of the numbers is equal to the product of the GCF and LCM.

Critical Thinking 39. Complete.

a. $18 \cdot 20 = ?$ 360
   GCF of 18 and 20 = ? 2
   LCM of 18 and 20 = ? 180
   GCF · LCM = ? 360

b. $16 \cdot 48 = ?$ 768
   GCF of 16 and 48 = ? 16
   LCM of 16 and 48 = ? 48
   GCF · LCM = ? 768

c. Write a rule that describes the relationship between the product of two numbers and their GCF and LCM.

d. Use your rule to describe how to find the GCF of two numbers if you already know the LCM.
   Divide the product of the two numbers by the LCM.

Applications 40. **Astronomy** Earth, Jupiter, and Saturn revolve around the Sun about once every 1, 12, and 30 years, respectively. The last time Jupiter and Saturn appeared close to each other in Earth's night sky was in 1982. When will this happen again? 2042

332 CHAPTER 8 RATIONAL EXPRESSIONS

Practice Masters Booklet, p. 64

Additional Answers

25. $\frac{2(x^3 + 1)}{x^2 - 1}$ or $\frac{2(x^2 - x + 1)}{x - 1}$

29. $\frac{-x^3 + x^2 + 3xy - 3y}{9xy^2}$ or $\frac{(3y - x^2)(x - 1)}{9xy^2}$

30. $\frac{a^3 + 7a^2 + 8a + 12}{(a + 2)^2(a - 2)}$

31. $\frac{2x^3 + 5x^2 - 3x}{(2x - 3)(2x + 3)^2}$

32. $\frac{1}{y^2 - 2y + 1}$

33. $\frac{x^2 + 6x - 11}{x^2 - 2x - 3}$

34. $\frac{4a^2 + 7a + 2}{(a + 3)(a - 3)(6a + 1)}$

35. $\frac{9m + 6}{(m + 2)^2(m + 1)}$

36. $\frac{10a^2 + 11a + 1}{(3a - 2)(2a + 1)}$

37. $\frac{x^2 + 12x + 2}{(x - 1)^2(x + 4)}$

38. $\frac{7a^2 + 3a - 12}{(3a + 2)(a - 4)^2}$

41. Agriculture When a certain farmer died, he left 17 cows to his children according to these terms: the eldest child was to receive $\frac{1}{2}$ of the cows, the second child was to receive $\frac{1}{3}$ of the cows, and the youngest child was to receive $\frac{1}{9}$ of the cows. Since none of these fractional parts of 17 cows was a whole number, the children were confused about how to carry out these terms. Finally a neighbor offered to lend a cow to the children. How many cows did each child get? **eldest: 9 cows; second: 6 cows; youngest: 2 cows**

42. Parades At the Veteran's Day parade, the local members of the Veterans of Foreign Wars (VFW) found that they could arrange themselves in rows of 6, 7, or 8, with no one left over. What is the least number of VFW members in the parade? **168 members**

43. Work At Migdalia Montenegro's retirement dinner, there were two sizes of banquet tables. One size seated 5 people and the other size seated 8 people. Seventy-nine people attended Mrs. Montengro's dinner. If there were no empty places, how many tables of each size were there? **3 tables of 5 people and 8 tables of 8 people or 11 tables of 5 people and 3 tables of 8 people**

44. Travel George Farquar spent, in this order, a third of his life in the United States, a sixth of his life in England, twelve years in Mexico, half the remainder in Australia, and as long in Canada as he spent in Spain. How many years did George live if he spent his 45th birthday in Mexico? **72 years**

Mixed Review

45. 50% more than what number is 25% less than 60% more than 20? **(Lesson 4-4)** **16**

46. Ping-pong Each ping-pong ball weighs about $\frac{1}{10}$ of an ounce. How many ping-pong balls weigh 1 pound altogether? **(Lesson 3-3)** **160 balls**

47. Find the degree of $51x^5yz$. **(Lesson 6-5)** **7**

48. Paula Robinson went to the corner store to buy four items. The clerk at the store had to add the four prices by hand since her cash register was broken. When the clerk figured Paula's bill, she mistakenly multiplied the four figures instead of adding them. Paula had already mentally computed her sum, so, realizing that the total was correct, she paid the clerk $7.11. How much was each item that Paula bought? **(Lesson 7-4)** **$3.16, $1.50, $1.25, $1.20**

49. Find $\frac{y}{y-1} - \frac{1}{y-1}$. **(Lesson 8-5)** **1**

50. Solve by listing the possibilities. **(Lesson 8-6)**

How many ways can you receive change for a half-dollar if you receive at least one dime and one quarter? **6 ways**

EXTENDING THE LESSON

Math Power: Reasoning

Find $\dfrac{2a^2 + 5a + 3}{2a^2 - a - 6} - \dfrac{a^2 - 4}{a^2 - a - 2}$ and simplify. $\dfrac{2a+5}{a^2-a-2}$

Lesson Resources

- Reteaching Master 8-8
- Practice Master 8-8
- Enrichment Master 8-8
- Activity Master, p. 23
- Video Algebra, 29

 Transparency 8-8 contains the 5-Minute Check and a teaching aid for this lesson.

INTRODUCING THE LESSON

5-Minute Check

(over Lesson 8-7)

1. Find the LCM of 48 and 56. **336**

2. Find the LCM of $3x^2y$ and $4x^3y^2z$. **$12x^3y^2z$**

Find each sum or difference. Simplify.

3. $\dfrac{5}{a} - \dfrac{3}{b}$ $\dfrac{5b - 3a}{ab}$

4. $\dfrac{7}{5} + \dfrac{a}{5b}$ $\dfrac{7b + a}{5b}$

5. $\dfrac{6}{3x - 9} + \dfrac{3}{x - 3}$ $\dfrac{5}{x - 3}$

Motivating the Lesson

Have the first student in a row identify a mixed number such as $3\frac{1}{2}$. The next student in the row must identify an equivalent improper fraction. A third student then identifies another mixed number. Continue the activity until all class members have had a turn speaking aloud.

TEACHING THE LESSON

Teaching Tip Help students to see that they are changing numbers with unlike denominators to numbers with like or common denominators. For example, consider $a + \dfrac{a^2 + b}{a - b}$ as $\dfrac{a}{1} + \dfrac{a^2 + b}{a - b}$. Changing the mixed expression to an algebraic fraction requires that $\dfrac{a}{1}$ be renamed with the LCD $a - b$ as its denominator.

8-8 Mixed Expressions and Complex Fractions

Objective
8-8

After studying this lesson, you should be able to:
- simplify mixed expressions and complex fractions.

Mixed expressions contain monomials and algebraic fractions.

Algebraic expressions such as $a + \dfrac{b}{c}$ and $5 + \dfrac{x - y}{x + 3}$ are called **mixed expressions**. Changing mixed expressions to rational expressions is similar to changing mixed numbers to improper fractions.

Mixed Number to Improper Fraction	Mixed Expression to Rational Expression
$3\frac{2}{5}$ or $3 + \dfrac{2}{5} = \dfrac{3(5)}{5} + \dfrac{2}{5}$	$a + \dfrac{a^2 + b}{a - b} = \dfrac{a(a - b)}{a - b} + \dfrac{a^2 + b}{a - b}$
$\qquad = \dfrac{3(5) + 2}{5}$	$\qquad = \dfrac{a(a - b) + (a^2 + b)}{a - b}$
$\qquad = \dfrac{15 + 2}{5}$	$\qquad = \dfrac{a^2 - ab + a^2 + b}{a - b}$
$\qquad = \dfrac{17}{5}$	$\qquad = \dfrac{2a^2 - ab + b}{a - b}$

Teaching Tip ①

Example 1

Find $8 + \dfrac{x^2 - y^2}{x^2 + y^2}$.

$$8 + \dfrac{x^2 - y^2}{x^2 + y^2} = \dfrac{8(x^2 + y^2)}{x^2 + y^2} + \dfrac{x^2 - y^2}{x^2 + y^2}$$

$$= \dfrac{8(x^2 + y^2) + (x^2 - y^2)}{x^2 + y^2}$$

$$= \dfrac{8x^2 + 8y^2 + x^2 - y^2}{x^2 + y^2}$$

$$= \dfrac{9x^2 + 7y^2}{x^2 + y^2}$$

If a fraction has one or more fractions in the numerator or denominator, it is called a **complex fraction**. Some complex fractions are shown below.

$$\dfrac{3\frac{1}{2}}{5\frac{2}{3}} \qquad \dfrac{8}{\frac{a}{b}} \qquad \dfrac{\frac{a + b}{a}}{\frac{a - b}{b}} \qquad \dfrac{\frac{1}{x} - \frac{1}{y}}{\frac{1}{x} + \frac{1}{y}}$$

Consider the complex fraction $\dfrac{\frac{3}{5}}{\frac{7}{8}}$. To simplify this fraction, rewrite it as $\dfrac{3}{5} \div \dfrac{7}{8}$ and proceed as follows.

$$\dfrac{3}{5} \div \dfrac{7}{8} = \dfrac{3}{5} \cdot \dfrac{8}{7} \text{ or } \dfrac{24}{35}$$

Recall that to find the quotient, you multiply by $\frac{8}{7}$, the reciprocal of $\frac{7}{8}$.

ALTERNATE TEACHING STRATEGIES

Using Logical Reasoning

Is it possible for a complex fraction to be its own reciprocal? Prove your answer with an example. **Yes, if it equals 1 or −1. Examples will vary.**

Similarly, to simplify $\dfrac{\frac{a}{b}}{\frac{c}{d}}$, rewrite it as $\dfrac{a}{b} \div \dfrac{c}{d}$ and proceed as follows.

$$\frac{a}{b} \div \frac{c}{d} = \frac{a}{b} \cdot \frac{d}{c} \text{ or } \frac{ad}{bc} \qquad \textit{The reciprocal of } \tfrac{c}{d} \textit{ is } \tfrac{d}{c}.$$

Simplifying Complex Fractions	Any complex fraction $\dfrac{\frac{a}{b}}{\frac{c}{d}}$, where $b \neq 0$, $c \neq 0$, and $d \neq 0$, may be expressed as $\dfrac{ad}{bc}$.

Example 2 Simplify $\dfrac{\frac{1}{x} + \frac{1}{y}}{\frac{1}{x} - \frac{1}{y}}$.

$$\frac{\frac{1}{x} + \frac{1}{y}}{\frac{1}{x} - \frac{1}{y}} = \frac{\frac{y}{xy} + \frac{x}{xy}}{\frac{y}{xy} - \frac{x}{xy}} \qquad \begin{array}{l}\textit{The LCD of the numerator } \frac{1}{x} + \frac{1}{y} \\ \textit{and the denominator } \frac{1}{x} - \frac{1}{y} \textit{ is xy.}\end{array}$$

$$= \frac{\frac{y + x}{xy}}{\frac{y - x}{xy}} \qquad \begin{array}{l}\textit{Add to simplify the numerator.} \\ \textit{Subtract to simplify the denominator.}\end{array}$$

$$= \frac{y + x}{xy} \cdot \frac{xy}{y - x} \qquad \textit{The reciprocal of } \tfrac{y - x}{xy} \textit{ is } \tfrac{xy}{y - x}.$$

$$= \frac{y + x}{\cancel{xy}_1} \cdot \frac{\cancel{xy}^1}{y - x} \qquad \textit{Eliminate common factors.}$$

$$= \frac{y + x}{y - x}$$

Example 3 Simplify $\dfrac{x + 4 - \frac{1}{x + 4}}{x + 11 + \frac{48}{x - 3}}$. **Teaching Tip** ②

$$\frac{x + 4 - \frac{1}{x + 4}}{x + 11 + \frac{48}{x - 3}} = \frac{\frac{(x + 4)(x + 4) - 1}{x + 4}}{\frac{(x + 11)(x - 3) + 48}{x - 3}} \qquad \begin{array}{l}\textit{The LCD of the numerator is } x + 4. \\ \textit{The LCD of the denominator is } x - 3.\end{array}$$

$$= \frac{\frac{x^2 + 8x + 16 - 1}{x + 4}}{\frac{x^2 + 8x - 33 + 48}{x - 3}} \qquad \begin{array}{l}\textit{Subtract to simplify the numerator.} \\ \textit{Add to simplify the denominator.}\end{array}$$

$$= \frac{\frac{x^2 + 8x + 15}{x + 4}}{\frac{x^2 + 8x + 15}{x - 3}} \qquad \textit{Simplify.}$$

$$= \frac{x^2 + 8x + 15}{x + 4} \cdot \frac{x - 3}{x^2 + 8x + 15} \qquad \begin{array}{l}\textit{Multiply by the reciprocal.} \\ x^2 + 8x + 15 \textit{ is a common factor.}\end{array}$$

$$= \frac{x - 3}{x + 4}$$

LESSON 8-8 MIXED EXPRESSIONS AND COMPLEX FRACTIONS 335

RETEACHING THE LESSON

Have students complete the following table.

single fraction	mixed expression
$\dfrac{6x^2 + 4x + 1}{3}$	$2x^2 + \dfrac{4x + 1}{3}$
$\dfrac{2x}{x + y}$	$\quad + \dfrac{x - y}{x + y}$
$\dfrac{x^2 + 5x + 6}{x + 1}$	$5 + \dfrac{x^2 + 5}{x + 1}$
$\dfrac{a + 3b}{a + b}$	$2 - \dfrac{a - b}{a + b}$

Chalkboard Examples

For Example 1
Simplify.

a. $4 + \dfrac{x - 3}{x + 7} \quad \dfrac{5x + 25}{x + 7}$

b. $3 + \dfrac{r - 4}{r^2 - 4} \quad \dfrac{3r^2 + r - 16}{r^2 - 4}$

For Example 2

Simplify $\dfrac{\frac{1}{a} - \frac{1}{b}}{\frac{1}{a} + \frac{1}{b}}$. $\dfrac{b - a}{b + a}$

For Example 3

Simplify $\dfrac{x - 2 + \frac{3}{x + 2}}{x + 1 - \frac{10}{x + 4}}$.

$\dfrac{(x + 1)(x + 4)}{(x + 2)(x + 6)}$

Teaching Tip ② All of these calculations may seem confusing to some students. Have students separate these into two problems: one involving the numerator and one involving the denominator. Then put the two together.

Reteaching Masters Booklet, p. 58

NAME _____ DATE _____

8-8 **Reteaching Worksheet**

Mixed Expressions and Complex Fractions

Algebraic expressions such as $a + \frac{b}{c}$ and $5 + \frac{x + y}{x + 3}$ are called **mixed expressions.** Changing mixed expressions to improper fractions is similar to changing mixed numbers to improper fractions.

If a fraction has one or more fractions in the numerator or denominator, it is called a **complex fraction.**

Simplifying Complex Fractions
Any complex fraction $\dfrac{\frac{a}{b}}{\frac{c}{d}}$, where $b \neq 0$, $c \neq 0$, and $d \neq 0$, may be expressed as $\frac{a}{b} \cdot \frac{d}{c}$, or $\frac{ad}{bc}$.

Example: Simplify $\dfrac{2 + \frac{4}{a}}{\frac{a + 2}{3}}$.

$\dfrac{2 + \frac{4}{a}}{\frac{a + 2}{3}} = \dfrac{\frac{2a}{a} + \frac{4}{a}}{\frac{a + 2}{3}}$

$= \dfrac{\frac{2a + 4}{a}}{\frac{a + 2}{3}}$

$= \dfrac{2a + 4}{a} \cdot \dfrac{3}{a + 2}$

$= \dfrac{2(a + 2)}{a} \cdot \dfrac{3}{a + 2}$

$= \dfrac{6}{a}$

Simplify.

1. $10 + \dfrac{60}{x + 5}$ $\dfrac{10x + 110}{x + 5}$

2. $12 + \dfrac{x - y}{x + y}$ $\dfrac{13x + 11y}{x + y}$

3. $4 - \dfrac{4}{2x + 1}$ $\dfrac{8x}{2x + 1}$

4. $\dfrac{2\frac{2}{5}}{3\frac{3}{4}}$ $\dfrac{16}{25}$

5. $\dfrac{\frac{3}{4}}{y}$ $\dfrac{3y}{4x}$

6. $\dfrac{\frac{3}{y + 2} - \frac{2}{y - 2}}{\frac{1}{y + 2} - \frac{2}{y - 2}}$ $\dfrac{y - 10}{-y - 6}$

7. $\dfrac{1 - \frac{1}{x}}{1 - \frac{1}{x^2}}$ $\dfrac{x}{x + 1}$

8. $\dfrac{\frac{1}{x - 3}}{\frac{2}{x^2 - 9}}$ $\dfrac{x + 3}{2}$

9. $\dfrac{\frac{x^2 - 25}{y}}{x^3 - 5x^2}$ $\dfrac{x + 5}{x^2 y}$

Example 4 | Simplify $\dfrac{x - \dfrac{x+4}{x+1}}{x-2}$.

$$\dfrac{x - \dfrac{x+4}{x+1}}{x-2} = \dfrac{\dfrac{x(x+1)-(x+4)}{x+1}}{x-2}$$

The LCD of the numerator is x + 1.
The LCD of the denominator is x − 2.

$$= \dfrac{\dfrac{x^2+x-x-4}{x+1}}{x-2}$$

Subtract to simplify the numerator.

$$= \dfrac{\dfrac{x^2-4}{x+1}}{\dfrac{x-2}{1}}$$

Simplify.

$$= \dfrac{x^2-4}{x+1} \cdot \dfrac{1}{x-2}$$

Multiply by the reciprocal.

$$= \dfrac{(x+2)\cancel{(x-2)}}{(x+1)\cancel{(x-2)}}$$

x − 2 is a common factor.

$$= \dfrac{x+2}{x+1}$$

CHECKING FOR UNDERSTANDING

Communicating Mathematics

Read and study the lesson to answer each question.

1. Is it possible for a complex fraction to be its own reciprocal? **Yes, if it equals 1 or −1.**

2. In the mixed expression $8 + \dfrac{x^2-y^2}{x^2+y^2}$, what is the denominator of 8? **1**

Guided Practice

Find each sum. 5-8. See margin.

3. $4 + \dfrac{2}{x}$ $\dfrac{4x+2}{x}$

4. $8 + \dfrac{5}{3y}$ $\dfrac{24y+5}{3y}$

5. $2m + \dfrac{4+m}{m}$

6. $3a + \dfrac{a+1}{2a}$

7. $b^2 + \dfrac{2}{b-2}$

8. $3r^2 + \dfrac{4}{2r+1}$

EXERCISES

Practice

Simplify.

9. $\dfrac{3\frac{1}{2}}{4\frac{3}{4}}$ $\dfrac{14}{19}$

10. $\dfrac{\frac{x^2}{y}}{\frac{y}{x^3}}$ $\dfrac{x^5}{y^2}$

11. $\dfrac{\frac{x+4}{y-2}}{\frac{x^2}{y^3}}$ $\dfrac{y^3(x+4)}{x^2(y-2)}$

12. $\dfrac{\frac{x^3}{y^2}}{\frac{x+y}{x-y}}$ $\dfrac{x^3(x-y)}{y^2(x+y)}$

13. $\dfrac{\frac{x+y}{a+b}}{\frac{x^2-y^2}{a^2-b^2}}$ $\dfrac{a-b}{x-y}$

14. $\dfrac{\frac{x-y}{x+y}}{\frac{x+y}{x-y}}$ $\dfrac{(x-y)^2}{(x+y)^2}$

Additional Answers

5. $\dfrac{2m^2+m+4}{m}$

6. $\dfrac{6a^2+a+1}{2a}$

7. $\dfrac{b^3-2b^2+2}{b-2}$

8. $\dfrac{6r^3+3r^2+4}{2r+1}$

15. $\dfrac{\frac{1}{x}+\frac{1}{y}}{\frac{1}{y}-\frac{1}{x}}$ $\dfrac{x+y}{x-y}$

16. $\dfrac{\frac{a+b}{x}}{\frac{a-b}{y}}$ $\dfrac{y(a+b)}{x(a-b)}$

17. $\dfrac{\frac{x^2+8x+15}{x^2+x-6}}{\frac{x^2+2x-15}{x^2-2x-3}}$ $\dfrac{x+1}{x-2}$

18. $\dfrac{\frac{a^2-6a+5}{a^2+13a+42}}{\frac{a^2-4a+3}{a^2+3a-18}}$ $\dfrac{a-5}{a+7}$

19. $\dfrac{\frac{y^2-1}{y^2+3y-4}}{y+1}$ $\dfrac{1}{y+4}$

20. $\dfrac{\frac{a^2-2a-3}{a^2-1}}{a-3}$ $\dfrac{1}{a-1}$

21. $\dfrac{\frac{a^2+2a}{a^2+9a+18}}{\frac{a^2-5a}{a^2+a-30}}$ $\dfrac{a+2}{a+3}$

22. $\dfrac{\frac{x^2+4x-21}{x^2-9x+18}}{\frac{x^2+3x-28}{x^2-10x+24}}$ 1

23. $\dfrac{x-\frac{15}{x-2}}{x-\frac{20}{x-1}}$ $\dfrac{(x+3)(x-1)}{(x-2)(x+4)}$

24. $\dfrac{m+\frac{35}{m+12}}{m-\frac{63}{m-2}}$ $\dfrac{(m+5)(m-2)}{(m+12)(m-9)}$

25. $7+\dfrac{x^2+y^2}{x^2-4y^2}$ $\dfrac{8x^2-27y^2}{x^2-4y^2}$

26. $5+\dfrac{a^2+11}{a^2-1}$ $\dfrac{6a^2+6}{a^2-1}$

27. $\dfrac{x+2+\frac{2}{x+5}}{x+6+\frac{6}{x+1}}$ $\dfrac{x+1}{x+5}$

28. $\dfrac{x+5+\frac{3}{x+1}}{x-1-\frac{3}{x+1}}$ $\dfrac{x+4}{x-2}$

29. $\dfrac{\frac{a^2-a-1}{a-1}}{a-\frac{1}{a-1}}$ 1

Critical Thinking

30. Simplify $\dfrac{1}{1-\frac{1}{1+a}}-\dfrac{1}{\frac{1}{1-a}-1}$. 2

Applications

31. **History** Construction of the Washington Monument began in 1848 and was put on hold in 1854. Construction resumed 26 years later and continued until the monument was completed 4 years later. The monument was finally opened to the public 4 years after it was completed. When was the Washington Monument opened to the public? **1888**

32. **Statistics** In 1988, New Jersey was the most densely populated state, and Alaska was the least densely populated. The population of New Jersey was 7,721,000, and the population of Alaska was 524,000. If the land area of New Jersey is 7,468 square miles and the land area of Alaska is 570,833 square miles, how many more people are there per square mile in New Jersey than in Alaska? **1033 people**

Mixed Review

33. **Sales** How many pounds of apples costing 64¢ per pound must be added to 30 pounds of apples costing 49¢ per pound to create a mixture that would sell for 58¢ per pound? **(Lesson 4-6)** **45 pounds**

34. If $\frac{4}{9}=0.\overline{4}$, $\frac{43}{99}=0.\overline{43}$, and $\frac{817}{999}=0.\overline{817}$, find fractions that are equivalent to the following decimals: $0.\overline{6}$, $0.\overline{57}$, $0.\overline{253}$, and $0.\overline{6001}$. **(Lesson 6-1)** $\frac{6}{9}$, $\frac{57}{99}$, $\frac{253}{999}$, $\frac{6001}{9999}$

35. Factor $12a^2-12$. **(Lesson 7-6)** $12(a+1)(a-1)$

36. Find $\dfrac{5b}{7x}+\dfrac{3a}{21x^2}$. **(Lesson 8-7)** $\dfrac{15bx+3a}{21x^2}$

EXTENDING THE LESSON

Math Power: Reasoning

Simplify.

$\dfrac{\frac{a^2-a-1}{a-1}}{a-\frac{1}{a-1}}$ 1

Closing the Lesson

Speaking Activity Have students describe the process used to simplify $\dfrac{\frac{5a^2-20}{2a+2}}{\frac{10a-20}{4a}}$.

$\dfrac{a^2+2a}{a+1}$

APPLYING THE LESSON

Homework Exercises

Assignment Guide

Basic: 9-23, 30-31, 33-36
Average: 11-28, 30-36
Enriched: 12-36

Chapter 8, Quiz C, (Lessons 8-6 through 8-8), is available in the Evaluation Masters Booklet, p. 108.

Enrichment Masters Booklet, p. 58

INTRODUCING THE LESSON

🕐 5-Minute Check
(over Lesson 8-8)

Simplify.

1. $8 + \dfrac{5}{3y}$ $\dfrac{24y + 5}{3y}$

2. $3r^2 + \dfrac{4}{2r + 1}$ $\dfrac{6r^3 + 3r^2 + 4}{2r + 1}$

3. $\dfrac{\frac{b^2}{t}}{\frac{t}{b^3}}$ $\dfrac{b^5}{t^2}$

4. $\dfrac{\frac{j^3}{t^2}}{\frac{j + t}{j - t}}$ $\dfrac{j^3(j - t)}{t^2(j + t)}$

Motivating the Lesson

Open this lesson with an examination of an equation that has no solution. You might begin with the equation $x = x + 4$. Then lead into equations containing fractions.

TEACHING THE LESSON

Teaching Tip ① Discuss Example 1 thoroughly. Olivia's rate of work is $\frac{1}{3}$ of the job per hour. In t hours, she can complete $\frac{t}{3}$ of the job. George's rate is $\frac{1}{4}$ of the job per hour. In t hours, he can complete $\frac{t}{4}$ of the job. If they work together for t hours, they can complete one job. Therefore, the equation is $\frac{t}{3} + \frac{t}{4} = 1$.

8-9 Solving Rational Equations

Objectives

8-9A
8-9B

After studying this lesson, you should be able to:
- solve rational equations, and
- solve problems involving work and uniform motion.

Rational equations are equations containing rational expressions.

Example 1

APPLICATION
Work

FYI ···

4-H Clubs began in the early 1900s. The members pledge their **H**eads, **H**earts, **H**ands, and **H**ealth to community service.

The Blendonville 4-H Club is holding their annual car wash to raise funds for club projects. Olivia can wash and wax 1 car in 3 hours. George can wash and wax 1 car in 4 hours. If Olivia and George work together, how long will it take them to wash and wax one car?

EXPLORE   In one hour, Olivia can complete $\frac{1}{3}$ of the job. In 2 hours, she can complete $\frac{1}{3} \cdot 2$ or $\frac{2}{3}$ of the job. In t hours, she can complete $\frac{1}{3} \cdot t$ or $\frac{t}{3}$ of the job. Use the following formula to solve the problem. **Teaching Tip ①**

$$\text{rate of work} \cdot \text{time} = \text{work done}$$
$$r \quad \cdot \quad t \quad = \quad w$$

Let t = time in hours of them to wash and wax one car.

PLAN   In t hours, Olivia can do $\frac{t}{3}$ of the job. In t hours, George can do $\frac{t}{4}$ of the job.

	r	t	w
Olivia	$\frac{1}{3}$	t	$\frac{t}{3}$
George	$\frac{1}{4}$	t	$\frac{t}{4}$

$$\frac{t}{3} + \frac{t}{4} = 1 \qquad \textit{Together they wash and wax 1 car.}$$

SOLVE $12\left(\frac{t}{3} + \frac{t}{4}\right) = 12(1)$ **Teaching Tip ②**

$$4t + 3t = 12 \qquad \textit{Multiply each side of the equation by the LCD, 12}$$
$$7t = 12$$
$$t = \frac{12}{7}$$

Olivia and George can wash and wax 1 car in $\frac{12}{7}$ hours or about one hour and 43 minutes. **Teaching Tip ③**

ALTERNATE TEACHING STRATEGIES

Using Logical Reasoning

Is it true that $\frac{a}{a + 1} - \frac{b}{b + 1} = 0$ whenever $a = b$?   Yes, as long as a and b do not equal -1. In that case, the denominator is 0 and division by 0 is undefined.

Using Connections

The measures of the sides of a triangle are $\frac{x}{x + 1}$, $\frac{x + 2}{x + 3}$, and $\frac{3}{3x - 1}$. If the measure of its perimeter is $\frac{2x^2 + 7x + 8}{x^2 + 4x + 3}$, find the value of x.   3

EXAMINE Olivia does $\frac{1}{3}t$ or $\frac{1}{3} \cdot \frac{12}{7}$ of the job. $\frac{1}{3} \cdot \frac{12}{7} = \frac{4}{7}$

George does $\frac{1}{4}t$ or $\frac{1}{4} \cdot \frac{12}{7}$ of the job. $\frac{1}{4} \cdot \frac{12}{7} = \frac{3}{7}$

Since $\frac{3}{7} + \frac{4}{7} = \frac{7}{7}$ or 1, the solution checks.

Example 2

Solve $\frac{11}{2x} - \frac{2}{3x} = \frac{1}{6}$.

$\frac{11}{2x} - \frac{2}{3x} = \frac{1}{6}$ *The LCD is 6x.*

$6x\left(\frac{11}{2x} - \frac{2}{3x}\right) = 6x\left(\frac{1}{6}\right)$ *Multiply each side of the equation by the LCD.*

$3(11) - 2(2) = x$ *The fractions are eliminated.*

$29 = x$ *Simplify.*

Check: $\frac{11}{2x} - \frac{2}{3x} = \frac{1}{6}$

$\frac{11}{2(29)} - \frac{2}{3(29)} \stackrel{?}{=} \frac{1}{6}$

$\frac{11}{58} - \frac{2}{87} \stackrel{?}{=} \frac{1}{6}$ *Use a calculator to check.*

$\frac{1}{6} = \frac{1}{6}$ ✔   The solution is 29.

Recall that uniform motion problems can be solved by using the formula below.

$$distance = rate \cdot time$$
$$d \quad = \quad r \quad \cdot \quad t$$

Example 3

APPLICATION

Fishing

Sally and her brother rented a boat to fish in Jones Creek. The maximum speed of the boat in still water was 3 miles per hour. At this rate, a 9-mile trip downstream with the current took the same amount of time as a 3-mile trip upstream against the current. What was the rate of the current?

EXPLORE   Let c = the rate of the current. The rate of the boat when traveling downstream, or with the current, is 3 miles per hour *plus* the rate of the current. That is, $3 + c$. The rate when traveling upstream, or against the current, is 3 miles per hour *minus* the rate of the current. That is $3 - c$.

Teaching Tip ❹

(continued on the next page)

LESSON 8-9 SOLVING RATIONAL EQUATIONS **339**

Chalkboard Example

For Example 4

Solve.

a. $-\frac{a}{a+1} + \frac{a+1}{4-a} = \frac{-5}{a^2 - 3a - 4}$ 2

b. $\frac{1}{x-4} - \frac{2}{16-x^2} = \frac{3}{x+4}$ 9

Teaching Tip 5 Another way to solve this equation is to cross multiply.

EVALUATING THE LESSON

Checking for Understanding

Exercises 1-14 are designed to help you assess understanding through reading, writing, and speaking. You should work through Exercises 1-2 with your students, and then monitor their work on Exercises 3-14.

PLAN To represent the time, t, solve $d = rt$ for t. Thus, $t = \frac{d}{r}$.

	d	r	t
Downstream	9	$3 + c$	$\frac{9}{3+c}$
Upstream	3	$3 - c$	$\frac{3}{3-c}$

SOLVE $\frac{9}{3+c} = \frac{3}{3-c}$ *time downstream = time upstream* *Note that $c \neq 3$ or -3. Why?*

$(3+c)(3-c)\left(\frac{9}{3+c}\right) = (3+c)(3-c)\left(\frac{3}{3-c}\right)$ *Multiply each side of the equation by the LCD.* **Teaching Tip 5**

$9(3-c) = (3+c)3$ *The fractions are eliminated.*

$27 - 9c = 3c + 9$

$-12c = -18$

$c = \frac{3}{2}$

The rate of the current was $\frac{3}{2}$ or $1\frac{1}{2}$ miles per hour. *Examine this solution.*

Example 4 **Solve $\frac{2m}{1-m} + \frac{m+3}{m^2-1} = 1$.**

$\frac{2m}{1-m} + \frac{m+3}{m^2-1} = 1$ *What values are excluded?*

$\frac{2m}{1-m} + \frac{m+3}{(m+1)(m-1)} = 1$ *Note that $1 - m = -(m-1)$.*

$-\frac{2m}{(m-1)} + \frac{m+3}{(m+1)(m-1)} = 1$ *The LCD is $(m+1)(m-1)$.*

$(m+1)(m-1)\left(-\frac{2m}{(m-1)} + \frac{m+3}{(m+1)(m-1)}\right) = (m+1)(m-1)1$

$-2m(m+1) + (m+3) = m^2 - 1$

$-2m^2 - 2m + m + 3 = m^2 - 1$

$-3m^2 - m + 4 = 0$

$3m^2 + m - 4 = 0$ *Why?*

$(3m+4)(m-1) = 0$ *Factor.*

$3m + 4 = 0$ or $m - 1 = 0$ *Zero product property*

$m = -\frac{4}{3}$ $\quad m = 1$

The solution is $-\frac{4}{3}$.

CHECKING FOR UNDERSTANDING

Communicating Mathematics

Read and study the lesson to answer each question.

1. In Example 3, what would happen if the maximum speed of the boat in still water was 1 mile per hour? **It would go backward.**
2. In Example 4, why is 1 not a solution? **It would make the denominator zero.**

RETEACHING THE LESSON

Give a set of work and uniform motion problems with a proposed answer to each student. Students are to determine if the answers are correct without solving the problems. Students will have to identify and examine the conditions in each problem.

Reteaching Masters Booklet, p. 59

NAME ________ DATE ________

8-9 Reteaching Worksheet

Solving Rational Equations

To solve equations containing fractions, eliminate the fractions by multiplying each side of the equation by a common denominator.

Example 1: Solve $\frac{x-3}{3} + \frac{x}{2} = 4$.

$6\left(\frac{x-3}{3} + \frac{x}{2}\right) = 6 \cdot 4$

$2(x-3) + 3(x) = 24$

$2x - 6 + 3x = 24$

$5x = 30$

$x = 6$

Problems involving work can be solved by calculating the rate of work and the time spent working as shown below.

(rate of working) · (time) = (work done)

$r \cdot t = w$

Uniform motion problems can be solved by using a formula similar to the one used to solve work problems.

(rate) · (time) = (distance)

$r \cdot t = d$

Example 2: Marla can paint Percy's kitchen in 3 hours. Percy can paint it in 2 hours. Working together, how long will it take Marla and Percy to paint the kitchen?

$\frac{t}{3} + \frac{t}{2} = 1$

$2t + 3t = 6$

$5t = 6$

$t = \frac{6}{5}$ or $1\frac{1}{5}$ hours

Together Marla and Percy can paint the kitchen in $1\frac{1}{5}$ hours, or 1 hour and 12 minutes.

Solve each equation.

1. $\frac{x-5}{5} + \frac{x}{4} = 8$ **20**
2. $\frac{4}{8y} - \frac{3y}{y-1} = -2$ **-1 or $-\frac{1}{2}$**
3. $s - \frac{4}{s+3} = s + 3$ **$-4\frac{1}{3}$**
4. $\frac{m+4}{m} + \frac{m}{3} = \frac{m}{3}$ **-4**
5. $\frac{q+4}{q-1} + \frac{q}{q+1} = 2$ **$-\frac{3}{2}$**
6. $\frac{5-2x}{2} - \frac{4x+3}{6} = \frac{7x+2}{6}$ **$\frac{10}{17}$**
7. A motorboat went upstream at 15 mi/h and returned downstream at 20 mi/h. How far did the boat travel one way if the round trip took 3.5 hours? **30 miles**
8. It takes Kenesha 45 minutes to prepare 20 greeting cards. It takes Paula 30 minutes to prepare the same cards. Working together at this rate, how long will it take them to prepare the cards? **18 minutes**

Guided Practice

Find the LCD for each set of rational expressions. 8-11. See margin.

3. $\dfrac{m}{2}, \dfrac{m}{3}$ 6

4. $\dfrac{x}{5}, \dfrac{2x}{3}$ 15

5. $\dfrac{3b}{4}, \dfrac{5b}{8}$ 8

6. $\dfrac{1}{x}, \dfrac{5x}{x+1}$ $x(x+1)$

7. $\dfrac{4}{r^2-1}, \dfrac{5}{r-1}$ r^2-1

8. $\dfrac{m}{2m^2+3m-35}, \dfrac{8}{2m-7}$

9. $\dfrac{5k}{k+5}, \dfrac{k^2}{k+3}, \dfrac{1}{k+3}$

10. $\dfrac{7}{h+1}, \dfrac{1}{2}, \dfrac{2h+5}{h-1}$

11. $\dfrac{2x+1}{4x^2-1}, \dfrac{1}{3}, \dfrac{1}{2x+1}$

12. Luisa can paint her house in 8 days. What part of it can she paint:
a. in 1 day? b. in 3 days? c. in x days? $\dfrac{1}{8}, \dfrac{3}{8}, \dfrac{x}{8}$

13. Drew can build a garage in n days. What part of it can he build:
a. in 1 day? b. in 4 days? c. in x days? $\dfrac{1}{n}, \dfrac{4}{n}, \dfrac{x}{n}$

14. Dimas can landscape a yard in 8 days. Stephanie can do the same job in 10 days.
a. What part of the job can Dimas do: in 1 day? in x days?
b. What part of the job can Stephanie do: in 1 day? in x days?
c. What part of the job can they do together: in 1 day? in x days?
a. $\dfrac{1}{8}, \dfrac{x}{8}$; b. $\dfrac{1}{10}, \dfrac{x}{10}$; c. $\dfrac{9}{40}, \dfrac{9x}{40}$

EXERCISES

Practice

Solve each equation.

A

15. $\dfrac{2a-3}{6} = \dfrac{2a}{3} + \dfrac{1}{2}$ -3

16. $\dfrac{3x}{5} + \dfrac{3}{2} = \dfrac{7x}{10}$ 15

Teaching Tip ⑥

17. $\dfrac{2b-3}{7} - \dfrac{b}{2} = \dfrac{b+3}{14}$ $-\dfrac{9}{4}$

18. $\dfrac{x+1}{x} + \dfrac{x+4}{x} = 6$ $\dfrac{5}{4}$

19. $\dfrac{18}{b} = \dfrac{3}{b} + 3$ 5

20. $\dfrac{3}{5x} + \dfrac{7}{2x} = 1$ $\dfrac{41}{10}$

B

21. $\dfrac{5x}{x+1} + \dfrac{1}{x} = 5$ $\dfrac{1}{4}$

22. $\dfrac{2}{3r} - \dfrac{3r}{r-2} = -3$ $-\dfrac{1}{4}$

23. $\dfrac{m}{m+1} + \dfrac{5}{m-1} = 1$ $-\dfrac{3}{2}$

24. $\dfrac{r-1}{r+1} - \dfrac{2r}{r-1} = -1$ 0

25. $\dfrac{4x}{2x+3} - \dfrac{2x}{2x-3} = 1$ $\dfrac{1}{2}$

26. $\dfrac{5}{5-p} - \dfrac{p^2}{5-p} = -2$ $-5, 3$

27. $\dfrac{14}{b-6} = \dfrac{1}{2} + \dfrac{6}{b-8}$ 20, 10

28. $\dfrac{2a-3}{a-3} - 2 = \dfrac{12}{a+3}$ 5

29. $\dfrac{r}{3r+6} - \dfrac{r}{5r+10} = \dfrac{2}{5}$ -3

30. $\dfrac{x-2}{x} - \dfrac{x-3}{x-6} = \dfrac{1}{x}$ 3

31. $\dfrac{z+3}{z-1} + \dfrac{z+1}{z-3} = 2$ 2

32. $\dfrac{x+2}{x-2} - \dfrac{2}{x+2} = \dfrac{-7}{3}$ $-1, \dfrac{2}{5}$

C

33. $\dfrac{7}{x^2-5x} + \dfrac{3}{5-x} = \dfrac{4}{x}$ $\dfrac{27}{7}$

34. $\dfrac{6}{z+2} + \dfrac{3}{z^2-4} = \dfrac{2z-7}{z-2}$ $-\dfrac{1}{2}, 5$

35. $\dfrac{3w}{w^2-5w+4} = \dfrac{2}{w-4} + \dfrac{3}{w-1}$ 7

36. $\dfrac{4}{k^2-8k+12} = \dfrac{k}{k-2} + \dfrac{1}{k-6}$ -1

37. $\dfrac{m+3}{m+5} + \dfrac{2}{m-9} = \dfrac{-20}{m^2-4m-45}$ 3, 1

38. $\dfrac{h^2-7h-8}{3h^2+2h-8} + \dfrac{1}{h+2} = 0$ 6

Critical Thinking

39. What number would you add to the numerator and denominator of $\dfrac{2}{11}$ to make a fraction equivalent to $\dfrac{1}{2}$? 7

LESSON 8-9 SOLVING RATIONAL EQUATIONS 341

Additional Answers

8. $(2m-7)(m+5)$
9. $(k+5)(k+3)$
10. $2(h+1)(h-1)$
11. $3(2x+1)(2x-1)$

Closing the Lesson
Speaking Activity Ask students to explain why 1 is not a solution to Example 4. It makes the denominator 0.

APPLYING THE LESSON

Homework Exercises

Assignment Guide

Basic: 15-32, 39-43, 47-51
Average: 18-35, 39-51
Enriched: 21-51

Teaching Tip ⑥ You may wish to have students name the restrictions on the domain of each equation before solving it.

Practice Masters Booklet, p. 66

8-9 **Practice Worksheet**

NAME _____ DATE _____

Solving Rational Equations

Solve each equation.

1. $\dfrac{2a+5}{6} - \dfrac{2a}{3} = -\dfrac{1}{2}$ $a=4$

2. $\dfrac{z-3}{10} + \dfrac{z-5}{5} = \dfrac{1}{2}$ $z=6$

3. $\dfrac{c+2}{c} + \dfrac{c+3}{c} = 7$ $c=1$

4. $\dfrac{2d-1}{6} - \dfrac{d}{3} = \dfrac{d+4}{18}$ $d=-7$

5. $\dfrac{1}{m} + \dfrac{4m}{m+1} = 4$ $m=\dfrac{1}{3}$

6. $\dfrac{3}{4r} - \dfrac{4r}{r-3} = -4$ $r=-\dfrac{1}{5}$

7. $\dfrac{5}{p-1} - \dfrac{3}{p+2} = 0$ $p=-\dfrac{13}{2}$

8. $\dfrac{y-2}{4} - \dfrac{y+2}{5} = -1$ $y=-2$

9. $\dfrac{x+2}{2} = 11 - \dfrac{3(28-x)}{8}$ $x=-4$

10. $\dfrac{3}{4x} + \dfrac{4x}{x-3} = 4$ $x=\dfrac{3}{17}$

11. $\dfrac{1}{z+1} - \dfrac{6-z}{6z} = 0$ $z=-3$ or $z=2$

12. $\dfrac{2}{m+2} - \dfrac{m+2}{m-2} = \dfrac{7}{3}$ $m=\dfrac{2}{5}$ or $m=-1$

13. $\dfrac{5e}{3e+1} - \dfrac{1}{9e+3} = \dfrac{7}{3}$ $e=1$

14. $\dfrac{u}{u+2} - \dfrac{2u}{2-u} = \dfrac{u^2}{u^2-4}$ $u=0$ or $u=-1$

Work: Use $rt = w$ to solve each problem.

40. Jane can wash the windows of a building in 4 hours. Jaime can do the same job in 6 hours. If they work together, how long will it take them to wash the windows? $2\frac{2}{5}$ hours

41. A swimming pool can be filled by one pipe in 10 hours. The drain pipe can empty the pool in 15 hours. If both pipes are open, how long will it take to fill the pool? 30 hours

42. Kiko and Marcus can clean the garage together in $3\frac{3}{5}$ hours. Kiko can do the job alone in 6 hours. How many hours would it take Marcus to do the job alone? 9 hours

Physics: Use $d = rt$ to solve each problem.

43. A long-distance cyclist pedaling at a steady rate travels 30 miles with the wind. He can travel only 18 miles against the wind in the same amount of time. If the rate of the wind is 3 miles per hour, what is the cyclist's rate without the wind? 12 mph

44. A tugboat pushing a barge up the Ohio River takes 1 hour longer to travel 36 miles up the river than to travel the same distance down the river. If the rate of the current is 3 miles per hour, find the speed of the tugboat and barge in still water. 15 mph

45. An airplane can fly at a rate of 600 miles per hour in calm air. It can fly 2520 miles with the wind in the same time it can fly 2280 miles against the wind. Find the speed of the wind. 30 mph

46. A motorboat takes $\frac{2}{3}$ as much time to travel 10 miles downstream as it takes to travel the same distance upstream. If the rate of the current is 5 miles per hour, find the speed of the motorboat in still water. 25 mph

Mixed Review

4,355 minutes or about 4 minutes 21 seconds

47. **World Records** The Huey P. Long Bridge, in Metairie, Louisiana, is the longest railroad bridge in the world. If you were traveling on a train going 60 miles per hour across the 22,996-foot bridge, how long would it take you to cross it? **(Lesson 4-7)**

48. **Physics** Shannon weighs 126 pounds and Minal weighs 154 pounds. They are seated at opposite ends of a seesaw. Shannon and Minal are 16 feet apart, and the seesaw is balanced. How far is Shannon from the fulcrum? **(Lesson 4-9)** 8.8 ft

49. Find $(4a + 6b) + (2a + 3b)$. **(Lesson 6-6)** $6a + 9b$

50. Factor $a^2 + 12a + 36$. **(Lesson 7-7)** $(a + 6)^2$

51. Find $x + \frac{x}{y}$. **(Lesson 8-8)** $\frac{xy + x}{y}$

EXTENDING THE LESSON

Math Power: Connections

A jet aircraft is flying from Honolulu to Los Angeles, a distance of 2570 miles. In still air, the plane flies at 600 mph. There is a 50 mph tailwind pushing the plane. At what point in the trip would it be quicker to go on to Los Angeles than to return to Honolulu? Give your answer in terms of distance from Honolulu. (Hint: Write expressions for equal times to continue or to return.) 1177.9 miles

---

Enrichment Masters Booklet, p. 59

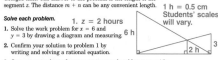

Objectives

8-10A
8-10B

After studying this lesson, you should be able to:
- solve formulas for a specified variable, and
- use formulas that involve rational expressions.

Rational expressions and rational equations often contain more than one variable. Sometimes it is useful to solve for one of the variables. Then you can find the values of any of the variables.

Example 1

CONNECTION

Geometry

Solve for *h* in $A = \frac{1}{2}h(a + b)$. *This is the formula for the area of a trapezoid.*

$$A = \frac{1}{2}h(a + b) \qquad \text{The LCD is 2. } \textbf{Teaching Tip } ❶$$

$$2A = 2\left(\frac{1}{2}h(a + b)\right) \qquad \text{Multiply each side by 2.}$$

$$2A = h(a + b)$$

$$\frac{2A}{a + b} = h \qquad \text{Divide each side by } (a + b).$$

FYI · · ·

The first photograph was taken in 1826 by Joseph Niépce, a French physicist. The photo of the view from his window took eight hours to develop.

The formula below applies to camera and lens systems.

object   lens   image

$\frac{1}{f} = \frac{1}{a} + \frac{1}{b}$

In the formula, *f* is the focal length of the lens, *a* is the distance from the object to the lens, and *b* is the distance from the image to the lens.

Example 2

APPLICATION

Photography

Solve the formula above for *f*.

$$\frac{1}{f} = \frac{1}{a} + \frac{1}{b} \qquad \textbf{Teaching Tip } ❷$$

$$abf\left(\frac{1}{f}\right) = abf\left(\frac{1}{a} + \frac{1}{b}\right) \qquad \text{Multiply each side by the LCD, } abf.$$

$$ab = bf + af$$

$$ab = (b + a)f \qquad \text{Factor } bf + af.$$

$$\frac{ab}{b + a} = f \qquad \text{Divide each side by } b + a.$$

ALTERNATE TEACHING STRATEGIES

Using Logical Reasoning

Find values for *f*, *a*, and *b* so
$\frac{1}{f} = \frac{1}{a} + \frac{1}{b}$.
Choose any nonzero values for *a* and
b with $a \neq -b$. Then $f = \frac{ab}{b + a}$.

Lesson Resources
- Reteaching Master 8-10
- Practice Master 8-10
- Enrichment Master 8-10

Transparency 8-10 contains the 5-Minute Check and a teaching aid for this lesson.

INTRODUCING THE LESSON

 5-Minute Check
(over Lesson 8-9)

Solve.

1. $\frac{3a}{5} + \frac{3}{2} = \frac{7a}{10}$ $a = 15$
2. $\frac{3}{4} + \frac{5x}{7} = 2$ $x = 1\frac{3}{4}$
3. $\frac{a}{3} - \frac{a}{4} = 3$ $a = 36$
4. $\frac{2y}{y - 4} - \frac{3}{5} = 3$ $y = 9$
5. $\frac{k}{6} + \frac{2k}{3} = -\frac{5}{2}$ $k = -3$

Motivating the Lesson

Begin the lesson by having the students draw a number of geometric figures such as a parallelogram, trapezoid, and triangle. Then they should write the formula used to calculate the area of each figure.

TEACHING THE LESSON

Teaching Tip ❶ Emphasize to students that although there are more variables in the equation, the process of solving for *h* does not change. Operations being performed on *h* must be undone.

Teaching Tip ❷ An alternate method of solving for *f* is shown below.

$$\frac{1}{f} = \frac{1}{a} + \frac{1}{b}$$

$$\frac{1}{f} = \frac{b + a}{ab}$$

$$\frac{f}{1} = \frac{ab}{b + a} \qquad \text{Note that } b + a \neq 0.$$

$$f = \frac{ab}{b + a}$$

Chalkboard Examples

For Example 1
Solve each formula for the variable indicated.

a. $P = 2w + 2l$. Solve for l
$$l = \frac{P}{2} - w$$

b. $I = Prt$. Solve for P. $P = \frac{I}{rt}$

For Example 2
Solve each formula for the variable indicated.

a. $\frac{a}{b} + n = 4n$. Solve for b.
$$b = \frac{a}{3n}$$

b. $\frac{3}{n} = \frac{2}{a} - \frac{3}{b}$. Solve for n.
$$n = \frac{3ab}{2b - 3a}$$

For Example 3
R_1 and R_2 are connected in series. Find R_T.

a. $R_1 = 5$ ohms
   $R_2 = 11$ ohms   **16 ohms**

b. $R_1 = 8.2$ ohms
   $R_2 = 4.6$ ohms   **12.8 ohms**

For Example 4
R_1 and R_2 are connected in parallel.

a. Find R_T if $R_1 = 6$ ohms and $R_2 = 9$ ohms.
   $\frac{18}{5}$ or $3\frac{3}{5}$ **ohms**

b. Find R_T if $R_1 = 4$ ohms and $R_2 = 10$ ohms.
   $\frac{20}{7}$ or $2\frac{6}{7}$ **ohms**

Teaching Tip ③   Point out that when more than two resistances are connected in series, the total resistance is the sum of the individual resistances.
$$R_T = R_1 + R_2 + R_3 + \ldots$$
When more than two resistors are connected in parallel, the following formula is used for total resistance.
$$\frac{1}{R_T} = \frac{1}{R_1} + \frac{1}{R_2} + \frac{1}{R_3} + \ldots$$

Electricity can be described as the flow of electrons through a conductor, such as a copper wire. Electricity flows more freely through some conductors than others. The force opposing the flow is called *resistance*. The unit of resistance commonly used is the *ohm*.

FYI · · ·

The *ohm* is named for German physicist Georg Simon Ohm. The unit of conductance, the reciprocal of resistance, is the *mho*—Ohm's name spelled backward.

Resistances can occur one after another, that is, *in series*. Resistances can also occur in branches of the conductor going in the same direction, or *in parallel*. Look at the diagrams below. Formulas for the total resistance, R_T, are given under the diagrams.   **Teaching Tip ③**

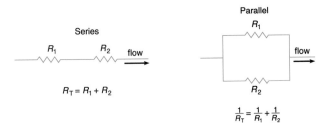

Series
$$R_T = R_1 + R_2$$

Parallel
$$\frac{1}{R_T} = \frac{1}{R_1} + \frac{1}{R_2}$$

Example 3

APPLICATION
Electronics

Assume that $R_1 = 4$ ohms and $R_2 = 3$ ohms. Compute the total resistance of the conductor when the resistances are in series.

$$R_T = R_1 + R_2$$
$$= 4 + 3$$
$$= 7$$

Thus, the total resistance is 7 ohms.

Example 4

APPLICATION
Electronics

Assume that $R_1 = 5$ ohms and $R_2 = 6$ ohms. Compute the total resistance of the conductor when the resistances are in parallel.

$$\frac{1}{R_T} = \frac{1}{R_1} + \frac{1}{R_2}$$
$$\frac{1}{R_T} = \frac{1}{5} + \frac{1}{6} \qquad R_1 = 5 \text{ and } R_2 = 6$$
$$\frac{1}{R_T} = \frac{11}{30} \qquad \frac{1}{5} + \frac{1}{6} = \frac{6}{30} + \frac{5}{30}$$
$$1 \cdot 30 = R_T \cdot 11 \qquad \textit{Find the cross products.}$$
$$\frac{30}{11} = R_T \qquad \textit{Divide each side by 11.}$$

Thus, the total resistance is $\frac{30}{11}$ or 2.727 ohms.

Additional Answers

1. Multiply each side by 2.
   Divide each side by h.
   Subtract b from each side.
2. Multiply each side by 2.
   Divide each side by h.
   Subtract a from each side.
3. Multiply each side by abf.
   Subtract af from each side.
   Factor and divide by $b - f$.
4. Multiply each side by abf.
   Subtract bf from each side.
   Factor and divide by $a - f$.

A *circuit*, or path for the flow of electrons, often has some resistances connected in series and others in parallel.

Example 5

A parallel circuit has one branch in series as shown at the right. Given that the total resistance is 2.25 ohms, $R_1 = 3$ ohms, and $R_2 = 4$ ohms, find R_3.

$$\frac{1}{R_T} = \frac{1}{R_1} + \frac{1}{R_2 + R_3}$$ *The total resistance of the branch in series is $R_2 + R_3$.*

$$\frac{1}{2.25} = \frac{1}{3} + \frac{1}{4 + R_3}$$ $R_T = 2.25$ and $R_1 = 3$

$$\frac{1}{2.25} - \frac{1}{3} = \frac{1}{4 + R_3}$$ $\frac{1}{2.25} - \frac{1}{3} = \frac{4}{9} - \frac{3}{9}$

$$\frac{1}{9} = \frac{1}{4 + R_3}$$

$4 + R_3 = 9$ *Find the cross products.*

$R_3 = 5$

Thus, R_3 is 5 ohms.

CHECKING FOR UNDERSTANDING

Communicating Mathematics

Read and study the lesson to answer each question. See margin.

1. In Example 1, what steps would you take to solve for *a*?

2. In Example 1, what steps would you take to solve for *b*?

3. In Example 2, what steps would you take to solve for *a*?

4. In Example 2, what steps would you take to solve for *b*?

Guided Practice

Exercises 5–10 refer to the diagram at the right.

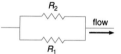

5. Find the total resistance, R_T, given that $R_1 = 8$ ohms and $R_2 = 6$ ohms. **3.429 ohms**

6. Find the total resistance, R_T, given that $R_1 = 4.5$ ohms and $R_2 = 3.5$ ohms. **1.969 ohms**

7. Find R_1, given that R_T is $2.\overline{2}$ ohms and R_2 is 5 ohms. **4 ohms**

8. Find R_1, given that R_T is $3\frac{3}{7}$ ohms and R_2 is 8 ohms. **6 ohms**

9. Find R_1 and R_2, given that the total resistance is $2.\overline{6}$ ohms and R_1 is two times as great as R_2. **8 ohms, 4 ohms**

10. Find R_1 and R_2, given that the total resistance is 2.25 ohms and R_1 is three times as great as R_2. **9 ohms, 3 ohms**

RETEACHING THE LESSON

To check the solution to solving a formula for a specified variable, substitute a set of values for all other variables in both the original formula and its equivalent that has been solved for a given variable. Find the value of the given variable in each and compare.

Chalkboard Example

For Example 5
Solve each example for the circuit shown in Example 5.

a. Find R_3 if $R_T = \frac{14}{3}$ ohms, $R_1 = 6$ ohms, and $R_2 = 9$ ohms.   **12 ohms**

b. Find R_1 if $R_T = 10$ ohms, $R_2 = 12$ ohms, and $R_3 = 8$ ohms.   **20 ohms**

EVALUATING THE LESSON

Checking for Understanding

Exercises 1-10 are designed to help you assess understanding through reading, writing, and speaking. You should work through Exercises 1-4 with your students, and then monitor their work on Exercises 5-10.

Reteaching Masters Booklet, p. 60

NAME _____   DATE _____

8-10 Reteaching Worksheet

Application: Formulas

Formulas and equations involving rational expressions often contain more than one variable. Sometimes it is useful to solve the equations or formulas for one of the variables.

Many scientific formulas, such as those for electrical resistance, contain rational expressions. The unit of resistance commonly used is the *ohm*.

In a series circuit, $R_T = R_1 + R_2$.

In a parallel circuit, $\frac{1}{R_T} = \frac{1}{R_1} + \frac{1}{R_2}$.

Example: $R_1 = 5$ ohms and $R_2 = \frac{1}{2}$ ohm. What is the total resistance if the resistors are in series?

$R_T = R_1 + R_2$

$R_T = 5 + \frac{1}{2}$

$R_T = 5\frac{1}{2}$ ohms

Thus, the total resistance is $5\frac{1}{2}$ ohms.

Solve each problem.

1. Six security alarms are connected in a series circuit. If the resistance of each alarm is 12 ohms, what is the total resistance? **72 ohms**

2. A lamp of 100 ohms resistance, a TV of 150 ohms resistance, and a VCR of 80 ohms resistance are connected in a parallel circuit. What is the total resistance? $\frac{240}{7}$, or $34\frac{2}{7}$ ohms

Solve each formula for the variable indicated.

3. $I = prt$, for t $t = \frac{I}{pr}$

4. $P = 2l + 2w$, for l $\frac{P - 2w}{2} = l$

5. $A = \frac{1}{2}bh$, for h $\frac{2A}{b} = h$

6. $V = \frac{1}{3}\pi r^2 h$, for h $\frac{3V}{\pi r^2} = h$

7. $C = \frac{5}{9}(F - 32)$, for F $\frac{9}{5}C + 32 = F$

8. $y = mx + b$, for x $\frac{y - b}{m} = x$

Use the diagram at the right to solve problems 9 and 10.

9. Find R_1 if $R_T = 3$ ohms and $R_2 = 10$ ohms. $4\frac{2}{7}$ ohms

10. Find R_T if $R_1 = 80$ ohms and $R_2 = 20$ ohms.   16 ohms

346 Chapter 8

Closing the Lesson

Speaking Activity Have students describe the similarities that exist between solving an equation for a specified variable and solving an equation for any real number. Ask them to give an example of each type of equation.

APPLYING THE LESSON

Homework Exercises

Assignment Guide

Basic: 11-37, 42, 44-49
Average: 15-40, 42-49
Enriched: 17-49

Chapter 8, Quiz D, (Lessons 8-9 through 8-10), is available in the Evaluation Masters Booklet, p. 108.

Teaching Tip ❹ Before students begin Exercises 18-20, have them identify what the variables *I, p, r,* and *t* represent.
interest, principle, rate, time

Practice Masters Booklet, p. 67

NAME _____ DATE _____

8-10 Practice Worksheet

Application: Formulas

Physics: Solve each formula for the variable indicated.

1. $a = \frac{v}{t}$, for v $v = at$

2. $v = r + at$, for t $t = \frac{v-r}{a}$

3. $s = vt + \frac{1}{2}at^2$, for a
   $a = \frac{2(s-vt)}{t^2}$

4. $f = \frac{W}{g} \cdot \frac{V^2}{R}$, for g $g = \frac{WV^2}{fR}$

Business: Solve each formula for the variable indicated.

5. $I = prt$, for p $p = \frac{I}{rt}$

6. $a = \frac{r}{2y} - 0.25$, for r
   $r = y(2a + 0.5)$

Electronics: Solve each formula for the variable indicated.

7. $H = (0.24)I^2Rt$, for t
   $t = \frac{H}{(0.24)I^2R}$

8. $\frac{1}{R_T} = \frac{1}{R_1} + \frac{1}{R_2}$, for R_2
   $R_2 = \frac{R_TR_1}{R_1 - R_T}$

9. $I = \frac{E}{r+R}$, for E
   $E = I(r + R)$

10. $I = \frac{nE}{nr+R}$, for r
    $r = \frac{nE - IR}{nI}$

Mathematics: Solve each formula for the variable indicated.

11. $A = \frac{1}{2}h(a + b)$, for h
    $h = \frac{2A}{a+b}$

12. $A = \frac{1}{2}h(a + b)$, for b
    $b = \frac{2A - ah}{h}$

13. $p = 2l + 2w$, for w
    $w = \frac{P - 2l}{2}$

14. $S = \frac{a}{1-r}$, for r $r = \frac{S-a}{S}$

Use the diagram at the right to solve problems 15 and 16.

15. Find R_1 if $R_T = 10$ ohms and $R_2 = 15$ ohms.   30 ohms

16. Find R_T if $R_1 = 90$ ohms and $R_2 = 60$ ohms.   36 ohms

---

EXERCISES

For answers not shown with exercises, see margin.

Applications   Physics: Solve each formula for the variable indicated.

11. $a = \frac{v}{t}$, for t $t = \frac{v}{a}$

12. $v = r + at$, for a $a = \frac{v-r}{t}$

13. $s = vt + \frac{1}{2}at^2$, for v

14. $s = vt + \frac{1}{2}at^2$, for a

15. $F = G\left(\frac{Mm}{d^2}\right)$, for M $M = \frac{Fd^2}{Gm}$

16. $f = \frac{W}{g} \cdot \frac{V^2}{R}$, for R $R = \frac{WV^2}{fg}$

Business: Solve each formula for variable indicated.   **Teaching Tip** ❹

17. $A = p + prt$, for p $p = \frac{A}{1 + rt}$

18. $I = prt$, for r $r = \frac{I}{pt}$

19. $I = \left(\frac{100 - P}{P}\right)\frac{365}{R}$, for P

20. $I = \frac{365d}{360 - dr}$, for d

21. $a = \frac{r}{2y} - 0.25$, for y

22. $c = \frac{P - 100}{P}$, for P $P = \frac{100}{1 - c}$

B   Electronics: Solve each formula for the variable indicated.

23. $H = (0.24)I^2Rt$, for R

24. $P = \frac{E^2}{R}$, for R $R = \frac{E^2}{P}$

25. $\frac{1}{R_T} = \frac{1}{R_1} + \frac{1}{R_2}$, for R_1

26. $I = \frac{E}{r + R}$, for R $R = \frac{E - Ir}{I}$

27. $I = \frac{nE}{nr + R}$, for n $n = \frac{IR}{E - Ir}$

28. $I = \frac{E}{\frac{r}{n} + R}$, for r $r = \frac{En - IRn}{I}$

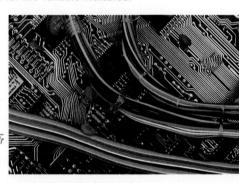

Mathematics: Solve each formula for the variable indicated.

29. $y = mx + b$, for m $m = \frac{y - b}{x}$

30. $S = \frac{n}{2}(A + t)$, for n $n = \frac{2S}{A + t}$

31. $m = \frac{y_2 - y_1}{x_2 - x_1}$, for y_2

32. $m = \frac{y_2 - y_1}{x_2 - x_1}$, for x_1

33. $\frac{P}{D} = Q + \frac{R}{D}$, for R $R = P - DQ$

34. $\frac{P}{D} = Q + \frac{R}{D}$, for D $D = \frac{P - R}{Q}$

Electronics: Exercises 35-37 refer to the diagram below.

35. Find R_T, given that $R_1 = 5$ ohms, $R_2 = 4$ ohms, and $R_3 = 3$ ohms.   2.916 ohms

36. Find R_1, given that $R_T = 2\frac{10}{13}$ ohms, $R_2 = 3$ ohms, and $R_3 = 6$ ohms.   4 ohms

37. Find R_2, given that $R_T = 3.5$ ohms, $R_1 = 5$ ohms, and $R_3 = 4$ ohms.

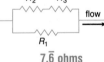

7.6 ohms

346   CHAPTER 8   RATIONAL EXPRESSIONS

Additional Answers

13. $v = \frac{2s - at^2}{2t}$

14. $a = \frac{2s - 2vt}{t^2}$

19. $P = \frac{36,500}{IR + 365}$

20. $d = \frac{360I}{Ir + 365}$

21. $y = \frac{r}{2a + 0.5}$

23. $R = \frac{H}{0.24I^2t}$

25. $R_1 = \frac{R_TR_2}{R_2 - R_T}$

31. $y_2 = mx_2 - mx_1 + y_1$

32. $x_1 = \frac{mx_2 - y_2 + y_1}{m}$

Electronics: Solve each problem.

38. Resistances of 3 ohms, 6 ohms, and 9 ohms are connected in series. What is the total resistance? **18 ohms**

39. Eight lights on a decorated tree are connected in series. Each has a resistance of 12 ohms. What is the total resistance? **96 ohms**

40. Three coils with resistances of 3 ohms, 4 ohms, and 6 ohms are connected in parallel. What is the total resistance? **1.3 ohms**

41. Three appliances are connected in parallel: a lamp with a resistance of 60 ohms, an iron with a resistance of 20 ohms, and a heating coil with a resistance of 80 ohms. Find the total resistance. **12.632 ohms**

42. $R_T = R_1 + \dfrac{R_2 R_3}{R_3 + R_2}$

Critical Thinking   **Electronics: Exercises 42–43 refer to the diagram below.**

42. Write an equation for the total resistance for the diagram at the right.

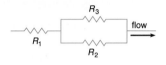

43. Find the total resistance, given that $R_1 = 5$ ohms, $R_2 = 4$ ohms, and $R_3 = 6$ ohms. **7.4 ohms**

Mixed Review

44. **Temperature**   The formula for finding the Celsius temperature (C) when you know the Fahrenheit temperature (F) is $C = \frac{5}{9}(F - 32)$. Find the Celsius temperature when the Fahrenheit temperature is 59°. **(Lesson 1-7)** **15°C**

45. Solve: $|4x + 4| \leq 14$.   **(Lesson 5-6)** $\left\{ x \mid -\frac{9}{2} \leq x \leq \frac{5}{2} \right\}$

46. **Finance**   The current balance on a car loan can be found by evaluating the expression $P\left[\dfrac{1 - (1 + r)^{k-n}}{r}\right]$, where P is the monthly payment, r is the monthly interest rate, k is the number of payments already made, and n is the total number of monthly payments. Find the current balance if $P = \$256$, $r = 0.01$, $k = 20$, and $n = 60$.   **(Lesson 6-2)** **$8405.68**

47. **Astronomy**   When a solar flare occurs on the sun, it can send out a blast wave that travels at 3×10^6 kilometers per hour. How long would it take for a blast wave to reach Earth where it could be detected by a satellite in orbit? (Assume that the distance from the sun to the satellite would be 1.5×10^8 kilometers.)   **(Lesson 6-4)** **50 hours or about 2 days**

48. Factor $2m^2 - 32n^2$.   **(Lesson 7-8)** $2(m + 4n)(m - 4n)$

49. **Work**   Hugo and Denise can mow a lawn together in 24 minutes. It takes Hugo 40 minutes to do the job alone. How long would it take Denise to do the job alone?   **(Lesson 8-9)** **60 minutes**

EXTENDING THE LESSON

Math Power: Connections

Given the formula $\dfrac{1}{R_T} = \dfrac{1}{R_1} + \dfrac{1}{R_2}$ for the resistance of a circuit, determine the resistance R_1 if $R_T = 1.2$ ohms and $R_2 = 4$ ohms.
1.71 ohms

Enrichment Masters Booklet, p. 60

NAME _____ DATE _____

8-10   Enrichment Worksheet

Using Rational Expressions and Equations

In 1985 Steve Cram set a world record for the mile run with a time of 3:46.31. In 1954, Roger Bannister ran the first mile under 4 minutes at 3:59.4. Had they run those times in the same race, how far in front of Bannister would Cram have been at the finish?

Use $\frac{d}{t} = r$. Since 3 min 46.31 s = 226.31 s, and 3 min 59.4 s = 239.4 s, Cram's rate was $\frac{5280 \text{ ft}}{226.31 \text{ s}}$ and Bannister's rate was $\frac{5280 \text{ ft}}{239.4 \text{ s}}$.

	r	t	d
Cram	$\frac{5280}{226.31}$	226.31	5280 feet
Bannister	$\frac{5280}{239.4}$	226.31	$\frac{5280}{239.4} \cdot 226.31$ or 4491.3 feet

Therefore, when Cram hit the tape, he would be 5280 − 4491.3, or 288.7 feet, ahead of Bannister. Let's see whether we can develop a formula for this type of problem.

Let D = the distance raced,
W = the winner's time,
and L = the loser's time.

Following the same pattern, you obtain the results shown in the table at the right.

The winning distance will be $D - \frac{DW}{L}$.

	r	t	d
Winner	$\frac{D}{W}$	W	$\frac{D}{W} \cdot W = D$
Loser	$\frac{D}{L}$	W	$\frac{D}{L} \cdot W = \frac{DW}{L}$

1. Show that the expression for the winning distance is equivalent to $\frac{D(L - W)}{L}$.
   $D - \frac{DW}{L} = \frac{DL}{L} - \frac{DW}{L}$
   $\frac{DL - DW}{L}$
   $\frac{D(L - W)}{L}$

Use the formula winning distance = $\frac{D(L - W)}{L}$ to find the winning distance for each of the following Olympic races.

2. women's 400 meter relay: Canada 48.4 s (1928); East Germany 41.6 s (1980) **56.2 meters**

3. men's 200 meter freestyle swimming: Mark Spitz 1 min 52.78 s (1972); Michael Gross 1 min 47.44 s (1984) **9.5 meters**

4. men's 50,000 meter walk: Thomas Green 4 h 50 min 10 s (1932); Hartwig Gauter 3 h 49 min 24 s (1980) **10,471 meters**

5. women's 400 meter freestyle relay: Great Britain 5 min 52.8 s (1912); East Germany 3 min 42.71 s (1980) **147.5 meters**

The Chapter Summary and
Review begins with an
alphabetical listing of the new
terms that were presented in the
chapter. Have students define
each term and provide an
example of it, if appropriate.

The Skills and Concepts
presented in the chapter are
reviewed using a side-by-side
format. Encourage students to
refer to the Objectives and
Examples on the left as they
complete the Review Exercises
on the right.

The Chapter Summary and
Review ends with exercises that
review Applications and
Connections.

CHAPTER SUMMARY AND REVIEW

VOCABULARY

Upon completing this chapter, you should be
familiar with the following terms:

complex fractions	334	316	multiplicative inverse
excluded values	306	338	rational equations
least common denominator (LCD)	330	306	rational expressions
least common multiple (LCM)	329	316	reciprocal
mixed expressions	334		

SKILLS AND CONCEPTS

OBJECTIVES AND EXAMPLES	REVIEW EXERCISES

Upon completing this chapter, you should be able to:

Use these exercises to review and prepare for the chapter test.

■ **simplify rational expressions**
(Lesson 8-1)

$$\frac{x + y}{x^2 + 3xy + 2y^2} = \frac{\overset{1}{\cancel{x + y}}}{(\cancel{x + y})(x + 2y)}$$

$$= \frac{1}{x + 2y}$$

Simplify. State the excluded values of the variables. 4. $\frac{x + 3}{x(x - 6)}$

1. $\frac{3x^2y}{12xy^3z}$ $\frac{x}{4y^2z}$

2. $\frac{z^2 - 3z}{z - 3}$ z

3. $\frac{a^2 - 25}{a^2 + 3a - 10}$ $\frac{a - 5}{a - 2}$

4. $\frac{x^2 + 10x + 21}{x^3 + x^2 - 42x}$

■ **multiply rational expressions**
(Lesson 8-2)

$$\frac{1}{x^2 + x - 12} \cdot \frac{x - 3}{x + 5}$$

$$= \frac{1}{(\cancel{x - 3})(x + 4)} \cdot \frac{\overset{1}{\cancel{x - 3}}}{x + 5}$$

$$= \frac{1}{x^2 + 9x + 20}$$

Find each product. Assume that no denominator is equal to zero.

5. $\frac{7}{9} \cdot \frac{a^2}{b}$ $\frac{7a^2}{9b}$

6. $\frac{5x^2y}{8ab} \cdot \frac{12a^2b}{25x}$ $\frac{3axy}{10}$

7. $\frac{x^2 + x - 12}{x + 2} \cdot \frac{x + 4}{x^2 - x - 6}$ $\frac{(x + 4)^2}{(x + 2)^2}$

8. $\frac{b^2 + 19b + 84}{b - 3} \cdot \frac{b^2 - 9}{b^2 + 15b + 36}$ $b + 7$

■ **divide rational expressions**
(Lesson 8-3)

$$\frac{y^2 - 16}{y^2 - 64} \div \frac{y + 4}{y - 8} = \frac{y^2 - 16}{y^2 - 64} \cdot \frac{y - 8}{y + 4}$$

$$= \frac{(\cancel{y + 4})(y - 4)}{(y + 8)(\cancel{y - 8})} \cdot \frac{\cancel{y - 8}}{\cancel{y + 4}}$$

$$= \frac{y - 4}{y + 8}$$

Find each quotient. Assume that no denominator is equal to zero. 10. See margin.

9. $\frac{p^3}{2q} \div \frac{-(p^2)}{4q}$ $-2p$

10. $\frac{n^2}{n - 3} \div (n + 4)$

11. $\frac{7a^2b}{x^2 + x - 30} \div \frac{3a}{x^2 + 15x + 54}$ $\frac{7ab(x + 9)}{3(x - 5)}$

12. $\frac{m^2 + 4m - 21}{m^2 + 8m + 15} \div \frac{m^2 - 9}{m^2 + 12m + 35}$ $\frac{(m + 7)^2}{(m + 3)^2}$

Additional Answers

10. $\frac{n^2}{(n - 3)(n + 4)}$

13. $x^2 + 4x + 2$

14. $x^3 + 5x^2 + 12x + 23 + \frac{52}{x - 2}$

15. $2a^2 + 18a + 159 + \frac{1422}{a - 9}$

16. $3a^2 - 2a - 4 - \frac{5}{2a - 5}$

24. $\frac{-m^3 + m^2 - 3m^2n - 3mn^2 - 2mn + n^2 - n^3}{(m + n)^2(m - n)}$

OBJECTIVES AND EXAMPLES	REVIEW EXERCISES

■ divide polynomials by binomials
(Lesson 8-4)

$$\begin{array}{r} x^2 + x - 19 \\ x - 3\overline{)x^3 - 2x^2 - 22x + 21} \\ \underline{x^3 - 3x^2} \\ x^2 - 22x \\ \underline{x^2 - 3x} \\ -19x + 21 \\ \underline{-19x + 57} \\ -36 \end{array}$$

The quotient is $x^2 + x - 19 - \dfrac{36}{x - 3}$.

Find each quotient. See margin.

13. $(x^3 + 7x^2 + 10x - 6) \div (x + 3)$

14. $(x^4 + 3x^3 + 2x^2 - x + 6) \div (x - 2)$

15. $(2a^3 - 3a - 9) \div (a - 9)$

16. $(6a^3 - 19a^2 + 2a + 15) \div (2a - 5)$

■ add and subtract rational expressions
with like denominators   (Lesson 8-5)

$$\frac{m^2}{4 + m} - \frac{16}{m + 4} = \frac{m^2}{m + 4} - \frac{16}{m + 4}$$
$$= \frac{m^2 - 16}{m + 4}$$
$$= \frac{\overset{1}{\cancel{(m + 4)}}(m - 4)}{\underset{1}{\cancel{m + 4}}}$$
$$= m - 4$$

Find each sum or difference.

17. $\dfrac{7}{x^2} + \dfrac{a}{x^2}$ $\dfrac{7 + a}{x^2}$

18. $\dfrac{a^2}{a^2 - b^2} + \dfrac{-(b^2)}{a^2 - b^2}$ 1

19. $\dfrac{2x}{x - 3} - \dfrac{6}{x - 3}$ 2

20. $\dfrac{x}{x^2 - 1} + \dfrac{1}{x^2 - 1}$ $\dfrac{1}{x - 1}$

■ add and subtract rational expressions
with unlike denominators   (Lesson 8-7)

$$\frac{m - 1}{m + 1} + \frac{4}{2m + 5}$$
$$= \frac{2m + 5}{2m + 5} \cdot \frac{m - 1}{m + 1} + \frac{4}{2m + 5} \cdot \frac{m + 1}{m + 1}$$
$$= \frac{2m^2 + 3m - 5}{(2m + 5)(m + 1)} + \frac{4m + 4}{(2m + 5)(m + 1)}$$
$$= \frac{2m^2 + 7m - 1}{2m^2 + 7m + 5}$$

Find each sum or difference.

21. $\dfrac{2}{x - y} + \dfrac{x}{y - x}$ $\dfrac{2 - x}{x - y}$

22. $\dfrac{x}{x + 3} - \dfrac{5}{x - 2}$ $\dfrac{x^2 - 7x - 15}{x^2 + x - 6}$

23. $\dfrac{2x + 3}{x^2 - 4} + \dfrac{6}{x + 2}$ $\dfrac{8x - 9}{x^2 - 4}$

24. $\dfrac{m - n}{m^2 + 2mn + n^2} - \dfrac{m + n}{m - n}$ See margin.

■ simplify mixed expressions and complex
fractions   (Lesson 8-8)

$$\frac{\dfrac{x - 3}{x + 5}}{\dfrac{x + 5}{x}} = \frac{x - 3}{x + 5} \cdot \frac{x}{x + 5}$$
$$= \frac{x^2 - 3x}{x^2 + 10x + 25}$$

Simplify.

25. $\dfrac{\dfrac{x^2}{y^3}}{\dfrac{3x}{9y^2}}$ $\dfrac{3x}{y}$

26. $\dfrac{\dfrac{a^2 - 13a + 40}{a^2 - 4a - 32}}{\dfrac{a - 5}{a + 7}}$ $\dfrac{a + 7}{a + 4}$

27. $\dfrac{x - \dfrac{35}{x + 2}}{x + \dfrac{42}{x + 13}}$ $\dfrac{(x - 5)(x + 13)}{(x + 2)(x + 6)}$ or $\dfrac{x^2 + 8x - 65}{x^2 + 8x + 12}$

NAME _____ DATE _____

Cumulative Review (Chapters 1–8)

1. Write an algebraic expression for *one-third the cube of a number.*
   1. $\frac{1}{3}n^3$

2. Solve $t = 7 - 6\frac{1}{3}$.
   2. $\frac{2}{3}$

3. State the property shown in $3a + 7c = 7c + 3a$.
   3. Comm., Add.

4. Write as an equation: y is n less than twice x.
   4. $y = 2x - n$

5. Graph $\{3, 4, 7, 8\}$ on a number line.
   5. (number line 0 1 2 3 4 5 6 7 8 9)

6. Find $-8.4 + 3.6$.
   6. -4.8

7. Solve $r - (-3) = 42$.
   7. 39

8. Read and explore the following problem. Then define a variable, write an equation, and solve. The sum of two integers is -12. One integer is 13. Find the other integer.
   8. n = the integer
      $n + 13 = -12$
      -25

9. Simplify $6(-4) + (-12)(-3)$.
   9. 12

Solve each equation.

10. $-\frac{3}{4}x = 30$
    10. -40

11. $2p - 3(p + 2) = 5(2p + 1)$
    11. -1

12. $\frac{7}{10} = \frac{3}{x+1}$
    12. $3\frac{2}{7}$

Solve each inequality.

13. $-6 + d > -14$
    13. $d > -8$

14. $10y - 3(y + 4) \le 0$
    14. $y \le \frac{12}{7}$

15. Solve the inequality $2 > 2t - 4$ and $2t - 4 > 8$. Then graph the solution set.
    15. no solutions

16. A clothing store makes a profit of $5.50 on each tie sold. How many ties must the store sell to make a profit of at least $352.00?
    16. at least 64

NAME _____ DATE _____

Cumulative Review (Chapters 1–8)

Simplify.

17. $-2(ax^2y^3)^2$
    17. $-2a^2x^4y^6$

18. $\frac{-25k^2m^3}{-5km^6}$
    18. $\frac{5k}{m^2}$

Solve each problem.

19. Emily received a discount of $7.65 on a new skirt. The discount price was $17.85. What was the percent of discount?
    19. 30%

20. How much salt must be added to 30 kg of a solution containing 15% salt to raise the salt content to 25%?
    20. 4 kg

Find each product.

21. $xy(x - y)$
    21. $x^2y - xy^2$

22. $(2a + 3)(3a - 7)$
    22. $6a^2 - 5a - 21$

23. $(m^2 + 5)(m^2 - 5)$
    23. $m^4 - 25$

24. The length of a rectangle is 5 cm more than twice the width. The perimeter is 70 cm. Find the dimensions of the rectangle.
    24. 10 cm by 25 cm

25. Find the GCF of $36x^2y$ and $45xy^2$.
    25. $9xy$

Factor, if possible.

26. $m^2 + 12m + 36$
    26. $(m + 6)^2$

27. $2ar + 2rt - a - t$
    27. $(2r - 1)(a + t)$

28. $36c^3 + 6c^2 - 6c$
    28. $6c(3c - 1)(2c + 1)$

Solve each equation.

29. $x(x + 12) = 0$
    29. $0, -12$

30. $r^2 - 10r + 25 = 0$
    30. 5

31. Find two consecutive odd integers whose product is 255.
    31. $15, 17; -17, -15$

32. Simplify $\frac{b^2 + 2b - 3}{2b^2 + 6b}$.
    32. $\frac{b - 1}{2b}$

33. For what value of k will the solution set of $\frac{x-7}{k} + \frac{1}{2} = 3$ be $\{-3\}$?
    33. -4

■ solve rational equations   **(Lesson 8-9)**

$$\frac{3}{x} + \frac{1}{x - 5} = \frac{1}{2x}$$

$$2x(x - 5)\left(\frac{3}{x} + \frac{1}{x-5}\right) = \left(\frac{1}{2x}\right)2x(x - 5)$$

$$6(x - 5) + 2x = x - 5$$

$$7x = 25$$

$$x = \frac{25}{7}$$

Solve each equation.

28. $\frac{4x}{3} + \frac{7}{2} = \frac{7x}{12}$ $-\frac{14}{3}$

29. $\frac{1}{h + 1} + \frac{2}{3} = \frac{2h + 5}{h - 1}$ $-2, -\frac{5}{2}$

30. $\frac{3x + 2}{x^2 + 7x + 6} = \frac{1}{x + 6} + \frac{4}{x + 1}$ $-\frac{23}{2}$

31. $\frac{3m - 2}{2m^2 - 5m - 3} - \frac{2}{2m + 1} = \frac{4}{m - 3}$ 0

■ solve formulas for a specified variable **(Lesson 8-10)**

Solve $\frac{1}{f} = \frac{1}{a} + \frac{1}{b}$ for a.

$$abf\left(\frac{1}{f}\right) = \left(\frac{1}{a} + \frac{1}{b}\right)abf$$

$$ab = bf + af$$

$$bf = a(b - f)$$

$$\frac{bf}{b - f} = a$$

Solve each equation for n.

32. $\frac{1}{2}n + b = n$ $n = 2b$

33. $\frac{n}{x} = \frac{y}{r}$ $\frac{xy}{r}$

34. $\frac{n}{a} + \frac{b}{c} = d$ $\frac{acd - ab}{c}$

35. $\frac{a}{c} = n + bn$ $\frac{a}{c + cb}$

APPLICATIONS AND CONNECTIONS

Geometry: Find the measure of the area of each rectangle in simplest form.   (Lesson 8-2)

36.

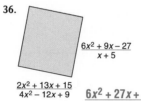

$6x^2 + 9x - 27$
$x + 5$

$2x^2 + 13x + 15$
$4x^2 - 12x + 9$

$\frac{6x^2 + 27x + 27}{2x - 3}$

37.

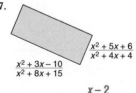

$x^2 + 5x + 6$
$x^2 + 4x + 4$

$x^2 + 3x - 10$
$x^2 + 8x + 15$

$\frac{x - 2}{x + 2}$

38.

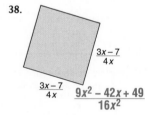

$3x - 7$
$4x$

$\frac{3x - 7}{4x}$ $\frac{9x^2 - 42x + 49}{16x^2}$

39. Solve by listing the possibilities.
    Which whole numbers less than 100 are divisible by both 3 and 11? **(Lesson 8-6)** 33, 66, 99

40. **Electronics** Assume that $R_1 = 4$ ohms and $R_2 = 6$ ohms. What is the total resistance of the conductor if R_1 and R_2 are:

    a. connected in series? **10 ohms**

    b. connected in parallel? **2.4 ohms**
       (Lesson 8-10)

Simplify.

1. $\dfrac{\frac{5}{9}}{\frac{2}{3}}$ $\dfrac{5}{6}$

2. $\dfrac{21x^2y}{28ax}$ $\dfrac{3xy}{4a}$

3. $\dfrac{x^2 + 7x - 18}{x^2 + 12x + 27}$ $\dfrac{x - 2}{x + 3}$

4. $\dfrac{x^2 - x - 56}{x^2 + x - 42}$ $\dfrac{x - 8}{x - 6}$

5. $\dfrac{7x^2 - 28}{5x^3 - 20x}$ $\dfrac{7}{5x}$

6. $\dfrac{2x^2 - 5x - 3}{x^2 + 2x - 15}$ $\dfrac{2x + 1}{x + 5}$

Perform the indicated operations. 9, 10, 12. See margin.

7. $\dfrac{3x}{x + 3} + \dfrac{5x}{x + 3}$ $\dfrac{8x}{x + 3}$

8. $\dfrac{2x}{x - 7} - \dfrac{14}{x - 7}$ 2

9. $\dfrac{2x}{x + 7} + \dfrac{4}{x + 4}$

10. $\dfrac{2a + 1}{2a - 3} + \dfrac{a - 3}{3a + 2}$

11. $\dfrac{x + 5}{x + 2} + 6$ $\dfrac{7x + 17}{x + 2}$

12. $\dfrac{x - 2}{x - 8} + x + 5$

13. $\dfrac{3x + 2}{4x + 1} + \dfrac{7}{x}$ $\dfrac{3x^2 + 30x + 7}{4x^2 + x}$

14. $\dfrac{x}{x + 1} + \dfrac{1}{x + 1}$ 1

15. $\dfrac{3x - 8}{x + 4} + \dfrac{9}{x + 1}$ $\dfrac{3x^2 + 4x + 28}{x^2 + 5x + 4}$

16. $\dfrac{x^2 + 4x - 32}{x + 5} \cdot \dfrac{x - 3}{x^2 - 7x + 12}$ $\dfrac{x + 8}{x + 5}$

17. $\dfrac{3x^2 + 2x - 8}{x^2 - 4} \div \dfrac{6x^2 + 13x - 28}{2x^2 - 3x - 35}$ $\dfrac{x - 5}{x - 2}$

18. $\dfrac{4x^2 + 11x + 6}{x^2 - x - 6} \div \dfrac{x^2 + 8x + 16}{x^2 + x - 12}$ $\dfrac{4x + 3}{x + 4}$

19. $\dfrac{3x^2 + 5x - 28}{3x^2 - 3x - 28} \cdot \dfrac{x^2 - 8x + 7}{3x - 7}$ $x - 1$

20. $\dfrac{x - \dfrac{24}{x + 5}}{x - \dfrac{72}{x - 1}}$ $\dfrac{(x - 3)(x - 1)}{(x - 9)(x + 5)}$

21. $\dfrac{\dfrac{x^2 - x - 6}{x^2 + 2x - 15}}{\dfrac{x^2 - 2x - 8}{x^2 + x - 20}}$ 1

22. $\dfrac{\dfrac{2}{3m} + \dfrac{3}{m^2}}{\dfrac{2}{5m} + \dfrac{5}{m}}$ $\dfrac{5(2m + 9)}{81m}$

Solve each equation.

23. $\dfrac{y + 3}{6} = \dfrac{y + 2}{12} - \dfrac{2}{5}$ $-\dfrac{44}{5}$

24. $\dfrac{x + 1}{x} + \dfrac{6}{x} = x + 7$ $1, -7$

25. $\dfrac{4m}{m - 3} + \dfrac{6}{3 - m} = m$ $6, 1$

26. $\dfrac{-2b - 9}{b^2 + 7b + 12} = \dfrac{b}{b + 3} + \dfrac{2}{b + 4}$ -5

27. $\dfrac{1}{y - 4} - \dfrac{2}{y - 8} = \dfrac{-1}{y + 6}$ $\dfrac{16}{9}$

28. $\dfrac{m + 3}{m - 1} + \dfrac{m + 1}{m - 3} = \dfrac{22}{3}$ $\dfrac{3}{2}, 4$

Solve each formula for the variable indicated.

29. $F = G\left(\dfrac{Mm}{d^2}\right)$, for G $G = \dfrac{Fd^2}{Mm}$

30. $\dfrac{1}{R_T} = \dfrac{1}{R_1} + \dfrac{1}{R_2}$, for R_2 $R_2 = \dfrac{R_1 R_T}{R_1 - R_T}$

Solve.

31. **Work** Willie can do a job in 6 days. Myra can do the same job in $4\frac{1}{2}$ days. If they work together, how long will it take to complete the job? $2\frac{4}{7}$ **days**

32. **Motion** The top speed of a boat in still water is 5 miles per hour. At this speed, a 21-mile trip downstream takes the same amount of time as a 9-mile trip upstream. Find the rate of the current. **2 mph**

33. **Electronics** Three appliances are connected in parallel: a lamp of resistance 120 ohms, a toaster of resistance 20 ohms, and an iron of resistance 12 ohms. Find the total resistance. $7\frac{1}{17}$ **ohms**

Bonus Complete.

$\dfrac{1}{x - y} + \dfrac{2}{y - x} + \dfrac{3}{x - y} + \dfrac{4}{y - x} + \dfrac{5}{x - y} + \dfrac{6}{y - x} + \dfrac{7}{x - y} + \dfrac{8}{y - x} = \dfrac{?}{x - y}$ -4

Test Generator Software is provided in both Apple and IBM versions. You may use this software to create your own tests, based on the needs of your students.

Additional Answers

9. $\dfrac{2x^2 + 12x + 28}{x^2 + 11x + 28}$

10. $\dfrac{8a^2 - 2a + 11}{6a^2 - 5a - 6}$

12. $\dfrac{x^2 - 2x - 42}{x - 8}$

Using the Chapter Test

This page may be used as a test or as a review. In addition, two multiple-choice tests and two free-response tests are provided in the Evaluation Masters Booklet. Chapter 8 Test, Form 1A is shown below.

Evaluation Masters Booklet, pp. 99-100

NAME _____ DATE _____

Chapter 8 Test, Form 1A

Write the letter for the correct answer in the blank at the right of each problem.

1. Simplify $\dfrac{y^2 + 2y - 24}{y^2 - 16}$.
   A. $\dfrac{3}{2}$ B. $\dfrac{y - 3}{-1}$ C. $\dfrac{y - 6}{y - 4}$ D. $\dfrac{y + 6}{y + 4}$ 1. __D__

2. Simplify $\dfrac{3x^2 - 5x + 2}{x^2 - 3x + 2}$.
   A. $\dfrac{3x - 2}{x - 2}$ B. $\dfrac{3x + 1}{x - 1}$ C. $\dfrac{3x - 5}{x - 3}$ D. $\dfrac{2}{3}$ 2. __A__

3. Find $\dfrac{2n^2y^2}{5n^5} \cdot \dfrac{5nc}{14y^3}$.
   A. $\dfrac{5n^3}{7y^3c^3}$ B. $\dfrac{n^3}{2y^3c^3}$ C. $\dfrac{5n^2}{7y^3c^4}$ D. $\dfrac{n^2}{2y^3c^4}$ 3. __A__

4. What are the excluded values of x in the expression $\dfrac{x + 7}{(x + 3)(1 - x)} \cdot \dfrac{3x - 8}{5x + 10}$?
   A. $x \neq -7, \dfrac{8}{3}, -3, -1, -2$ B. $x \neq -3, -1, -10$
   C. $x \neq 1, -2, -3, -7, 8$ D. $x \neq -2, 1, -3$ 4. __D__

5. Find $\dfrac{4m^7n}{p^3} \div \dfrac{mn}{6p^4}$.
   A. $24mp$ B. $\dfrac{1}{24mp}$ C. $\dfrac{2m^3n^2}{3p^7}$ D. $\dfrac{1}{10mp}$ 5. __A__

6. Find $\dfrac{v + y}{v - y} \div \dfrac{y + v}{y - v}$.
   A. 1 B. -1 C. $\dfrac{(v + y)^2}{(v - y)(y - v)}$ D. none of these 6. __B__

7. In the long division $x - 2\overline{)3x^3 + x^2 - 8x - 5}$, the remainder is
   A. 7 B. -9 C. -41 D. none of these 7. __A__

8. Find $\dfrac{x}{x - 2} + \dfrac{5x}{x - 2}$.
   A. -3 B. $\dfrac{5x^2}{x - 2}$ C. $\dfrac{6x}{2x - 4}$ D. $\dfrac{6x}{x - 2}$ 8. __D__

9. Find $\dfrac{8w + 25}{5w} - \dfrac{3w - 15}{5w}$.
   A. $\dfrac{w + 2}{w}$ B. $\dfrac{w + 8}{w}$ C. 40 D. 10 9. __B__

10. Find $\dfrac{7}{6n} - \dfrac{6}{4n^2}$.
    A. $\dfrac{1}{12n^2}$ B. $\dfrac{7n - 9}{6n^2}$ C. $\dfrac{28n - 1}{4n^2}$ D. $\dfrac{1}{24n^3}$ 10. __B__

11. Find $\dfrac{x}{x - 3} - \dfrac{4}{x^2 - 9}$.
    A. $\dfrac{x - 4}{x - 3}$ B. $\dfrac{x - 4}{x^2 - 9}$ C. $\dfrac{(x + 4)(x - 1)}{(x + 3)(x - 3)}$ D. $\dfrac{(x + 1)(x - 1)}{(x + 3)(x - 3)}$ 11. __C__

12. Find $\dfrac{3m + 2}{2m + 3} + \dfrac{1}{3m + 2}$.
    A. $\dfrac{9m^2 + 14m + 7}{(2m + 3)(3m + 2)}$ B. $\dfrac{3}{5}$
    C. $\dfrac{9m^2 + 12m + 5}{(2m + 3)(3m + 2)}$ D. $\dfrac{3(m + 1)}{(2m + 3)(3m + 2)}$ 12. __A__

NAME _____ DATE _____

Chapter 8 Test, Form 1A (continued)

13. What is the simplest form of $\dfrac{\dfrac{3x + 6}{5x - 10}}{\dfrac{x^2 - 4}{15}}$?
    A. $9(x + 2)^2$ B. $\dfrac{(x + 2)^2}{25}$ C. $\dfrac{9}{(x - 2)^2}$ D. 1 13. __C__

14. Solve $\dfrac{1}{4x} + \dfrac{2}{3} = 5$.
    A. $\dfrac{52}{3}$ B. $\dfrac{3}{52}$ C. 4 D. $\dfrac{1}{4}$ 14. __B__

15. Solve $\dfrac{x}{x - 2} - \dfrac{4}{x^2 - 2x} = \dfrac{1}{x}$.
    A. 2 B. -1 C. $-1, 2$ D. none of these 15. __B__

16. One pipe can fill a tank in 6 hours. A second pipe can fill the same tank in 10 hours. How many hours will it take to fill the tank if both pipes are used?
    A. 2 hours B. $\dfrac{4}{15}$ hours C. 8 hours D. 3.75 hours 16. __D__

17. An airplane can fly at a rate of 540 mi/h in calm air. It can fly 2668 miles with the wind in the same time it can fly 2300 miles against the wind. If x represents the speed of the wind, which equation must be true?
    A. $2668(540 + x) = 2300(540 - x)$
    B. $2668(x + 540) = 2300(x - 540)$
    C. $2668(540 - x) = 2300(540 + x)$
    D. $2668(x - 540) = 2300(x + 540)$ 17. __C__

18. In which of the following is $s = \dfrac{1}{2}at^2$ solved for a?
    A. $a = \dfrac{2s}{t^2}$ B. $a = \dfrac{s}{2t^2}$ C. $a = \dfrac{2t^2}{s}$ D. $a = \dfrac{t^2}{2s}$ 18. __A__

19. In a twelve-hour period of time, how many times are the digits on a digital clock all the same?
    A. 12 times B. 11 times C. 8 times D. 6 times 19. __D__

20. Given the formula $\dfrac{1}{R_T} = \dfrac{1}{R_1} + \dfrac{1}{R_2 + R_3}$ for the resistance of a circuit, what is the resistance R_2 if $R_T = 4.5$ ohms, $R_1 = 6$ ohms, and $R_3 = 9$ ohms?
    A. 27 ohms B. 9 ohms C. 3 ohms D. 6 ohms 20. __B__

Bonus: $x - 4$ is a factor of $x^3 + x^2 - 14x - 24$. Find the other two factors. **Bonus:** $(x + 2)(x + 3)$

Functions and Graphs

PREVIEWING THE CHAPTER

This chapter makes the connection between algebraic equations and their geometric models. Starting with examples from real-life, students identify coordinates and locate points on the coordinate plane, identify the domain, range, and inverse of a relation, and solve linear equations for a specific variable or a given domain. Then they graph relations from a table of ordered pairs and determine whether the relation is a function. Students expand their understanding to include graphing inequalities, and conclude by writing an equation for a relation, given a chart of values.

Problem-Solving Strategy Students learn to solve problems by using a statistical graph that presents the data in graphical form that helps them identify relationships among subsets of the data.

Lesson Objective Chart

Lesson (Pages)	Lesson Objectives	State/Local Objectives
9-1 (354-358)	**9-1:** Graph ordered pairs on a coordinate plane.	
9-2 (359-363)	**9-2A:** Identify the domain, range, and inverse of a relation.	
	9-2B: Show relations as sets of ordered pairs and mappings.	
9-3 (364-368)	**9-3A:** Solve linear equations for a specific variable.	
	9-3B: Solve linear equations for a given domain.	
9-4 (369-373)	**9-4:** Graph linear equations on a coordinate plane.	
9-5 (374-378)	**9-5A:** Determine whether a given relation is a function.	
	9-5B: Calculate functional values for a given function.	
9-6 (379-383)	**9-6:** Graph inequalities in the coordinate plane.	
9-7 (385-388)	**9-7:** Write an equation to represent a relation, given a chart of values.	
9-8 (389-391)	**9-8:** Solve problems by using bar graphs and line graphs.	

ORGANIZING THE CHAPTER

You may want to refer to the **Course Planning Calendar** on page T36.

Lesson (Pages)	Pacing Chart (days) Course I	II	III	Reteaching	Practice	Enrichment	Evaluation	Technology	Lab Manual	Mixed Problem Solving	Applications	Cooperative Learning Activity	Multicultural	Transparencies
9-1 (354-358)	1.5	1.5	1.5	p. 61	p. 68	p. 61								9-1
9-2 (359-363)	1.5	1.5	1.5	p. 62	p. 69	p. 62	Quiz A, p. 121						p. 54	9-2
9-3 (364-368)	1.5	1.5	1	p. 63	p. 70	p. 63		p. 9						9-3
9-4 (369-373)	1.5	1	1	p. 64	p. 71	p. 64	Quiz B, p. 121 Mid-Chapter Test, p. 125	p. 24						9-4
9-5 (374-378)	1.5	1.5	1	p. 65	p. 72	p. 65					p. 24	p. 39		9-5
9-6 (379-383)	1.5	1	1	p. 66	p. 73	p. 66	Quiz C, p. 122		pp. 35-36					9-6
9-7 (385-388)	1	1	1	p. 67	p. 74	p. 67								9-7
9-8 (389-391)	1	1	1		p. 75		Quiz D, p. 122			p. 9				9-8
Review (392-394)	1	1	1	Multiple Choice Tests, Forms 1A and 1B, pp. 113-116 Free Response Tests, Forms 2A and 2B, pp. 117-120										
Test (395)	1	1	1	Cumulative Review, pp. 123-124 Standardized Test Practice Questions, p. 126										

Course I: Chapters 1-13; Course II: Chapters 1-14: Course III: Chapters 1-15

Other Chapter Resources

Student Edition

Mid-Chapter Review, p. 373
History Connection, p. 383
Technology, p. 384
Cooperative Learning Activity, p. 391

Teacher Resource Package

Activity Masters Booklet
    Mixed Problem Solving, p. 9
    Applications, p. 24
    Cooperative Learning Activity, p. 39
    Multicultural Activity, p. 54

Technology Masters Booklet
    Scientific Calculator Activity, p. 9
    Graphing Calculator Activity, p. 24

Lab Manual
    Lab Activity, pp. 35-36

Other Supplements

Transparency for Chapter Opener
Problem-of-the-Week Activity
    Cards, 21-23
Video Algebra, 34-35, 44

Software

Algebra 1 Test and Review
    Generator Software
    Available for Apple and IBM.

ENHANCING THE CHAPTER

Cooperative Learning

Specifying Desired Student Behavior

To make sure that students will exhibit the group skills required for a successful cooperative-learning experience, you should clearly define the behaviors that are appropriate and desirable. Initially, skills will include the more obvious, such as "stay with your group," "use quiet voices," and "take turns." As groups begin to operate more effectively, add other expected behaviors, such as "criticize ideas, not people," "encourage everyone to participate," "use names and look at the other members when speaking," "paraphrase statements made by others," "seek elaboration," "probe by asking in-depth questions," "check to make sure every member understands and can explain the material," and so on. Research indicates that it is more effective if you define and focus on only one or two of these skills in each session. Although students do need to know what behavior is appropriate and desirable within a cooperative-learning group, they should not be subjected to information overload.

Technology

The Technology Feature in this chapter presents graphing lines and inequalities on a graphing calculator. The connection is made between the equation of a line and what the graph of that equation looks like. It is an introduction to the concept of intercepts and slope and can also help students with building tables of values. Students will be graphing equations in two variables (even though they may not realize it at the time), and they will also be graphing inequalities. This feature offers the students an opportunity to understand shading in a new way.

Critical Thinking

Very young children who have difficulty with addition and subtraction often display excellent ability to apply these concepts when making sure they have received the right amount of allowance or the correct amount of change when spending the allowance. Their school experience had not revealed a connection between the concept of these operations and the kinds of interesting and challenging questions that were considered when dealing with their own money. Many algebra students also fail to make similar important connections between their content knowledge and real-life applications. After students work with the applications presented in the textbook, have them describe other real-life situations where the same concepts and skills are applied.

Cooperative Learning, p. 39

CHAPTER 9   NAME _____   DATE _____

Cooperative Learning Activity (Use after Lesson 9-5)

Functions or Not?

Work in pairs. Use the materials listed below to complete the activities on this page. **Answers will vary.**

Materials needed: one red die, one green die, graph paper, ruler

Roll each die four times to complete the chart. Write the results as ordered pairs.

Red	Green

Plot the ordered pairs on the grid below.

Use the information from the activity above to answer the following questions.

1. What is the relation? Write as a set of ordered pairs.

2. What is the domain of the relation?

3. What is the range?

4. The vertical line test for a function states that if any vertical line passes through no more than one point of the graph of a relation, then the relation is a function. Does the vertical line test indicate that this relation is a function?

5. Repeat the experiment three times. Answer the questions for each experiment. Can you make any generalizations about the results? Students may find in individual experiments that the vertical line test indicates that the relation is a function. However, it is likely that sooner or later the relation will prove not to be a function. That is, a result on the red die will be paired with two or more results on the green die.

Technology, p. 9

CHAPTER 9   NAME _____   DATE _____

Scientific Calculator Activity (Use after Lesson 9-3)

Solving Linear Equations

Suppose you want to make a table of values for a linear equation, given its domain. A calculator can be used to find the values.

Example: Give a table of values for $y - 3x = -1$ if the domain is $\{-3, -1, 0, 1, 3\}$.

First solve for y. Then make a table using each domain value.

$$y - 3x = -1$$
$$y = 3x - 1$$

x	$3x - 1$	y	(x, y)
-3	$3(-3) - 1$	-10	$(-3, -10)$
-1	$3(-1) - 1$	-4	$(-1, -4)$
0	$3(0) - 1$	-1	$(0, -1)$
1	$3(1) - 1$	2	$(1, 2)$
3	$3(3) - 1$	8	$(3, 8)$

Substitute each value of x from the domain to determine the corresponding value for y.

ENTER 3 [X] 3 [%] [-] 1 [=]   Result: -10

Therefore, if x is -3, y is -10. The corresponding point is $(-3, -10)$. Find the other values in the table above.

Use a calculator to solve each equation for the given domain. Make a table and give the answers as ordered pairs.

1. $y = -2x + 3$; $\{0, 1, 2, 3, 4, 5\}$
   (0, 3); (1, 1); (2, −1); (3, −3);
   (4, −5); (5, −7)

2. $y + 4x = 8$; $\{-3, -2, -1, 0, 1, 2, 3\}$
   (−3, 20); (−2, 16); (−1, 12); (0, 8);
   (1, 4); (2, 0); (3, −4)

3. $2y = 6x - 10$; $\{-4, -3, -2, -1, 0\}$
   (−4, −17); (−3, −14); (−2, −11);
   (−1, −8); (0, −5)

4. $y = 200 + 10x$; $\{10, 20, 30, 40, 50\}$
   (10, 300); (20, 400); (30, 500);
   (40, 600); (50, 700)

5. $y = 0.75x - 2$; $\{10, 15, 20, 25, 30\}$
   (10, 5.5); (15, 9.25); (20, 13);
   (25, 16.75); (30, 20.5)

6. $0.5x - 0.25y = 10$; $\{10, 20, 30, 40, 50\}$
   (10, −20); (20, 0); (30, 20); (40, 40);
   (50, 60)

7. $y = x^2 + 4$; $\{-2, -1, 0, 1, 2, 3\}$
   (−2, 8); (−1, 5); (0, 4); (1, 5); (2, 8); (3, 13)

8. $y = |2x - 5|$; $\{-20, -10, 0, 10, 20\}$
   (−20, 45); (−10, 25); (0, 5); (10, 15); (20, 35)

Problem of the Week Activity

The card shown below is one of three available for this chapter. It can be used as a class or small group activity.

Activity Card

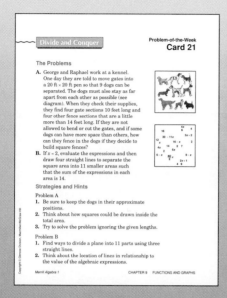

Manipulatives and Models

The following materials may be used as models or manipulatives in Chapter 9.

- geoboard (Lessons 9-2 and 9-5)
- magazines (Lesson 9-8)
- newspapers (Lesson 9-8)

Outside Resources

Books/Periodicals

Cleveland, William S. *The Elements of Graphing Data.* Wadsworth Advanced Books and Software.

White, Jan V. *Using Charts and Graphs.* R.R. Bowker Company.

Films/Videotapes/Videodiscs

Math-Wise — A Series: Graphs, Agency for Instructional Television

Polar Coordinates, Phoenix/BFA Films and Video, Inc.

Software

Super Graph, Ventura Educational Systems

Green Globs and Graphing Equations, Sunburst Communications, Inc.

Multicultural

Multicultural Activity, p. 54

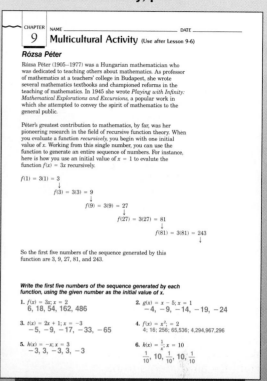

Lab Manual

Lab Activity, pp. 35-36

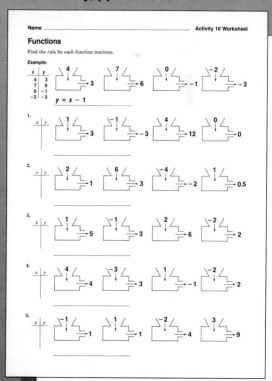

Using the Chapter Opener

Transparency 9-0 is available in the Transparency Package. It provides a full-color visual and motivational activity that you can use to engage students in the mathematical content of the chapter.

Background Information

Researchers use graphs in virtually every area of science and math. We can often gain more insight by studying the graph of an event than by studying the event itself. Solutions to questions that become lost in volumes of data can become quite clear when the data are plotted on a graph. The parabolic line graphs in the chapter opener, for example, demonstrate far more clearly the danger of speeding than do the same data in the accompanying chart. As graphs become more complex, it becomes increasingly important for all students to have a knowledge of graphing fundamentals.

CHAPTER OBJECTIVES

In this chapter, you will:

- Identify the domain and range of a relation.
- Graph linear equations and inequalities in the coordinate plane.
- Solve linear equations for a given domain.
- Calculate functional values.
- Represent data by using graphs.

Chapter Project

Materials: graph paper, pencil

Organize students into cooperative groups. Instruct each group to graph the data in the following chart of the distance an object falls versus time.

Distance (d) (meters)	Time (t) (seconds)
−4.9	1
−19.6	2
−44.1	3
−78.4	4
−122.5	5
−176.4	6

Ask each group to write a description of its resulting graph. (It should be parabolic.) Ask each group to describe how the distance an object falls varies according to time. (The distance an object falls varies according to the square of the time it continues to fall.) Finally, if the distance an object falls can be represented by the equation $y = kt^2$, ask students to find the value of the constant k. (−4.9 m/s^2, or one-half the acceleration of gravity of −9.8 m/s^2)

9

Functions and Graphs

Lesson	Connections (C) and Applications (A)	Examples	Exercises
9-1	A: Cartography Entertainment	3	61-65 67
9-2	C: Probability Statistics A: Food Chemistry Electronics	4	33-34 43 44 46 49
9-3	A: Career Gardening Physics Work	4	45 46 51
9-4	A: Meteorology Science Business Temperature Gardening	4	48 49 50 55
9-5	A: Physics Car Rental Business Construction	7	53 54 57
9-6	A: Sales Manufacturing Physics	2, 3	49 50 56
9-7	A: Business Geology Sales Finance	3	34 35 36
9-8	C: Statistics	1	

Automobile manufacturers have yet to build a car that can "stop on a dime." Cars all follow one basic rule: the faster they are traveling, the farther they go before stopping once their brakes are applied.

APPLICATION IN AUTOMOBILE SAFETY

One thing driver's education teachers always emphasize is to keep a safe distance behind the car in front of you so there is enough time to stop. But what exactly is a "safe distance?" For each situation, a safe distance will depend upon the *total stopping distance* for that situation. Total stopping distance is how far your car travels from the time you decide to apply the brakes until the car stops.

One factor in total stopping distance is called *braking distance.* This is how far the car travels from the time you apply the brakes until the time it actually stops. The road surface, the car's condition (especially its tires), the weather, and the car's speed all affect braking distance. The other factor in total stopping distance is called *thinking distance.* This is how far the car travels from the time you decide to apply the brakes until the time you actually apply them. The driver's mental and physical condition as well as the car's speed affect thinking distance. As the chart and graph below indicate, thinking distance and braking distance are both affected by speed. We can say that each of these distances is a *function* of speed.

ALGEBRA IN ACTION

Based on the information in the chart and graph below, what would be the approximate thinking distance, braking distance, and total stopping distance for a car traveling 65 miles per hour?

71 ft, 231 ft, 302 ft

Original Speed (mph)	Thinking Distance (ft)	Braking Distance (ft)	Total Stopping Distance (ft)
15	16	12	28
25	27	34	61
35	38	67	105
45	49	111	160
55	60	165	225

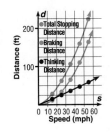

353

INTRODUCING THE LESSON

🕐 5-Minute Check
(over Chapter 8)

Solve each formula for the variable indicated.

1. $P = 2\ell + 2w$, solve for w.
   $w = \frac{P}{2} - \ell$

2. $d = rt$, solve for r. $r = \frac{d}{t}$

3. $C = 2\pi r$, solve for r.
   $r = \frac{C}{2\pi}$

4. $P = \frac{300T}{v}$, solve for v.
   $v = \frac{300T}{P}$

5. $A = \frac{bh}{2}$, solve for h. $h = \frac{2A}{b}$

Motivating the Lesson

Introduce the concept of ordered pairs through the following activity. Identify the student sitting in the second seat of the third row of desks in your classroom. Tell students that this student will now be referred to as (3, 2). Identify the student sitting in the third seat of the second row. Tell students this person will now be referred to as (2, 3). Challenge students to identify the procedure you are using to name the students. Then have each student name their new identity based on their seat assignment.

TEACHING THE LESSON

Teaching Tip ❶   Students often confuse horizontal and vertical. Emphasize that a horizontal line runs in the same direction as the horizon. A vertical line runs up and down, or perpendicular to the horizontal line.

9-1 Ordered Pairs

Objective
9-1

After studying this lesson, you should be able to:
- graph ordered pairs on a coordinate plane.

Application

Ms. Miyashiro makes seating charts for her classes. Her classroom has 5 rows of desks with 6 desks in each row. She assigns desks by using two numbers. The first number is for the row of the desk, and the second number is for the desk in that row. Ms. Miyashiro assigns desk (3, 2) to Gene and desk (2, 3) to Lori. This means Gene will sit in the third row at the second desk, and Lori will sit in the second row at the third desk.

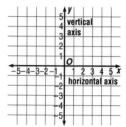

Notice that (3, 2) and (2, 3) do *not* name the same desk in the seating chart. (3, 2) and (2, 3) are called **ordered pairs** because the order in which the pair of numbers are written is important.

Perpendicular lines are lines that meet to form 90° angles.

Ordered pairs are used to locate points in a plane. The points are in reference to two *perpendicular* number lines. The point at which the number lines intersect is called the **origin**. The ordered pair that names the origin is (0, 0). The two number lines are called the **x-axis** and the **y-axis**. The plane that contains the x- and the y-axis is called the **coordinate plane**.

Teaching Tip ❶

A point is often referred to by just a letter. Thus, A can be used to mean point A.

Teaching Tip ❷

The first number, or **coordinate**, of an ordered pair corresponds to a number on the x-axis. The second number of the ordered pair corresponds to a number on the y-axis. To find the ordered pair for point A, shown at the right, think of a horizontal line and a vertical line passing through point A. Notice where these lines intersect each axis. The number on the x-axis that corresponds to A is -3. The number on the y-axis that corresponds to A is 4. Thus, the ordered pair for point A is $(-3, 4)$. The first coordinate, -3, is called the **x-coordinate** of point A. The second coordinate, 4, is called the **y-coordinate** of point A.

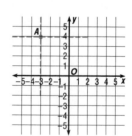

ALTERNATE TEACHING STRATEGIES

Using Logical Reasoning

Are there any points in the plane that can be described by two different locations?   **The origin is in both the x-axis and y-axis.**

Using Applications

Have students write a short essay explaining the similarities between meridians of latitude and parallels of longitude and the axes of a graph. Then have the students identify the latitude and longitude of five locations that they have visited.

Example 1

Write the ordered pairs that name points *R, S, T,* and *U.*

Think of a horizontal and a vertical line passing through each point.

Point R: The x-coordinate is 4 and the y-coordinate is −3. Thus, the ordered pair is (4, −3).

Point S: The x-coordinate is 1 and the y-coordinate is 4. Thus, the ordered pair is (1, 4).

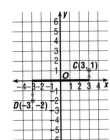

The ordered pair for point *T* is (−3, −5), and the ordered pair for point *U* is (−5, 0). *Why?* **Teaching Tip ③**

R(4, 3) also means that the location of point R is (4, 3).

Teaching Tip ④

Sometimes, a point is named by both a letter and its ordered pair. For example, R(4, 3) means that the point *R* is named by the ordered pair (4, 3).

To **graph** an ordered pair means to draw a dot at the point that corresponds to the ordered pair. This is sometimes called *plotting* the point. When graphing an ordered pair, start at the origin. The x-coordinate indicates the number of units to move left or right. The y-coordinate indicates the number of units to move up or down.

Example 2

Plot the following points on a coordinate plane.

a. C(3, 1)

Start at the origin, O. Move 3 units to the right. Then move 1 unit up and draw a dot. Label this dot with the letter C. *Check that 3 on the x-axis and 1 on the y-axis correspond to C.*

b. D(−3, −2)

Start at the origin, O. Move 3 units to the left, since the x-coordinate is −3. Then move 2 units down, since the y-coordinate is −2, and draw a dot. Label this dot with the letter D. *Check that −3 on the x-axis and −2 on the y-axis correspond to D.*

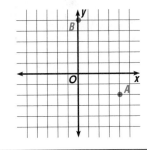

The correspondence between points in the plane and ordered pairs of real numbers is given by the following property.

Completeness Property for Points in the Plane	1. Exactly one point in the plane is named by a given ordered pair of numbers. 2. Exactly one ordered pair of numbers names a given point in the plane.

Teaching Tip ③ The x-coordinate of point *T* is −3, and its y-coordinate is −5. The x-coordinate of point *U* is −5, and its y-coordinate is 0.

Teaching Tip ④ Help students to see the ordered pair as a set of directions when plotting the point. Discuss why the moves for positive numbers are to the right or up, and the moves for negative numbers are to the left or down.

Chalkboard Examples

For Example 1
Name the ordered pairs for the points M, N, and R.

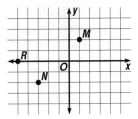

M(1, 2), N(−3, −2), R(−5, 0)

For Example 2
Graph the points A(4, −2) and B(0, 5).

356   **Chapter 9**

Example 3

APPLICATION
Cartography

On the map at the right, letters and numbers are used to form ordered pairs that name sectors on the map. Name all the sectors that the Scioto River passes through.

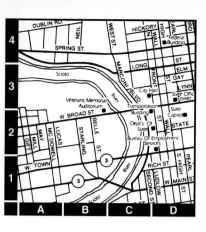

The Scioto River first appears at the bottom of the map in sectors (B, 1) and (C, 1). It then travels up through sectors (C, 2) and (C, 3) and left through sector (B, 3) before exiting the map through sectors (A, 3) and (A, 4).

Teaching Tip 5

The x-axis and the y-axis separate the coordinate plane into four regions, called **quadrants**. The quadrants are numbered as shown at the right. Notice that the axes are not located in any of the quadrants. *Why?*

Quadrant II (−, +)	Quadrant I (+, +)
Quadrant III (−, −)	Quadrant IV (+, −)

Example 4

Name the quadrant in which each point is located.

a. $A(5, -4)$

Since the x-coordinate of $A(5, -4)$ is positive and the y-coordinate is negative, point A is located in Quadrant IV.

b. $B(-2, -7)$

Since the x-coordinate of $B(-2, -7)$ is negative and the y-coordinate is negative, point B is located in Quadrant III.

c. $C(2, 0)$

Since point C lies on the x-axis, it is not located in a quadrant.

CHECKING FOR UNDERSTANDING

Communicating Mathematics

Read and study the lesson to answer each question. 1–3. See margin.

1. Draw a coordinate plane. Label the origin, the x-axis, the y-axis, and quadrants I, II, III, and IV.

2. Explain the difference between the ordered pairs (5, 3) and (3, 5).

3. State the completeness property for points in a plane in your own words.

4. Name three ordered pairs whose graphs are not located in one of the four quadrants. **Answers will vary; typical answers are (0, 0), (1, 0), and (0, −2**

356   CHAPTER 9   FUNCTIONS AND GRAPHS

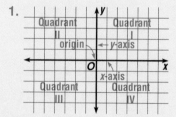

Write the ordered pair for each point shown at the right.

5. A (1, 4)   6. C (−3, 3)
7. E (−1, −2)   8. G (4, 0)
9. T (3, −1)   10. U (0, −5)

Name the quadrant in which the point named by each ordered pair is located.

11. (5, 2) I   12. (−3, −1) III
13. (−2, 3) II   14. (6, 0) none
15. (0, −2) none   16. (4, −3) IV

EXERCISES

Practice

Write the ordered pair for each point shown above.

17. B (−1, 1)   18. D (−4, −3)   19. F (3, −2)   20. H (4, 2)
21. I (1, 1)   22. J (0, −1)   23. K (−1, −1)   24. L (−3, 0)
25. N (2, −3)   26. P (−3, −4)   27. Q (−4, 1)   28. S (5, 1)

If the graph of $P(x, y)$ satisfies the given conditions, name the quadrant in which point P is located.

29. $x > 0, y < 0$ IV   30. $x < 0, y < 0$ III   31. $x < 0, y > 0$ II
32. $x = 0, y > 0$ none   33. $x = 1, y < 0$ IV   34. $x = -1, y < 0$ III
35. $x < 0, y = 3$ II   36. $x > 0, y = 3$ I   37. $x > 0, y = 0$ none

Graph each point. See margin.

38. $A(5, -2)$ 39. $B(3, 5)$ 40. $C(-6, 0)$ 41. $D(-3, 4)$
42. $E(-3, -3)$ 43. $F(-5, 1)$ 44. $G(2, -1)$ 45. $H(4, 0)$
46. $I(3, -4)$ 47. $J(-3, 0)$ 48. $K(-5, -2)$ 49. $L(4, 2)$
50. $M(0, 3)$ 51. $N(1, 4)$ 52. $P(2, -3)$ 53. $Q(0, -2)$

If x and y are integers, graph all ordered pairs that satisfy the given conditions. See Solutions Manual.

54. $-3 \leq x \leq 2$ and $-1 \leq y < 3$ 55. $|x| < 3$ and $|y| \leq 2$

Graph each point. Then connect the points in alphabetical order and identify the figure. See margin.

56. $A(4, 6)$, $B(3, 7)$, $C(2, 6)$, $D(1, 7)$, $E(0, 6)$, $F(1, 8)$, $G(4, 9)$, $H(7, 8)$, $I(8, 6)$, $J(7, 7)$, $K(6, 6)$, $L(5, 7)$, $M(4, 6)$, $N(4, 0)$, $P(5, 0)$, $Q(5, 1)$

57. $A(-3, 0.5)$, $B(1, 0)$, $C(4, 0)$, $D(7, -4)$, $E(8, -4)$, $F(7, 0)$, $G(10, 0)$, $H(11, -2)$, $I(12, -2)$, $J(11.5, 0)$, $K(11.5, 1)$, $L(12, 3)$, $M(11, 3)$, $N(10, 1)$, $P(7, 1)$, $Q(8, 5)$, $R(7, 5)$, $S(4, 1)$, $T(1, 1)$, $U(-3, 0.5)$

Additional Answers

2. (5, 3) represents a point 5 units to the right and 3 units up from the origin. (3, 5) represents a point 3 units to the right and 5 units up from the origin.

3. Each point in the plane is named by exactly one ordered pair, and each ordered pair names exactly one point in the plane.

38-53.

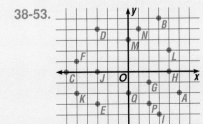

APPLYING THE LESSON

Homework Exercises

Assignment Guide
Basic: 17-53, 58-63, 66-72
Average: 24-72
Enriched: 24-72

Practice Masters Booklet, p. 68

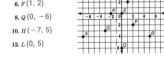

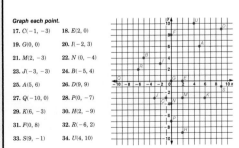

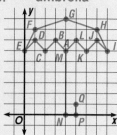
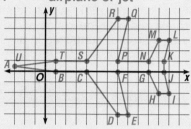

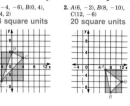
Critical Thinking

Describe the possible locations, in terms of quadrants or axes, for the graph of (x, y) if x and y satisfy the given conditions.

58. $xy > 0$ I or III   **59.** $xy < 0$ II or IV   **60.** $xy = 0$ x- or y-axis

Applications: Cartography

Refer to the map at the right to answer each question.

61. What city is in sector (A, 4)? Irving

62. In what sector is the city of Garland? (F, 6)

63. In what 4 sectors is Love Field? (B,4), (B,5), (C,4), (C,5)

64. What highway goes from sector (A, 1) to sector (F, 3)? I-20

65. Name all the sectors that Interstate Highway 30 passes through. (A,3), (B,3), (C,3), (D,3), (E,3), (E,4), (F,4)

Mixed Review

66. Simplify $2x^2 + 3y + z^2 + 8x^2$. (Lesson 1-6) $10x^2 + 3y + z^2$

67. Entertainment A theater was filled to 75% of capacity. How many of the 720 seats were filled? (Lesson 4-2) 540 seats

68. Find $(5a-b)^2$. (Lesson 6-9) $25a^2 - 10ab + b^2$

69. Graph the solution set of $3 - 2p \geq -3$ or $3 - 2p \leq 7$. (Lesson 5-5) See margin.

70. Evaluate $\frac{8.5 \times 10^{-3}}{1.7 \times 10^{-8}}$. Express the result in scientific notation and decimal notation. (Lesson 6-4) 5×10^5; 500,000

71. Factor $4x^2 - 64y^2$ completely. (Lesson 7-6) $4(x + 4y)(x - 4y)$

72. Simplify $\frac{z^2 + 16z + 39}{z^2 + 9z + 18} \cdot \frac{z + 5}{z^2 + 18z + 65}$. (Lesson 8-2) $\frac{1}{z + 6}$

358 CHAPTER 9 FUNCTIONS AND GRAPHS

EXTENDING THE LESSON

Math Power: Connections

A parallelogram has three of its vertices at $(0, 0)$, $(2, 2)$, and $(7, 1)$. Find the possible ordered pairs that could correspond to its fourth vertex. (9, 3) and (5, -1)

Additional Answer

69.

-2 -1 0 1 2 3 4 5 6

Relations

Objectives

9-2A

9-2B

After studying this lesson, you should be able to:

- identify the domain, range, and inverse of a relation, and
- show relations as sets of ordered pairs and mappings.

Application

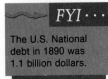

The U.S. National debt in 1890 was 1.1 billion dollars.

As part of a project for his U.S. History class, Ramón researched the growth of the national debt since 1965. He organized his research in a table, as shown at the right.

OUR NATIONAL DEBT:
$ 2,926,460,770,438
YOUR *Family share* $45,016
THE NATIONAL DEBT CLOCK

National Debt	
Year	Billions of Dollars
1965	322
1970	381
1975	542
1980	909
1985	1817
1990	2601

Ramón could also have shown this data using a set of ordered pairs. Each first coordinate would be the year, and each second coordinate would be the national debt, in billions of dollars.

$$\{(1965, 322), (1970, 381), (1975, 542),$$
$$(1980, 909), (1985, 1817), (1990, 2601)\}$$

Teaching Tip ❶

A **relation** is a set of ordered pairs, like the set shown above. The set of first coordinates of the ordered pairs is called the **domain** of the relation. The set of second coordinates is called the **range** of the relation.

Definition of the Domain and Range of a Relation	The domain of a relation is the set of all first coordinates from the ordered pairs. The range of the relation is the set of all second coordinates from the ordered pairs.

For the relation given above, the domain is $\{1965, 1970, 1975, 1980, 1985, 1990\}$, and the range is $\{322, 381, 542, 909, 1817, 2601\}$.

A relation can also be shown using a table, a mapping, or a graph. A **mapping** illustrates how each element of the domain is paired with an element in the range. For example, the relation $\{(2, 2), (-2, 3), (0, -1)\}$ can be shown in each of the following ways.

Table

x	y
2	2
-2	3
0	-1

Mapping

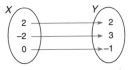

Graph

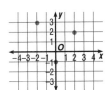

LESSON 9-2   RELATIONS   359

ALTERNATE TEACHING STRATEGIES

Using Discussion

The relation $\{(3, 6), (-2, -4), (6, 12), (-4, -8), (0, 0)\}$ suggests a relationship between the x- and y-coordinates of the ordered pairs. Given x, how do you determine y?
$y = 2x$
In the inverse of the above relation, how would you determine y when given x?
$y = \frac{x}{2}$

Using Manipulatives

Use a geoboard to show $\triangle ABC$ with points A (0, 0), B (6, 0), and C (0, 4). List the ordered pairs of the relation that contain the points in the interior of $\triangle ABC$. $\{(1, 1), (1, 2), (1, 3), (2, 1), (2, 2), (3, 1), (4, 1)\}$

9-2 Lesson Notes

Lesson Resources

- Reteaching Master 9-2
- Practice Master 9-2
- Enrichment Master 9-2
- Video Algebra, 34
- Transparency 9-2 contains the 5-Minute Check and a teaching aid for this lesson.

INTRODUCING THE LESSON

⏱ 5-Minute Check
(over Lesson 9-1)

Identify the quadrant in which each point lies.

1. $(-3, 2)$ Quadrant II
2. $(6, 2)$ Quadrant I
3. $(-8, -1)$ Quadrant III
4. $(4, -7)$ Quadrant IV
5. $(9, 0)$ It lies on the x-axis.

Motivating the Lesson

Tell the students you are going to say two pairs of numbers. The numbers in each pair are related in the same way. The students need to identify the relationship and then name an additional pair related in the same way. For example, you might say "7 and 2, 4 and −1". The students might respond with "difference of 5". Continue the activity as time permits with different number pairs.

TEACHING THE LESSON

Teaching Tip ❶   The word *relation* simply indicates a set pair of numbers. There may or may not be a reason for the pairing. Stress that a relation can be shown in many different ways. Remind students that the domain is a set of numbers, not a set of ordered pairs. The same is true of the range.

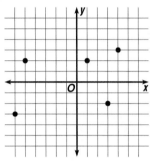
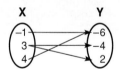
Example 1

Express the relation shown in the table below as a set of ordered pairs. Then determine its domain and range.

x	y
0	5
2	3
1	−4
−3	3
−1	−2

The set of ordered pairs for the relation is {(0, 5), (2, 3), (1, −4), (−3, 3), (−1, −2)}.

The domain is the set of all first coordinates: {0, 2, 1, −3, −1}.

The range is the set of all second coordinates: {5, 3, −4, −2}.

Example 2

Express the relation shown in the graph below as a set of ordered pairs. Determine its domain and range. Then show the relation using a mapping.

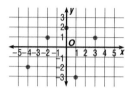

The set of ordered pairs for the relation is {(3, 1), (0, 2), (−2, 1), (−4, −2), (1, −3)}.

The domain is {3, 0, −2, −4, 1}.

The range is {1, 2, −2, −3}.

In this relation, 3 maps to 1, 0 maps to 2, −2 maps to 1, −4 maps to −2, and 1 maps to −3. This mapping is shown at the right.

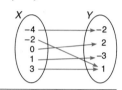

  The **inverse** of any relation is obtained by switching the coordinates in each ordered pair of the relation. Thus, the inverse of the relation {(2, 2), (−2, 3), (0, −1)} is the relation {(2, 2), (3, −2), (−1, 0)}. Notice that the domain of the relation becomes the range of the inverse and the range of the relation becomes the domain of the inverse.

Definition of the Inverse of a Relation	Relation *Q* is the inverse of relation *S* if and only if for every ordered pair (*a, b*) in *S*, there is an ordered pair (*b, a*) in *Q*.

Example 3

Express the relation shown in the mapping below as a set of ordered pairs. Write the inverse of this relation. Then determine the domain and range of the inverse.

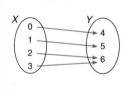

The set of ordered pairs for the relation is {(0, 4), (1, 5), (2, 6), (3, 6)}.

The inverse of the relation is {(4, 0), (5, 1), (6, 2), (6, 3)}.

The domain of the inverse is {4, 5, 6}.

The range of the inverse is {0, 1, 2, 3}.

360   CHAPTER 9   FUNCTIONS AND GRAPHS

Example 4

CONNECTION

Probability

Write a relation to show the 36 different possible outcomes when two six-sided dice are tossed. Then use this relation to help determine how many ways the faces of the dice can show a sum of 7.

Let the first coordinate of each ordered pair be the outcome on the first die. Let the second coordinate be the outcome on the second die. Each die can land in six ways. Thus, the relation can be written as follows.

$$\{(1, 1), (1, 2), (1, 3), (1, 4), (1, 5), (1, 6),$$
$$(2, 1), (2, 2), (2, 3), (2, 4), (2, 5), (2, 6),$$
$$(3, 1), (3, 2), (3, 3), (3, 4), (3, 5), (3, 6),$$
$$(4, 1), (4, 2), (4, 3), (4, 4), (4, 5), (4, 6),$$
$$(5, 1), (5, 2), (5, 3), (5, 4), (5, 5), (5, 6),$$
$$(6, 1), (6, 2), (6, 3), (6, 4), (6, 5), (6, 6)\}$$

The ordered pairs in this relation that show a sum of 7 are $(1, 6)$, $(2, 5)$, $(3, 4)$, $(4, 3)$, $(5, 2)$, and $(6, 1)$. Thus, there are 6 ways that the faces of the dice can show a sum of 7.

CHECKING FOR UNDERSTANDING

Communicating Mathematics

Read and study the lesson to answer each question. **See margin.**

1. What is the inverse of the national debt relation?

2. What are four different ways to show a relation?

3. What is the difference between the domain and the range of a relation?

Guided Practice

State the domain and the range of each relation. **See margin.**

4. $\{(0, 2), (1, -2), (2, 4)\}$

5. $\{(5, 2), (0, 0), (-9, -1)\}$

6. $\{(-4, 2), (-2, 0), (0, 2), (2, 4)\}$

7. $\{(7, 5), (-2, -3), (4, 0), (5, -7), (-9, 2)\}$

8. $\{(3.1, -1), (-4.7, 3.9), (2.4, -3.6), (-9, 12.12)\}$

9. $\left\{\left(\frac{1}{2}, \frac{1}{4}\right), \left(1\frac{1}{2}, -\frac{2}{3}\right), \left(-3, \frac{2}{5}\right), \left(-5\frac{1}{4}, -6\frac{2}{7}\right)\right\}$

Express each relation shown in each table as a set of ordered pairs. Then state the domain, range, and inverse of the relation. **See margin.**

10.

x	y
1	5
2	7
3	9
4	11

11.

x	y
1	3
2	2
4	9
6	5

12.

x	y
1	4
3	-2
4	4
6	-2

LESSON 9-2 RELATIONS 361

Additional Answers

5. $\{5, 0, -9\}$; $\{2, 0, -1\}$

6. $\{-4, -2, 0, 2\}$; $\{0, 2, 4\}$

7. $\{7, -2, 4, 5, -9\}$; $\{5, -3, 0, -7, 2\}$

8. $\{3.1, -4.7, 2.4, -9\}$; $\{-1, 3.9, -3.6, 12.12\}$

9. $\left\{\frac{1}{2}, 1\frac{1}{2}, -3, -5\frac{1}{4}\right\}$; $\left\{\frac{1}{4}, -\frac{2}{3}, \frac{2}{5}, -6\frac{2}{7}\right\}$

10. $\{(1, 5), (2, 7), (3, 9), (4, 11)\}$; $\{1, 2, 3, 4\}$; $\{5, 7, 9, 11\}$; $\{(5, 1), (7, 2), (9, 3), (11, 4)\}$

11. $\{(1, 3), (2, 2), (4, 9), (6, 5)\}$; $\{1, 2, 4, 6\}$; $\{3, 2, 9, 5\}$; $\{(3, 1), (2, 2), (9, 4), (5, 6)\}$

12. $\{(1, 4), (3, -2), (4, 4), (6, -2)\}$; $\{1, 3, 4, 6\}$; $\{4, -2\}$; $\{(4, 1), (-2, 3), (4, 4), (-2, 6)\}$

EXERCISES

Practice   Express the relation shown in each mapping as a set of ordered pairs.

 13. 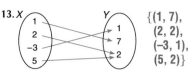   {(1, 7), (2, 2), (−3, 1), (5, 2)}

14. 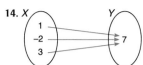   {(1, 7), (−2, 7), (3, 7)}

15. 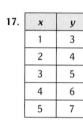   {(5, 4), (5, 8), (2, 9), (−7, 2), (3, 2), (3, 4)}

16. 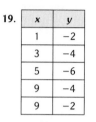   {(−1, 5), (−2, 5), (−2, 4), (−2, 1), (−6, 1)}

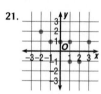 Draw a mapping for the relation shown in each table. Then express the relation and its inverse as sets of ordered pairs. **See Solutions Manual.**

17.

x	y
1	3
2	4
3	5
4	6
5	7

18.

x	y
−4	1
−2	3
0	1
2	3
4	1

19.

x	y
1	−2
3	−4
5	−6
9	−4
9	−2

20.

x	y
1	3
2	5
1	−7
2	9
3	3

Express the relation shown in each graph as a set of ordered pairs. Then state the domain and range of the relation. **See margin.**

21. 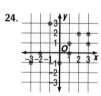   22. 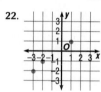   23.

24. 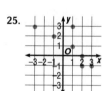   25. 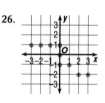   26. (graph)

27–32. Write the inverse of the relation in Exercises 21–26. **See margin.**

Additional Answers

24. {(−3, −1), (−2, 0), (−1, 3), (0, −1), (1, 0), (1, 1), (2, 2), (3, 1), (3, 2)};
{−3, −2, −1, 0, 1, 2, 3};
{−1, 0, 3, 1, 2}
25. {(−3, 3), (−1, 2), (1, 1), (1, 3), (2, 0), (2, −1), (3, −1)};
{−3, −1, 1, 2, 3};
{3, 2, 1, 0, −1}
26. {(−3, 1), (−2, 1), (−1, 1), (0, 1), (0, 0), (0, −1), (1, −1), (2, −2), (3, −2)};
{−3, −2, −1, 0, 1, 2, 3};
{1, 0, −1, −2}
27. {(2, −2), (1, −1), (1, 0), (1, 1), (−1, 1), (−1, 2), (1, 3)}
28. {(−2, −3), (−1, −2), (0, 0), (1, 1)}

Use the relation in Example 4 to complete the following. **See margin.**

33. Determine how many ways the faces of two dice can show each sum. For example, there are three ways to show a sum of 10: (5, 5), (4, 6), and (6, 4).

34. Do you notice a pattern in the answers to Exercise 33?

Draw a mapping for each relation. See Solutions Manual.

35. {(0, 1)}

36. {(2, 3), (3, 2)}

37. {(1, 3), (2, 3), (2, 1), (3, 2)}

38. {(−6, 0), (−1, 2), (−3, 4)}

39. {(4, −3), (6, −4), (5, −3), (6, 0)}

40. {(1, 3), (2, 7), (4, 1), (−3, 3), (3, 3)}

41. {(4, 2), (7, 5), (−3, 2), (8, −9), (8, 2)}

Critical Thinking 42. Graph the relation {(5, 5), (1, 3), (2, −1), (4, 0)}. Connect these points in the order given. Then show the inverse of this relation as a graph and connect those points in the same order. What conclusions can be made about the two graphs? **They are mirror images, or reflections, of each other.**

Applications 43. **Statistics** Fifteen students participated in a free-throw shooting contest. The number of free throws made by each student is as follows: 3, 3, 4, 5, 4, 1, 2, 3, 4, 2, 2, 4, 5, 4, 4. Show this as the graph of a relation where the first coordinate is the number of free throws made and the second coordinate is the number of students who made that many free throws. Then connect the points from left to right. *This graph is called a line graph.* **See margin.**

44. **Food** Lisa buys a dozen doughnuts for a morning meeting. She knows that the staff prefers glazed doughnuts over cake doughnuts. If she buys at least twice as many glazed doughnuts as cake doughnuts, write a relation to show the different possibilities. (*Hint:* Let the domain be the number of glazed doughnuts.) **{(8, 4), (9, 3), (10, 2), (11, 1), (12, 0)}**

Mixed Review 45. Solve $2(5 − 8n) = −4(3 + 4n)$. **(Lesson 3-6) no solution**

46. **Chemistry** A chemist has 800 mL of a solution that is 25% acid. How much pure (100%) acid must be added to the 25% solution to obtain a 40% acid solution? **(Lesson 4-6) 200 mL**

47. Simplify $7a^2b^2(a^4 − 5a^2b + 6b^2)$. **(Lesson 6-7) $7a^6b^2 − 35a^4b^3 + 42a^2b^4$**

48. Factor $144n^2 + 168n + 49$. **(Lesson 7-7)($(12n + 7)^2$**

49. **Electronics** Three coils with resistances of 4 ohms, 6 ohms, and 15 ohms are connected in parallel. What is the total resistance? Use the formula $\frac{1}{R_T} = \frac{1}{R_1} + \frac{1}{R_2} + \frac{1}{R_3}$. **(Lesson 8-10) $2\frac{2}{29}$ ohms**

50. Graph the points $A(6, 2)$, $B(−3, 6)$, and $C(−5, −4)$. **(Lesson 9-1)**
See Solutions Manual.

LESSON 9-2 RELATIONS **363**

EXTENDING THE LESSON

Math Power: Reasoning

A relation has domain $A = \{2, 4, 6\}$ and range $B = \{1, 3\}$. The Cartesian Product $A \times B$ is defined as the relation that contains all possible pairings of elements of A with elements of B.

1. What is the relation $A \times B$?
   {(2, 1), (2, 3), (4, 1), (4, 3), (6, 1), (6, 3)}

2. How many elements are contained in $A \times B$? **6**

3. Suppose the domain A contains 213 elements and range B contains 432 elements. How many elements are contained in $A \times B$?
   213 × 432 = 92,016 ordered pairs

 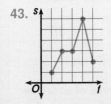

Lesson Resources

- Reteaching Master 9-3
- Practice Master 9-3
- Enrichment Master 9-3
- Video Algebra, 35

 Transparency 9-3 contains the 5-Minute Check and a teaching aid for this lesson.

INTRODUCING THE LESSON

⏱ 5-Minute Check

(over Lesson 9-2)

State the domain and range of each relation.

1. $\{(0, -3), (1, 4), (1, -3)\}$
   $D = \{0, 1\}, R = \{-3, 4\}$
2. $\{(1, 5), (2, 5), (3, 5), (4, 5)\}$
   $D = \{1, 2, 3, 4\}, R = \{5\}$
3. **Show the inverse of Exercise 1 as a table.**

x	y
-3	0
4	1
-3	1

4. **A relation contains five ordered pairs. If its domain is {2, 4, 6, 8, 10} and each y-coordinate is three more than the x-coordinate, then what are the ordered pairs in the relation?** $\{(2, 5), (4, 7), (6, 9), (8, 11), (10, 13)\}$

Motivating the Lesson

The French Club will receive a base fee of $10 plus 15% of its sales for a flag sale. If each flag sells for $5.00, what equation represents their profit?
$p = 0.15s + 10$
What is the club's profit if its sales are $200? $40

Objectives

9-3A
9-3B

After studying this lesson, you should be able to:
- solve linear equations for a specific variable, and
- solve linear equations for a given domain.

Application

FYI · · ·

Most American car horns beep in the key of F.

Anne Thompson is saving money to buy a used car for $1900. She already has $500 in her savings account. She plans to add $80 each week from the money she earns working at Readalot Bookstore. Anne uses a chart to help determine when she will have enough money in savings to buy the car. Let x represent the number of weeks and let y represent her total savings in dollars. Then $500 + 80x$ represents her savings after x weeks.

x (weeks)	500 + 80x	y (savings)	(x, y)
5	500 + 80(5)	900	(5, 900)
10	500 + 80(10)	1300	(10, 1300)
12	500 + 80(12)	1460	(12, 1460)
15	500 + 80(15)	1700	(15, 1700)
18	500 + 80(18)	1940	(18, 1940)
20	500 + 80(20)	2100	(20, 2100)

Based on this chart, Anne knows that in 18 weeks her total savings will be over $1900.

The equation $y = 500 + 80x$ describes Anne's total savings (y) after any number of weeks (x). Each of the ordered pairs listed in the chart above is a *solution* of the equation $y = 500 + 80x$.

Definition of the Solution of an Equation in Two Variables	If a true statement results when the numbers in an ordered pair are substituted into an equation in two variables, then the ordered pair is a solution of the equation.

Since the solutions of an equation in two variables are ordered pairs, such an equation describes a relation. The set of values of x is the domain of the relation. The set of corresponding values of y is the range of the relation.

ALTERNATE TEACHING STRATEGIES

Using Discussion

Is the ordered pair (3, 4) a solution of the equation $2x + 3y = 25$? no
Is the ordered pair (5, 5) a solution of the equation? yes
Is there a way to rewrite the equation so that it is easier to find the ordered pairs that make up its solution set?
Yes, solve the equation for either x or y.

Example 1

Solve $y = 2x + 3$ if the domain is $\{-5, -3, -1, 0, 1, 3, 5, 7, 9\}$.

Make a table. The values of x come from the domain. Substitute each value of x into the equation to determine the corresponding value of y.

x	2x + 3	y	(x, y)
−5	2(−5) + 3	−7	(−5, −7)
−3	2(−3) + 3	−3	(−3, −3)
−1	2(−1) + 3	1	(−1, 1)
0	2(0) + 3	3	(0, 3)
1	2(1) + 3	5	(1, 5)
3	2(3) + 3	9	(3, 9)
5	2(5) + 3	13	(5, 13)
7	2(7) + 3	17	(7, 17)
9	2(9) + 3	21	(9, 21)

The solution set is $\{(-5, -7), (-3, -3), (-1, 1), (0, 3), (1, 5), (3, 9), (5, 13), (7, 17), (9, 21)\}$.

The solutions of an equation in two variables are usually easier to determine when the equation is solved for one of the variables.

Example 2

Solve $3y + 6x = 12$ if the domain is $\{-4, -3, -2, 2, 3, 4\}$.

First solve the equation for y in terms of x. **Teaching Tip ❶**

$$3y + 6x = 12$$
$$3y = 12 - 6x \qquad \text{\textit{Subtract 6x from each side.}}$$
$$\frac{3y}{3} = \frac{12 - 6x}{3} \qquad \text{\textit{Divide each side by 3.}}$$
$$y = 4 - 2x$$

Now substitute each value of x from the domain to determine the corresponding values of y.

x	4 − 2x	y	(x, y)
−4	4 − 2(−4)	12	(−4, 12)
−3	4 − 2(−3)	10	(−3, 10)
−2	4 − 2(−2)	8	(−2, 8)
2	4 − 2(2)	0	(2, 0)
3	4 − 2(3)	−2	(3, −2)
4	4 − 2(4)	−4	(4, −4)

Teaching Tip ❷

The solution set is $\{(-4, 12), (-3, 10), (-2, 8), (2, 0), (3, -2), (4, -4)\}$.

LESSON 9-3 EQUATIONS AS RELATIONS 365

TEACHING THE LESSON

Teaching Tip ❶ Transforming equations gives good practice in applying the properties of solving equations.

Teaching Tip ❷ To insure that students have correctly solved for y, have them check several of their ordered pairs in the original equation.

Chalkboard Examples

For Example 1
Solve $y = -2x + 1$ if the domain is $\{-4, -2, 0, 2, 4\}$. The solution set is $\{(-4, 9), (-2, 5), (0, 1), (2, -3), (4, -7)\}$.

For Example 2
Solve the equation $3x = 4y + 6$ for y. $y = \frac{3}{4}x - \frac{3}{2}$

In this textbook, when variables other than x and y are used in an equation, you may assume that the values of the variable that comes first alphabetically are from the domain. **Teaching Tip 3**

Example 3

Solve 3a + 2b = 11 if the domain is {−3, 0, 1, 2, 5}.

Assume that the values of a come from the domain. Therefore, the equation should be solved for b in terms of a. **Teaching Tip 4**

$3a + 2b = 11$
$\quad 2b = 11 - 3a$ *Subtract 3a from each side.*
$\quad b = \frac{11 - 3a}{2}$ *Divide each side by 2.*

Now substitute the values of a from the domain to determine the corresponding values of b.

a	$\frac{11-3a}{2}$	b	(a, b)
−3	$\frac{11-3(-3)}{2}$	10	(−3, 10)
0	$\frac{11-3(0)}{2}$	$\frac{11}{2}$	$\left(0, \frac{11}{2}\right)$
1	$\frac{11-3(1)}{2}$	4	(1, 4)
2	$\frac{11-3(2)}{2}$	$\frac{5}{2}$	$\left(2, \frac{5}{2}\right)$
5	$\frac{11-3(5)}{2}$	−2	(5, −2)

The solution set is $\left\{(-3, 10), \left(0, \frac{11}{2}\right), (1, 4), \left(2, \frac{5}{2}\right), (5, -2)\right\}$.

Example 4

APPLICATION
Career

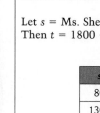

Ms. Shell works as a sales representative for Stokes Electronics. She receives a salary of $1800 per month plus a 6% commission on monthly sales over her target. Her sales in July will be $800, $1300, or $2000 over target, depending on when her orders are filled by the company distribution center. Will her total income for July be more than $1850?

Let s = Ms. Shell's sales for July, and let t = her total income. Then t = 1800 + 0.06s where the domain is {800, 1300, 2000}.

s	1800 + 0.06s	t	(s, t)
800	1800 + 0.06(800)	1848	(800, 1848)
1300	1800 + 0.06(1300)	1878	(1300, 1878)
2000	1800 + 0.06(2000)	1920	(2000, 1920)

Her total income for July will be more than $1850 only if her sales are $1300 or $2000, and not $800.

366   CHAPTER 9   FUNCTIONS AND GRAPHS

RETEACHING THE LESSON

Demonstrate two approaches to solving an equation given its domain. First, substitute each value of the domain for x and solve for the corresponding y-value. Second, solve for y in general. Then substitute each value of the domain for x into the phrase found equal to y.

1. She can solve the equation $1900 = 80x + 500$.

CHECKING FOR UNDERSTANDING

Communicating Mathematics

Read and study the lesson to answer each question.

1. Refer to the application at the beginning of the lesson. How can Anne determine during which week she will have saved $1900?

2. Why does the equation $y = 2x + 1$ describe a relation? $\{-1, 0\}$

3. If the domain of the equation $m = n + 1$ is $\{0, 1\}$, what is the range?

2. All of the solutions of this equation form a set of ordered pairs.

Guided Practice

Copy and complete each table for the given equation.

4. $y = 4x - 3$

x	y	(x, y)
-3	-15	$(-3, -15)$
-2	-11	$(-2, -11)$
-1	-7	$(-1, -7)$
0	-3	$(0, -3)$
2	5	$(2, 5)$
4	13	$(4, 13)$

5. $n = \dfrac{2m + 5}{3}$

m	n	(m, n)
-4	-1	$(-4, -1)$
-2	$\frac{1}{3}$	$\left(-2, \frac{1}{3}\right)$
0	$\frac{5}{3}$	$\left(0, \frac{5}{3}\right)$
1	$\frac{7}{3}$	$\left(1, \frac{7}{3}\right)$
3	$\frac{11}{3}$	$\left(3, \frac{11}{3}\right)$

Which of the ordered pairs given are solutions of the equation?

6. $3x + y = 8$ **a, c**   a. $(2, 2)$ b. $(3, 1)$ c. $(4, -4)$ d. $(8, 0)$

7. $2x + 3y = 11$ **b, c**   a. $(3, 1)$ b. $(1, 3)$ c. $(-2, 5)$ d. $(4, -1)$

8. $2m - 5n = 1$ **a, d**   a. $(-2, -1)$ b. $(2, 1)$ c. $(7, 3)$ d. $(-7, -3)$

Solve each equation for the variable indicated.

9. $x + y = 5$ for y $y = 5 - x$

10. $3x + y = 7$ for y $y = 7 - 3x$

11. $b - 5a = 3$ for b $b = 3 + 5a$

12. $4m + n = 7$ for n $n = 7 - 4m$

EXERCISES

Practice

Which of the ordered pairs given are solutions of the equation?

13. $3r = 8s - 4$ **a, b, c**   a. $\left(\frac{2}{3}, \frac{3}{4}\right)$ b. $\left(0, \frac{1}{2}\right)$ c. $(4, 2)$ d. $(2, 4)$

14. $3y = x + 7$ **c, d**   a. $(2, 4)$ b. $(2, -1)$ c. $(2, 3)$ d. $(-1, 2)$

15. $4x = 8 - 2y$ **a**   a. $(2, 0)$ b. $(0, 2)$ c. $(0.5, -3)$ d. $(1, -2)$

Solve each equation for the variable indicated.

16. $8x + 2y = 6$ for y $y = 3 - 4x$

17. $6x + 3y = 12$ for y $y = 4 - 2x$

18. $4a + 3b = 7$ for b $b = \dfrac{7 - 4a}{3}$

19. $6r + 5s = 2$ for s $s = \dfrac{2 - 6r}{5}$

20. $6x = 3y + 2$ for y $y = \dfrac{6x - 2}{3}$

21. $3a = 7b + 8$ for b $b = \dfrac{3a - 8}{7}$

22. $4p = 7 - 2r$ for r $r = \dfrac{7 - 4p}{2}$

23. $-4 = 5n - 7r$ for r $r = \dfrac{4 + 5n}{7}$

LESSON 9-3 EQUATIONS AS RELATIONS **367**

EXTENDING THE LESSON

Math Power: Reasoning

When variables other than x and y are used in examples in this lesson, we have assumed that the alphabetical ordering of the variables determines which variable represents the domain element. Give an example of a situation where this might not be the case. **Answer will vary.**

Possible answers include $A = s^2$, where the area depends on the length of a side of a square, and $d = 50t$ where the distance (d) covered at 50 mph depends on the number of hours (t).

Checking for Understanding

Exercises 1-12 are designed to help you assess understanding through reading, writing, and speaking. You should work through Exercises 1-3 with your students, and then monitor their work on Exercises 4-12.

Closing the Lesson

Writing Activity For each equation, find the range for the given domain.
1. $5y - 3x = 8$, where the domain is $\{-2, 0, 5\}$.
$R = \left\{\frac{2}{5}, 1\frac{3}{5}, 4\frac{3}{5}\right\}$
2. $3z - 6w = 1$, where the domain is $\{-1, 0, 2\}$.
$R = \left\{-1\frac{2}{3}, \frac{1}{3}, 4\frac{1}{3}\right\}$

APPLYING THE LESSON

Homework Exercises

Assignment Guide
Basic: 13-35, 42-45, 47-52
Average: 16-38, 42-52
Enriched: 20-52

Practice Masters Booklet, p. 70

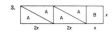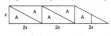

368   Chapter 9

Solve each equation if the domain is $\{-2, -1, 0, 2, 5\}$. **See margin.**

24. $y = 3x$ 25. $y = 2x + 1$ 26. $x + y = 7$

27. $x - y = 4$ 28. $5x + y = 4$ 29. $2a + 3b = 13$

30. $4r + 3s = 16$ 31. $2t = 3 - 5s$ 32. $5a - b = -3$

33. $3x = 5 + 2y$ 34. $5a = 8 - 4b$ 35. $6b - a = 32$

 Solve each equation if the range is $\{-3, -1, 0, 2, 3\}$. **See margin.**

36. $y = 2x$ 37. $y = 5x + 1$ 38. $2a + b = 4$

39. $4r + 3s = 13$ 40. $5b = 8 - 4a$ 41. $6m - n = -3$

Critical Thinking   Find the domain of each relation if the range is $\{0, 4, 36\}$.

42. $y = x^2$ 43. $y = |2x| - 4$ 44. $y = |2x - 4|$
    $\{-6, -2, 0, 2, 6\}$ $\{-20, -4, -2, 2, 4, 20\}$ $\{-16, 0, 2, 4, 20\}$

Applications   45. **Gardening**   Paquita has only 16 m of fencing to use for enclosing her rectangular garden. She wants the garden to have the largest possible area given that the sides have integral lengths. What are the dimensions of her garden? (*Hint:* $P = 2\ell + 2w$ and $A = \ell w$.) **4 m by 4 m**

46. **Physics**   A ball is thrown upward with an initial velocity of 96 feet per second. The height h, in feet, of the ball above the ground after t seconds is given by the equation $h = 96t - 16t^2$. Make a table of values for this equation to determine when the ball will reach its maximum height and when the ball will hit the ground. **3 seconds; 6 seconds**

Mixed Review   47. Solve $5s - 6.5 < -13.4 + 4s$.   **(Lesson 5-1)** $\{s | s < -6.9\}$

48. Find $(2xy + 6xy^2 + y^2) - (3x^2y + 2xy + 3y^2)$.   **(Lesson 6-6)**
              $-3x^2y + 6xy^2 - 2y^2$

49. Factor $42abc - 12a^2b^2 + 3a^2c^2$.   **(Lesson 7-2)** $3a(14bc - 4ab^2 + ac^2)$

50. Solve $5m^2 + 5m = 0$.   **(Lesson 7-9)** $\{-1, 0\}$

51. **Work**   A swimming pool can be filled by one pipe in 12 hours and by another pipe in 4 hours. How long will it take to fill the pool if the water flows through both pipes?   **(Lesson 8-9) 3 hours**

52. Determine the domain, range, and inverse of the relation $\{(8, 1), (4, 2), (6, -4), (5, -3), (6, 0)\}$.   **(Lesson 9-2) See margin.**

368   CHAPTER 9   FUNCTIONS AND GRAPHS

Graphing Linear Relations

Objective
9-4

After studying this lesson, you should be able to:
- graph linear equations on a coordinate plane.

Lesson Resources

- Reteaching Master 9-4
- Practice Master 9-4
- Enrichment Master 9-4
- Video Algebra, 35

 Transparency 9-4 contains the 5-Minute Check and a teaching aid for this lesson.

Application

Every April, Maxine's Pie Shop has a $1 off sale. The following chart shows the prices for selected pies.

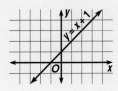

Pie	Original Price	Sale Price
Banana Cream	$6.00	$5.00
Lemon Meringue	$7.00	$6.00
Strawberry	$9.00	$8.00
Pecan	$10.00	$9.00

Let x represent the original price of a pie and let y represent the sale price. Then the equation $y = x - 1$ describes the sale price for any pie. For the chart above, the domain is {6, 7, 9, 10} and the solution set is {(6, 5), (7, 6), (9, 8), (10, 9)}. The solutions can also be shown in a graph like the one at the right.

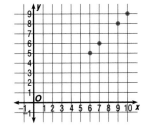

Remember, the values of the first coordinates in the ordered pairs of a relation represent its domain.

If the domain of $y = x - 1$ is the set of all real numbers, then an infinite number of ordered pairs are solutions of the equation. Suppose you draw a line connecting the points in the graph at the right. The graph of every solution of $y = x - 1$ lies on this line. The coordinates of any point on this line satisfy the equation. Hence the line is called the *graph* of $y = x - 1$.

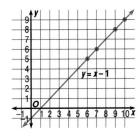

The equation $y = x - 1$ is equivalent to equations like $-y = 1 - x$ and $x - y = 1$. All of these equations have the same graph. An equation whose graph is a straight line is called a **linear equation**.

Teaching Tip ❶

Definition of a Linear Equation	A linear equation is an equation that can be written in the form $Ax + By = C$, where A, B, and C are any numbers, and A and B are not both zero.

LESSON 9-4 GRAPHING LINEAR RELATIONS **369**

INTRODUCING THE LESSON

⏱ 5-Minute Check
(over Lesson 9-3)

Solve each equation for the variable indicated.

1. $2x + 3y = 15$, for y
   $y = 5 - \frac{2}{3}x$
2. $7m - n = 8$, for n
   $n = 7m - 8$
3. $m + 3k = 14$, for m
   $m = 14 - 3k$

Solve each equation if the domain is {−2, −1, 0, 1, 2}.

4. $y = 4x - 1$ {(−2, −9), (−1, −5), (0, −1), (1, 3), (2, 7)}
5. $3r + 2s = 4$ {(−2, 5), $\left(-1, \frac{7}{2}\right)$, (0, 2), $\left(1, \frac{1}{2}\right)$, (2, −1)}

Motivating the Lesson

Ask students to identify some applications from previous lessons in which there appears to be a linear relationship between the two variables in a relation. Some examples might include a salary that is dependent upon the number of hours worked and commission based on the amount of sales.

TEACHING THE LESSON

Teaching Tip ❶ Make sure students understand this definition. The phrase "can be written" does not mean the equation has to appear in that form. However, the equation must be equivalent to an equation in the form $Ax + By = C$. All such equations have degree 1.

ALTERNATE TEACHING STRATEGIES

Using Logical Reasoning

The following is a graph of $y = x + 1$. Equivalent equations have the same graph.

Can you write an equation that is equivalent to $y = x + 1$? **Answers will vary but may include $y - 1 = x$, $y - x = 1$, and $-2 = 2x - 2y$.**

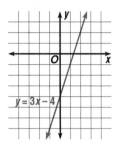
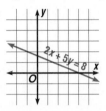
Example 1

Determine whether each equation is a linear equation.

a. $2x = 8 + y$

An equivalent form of this equation is $2x - y = 8$. Therefore, this is a linear equation with $A = 2$, $B = -1$, and $C = 8$.

b. $3x + y^2 = 7$

The exponent of all variables in a linear equation must be 1. Therefore, this is *not* a linear equation.

c. $y = 7$

An equivalent form of this equation is $0x + y = 7$. Therefore, this is a linear equation with $A = 0$, $B = 1$, and $C = 7$.

Example 2

Draw the graph of $y = 2x - 1$.

An equivalent form of this equation is $2x - y = 1$. Thus, it is a linear equation. Set up a table of values for x and y. Then graph the ordered pairs and connect the points with a line. **Teaching Tip ②**

x	$2x - 1$	y	(x, y)
-2	$2(-2) - 1$	-5	$(-2, -5)$
-1	$2(-1) - 1$	-3	$(-1, -3)$
0	$2(0) - 1$	-1	$(0, -1)$
1	$2(1) - 1$	1	$(1, 1)$
2	$2(2) - 1$	3	$(2, 3)$

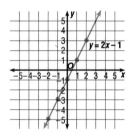

Usually, values of x such as 0 and integers near 0 are chosen.

Example 3

Draw the graph of $3x + 2y = 4$.

Solve the equation for y.

$3x + 2y = 4$ **Teaching Tip ③**

$2y = 4 - 3x$

$y = \dfrac{4 - 3x}{2}$

x	$\dfrac{4 - 3x}{2}$	y	(x, y)
-2	$\dfrac{4 - 3(-2)}{2}$	5	$(-2, 5)$
-1	$\dfrac{4 - 3(-1)}{2}$	$\dfrac{7}{2}$	$\left(-1, \dfrac{7}{2}\right)$
0	$\dfrac{4 - 3(0)}{2}$	2	$(0, 2)$
1	$\dfrac{4 - 3(1)}{2}$	$\dfrac{1}{2}$	$\left(1, \dfrac{1}{2}\right)$
2	$\dfrac{4 - 3(2)}{2}$	-1	$(2, -1)$

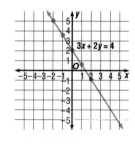

Example 4

During May of 1990, southwest Missouri received 30 inches of rain. The water level of a flooded river dropped by 3 inches per hour after cresting at 3 feet above its normal level. Let x represent the number of hours and y represent the water's height above the normal level. Then the equation $y = 36 - 3x$ describes the water's height above its normal level for any number of hours. Draw the graph of this equation. Then use the graph to estimate when the river will return to its normal level.

Set up a table of values for x and y. Then graph the ordered pairs and connect them with a line.

x	$36 - 3x$	y	(x, y)
0	$36 - 3(0)$	36	$(0, 36)$
1	$36 - 3(1)$	33	$(1, 33)$
3	$36 - 3(3)$	27	$(3, 27)$
6	$36 - 3(6)$	18	$(6, 18)$

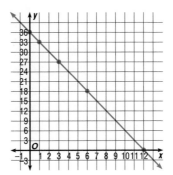

Why is it not necessary to choose negative values for x?

Based on the graph, the river should return to its normal level after 12 hours.

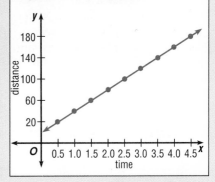

CHECKING FOR UNDERSTANDING

Communicating Mathematics

Read and study the lesson to answer each question.

1. What are the values of A, B, and C for the linear equation $3x = 2y$? $A = 3, B = -2, C = 0$ or $A = -3, B = 2, C = 0$
2. Describe the graph of a linear equation with $A = 0$. horizontal line
3. Describe the graph of a linear equation with $B = 0$. vertical line
4. The graph of a linear equation with $C = 0$ always passes through what point? the origin

Guided Practice

Determine whether each equation is a linear equation.

5. $5x + 2y = 7$ yes   6. $3x^2 + 2y = 4$ no   7. $x + \frac{1}{y} = 7$ no

8. $\frac{1}{x} - \frac{1}{y} = \frac{1}{2}$ no   9. $\frac{3}{5}x - \frac{2}{3}y = 5$ yes   10. $x = y^2$ no

11. $\frac{3}{5x} = y$ no   12. $\frac{3}{5}x = y$ yes   13. $\frac{y}{2} = 2$ yes

Solve each equation for y. Then graph each equation.

14. $6x + 7 = -14y$
$y = -\frac{6x + 7}{14}$

15. $8x - y = 16$
$y = 8x - 16$

16. $x + 5y = 16$
$y = \frac{16 - x}{5}$

LESSON 9-4 GRAPHING LINEAR RELATIONS 371

Error Analysis

Students often confuse the graphs of $y = a$ and $x = b$. Invite students to reconstruct which line, horizontal or vertical, corresponds to which graph by making (x, y) tables that fit the equations. To differentiate these similar concepts, focus on just one of the ideas.

Closing the Lesson

Writing Activity Have students select a formula from Lesson 8-9, set up a table of values, and graph the relation. Have them determine whether the relation is linear.

APPLYING THE LESSON

Homework Exercises

Assignment Guide

Basic: 17-43, 47-48, 51-56
Average: 21-45, 47-56
Enriched: 23-56
All: Mid-Chapter Review, 1-15

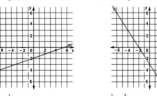

NAME _____ DATE _____

9-4 | **Practice Worksheet**

Graphing Relations

Solve each equation for y.

1. $2x + 3y = 6$ $y = -\frac{2}{3}x + 2$
2. $4x - 2y = 3$ $y = 2x - \frac{3}{2}$
3. $\frac{1}{2}y - 2x = 4$ $y = 4x + 8$
4. $\frac{1}{4}x - \frac{5}{8}y = 1$ $y = \frac{2x - 8}{5}$

Determine whether each equation is a linear equation.

5. $xy = 6$ no
6. $y^2 - 4x = 6$ no
7. $y = 0$ yes
8. $x - y = 0$ yes
9. $4x = 2y$ yes
10. $5r + 6t = 3r - 2$ yes

Graph each equation.

11. $x - 3y = 6$
12. $3x + 2y = -6$
13. $\frac{1}{3}x - \frac{1}{6}y = 0$
14. $\frac{1}{2}x + \frac{3}{4}y = 1$

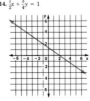

EXERCISES

Practice

Solve each equation for y. 19. $y = \frac{3}{4}x - 15$

 17. $3x + 4y = 12$ $y = \frac{12 - 3x}{4}$

18. $4x - \frac{3}{8}y = 1$ $y = \frac{32x - 8}{3}$

19. $\frac{1}{2}x - \frac{2}{3}y = 10$

Determine whether each equation is a linear equation.

20. $xy = 2$ no
21. $3x = 2y$ yes
22. $x^2 = y^2$ no

23. $2x - 3 = y^2$ no
24. $3m - 2n = 8$ yes
25. $3m - 2n = 0$ yes

26. $4x^2 - 3x = y$ no
27. $2m + 5m = 7n$ yes
28. $8a - 7b = 2a - 5$ yes

Graph each equation. See Solutions Manual.

29. $3m + n = 4$
30. $2x - y = 8$
31. $b = 5a - 7$

32. $y = 3x + 1$
33. $4x + 3y = 12$
34. $2x + 7y = 9$

35. $3x - 2y = 12$
36. $\frac{1}{2}x + y = 8$
37. $x + \frac{1}{3}y = 6$

38. $x = -\frac{5}{2}$
39. $y = \frac{4}{3}$
40. $\frac{3}{5}x = 6$

41. $-\frac{3}{4}y = 6$
42. $\frac{3}{4}x + \frac{1}{2}y = 6$
43. $\frac{4}{3}x - \frac{3}{4}y = 1$

Find a linear equation that represents each relation.

44. $\{(0, 0), (1, 1), (2, 2), (-1, -1)\}$ $y = x$ or $x - y = 0$

45. $\{(0, 0), (1, -3), (2, -6), (-1, 3)\}$ $y = -3x$ or $3x + y = 0$

46. $\{(0, -1), (1, 1), (2, 3), (3, 5), (-1, -3)\}$ $y = 2x - 1$ or $2x - y = 1$

Critical Thinking

47. Graph the four equations given below on the same coordinate plane. Then compare the graphs. See margin.

$$y = x - 1 \qquad y = 2x - 1 \qquad y = 3x - 1 \qquad y = 4x - 1$$

Applications

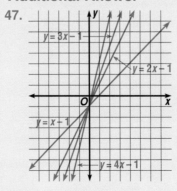

48. Science As a thunderstorm approaches, you see lightning as it occurs, but you hear the accompanying sound of thunder a short time afterward. The distance y, in miles, that sound travels in t seconds is given by the equation $y = 0.21t$.

a. Draw a graph of this equation. **See Solutions Manual.**

b. Use the graph to estimate how long it will take you to hear the thunder from a storm that is 3 miles away. **about 14 seconds**

49. Business Creative Catering charges a basic fee of $100 to cater a banquet plus an additional charge of $3 per person invited to the banquet. The total charge t, in dollars, for a banquet where p people are invited is given by the equation $t = 3p + 100$.

a. Draw a graph of this equation. **See Solutions Manual.**

b. Use the graph to determine how many people were invited to a banquet if Creative Catering charged $850. **250 people**

Additional Answer

47.

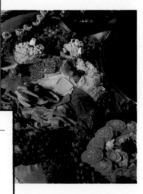

50. **Temperature** The relationship between Celsius temperature (C) and Fahrenheit temperature (F) is given by the formula $F = \frac{9}{5}C + 32$.

    a. Draw a graph of this equation. **See Solutions Manual.**

    b. Use the graph to determine at what point the values for C and F are equal. **−40**

Mixed Review

51. Arrange the terms of $12n^4xy^3 - 4n^2x^3 + 2nxy^5$ so that the powers of y are in descending order. **(Lesson 6-5)** $2nxy^5 + 12n^4xy^3 - 4n^2x^3$

Simplify each expression. **(Lessons 6-3, 8-1, and 8-4)** 54. $5x^2 - 4x + 7$

52. $\dfrac{(-m)^3n^{-4}}{(3m^2n)^{-2}}$ $\dfrac{-9m^7}{n^2}$ 53. $\dfrac{k^2 - 1}{k^2 + 2k + 1}$ $\dfrac{k - 1}{k + 1}$ 54. $\dfrac{20x^3 + 19x^2 + 49}{4x + 7}$

55. **Gardening** A rectangular garden is 5 meters wide and 16 meters long. When the length and width are increased by the same amount in order to plant more vegetables, the area is increased by 72 square meters. What are the dimensions of the new garden? **(Lesson 7-10)** 8 m by 19 m

56. Solve $3n = 10 - 4m$ if the domain is $\{-3, -1, 0, 1, 4\}$. **(Lesson 9-3)**
$\{(-3, \frac{22}{3}), (-1, \frac{14}{3}), (0, \frac{10}{3}), (1, 2), (4, -2)\}$

MID-CHAPTER REVIEW

Graph each point. **(Lesson 9-1) See Solutions Manual.**

1. $A(-5, 7)$ 2. $B(5, -7)$ 3. $C(5, 0)$ 4. $D(-2, -6)$

Express each relation as a set of ordered pairs. Then state the domain, the range, and the inverse of the relation. **(Lesson 9-2) See margin.**

x	y
4	2
1	3
3	3
6	4

5.

6.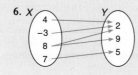

7.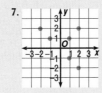

Solve each equation if the domain is $\{-5, -2, 0, 1, 3\}$. **(Lesson 9-3) See margin.**

8. $y = 5x + 3$ 9. $2x - y = 7$ 10. $3s - 4r = 16$ 11. $6x = 11 + 5y$

Determine whether each equation is a linear equation. If it is, then graph the equation. **(Lesson 9-4) For graphs, see Solutions Manual.**

12. $3x - y = 4$ **yes**   13. $b = 7a - 5$ **yes**   14. $m = 5n^2 - 7$ **no**   15. $2x - 3y = 12$ **yes**

LESSON 9-4 GRAPHING LINEAR RELATIONS **373**

EXTENDING THE LESSON

Math Power: Reasoning

Write a linear equation for y in terms of x for the following ordered pairs: (1, 4), (2, 9), (3, 14), (5, 24), (8, 39).
$y = 5x - 1$

Mid-Chapter Review

The Mid-Chapter Review provides students with a brief review of the concepts and skills in Lessons 9-1 through 9-4. Lesson numbers are given at the end of problems or instruction lines so students may review concepts not yet mastered.

Chapter 9, Quiz B, (Lessons 9-3 through 9-4), is available in the Evaluation Masters Booklet, p. 121.

Additional Answers to Mid-Chapter Review

5. $\{(4, 2), (1, 3), (3, 3), (6, 4)\}$; $\{4, 1, 3, 6\}$; $\{2, 3, 4\}$; $\{(2, 4), (3, 1), (3, 3), (4, 6)\}$

6. $\{(4, 2), (-3, 2), (8, 2), (8, 9), (7, 5)\}$; $\{4, -3, 8, 7\}$; $\{2, 9, 5\}$; $\{(2, 4), (2, -3), (2, 8), (9, 8), (5, 7)\}$

7. $\{(-2, 2), (-1, 1), (1, 1), (1, -1), (2, 2), (2, -2)\}$; $\{-2, -1, 1, 2\}$; $\{2, 1, -1, -2\}$; $\{(2, -2), (1, -1), (1, 1), (-1, 1), (2, 2), (-2, 2)\}$

8. $\{(-5, -22), (-2, -7), (0, 3), (1, 8), (3, 18)\}$

9. $\{(-5, -17), (-2, -11), (0, -7), (1, -5), (3, -1)\}$

10. $\{(-5, -\frac{4}{3}), (-2, \frac{8}{3}), (0, \frac{16}{3}), (1, \frac{20}{3}), (3, \frac{28}{3})\}$

11. $\{(-5, -\frac{41}{5}), (-2, -\frac{23}{5}), (0, -\frac{11}{5}), (1, -1), (3, \frac{7}{5})\}$

Enrichment Masters Booklet, p. 64

NAME _____ DATE _____

9-4 **Enrichment Worksheet**

Taxicab Graphs

You have used a rectangular coordinate system to graph equations such as $y = x - 1$ on a coordinate plane. In a coordinate plane, the numbers in an ordered pair (x, y) can be any two real numbers.

A **taxicab plane** is different from the usual coordinate plane. The only points allowed are those that exist along the horizontal and vertical grid lines. You may think of the points as taxicabs that must stay on the streets.

The taxicab graph shows the equations $y = -2$ and $y = x - 1$. Notice that one of the graphs is no longer a straight line. It is now a collection of separate points.

Taxicab Graph of $y = x - 1$

Graph these equations on the taxicab plane at the right.

1. $y = x + 1$ 2. $y = -2x + 3$

3. $y = 2.5$ 4. $x = -4$

Use your graphs for these problems.

5. Which of the equations would have the same graph in both the usual coordinate plane and the taxicab plane? $x = -4$

6. Describe the form of equations that have the same graph in both the usual coordinate plane and the taxicab plane.
$x = A$ and $y = B$, where A and B are integers

In the taxicab plane, distances are not measured diagonally, but along the streets. Write the taxi-distance between each pair of points.

7. $(0, 0)$ and $(5, 2)$ 8. $(0, 0)$ and $(-3, 2)$ 9. $(0, 0)$ and $(2, 1.5)$
7 units   5 units   3.5 units

10. $(1, 2)$ and $(4, 3)$ 11. $(2, 4)$ and $(-1, 3)$ 12. $(0, 4)$ and $(-2, 0)$
4 units   4 units   6 units

Draw these graphs on the taxicab grid at the right.

13. The set of points whose taxi-distance from $(0, 0)$ is 2 units. indicated by crosses

14. The set of points whose taxi-distance from $(2, 1)$ is 3 units. indicated by dots

Lesson Resources

- Reteaching Master 9-5
- Practice Master 9-5
- Enrichment Master 9-5
- Video Algebra, 34

 Transparency 9-5 contains the 5-Minute Check and a teaching aid for this lesson.

INTRODUCING THE LESSON

 5-Minute Check

(over Lesson 9-4)

Identify each equation as linear or not linear.

1. $2a - 3b = 7$ linear
2. $y = \frac{1}{x}$ not linear
3. $4x + 2y^2 = 15$ not linear

Solve each equation for the variable indicated.

4. $2m - 3n = 6$, solve for n.
   $n = \frac{2}{3}m - 2$
5. $4y - 8 = 3x$, solve for y.
   $y = \frac{3}{4}x + 2$

Motivating the Lesson

Ask students to consider the statement, "Your shoe size is a function of the size of your foot". Develop the idea that "is a function of" actually means "depends on". Have students give examples of additional situations in which the value of one variable results in only one true value for a second variable.

TEACHING THE LESSON

Teaching Tip ① Have students express the definition of a function in their own words.

Teaching Tip ② Emphasize that values in the domain will not be used more than once in a function. Values in the range may occur more than once as Example 1 demonstrates. Point out that in (3, 2) and (−2, 2), the values of the domain are different.

9-5 Functions

Objectives
9-5A
9-5B

After studying this lesson, you should be able to:
- determine whether a given relation is a function, and
- calculate functional values for a given function.

Connection

FYI · · ·

The ancient Greeks made dice from the ankle bones and shoulder blades of sheep.

In Example 4 on page 361, you found the 36 possible outcomes when two dice are tossed and those outcomes where the faces of the dice show a sum of 7. The graphs of these relations are shown below.

Possible outcomes when two six-sided dice are tossed

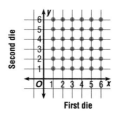

Those outcomes where the faces of the dice show a sum of 7

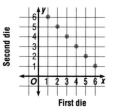

Teaching Tip ①

In the first relation, for each value of x, there are six different values of y: 1, 2, 3, 4, 5, and 6. In the second relation, for each value of x, there is *exactly* one value of y. The second relation is called a **function**. A function is a relation in which each element of the domain is paired with *exactly* one element of the range.

Example 1

Is {(5, −2), (3, 2), (4, −1), (−2, 2)} a function?

Since each element of the domain is paired with exactly one element of the range, this relation is a function.   **Teaching Tip ②**

Example 2

Which mapping represents a function?

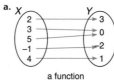

a.

a function

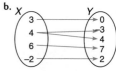

b.

not a function

The mapping in **a** represents a function since, for each element of the domain, there is *only one* corresponding element in the range.

The mapping in **b** does not represent a function since the element 4 in the domain maps to two elements, −3 and 4, in the range. **Teaching Tip ③**

ALTERNATE TEACHING STRATEGIES

Using Models

Form several different polygons on a geoboard, some of which have the same perimeter. Ask students to find the perimeter of each polygon and to describe the relation that maps each polygon (the domain) to its perimeter (the range). Then have each student form several different polygons on a geoboard and proceed as described

above. In each case, students should see that for each polygon there is exactly one perimeter. Explain that this type of a relation is called a function. Then ask students if the relation that maps the perimeter of each polygon to itself is a function. In some cases their answers should be "yes" and in some cases "no".

Example 3

Is the relation represented by the equation $x + 2y = 8$ a function?

Substitute a value for x in the equation. What is the corresponding value of y? Is there more than one value for y? For example, if x is 2, then y is 3 *and* that is the only value of y that will satisfy the equation. If you try other values of x, you will see that there is always only one corresponding value of y. Therefore, the equation $x + 2y = 8$ represents a function.

For equations like $x + 2y = 8$, it may not be easy to determine whether there is an element of the domain that is paired with more than one element of the range. Often, it is simpler to look at the graph of the relation. Suppose you graph $x + 2y = 8$.

Solve $x + 2y = 8$ for y.

$x + 2y = 8$

$2y = 8 - x$

$y = \dfrac{8 - x}{2}$

Make a table of values and graph the equation.

x	2	0	8
y	3	4	0

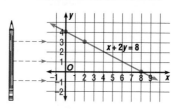

Now place your pencil at the left of the graph to represent a vertical line. Slowly move the pencil to the right across the graph.

For each value of x, this vertical line passes through no more than one point on the graph. This is true for *every* function. **Teaching Tip** ④

Vertical Line Test for a Function

If any vertical line passes through no more than one point of the graph of a relation, then the relation is a function.

Example 4

Use the vertical line test to determine if each relation is a function.

a.   b.   c.   d.

The relations in **a** and **c** are functions since any vertical line passes through no more than one point of the graph of the relation. The relation in **b** is *not* a function, since a vertical line near the y-axis will pass through *three* points. The relation in **d** is not a function since a vertical line passing through point P will also intersect the horizontal line.

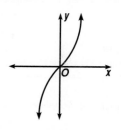

Equations that represent functions can be written in a form called **functional notation**. The equation $y = 2x + 1$ can be written in the form $f(x) = 2x + 1$. The symbol $f(x)$ is read "f of x" and represents the value in the range of the function that corresponds to the value of x in the domain. For example, $f(3)$ is the element in the range that corresponds to the element $x = 3$ in the domain. We say $f(3)$ is the **functional value** of f for $x = 3$.

Letters other than f are also used for names of functions.

The ordered pair $(3, f(3))$ is a solution of the function f.

You can determine a functional value by substituting the given value for x into the equation. For example, if $f(x) = 2x + 1$ and $x = 3$, then $f(3) = 2(3) + 1$ or 7.

Example 5 | If $f(x) = 3x - 7$, find each of the following.

a. $f(2)$ **b.** $f(5)$ **c.** $f(-3)$

$\quad f(2) = 3(2) - 7 \quad\quad f(5) = 3(5) - 7 \quad\quad f(-3) = 3(-3) - 7$
$\quad\quad = 6 - 7 \quad\quad\quad\quad = 15 - 7 \quad\quad\quad\quad\quad = -9 - 7$
$\quad\quad = -1 \quad\quad\quad\quad\quad = 8 \quad\quad\quad\quad\quad\quad = -16$

Example 6 | If $g(x) = x^2 - 2x + 1$, find each of the following.

a. $g(6a)$ **Teaching Tip ⑤**

$\quad g(6a) = (6a)^2 - 2(6a) + 1 \quad$ *Substitute 6a for x.*
$\quad\quad = 36a^2 - 12a + 1$

b. $6[g(a)]$

$\quad 6[g(a)] = 6[(a)^2 - 2(a) + 1] \quad$ *6[g(a)] means 6 times the value of g(a).*
$\quad\quad = 6a^2 - 12a + 6 \quad\quad\quad$ *Notice that $g(6a) \neq 6[g(a)]$.*

Example 7 | A rocket is launched with an initial velocity of 100 meters per second. Its height above the ground after t seconds is given by the formula $h(t) = 100t - 4.9t^2$, where $h(t)$ represents the height in meters. What is the height of this rocket 15 seconds after it is launched?

APPLICATION

Physics

The height of the rocket after 15 seconds is $h(15)$.

$\quad h(t) = 100t - 4.9t^2$
$\quad h(15) = 100(15) - 4.9(15)^2 \quad$ *Replace t with 15.*
$\quad\quad = 1500 - 4.9(225)$
$\quad\quad = 1500 - 1102.5$ or 397.5

The rocket is 397.5 meters high after 15 seconds.

RETEACHING THE LESSON

Demonstrate how functional notation $f(x)$ has an advantage to using "y".

$y = 2x - 3$	vs.	$f(x) = 2x - 3$
Find y when x is 4.		Find $f(4)$.
$y = 2(4) - 3$		$f(4) = 2(4) - 3$
$y = 5$ when $x = 4$.		$f(4) = 5$

CHECKING FOR UNDERSTANDING

Communicating Mathematics

Read and study the lesson to answer each question. 1–3. See margin.

1. Does a linear equation always represent a function? Explain.
2. Explain the vertical line test for a function in your own words.
3. Given a function $g(x)$, how can you determine $g(1)$?
4. Give an example of a function whose inverse is *not* a function.
   Answers will vary; typical answer is {(0, 1), (1, 1)}.

Guided Practice

Determine whether each relation is a function.

5. $\{(5, 4), (-2, 3), (5, 3)\}$ **no**
6. $\{(6, 3), (5, -2), (2, 3)\}$ **yes**
7. $5a^2 - 7 = b$ **yes**
8. $3s^2 + 2t^2 = 7$ **no**

Use the vertical line test to determine if each relation is a function.

9. 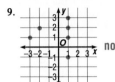 **no**
10. 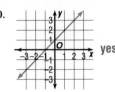 **yes**
11. 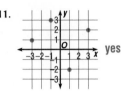 **yes**

Given $g(x) = 2x - 1$, determine each value.

12. $g(2)$ **3**
13. $g(-4)$ **−9**
14. $g(0)$ **−1**
15. $g\left(\frac{1}{2}\right)$ **0**

EXERCISES

Practice

 A

Determine whether each relation is a function.

16. **no**
17. **yes**
18. 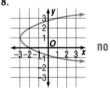 **no**

Determine whether each relation is a function. Then state the inverse of the relation and determine whether it is a function. **See margin.**

 B

19. $\{(3, 1), (5, 1), (7, 1)\}$
20. $\{(1, 3), (1, 5), (1, 7)\}$
21. $\{(-2, 4), (1, 3), (5, 2), (1, 4)\}$
22. $\{(6, -1), (1, 4), (2, 3), (6, 1)\}$
23. $\{(5, 4), (-6, 5), (4, 5), (0, 4)\}$
24. $\{(3, -2), (4, 7), (-2, 5), (4, 5)\}$

Determine whether each relation is a function.

25. $3x + 5y = 7$ **yes**
26. $y = 2$ **yes**
27. $4x - 7y = 3$ **yes**
28. $x^2 + y = 11$ **yes**
29. $x + y^2 = 11$ **no**
30. $x = -3$ **no**
31. $1 = yx$ **yes**
32. $x^2 - y^2 = 3$ **no**

LESSON 9-5 FUNCTIONS 377

Additional Answers

1. No, since the graph of any linear equation of the form $x = a$ is a vertical line.
2. A relation is a function if no two distinct points on the graph of the relation have the same x-coordinate.
3. Substitute 1 for each x in the equation of $g(x)$ and simplify.
19. yes; $\{(1, 3), (1, 5), (1, 7)\}$; no
20. no; $\{(3, 1), (5, 1), (7, 1)\}$; yes

21. no; $\{(4, -2), (3, 1), (2, 5), (4, 1)\}$; no
22. no; $\{(-1, 6), (4, 1), (3, 2), (1, 6)\}$; yes
23. yes; $\{(4, 5), (5, -6), (5, 4), (4, 0)\}$; no
24. no; $\{(-2, 3), (7, 4), (5, -2), (5, 4)\}$; no

Checking for Understanding

Exercises 1-15 are designed to help you assess understanding through reading, writing, and speaking. You should work through Exercises 1-4 with your students, and then monitor their work on Exercises 5-15.

Error Analysis

Students sometimes misinterpret the "exactly one element of the range" condition in the definition of a function as "one distinct range element". The misinterpretation leads to classifying the relation $\{(1, 3), (2, 3), (3, 4)\}$ as a nonfunction.

Assignment Guide

Basic: 16-40, 49-60
Average: 19-44, 49-60
Enriched: 21-60

Practice Masters Booklet, p. 72

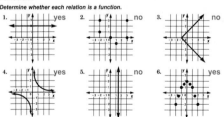

Chapter 9 377

Closing the Lesson

Writing Activity Have students show a relation that is a function and one that is not a function. Ask them to explain their reasoning.

APPLYING THE LESSON

Homework Exercises

See assignment guide on page 377.

Additional Answers

55a. See Solutions Manual for graph. The graphs all intersect at (0, 2).

55b. See Solutions Manual for graph. The coefficients of *x* are the additive inverses of those in Exercise a.

Enrichment Masters Booklet, p. 65

Composite Functions

Three things are needed to have a function—a set called the *domain*, a set called the *range*, and a *rule* that matches each element in the domain with only one element in the range. Here is an example.

Rule: $f(x) = 2x + 1$

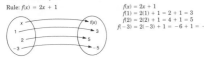

$f(x) = 2x + 1$
$f(1) = 2(1) + 1 = 2 + 1 = 3$
$f(2) = 2(2) + 1 = 4 + 1 = 5$
$f(-3) = 2(-3) + 1 = -6 + 1 = -5$

Suppose we have three sets A, B, and C and two functions described as shown below.

Rule: $f(x) = 2x + 1$ Rule: $g(y) = 3y - 4$

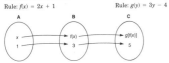

$g(y) = 3y - 4$
$g(3) = 3(3) - 4 = 5$

Let's find a rule that will match elements of set A with elements of set C without finding any elements in set B. In other words, let's find a rule for the **composite function** $g[f(x)]$.

Since $f(x) = 2x + 1$, $g[f(x)] = g(2x + 1)$.
Since $g(y) = 3y - 4$, $g(2x + 1) = 3(2x + 1) - 4$, or $6x - 1$.
Therefore, $g[f(x)] = 6x - 1$.

Find a rule for the composite function $g[f(x)]$.

1. $f(x) = 3x$ and $g(y) = 2y + 1$
   $g[f(x)] = 6x + 1$

2. $f(x) = x^2 + 1$ and $g(y) = 4y$
   $g[f(x)] = 4x^2 + 4$

3. $f(x) = -2x$ and $g(y) = y^2 - 3y$
   $g[f(x)] = 4x^2 + 6x$

4. $f(x) = \frac{1}{x-3}$ and $g(y) = y^{-1}$
   $g[f(x)] = x - 3$

5. Is it always the case that $g[f(x)] = f[g(x)]$? Justify your answer.
   No. For example, in Exercise 1, $f[g(x)] = f(2x + 1) = 3(2x + 1) = 6x + 3$, not $6x + 1$

Given $f(x) = 3x - 5$ and $g(x) = x^2 - x$, determine each value.

33. $f(-3)$ -14 **34.** $g(3)$ 6 **35.** $g\left(\frac{1}{3}\right)$ $\frac{-2}{9}$ **36.** $f\left(\frac{2}{3}\right)$ -3

37. $f(5.5)$ 11.5 **38.** $3[f(5)]$ 30 **39.** $2[g(-2)]$ 12 **40.** $g(0.5)$ -0.25

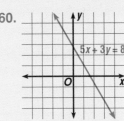

41. $f(4a)$ $12a - 5$ **42.** $g(4b)$ $16b^2 - 4b$ **43.** $3[f(2n)]$ $18n - 15$ **44.** $2[f(3n)]$ $18n - 10$

45. $3[g(2m)]$ $12m^2 - 6m$ **46.** $2[g(3m)]$ $18m^2 - 6m$ **47.** $f(a + 3)$ $3a + 4$ **48.** $g(b - 3)$ $b^2 - 7b + 12$

Critical Thinking The inverse of a relation can be found by interchanging the variables. For example, the inverse of the relation $y = 3x - 1$ is $x = 3y - 1$. Determine if the inverse of each relation is a function.

49. $3x + 2y = 1$ yes   **50.** $y = -3x^2$ no   **51.** $3x^2 - y^2 = 3$ no   **52.** $x + 3y^2 = 3$ yes

Applications **53. Car Rental** The cost of a one-day car rental from Rossi Rentals is given by the formula $C(m) = 31 + 0.13m$, where m is the number of miles that the car is driven, $0.13 is the cost per mile driven, and $C(m)$ is the total cost. If Sheila drove a distance of 110 miles and back in one day, what is the cost of the car rental? **$59.60**

54. Business The owner of Clean City Car Wash found that if n cars were washed in a day, the average daily profit $P(n)$, in dollars, was given by the formula $P(n) = -0.027n^2 + 8n - 280$. Find values of $P(n)$ for various values of n to determine the least number of cars that must be washed each day for Clean City Car Wash to make a profit. **41 cars**

Computer **55.** The BASIC program at the right uses a FOR/NEXT loop to generate several ordered pairs that could be used to graph the equation $y = 2x - 1$.

```
10 FOR X = -2 TO 2
20 LET Y = 2*X-1
30 PRINT "(";X;", ";Y;")"
40 NEXT X
50 END
```

a–b. See margin.

a. Modify line 20 to generate ordered pairs for $y = x + 2$, $y = 2x + 2$, $y = 3x + 2$, $y = 10x + 2$, and $y = 0.5x + 2$. Graph the five equations on the same axes. At what point do the graphs intersect the y-axis?

b. Modify line 20 to generate ordered pairs for $y = -x + 2$, $y = -2x + 2$, $y = -3x + 2$, $y = -10x + 2$, and $y = -0.5x + 2$. Graph the five equations on the same axes. How do these equations differ from those in exercise **a**?

Mixed Review **56.** Simplify $6(3x + 7x) + 7(-4x + 8x)$. **(Lesson 2-6)** $88x$

57. Construction A rectangular pool is 10 meters longer than it is wide. A deck 4 meters wide is built around the pool. If the total area of the deck is 592 m², what are the dimensions of the pool? **(Lesson 6-8)** **28 m by 38 m**

58. Factor $7n^2 - 22n + 3$. **(Lesson 7-5)** $(7n - 1)(n - 3)$

59. Simplify $\frac{-3}{5 - a} + \frac{5}{a^2 - 25}$. **(Lesson 8-7)** $\frac{3a + 20}{a^2 - 25}$

60. Graph $5x + 3y = 8$. **(Lesson 9-4)** **See margin.**

EXTENDING THE LESSON

Math Power:
Problem Solving

If $h(x) = 4x^3 + 3x^2 + x - 12$, find $3[h(2)]$. **102**

Additional Answer

60.

(graph of $5x + 3y = 8$)

Graphing Inequalities in Two Variables

Objective
9-6

After studying this lesson, you should be able to:
- graph inequalities in the coordinate plane.

Application

Mr. Harris is taking his drama class to see the play *Hansel and Gretel* at the Granada Theatre. Tickets for the play cost either $15 or $20. If he plans to spend no more than $240 on tickets, how many of each ticket can Mr. Harris purchase?

Let x = the number of $15 tickets purchased, and let y = the number of $20 tickets purchased. Then the following inequality can be used to represent this problem.

Cost of $15 tickets	plus	cost of $20 tickets	is no more than	$240.
15x	+	20y	≤	240

There are an infinite number of ordered pairs that are solutions to this inequality. The easiest way to show all of these solutions is to draw a *graph* of the inequality. Before doing this, let's consider some simpler inequalities.   *The problem above is solved in Example 2.* **Teaching Tip ❶**

Suppose you want to draw the graph of the inequality $x < 3$. First, you need to draw the graph of the equation $x = 3$. This graph is a line that separates the coordinate plane into two regions. In the figure at the right, one of the regions is shaded blue and the other is shaded yellow. Each region is called a **half-plane**. The line $x = 3$ is called the **boundary**, or **edge**, for each half-plane.

The line x = 3 means the line that is the graph of the equation x = 3.

To determine which half-plane $x < 3$ describes, choose a value of x that appears in the blue region, like 0. Since $0 < 3$, the blue region is described by $x < 3$. The x-coordinate of *every* point in that region is less than 3. The inequality $x > 3$ describes the yellow region. The points on the line $x = 3$ are in neither of these two regions.

Consider the graph of $y > x + 1$. The boundary line for this graph is the line $y = x + 1$. Since the boundary is *not* part of the graph, it is shown as a dashed line on the graph. To determine which half-plane is the graph of $y > x + 1$, test a point *not* on the boundary. For example, you can test the origin, $(0, 0)$. Since $0 > 0 + 1$ is

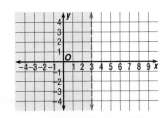

What happens if you test (0, 4)?

false, $(0, 0)$ is *not* a solution of $y > x + 1$. Thus, the graph is all points in the half-plane that does *not* contain $(0, 0)$. This graph is called an **open half-plane** since the boundary is not part of the graph.

LESSON 9-6 GRAPHING INEQUALITIES IN TWO VARIABLES   379

ALTERNATE TEACHING STRATEGIES

Using Applications

The cost of five pencils and three pens is at most $4.25. Use a graph to determine all the possible costs of a pencil and a pen.

Lesson Resources

- Reteaching Master 9-6
- Practice Master 9-6
- Enrichment Master 9-6
- Video Algebra, 44

 Transparency 9-6 contains the 5-Minute Check and a teaching aid for this lesson.

INTRODUCING THE LESSON

🕐 5-Minute Check
(over Lesson 9-5)

1. Is the relation {(1, 3), (2, 4), (3, 5), (−1, 3), (−2, 4), (−3, 5)} a function?   **yes**
2. Is the inverse of the relation shown in problem 1 a function?   **no**
3. Is the relation described by $y = −2$ a function?   **yes**

If $f(x) = 3x^2 − 4$, determine each of the following.

4. $f(−2)$ **8**
5. $f(0)$ **−4**

Motivating the Lesson

Have students consider each of the following situations.
1. Your height must be less than 4 feet to go on a kiddy ride at the amusement park.
2. The center must score at least 24 points to set a new record.
3. The cost of five pencils and three pens is at most $4.25.

Ask the students to show a relation to represent each of the above sentences.

TEACHING THE LESSON

Teaching Tip ❶   Point out to students that the graphs shown on this page are graphs of relations. Every x-value is paired with many y-values. Have them consider the vertical line test to verify that these relations are not functions.

For Example 1

Graph $y > x - 1$.

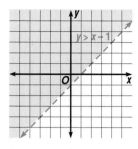

For Example 2

Graph $3y - 2x \leq 6$.

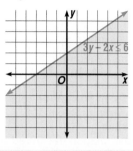

Teaching Tip ② Relate the open and closed half-planes used in graphing inequalities in two variables to the open and closed endpoints used in graphing inequalities in one variable.

Now consider the graph of $y \leq x + 1$. The boundary line for this graph is also the line $y = x + 1$. Since the inequality $y \leq x + 1$ means $y < x + 1$ or $y = x + 1$, this boundary *is* part of the graph. Therefore, the boundary is shown as a solid line on the graph.

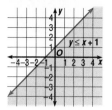

The origin, $(0, 0)$, is a part of the graph of $y \leq x + 1$ since $0 \leq 0 + 1$ is true. Thus, the graph is all points in the half-plane that contains the origin and the line $y = x + 1$. This graph is called **a closed half-plane.** Teaching Tip ②

Example 1

Graph $y > -4x - 3$.

Graph the line $y = -4x - 3$. Draw it as a dashed line since this boundary is *not* part of the graph. The origin, $(0, 0)$, is part of the graph since $0 > -4(0) - 3$ is true. Thus, the graph is all points in the half-plane that contains the origin.

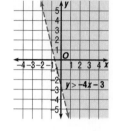

Check: Test a point on the other side of the boundary, say $(-2, -2)$. Since $-2 > -4(-2) - 3$, or $-2 > 5$ is false, $(-2, -2)$ is *not* part of the graph.

Example 2

APPLICATION

Sales

Graph $15x + 20y \leq 240$ to answer the application at the beginning of the lesson. How many of each ticket can Mr. Harris purchase?

First solve for y in terms of x.

$$15x + 20y \leq 240$$
$$20y \leq 240 - 15x$$
$$y \leq 12 - \frac{3}{4}x$$

Then graph $y = 12 - \frac{3}{4}x$ as a solid line since the boundary is part of the graph. The origin is part of the graph since $15(0) + 20(0) \leq 240$ is true. Thus, the graph is all points in the half-plane that contains the origin.

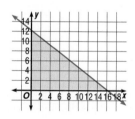

Mr. Harris cannot buy fractional or negative numbers of tickets. So, any point in the shaded region whose x- and y-coordinates are whole numbers is a possible solution. For example, $(5, 8)$ is a solution. This corresponds to buying five \$15 tickets and eight \$20 tickets for a total cost of $15(5) + 20(8)$ or \$235.

Example 3

APPLICATION

Sales

Jessica is selling two types of school notebooks. She knows that one type of notebook is much more popular with students than the other. She prices the popular notebook so that she will make $3 profit on each sale. To help sell the other notebook, she prices it cheaply and expects to lose $1 on each sale. How many of each type of notebook can she sell and not lose any money?

Let x = the number of the more popular notebooks sold.
Let y = the number of the other notebooks sold.
Then $3x$ = the profit from the sales of the more popular notebook, and $-1y$ = the profit (or loss) from the sales of the other notebook.

Write an inequality to represent the problem. Then graph this inequality to determine all of the possible solutions.

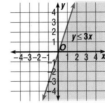

Profit from popular notebook	*plus*	*profit from other notebook*	*must be at least*	*0.*
$3x$	$+$	$-1y$	$\geq$	0

$$3x - y \geq 0$$
$$3x \geq y$$

Graph the equation $3x = y$. Draw it as a solid line since this boundary is part of the graph. Since the origin is on the boundary, you must test another point, say $(1, 1)$. Since $3(1) \geq 1$ is true, the graph of $3x \geq y$ is the half-plane that contains the point $(1, 1)$.

Any point in the shaded region above whose x-coordinate and y-coordinate are *whole* numbers is a possible solution. For example, since the point $(3, 5)$ is in this region, Jessica can sell 3 of the popular notebook and 5 of the other, giving her a total profit of $3(3) + (-1)(5)$ or $4.

CHECKING FOR UNDERSTANDING

Communicating Mathematics

Complete.

1. The graph of a linear equation separates the coordinate plane into two _____?_____. **half-planes**

2. For a(n) _____?_____ half-plane, the boundary is part of the graph. **closed**

3. If the coordinates of a point satisfy an inequality, then the graph of the inequality is the half-plane that _____?_____ the point. **contains**

Guided Practice

State whether the boundary is included in the graph of each inequality.

4. $2x + y \geq 3$ **yes**   5. $3x - 2y \leq 1$ **yes**   6. $5x - 2 > 3y$ **no**

LESSON 9-6 GRAPHING INEQUALITIES IN TWO VARIABLES   381

RETEACHING THE LESSON

An alternate strategy in determining which half-plane contains the solution to an inequality in two variables starts by transforming the inequality so y is the left member. Shade the lower half-plane for the "$y<$" form or shade the upper half-plane for the "$y>$" form.

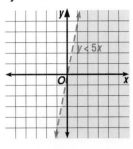
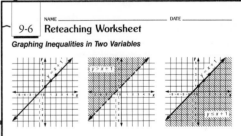
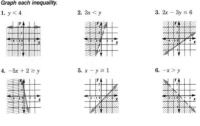

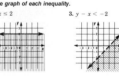

9-6 Practice Worksheet

Graphing Inequalities in Two Variables

Determine which half-plane is the graph of each inequality.

1. $y > 2x$ 2. $x \leq 2$ 3. $y - x < -2$

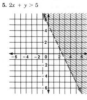

Graph each inequality.

4. $y - x \leq 4$ 5. $2x + y > 5$

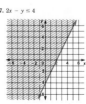

6. $x + 2y < -6$ 7. $2x - y \leq 4$

Determine which of the ordered pairs are solutions to the inequality.

7. $x + 2y \geq 3$ a. $(-2, 2)$ b. $(4, -1)$ c. $(3, 1)$ **c**
8. $2x - 3y \leq 1$ a. $(2, 1)$ b. $(5, -1)$ c. $(1, 1)$ **a, c**
9. $3x + 4y < 7$ a. $(1, 1)$ b. $(2, -1)$ c. $(-2, 4)$ **b**
10. $4y - 8 \geq 0$ a. $(0, 2)$ b. $(2, 5)$ c. $(-2, 0)$ **a, b**
11. $-2x < 8 - y$ a. $(5, 10)$ b. $(3, 6)$ c. $(-4, 0)$ **a, b**
12. $5x + 2 > 3y$ a. $(-2, -3)$ b. $(2, 3)$ c. $(4, 7)$ **a, b, c**

Use the point $(0, 0)$ to determine which half-plane is the graph of each inequality.

13. $x < 4$ 14. $y > -2$ 15. $3m + n > 4$

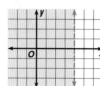

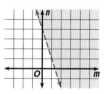

EXERCISES

Practice   Determine which half-plane is the graph of each inequality.

A   16. $2x - y < 6$ 17. $5a - b < 5$ 18. $3x < 2y$

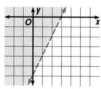
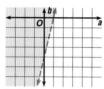

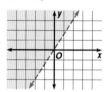

Teaching Tip ③   Graph each inequality. **See Solutions Manual.**

19. $y > 3$ 20. $y \leq -2$ 21. $x \geq -1$ 22. $x < 4$
23. $x + y > 1$ 24. $x + y < 2$ 25. $x + y < -2$ 26. $x + y > -4$
B   27. $y > x - 1$ 28. $y \leq x + 1$ 29. $y \leq 3x - 1$
30. $y > 4x - 1$ 31. $2x - y < 1$ 32. $3x + y > 1$
33. $2x + 3y \geq -2$ 34. $3y - 2x \leq 2$ 35. $x - 2y < 4$
36. $4y + x < 16$ 37. $x < y$ 38. $2x > 3y$
39. $-x < -y$ 40. $-y > x$ 41. $2x < -y$
C   42. $y > |x|$ 43. $|y| \geq 2$ 44. $y > 2$ and $x < 3$
45. $y > 2$ or $y < 1$ 46. $y \leq -x$ or $x \geq -3$ 47. $3y \geq x$ and $y < 0$

Critical Thinking   48. What compound inequality is described by the graph at the right? Find an inequality that also describes this graph. $(x \geq 0$ and $y \geq 0)$ or $(x \leq 0$ and $y \leq 0)$; $xy \geq 0$

Applications

49. **Sales** Tickets for Southside High School's annual talent show are $3 for adults and $2 for students. In order to cover the expenses for the show, a total of $600 must be made from ticket sales. **See margin.**

   a. Use a graph to determine how many of each type of ticket must be sold to cover the expenses.

   b. List three of the solutions.

50. **Manufacturing** A furniture factory can produce a table in 30 minutes and a chair in 12 minutes. **See margin.**

   a. Use a graph to determine how many of each can be produced during an 8-hour shift.

   b. List three possible solutions where at least 30 chairs are produced.

Mixed Review

51. Solve $2(x - 4) - 10x \leq 0$. **(Lesson 5-3)** $\{x | x \geq -1\}$

Simplify each expression. **(Lessons 6-2, 8-5, and 8-8)**

52. $(r^2xy)(-2r^3x)^2$ $4r^8x^3y$ 53. $\dfrac{12n}{3n - 2} + \dfrac{8}{2 - 3n}$ 4 54. $\dfrac{\frac{x + y}{a + b}}{\frac{x^2 - y^2}{b^2 - a^2}}$ $\dfrac{b - a}{x - y}$

55. Factor $15a^2 - 28bc - 21ab + 20ac$. **(Lesson 7-3)** $(3a + 4c)(5a - 7b)$

56. **Physics** A ball is dropped from a 100-meter tower. Its height $h(t)$, in meters, after t seconds is given by the formula $h(t) = 100 - 4.9t^2$. Will the ball have hit the ground after 4 seconds? Why or why not? **(Lesson 9-6)** No; after 4 seconds, the ball will be $100 - 4.9(4)^2$ or 21.6 meters above the ground.

HISTORY CONNECTION

René Descartes

René Descartes (1596–1650) was one of the greatest scientists of the seventeenth century. It was he who used two perpendicular number lines to identify points in a plane. This rectangular coordinate system is called the *Cartesian coordinate system*, in honor of Descartes. The connecting of algebra and geometry through graphing is called *analytic geometry*. Although Descartes is considered to be the founder of analytic geometry, he did not consider himself a mathematician. He is often called the "father of modern philosophy," his great love.

EXTENDING THE LESSON

Math Power: Connections

Find the area of the triangular region determined as the intersection of the closed half-planes $x \leq 4$, $y \geq -\dfrac{1}{2}x + 3$, and $y \leq \dfrac{1}{2}x + 5$. **Area = 18 units²**

History Connection

The History Connection features introduce students to persons or cultures who were involved in the development of mathematics. You may want students to further research Descartes or to research analytic geometry.

Additional Answers

49.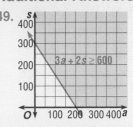

Answers will vary; typical answers are 200 adult and 0 student tickets, 0 adult and 300 student tickets, and 100 adult and 200 student tickets.

50.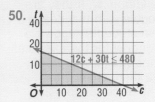

Answers will vary; typical answers are 40 chairs and 0 tables, 30 chairs and 4 tables, and 35 chairs and 2 tables.

Enrichment Masters Booklet, p. 66

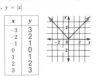

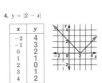

NAME _____ DATE _____

9-6 **Enrichment Worksheet**

Absolute Value Functions

Some types of functions that occur frequently have special names. Absolute value functions are an example.

Example: Graph $y = |x + 2|$.

x	y
-4	2
-3	1
-2	0
-1	1
0	2
1	3
2	4

Complete the table for each equation. Then, draw the graph.

1. $y = |x|$

x	y
-3	3
-2	2
-1	1
0	0
1	1
2	2
3	3

2. $y = |x| - 2$

x	y
-3	1
-2	0
-1	-1
0	-2
1	-1
2	0
3	1

3. $y = |x - 1|$

x	y
-2	3
-1	2
0	1
1	0
2	1
3	2
4	3

4. $y = |2 - x|$

x	y
-2	4
-1	3
0	2
1	1
2	0
3	1
4	2

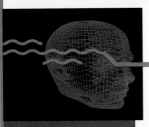

Using Technology

Objective This optional page shows how the graphing calculator can be used to perform mathematical computations and to enhance and extend mathematical concepts.

Teaching Suggestions

Take some time discussing range with students. It is an important concept and will pose great difficulty later if they do not grasp the idea now. If they are having trouble with the idea of range have students suggest a viewing window for the exercises that are not a complete graph. Then have them change the range on their calculators and graph the lines.

You can build a table of values with students by tracing along the graph of the line. If you are using the TI-81, it will show you both *x*- and *y*-values. You can use the [*X↔Y*] key on the Casio to find the *y*-value. Take these values and put them back into the equation to show students the connection between the graph and the algebra. Move along the line and do the same with two more values.

Technology

Graphing Relations

You can use a graphing calculator to graph linear relations. To graph a line on a graphing calculator, you first need to set the range. Press the [Range] key. Make sure it is set for the standard viewing window of Xmin = −10, Xmax = 10, Xscl = 1, Ymin = −10, Ymax = 10, Yscl = 1. To change the range on the TI-81, enter the following.

[RANGE] [(-)] 10 [ENTER] 1 [ENTER] [(-)] 10 [ENTER] 10 [ENTER] 1 [ENTER]

To change the range on the Casio, enter the following.

[Range] [(-)] 10 [EXE] 10 [EXE] 1 [EXE] [(-)] 10 [EXE] 10 [EXE] 1 [EXE]

Be sure to use the [(-)] key, not the [−] key, when typing in a negative value. After setting the range, enter the function and graph it.

Example 1

Graph $y = 2x + 3$.

For the TI-81

[Y =] [CLEAR] 2 [X|T] [+] 3 [GRAPH]

For the Casio

[Graph] 2 [Alpha] [x] [+] 3 [EXE]

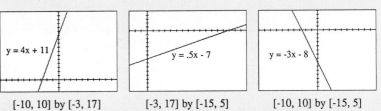

When you graph a line, you should be able to see the points at which the line crosses the *x*- and *y*-axes. When this is the case, we will call the graph a *complete graph*. Some examples follow. The range values are given below each graph.

$y = 4x + 11$	$y = .5x - 7$	$y = -3x - 8$
[-10, 10] by [-3, 17]	[-3, 17] by [-15, 5]	[-10, 10] by [-15, 5]

EXERCISES

Graph each equation in the standard viewing window. State whether the graph is a complete graph. See Solutions Manual for graphs.

1. $y = 5x + 6$ yes
2. $y = -10x - 7$ yes
3. $y = 0.01x + 4$ no
4. $y = 5$ yes
5. $y = 10x + 15$ no
6. $y = 3x - 5$ yes

384 CHAPTER 9 FUNCTIONS AND GRAPHS

Finding Equations from Relations

Objective
9-7

After studying this lesson, you should be able to:
■ write an equation to represent a relation, given a chart of values.

Application

Teaching Tip ➊

Video Village sells blank videocassettes in packages of 5. You can make a chart to show the relationship between the number of videocassettes and the number of packages. Let *y* represent the number of videocassettes and let *x* represent the number of packages.

x	1	2	3	4	5	6
y	5	10	15	20	25	30

This relation can also be shown using an equation. Study the differences between successive values of *x* and *y*.

		+1	+1	+1	+1	+1	
x	1	2	3	4	5	6
y	5	10	15	20	25	30
		+5	+5	+5	+5	+5	

Notice that the differences of the *y*-values are exactly five times the differences of the corresponding *x*-values. This pattern suggests the relation $y = 5x$. You can check to see if this equation is correct by substituting values of *x* into the equation. For example, if $x = 2$, then $y = 5(2)$ or 10, as given in the chart.

Example 1

Write an equation for the relation given in the chart at the right.

a	1	2	3	4	5	6
b	1	4	7	10	13	16

Find the differences between successive values of *a* and *b*.

Teaching Tip ➋

		+1	+1	+1	+1	+1	
a	1	2	3	4	5	6
b	1	4	7	10	13	16
		+3	+3	+3	+3	+3	

Notice that the differences of the *b*-values are 3 times the differences of the corresponding *a*-values. This pattern suggests the relation $b = 3a$. However, if $a = 1$, then $b = 3(1)$ or 3, not 1, as given in the chart. Thus, the equation $b = 3a$ does *not* describe the relation. To obtain 1 for *b* when *a* is 1, you need to subtract 2. This suggests the relation $b = 3a - 2$. Check this by using other values from the chart.

Check: If $a = 2$, then $b = 3(2) - 2$ or 4. ✔
If $a = 5$, then $b = 3(5) - 2$ or 13. ✔

LESSON 9-7 FINDING EQUATIONS FROM RELATIONS **385**

ALTERNATE TEACHING STRATEGIES

Using Discussion

Suppose $x = 1$ and $y = 3$. Can you write an equation using *x* and *y* such that these values are a solution to the equation? **Answers may vary. A sample answer would be $y = 3x$.**
What if $x = 3$ and $y = 1$? **Answers may vary. A sample answer would be $y = \frac{1}{3}x$.**

Lesson Resources
• Reteaching Master 9-7
• Practice Master 9-7
• Enrichment Master 9-7
 Transparency 9-7 contains the 5-Minute Check and a teaching aid for this lesson.

INTRODUCING THE LESSON

🕐 **5-Minute Check**
(over Lesson 9-6)

Does the graph of the relation contain the origin?

1. $4x - 8 > 0$ no
2. $3x - 2y \le 0$ yes
3. $x \le 5$ yes

4. **Graph $x - 2y < 4$.**

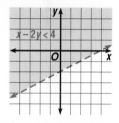

Motivating the Lesson
Present the following number sequences to the students. Ask them to determine what number is added to each term as well as what are missing terms.
1. 3, 7, 11, 15, ___, ___
   Add 4; 19, 23.
2. 6, 4, 2, 0, −2, ___, ___
   Add −2; −4, −6.
3. 3, −1, −5, −9, ___, ___
   Add −4; −13, −17.

TEACHING THE LESSON

Teaching Tip ➊   It may help students to consider the question "What must I do to *x* to get *y*?"

Teaching Tip ➋   For advanced students, you could show the set of builder notation for each relation. The relation in this chart is equivalent to $\{(x, y): y = 3x - 2, x \in \{1, 2, 3, 4, 5, 6\}\}$.

Chalkboard Examples

For Example 1

Write an equation for the relation given in the chart.

x	1	2	3	4	5
y	6	12	18	24	30

$y = 6x$

For Example 2

Write an equation for the relation given in the chart.

x	1	2	3	4	5	6
y	−1	1	3	5	7	9

$y = 2x - 3$

For Example 3

Write an equation for the relation given in the chart.

x	1	2	3	4	5	6
y	5	7	9	11	13	15

$y = 2x + 3$

Example 2

Write an equation for the relation given in the chart at the right.

m	1	2	4	5	6	9
n	9	6	0	−3	−6	−15

Find the differences.

| | +1 | +2 | +1 | +1 | +3 | |
m	1	2	4	5	6	9
n	9	6	0	−3	−6	−15
	−3	−6	−3	−3	−9	

Notice that the values for m are increasing, but the values for n are decreasing.

The differences suggest the relation $n = -3m$. However, if $m = 1$, then $n = -3(1)$ or -3, not 9, as given in the chart. Thus, $n = -3m$ does *not* describe the relation.

To obtain 9 for n when m is 1, you need to add 12. This suggests the relation $n = -3m + 12$, or $n = 12 - 3m$.

Check: If $m = 4$, then $n = 12 - 3(4)$ or 0. ✔
If $m = 9$, then $n = 12 - 3(9)$ or -15. ✔

Example 3

APPLICATION

Business

McGaffin Plumbing has a standard charge for every housecall it makes. In addition, there is an hourly rate. Suppose the charges are $60 for a one-hour job, $95 for a two-hour job, and $130 for a three-hour job. Write an equation to describe the relationship between the number of hours worked and the charge. Then use this equation to find the standard charge for each job and the hourly rate.

Let x = the number of hours worked, and let y = the total charge. Make a chart for this relation. Then find the differences.

| | +1 | +1 | |
x	1	2	3
y	60	95	130
	+35	+35	

The differences suggest the relation $y = 35x$. However, if $x = 1$, then $y = 35(1)$ or 35, not 60, as given in the chart. To obtain 60 for y when $x = 1$, you need to add 25.

Thus, the equation that describes this relation is $y = 35x + 25$.

Check: If $x = 2$, then $y = 35(2) + 25$ or 95. ✔
If $x = 3$, then $y = 35(3) + 25$ or 130. ✔

In the equation $y = 35x + 25$, x represents the number of hours worked. Thus, the hourly charge for each plumber is $35. This means that the standard charge for each job is $25.

386 CHAPTER 9 FUNCTIONS AND GRAPHS

RETEACHING THE LESSON

For a fun way to practice finding equations from relations, play the function rule game. A person thinks of an equation like $y = 10 - 2x$. Students give input values and are given the functional output values. For example, $1 \rightarrow 8$, $3 \rightarrow 4$. The goal is to guess the function rule.

Reteaching Masters Booklet, p. 67

9-7 **Reteaching Worksheet**

NAME _____ DATE _____

Finding Equations From Relations

You can find equations from relations. Suppose you purchased a number of packages of blank cassette tapes. If each package contained three tapes, you could make a chart to show the relationship between the number of packages of blank cassette tapes and the number of tapes purchased. Use x for the number of packages and y for the number of tapes.

x	1	2	3	4	5	6
y	3	6	9	12	15	18

This relation can also be shown as an equation. Since y is always three times x, the equation is $y = 3x$. Another way to discover this relationship is to study the difference between successive values of x and y.

| x | 1 | 2 | 3 | 4 | 5 | 6 | This suggests the relation $y = 3x$.
|---|---|---|---|---|---|---|
| y | 3 | 6 | 9 | 12 | 15 | 18 |

Complete.

1. 4, −8, 16, −32, ____, ____ 64, −128
2. 5, 2, −1, −4, ____, ____ −7, −10
3. 125, 25, ____, 1, ____ 5, $\frac{1}{5}$
4. 7.5, ____, 8.5, 9, ____ 10 8, 9.5

Write an equation for the relation shown in each chart. Then complete each chart.

5.
x	−1	0	1	2	3	4
y	−2	2	6	10	14	18

$y = 4x + 2$

6.
x	−2	−1	0	1	2	3
y	10	7	4	1	−2	−5

$y = -3x + 4$

7.
x	−4	−3	−2	−1	0	1
y	$\frac{5}{2}$	$\frac{9}{4}$	2	$\frac{7}{4}$	$\frac{3}{2}$	$\frac{5}{4}$

$y = -\frac{1}{4}x + 1\frac{1}{2}$

8.
x	0	2	2	3	4	5
y	3	$\frac{12}{5}$	$\frac{9}{5}$	$\frac{6}{5}$	$\frac{3}{5}$	0

$y = -\frac{3}{5}x + 3$

Write an equation to represent each relation.

9. $\{(-10, -5), (-4, -2), (0, 0), (2, 1), (5, \frac{5}{2})\}$ $y = \frac{1}{2}x$

10. $\{(-3, -10), (-1, -4), (0, -1), (2, 5), (4, 11)\}$ $y = 3x - 1$

---

386 **Chapter 9**

CHECKING FOR UNDERSTANDING

Communicating Mathematics

Read and study the lesson to answer each question.

1. When you study successive differences of a relation shown in a chart, you are applying what problem-solving strategy to find an equation that describes the relation? **look for a pattern**

2. How can you determine whether an equation represents a relation that is given in a chart? **Check the equation with values from the chart.**

3. Find a linear equation that has both $(1, 1)$ and $(0, 3)$ as solutions. Is this the only linear equation that has these two solutions?
Answers may vary; a typical answer is $2x + y = 3$; no.

Guided Practice

In Exercises 4–7, match each equation with a relation in charts a-d.

4. $y = 2x + 6$ **c**   5. $y = 4x + 3$ **d**   6. $x - 2y = 10$ **a**   7. $2x + 3y = 3$ **b**

a.
x	2	4	6	8	10
y	−4	−3	−2	−1	0

b.
x	3	6	9	12	15
y	−1	−3	−5	−7	−9

c.
x	3	4	5	6	7
y	12	14	16	18	20

d.
x	1	2	3	4	5
y	7	11	15	19	23

Complete.

8. $5, 7, 9, 11, \underline{\ ?\ }, \underline{\ ?\ }$ **13, 15**

9. $12, 9, 6, 3, \underline{\ ?\ }, \underline{\ ?\ }$ **0, −3**

10. $-1, -4, -7, -10, \underline{\ ?\ }, \underline{\ ?\ }$ **−13, −16**

11. $5, \underline{\ ?\ }, 15, \underline{\ ?\ }, 25, 30$ **10, 20**

EXERCISES

Practice

A

Complete.   14. **−8.2, −8.8**   11.25, 10.75

12. $3, 3.5, 4, 4.5, \underline{\ ?\ }, \underline{\ ?\ }$ **5, 5.5**

13. $11.75, 11.5, \underline{\ ?\ }, 11, \underline{\ ?\ }$ **11.25, 10.75**

14. $-8, \underline{\ ?\ }, -8.4, -8.6, \underline{\ ?\ }$ **−8.2, −8.8**

15. $1, 2, 4, 8, \underline{\ ?\ }, \underline{\ ?\ }$ **16, 32**

16. $27, 9, 3, \underline{\ ?\ }, \underline{\ ?\ }, 1, \frac{1}{3}$

17. $8, \underline{\ ?\ }, 2, -1, \underline{\ ?\ }$ **−4, $\frac{1}{2}$**

Write an equation for the relation shown in each chart. Then copy and complete each chart.

18.
x	1	2	3	4	5
y	4	8	12	**16**	**20**

$y = 4x$

19.
m	−3	−2	−1	0	1
n	−5	−3	−1	**1**	**3**

$n = 2m + 1$

20.
a	−2	−1	0	1	2
b	−3	1	5	**9**	**13**

$b = 4a + 5$

21.
a	−4	−2	0	2	4
b	−13	−5	3	**11**	**19**

$b = 4a + 3$

22.
x	1	2	3	4	5	6	7
y	14	13	12	**11**	**10**	9	8

$y = 15 - x$

23.
m	−2	−1	0	1	2	3	4
n	13	12	11	10	**9**	**8**	7

$n = 11 - m$

LESSON 9-7 FINDING EQUATIONS FROM RELATIONS 387

Chapter 9 387

33. Find the differences between successive x-values and y-values for the three points.
For (−2, −3) and (0, 5)
x: 0 − (−2) = 2;
y: 5 − (−3) = 8
For (0, 5) and (4, 22):
x: 4 − 0 = 4; y: 22 − 5 = 17
Since 4 = 2(2) and
17 ≠ 2(8), the 3 points cannot be solutions to the same linear equation.

40.
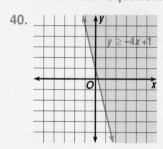

Enrichment Masters Booklet, p. 67

NAME _____ DATE _____
9-7 Enrichment Worksheet

Polynomial Functions

Suppose a linear equation such as −3x + y = 4 is solved for y. Then an equivalent equation, y = 3x + 4, is found. Expressed in this way, y is a function of x, or f(x) = 3x + 4. Notice that the right side of the equation is a binomial of degree 1.

Higher degree polynomials in x may also form functions. An example is f(x) = x³ + 1, which is a polynomial function of degree 3. You can graph this function using a table of ordered pairs.

x	y
$-1\frac{1}{2}$	$-2\frac{3}{8}$
−1	0
0	1
1	2
$1\frac{1}{2}$	$4\frac{3}{8}$

For each of the following polynomial functions, make a table of values for x and y = f(x). Then draw the graph on the grid.

1. f(x) = 1 − x²

2. f(x) = x² − 5

3. f(x) = x² + 4x − 1

4. f(x) = x³

Write an equation for the relation shown in each chart. Then copy and complete each chart.

24.

a	−5	−3	−1	1	2	4	7
b	28	18	8	−2	−7	−17	−32

b = 3 − 5a

25.

x	−4	−2	0	2	4	6	8
y	26	22	18	14	10	6	2

y = 18 − 2x

26.

r	−4	−2	0	2	4	6	8
s	−1	0	1	2	3	4	5

$s = \frac{1}{2}r + 1$

27.

c	6	12	18	24	30	36	42
d	0	2	4	6	8	10	12

$d = \frac{1}{3}c - 2$

C Write an equation to represent each relation.

28. {(−2, 4), (−1, 1), (0, 0), (1, 1), (2, 4)} y = x²

29. {(1, 2), (2, 9), (3, 28), (4, 65), (5, 126)} y = x³ + 1

30. {(−6, 4), (−3, 8), (1, −24), (2, −12), (6, −4)} xy = −24

31. {(−2, 11), (−1, 14), (0, 15), (1, 14), (2, 11)} y = 15 − x²

32. {(−4, 3), (−2, 12), (−1, 48), (1, 48), (2, 12)} x²y = 48

Critical Thinking

33. How can you determine whether there is *one* linear equation that has (−2, −3), (0, 5), and (4, 22) as solutions? **See margin.**

Applications

34. Geology   The underground temperature of rocks varies with their depth below the surface. The temperature at the surface is about 20°C. At a depth of 2 km, the temperature is about 90°C, and at a depth of 10 km, the temperature is about 370°C.

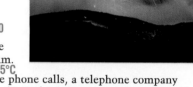

 a. Write an equation to describe this relationship. y = 35x + 20

 b. Use the equation to predict the temperature at a depth of 13 km. 475°C

35. Sales   For intrastate long distance phone calls, a telephone company charges $1.72 for a 4-minute call, $2.40 for a 6-minute call, and $5.46 for a 15-minute call.

 a. Write an equation to describe this relationship. y = $0.34x + $0.36

 b. Use the equation to determine the charge for a 1-minute call and the charge per minute. $0.70; $0.34

Mixed Review

36. Finance   Beatriz invested $12,200, part at 5% annual interest and the remainder at 6.5% annual interest. After one year, the total value of her investment, including interest, was $12,870. How much money did she invest at each rate? **(Lesson 4-4)** $8200 at 5%, $4000 at 6.5%

37. Find the GCF of 24x²y, 28mnx, and 36nx. **(Lesson 7-1)** 4x

38. Factor 3x³ + 24x²y − 99xy². **(Lesson 7-8)** 3x(x + 11y)(x − 3y)

39. Simplify $\frac{x^2 + 2x - 15}{x^2 - x - 30} \div \frac{x^2 - 3x - 18}{x^2 - 2x - 24}$. **(Lesson 8-3)** $\frac{x^2 + x - 12}{x^2 - 3x - 18}$

40. Graph y ≥ −4x + 1. **(Lesson 9-6) See margin.**

388   CHAPTER 9   FUNCTIONS AND GRAPHS

EXTENDING THE LESSON

Math Power: Problem Solving

Tables are given for two linear functions. If the domains of these functions are the set of all numbers, find the value(s) of x that make f(x) = g(x). x = 3

x	2	4	6	8
f(x)	5	9	13	17

y = 2x + 1

x	2	4	6	8
g(x)	4	10	16	22

y = 3x − 2

Problem-Solving Strategy:
Use a Graph

Objective 9-8

After studying this lesson, you should be able to:
- solve problems by using bar graphs and line graphs.

Connection

Statistical graphs are often used to present data and show relationships between sets of data. Two examples are shown below.

Bar graphs show how specific quantities compare. The bar graph at the right illustrates the relationship between average household income and the level of education achieved by the head of the household.

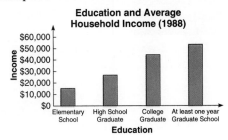

Education and Average Household Income (1988)

Line graphs show trends or changes. The line graph at the right shows the growth of the world's population.
Teaching Tip ❶

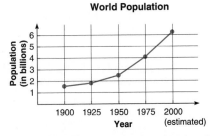

World Population

To fully understand the information presented in a graph, ask yourself the following questions.

1. What information does the title give you about the data?
2. What variable is represented along each axis?
3. What units are used along each axis?

Apply each of the three questions to the graph below.

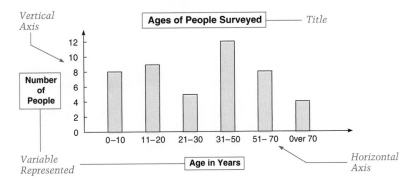

Vertical Axis — **Ages of People Surveyed** — *Title*

Number of People

Variable Represented — **Age in Years** — *Horizontal Axis*

LESSON 9-8 PROBLEM-SOLVING STRATEGY: USE A GRAPH **389**

9-8 Lesson Notes

Lesson Resources

- Practice Master 9-8
 Transparency 9-8 contains the 5-Minute Check and a teaching aid for this lesson.

INTRODUCING THE LESSON

🕐 5-Minute Check
(over Lesson 9-7)

Find the missing terms in each sequence.

1. $-5, -2, 1, 4, \underline{\quad}, \underline{\quad}$
   7, 10
2. $-32, -24, -16, \underline{\quad}, \underline{\quad}$
   $-8, 0$
3. $4.5, 3.0, 1.5, \underline{\quad}, \underline{\quad}$
   $0, -1.5$
4. $2.5, 1.8, 1.1, \underline{\quad}, \underline{\quad}$
   $0.4, -0.3$
5. $17, 29, 41, \underline{\quad}, \underline{\quad}$ 53, 65

Motivating the Lesson

Ask students to identify various types of graphs they have created. Have them explain advantages of presenting information in graph form.

TEACHING THE LESSON

Teaching Tip ❶ Emphasize to the students the idea that all kinds of graphs are used to show the relationship between two different sets of data.

ALTERNATE TEACHING STRATEGIES

Using Discussion

Explain how someone in advertising could use a misleading graph to sell a product.

Using Applications

Have students look through magazines and newspapers for examples of graphs. Ask them to analyze the graphs to determine whether they were designed to support a particular point of view.

EVALUATING THE LESSON

Checking for Understanding

Exercises 1-11 are designed to help you assess understanding through reading, writing, and speaking. You should work through Exercises 1-6 with your students, and then monitor their work on Exercises 7-11.

Closing the Lesson

Speaking Activity Ask students to identify the steps to follow in making a graph.

Additional Answers

1. how specific quantities compare
2. trends and changes in quantities
9. In Graph A, Restaurant III does not appear as unpopular as it does in Graph B.
10. The scale on the vertical axis is much smaller.
11. Graph A

The title indicates that the graph illustrates the number of people in each age group who were surveyed. The vertical axis shows the number of people in each age group. Each unit on the vertical axis represents two people. The horizontal axis shows age groups in years. Notice that the units used for the axes do not have to be the same.

Some graphs can be misleading, as shown in the example below.

Example

CONNECTION
Statistics

Greg received scores of 72, 74, 75, 77, and 78 on his first five algebra exams. The two graphs below were made to show how his test scores have improved. Do they show the same results? Teaching Tip 2

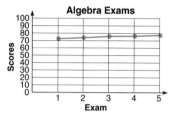 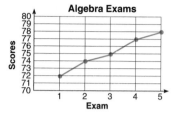

Both graphs use the same data but appear to show different results. In the graph on the left, Greg's scores show slight improvement. In the graph on the right, Greg's scores appear to show great improvement. While both graphs are correct, the graph on the right is misleading.

CHECKING FOR UNDERSTANDING

Communicating Mathematics

Read and study the lesson to answer each question. **See margin.**

1. What do bar graphs illustrate best?
2. What do line graphs illustrate best?

Identify each part labeled.

3. a **vertical axis**
4. b **variables represented**
5. c **title**
6. d **horizontal axis**

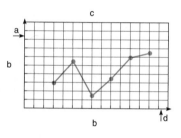

Guided Practice

The graphs below show the results of a survey on favorite restaurants.

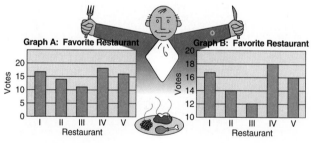

390 CHAPTER 9 FUNCTIONS AND GRAPHS

RETEACHING THE LESSON

Driver A drives 40 mph and has a 60-mile headstart when driver B sets out at 55 mph to overtake driver A. In how many hours will driver B overtake driver A? in how many miles? Solve by graphing. **4 hours, 220 miles**

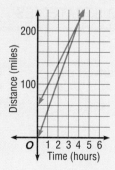

7. Do Graphs A and B display the same data? **yes**

8. In Graph B, the bar for Restaurant II is twice as high as the bar for Restaurant III. Does this mean that there are twice as many votes? **no**

9. Why would Restaurant III prefer Graph A?

10. What causes the difference in voting to appear greater in Graph B?

11. Which graph better represents the result?

9–11. See margin.

EXERCISES

Practice

Strategies
Look for a pattern.
Solve a simpler problem.
Act it out.
Guess and check.
Draw a diagram.
Make a chart.
Work backwards.

Solve. Use any strategy.

12. Lesharo has ten boxes. Four of his boxes contain pencils, five contain pens, and two contain both pens and pencils. How many of Lesharo's boxes are empty? **3 boxes**

13. Numero Uno says, "I am thinking of a three-digit number. If the digits of my number are added together and the result is cubed, the answer will be the original number. What is my number?" **512**

14. Paula spends $\frac{1}{3}$ of her monthly income on rent and $\frac{1}{4}$ of the remainder on food. She spends $\frac{1}{6}$ of what's left on clothes and $\frac{1}{5}$ of the remainder on entertainment. After she saves $\frac{1}{2}$ of what's left and makes a $200 car payment, she has $40 left. What is her monthly income? **$1440**

15. Al is two or three years younger than Betty, who is two or three times as old as Carmelita. But Al is two or three times as old as Dwayne, who is two or three years younger than Carmelita. If they are all older than three years old, how old are they? **Al, 12 years old; Betty, 14 years old; Carmelita, 7 years old; Dwayne, 4 years old**

COOPERATIVE LEARNING ACTIVITY

Work in groups of four. Each person must understand the solution and be able to explain it to any person in the class.

Find the solution to the puzzle. The solution is unique.

¹3	²2	³4
⁴7	2	9
⁵7	5	6

Across

1. a square
4. a cube
5. a multiple of a square

Down

1. a Fibonacci number
2. a square
3. a perfect number

LESSON 9-8 PROBLEM-SOLVING STRATEGY: USE A GRAPH **391**

APPLYING THE LESSON

Homework Exercises

Assignment Guide
Basic: 12-15
Average: 12-15
Enriched: 12-15

Chapter 9, Quiz D, (Lessons 9-7 through 9-8), is available in the Evaluation Masters Booklet, p. 122.

Practice Masters Booklet, p. 75

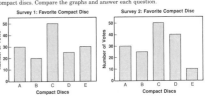

EXTENDING THE LESSON

Math Power: Communication

Have student pairs identify a set of data they wish to present in graph form such as school or state population, information on teacher's salaries, or the budget of a local government. Student pairs then construct two graphs that present the data to support opposing points of view.

Cooperative Learning Activity

This activity provides students with an opportunity to *learn* things together, not just do things together. You may wish to refer to pages T6 - T8 and page 6C for the various elements of cooperative groups and specific goals and strategies for using them.

Additional Answers

1-4.
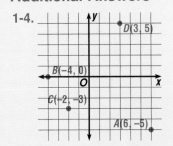

9. {4}; {1, −2, 6, −1}; {(1, 4), (−2, 4), (6, 4), (−1, 4)}
10. {−3, 4}; {5, 6}; {(5, −3), (6, −3), (5, 4), (6, 4)}
11. {{−2, −5, −7}; {1}; {(1, −2), (1, −5), (1, −7)}
12. {−3, −2, −1, 0}; {1, 0, 2}; {(1, −3), (0, −2), (1, −1), (2, 0)}
16. {(−4, −11), (−2, −3), (0, 5), (2, 13), (4, 21)}

SUMMARY AND REVIEW

VOCABULARY

Upon completing this chapter, you should be familiar with the following terms:

boundary	379	359	mapping
coordinate plane	354	354	ordered pair
domain	359	354	origin
function	374	356	quadrant
functional notation	376	359	range
functional value	376	359	relation
graph	355	354	x-axis
half-plane	379	354	x-coordinate
inverse of a relation	360	354	y-axis
linear equation	369	354	y-coordinate

SKILLS AND CONCEPTS

OBJECTIVES AND EXAMPLES	REVIEW EXERCISES
Upon completing this chapter, you should be able to:	Use these exercises to review and prepare for the chapter test.

■ graph ordered pairs on a coordinate plane (Lesson 9-1)

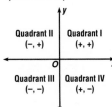

Graph each point. See margin.

1. A(6, −5) 2. B(−4, 0)
3. C(−2, −3) 4. D(3, 5)

If the graph of P(x, y) satisfies the given condition, name the quadrant in which point P is located. 6. III 8. none

5. x > 0, y > 0 I 6. x < 0, y = −3
7. x = −2, y > 0 II 8. x < −3, y = 0

■ identify the domain, range, and inverse of a relation (Lesson 9-2)

Determine the domain, range, and inverse of {(3, 5), (2, 6), (5, 6)}.
The domain is {3, 2, 5}.
The range is {5, 6}.
The inverse is {(5, 3), (6, 2), (6, 5)}.

Determine the domain, range, and inverse of each relation. See margin.

9. {(4, 1), (4, −2), (4, 6), (4, −1)}
10. {(−3, 5), (−3, 6), (4, 5), (4, 6)}
11. {(−2, 1), (−5, 1), (−7, 1)}
12. {(−3, 1), (−2, 0), (−1, 1), (0, 2)}

Additional Answers

17. {(−4, −13), (−2, −11), (0, −9), (2, −7), (4, −5)}
18. {(−4, 21/2), (−2, 15/2), (0, 9/2), (2, 3/2), (4, −3/2)}
19. {(−4, −16/3), (−2, −8/3), (0, 0), (2, 8/3), (4, 16/3)}

OBJECTIVES AND EXAMPLES	REVIEW EXERCISES

■ solve linear equations for a specific variable **(Lesson 9-3)**

Solve for y.

$2x - 5y = 9$
$\quad -5y = 9 - 2x$
$\quad\quad y = \dfrac{9 - 2x}{-5}$

Solve each equation for y in terms of x.

13. $3x + y = 7$ $y = 7 - 3x$
14. $4x - 3y = 9$ $y = \dfrac{4x - 9}{3}$
15. $x + 6y = 12$ $y = \dfrac{12 - x}{6}$

■ solve linear equations for a given domain **(Lesson 9-3)**

Solve $2x + y = 7$ if the domain is $\{-2, 0\}$. $2x + y = 7 \rightarrow y = 7 - 2x$

x	$7 - 2x$	y	(x, y)
-2	$7 - 2(-2)$	11	$(-2, 11)$
0	$7 - 2(0)$	7	$(0, 7)$

Solve each equation if the domain is $\{-4, -2, 0, 2, 4\}$. See margin.

16. $y = 4x + 5$
17. $x - y = 9$
18. $3x + 2y = 9$
19. $4x - 3y = 0$

■ graph linear equations on a coordinate plane **(Lesson 9-4)**

Graph $y = 3x - 5$.

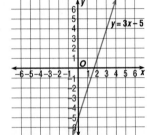

Graph each equation. See Solutions Manual.

20. $x + 5y = 4$
21. $2x - 3y = 6$
22. $5x + 2y = 10$
23. $\frac{1}{2}x + \frac{1}{3}y = 3$

■ determine whether a given relation is a function **(Lesson 9-5)**

Is $\{(3, 2), (5, 3), (4, 3), (5, 2)\}$ a function?

Because there are 2 values of y for one value of x, 5, the relation is *not* a function.

Determine whether each relation is a function.

24. $\{(3, 8), (9, 3), (-3, 8), (5, 3)\}$ yes
25. $x - y^2 = 4$ no
26. $xy = 6$ yes
27. $3x - 4y = 7$ yes

■ calculate functional values for a given function **(Lesson 9-5)**

Given $g(x) = 2x - 1$, find $g(-6)$.
$g(-6) = 2(-6) - 1$
$\quad\quad = -12 - 1$
$\quad\quad = -13$

Given $g(x) = x^2 - x + 1$, determine each value.

28. $g(2)$ 3
29. $g(-1)$ 3
30. $g\left(\frac{1}{2}\right)$ $\frac{3}{4}$
31. $g(a + 1)$ $a^2 + a + 1$
32. $g(-2a)$ $4a^2 + 2a + 1$

Alternate Review Strategy

To provide a brief in-class review, you may wish to read the following questions to the class and require a verbal response.

1. Name the quadrant for the graph of (x, y) given the condition $x = -1, y < 0$.   **III**
2. Determine the domain, range, and inverse of the following relation: $\{(2, 5), (6, 3), (7, 8)\}$. **D = {2, 6, 7}, R = {5, 3, 8}, Inverse = {(5, 2), (3, 6), (8, 7)}**
3. Solve for r, $r - 5s = 3$. **$r = 3 + 5s$**
4. Graph $4x + 3y = 12$.

5. Determine whether $\{(5, 4), (-6, 5), (4, 5), (0, 4)\}$ is a function. Then state the inverse relation and determine whether it is a function. **yes; $\{(4, 5), (5, -6), (5, 4), (4, 0)\}$; no**
6. Write an equation for the relation given in the chart.

m	-2	-1	0	1	2
n	13	12	11	10	9

$n = 11 - m$

The Cumulative Review shown below can be used to review skills and concepts presented thus far in the text. Standardized Test Practice Questions are also provided in the Evaluation Masters Booklet.

Evaluation Masters Booklet, pp. 123-124

OBJECTIVES AND EXAMPLES	REVIEW EXERCISES

■ graph inequalities in the coordinate plane (Lesson 9-6)

Graph $2x + 7y < 9$.

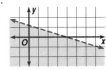

Graph each inequality. **See Solutions Manual.**

33. $x + 2y > 5$

34. $4x - y \leq 8$

35. $3x - 2y < 6$

36. $\frac{1}{2}y \geq x + 4$

■ write an equation to represent a relation, given a chart of values. (Lesson 9-7)

Write an equation for the relation given in the chart below.

	+1	+1	+1	+1
a	-2	-1	0	1	2
b	20	17	14	11	8
	-3	-3	-3	-3

The equation is $b = 14 - 3a$.

Write an equation for the relation given in each chart.

37.

x	0	1	2	3	4
y	5	8	11	14	17

$y = 3x + 5$

38.

x	2	4	5	7	10
y	-2	0	1	3	6

$y = x - 4$

APPLICATIONS AND CONNECTIONS

39. **Physics** A ball is dropped from a 324-foot tower. Its height h, in feet, after t seconds is given by the formula $h = 324 - 16t^2$. Make a table of values for this equation to determine how many seconds it takes for the ball to hit the ground. **4.5 seconds**

40. **Sales** At Recordville, Emilio earns a weekly salary of $150 plus $0.30 for each record over 100 that he sells each week. If Emilio sells r records in a week, then his total weekly salary is $C(r) = 150 + 0.30(r - 100)$ for $r > 100$. If he earned $225 last week, how many records did he sell? **350 records**

41. **Statistics** Eric's scores on the first three of five 100-point tests were 83, 72, and 73. Eric wants to have an average of at least 75 on all the tests.
    a. Use a graph to determine what scores Eric can receive on the last two tests.
    b. List three possible solutions where both of his last two scores are no more than 75. **See margin.**

42. **Car Rental** The cost of a one-day car rental from A-1 Car Rental is $41 if you drive 100 miles, $51.80 if you drive 160 miles, and $63.50 if you drive 225 miles.
    a. Write an equation to describe this relationship. $y = 0.18x + 23$
    b. Use the equation to determine the per-mile charge. **$0.18 per mile**

Additional Answer

41.

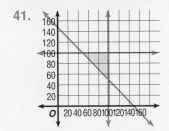

Answers will vary; typical answers are 74 and 73, 80 and 67, and 100 and 47.

Additional Answer to Chapter Test

1.

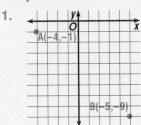

1. Graph the points $A(-4, -1)$ and $B(5, -9)$. **See margin.**

2. Name the quadrant in which the point $C(-3, 5)$ is located. **II**

Express each relation as a set of ordered pairs. Then state the domain, range, and inverse.

See margin.

3.

x	y
1	3
2	7
3	-3
5	-2

4.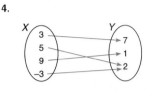

5.

Solve each equation if the domain is $\{-2, -1, 0, 1, 3\}$. See margin.

6. $y = 3x + 10$

7. $2x - 5y = 4$

8. $2y - 8 = x$

Determine whether each equation is a linear equation.

9. $5x = 17 - 4x$ **yes**

10. $y = x^2 - 4$ **no**

11. $y = xy + 1$ **no**

Determine whether each relation is a function.

12. $\{(2, 4), (3, 2), (4, 6), (5, 4)\}$ **yes**

13. $8y = 7 + 3x$ **yes**

14. $2x = 9$ **no**

15. Given $f(x) = 2x - 3$, determine the value of $f(-3)$, $f(7)$, and $f(0)$. **−9, 11, −3**

Graph each equation or inequality. See Solutions Manual.

16. $x - 2y = 8$

17. $4x + 3y = 12$

18. $3x - 2y < 6$

19. $y \geq 5x + 1$

20. $4x + 2y > 9$

21. $5x - 2y = 8$

Write an equation for the relation given in each chart.

22.

x	1	2	3	4	7
y	3	8	13	18	33

$y = 5x - 2$

23.

x	1	3	5	7	9	11	13
y	5	17	29	41	53	65	77

$y = 6x - 1$

Solve.

24. **Physics** If a ball is thrown upward with an initial velocity of 72 meters per second, its height $h(t)$, in meters, after t seconds is given by the formula $h(t) = 72t - 4.9t^2$. Will the ball have hit the ground after 15 seconds? **yes**

25. **Sales** When you use Jay's Taxi Service, a two-mile trip costs $6.30, a five-mile trip costs $11.25, and a ten-mile trip costs $19.50. Write an equation to describe this relationship and use it to find the cost of a one-mile trip. $y = 1.65x + 3$; **$4.65**

Bonus If $f(a) = (2a + 3)^2$ and $g(a) = \sqrt{a} - 5$, for what value(s) of a does $g[f(a)] = 8$? **5**

Additional Answers

3. $\{(1, 3), (2, 7), (3, -3), (5, -2)\}$;
$\{1, 2, 3, 5\}$; $\{\{3, 7, -3, -2\}$;
$\{(3, 1), (7, 2), (-3, 3), (-2, 5)\}$

4. $\{(3, 7), (5, 2), (9, 1), (-3, 2)\}$;
$\{3, 5, 9, -3\}$; $\{7, 1, 2\}$; $\{(7, 3),$
$(2, 5), (1, 9), (2, -3)\}$

5. $\{(-1, 1), (0, 2), (1, -1), (2, 0),$
$(2, 1)\}$; $\{-1, 0, 1, 2\}$; $\{1, -1, 2,$
$0\}$; $\{(1, -1), (2, 0), (-1, 1),$
$(0, 2), (1, 2)\}$

6. $\{(-2, 4), (-1, 7), (0, 10),$
$(1, 13), (3, 19)\}$

7. $\left\{\left(-2, -\frac{8}{5}\right), \left(-1, -\frac{6}{5}\right), \left(0, -\frac{4}{5}\right),\right.$
$\left.\left(1, -\frac{2}{5}\right), \left(3, \frac{2}{5}\right)\right\}$

8. $\left\{(-2, 3), \left(-1, \frac{7}{2}\right), (0, 4), \left(1, \frac{9}{2}\right),\right.$
$\left.\left(3, \frac{11}{2}\right)\right\}$

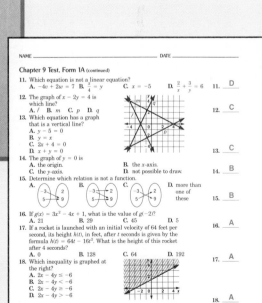

The questions on these pages involve comparing two quantities, one in Column A and one in Column B. In certain questions, information related to one or both quantities is centered above them. All variables used stand for real numbers.

Directions:
Write A if the quantity in Column A is greater. Write B if the quantity in Column B is greater. Write C if the quantities are equal. Write D if there is not enough information to determine the relationship.

	Column A	Column B
	$x \geq 13$	
1. B	$\dfrac{37}{3}$	x
2. A	$\dfrac{0.4}{20}$	0.002
3. B	$10 + 5 \div 4 - 3$	$10 - 5 \div 4 + 3$
	$b > c + 1$	
4. A	b	c
	$b < c + 1$	
5. D	b	c
	$r < 0 < s$	
6. D	r^2	$\dfrac{s}{2}$
7. D	a	$|a|$

	Column A	Column B
	$a = b$	
8. C	$-5(a - b)$	$7(3b - 3a)$
9. B	$\dfrac{3}{4}(5 + 1)\left(\dfrac{6 - 6}{2}\right)$	$\dfrac{1}{6}(1 + 3)(12 \div 2)$
10. C	25% of $\dfrac{4}{7}$	$\dfrac{4}{7}$ of $\dfrac{1}{4}$
11. B	$0.02 \div 0.2$	$0.2 \div 0.02$
12. B	The value of $2y + 7$ when $y = -2$.	The value of $2x - 8$ when $x = 6$.

13. B

	The number indicated by arrow A on the number line above.	The number indicated by arrow B on the number line above.
14. A	The price of a CD player increased by 20% and then decreased by 20%.	
	the original price of the CD player	the new price of the CD player
	$a : b = c : d$	
15. C	ad	bc
	$3x - 3y = 24$	
16. D	xr	y
17. B	The number of which 6 is 20%.	10% of 310

Column A	Column B

18.   Point P with coordinates (x, y)
B   is in the second quadrant.

x	y

19. the greatest   the greatest
B prime factor   prime factor
of 1540   of 1530

20. the number of   the number of
C prime numbers   prime numbers
between 1   between 10
and 10   and 20

21. a, b, and c are odd
C   consecutive integers.

$a + c$	$2b$

22.   The perimeter of each figure is P.
B

the area of   the area of
the rectangle   the square

23.   If $y = 2$, then $x = 8$.
A

The value of   The value of
x when $y = 5$ x when $y = 5$
if y varies   if y varies
directly as x.   indirectly as x.

24. A portion of $10,000 was invested at
C 6% interest and the balance at 8%
interest. The total interest was $700.

the amount   the amount
invested   invested
at 6%   at 8%

TEST TAKING TIP

Treat the two expressions given as the two sides of an inequality. Add, subtract, multiply and divide by the same terms until you can more easily compare the two columns. Do not change the sense of the inequality by multiplying or dividing by negative numbers.

Substitute values for the unknown or unknowns. Be sure to use many types and combinations of numbers. Use positive and negative numbers, fractions and mixed numbers. Do not make assumptions.

Perform any indicated mathematical operations. Change the common information.

If the use of As and Bs in both the column names and answer choices is confusing, change the column names to another pair of letters or numbers, such as x and y or I and II.

Column A	Column B

B
25. $x < 0$

$x - 5$	$5 - x$

26. D a a^2

     $f(x) = x^2 + 2x - 5$
A
27. $f(3)$ $f(-3)$

Graphing Linear Equations

PREVIEWING THE CHAPTER

The chapter begins with a lesson where students find the slope of a line given the coordinates of two points on the line. Next, students study the point-slope form, standard form, and slope-intercept form of linear equations, and then use slopes and intercepts to graph equations. Students use the slope-intercept form of a line to write the equation of a line and then learn how to write an equation for a parallel or perpendicular line. The chapter concludes with a lesson where students find the coordinates of the midpoint of a line given the coordinates of the endpoints.

Problem-Solving Strategy   Students learn to work with data presented in pictographs, circle graphs, and comparative graphs to solve problems.

Lesson Objective Chart

Lesson (Pages)	Lesson Objectives	State/Local Objectives
10-1 (400–404)	**10-1:** Find the slope of a line, given the coordinates of two points on the line.	
10-2 (405–409)	**10-2A:** Write a linear equation in standard form given the coordinates of a point on the line and the slope of the line.	
	10-2B: Write a linear equation in standard form given the coordinates of two points on the line.	
10-3 (410–414)	**10-3A:** Write an equation in slope-intercept form given the slope and y-intercept.	
	10-3B: Determine the x- and y-intercept of a graph.	
	10-3C: Determine the x- and y-intercepts of a graph.	
10-4 (415–418)	**10-4:** Graph linear equations using the x- and y-intercepts or the slope and y-intercept.	
10-5 (419–422)	**10-5A:** Write a linear equation in slope-intercept form given the slope of a line and the coordinates of a point on the line.	
	10-5B: Write a linear equation in slope-intercept form given the coordinates of two points on the line.	
10-6 (423–426)	**10-6:** Write an equation of a line that passes through a given point and is parallel or perpendicular to the graph of a given equation.	
10-7 (428–431)	**10-7:** Find the coordinates of the midpoint of a line segment in the coordinate plane given the coordinates of the endpoints.	
10-8 (432–433)	**10-8:** Solve problems by using pictographs, circle graphs, and comparative graphs.	

ORGANIZING THE CHAPTER

You may want to refer to the **Course Planning Calendar** on page T36.

Lesson Planning Guide

Lesson (Pages)	Pacing Chart (days) Course I	II	III	Reteaching	Practice	Enrichment	Evaluation	Technology	Lab Manual	Mixed Problem Solving	Applications	Cooperative Learning Activity	Multicultural	Transparencies
10-1 (400-404)	1.5	1.5	1.5	p. 68	p. 76	p. 68	Quiz A, p. 135							10-1
10-2 (405-409)	1.5	1	1	p. 69	p. 77	p. 69							p. 55	10-2
10-3 (410-414)	1.5	1.5	1.5	p. 70	p. 78	p. 70	Quiz B, p. 135 Mid-Chapter Test, p. 139				p. 25			10-3
10-4 (415-418)	1.5	1	1	p. 71	p. 79	p. 71		p. 25						10-4
10-5 (419-422)	1	1	1	p. 72	p. 80	p. 72	Quiz C, p. 136			p. 10		p. 40		10-5
10-6 (423-426)	1	1	1	p. 73	p. 81	p. 73								10-6
10-7 (428-431)	1	1	1	p. 74	p. 82	p. 74	Quiz D, p. 136	p. 10	pp. 31-32					10-7
10-8 (432-433)	1	1	1		p. 83									10-8
Review (434-436)	1	1	1	Multiple Choice Tests, Forms 1A and 1B, pp. 127-130 Free Response Tests, Forms 2A and 2B, pp. 131-134										
Test (437)	1	1	1	Cumulative Review, pp. 137-138 Standardized Test Practice Questions, p. 140										

Course I: Chapters 1-13; Course II: Chapters 1-14: Course III: Chapters 1-15

Other Chapter Resources

Student Edition

History Connection, p. 409
Mid-Chapter Review, p. 418
Technology, p. 427
Cooperative Learning Activity, p. 433
Algebraic-Skills Review, p. 663
   (ex. 1-36)

Teacher Resource Package

Activity Masters Booklet
   Mixed Problem Solving, p. 10
   Applications, p. 25
   Cooperative Learning Activity, p. 40
   Multicultural Activity, p. 55
Technology Masters Booklet
   Scientific Calculator Activity, p. 10
   Graphing Calculator Activity, p. 25
Lab Manual
   Lab Activity, pp. 31-32

Other Supplements

Transparency for Chapter Opener
Problem-of-the-Week Activity
   Cards, 24-25
Video Algebra, 35-38

Software

Algebra 1 Test and Review
   Generator Software
   Available for Apple and IBM.

ENHANCING THE CHAPTER

Cooperative Learning

Explaining the Task and the Criteria for Success

Before any group session begins, make sure that students have a clear understanding of the academic task to be completed by the group. You should thoroughly explain the objectives that are to be achieved and the procedures that students are expected to follow. Provide examples and ask specific questions to make sure all students understand what the assignment is and how they are to proceed. You should clearly explain the criteria by which the final work will be evaluated. These criteria should be structured so that students may achieve them without penalizing or being penalized by other students in the group. The criteria also should be fashioned so that they are challenging but also realistic for each and every member of the group. For some activities, the criteria can be as explicit as a set number of problems to be answered correctly. For other activities, simply completing the assignment or just doing better this time than last time may be sufficient criteria for success.

Technology

The Technology Feature after Lesson 10-6 shows how to use the *Mathematical Exploration Toolkit* to explore the graphs of lines. MET has a powerful graphing utility which (unlike graphing calculators) supports equations not in function form. Students will enter sets of linear equations in standard form, $Ax + By = C$. By varying the parameters A, B, and C, they can induce the effect on the graphs. MET includes many Guided Explorations about lines. Some focus on slope, some intercepts, and other forms of equations. Refer to the manual for teaching suggestions and blackline masters for student worksheets.

Critical Thinking

Complementing Bloom's research (1956) that led to his taxonomy is the research done by Williams (1969) in which he identified eight student behaviors involving creative thinking: the four cognitive factors are *fluency, flexibility, originality,* and *elaboration*; and the four affective factors are *risk taking, complexity, curiosity,* and *imagination*. Brainstorming activities, creative problem writing, paraphrasing and elaboration, making and testing predictions, justifying conclusions, and seeking many alternatives are just some ways to encourage positive behavior. Remember that all such behaviors are cultivated best when students are encouraged to explore, express different opinions, and defend ideas in a non-judgmental environment.

Cooperative Learning, p. 40

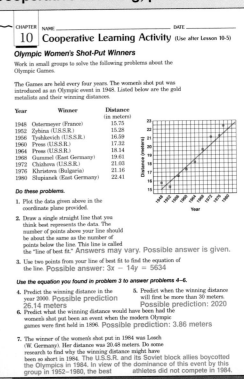

Technology, p. 25

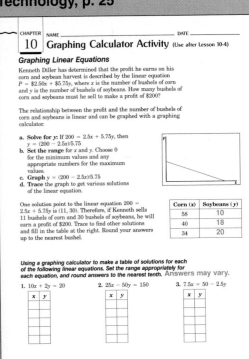

Problem of the Week Activity

The card shown below is one of two available for this chapter. It can be used as a class or small group activity.

Activity Card

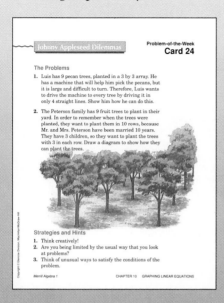

Manipulatives and Models

The following materials may be used as models or manipulatives in Chapter 10.

grid paper (Lesson 10-2)
meterstick (Lesson 10-2)

Outside Resources

Books/Periodicals

Closs, Michael P. *Native American Mathematics.* University of Texas Press.

Osen, Lynn M. *Women in Mathematics.* The MIT Press.

Films/Videotapes/Videodiscs

Equations of Lines and Planes, Massachusetts Institute of Technology

Graphs of Linear Equations, Phoenix/BFA Films and Video, Inc.

Software

Baffles, Conduit Educational Software

Graphmaster, Learning Arts

Mathematical Exploration Toolkit, IBM

Multicultural

Multicultural Activity, p. 55

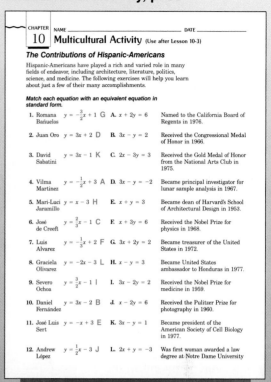

Lab Manual

Lab Activity, pp. 31-32

Using the Chapter Opener

Transparency 10-0 is available in the Transparency Package. It provides a full-color visual and motivational activity that you can use to engage students in the mathematical content of the chapter.

Background Information

In actuality, a ski slope cannot usually be represented by a line. Often the hill will have some sections that are quite steep and others that are fairly flat, instead of having the same steepness all the way down the hill. Thus, the graph that best represents a ski slope would be a series of line segments that show the steepness of each of the sections of the hill. Then the slopes of these line segments represent the steepness of the sections of the hill. The steeper the section of hill, the greater the slope of its line segment on the graph. If a section of hill is flat, then the slope of its line segment will be zero.

In this chapter, you will:
- Write an equation of a line given the coordinates of two points on the line.
- Determine the slope, x-intercept, and y-intercept of a line.
- Graph linear equations using the slope and y-intercept.
- Write an equation of a line that is parallel to or perpendicular to a given line.
- Represent data by using graphs.

Chapter Project

Materials: plant seeds, pots, water, fertilizer, graph paper, pencil

Organize students into cooperative groups of research scientists. Instruct each group to plant seeds of a rapidly growing plant such as beans in at least three separate pots. Have each group grow its seeds under a different condition for each pot. One pot might get ample water and fertilizer and sunlight; another ample water and fertilizer but no sunlight; and so on. Once plants begin to grow, instruct each group to measure the height of each plant each day, and plot the height versus time in days on a separate graph for each plant. After several days of growth, have each group construct a graph by drawing line segments connecting the points for consecutive days. The slopes of these line segments can be used as a measure for the rate of growth for each plant. Assign each group the task of preparing a comparative report of (1) rates of growth - the slopes of each of the line segments on each of the graphs - and (2) differences in rates of growth - slopes - among the three plants.

Graphing Linear Equations

APPLICATION IN SKIING

When we talk about the *slope* of a hillside, we are referring to the steepness of that hillside. Similarly, when we talk about *slope* in mathematics, we are usually referring to the steepness of a line drawn in the coordinate plane. In each case, *slope* is used to describe steepness.

Imagine you are a first-time skier facing your first run down the beginner's ski slope or "bunny hill." You certainly do not want this hill to be too steep for your level of expertise. That is, you hope the hill rises very little vertically compared to the horizontal distance, or run, from the top to the bottom of the hill. Perhaps in a few days, after you have had some lessons and practice, you might find the beginner's slope is too slow. Then you could move over to the intermediate slope where the hill rises a greater vertical distance compared to its horizontal run. In other words, you now are skiing on a steeper slope.

ALGEBRA IN ACTION

In the graph below, lines are used to represent the steepness of the beginner, intermediate, and expert slopes at a ski resort. Notice from the graph that the beginner slope rises 2 feet for every 10 horizontal feet. How many feet do the intermediate slope and the expert slope rise for every 10 horizontal feet? **5 ft, 8 ft**

Does the word *slopes* bring to mind pictures of skiers going down steep snow-covered hills? If so, then you have a pretty good idea of the mathematical meaning of the term *slope*.

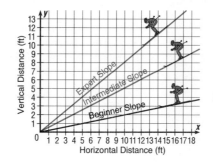

Lesson	Connections (C) and Applications (A)	Examples	Exercises
10-1	A: Driving Construction Carpentry Aviation	1	43 42 44 45
10-2	A: Entertainment Shipping Work National Landmarks	3	36 37 42
10-3	A: Travel Finance Education Tennis	2	55 56 57
10-4	A: Communica- tion Aviation Manufacturing National Landmarks	2	37 38 39
10-5	A: Manufacturing Business Skydiving	2	33 34
10-6	C: Geometry A: Sales Geography	1	31-32 33
10-7	C: Geometry A: Driving	1	62
10-8	A: Number Theory		10

399

Lesson Resources

- Reteaching Master 10-1
- Practice Master 10-1
- Enrichment Master 10-1
- Video Algebra, 36

 Transparency 10-1 contains the 5-Minute Check and a teaching aid for this lesson.

INTRODUCING THE LESSON

 5-Minute Check

(over Chapter 9)

State the domain and range of each relation.

1. {(5, 2), (0, 0), (−9, −1)}
   Domain = {5, 0, −9};
   Range = {2, 0, −1}
2. {(1, 1), (2, 4), (−2, 4), (3, 9)}
   Domain = {1, 2, −2, 3};
   Range = {1, 4, 9}

Determine whether each relation is a function. Then state the inverse relation and determine whether it is a function.

3. {(3, 1), (5, 1), (7, 1)}   yes;
   {(1, 3), (1, 5), (1, 7)}; no
4. {(5, 4), (−6, 5), (4, 5), (0, 4)}
   yes; {(4, 5), (5, −6), (5, 4),
   (4, 0)}; no
5. If *f(x)* = 3*x* − 5, determine the value of *f*(2).   1

Motivating the Lesson

Introduce this lesson on slope by discussing the pitch of a roof with students. Ask why the pitch varies in different parts of the country. What determines the pitch of a roof when an architect draws up building plans? Develop the idea that a relationship exists between the amount of precipitation an area generally receives and the roof structures used in the region.

TEACHING THE LESSON

Teaching Tip ❶   In this introductory example,
$$\text{slope} = \frac{\text{rise}}{\text{run}} = \frac{6'}{100'} \text{ or } \frac{3}{50}.$$

Objective
10-1

After studying this lesson, you should be able to:
- find the slope of a line, given the coordinates of two points on the line.

Application

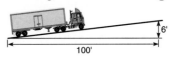 *FYI* · · ·

The steepest streets in the United States are in San Francisco with grades of 31.5% or a rise of 3.15 feet for every 10 feet.

Do you ever recall seeing a sign along the highway like the one at the right? These signs are designed to inform the driver that there is a steep hill ahead. If a hill has a *grade* of 6%, this means that for every 100 feet of horizontal change, there is a vertical change of 6 feet. **Teaching Tip** ❶

$$\text{grade} = \frac{\text{vertical change}}{\text{horizontal change}} = \frac{6}{100} \text{ or } 6\%$$

Example 1

 **APPLICATION**

Driving

How many feet does a road with a 6% grade drop in 3 miles?

Using 0.06 for 6%, the grade can be expressed as follows.

$0.06 = \frac{v}{h}$ *v represents the vertical change.*
                        h represents the horizontal change.

$v = 0.06h$

$v = 0.06(3)$ *The horizontal change is 3 miles.*

$v = 0.18$ *The vertical change is 0.18 miles.*

Since 1 mile equals 5280 feet, 0.18 miles equals 0.18(5280) or 950.4 feet. Thus, a road with a 6% grade drops 950.4 feet in 3 miles.

Sometimes the vertical distance is referred to as the *rise*, and the horizontal distance is referred to as the *run*. The ratio of *rise* to *run* is called **slope**. The slope of a line describes its steepness, or rate of change.

On the graph below, the line passes through the origin, (0, 0), and (4, 3). The change in y or rise is 3, while the change in x or run is 4. Therefore, the slope of this line is $\frac{3}{4}$.

$$\text{slope} = \frac{\text{rise}}{\text{run}} = \frac{\text{change in y}}{\text{change in x}}$$

ALTERNATE TEACHING STRATEGIES

Using Applications

Have students determine the slope of their driveway or curb ramp. Ask them to describe the procedure they used in calculating the value of this slope.

<table>
<tr><td>Definition
of Slope</td><td>The slope m of a line is the ratio of the change in y to the corresponding change in x.

$$\text{slope} = \frac{\text{change in } y}{\text{change in } x} \quad \text{or} \quad m = \frac{\text{change in } y}{\text{change in } x}$$</td></tr>
</table>

Example 2

Determine the slope of each line. **Teaching Tip**

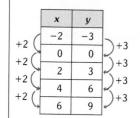

$$\frac{\text{change in } y}{\text{change in } x} = \frac{2}{3}$$

$$\frac{\text{change in } y}{\text{change in } x} = \frac{2}{-1}$$
$$= -2$$

$$\frac{\text{change in } y}{\text{change in } x} = \frac{0}{1}$$
$$= 0$$

$$\frac{\text{change in } y}{\text{change in } x} = \frac{y}{0}$$
The slope is undefined.

Notice that in Example 2, the line extending from lower left to upper right has a positive slope. The line extending from upper left to lower right has a negative slope. The slope of the horizontal line is zero. For a vertical line, the change in x would be zero. Since division by zero is not defined, the slope of a vertical line is undefined. We say that a vertical line *has no slope*.

Example 3

Determine the slope of the line containing the points with the coordinates listed in the table.

x	y
−2	−3
0	0
2	3
4	6
6	9

+2 ... +3 (between each row)

Notice that y increases 3 units for each 2 units that x increases.

$$\text{slope} = \frac{\text{change in } y}{\text{change in } x}$$
$$= \frac{3}{2}$$

These examples suggest that the slope of a nonvertical line can be determined from the coordinates of any two points on the line.

<table>
<tr><td>Determining
Slope Given
Two Points</td><td>Given the coordinates of two points on a line, (x_1, y_1) and (x_2, y_2), the slope, m, can be found as follows.

$$m = \frac{y_2 - y_1}{x_2 - x_1}, \text{ where } x_2 \neq x_1.$$</td></tr>
</table>

y_2 is read "y sub 2." The 2 is called a *subscript*.

LESSON 10-1 SLOPE OF A LINE 401

Teaching Tip 2 Emphasize that the line in Example 2 with a slope of 0 is horizontal (parallel to the *x*-axis) and the line with an undefined slope is vertical (parallel to the *y*-axis).

Chalkboard Examples

For Example 1

How many feet does a road with a 4% grade drop in 5 miles?
1056 feet

For Example 2

Determine the slope of the line through the origin and the point named.

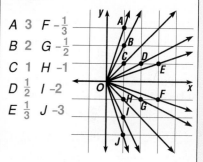

A 3   F $-\frac{1}{3}$
B 2   G $-\frac{1}{2}$
C 1   H -1
D $\frac{1}{2}$ I -2
E $\frac{1}{3}$ J -3

For Example 3

Determine the slope of the line containing the following points.

a.

x	0	1	2	3
y	5	7	9	11

2

b.

x	−3	−1	1	3
y	5	4	3	2

$-\frac{1}{2}$

c.

x	−1	0	1	2
y	5	5	5	5

0

For Example 4

Determine the slope of the line passing through each pair of points.

a. $(-5, 3), (2, 1)$ $-\frac{2}{7}$

b. $(4, 3), (1, -1)$ $\frac{4}{3}$

For Example 5

Determine the value of _n_ so the line through the two given points has the indicated slope.

a. $(-2, 4), (n, 5), m = \frac{1}{5}$ 3

b. $(3, 4), (-1, n), m = -\frac{3}{4}$ 7

Teaching Tip ③   Students should be aware that the y-coordinates can be subtracted in any order as long as the corresponding x-coordinates are subtracted in that same order.
$\frac{y_1 - y_2}{x_1 - x_2}$ or $\frac{y_2 - y_1}{x_2 - x_1}$, not $\frac{y_2 - y_1}{x_1 - x_2}$.

Teaching Tip ④   Have students graph the line through $(9, -2)$ with slope $-\frac{3}{2}$ to verify that the point $(5, 4)$ is on this line. They can think of slope as directions from one point to another on a line. That is, from $(9, -2)$, go 2 units right and 3 units down to locate another point on the line.

Reteaching Masters Booklet, p. 68

Example 4   Determine the slope of the line passing through $(3, -9)$ and $(4, -12)$.

$$m = \frac{y_2 - y_1}{x_2 - x_1}$$

$$= \frac{-12 - (-9)}{4 - 3} \quad (x_1, y_1) = (3, -9) \text{ and } (x_2, y_2) = (4, -12)$$

$$= \frac{-3}{1}$$

$$= -3$$

The slope is -3.

In Example 4, the difference of the y-coordinates was expressed as $-12 - (-9)$. Suppose $-9 - (-12)$ had been used as the change in y-coordinates and $3 - 4$ had been used as the change in x-coordinates. Since $\frac{-9 - (-12)}{3 - 4}$ is also equal to -3, it does not matter which point is chosen to be (x_1, y_1). However, the coordinates of both points must be used in the same order. **Teaching Tip ③**

Example 5   Determine the value of r so the line through $(r, 4)$ and $(9, -2)$ has a slope of $-\frac{3}{2}$.

$$m = \frac{y_2 - y_1}{x_2 - x_1}$$

$$-\frac{3}{2} = \frac{-2 - 4}{9 - r} \quad \textit{Replace each variable with its appropriate value.}$$

$$-\frac{3}{2} = \frac{-6}{9 - r}$$

$$-3(9 - r) = -6(2) \quad \textit{Means-extremes property}$$

$$-27 + 3r = -12 \quad \textit{Solve for r.}$$

$$3r = 15$$

$$r = 5 \quad \textbf{Teaching Tip ④}$$

CHECKING FOR UNDERSTANDING

Communicating Mathematics

Read and study the lesson to answer each question. See margin.

1. What is meant by a road sign stating that the grade of the road is 5%?

2. Explain the meaning of the slope of a line.

3. Draw a graph of a line having each of the following.

    a. a positive slope   **b.** a negative slope

    c. zero slope   **d.** no slope

402 CHAPTER 10 GRAPHING LINEAR EQUATIONS

RETEACHING THE LESSON

On the chalkboard or overhead, draw lines that go through the origin and also the points: $(4, 0)$, $(6, 2)$, $(2, 2)$, $(2, 6)$, $(0, 4)$, $(-2, 4)$, $(-2, 2)$, $(-4, 2)$, and $(-6, 0)$. Have students determine and compare the slopes of the lines.

Additional Answers

1. For every 100 feet of horizontal change, there is a vertical change of 5 feet.

2. Slope is a ratio, rise to run, or the change in y to the change in x.

3. Answers may vary; typical answers are given at the right.

NAME _____ DATE _____

10-1   **Reteaching Worksheet**

Slope of a Line

The ratio of *rise* to *run* is called **slope**. The slope of a line describes its steepness, or rate of change.

On a coordinate plane, a line extending from lower left to upper right has a positive slope. A line extending from upper left to lower right has a negative slope. The slope of a horizontal line is zero. A vertical line has *no slope*.

The slope of a nonvertical line can be determined from the coordinates of any two points on the line.

Definition of Slope
The slope of a line is the ratio of the change in *y* to the corresponding change in *x*.
Slope = $\frac{\text{change in } y}{\text{change in } x}$ or $m = \frac{\text{change in } y}{\text{change in } x}$

Determining Slope Given Two Points
Given the coordinates of two points on a line, (x_1, y_1) and (x_2, y_2), the slope, m, can be found as follows.
$m = \frac{y_2 - y_1}{x_2 - x_1}$, where $x_2 \neq x_1$

Example: Determine the slope of the line passing through $(-1, 5)$ and $(4, -2)$.

$$m = \frac{y_2 - y_1}{x_2 - x_1}$$
$$= \frac{-2 - 5}{4 - (-1)}$$
$$= \frac{-7}{5} = -\frac{7}{5}$$

Determine the slope of the line passing through each pair of points.

1. $(2, 1), (8, 9)$ $\frac{4}{3}$ 2. $(4, 9), (1, 6)$ 1 3. $(7, -8), (14, -6)$ $\frac{2}{7}$

4. $(-10, 7), (-20, 8)$ $-\frac{1}{10}$ 5. $(3, 11), (-12, 18)$ $-\frac{7}{15}$ 6. $(-4, -1), (-2, -5)$ -2

Determine the value of r so the line passing through each pair of points has the given slope.

7. $(10, r), (3, 4), m = -\frac{2}{7}$ 2   8. $(-1, -3), (7, r), m = \frac{3}{4}$ 3   9. $(-2, r), (10, 4),$ $m = -\frac{1}{2}$ 10

10. $(12, r), (r, 6), m = 2$ 10   11. $(6, 8), (r, -2), m = -3$ $\frac{28}{3}$ 12. $(r, 9), (7, 5), m = 6$ $\frac{23}{3}$

For each table, state the change in y and the change in x. Then determine the slope of the line passing through the points with the coordinates listed.

4.

x	y
0	0
1	1
2	2
3	3
4	4

$\frac{1}{1} = 1$

5.

x	y
-2	2
-1	1
0	0
1	-1
2	-2

$\frac{-1}{1} = -1$

6.

x	y
-2	-8
-1	-4
0	0
1	4
2	8

$\frac{4}{1} = 4$

7.

x	y
-6	8
-3	4
0	0
3	-4
6	-8

$\frac{-4}{3} = -\frac{4}{3}$

See Solutions Manual.

Draw a line through the given point that has the given slope.

8. $(2, 4)$, $m = \frac{1}{3}$ **9.** $(4, -1)$, $m = -\frac{2}{5}$ **10.** $(-3, 4)$, $m = 4$

11. $(-1, 5)$, $m = -2$ **12.** $(-3, -3)$, $m = \frac{4}{3}$ **13.** $(2, -4)$, $m = 0$

EXERCISES

Practice

Determine the slope of each line named below.

A

14. a **3**

15. b **-1**

16. c $\frac{3}{2}$

17. d **0**

18. e **no slope**

19. f $-\frac{1}{5}$

20. g $\frac{1}{3}$

21. h **-2**

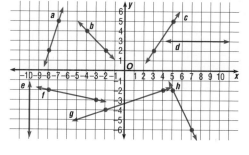

B

Determine the slope of the line passing through each pair of points.

22. $(3, 4)$, $(4, 6)$ **2** **23.** $(-3, 6)$, $(-5, 9)$ $-\frac{3}{2}$

24. $(-1, 11)$, $(-5, 4)$ $\frac{7}{4}$ **25.** $(7, -4)$, $(9, -1)$ $\frac{3}{2}$

26. $(18, -4)$, $(6, -10)$ $\frac{1}{2}$ **27.** $(14, 3)$, $(-11, 3)$ **0**

28. $(-4, -6)$, $(-3, -8)$ **-2** **29.** $(0, 0)$, $(0.5, 0.25)$ **0.5**

30. $\left(\frac{3}{4}, 1\right)$, $\left(\frac{3}{4}, -1\right)$ **none** **31.** $\left(3\frac{1}{2}, 5\frac{1}{4}\right)$, $\left(2\frac{1}{2}, 6\right)$ $-\frac{3}{4}$

LESSON 10-1 SLOPE OF A LINE 403

Additional Answers

3a.

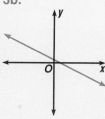

3b.

3c.

3d.

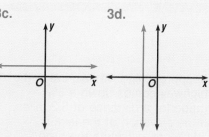

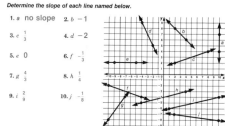

Determine the value of r so the line passing through each pair of points has the given slope.

32. $(9, r)$, $(6, 3)$, $m = -\frac{1}{3}$ **2**

33. $(r, 4)$, $(7, 3)$, $m = \frac{3}{4}$ **$\frac{25}{3}$**

34. $(4, -7)$, $(-2, r)$, $m = \frac{8}{3}$ **-23**

35. $(6, -2)$, $(r, -6)$, $m = -4$ **7**

C

36. $(r, 7)$, $(11, r)$, $m = -\frac{1}{5}$ **6**

37. $(4, r)$, $(r, 2)$, $m = -\frac{5}{3}$ **7**

38. $(9, r)$, $(6, 2)$, $m = r$ **-1**

39. $(8, r^2)$, $(3, -6)$, $m = r$ **2, 3**

Critical Thinking

40. Look at lines a, c, and g on the previous page. These lines have positive slopes. What is the general direction of lines with positive slopes? **The lines go from lower left to upper right.**

41. Look at lines b, f, and h on the previous page. These lines have negative slopes. What is the general direction of lines with negative slopes? **The lines go from upper left to lower right.**

Applications

42. Construction A ramp installed to give handicapped people access to a building has a 3-foot rise and a 36-foot run. What is the slope of the ramp? **$\frac{1}{12}$**

43. Driving The eastern entrance of the Eisenhower Tunnel in Colorado is at an elevation of 11,080 feet. The tunnel is 8941 feet long and has an upgrade of 0.895% toward the western end. What is the elevation of the western end of the tunnel? **11,160 feet**

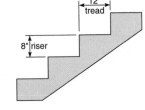

44. Carpentry When building a stairway, a carpenter considers the ratio of riser to tread. Write a ratio to describe the steepness of the stairs. **$\frac{2}{3}$**

45. Aviation An airplane passing over Albuquerque at an elevation of 33,000 feet begins its descent to land at Santa Fe, 50 miles away. If the elevation of Santa Fe is 7000 feet, what should be the approximate slope of descent, expressed as a percent? **9.8%**

Mixed Review

46. Name the property illustrated by $8 + (12 + 34) = (8 + 12) + 34$. **(Lesson 1-6) associative (+)**

47. Find the degree of $2xy^2z + 5xyz^5 + x^4$. **(Lesson 6-5) 7**

48. Factor $5a^3 + 3a^2b - 5ab^2 - 3b^3$. **(Lesson 7-3) $(5a + 3b)(a + b)(a - b)$**

49. Find $\frac{6}{x} - \frac{5}{x^2}$. **(Lesson 8-7) $\frac{6x - 5}{x^2}$**

50. Complete: $1, 6, 11, \underline{\ ?\ }, \underline{\ ?\ }, 26, \underline{\ ?\ }$. **(Lesson 9-7) 16, 21, 31**

EXTENDING THE LESSON

Math Power: Problem Solving

In approaching Castaic Lake, the highway comes down a 5% grade for a distance of 5.2 miles. If the elevation of the lake is 1440 feet, calculate the drop from the top of the grade to the lake. What is the elevation of the top of the grade? **The drop is about 1373 ft. The top of the grade is about 2813 feet.**

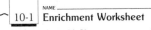
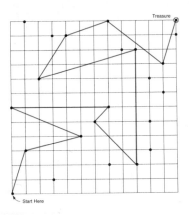

Point-Slope and Standard Forms of Linear Equations

Objectives

After studying this lesson, you should be able to:

10-2A
- write a linear equation in standard form given the coordinates of a point on the line and the slope of the line, and

10-2B
- write a linear equation in standard form given the coordinates of two points on the line.

Lesson Resources

- Reteaching Master 10-2
- Practice Master 10-2
- Enrichment Master 10-2
- Activity Master, p. 55
- Video Algebra, 37

 Transparency 10-2 contains the 5-Minute Check and a teaching aid for this lesson.

Application

FYI · · ·

The book *Men of Good Will*, first published in 1933, consists of 4949 pages and is estimated to have 2,070,000 words.

Seth is reading a book for a book report. He decides to avoid a last-minute rush by reading 2 chapters each day. A graph representing his plan is shown at the right. By the end of the first day, Seth should have read 2 chapters, so one point on the graph has coordinates (1, 2). Since he plans to read 2 chapters in 1 day, the slope is $\frac{2}{1}$ or 2.

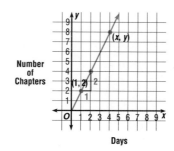

INTRODUCING THE LESSON

Let (x, y) represent the coordinates of any other point on the line. The equation for the slope of a line can be used to find an equation that describes Seth's plan. Replace (x_1, y_1) with (1, 2) and (x_2, y_2) with any other point (x, y). We know that the slope is 2, so replace m with 2.

$$\frac{y_2 - y_1}{x_2 - x_1} = m$$

$$\frac{y - 2}{x - 1} = 2 \qquad \text{\textit{Replace } } y_2 \text{ \textit{with} } y, y_1 \text{ \textit{with} } 2, \\ x_2 \text{ \textit{with} } x, x_1 \text{ \textit{with} } 1, \text{ \textit{and} } m \text{ \textit{with} } 2.$$

$$y - 2 = 2(x - 1) \qquad \text{\textit{Multiply each side by} } (x - 1).$$

This linear equation is said to be in **point-slope form**.

Point-Slope Form	For a given point (x_1, y_1) on a nonvertical line with slope m, the point-slope form of a linear equation is as follows.

Teaching Tip ❶

$$y - y_1 = m(x - x_1)$$

In general, you can write an equation in point-slope form for the graph of any nonvertical line. If you know the slope of a line and the coordinates of one point on the line, you can write an equation of the line.

Motivating the Lesson

Develop student understanding of how to identify approximate slopes of lines by putting a grid on an overhead projector and placing lines in various positions. Ask students what would be a reasonable slope. The same kind of drill can be done on the chalkboard using a meter stick as a line.

ALTERNATE TEACHING STRATEGIES

Using Charts

Have the students make a chart with the following headings: Standard Form, Point-Slope Form, Slope, *x*-Intercept, *y*-Intercept, Points. In the first line, have them write $3x - 2y = 12$ under Standard Form. In the second line, have them write 4 under *x*-Intercept and −1 under *y*-Intercept. In the third line, write (4, 1) and (−3, 5) under Points. Then have the students complete the chart.

TEACHING THE LESSON

Teaching Tip ❶ The point-slope form of a linear equation is not unique. This form is used as an intermediate step when finding the standard form or slope-intercept form. Ask students why the definition of the point-slope form includes the phrase "a nonvertical line."

For Example 1

Write the point-slope form of an equation of the line passing through the given point and having the given slope.

a. $(3, 5)$, $\frac{4}{3}$ $y - 5 = \frac{4}{3}(x - 3)$

b. $(-2, 0)$, $-\frac{3}{2}$ $y = -\frac{3}{2}(x + 2)$

c. $(-3, 2)$, $-\frac{1}{2}$
$y - 2 = -\frac{1}{2}(x + 3)$

d. $(0, 5)$, -3 $y - 5 = -3x$

For Example 2

Write each of the following equations in standard form.

a. $2y = x - 4$ $x - 2y = 4$

b. $y = \frac{3}{4}x - 5$ $3x - 4y = 20$

c. $y = -\frac{3}{5}(x + 10)$
$3x + 5y = -30$

d. $y = 4x - 3$ $4x - y = 3$

For Example 3

Sue is taking a group of students and chaperones to a local theater. She has enough money to buy 5 adult tickets and 4 student tickets or 6 adult tickets and 3 student tickets. Write an equation in standard form that represents the amount of money Sue has. $x + y = 9$ **where x is cost of student tickets, y is cost of adult tickets, and $9 is amount of money Sue has.**

Teaching Tip ❷   Point out that $(2, -4)$ is just one point that lies on the line. The variables x and y in the equation represent all of the other points (x, y) that lie on the line.

Teaching Tip ❸   Some students may need to see this multiplication in greater detail. You may want to insert the following step.
$4(y + 4) = \cancel{4}\left(\frac{3}{\cancel{4}}\right)(x - 2)$

Example 1 | Write the point-slope form of an equation of the line passing through $(2, -4)$ and having a slope of $\frac{2}{3}$.

$y - y_1 = m(x - x_1)$

$y - (-4) = \frac{2}{3}(x - 2)$ *Replace x_1 with 2, y_1 with -4, and m with $\frac{2}{3}$.*

$y + 4 = \frac{2}{3}(x - 2)$

An equation of the line is $y + 4 = \frac{2}{3}(x - 2)$. **Teaching Tip ❷**

Any linear equation can be expressed in the form $Ax + By = C$ where A, B, and C are integers and A and B are not both zero. This is called the **standard form**. An equation that is written in point-slope form can be written in standard form.

Example 2 | Write $y + 4 = \frac{3}{4}(x - 2)$ in standard form.

$y + 4 = \frac{3}{4}(x - 2)$ **Teaching Tip ❸**

$4(y + 4) = 3(x - 2)$ *Multiply each side by 4 to eliminate the fraction.*

$4y + 16 = 3x - 6$ *Distributive property*

$-3x + 4y = -22$

$3x - 4y = 22$ *Multiply each side by -1 to get a positive coefficient for x.*

$3x - 4y = 22$ is in standard form.

You can also find an equation of a line if you know the coordinates of two points on the line.

Example 3

APPLICATION
Entertainment

Alejandra is selling tickets to the music program at school. Mr. Foster says that he has enough money to buy 9 student tickets and 2 adult tickets or 3 student tickets and 6 adult tickets. Write an equation in standard form that represents the cost of each ticket and the amount of money that Mr. Foster has.

EXPLORE   Let x = the number of student tickets and let y = the number of adult tickets. In $Ax + By = C$, A is the price in dollars of a student ticket, B is the price in dollars of an adult ticket, and C is the amount of money Mr. Foster has. The two points $(9, 2)$ and $(3, 6)$ lie on the graph of this equation.

PLAN   Use $(9, 2)$ and $(3, 6)$ to find the slope. Then use the point-slope form to write the equation in standard form.

SOLVE
$$m = \frac{y_2 - y_1}{x_2 - x_1}$$

$$= \frac{6 - 2}{3 - 9}$$ *Replace y_2 with 6, y_1 with 2, x_2 with 3, and x_1 with 9.*

$$= \frac{4}{-6} \text{ or } -\frac{2}{3}$$

Now use the point-slope form. The slope is $-\frac{2}{3}$. Either $(9, 2)$ or $(3, 6)$ can be substituted for (x_1, y_1).

$$y - y_1 = m(x - x_1) \quad \textit{Let } (x_1, y_1) = (9, 2).$$

$$y - 2 = -\frac{2}{3}(x - 9) \quad \textit{Point-slope form}$$

$$3(y - 2) = -2(x - 9) \quad \textit{Multiply by 3 to eliminate the fraction.}$$

$$3y - 6 = -2x + 18$$

$$2x + 3y = 24 \quad \textit{This equation is in standard form.}$$

The equation in standard form is $2x + 3y = 24$. So, Mr. Foster has $24, if the student tickets are $2 each and the adult tickets are $3 each.

EXAMINE   Check the solution by replacing (x, y) with $(9, 2)$ and $(3, 6)$.

$2x + 3y = 24$	$2x + 3y = 24$
$2(9) + 3(2) \stackrel{?}{=} 24$	$2(3) + 3(6) \stackrel{?}{=} 24$
$18 + 6 \stackrel{?}{=} 24$	$6 + 18 \stackrel{?}{=} 24$
$24 = 24$ ✔	$24 = 24$ ✔

The solution checks.

A horizontal line has a slope of zero. The point-slope form can be used to write equations of horizontal lines. For example, the equation of a line through $(5, 2)$ and $(-9, 2)$ is $y - 2 = 0(x - 5)$ or $y = 2$. **Teaching Tip ④**

A vertical line has no slope. Therefore, the point-slope form cannot be used for vertical lines. The equation of a line through $(3, 5)$ and $(3, -9)$ is $x = 3$ since the x-coordinate of every point on the line is equal to 3.

CHECKING FOR UNDERSTANDING

Communicating Mathematics

Read and study the lesson to answer each question.

1. In the point-slope form of a linear equation, what do x_1 and y_1 represent? **The coordinates of a point on the line.**

2. What is the standard form of a linear equation? *Ax + By = C*

3. Describe the graph of the equation $y = c$, where c is any number. **horizontal line with y-coordinate c**

4. Describe the graph of the equation $x = c$, where c is any number. **vertical line with x-coordinate c**

LESSON 10-2   POINT-SLOPE FORM AND STANDARD FORMS OF LINEAR EQUATIONS   407

RETEACHING THE LESSON

Have students name two points and then graph them. Determine the slope from the graph. Have half the class use one of the points and the slope to find the standard form of the equation and the other half of the class use the other point and the slope to find the standard form of the equation.

Closing the Lesson

Writing Activity Place several lines on a grid and have the students estimate their slopes and y-intercepts. Have them write a linear equation in point-slope form for each line.

APPLYING THE LESSON

Homework Exercises

Assignment Guide

Basic: 15-30, 35-36, 38-42
Average: 19-32, 38-42
Enriched: 21-42

Chapter 10, Quiz A, (Lessons 10-1 through 10-2), is available in the Evaluation Masters Booklet, p. 135.

Guided Practice State the slope and a point through which the line for each linear equation passes. 6. -2; $(-1, -5)$

5. $y - 2 = 3(x - 5)$ 3; (5, 2)

6. $y - (-5) = -2(x + 1)$

7. $y + 6 = -\frac{3}{2}(x + 5)$ $-\frac{3}{2}$; $(-5, -6)$

8. $2(x - 3) = y + \frac{3}{2}$ 2; $\left(3, -\frac{3}{2}\right)$

9. $y = 3$ 0; (0, 3)

10. $x = 1$ none; (1, 0)

Write each equation in standard form.

11. $y - 3 = 2\left(x + \frac{3}{2}\right)$ $2x - y = -6$

12. $y + 5 = -3\left(x - \frac{1}{3}\right)$ $3x + y = -4$

13. $y + 1 = \frac{2}{3}(x + 2)$ $2x - 3y = -1$

14. $y + \frac{3}{2} = \frac{1}{2}(x + 4)$ $x - 2y = -1$

EXERCISES

Practice Write the standard form of an equation of the line passing through the given point and having the given slope.

15. (5, 4), $-\frac{2}{3}$ $2x + 3y = 22$

16. $(-6, -3)$, $-\frac{1}{2}$ $x + 2y = -12$

17. (9, 1), $\frac{2}{3}$ $2x - 3y = 15$

18. (4, -3), 2 $2x - y = 11$

19. $(-2, 4)$, -3 $3x + y = -2$

20. $(6, -2)$, $\frac{4}{3}$ $4x - 3y = 30$

21. $(-2, 6)$, 0 $y = 6$

22. (1, 3), none $x = 1$

Write the standard form of an equation of the line passing through each pair of points.

23. (5, 4), (6, 3) $x + y = 9$

24. (6, 1), (7, -4) $5x + y = 31$

25. $(4, -2)$, (4, 8) $x = 4$

26. $(4, -2)$, $(8, -3)$ $x + 4y = -4$

27. $(-6, 1)$, $(-8, 2)$ $x + 2y = -4$

28. (5, 3), $(-6, 3)$ $y = 3$

29. $(-5, 1)$, $(6, -2)$ $3x + 11y = -4$

30. $(-8, 2)$, $(-1, -2)$ $4x + 7y = -18$

31. (0.75, 1), (2, 0.5) $4x + 10y = 13$

32. $(-8, 0.5)$, (9, 0.5) $2y = 1$

33. $\left(2\frac{1}{2}, \frac{1}{3}\right)$, $\left(\frac{3}{4}, 1\frac{1}{2}\right)$ $2x + 3y = 6$

34. $(-2, 7)$, $\left(-2, \frac{16}{3}\right)$ $x = -2$

Critical Thinking 35. A line contains the points (9, 1) and (5, 5). Write a convincing argument that the same line intersects the y-axis at (10, 0). See margin.

Applications 36. **Shipping** The number of books shipped in one box is limited by the weight of the books. Six algebra books and 18 geometry books can be shipped together. Eleven algebra and 14 geometry books can also be shipped together. Write an equation in standard form that relates the number of algebra and geometry books that can be shipped in one box.
See margin.

Practice Masters Booklet, p. 77

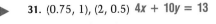

| NAME | DATE |

10-2 Practice Worksheet

Point-Slope and Standard Forms of Linear Equations

Write the standard form of an equation of the line passing through the given point and having the given slope.

1. (1, 1), $\frac{1}{4}$ $x - 4y = -3$

2. (6, 0), $-\frac{1}{2}$ $x + 2y = 6$

3. $(-2, 1)$, 1 $x - y = -3$

4. $(-6, -2)$, $-\frac{1}{3}$ $x + 3y = -12$

5. (3, -4), 0 $y = -4$

6. $(-4, 1)$, $\frac{3}{2}$ $3x - 2y = -14$

7. (0, 0), -3 $3x + y = 0$

8. (5, -3), none $x = 5$

Write the standard form of an equation of the line passing through each pair of points.

9. $(-1, -7)$, (1, 3) $5x - y = 2$

10. (5, 3), $(-4, 3)$ $y = 3$

11. $(-4, 6)$, $(-2, 5)$ $x + 2y = 8$

12. (2, -6), (2, 5) $x = 2$

13. $(-3, -2)$, (4, 5) $x - y = -1$

14. $(-5, 1)$, $(0, -2)$ $3x + 5y = -10$

Additional Answers

35. $m = \frac{5 - 1}{5 - 9} = \frac{4}{-4} = -1$

$y - 5 = -1(x - 5)$
$y - 5 = -x + 5$
$y = -x + 10$
Let $x = 10$. $y = -(10) + 10$
$y = 0$
Since $y = 0$ when $x = 10$, this line intersects the y-axis at (10, 0).

36. Let $x =$ the number of algebra books and $y =$ the number of geometry books.
$4x + 5y = 114$

37. Let $x =$ the number of weeks that have passed and $y =$ the amount of money he has left. Kyung started with $90 since he had $75 left after 3 weeks.
$y = -5x + 90$

37. **Work** Kyung earned some money by baby-sitting during spring vacation. He decides to allow himself to spend $5 of the money each week. After 3 weeks, he has $75 left. Write an equation in standard form that relates the money left with the number of weeks that have passed. (*Hint:* The slope is −5.) **See margin.**

Mixed Review

38. $56a^2 + 77a$
39. $(x - 7)(x - 2)$

38. Multiply $7a(8a + 11)$. **(Lesson 6-7)**

39. Factor $x^2 - 9x + 14$. **(Lesson 7-5)**

40. Find $\dfrac{y^2 + 3y^3}{y^2 - 4} \cdot \dfrac{2y + y^2}{y + 4y^2 + 3y^3}$. **(Lesson 8-2)** $\dfrac{y^2}{y^2 - y - 2}$

41. Name the quadrant for the graph of (x, y), given that $x > 0$ and $y > 0$. **(Lesson 9-1)** **Quadrant I**

42. **National Landmarks** At the Royal Gorge in Colorado, an inclined railway takes visitors down to the Arkansas River. If the grade is 100% and the vertical drop is 1015 feet, what is the horizontal change of the railway? **(Lesson 10-1)** **1015 feet**

HISTORY CONNECTION

Benjamin Banneker

Benjamin Banneker (1731–1806), a free African-American man, was a self-taught genius in the areas of mathematics, astronomy, and surveying. He was often referred to as the "sable (Black) genius." At the age of 20, Banneker obtained a book on geometry and, armed with a compass and ruler, designed and built the first clock ever built in the United States. It kept perfect time for 40 years. Banneker corresponded often with Thomas Jefferson, and it was on Jefferson's recommendation that President Washington appointed Banneker as the assistant surveyor on the team responsible for designing and building the new capital at Washington, D.C. Long before the project was completed, Pierre L'Enfant, the French engineer in charge of the project, resigned and returned to France with all of the plans and maps. But having worked closely with L'Enfant, Banneker was able to reproduce all of the plans from memory in only two days. The nation's capital stands today as a monument to Banneker's genius.

LESSON 10-2 POINT-SLOPE FORM AND STANDARD FORMS OF LINEAR EQUATIONS **409**

EXTENDING THE LESSON

Math Power: Connections

The coordinates of the vertices of a triangle are $A(2, 1)$, $B(-3, 4)$, and $C(-5, -2)$. Write the standard form of the equations of the lines that form the sides of the triangle.

side $\overline{AB}$: $3x + 5y = 11$
side $\overline{AC}$: $3x - 7y = -1$
side $\overline{BC}$: $3x - y = -13$

History Connection

The History Connection features introduce students to persons or cultures who were involved in the development of mathematics. You may want students to further research Banneker or to research the building of the U.S. capital.

Lesson Resources
- Reteaching Master 10-3
- Practice Master 10-3
- Enrichment Master 10-3
- Activity Master, p. 25
- Video Algebra, 36

 Transparency 10-3 contains the 5-Minute Check and a teaching aid for this lesson.

INTRODUCING THE LESSON

 5-Minute Check

(over Lesson 10-2)

Write the standard form of an equation of the line passing through the given point and having the given slope.

1. $(-2, 6)$, 0 $y = 6$
2. $(4, -3)$, 2 $2x - y = 11$
3. $(5, 7)$, 0 $y = 7$

Write the standard form of an equation of the line passing through each pair of points.

4. $(5, 3)$, $(-6, 3)$ $y = 3$
5. $(9, 1)$, $(8, 2)$ $x + y = 10$

Motivating the Lesson

Graph $y = 2x - 1$.

Ask students what the y-intercept and slope of the line is. Then ask them if they can find these numbers in the equation $y = 2x - 1$. You may graph several linear equations to convince students of the relationship.

TEACHING THE LESSON

Teaching Tip ❶ Make students aware that each time they are given an intercept, they know a point on the line. For example, for a y-intercept of 3, the point $(0, 3)$ is on the line. For an x-intercept of -2, the point $(-2, 0)$ is on the line.

10-3 Slope-Intercept Form of Linear Equations

Objectives

After studying this lesson, you should be able to:

10-3A ▪ write an equation in slope-intercept form given the slope and y-intercept,

10-3B ▪ determine the slope and y-intercept of a graph, and

10-3C ▪ determine the x- and y-intercepts of a graph.

Application

FYI ···

The average American consumes about 73.4 pounds of beef and 62.7 pounds of chicken each year.

Larry is taking home economics. As a class project, he is cooking dinner for some friends. Larry plans to spend $15 on beef and/or chicken. If beef costs $5 per pound and chicken costs $3 per pound, the graph at the right shows all the possible combinations of beef and chicken he can buy. If he buys no beef, he can buy 5 pounds of chicken. If he buys no chicken, he can buy 3 pounds of beef. The point at 5 on the x-axis and the point at 3 on the y-axis are called the **intercepts**.

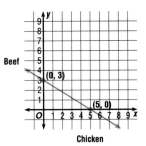

The x-coordinate of the point where a line crosses the x-axis is called the **x-intercept** of the line. The line graphed on the coordinate plane above crosses the x-axis at $(5, 0)$. Therefore the x-intercept is 5. Note that the corresponding y-coordinate is 0. Similarly, the y-coordinate of the point where the line crosses the y-axis is called the **y-intercept** of the line. The line above crosses the y-axis at $(0, 3)$. Therefore, the y-intercept is 3. Note that the corresponding x-coordinate is 0. **Teaching Tip** ❶

Consider the graph at the right. The line with slope m crosses the y-axis at $(0, b)$. You can write an equation for this line using the point-slope form. Let $(x_1, y_1) = (0, b)$.

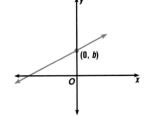

$$y - y_1 = m(x - x_1) \quad \text{Point-slope form}$$
$$y - b = m(x - 0) \quad \begin{array}{l}\text{Replace } y_1 \text{ with } b.\\ \text{Replace } x_1 \text{ with } 0.\end{array}$$
$$y = \underset{\uparrow}{m}x + \underset{\uparrow}{b}$$
$$\text{slope}\quad\text{y-intercept}$$

Slope-Intercept Form	Given the points (x, y) and $(0, b)$ and slope m, the slope-intercept form of an equation for the line through the points is $y = mx + b$.

ALTERNATE TEACHING STRATEGIES

Using Applications

Have students measure three sets of stairs in the school or their homes. Tell them to determine the slope of the stairs. Ask them to make some generalizations about the run (tread) and rise of the steps. Have them explain how the slope of each set of stairs is determined.

Using Discussion

Explain why the equations of vertical lines cannot be written in slope-intercept form.

Example 1

State the slope and y-intercept of the graph of $y = 5x - 3$.

$$y = 5x + (-3)$$
$$\downarrow \qquad \downarrow$$
$$y = mx + \quad b$$

Since $m = 5$, the slope is 5. Since b is -3, the y-intercept is -3.

Example 2

APPLICATION
Travel

Mini and her family are taking a trip to see her grandmother. After traveling a while, she begins to keep track of their time and mileage. Let d represent the total distance traveled in miles and let t represent the time in hours. Then $d = 50t + 83$ represents the total distance traveled.

a. How far had Mini's family traveled before she began keeping track of their mileage?

b. What is their average rate of speed?

a. The distance traveled would be the value of d when $t = 0$.

$$d = 50t + 83$$
$$d = 50(0) + 83 \qquad \textit{Replace t with 0.}$$
$$d = 83 \qquad \text{They had traveled 83 miles.}$$

b. Their average rate of speed is the slope, or 50 miles per hour.

Compare the slope-intercept form of a linear equation with the standard form, $Ax + By = C$. Solve for y.

$$Ax + By = C$$
$$By = -Ax + C \qquad \textit{Assume B} \neq 0.$$
$$y = -\frac{Ax}{B} + \frac{C}{B} \qquad \textit{This equation is in slope-intercept form.}$$
$$\uparrow \qquad \uparrow$$
$$\textit{slope} \quad \textit{y-intercept}$$

If the equation is given in standard form and B is *not* zero, the slope of the line is $-\frac{A}{B}$ and the y-intercept is $\frac{C}{B}$. **Teaching Tip ❷**

Example 3

State the slope and y-intercept of the graph of $3x + 2y = 12$.

In the equation $3x + 2y = 12$, $A = 3$, $B = 2$, and $C = 12$.

slope: $-\frac{A}{B} = -\frac{3}{2}$ $\qquad$ y-intercept: $\frac{C}{B} = \frac{12}{2}$ or 6

Check: Write the equation in slope-intercept form.

$$3x + 2y = 12$$
$$2y = -3x + 12$$
$$y = -\frac{3}{2}x + 6$$

The slope is $-\frac{3}{2}$ and the y-intercept is 6. The solution checks.

LESSON 10-3 SLOPE-INTERCEPT FORM OF LINEAR EQUATIONS 411

Teaching Tip ③   You may wish to have advanced students discover on their own the formula for the x-intercept.

Teaching Tip ④   Point out that vertical lines have no y-intercept, while horizontal lines have no x-intercept.

EVALUATING THE LESSON

Checking for Understanding

Exercises 1-19 are designed to help you assess understanding through reading, writing, and speaking. You should work through Exercises 1-4 with your students, and then monitor their work on Exercises 5-19.

Reteaching Masters Booklet, p. 70

Recall that the x-coordinate of the ordered pair for the y-intercept is 0 and the y-coordinate of the ordered pair for the x-intercept is 0. You can use these facts to find the x- and y-intercepts of the graph of a linear equation.

Example 4

Determine the x- and y-intercepts of the graph of $4x - 5y = 10$.

To find the x-intercept, let $y = 0$.

$$4x - 5y = 10$$
$$4x - 5(0) = 10 \qquad \textit{Let y = 0.}$$
$$4x = 10$$
$$x = \frac{5}{2}$$

The x-intercept is $\frac{5}{2}$. The graph crosses the x-axis at $\left(\frac{5}{2}, 0\right)$.

To find the y-intercept, let $x = 0$.

$$4x - 5y = 10$$
$$4(0) - 5y = 10 \qquad \textit{Let x = 0.}$$
$$-5y = 10$$
$$y = -2$$

The y-intercept is −2. The graph crosses the y-axis at $(0, -2)$.

The y-intercept of the graph of an equation in the form $Ax + By = C$ is $\frac{C}{B}$. To find a formula for the x-intercept, let $y = 0$. **Teaching Tip ③**

$$Ax + By = C$$
$$Ax + B(0) = C \qquad \textit{Let y = 0.}$$
$$Ax = C$$
$$x = \frac{C}{A}$$

The x-intercept is $\frac{C}{A}$, $A \neq 0$. Therefore, for the graph of $2x - 3y = 8$, the x-intercept is $\frac{8}{2}$ or 4, and the y-intercept is $-\frac{8}{3}$. **Teaching Tip ④**

CHECKING FOR UNDERSTANDING

Communicating Mathematics

Read and study the lesson to answer each question.

1. Does the graph of every linear equation have an x-intercept?
   No; equations of the form $y = c$ do not.
2. How can you find the x-intercept using the equation $y = mx + b$?
   Let $y = 0$ and solve for x.
3. Write the equation of a line that has no slope.
   $x = c$ (c is any number)
4. Write the equation of a line that has no y-intercept.
   $x = c$ (c is any number)

RETEACHING THE LESSON

Have students find the x- and y-intercepts of a linear equation and graph them. Then write the equation in slope-intercept form. Using the graph, find another point on the line and replace that point into the original equation to check for equality. Also, find the slope from the graph and check with their slope-intercept form equation.

Guided Practice

State the slope and y-intercept of the graph of each equation.

5. $y = 5x + 3$ 5, 3

6. $y = 3x - 7$ 3, −7

7. $y = \frac{1}{3}x$ $\frac{1}{3}$, 0

8. $y = \frac{3}{5}x - \frac{1}{4}$ $\frac{3}{5}$, $-\frac{1}{4}$

9. $2x + 3y = 5$ $-\frac{2}{3}$, $\frac{5}{3}$

10. $-x + 4y = 3$ $\frac{1}{4}$, $\frac{3}{4}$

11. $y - 6x = 5$ 6, 5

12. $3y - 8x = 2$ $\frac{8}{3}$, $\frac{2}{3}$

13. $5y = -8x - 2$
$-\frac{8}{5}$, $-\frac{2}{5}$

Write an equation in slope-intercept form of the line with the given slope and y-intercept.

14. $m = 3, b = 1$ $y = 3x + 1$

15. $m = -3, b = 5$ $y = -3x + 5$

16. $m = 4, b = -2$ $y = 4x - 2$

17. $m = \frac{1}{2}, b = 5$ $y = \frac{1}{2}x + 5$

18. $m = -3.1, b = 0.6$
$y = -3.1x + 0.6$

19. $m = 0, b = 14$ $y = 14$

EXERCISES

24. $-\frac{11}{2}$, $-\frac{11}{5}$

Practice

Determine the x- and y-intercepts of the graph of each equation.

20. $3x + 2y = 6$ 2, 3

21. $5x + y = 10$ 2, 10

22. $3x + 4y = 24$ 8, 6

23. $2x - 7y = 28$ 14, −4

24. $2x + 5y = -11$

25. $x = -2$ −2, none

26. $\frac{3}{4}x - 2y = 7$ $\frac{28}{3}$, $-\frac{7}{2}$

27. $3y = 12$ none, 4

28. $1.8x - 2.5y = 5.4$
3, 2.16

Determine the slope and y-intercept of the graph of each equation. Then write each equation in slope-intercept form. **29–48. See margin.**

29. $2x + 5y = 10$

30. $5x - y = 15$

31. $7x + 4y = 8$

32. $5x - 4y = 11$

33. $12x + 9y = 15$

34. $13x - 11y = 22$

35. $2x + \frac{1}{3}y = 5$

36. $3x - \frac{1}{4}y = 6$

37. $\frac{2}{3}x + \frac{1}{6}y = 2$

38. $3x = 2y - 7$

39. $5x = 8 - 2y$

40. $8y = 4x + 12$

41. $1.1x - 0.2y = 3.2$

42. $3(x - 7) = 2y + 5x + 8$

43. $y - 3x = 6(y + 7x) + 10$

44. $4y + x = 9 - 3(2y - 2x)$

45. $\frac{4}{5}(2x - y) = 6x + \frac{2}{5}y - 10$

46. $\frac{3}{2}(4x + 9y) = 4(7x - \frac{1}{2}y)$

47. Write an equation in slope-intercept form of the line with slope $\frac{4}{5}$ and y-intercept the same as the line whose equation is $3x + 4y = 6$.

48. Write an equation in slope-intercept form of the line with slope $-\frac{3}{5}$ and y-intercept the same as the line whose equation is $7x - 3y = 12$.

LESSON 10-3 SLOPE-INTERCEPT FORM OF LINEAR EQUATIONS 413

Additional Answers

29. $-\frac{2}{5}$, 2; $y = -\frac{2}{5}x + 2$

30. 5, −15; $y = 5x - 15$

31. $-\frac{7}{4}$, 2; $y = -\frac{7}{4}x + 2$

32. $\frac{5}{4}$, $-\frac{11}{4}$; $y = \frac{5}{4}x - \frac{11}{4}$

33. $-\frac{4}{3}$, $\frac{5}{3}$; $y = -\frac{4}{3}x + \frac{5}{3}$

34. $\frac{13}{11}$, −2; $y = \frac{13}{11}x - 2$

35. −6, 15; $y = -6x + 15$

36. 12, −24; $y = 12x - 24$

37. −4, 12; $y = -4x + 12$

38. $\frac{3}{2}$, $\frac{7}{2}$; $y = \frac{3}{2}x + \frac{7}{2}$

39. $-\frac{5}{2}$, 4; $y = -\frac{5}{2}x + 4$

40. $\frac{1}{2}$, $\frac{3}{2}$; $y = \frac{1}{2}x + \frac{3}{2}$

41. $\frac{11}{2}$, −16; $y = \frac{11}{2}x - 16$

42. −1, $-\frac{29}{2}$; $y = -x - \frac{29}{2}$

49. Write an equation in slope-intercept form of the line with y-intercept 12 and slope the same as the line whose equation is $2x - 5y - 10 = 0$.
$$y = \tfrac{2}{5}x + 12$$

50. Write an equation in slope-intercept form of the line with y-intercept -0.65 and slope the same as the line whose equation is $\tfrac{1}{2}x - \tfrac{3}{4}y = 6$.
$$y = \tfrac{2}{3}x - 0.65$$

Critical Thinking

51. Find the coordinates of a point on the graph of $3x - 4y = -20$, if the y-coordinate is twice the x-coordinate. **(4, 8)**

52. Find the coordinates of a point on the graph of $4x - y = -2$, if the y-coordinate is three times the x-coordinate. **(−2, −6)**

53. Find the coordinates of a point on the graph of $x + 2y = 11$, if the y-coordinate is 5 less than the x-coordinate. **(7, 2)**

54. Find the coordinates of a point on the graph of $7x + 3y = 2$, if the y-coordinate is 4 more than the x-coordinate. **(−1, 3)**

Applications

55. Finance To save for a new bicycle, Cesár begins a savings plan. Cesár's savings are described by the equation $s = 5w + 56$, where s represents his total savings in dollars and w represents the number of weeks since the start of the savings plan.

  a. How much money had Cesár already saved when the plan started? **$56**

  b. How much does Cesár save each week? **$5**

56. Education In order to "curve" a set of test scores, a teacher uses the equation $g = 2.5p + 10$, where g is the curved test score and p is the number of problems answered correctly.

  a. How many extra points does each student receive for the test? **10 points**

  b. How many points is each problem worth? **2.5 points**

Mixed Review

57. Tennis The diameter of a circle is the distance across the circle. If the diameter of a tennis ball is $2\tfrac{1}{2}$ inches, how many tennis balls will fit in a can 12 inches high? **(Lesson 2-7) 4 tennis balls**

58. Simplify $(3x^4)(-2x^4y^3)$. **(Lesson 6-2)** $-6x^8y^3$

59. Factor $m^4 + 12m^2n^2 + 36n^4$. **(Lesson 7-7)** $(m^2 + 6n^2)^2$

60. Find $\dfrac{y^2}{x+2} \div \dfrac{y}{x+2}$. **(Lesson 8-4)** y

61. Given $g(x) = 2x - 1$, find $g\!\left(\tfrac{5}{2}\right)$. **(Lesson 9-5) 4**

62. Write the standard form of an equation of the line passing through $(5, 7)$ and having slope 0. **(Lesson 10-2)** $y = 7$

414 CHAPTER 10 GRAPHING LINEAR EQUATIONS

EXTENDING THE LESSON

Math Power:
Problem Solving

Write an equation in slope-intercept form of the line with y-intercept 6 passing through the point (3, 4).
$$y = -\tfrac{2}{3}x + 6$$

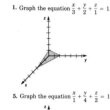

414 Chapter 10

10-4 Graphing Linear Equations

Objective
10-4

After studying this lesson, you should be able to:
- graph linear equations using the x- and y-intercepts or the slope and y-intercept.

Application

Nicki is starting a training program to shape up for summer. She plans to walk and/or jog a total of 6 miles each day. Let x represent the distance she walks and let y represent the distance she jogs. Then each day $x + y$ must equal 6.

$$x + y = 6$$

For this equation, both the x-intercept and the y-intercept are 6. A simple method of graphing this equation is to graph $(6, 0)$ and $(0, 6)$. Then draw the line that passes through these points.

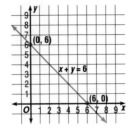

In terms of Nicki's training program, what does any point on the line represent?

Example 1

Graph $3x - 2y = 12$ using the x- and y-intercepts.

To find the x-intercept, let $y = 0$.

$$3x - 2y = 12$$
$$3x - 2(0) = 12$$
$$3x = 12$$
$$x = 4$$

To find the y-intercept, let $x = 0$.

$$3x - 2y = 12$$
$$3(0) - 2y = 12$$
$$-2y = 12$$
$$y = -6$$

Graph $(4, 0)$ and $(0, -6)$. Then draw the line that passes through these points.

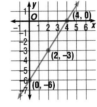

To check, choose some other point on the line and determine whether it is a solution of $3x - 2y = 12$. Try $(2, -3)$. **Teaching Tip ①**

$$3x - 2y = 12$$
$$3(2) - 2(-3) \stackrel{?}{=} 12$$
$$6 + 6 \stackrel{?}{=} 12$$
$$12 = 12 \;\checkmark$$

LESSON 10-4 GRAPHING LINEAR EQUATIONS **415**

ALTERNATE TEACHING STRATEGIES

Using Reasoning

A friend told you she finds it much easier to work with the slope-intercept form of a linear equation than with the standard form. Do you agree? Write a brief paragraph describing your beliefs. Be sure to back it up with examples to support your point of view.

Using Discussion

State an equation of a line that has the same x- and y-intercepts. What is the slope of the line? −1

Lesson Resources

- Reteaching Master 10-4
- Practice Master 10-4
- Enrichment Master 10-4
- Technology Master, p. 25
- Video Algebra, 35

 Transparency 10-4 contains the 5-Minute Check and a teaching aid for this lesson.

INTRODUCING THE LESSON

⏱ **5-Minute Check**
(over Lesson 10-3)

Find the slope, x-intercept, and y-intercept for the graph of each equation.

1. $4x - y = 16$ $\;4, 4, -16$
2. $2x + 3y = 8$ $\;-\frac{2}{3}, 4, \frac{8}{3}$
3. $y = 2x + 7$ $\;2, -\frac{7}{2}, 7$
4. $3x = y - 1$ $\;3, -\frac{1}{3}, 1$
5. $y = \frac{3}{4}x - 7$ $\;\frac{3}{4}, \frac{28}{3}, -7$

Motivating the Lesson

Introduce this lesson with a review of graphing a linear equation using two ordered pairs that satisfy the equation. Ask students to describe the procedure they would follow in graphing $x + 3y = 3$. Then have them graph the equation.

TEACHING THE LESSON

Teaching Tip ① The method shown in this example for checking graphs should be used only when a point on the graph appears to have integral coordinates. Point out that if the coordinates are not integers, the equation probably will not check. The best way to check such equations is to find another ordered pair that satisfies the equation, and determine whether the point for the ordered pair lies on the line.

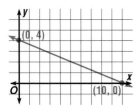
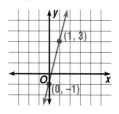
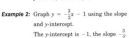

When A = 0, the graph is horizontal. When B = 0, the graph is vertical. When C = 0, the graph passes through the origin.

If an equation is in standard form and *A*, *B*, or *C* is zero, the graph of the equation has at most one intercept. In these cases, you will need to find some other ordered pairs that satisfy the equation. If the equation is in slope-intercept form, then it is convenient to use the slope and *y*-intercept to draw the graph of the equation.

Example 2

APPLICATION

Communication

The cost of a long-distance call using a certain long-distance carrier is 50¢ plus 75¢ per minute. The equation $C = 0.75t + 0.50$, where *t* represents the time in minutes, represents the total cost of any call. Make a graph that can be used to find the cost of a call of any length.

The *y*-intercept is 0.50 or $\frac{1}{2}$ so the graph passes through $\left(0, \frac{1}{2}\right)$.

The slope is 0.75 or $\frac{3}{4}$. $\frac{3}{4} = \frac{\text{change in y}}{\text{change in x}}$

Starting at $\left(0, \frac{1}{2}\right)$, go to the right 4 units and up 3 units. This will be the point $\left(4, 3\frac{1}{2}\right)$. Then draw the line through $\left(0, \frac{1}{2}\right)$ and $\left(4, 3\frac{1}{2}\right)$. *What does the ordered pair $\left(4, 3\frac{1}{2}\right)$ represent in terms of a long-distance call?*

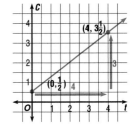

To check, substitute the points $\left(0, \frac{1}{2}\right)$ and $\left(4, 3\frac{1}{2}\right)$ or (0, 0.5) and (4, 3.5) in the equation $C = 0.75t + 0.50$ to determine whether they are solutions of the equation. **Teaching Tip ②**

If the equation is in standard form, it may be more convenient to use the slope and y-intercept to draw the graph. Recall that for an equation in standard form, $-\frac{A}{B}$ is the slope and $\frac{C}{B}$ is the y-intercept. Consider $-4x + 3y = 12$. The slope of its graph, $-\frac{A}{B}$, is $\frac{4}{3}$. The y-intercept of its graph, $\frac{C}{B}$, is $\frac{12}{3}$ or 4. To draw the graph, use the slope and y-intercept, as in Example 2. To check, choose another point on the line and determine whether it is a solution of $-4x + 3y = 12$.

CHECKING FOR UNDERSTANDING

Communicating Mathematics

Read and study the lesson to answer each question.

1. How many points are needed to draw the graph of a linear equation?
   2 points
2. In the equation $Ax + By = C$, suppose either *A* or *B* equals zero. What can you say about the graph of the equation? **If A = 0, the line is parallel to the x-axis. If B = 0, the line is parallel to the y-axis.**

416   CHAPTER 10   GRAPHING LINEAR EQUATIONS

Guided Practice

State the *x*- and *y*-intercepts for the graph of each equation. Then graph each equation using the intercepts. **See students' work for graphs.**

3. $4x + y = 8$ **2, 8**   4. $3x + 4y = 6$ **2, $\frac{3}{2}$**   5. $2x - y = 8$ **4, −8**

6. $3x - 2y = 6$ **2, −3**   7. $7x + 2y = 10$ **$\frac{10}{7}$, 5**   8. $5x - \frac{1}{2}y = 2$ **$\frac{2}{5}$, −4**

9–14. Answers may vary. See Solutions Manual for possible answers.

Given the slope of a line and a point on a line, graph the line and name two other points on the line.

9. $m = 2$, $(0, 1)$ 10. $m = -7$, $(0, 4)$ 11. $m = 0$, $(3, 2)$

12. $m = \frac{4}{3}$, $(0, 1)$ 13. $m = \frac{1}{2}$, $(5, 2)$ 14. $m = -\frac{2}{3}$, $(-3, 2)$

15–36. See Solutions Manual.

EXERCISES

Practice

Graph each equation using the *x*- and *y*-intercepts.

A

15. $6x - 3y = 6$ 16. $4x + 5y = 20$ 17. $5x - y = -10$

18. $2x + 5y = -10$ 19. $7x - 2y = -7$ 20. $y = 6x - 9$

21. $x + \frac{1}{2}y = 4$ 22. $x = 8y - 4$ 23. $\frac{2}{3}y = \frac{1}{2}x + 6$

B

Graph each equation using the slope and *y*-intercept.

24. $y = \frac{2}{3}x + 3$ 25. $y = \frac{3}{4}x + 4$ 26. $y = -\frac{3}{4}x + 4$

27. $-4x + y = 6$ 28. $-2x + y = 3$ 29. $3y - 7 = 2x$

30. $y = -\frac{3}{5}x - 1$ 31. $y = \frac{3}{2}x - 5$ 32. $\frac{3}{4}x + \frac{1}{2}y = 4$

Critical Thinking

33. Compare the equations and graphs of Exercises 24 and 28. What is true about their *y*-intercepts? What is their point of intersection?

34. Compare the equations and graphs of Exercises 25 and 26. What is true about their slopes? What is the relationship between the lines?

35. Compare the equations and graphs of Exercises 24 and 29. What is true about their slopes? What is the relationship between the lines?

36. Compare the equations and graphs of Exercises 29 and 32. What is true about their slopes? What is the relationship between the lines?

Applications

37. **Aviation** The equation $a = 25,000 - 1500t$, where *t* is the time in minutes and *a* is the altitude in feet, represents the steady descent of a certain airplane.

a. Graph the equation. **See margin.**

b. How long will it be before the airplane reaches the ground? **$16\frac{2}{3}$ minutes**

38. **Manufacturing** The Comfort Furniture Company plans to spend $300,000 on the manufacture of chairs and sofas. The cost of manufacturing a chair is $150. The cost of manufacturing a sofa is $300. The accountant of the company knows that the equation $150c + 300s = 300,000$ represents all of the possibilities for the manufacture of these items. Make a graph that she can use to present this information to the president of the company. **See margin.**

LESSON 10-4   GRAPHING LINEAR EQUATIONS   417

Additional Answers

37a.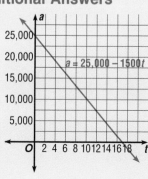

38.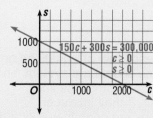

EVALUATING THE LESSON

Checking for Understanding

Exercises 1-14 are designed to help you assess understanding through reading, writing, and speaking. You should work through Exercises 1-2 with your students, and then monitor their work on Exercises 3-14.

Closing the Lesson

Writing Activity Have students write a brief explanation to a friend describing how to graph a linear equation from its equation.

APPLYING THE LESSON

Homework Exercises

Assignment Guide

Basic: 15-29, 33-37, 40-44
Average: 19-30, 33-44
Enriched: 21-44
All: Mid-Chapter Review, 1-15

Chapter 10, Quiz B, (Lessons 10-3 through 10-4), is available in the Evaluation Masters Booklet, p. 135.

Practice Masters Booklet, p. 79

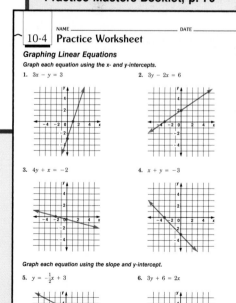

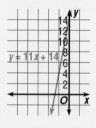
Enrichment Masters Booklet, p. 71

Mixed Review

39. **National Landmarks** The Statue of Liberty and the pedestal on which it stands are 302 feet tall altogether. The pedestal is 2 feet shorter than the statue. How tall is the statue? (Lesson 3-5) 152 feet

40. Multiply: $(3y + 2)(y - 3)$. (Lesson 6-8) $3y^2 - 7y - 6$

41. Find the GCF of 16, 24, 30. (Lesson 7-1) 2

42. Solve: $\frac{3a}{2} + \frac{5}{4} = \frac{5a}{2}$. (Lesson 8-9) $\frac{5}{4}$

43. Complete: 1, 11, 21, 31, __?__, __?__, __?__. (Lesson 9-8) 41, 51, 61

44. Determine the x- and y-intercepts of the graph of $2x + y = 6$. (Lesson 10-3) 3, 6

MID-CHAPTER REVIEW

Determine the slope of the line passing through each pair of points. (Lesson 10-1)

1. (5, 2), (7, 6) 2

2. (−2, 1), (−6, 3) $-\frac{1}{2}$

3. $\left(\frac{3}{4}, \frac{1}{2}\right)$, $\left(\frac{1}{2}, \frac{3}{4}\right)$ −1

Write the standard form of an equation of the line passing through the given point and having the given slope. (Lesson 10-2) 4. $3x - 4y = 16$ 5. $3x - 2y = -20$

4. (8, 2), $\frac{3}{4}$

5. (−6, 1), $\frac{3}{2}$

6. (−2, 1), undefined $x = -2$

Write the standard form of an equation of the line passing through each pair of points. (Lesson 10-2) 7. $x + y = 10$ 8. $x = 5$ 9. $3x - 10y = -6$

7. (9, 1), (8, 2)

8. (5, −4), (5, 5)

9. $\left(\frac{1}{2}, \frac{3}{4}\right)$, $\left(\frac{2}{3}, \frac{4}{5}\right)$

Determine the x- and y-intercepts of the graph of each equation. Then graph each equation. (Lesson 10-3, 10-4)

10. $5x + 3y = 15$ 3, 5

11. $3x - 2y = -5$ $-\frac{5}{3}, \frac{5}{2}$

12. $3x + \frac{1}{2}y = 8$ $\frac{8}{3}$, 16

13–15. See margin.

Determine the slope and y-intercept of the graph of each equation. Then write each equation in slope-intercept form and graph the equation. (Lesson 10-3, 10-4)

13. $3x + 4y = 12$

14. $10x - 14y = 21$

15. $5(x + 2) = y - 6x - 4$

EXTENDING THE LESSON

Math Power: Problem Solving

Graph each pair of equations on the same coordinate system, and determine whether the lines intersect. If they intersect, determine the coordinates of the point of intersection and check the coordinates in the original equations.

1. $2x - y - 5 = 0$
   $x + 2y + 5 = 0$ yes; (1, 3)

2. $2x - 3y + 5 = 0$
   $4x + 3y - 17 = 0$ yes; (2, 3)

3. $4x - 6y = -16$
   $2x - 3y + 6 = 0$ no

10-5 Writing Slope-Intercept Equations of Lines

Objectives

After studying this lesson, you should be able to:

10-5A ■ write a linear equation in slope-intercept form given the slope of a line and the coordinates of a point on the line, and

10-5B ■ write a linear equation in slope-intercept form given the coordinates of two points on the line.

Application

FYI ···

The world's population increases by 155 people every minute.

The present population of Cedarville is 55,000. If the population increases by 600 people each year, the equation $y = 600x + 55,000$ can be used to find the population x years from now. Notice that 55,000 (the present population) is the y-intercept and 600 (the growth per year) is the slope.

In the problem above, the slope and the y-intercept were used to write an equation. Other information can also be used to write an equation for a line. In fact, given any one of the three types of information below about a line, you can write an equation for that line.

1. the slope and a point on the line
2. two points on the line
3. the x- and y-intercepts

Example 1

Write an equation of the line whose slope is 3 that passes through (4, −2).

$y = mx + b$	*Use slope-intercept form.* **Teaching Tip**
$y = 3x + b$	*The slope is 3.*
$-2 = 3(4) + b$	*Substitute 4 for x and −2 for y.*
$-2 = 12 + b$	*Solve for b.*
$-14 = b$	

The slope-intercept form of the equation of the line is $y = 3x + (-14)$ or $y = 3x - 14$. In standard form, the equation is $3x - y = 14$.

Example 2 illustrates a procedure that can be used to write an equation of a line when two points on the line are known.

LESSON 10-5 WRITING SLOPE-INTERCEPT EQUATIONS OF LINES **419**

ALTERNATE TEACHING STRATEGIES

Using Discussion

Is it possible to write an equation of a line given its graph? How? What difficulties might occur? **Yes; find the coordinates of two points on the line; the graph could be inaccurate, or difficult to interpret exact points.**

Lesson Resources

- Reteaching Master 10-5
- Practice Master 10-5
- Enrichment Master 10-5
- Activity Master, pp. 10, 40
- Video Algebra, 36

Transparency 10-5 contains the 5-Minute Check and a teaching aid for this lesson.

INTRODUCING THE LESSON

🕐 5-Minute Check
(over Lesson 10-4)

Graph each equation using the x- and y-intercepts. See students' work.

1. $4x + y = 6$
2. $3x - 2y = -8$

Graph each equation using the slope and y-intercept. See students' work.

3. $y = -2x + 5$
4. $y = \frac{3}{4}x - 1$
5. What is the slope, x-intercept, and y-intercept of the line represented by $mx + ny = k$?
$-\frac{m}{x}, \frac{k}{m}, \frac{k}{n}$

Motivating the Lesson

Draw the graph below on the board. Ask students to write an equation for each of the five lines shown.

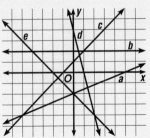

a: $2x - 5y = 10$; b: $y = 2$;
c: $x - y = -1$; d: $4x + y = 4$;
e: $x + y = -2$

Teaching Tip ❶ An alternate way to solve this example is to begin with the point-slope form of a linear equation as shown below.

$$y - y_1 = m(x - x_1)$$
$$y - (-2) = 3(x - 4)$$
$$y + 2 = 3x - 12$$
$$y = 3x - 14$$

Chalkboard Examples

For Example 1

Write an equation in slope-intercept form of the line whose slope is 3 and passing through (1, 4). $y = 3x + 1$

For Example 2

Write an equation in slope-intercept form of a line that passes through (1, 2) and (5, 6). $y = x + 1$

For Example 3

Write an equation in slope-intercept form of a line that passes through (−1.225, −1.066) and (2.4, 5.24). $y = 1.740x + 1.065$

Reteaching Masters Booklet, p. 72

NAME _____ DATE _____

10-5 | Reteaching Worksheet

Writing Slope-Intercept Equations of Lines

Given any of the three facts below, you can write an equation for a line.

the slope and a point on the line   two points on the line
the x- and y-intercepts

Example 1: Write an equation in slope-intercept form of the line that passes through (−1, 2) and has a slope of 3.

$y = mx + b$ Use slope-intercept form.
$2 = 3(-1) + b$ Substitute 3 for m, −1 for x, and 2 for y.
$5 = b$ Solve for b.

The slope-intercept form of the equation of the line is $y = 3x + 5$.

Example 2: Write an equation in slope-intercept form of the line that passes through (4, 7) and (−2, 9).

$m = \frac{y_2 - y_1}{x_2 - x_1}$

$= \frac{9 - 7}{-2 - 4} = \frac{2}{-6}$, or $-\frac{1}{3}$ The slope is $-\frac{1}{3}$.

$y = -\frac{1}{3}x + b$

Next choose either (4, 7) or (−2, 9) and substitute.

$7 = -\frac{1}{3}(4) + b$ (4, 7) is chosen.

$b = \frac{25}{3}$

The equation is $y = -\frac{1}{3}x - \frac{25}{3}$.

Write an equation in slope-intercept form of the line having the given slope that passes through the given point.

1. 4; (6, 3)   2. 5; (7, 9)   3. $\frac{1}{2}$; (0, 1)   4. $\frac{3}{4}$; (3, 2)
$y = 4x - 21$ $y = 5x - 26$ $y = \frac{1}{2}x + 1$ $y = \frac{3}{4}x - \frac{1}{4}$

Write an equation in slope-intercept form of the line that passes through each pair of points.

5. (−1, 6), (4, 0)   6. (10, −12), (8, −6)   7. (8, 12), (9, 6)
$y = -\frac{6}{5}x + \frac{24}{5}$ $y = -3x + 18$ $y = -6x + 60$

8. (−2, −4), (−5, −7)   9. (−15, 10), (−20, 25)   10. (6, 0), (0, −5)
$y = x - 2$ $y = -3x - 35$ $y = \frac{5}{6}x - 5$

Example 2

APPLICATION

Manufacturing

The Super Duper Toy Company has introduced an exciting new toy called a Gizmo Gadget. At the end of the first month, the company had manufactured 1200 Gizmo Gadgets. At the end of the fifth month, it had manufactured a total of 5800 Gizmo Gadgets. Assume that the planned production of this toy can be represented by a straight line. Write an equation for the graph used to show stockholders the planned production of Gizmo Gadgets.

The ordered pair (1, 1200) means that after 1 month, 1200 Gizmo Gadgets had been manufactured. Therefore, the line passes through the points (1, 1200) and (5, 5800). Use this information to find the slope.

$$m = \frac{y_2 - y_1}{x_2 - x_1}$$
$$= \frac{5800 - 1200}{5 - 1}$$
$$= \frac{4600}{4}$$
$$= 1150 \qquad \text{The slope is 1150.}$$

Now, substitute the coordinates of either point into the equation $y = mx + b$ and solve for b.

$$y = 1150x + b$$
$$1200 = 1150(1) + b \qquad (x, y) = (1, 1200)$$
$$50 = b$$

The y-intercept is 50, so the equation is $y = 1150x + 50$, where x is the number of months and y is the number of Gizmo Gadgets. In standard form, the equation is $1150x - y = -50$.

Example 3

Write an equation of the line that passes through (7.6, 10.8) and (12.2, 93.7). Round values to the nearest thousandth.

The ⎝ and ⎠ keys on a calculator can be used to find the slope using the equation $m = \frac{y_2 - y_1}{x_2 - x_1}$.

Enter: ⎝ 93.7 ⊟ 10.8 ⎠ ÷ ⎝ 12.2 ⊟ 7.6 ⎠ ⊜ STO 18.021729

Rounded to the nearest thousandth, the slope is 18.022. In slope-intercept form, $y = 18.022x + b$. To determine the y-intercept, solve for b. Thus, $b = y - 18.022x$. Then let $(x, y) = (7.6, 10.8)$.

Enter: 10.8 ⊟ RCL ✕ 7.6 ⊜ −126.16522

Rounded to the nearest thousandth, the y-intercept is −126.165. Therefore, the slope-intercept form of the equation is $y = 18.022x - 126.165$. In standard form, the equation is $18.022x - y = 126.165$.

RETEACHING THE LESSON

Divide the class in half. Put a graph of a line on the overhead and have one group find the slope-intercept form of the line using any two points on the line and the other group find the slope-intercept form of the line using any point and the slope. Have students compare equations.

You can also use the slope and y-intercept obtained from the graph to write an equation of a line.

Example 4

Write an equation for line *PQ* whose graph is shown below.

First determine the slope. Start at *P*. The y-coordinate *decreases* by 4 as you move from *P* to *Q*. The x-coordinate *increases* by 3 as you move from *P* to *Q*.

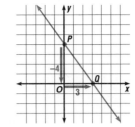

$$\text{slope} = \frac{\text{change in y}}{\text{change in x}} = \frac{-4}{3} = -\frac{4}{3}$$

The line intersects the y-axis at (0, 4). Thus, the y-intercept is 4. Now substitute these values into the slope-intercept form.

$$y = mx + 4$$
$$y = -\frac{4}{3}x + 4 \qquad m = -\frac{4}{3} \text{ and } b = 4$$

The equation for line *PQ* is $y = -\frac{4}{3}x + 4$.
In standard form, the equation is $4x + 3y = 12$.

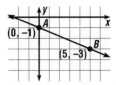
CHECKING FOR UNDERSTANDING

Communicating Mathematics

Read and study the lesson to answer each question. **1. See margin.**

1. List the information that can be used to find the equation of a line.

2. Given the coordinates of one point on a line and the slope of the line, what is the first thing that you should do in order to find the equation of the line? **Use the slope-intercept form to find *b*.**

3. Given the coordinates of two points, what is the first thing that you should do in order to find the equation of the line passing through these points? **Find the slope of the line.**

Guided Practice

Given the equation of a line and a point on the line, determine the y-intercept, *b*.

4. $y = 3x + b$, (2, 1) **−5**

5. $y = -2x + b$, (6, 2) **14**

6. $y = -\frac{2}{3}x + b$, (−6, 5) **1**

7. $y = \frac{5}{6}x + b$, (3, −1) **$-\frac{7}{2}$**

State the slope and y-intercept for each line. Then write an equation of the line in slope-intercept form.

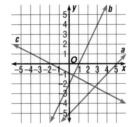

8. *a* **1, −5, $y = x - 5$**

9. *b* **2, −2, $y = 2x - 2$**

10. *c* **$-\frac{1}{2}$, −1, $y = -\frac{1}{2}x - 1$**

LESSON 10-5 WRITING SLOPE-INTERCEPT EQUATIONS OF LINES **421**

Additional Answer

1. the slope and a point on the line; two points on the line; x- and y-intercepts of the line

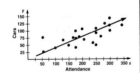
EXERCISES

Practice
A

State the slope and y-intercept for each line. Then write an equation of the line in slope-intercept form.

11. d $-4, 4, y = -4x + 4$

12. e $2, -4, y = 2x - 4$

13. f $-\frac{2}{3}, 2, y = -\frac{2}{3}x + 2$

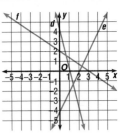

B

Write an equation in slope-intercept form of the line having the given slope that passes through the given point. **See margin.**

14. $3; (5, -2)$ 15. $\frac{2}{3}; (-1, 0)$ 16. $-5; (5, 4)$

17. $\frac{3}{4}; (-2, -4)$ 18. $-\frac{5}{3}; (-3, -5)$ 19. $\frac{1}{4}; (0, 8)$

Write an equation in slope-intercept form of the line that passes through each pair of points. **See margin.**

20. $(-1, 7), (8, -2)$ 21. $(6, 0), (0, 4)$ 22. $(8, -1), (7, -1)$

23. $(1, 0), (0, 1)$ 24. $(5, 7), (-1, 6)$ 25. $(-6, 2), (3, -5)$

C

Use a calculator to write an equation in slope-intercept form of the line that passes through each pair of points. Round values to the nearest thousandth. **See margin.**

26. $(4.67, 5.235), (0.25, -1.5)$ 27. $(-3.2, 7.198), (12.34, -0.8)$

28. $(0.4, 2.63), (6.25, 12.05)$ 29. $(-2.1, -4.08), (-0.2, -7.11)$

30. $(6.27, -0.001), (4.33, 1.33)$ 31. $(18.2, 1.008), (-4.3, -11.5)$

Critical Thinking

32. The x-intercept of a line is s, and the y-intercept is t. Write the equation of the line. $y = -\frac{tx}{s} + t$

Applications

33. **Business**   Velma's Housecleaning Service charges $65 for a three-hour job and $115 for a six-hour job. Define variables and write an equation that Velma can use to determine what amount to bill customers for a job of any length. **See margin.**

34. **Skydiving**   Kevin Byrd jumps from an airplane flying at 6400 feet. The wind carries him to a landing spot 580 feet away. Define variables and write an equation that represents his path of descent. **See Solutions Manual.**

Mixed Review

35. Write 82,100,000 in scientific notation.   **(Lesson 6-4)** 8.21×10^7

36. Factor $36x^2 - 81y^4$.   **(Lesson 7-6)** $9(2x - 3y^2)(2x + 3y^2)$

37. Find $\frac{a^2 + 3a - 10}{a^2 + 8a + 15} \div \frac{a^2 - 6a + 8}{12 + a - a^2}$.   **(Lesson 8-3)** -1

38. See margin.   38. Solve $y = 5x - 3$ if the domain is $\{-2, -1, 0, 2, 5\}$.   **(Lesson 9-3)**

39. Graph $2x + 10y = 5$ using the x- and y-intercepts.   **(Lesson 10-4)**
See Solutions Manual.

EXTENDING THE LESSON

Math Power: Reasoning

Show that the equation of a line with x-intercept p and y-intercept q is $\frac{x}{p} + \frac{y}{q} = 1$ where $p \neq 0$ and $q \neq 0$.

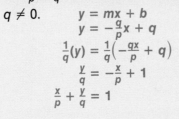

$$y = mx + b$$
$$y = -\frac{q}{p}x + q$$
$$\frac{1}{q}(y) = \frac{1}{q}\left(-\frac{qx}{p} + q\right)$$
$$\frac{y}{q} = -\frac{x}{p} + 1$$
$$\frac{x}{p} + \frac{y}{q} = 1$$

Additional Answers

29. $y = -1.595x - 7.429$
30. $y = -0.686x + 4.301$
31. $y = 0.556x - 9.110$
33. Let h = the number of hours worked and d = the total charge.
$$d = \frac{50}{3}h + 15$$
38. $\{(-2, -13), (-1, -8), (0, -3), (2, 7), (5, 22)\}$

Parallel and Perpendicular Lines

Objective
10-6

After studying this lesson, you should be able to:

- write an equation of a line that passes through a given point and is parallel or perpendicular to the graph of a given equation.

Application

Isabel starts riding her bicycle at the rate of 10 miles per hour. At the same time, Heather starts riding her bike in the same direction from a point 5 miles north of Isabel. Heather also rides at a rate of 10 miles per hour. If the girls continue to ride at the same rate of speed, will Isabel ever catch up with Heather?

The equation $y = 10x$ represents Isabel's position at any given time x. The equation $y = 10x + 5$ represents Heather's position. The graph at the right represents the bike rides. Because $10x$ is never equal to $10x + 5$, Isabel will never catch up with Heather and the graphs of these two equations will never intersect. These lines are **parallel**.

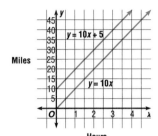

What is the slope of the line $y = 10x$?
What is the slope of the line $y = 10x + 5$?

Definition of Parallel Lines	If two lines have the same slope, then they are parallel. All vertical lines are parallel. Teaching Tip ❶

A *quadrilateral* is a four-sided figure. A *parallelogram* is a quadrilateral with two sets of parallel sides.

Example 1

CONNECTION
Geometry

Determine if the quadrilateral shown at the right is a parallelogram.

Since parallel lines have the same slope, find and compare the slope of the lines containing each side. Use $m = \frac{y_2 - y_1}{x_2 - x_1}$.

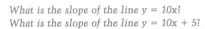

Side *a:* $m = \frac{-1 - 2}{1 - (-2)} = \frac{-3}{3}$ or -1

Side *b:* $m = \frac{-1 - 2}{1 - 7} = \frac{-3}{-6}$ or $\frac{1}{2}$

Side *c:* $m = \frac{2 - 5}{7 - 4} = \frac{-3}{3}$ or -1 *Lines a and c have slope -1.*

Side *d:* $m = \frac{5 - 2}{4 - (-2)} = \frac{3}{6}$ or $\frac{1}{2}$ *Lines b and d have slope $\frac{1}{2}$.*

The lines containing the opposite sides of the quadrilateral are parallel. Therefore, the quadrilateral is a parallelogram.

LESSON 10-6 PARALLEL AND PERPENDICULAR LINES 423

ALTERNATE TEACHING STRATEGIES

Using Models

Have students identify five examples of parallel lines and five examples of perpendicular lines in the classroom. For example, the lines formed where a wall meets the ceiling and where a wall meets the floor are parallel lines. The lines formed where the side of the chalkboard meets the top of the chalkboard are perpendicular lines.

Using Questioning

1. What is an example of an equation of a line that is perpendicular to a line that has an undefined slope?
   $y = b$, *b is a constant*
2. What is an example of an equation of a line that is parallel to a line that has an undefined slope?
   $x = c$, *c is a constant*

Lesson Resources

- Reteaching Master 10-6
- Practice Master 10-6
- Enrichment Master 10-6
- Video Algebra, 38
- Transparency 10-6 contains the 5-Minute Check and a teaching aid for this lesson.

INTRODUCING THE LESSON

⏱ 5-Minute Check
(over Lesson 10-5)

Write an equation in slope-intercept form for the line with the given slope and passing through the indicated point.

1. $m = -\frac{5}{2}$, $(4, -3)$
   $y = -\frac{5}{2}x + 7$
2. $m = 6$, $(-1, 7)$
   $y = 6x + 13$
3. $m = 2$, $(4, -2)$
   $y = 2x - 10$

Write an equation in slope-intercept form for a line passing through the pair of points.

4. $(-3, -2)$, $(5, -1)$
   $y = \frac{1}{8}x - \frac{13}{8}$
5. $(5, 6)$, $(2, -3)$
   $y = 3x - 9$

Motivating the Lesson

Review the terms *parallel* and *perpendicular* with students. Ask student volunteers to draw examples of pairs of lines that are parallel and those that are perpendicular on the chalkboard.

TEACHING THE LESSON

Teaching Tip ❶   Point out that the converse of this statement is also true: If two lines are parallel, then they have the same slope. Ask students why it must be specified that vertical lines are parallel.

Chalkboard Examples

For Example 1

Determine if the quadrilateral shown below is a parallelogram.

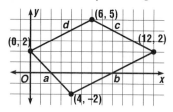

Since the lines containing sides *a* and *c* do not have the same slope, the quadrilateral is not a parallelogram.

For Example 2

Write the equation of the line parallel to the graph of each equation and passing through the given point.

a. $3x - 2y = 7, (-3, 1)$
   $3x - 2y = -11$

b. $5x + y = 2, (2, 3)$
   $5x + y = 13$

For Example 3

Classify each pair of equations as representing lines that are parallel, perpendicular, or neither.

a. $5x - 3y = 8, 5x - 3y = 9$
   parallel

b. $2x + 3y = 7, 2x - 3y = 8$
   neither

Reteaching Masters Booklet, p. 73

NAME _____ DATE _____

10-6 | **Reteaching Worksheet**

Parallel and Perpendicular Lines

When you graph two lines, you may encounter the two special types of graphs described at the right.

Parallel Lines and Perpendicular Lines
If two lines have the same slope, then they are **parallel**. All vertical lines are parallel.
If the product of the slope of two lines is -1, then the lines are **perpendicular**. In a plane, vertical lines are perpendicular to horizontal lines.

Example: Write an equation of the line that is parallel to the graph of the equation $2x - y = -12$ and passes through $(0, 6)$. Use slope-intercept form.

The slope of the graph is 2. $-\frac{A}{B} = -\frac{2}{-1}$, or 2

The slope-intercept form of an equation whose graph is parallel to the original graph is $y = 2x + b$. Substitute $(0, 6)$ into the equation and solve for *b*.
$6 = 0x + b$
$b = 6$ *The y-intercept is b.*
The equation of the line is $y = 2x + 6$.

Since $2 \cdot \left(-\frac{1}{2}\right) = -1$, any line that is perpendicular to the line of the Example has an equation of the form $y = -\frac{1}{2}x + b$. If the line includes the point $(-4, 3)$, then $3 = -\frac{1}{2}(-4) + b$ and thus $b = 1$. The equation of the line is $y = -\frac{1}{2}x + 1$.

Write an equation of the line that is parallel to the graph of each equation and passes through the given point. Use slope-intercept form.

1. $y = -\frac{2}{3}x + 4; (1, -3)$ 2. $y = \frac{1}{2}x + 1 (4, 2)$ 3. $2x + y = 5; (4, -6)$
   $y = -\frac{2}{3}x - \frac{7}{3}$ $y = \frac{1}{2}x$ $y = -2x + 2$
4. $3x - y = 0; (7, 2)$ 5. $x - 8y = 10; (0, 5)$ 6. $7x + 2y = 3; (1, 6)$
   $y = 3x - 19$ $y = \frac{1}{8}x + 5$ $y = -\frac{7}{2}x + \frac{19}{2}$

Write an equation of the line that is perpendicular to the graph of each equation and passes through the given point. Use slope-intercept form.

7. $4x - 3y = 7; (5, -2)$ 8. $6x + 16y = 8; (0, 4)$ 9. $y = 7x + 1; (6, 4)$
   $y = -\frac{3}{4}x + \frac{7}{4}$ $y = \frac{8}{3}x + 4$ $y = -\frac{1}{7}x + \frac{34}{7}$

Example 2 | Find an equation of the line that passes through $(4, -2)$ and is parallel to the graph of $5x - 2y = 6$. Use slope-intercept form.

The slope of the graph of $5x - 2y = 6$ is $\frac{5}{2}$. $-\frac{A}{B} = \frac{5}{2}$

Therefore, the slope-intercept form of an equation whose graph is parallel to the graph of $5x - 2y = 6$ is $y = \frac{5x}{2} + b$. *Why?*

Now, substitute $(4, -2)$ into the equation above and solve for *b*.

$y = \frac{5}{2}x + b$

$-2 = \frac{5}{2}(4) + b$ *Let (x, y) = (4, -2).*

$-2 = 10 + b$

$-12 = b$ *The y-intercept is -12.*

The equation of the line is $y = \frac{5}{2}x - 12$.

ℓ' is read "ℓ prime."

Line ℓ is shown in the figure below at left. Suppose line ℓ is rotated counterclockwise 90° to form line ℓ'. After the rotation, line ℓ' is perpendicular to line ℓ.

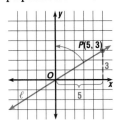 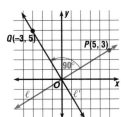 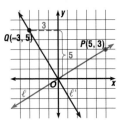

slope of ℓ

$\frac{y_2 - y_1}{x_2 - x_1} = \frac{0 - 3}{0 - 5}$

$= \frac{-3}{-5}$

$= \frac{3}{5}$

slope of ℓ'

$\frac{y_2 - y_1}{x_2 - x_1} = \frac{0 - 5}{0 - (-3)}$

$= \frac{-5}{3}$

$= -\frac{5}{3}$

Compare the slopes. What is their product?

Definition of Perpendicular Lines	If the product of the slopes of two lines is -1, then the lines are perpendicular. In a plane, vertical lines are perpendicular to horizontal lines.

424 CHAPTER 10 GRAPHING LINEAR EQUATIONS

RETEACHING THE LESSON

Put a graph of a line on the overhead and ask each row of students to pick a point not on the line. Students should then find the line that is perpendicular to the original line and passes through the point they chose. Then find the line that is parallel to the original line and passes through the point they chose. Use slope-intercept form.

Example 3

Show that the lines whose equations are $7x + 3y = 4$ and $3x - 7y = 1$ are perpendicular.

The slope of the graph of $7x + 3y = 4$ is $-\frac{7}{3}$. $-\frac{A}{B} = -\frac{7}{3}$

The slope of the graph of $3x - 7y = 1$ is $\frac{3}{7}$. $-\frac{A}{B} = -\frac{3}{-7} = \frac{3}{7}$

Since $-\frac{7}{3} \cdot \frac{3}{7} = -1$, the lines are perpendicular.

Example 4

Find an equation of the line that passes through $(-2, 7)$ and is perpendicular to the line whose equation is $2x - 5y = 3$. Use slope-intercept form.

The slope of the graph of $2x - 5y = 3$ is $\frac{2}{5}$. $-\frac{A}{B} = -\frac{2}{-5} = \frac{2}{5}$

The slope of the line perpendicular to that line is $-\frac{5}{2}$.

Thus, the equation in slope-intercept form of the line perpendicular to the line whose equation is $2x - 5y = 3$ is $y = -\frac{5}{2}x + b$. Substitute $(-2, 7)$ into the equation and solve for b.

$$y = -\frac{5}{2}x + b$$
$$7 = -\frac{5}{2}(-2) + b \quad \text{Let } (x, y) = (-2, 7).$$
$$7 = 5 + b$$
$$2 = b$$

In slope-intercept form the equation is $y = -\frac{5}{2}x + 2$.

1. The slopes are equal.

CHECKING FOR UNDERSTANDING

Communicating Mathematics

Read and study the lesson to complete the following.

1. Describe the relationship between the slopes of two parallel lines.

2. Describe the relationship between the slopes of two perpendicular lines. **The slopes are negative reciprocals.**

3. Write some equations of lines that are perpendicular to a line that has an undefined slope. $y = c$, c is a constant

4. Write some equations of lines that are parallel to a line that has an undefined slope. $x = c$, c is a constant

Guided Practice

State the slopes of the lines parallel to and perpendicular to the graph of each equation. **See margin.**

5. $5x - y = 7$ 6. $3x + 4y = 2$ 7. $2x - 3y = 7$

8. $7x + y = 4$ 9. $x = 7$ 10. $y = 4x + 2$

11. $3y = 2x + 5$ 12. $y = -4$ 13. $3x = 4 - 3y$

LESSON 10-6 PARALLEL AND PERPENDICULAR LINES 425

Additional Answers

5. $5, -\frac{1}{5}$

6. $-\frac{3}{4}, \frac{4}{3}$

7. $\frac{2}{3}, -\frac{3}{2}$

8. $-7, \frac{1}{7}$

9. undefined, 0

10. $4, -\frac{1}{4}$

11. $\frac{2}{3}, -\frac{3}{2}$

12. 0, undefined

13. $-1, 1$

For Example 4
Write the equation of the line perpendicular to the graph of each equation and passing through the given point.

a. $7x - 2y = 3$, $(4, -1)$
$2x + 7y = 1$

b. $2x + 5y = -3$, $(2, -3)$
$5x - 2y = 16$

EVALUATING THE LESSON

Checking for Understanding

Exercises 1-13 are designed to help you assess understanding through reading, writing, and speaking. You should work through Exercises 1-4 with your students, and then monitor their work on Exercises 5-13.

Error Analysis

Watch that students do not just use the coefficient of x for the slope. They must solve for y first.
Example: $-x - 4y = 2$
The slope is not -1. Solve for y.
$$-4y = x + 2$$
$$y = -\frac{1}{4}x - \frac{1}{2}$$
The slope is $-\frac{1}{4}$.

Practice Masters Booklet, p. 81

NAME _____ DATE _____

10-6 Practice Worksheet

Parallel and Perpendicular Lines

Write an equation of the line that is parallel to the graph of each equation and passes through the given point. Use slope-intercept form.

1. $2x + y = 5$; $(3, 1)$
$y = -2x + 7$

2. $3x - y = 5$; $(-1, -2)$
$y = 3x + 1$

3. $5x - 4y = 1$; $(-8, 2)$
$y = \frac{5}{4}x + 12$

4. $9x + 3y = 8$; $(-1, -4)$
$y = -3x - 7$

5. $y = \frac{4}{3}x + 5$; $(12, 3)$
$y = \frac{4}{3}x - 13$

6. $y = -\frac{3}{4}x + \frac{1}{4}$; $(4, -2)$
$y = -\frac{3}{4}x + 1$

Write an equation of the line that is perpendicular to the graph of each equation and passes through the given point. Use slope-intercept form.

7. $x - 6y = 2$; $(2, 4)$
$y = -6x + 16$

8. $3x + 2y = -7$; $(1, 1)$
$y = \frac{2}{3}x + \frac{1}{3}$

9. $5x + 4y = 8$; $(10, 5)$
$y = \frac{4}{5}x - 3$

10. $4x + 3y = -6$; $(2, 1)$
$y = \frac{3}{4}x - \frac{1}{2}$

11. $y = \frac{1}{4}x - 4$; $(-2, 3)$
$y = -4x - 5$

12. $2x + 10y = 3$; $(2, 3)$
$y = 5x - 7$

13. $x = 2y - 1$; $(0, 0)$
$y = -2x$

14. $4x + 7y = 6$; $(-4, 1)$
$y = \frac{7}{4}x + 8$

Closing the Lesson

Speaking Activity Ask students to explain the relationship of the line represented by $ax + by = c$ and all the lines parallel to it and perpendicular to it.

APPLYING THE LESSON

Homework Exercises

Assignment Guide
Basic: 14–25, 30–31, 33–37
Average: 17–27, 30–37
Enriched: 20–37

Chapter 10, Quiz C, (Lessons 10-5 through 10-6), is available in the Evaluation Masters Booklet, p. 136.

Additional Answers

14. $y = -\frac{3}{5}x - 1$

15. $y = \frac{3}{4}x$

16. $y = -6x - 9$

17. $y = -\frac{2}{3}x + \frac{14}{3}$

18. $y = \frac{5}{2}x + 4$

19. $y = \frac{4}{3}x - \frac{16}{3}$

20. $y = -\frac{1}{3}x - \frac{13}{3}$

21. $y = x - 9$

Enrichment Masters Booklet, p. 73

Practice   Write an equation of the line that is parallel to the graph of each equation and passes through the given point. Use slope-intercept form. **See margin.**

14. $y = -\frac{3}{5}x + 4$; $(0, -1)$

15. $y = \frac{3}{4}x - 1$; $(0, 0)$

16. $6x + y = 4$; $(-2, 3)$

17. $2x + 3y = 1$; $(4, 2)$

18. $5x - 2y = 7$; $(0, 4)$

19. $4x - 3y = 2$; $(4, 0)$

20. $y = -\frac{1}{3}x + 7$; $(2, -5)$

21. $x = y$; $(7, -2)$

22-26. See margin.

Write an equation of the line that is perpendicular to the graph of each equation and passes through the given point. Use slope-intercept form.

22. $5x - 3y = 7$; $(8, -2)$

23. $3x + 8y = 4$; $(0, 4)$

24. $y = 3x - 2$; $(6, -1)$

25. $y = -3x + 7$; $(-3, 1)$

26. $y = 5x - 3$; $(0, -1)$

27. $y = \frac{2}{3}x + 1$; $(-3, 0)$

28. $5x + 9y = 3$; $(0, 0)$

29. $y = 2x - 7$; $(4, -6)$

27. $y = -\frac{3}{2}x - \frac{9}{2}$

28. $y = \frac{9}{5}x$

29. $y = -\frac{1}{2}x - 4$

Critical Thinking   30. The graphs of $5x + 8y = 3$ and $5x + 8y = 6$ are parallel lines. Find the equation of the line that is parallel to both lines and lies midway between them. $5x + 8y = \frac{9}{2}$

Applications   To solve each problem, write two equations and determine if the graphs of the equations are parallel. Assume that there were no price increases or decreases during the period.

31. **Sales** On Tuesday, Joey's Pizza sold 52 pizzas and 28 gallons of soda for $518. On Wednesday, Joey's Pizza sold 39 pizzas and 21 gallons of soda. Could their total sales have been $396? **no**

32. **Sales** Lisa operates a lemonade stand. During the month of July, Lisa sold 1200 lemonades and 500 fruit punches. During the month of August, Lisa sold 1800 lemonades and 750 fruit punches. If Lisa made $1650 during July, is it possible that she made $2475 during August? **yes**

Mixed Review   33. **Geography** There is three times as much water as land on Earth's surface. What percent of Earth is covered by water? **(Lesson 4-2)** 75%

34. Multiply $(4x^3 - 3y^2)^2$. **(Lesson 6-9)** $16x^6 - 24x^3y^2 + 9y^4$

35. Find the number that each digit represents. (*Hint:* $T \neq 0$.) **(Lesson 7-4)**
$T = 5, W = 4, E = 6, N = 2$ or 7,
$Y = 0, H = 9, I = 3, R = 7$ or $2, S = 1, V = 8$

```
  TWENTY
  TWENTY
+ THIRTY
-------
 SEVENTY
```

36. Simplify $\frac{x^2 - 49}{x^2 - 2x - 35}$. **(Lesson 8-1)** $\frac{x + 7}{x + 5}$

37. Is $\{(-3, 3), (-2, 2), (-1, 1), (0, 0)\}$ a function? **(Lesson 9-6)** yes

EXTENDING THE LESSON

Math Power: Problem Solving

Write an equation in standard form of the line satisfying the given conditions.

1. passes through $(6, -2)$ and parallel to the x-axis $y = -2$

2. passes through $(-4, -1)$ and perpendicular to the x-axis
$x = -4$

Additional Answers

22. $y = -\frac{3}{5}x + \frac{14}{5}$

23. $y = \frac{8}{3}x + 4$

24. $y = -\frac{1}{3}x + 1$

25. $y = \frac{1}{3}x + 2$

26. $y = -\frac{1}{5}x - 1$

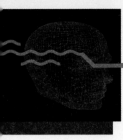

Technology

Graphing Linear Equations

BASIC
Graphing calculators
▶ Graphing software
Spreadsheets

The *Mathematics Exploration Toolkit* can be used to graph lines. The following CALC commands will be used.

CLEAR F (clr f)   GRAPH (gra)   SCALE (sca)

The CLEAR F command removes any previous graphs from the graphing window. The GRAPH command graphs the most recent equation in the expression window. The SCALE command sets limits on the x- and y-axes.

To set up the graphing window, enter clr f. Then enter sca 10. This sets limits on the axes at -10 to 10 for x and y. Only two points are needed to graph a line. So, use the command gra 2.

Example

Graph $x + y = 4$ and $x + y = -4$ on the same set of axes.

Enter	Result
$x + y = 4$	$x + y = 4$
gra 2	graphs the line
$x + y = -4$	$x + y = -4$
gra 2	graphs the line

Notice that since CLEAR was not used, the lines were graphed on the same axes. The lines have the same slope but different x- and y-intercepts.

EXERCISES

Graph each set of equations on the same set of axes. See margin.

1a. $2x + 3y = -12$ b. $2x + 3y = -6$ c. $2x + 3y = 0$

d. $2x + 3y = 6$ e. $2x + 3y = 12$

f. As the value of C increases, what is the effect on the slope? the x-intercept? the y-intercept?

2a. $-4x + 3y = 12$ b. $-2x + 3y = 12$ c. $-x + 3y = 12$

d. $x + 3y = 12$ e. $2x + 3y = 12$ f. $4x + 3y = 12$

g. As the value of A increases, what is the effect on the slope? the x-intercept? the y-intercept?

3a. $2x - 6y = 12$ b. $2x - 3y = 12$ c. $2x - y = 12$

d. $2x + y = 12$ e. $2x + 3y = 12$ f. $2x + 6y = 12$

g. As the value of B increases, what is the effect on the slope? the x-intercept? the y-intercept?

TECHNOLOGY: GRAPHING LINEAR EQUATIONS   427

Using Technology

Objective This optional page shows how graphing software can be used to perform mathematical computations and to enhance and extend mathematical concepts.

Teaching Suggestions

You may wish to introduce the CALC commands COLOR, LINE, and POINT at this time. COLOR 1 (col 1) sets the graphing color to cyan (blue). COLOR 2 (col 2) sets the graphing color to magenta (red), and COLOR 3 (col 3) sets it to white. The command LINE (lin) x_1 y_1 x_2 y_2 draws a line through the points (x_1, y_1) and (x_2, y_2). For example, if line 1 2 3 4 is entered, a line is generated through the points $(1, 2)$ and $(3, 4)$. The command POINT (poi) x y graphs a dot at the point (x, y).

Additional Answers

1a.-1e. See Solutions Manual.
1f. As the value of C increases, the slope remains the same and the x- and y-intercepts both increase.
2a.-2f. See Solutions Manual.
2g. As the value of A increases, the slope decreases and the y-intercept remains the same. The x-intercept decreases until A changes from positive to negative. Then it changes from negative to positive and continues decreasing.
3a-3f. See Solutions Manual.
3g. As the value of B increases, the x-intercept remains the same. The slope increases and the y-intercept decreases until B changes from negative to positive. Then the slope changes from positive to negative and continues increasing, and the y-intercept changes from negative to positive and continues decreasing.

INTRODUCING THE LESSON

 5-Minute Check

(over Lesson 10-6)

Write the equation of a line parallel and a line perpendicular to the given line and passing through the indicated point.

1. $5x - 3y = 8$, $(4, -2)$
   $5x - 3y = 26$, $3x + 5y = 2$
2. $7x + 2y = 4$, $(-6, 1)$
   $7x + 2y = -40$,
   $2x - 7y = -19$
3. $x = 7$, $(4, -3)$
   $x = 4$, $y = -3$
4. $x - y = 3$, $(4, 6)$
   $x - y = -2$, $x + y = 10$

Motivating the Lesson

Introduce this lesson with a discussion of arithmetic mean or average. Pose the following problem to the students. Tamara has taken five 100-point algebra exams. Her average on the first four was 88. Is it possible for her to have an average of 91 after the fifth exam? **No, she would need a score of 103 and only 100 is possible.**

TEACHING THE LESSON

Teaching Tip ① Point out that this is the average of the *x*-coordinates and the *y*-coordinates.

Objective
10-7

After studying this lesson, you should be able to:
- find the coordinates of the midpoint of a line segment in the coordinate plane given the coordinates of the endpoints.

The **midpoint** of a line segment is the point on that segment that separates it into two segments of equal length.

The coordinate of the midpoint, *P*, of line segment *AB* shown on the number line above can be found as follows. Find the average of the coordinates by adding the coordinates and dividing by 2.

$$P = \frac{-5 + 3}{2} = \frac{-2}{2} = -1$$

The coordinate of the midpoint is -1.

Midpoint on a Number Line	The coordinate of the midpoint, *P*, of two points, x_1 and x_2, on a number line is $$P = \frac{x_1 + x_2}{2}.$$

This method can be extended to find the coordinates of the midpoint of a line segment in the coordinate plane.

Midpoint of a Line Segment **Teaching Tip ①**	The coordinates of the midpoint (*x*, *y*) of a line segment whose endpoints are at (x_1, y_1) and (x_2, y_2) are $$(x, y) = \left(\frac{x_1 + x_2}{2}, \frac{y_1 + y_2}{2}\right).$$

Example 1

CONNECTION
Geometry

The endpoints of a diameter of a circle are $(-1, 2)$ and $(3, -3)$. Find the coordinates of the center of the circle.

The diameter of a circle is a line segment. The center of a circle is the midpoint of the diameter.

$$(x, y) = \left(\frac{x_1 + x_2}{2}, \frac{y_1 + y_2}{2}\right)$$

$$= \left(\frac{-1 + 3}{2}, \frac{2 + (-3)}{2}\right)$$

$$= \left(1, -\frac{1}{2}\right)$$

The center of the circle is at $\left(1, -\frac{1}{2}\right)$.

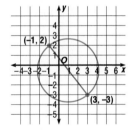

ALTERNATE TEACHING STRATEGIES

Using Cooperative Groups

In a group, discuss how to find the coordinate of a point $\frac{1}{3}$ of the way from $A(-6, 2)$ to $B(9, 8)$. Make a presentation to the class on the group's conclusion. Explain how it could be extended to find the coordinates $\frac{5}{7}$ of the way from *A* to *B*.

Using Logical Reasoning

Find the general form of the coordinates of the endpoints of line segments whose midpoint is the origin. **(a, b) and (−a, −b)**

Example 2

If one endpoint of a line segment is (2, 8) and the midpoint is (−1, 4), find the coordinates of the other endpoint.

$$(x, y) = \left(\frac{x_1 + x_2}{2}, \frac{y_1 + y_2}{2}\right)$$

$$(-1, 4) = \left(\frac{2 + x_2}{2}, \frac{8 + y_2}{2}\right)$$ *Substitute (−1, 4) for (x, y).*
Substitute (2, 8) for (x₁, y₁).

Now separate this into two equations. The x-coordinates are equal and the y-coordinates are equal.

$$-1 = \frac{2 + x_2}{2}$$ *Solve for x₂.* $$4 = \frac{8 + y_2}{2}$$ *Solve for y₂.*

$$-2 = 2 + x_2$$ $$8 = 8 + y_2$$

$$-4 = x_2$$ $$0 = y_2$$

Thus, the coordinates of the other endpoint are (−4, 0).

CHECKING FOR UNDERSTANDING

Communicating Mathematics

Read and study the lesson to complete the following. See margin.

1. Explain how to find the coordinates of a point midway between two points on a number line.

2. Explain how to find the coordinates of the midpoint of a line segment on the coordinate plane.

Guided Practice

State the coordinate of the point midway between each pair of points on a number line.

3. 4 and 8   **6**

4. −2 and 6   **2**

5. −3 and 13   **5**

6. −4 and −10   **−7**

7. −3 and 6 $\frac{3}{2}$

8. −10 and 15 $\frac{5}{2}$

State the coordinates of the midpoint of each line segment named below.

9. a   **(2, 2)**

10. b $(5\frac{1}{2}, 1)$

11. c   **(7, 4.5)**

12. d   **(−3, 6)**

13. e   **(−1, −1)**

14. f   **(−3, −4)**

15. g   **(−2, 3.5)**

16. h   **(3.5, −4.5)**

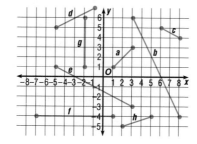

Additional Answers

1. Find the average of the coordinates of the two points.
2. Find the average of the x-coordinates and y-coordinates of the two endpoints of the line segment.

Closing the Lesson

Speaking Activity Ask students to explain the procedure they would use to determine the midpoint of a line segment.

APPLYING THE LESSON

Homework Exercises

Assignment Guide

Basic: 17-42, 47-48, 51-63
Average: 20-44, 47-63
Enriched: 23-63

EXERCISES

Practice Find the coordinates of the midpoint of the line segment whose endpoints are given.

A

17. (8, 4), (12, 2) **(10, 3)**

18. (9, 5), (17, 3) **(13, 4)**

19. (17, 9), (11, −3) **(14, 3)**

20. (19, −3), (11, 5) **(15, 1)**

21. (4, 2), (8, −6) **(6, −2)**

22. (−6, 5), (8, −11) **(1, −3)**

B

23. (5, −2), (7, 3) $\left(6, \frac{1}{2}\right)$

24. (−11, 6), (13, 4) **(1, 5)**

25. (9, 10), (−8, 4) $\left(\frac{1}{2}, 7\right)$

26. (x, y), (a, b) $\left(\frac{x+a}{2}, \frac{y+b}{2}\right)$

27. (2x, 3y), (6x, y) **(4x, 2y)**

28. $\left(\frac{5}{6}, \frac{1}{3}\right), \left(\frac{1}{6}, \frac{1}{3}\right)$ $\left(\frac{1}{2}, \frac{1}{3}\right)$

If *P* is the midpoint of line segment *AB,* find the coordinates of the missing point *A, B,* or *P.*

29. A(3, 5), P(11, 7) **B(19, 9)**

30. A(3, 5), P(5, −7) **B(7, −19)**

31. A(5, 9), B(−7, 3) **P(−1, 6)**

32. B(11, −4), P(3, 8) **A(−5, 20)**

33. B(5, 3), P(9, 7) **A(13, 11)**

34. A(11, −6), B(5, −9) $P\left(8, -\frac{15}{2}\right)$

35. P(5, −9), A(4, −11) **B(6, −7)**

36. P(3, 9), B(−4, 1) **A(10, 17)**

37. A(4, −7), B(−8, 1) **P(−2, −3)**

38. A(7, 4), P(9, −3) **B(11, −10)**

39. P(3, −5), A(−3, 8) **B(9, −18)**

40. P(5, 6), B(5, 7) **A(5, 5)**

CONNECTION
Geometry

41. The two endpoints of a diameter of a circle are (8, −2) and (4, −6). Find the coordinates of the center. **(6, −4)**

42. The center of a circle is (3, −2) and one endpoint of a diameter is (8, 3). Find the other endpoint of the diameter. **(−2, −7)**

C Find the coordinates of *P* on line segment *AB* if *P* is one fourth of the distance from *A* to *B.*

43. A(8, 4), B(12, 12) **(9, 6)**

44. A(−3, 9), B(5, 1) **(−1, 7)**

45. A(−3, 2), B(5, 4) $\left(-1, \frac{5}{2}\right)$

46. A(2, −6), B(9, 5) $\left(\frac{15}{4}, -\frac{13}{4}\right)$

Critical Thinking For quadrilateral *ABCD,* determine whether the diagonals of *ABCD* bisect each other. Justify your answer.

47. A(−2, 6), B(2, 11), C(3, 8), D(−1, 3) **yes**

48. A(11, 6), B(1, −2), C(−2, 4), D(3, 8) **no**

430 CHAPTER 10 GRAPHING LINEAR EQUATIONS

49. The BASIC program at the right tests if three points are on the same line. In the program, the points are (A, B), (C, D), and (E, F). If the slope of the line from (A, B) to (C, D) equals the slope of the line from (C, D) to (E, F), then the three points are on the same line. Points on the same line are said to be *collinear*.
Teaching Tip ❷

```
10 PRINT "ENTER THE COORDINATES
   OF THREE POINTS."
20 INPUT A, B, C, D, E, F
30 PRINT "(";A;", ";B;")","(";C;
   ", ";D;")","(";E;", ";F;")"
40 IF (D-B)/(C-A)=(F-D)/(E-C)
   THEN 70
50 PRINT "ARE NOT COLLINEAR."
60 GOTO 10
70 PRINT "ARE COLLINEAR."
80 GOTO 10
90 END
```

Teaching Tip ❷ Discuss with students the utility of using a computer to check for collinearity. Point out the speed of calculation and the difficulties of checking by graphing. Coordinates can be too large or too spread apart for practical graphing by hand.

Additional Answer

63.

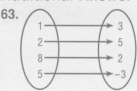

Use the program to determine whether each set of points is collinear.

a. $(1, 5)$, $(16, 14)$, $(-4, 2)$ **yes**

b. $(-2, -3)$, $(2, 1)$, $(5, 6)$ **no**

c. $(-459, -80)$, $(865, 163)$, $(54, 1)$ **no**

d. $(5, 14)$, $(-5, 10)$, $(-6, 8)$ **no**

50. Modify the program to print the slope for each segment if the points are collinear. **75 PRINT (D-B)/(C-A)**

Applications

The map coordinates of certain cities are given below.

Los Angeles $(-6, -1)$ Dallas $(1, -3)$
Chicago $(3, 3)$ Atlanta $(5, -1)$
Miami $(6, -4)$ Boston $(7, 5)$

Find the coordinates of the point on the map midway between each pair of cities.

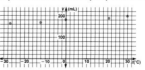

51. Los Angeles and Boston $\left(\frac{1}{2}, 2\right)$

52. Atlanta and Dallas $(3, -2)$

53. Chicago and Miami $\left(\frac{9}{2}, -\frac{1}{2}\right)$

54. Boston and Atlanta $(6, 2)$

55. Dallas and Boston $(4, 1)$

56. Miami and Dallas $\left(\frac{7}{2}, -\frac{7}{2}\right)$

57. Chicago and Los Angeles $\left(-\frac{3}{2}, 1\right)$

58. Boston and Chicago $(5, 4)$

Mixed Review

59. Solve $3y + 7 \le 4y + 8$. **(Lesson 5-3)** $\{y \mid y \ge -1\}$

60. Subtract $(7y + 9x) - (6x + 5y)$. **(Lesson 6-6)** $3x + 2y$

61. Factor $5x^2 + 20y^2$. **(Lesson 7-2)** $5(x^2 + 4y^2)$

62. **Driving** The toll for the Overbrook Bridge is 50¢ per car. The machines in the exact change lanes accept any type of coin except pennies and half dollars. In how many different ways can a driver pay the toll in the exact change lane? **(Lesson 8-6)** **10 ways**

63. Draw a mapping for the relation $\{(1, 3), (2, 5), (8, 2), (5, -3)\}$. **(Lesson 9-2)** **See margin.**

EXTENDING THE LESSON

Math Power: Connections

The diameter of a circle has the endpoints $(8, 6)$ and $(2, -2)$. Find the center of the circle and at least two other points on the circle. **Center is $(5, 2)$; Answers may vary for other points on the circle. Possible answers include $(2, 6)$, $(8, -2)$, $(9, 5)$, $(9, -1)$, $(1, 5)$, $(1, -1)$, $(10, 2)$, and $(0, 2)$.**

Enrichment Masters Booklet, p. 74

NAME _____ DATE _____

10-7 Enrichment Worksheet

Celsius and Kelvin Temperatures

If you blow up a balloon and put it in the refrigerator, the balloon will shrink as the temperature of the air in the balloon decreases.

The volume of a certain gas is measured at 30° Celsius. The temperature is decreased and the volume is measured again.

Temperature (t)	Volume (v)
30°C	202 mL
21°C	196 mL
0°C	182 mL
−12°C	174 mL
−27°C	164 mL

1. Graph this table on the coordinate plane provided below.

2. Find the equation of the line that passes through the points you graphed in Exercise 1. $y = \frac{2}{3}x + 182$ or $v = \frac{2}{3}t + 182$

3. Use the equation you found in Exercise 2 to find the temperature that would give a volume of zero. This temperature is the lowest one possible and is called "absolute zero." −273°C

4. In 1848 Lord Kelvin proposed a new temperature scale with 0 being assigned to absolute zero. The size of the degree chosen was the same size as the Celsius degree. Change each of the Celsius temperatures in the table above to degrees Kelvin. 303°, 294°, 273°, 261°, 246°

INTRODUCING THE LESSON

🕐 5-Minute Check

(over Lesson 10-7)

Find the coordinates of the midpoint of the line segment whose endpoints are given.

1. (1, 2), (7, 6) **(4, 4)**
2. (−3, 4), (1, 2) **(−1, 3)**
3. (−3, 4), (7, 6) **(2, 5)**

Segment AB has midpoint M. Find the missing coordinate.

4. $A(−2, 5)$, $B(6, 3)$
   $M = (2, 4)$
5. $B(−7, 1)$, $M(4, 5)$
   $A = (15, 9)$

Motivating the Lesson

Review student understanding of bar graphs and line graphs. Develop the idea that both bar graphs and line graphs compare two different variables.

TEACHING THE LESSON

Teaching Tip ❶ Note that circle graphs are commonly used to represent budgets for governmental agencies, for businesses, and for individual concerns.

10-8 Problem-Solving Strategy: Use a Graph

Objective
10-8

After studying this lesson, you should be able to:
■ solve problems by using pictographs, circle graphs, and comparative graphs.

Connection

In Chapter 9, you studied how bar graphs and line graphs are used to represent data. Three other types of graphs are shown below.

Pictographs use pictures or illustrations to show how specific quantities compare. The pictograph at the right shows the average motor fuel consumption in the United States. *Why do you think fuel consumption dropped so much in the 1970s?*

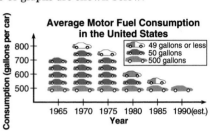

Average Motor Fuel Consumption in the United States

49 gallons or less
50 gallons
500 gallons

Circle graphs show how parts are related to the whole. The circle graph at the right shows how often Americans eat at fast-food restaurants each week. **Teaching Tip ❶**

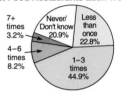

How Often Americans Eat at Fast-Food Restaurants Each Week

7+ times 3.2%
Never/ Don't know 20.9%
Less than once 22.8%
4–6 times 8.2%
1–3 times 44.9%

Comparative graphs show trends. These graphs are often used to compare results in two or more similar groups. The graph at the right compares the college enrollments of men and women.

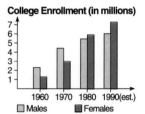

College Enrollment (in millions)

1960 1970 1980 1990(est.)
☐ Males   ■ Females

CHECKING FOR UNDERSTANDING

Communicating Mathematics

Match.

b 1. Shows how parts are related to the whole.
d 2. Shows trends or changes of a single quantity.
a, c 3. Shows how specific quantities compare.
e 4. Uses pictures or illustrations to show how specific quantities compare.
c 5. Compares results in two or more similar groups.

a. bar graph
b. circle graph
c. comparative graph
d. line graph
e. pictograph

432 CHAPTER 10 GRAPHING LINEAR EQUATIONS

RETEACHING THE LESSON

Have groups of students think of data that could be portrayed using one of the three types of graphs and construct their own graph using their data. Also write five questions that pertain to the graph. Make copies of each of the groups graphs and questions and distribute to each of the other groups to answer the questions.

Use the graphs below to answer each question.

U.S. Resident Population Age Distribution

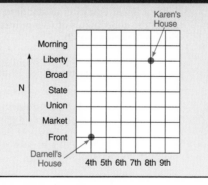

under 18 35.8% | 18–64 55% | over 65 9.2% | 1960

under 18 26.0% | 18–64 61.7% | over 65 12.3% | 1990

6. Did the percentage of people under 18 increase or decrease from 1960 to 1990? **decrease**

7. Which age group had the least number of people in both years? **over 65**

8. If the population in 1960 was 200 million and in 1990 it was 250 million, how many more people were in the 18–64 age group in 1990 than in 1960? **44,250,000**

EXERCISES

Practice

Solve. Use any strategy. 9. Ana and Carl, Betty and Frank, Daisy and Ed

Strategies
Look for a pattern.
Solve a simpler problem.
Act it out.
Guess and check.
Draw a diagram.
Make a chart.
Work backwards.

9. Three couples received a total of $5400 in income tax refunds. Altogether, the wives received $2400. Ana received $200 more than Daisy, and Betty received $200 more than Ana. Carl received half as much as his wife, Ed received the same amount as his wife, and Frank received twice as much as his wife. Who is married to whom?

10. **Number Theory** The *persistence* of a number is the number of times you can multiply the digits until you get a one-digit product. For example, 34 has a persistence of 2 since $34 \rightarrow 12 \rightarrow 2$ (2 steps). If 0 is the least number with a persistence of 0, and 10 is the least number with a persistence of 1, find the least numbers that have persistences of 2, 3, and 4. **25, 39, 77**

COOPERATIVE LEARNING ACTIVITY

Work in groups of three. Each person must understand the solution and be able to explain it to any person in the class.

The map of Hokeyville is shown at the right. Darnell plans to visit Karen once a day until he has tried every route between his house and Karen's house.

If Darnell goes only east or north, how many routes can he take? (*Hint:* Find the number of different routes to each point on the grid.) **126 routes**

Karen's House

Morning
Liberty
Broad
N State
Union
Market
Front
Darnell's House   4th 5th 6th 7th 8th 9th

LESSON 10-8 PROBLEM-SOLVING STRATEGY: USE A GRAPH   433

EXTENDING THE LESSON

Math Power: Communication

Classify the following data according to the type of graph best suited to communicating each main idea.
1. Show the results of students from three different high schools on a standardized test. **comparative graph**
2. Show the breakdown of a town budget. **circle graph**

Cooperative Learning Activity

This activity provides students with an opportunity to *learn* things together, not just do things together. You may wish to refer to pages T6 - T8 and page 6C for the various elements of cooperative groups and specific goals and strategies for using them.

10-8 **Practice Worksheet**

NAME _____ DATE _____

Problem-Solving: Use a Graph

The circle graphs show the weekly budgets for Chico and Ling. Use the graphs to answer each question.

Chico: Lunches 24%, Savings 15%, Music 10%, Clothing 30%, Recreation 21%

Ling: Lunches 22%, Savings 17%, Recreation 18%, Music 8%, Clothing 35%

1. How does Ling's budget for recreation compare to Chico's budget for recreation? **3% less than Chico's**

2. Which budget item for both Chico and Ling had the greatest percent? **clothing** the least percent? **music**

3. If Chico earns $30 per week, how much of it does he save? **$4.50**

4. If Ling earns $10 per week more than Chico, how much of it does she spend on both music and clothing? **$17.20**

5. What two items does each spend the most on? **clothing and lunches**

6. How much does each spend on the items named in Exercise 5? **Chico, $16.20; Ling, $22.80**

Solve. Use any strategy.

7. Triangular numbers are numbers that can be represented by dots in the shape of a triangle. The first four triangular numbers are 1, 3, 6, and 10. Find the greatest two-digit triangular number. **91**

1 , 3 , 6 , 10 .

8. Three couples collected a total of $7800 for charities. Altogether, the husbands collected $4800. Corey collected $400 more than Bob, and Gene collected $400 more than Corey. June collected half as much as her husband, and Ella collected the same amount as her husband. Judy collected $800 less than her husband. Who is married to whom? Which couples collected the most? the least? **Corey, Ella; Bob, Judy; Gene, June; most: Corey, Ella; least: Bob, Judy**

Using the Chapter Summary and Review

The Chapter Summary and Review begins with an alphabetical listing of the new terms that were presented in the chapter. Have students define each term and provide an example of it, if appropriate.

The Skills and Concepts presented in the chapter are reviewed using a side-by-side format. Encourage students to refer to the Objectives and Examples on the left as they complete the Review Exercises on the right.

The Chapter Summary and Review ends with exercises that review Applications and Connections.

CHAPTER **10** SUMMARY AND REVIEW

VOCABULARY

Upon completing this chapter, you should be familiar with the following terms:

intercepts	**410**	**400**	slope
midpoint	**428**	**406**	standard form
parallel	**423**	**410**	x-intercept
perpendicular	**424**	**410**	y-intercept
point-slope form	**405**		

SKILLS AND CONCEPTS

OBJECTIVES AND EXAMPLES	REVIEW EXERCISES
Upon completing this chapter, you should be able to:	Use these exercises to review and prepare for the chapter test.

■ find the slope of a line, given the coordinates of two points on the line **(Lesson 10-1)**

Determine the slope of the line passing through $(-3, 5)$ and $(4, 5)$.

$$m = \frac{y_2 - y_1}{x_2 - x_1}$$
$$= \frac{5 - 5}{4 - (-3)}$$
$$= 0 \qquad \text{The slope is 0.}$$

Determine the slope of the line passing through each pair of points.

1. $(8, 3), (2, 5)$ $\frac{1}{2}$

2. $(-2, 5), (-2, 9)$ undefined

3. $(-3, -5), (9, -1)$ $\frac{1}{3}$

4. $(-3, 6), (-8, 4)$ $\frac{2}{5}$

5. $(11, -1), (14, -6)$ $-\frac{5}{3}$

■ write a linear equation in standard form given the coordinates of two points on the line   **(Lesson 10-2)**

Write the standard form of an equation of the line passing through $(8, 1)$ and $(-3, 5)$.

$$m = \frac{y_2 - y_1}{x_2 - x_1} \qquad y - y_1 = m(x - x_1)$$
$$= \frac{5 - 1}{-3 - 8} \qquad y - 1 = -\frac{4}{11}(x - 8)$$
$$= \frac{4}{-11} \qquad 11y - 11 = -4x + 32$$
$$\qquad\qquad 4x + 11y = 43$$

Write the standard form of an equation of the line passing through each pair of points.

6. $(-2, 5), (9, 5)$ $y = 5$

7. $(0, 5), (-2, 0)$ $5x - 2y = -10$

8. $(-3, 0), (0, -6)$ $2x + y = -6$

9. $(4, 2), (-7, 2)$ $y = 2$

10. $\left(-2, \frac{2}{3}\right), \left(-2, \frac{2}{7}\right)$ $x = -2$

■ determine the slope and y-intercept of a graph **(Lesson 10-3)**

Determine the slope and y-intercept of the graph of $3x - 2y = 7$.

$$3x - 2y = 7$$
$$-2y = -3x + 7$$
$$y = \frac{3}{2}x - \frac{7}{2}$$

The slope is $\frac{3}{2}$; the y-intercept is $-\frac{7}{2}$.

■ determine the x- and y-intercepts of a graph **(Lesson 10-3)**

Determine the x- and y-intercepts of $2x + 5y = 10$.

$$2x + 5(0) = 10 \qquad 2(0) + 5y = 10$$
$$2x = 10 \qquad\qquad 5y = 10$$
$$x = 5 \qquad\qquad\quad y = 2$$

x-intercept = 5, y-intercept = 2

■ graph linear equations using the x- and y-intercepts or the slope and y-intercept **(Lesson 10-4)**

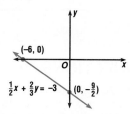

(-6, 0)

$\frac{1}{2}x + \frac{2}{3}y = -3$ $(0, -\frac{9}{2})$

■ write a linear equation in slope-intercept form **(Lesson 10-5)**

Write an equation in slope-intercept form of the line passing through $(4, -2)$ with slope 2.

$$y = mx + b$$
$$-2 = 2(4) + b$$
$$-10 = b$$

The slope-intercept form is $y = 2x - 10$.

Determine the slope and y-intercept of the graph of each equation.

11. $y = \frac{1}{4}x + 3$ $\frac{1}{4}$, 3

12. $8x + y = 4$ -8, 4

13. $x = 2y - 7$ $\frac{1}{2}$, $\frac{7}{2}$

14. $14x + 20y = 10$ $-\frac{7}{10}$, $\frac{1}{2}$

15. $\frac{1}{2}x + \frac{1}{4}y = 3$ -2, 12

Determine the x- and y-intercepts of the graph of each equation.

16. $3x + 4y = 15$ 5, $\frac{15}{4}$

17. $8x + y = 4$ $\frac{1}{2}$, 4

18. $6x + 2y = 3$ $\frac{1}{2}$, $\frac{3}{2}$

19. $\frac{1}{2}x - \frac{3}{2}y = 4$ 8, $-\frac{8}{3}$

20. $2.2x + 0.5y = 1.1$ 0.5, 2.2

Graph each equation using the x- and y-intercepts. See Solutions Manual.

21. $3x - y = 9$

22. $5x + 2y = 12$

Graph each equation using the slope and y-intercept. See Solutions Manual.

23. $y = \frac{2}{3}x + 4$

24. $y = -\frac{3}{2}x - 6$

Write an equation of the line satisfying the given conditions. Use the slope-intercept form. See margin.

25. slope = 4, passes through $(6, -2)$

26. passes through $(9, 5)$ and $(-3, -4)$

27. passes through $(2, 2)$, y-intercept 7

28. slope = $-\frac{3}{5}$, y-intercept = 3

To provide a brief in-class review, you may wish to read the following questions to the class and require a verbal response.

1. Determine the slope of a line passing through points $(5, 2)$ and $(7, 6)$. **2**
2. Write the standard form of an equation of the line passing through points $(6, 1)$ and $(7, -4)$. **$5x + y = 31$**
3. Determine the slope and y-intercept of the graph of $2x - y = 1$. **2, -1**
4. Write an equation in slope-intercept form of the line having a slope of 3 and passing through the point $(5, -2)$. **$y = 3x - 17$**
5. Write an equation of the line that is perpendicular to the graph of the equation $2x + 3y = 9$ and passes through point $(5, 2)$. **$y = \frac{3}{2}x - \frac{11}{2}$**
6. Segment AB has midpoint M. Find A if M is $(5, -2)$ and B is $(3, -1)$. **$(7, -3)$**

Additional Answers

25. $y = 4x - 26$

26. $y = \frac{3}{4}x - \frac{7}{4}$

27. $y = -\frac{5}{2}x + 7$

28. $y = -\frac{3}{5}x + 3$

The Cumulative Review shown below can be used to review skills and concepts presented thus far in the text. Standardized Test Practice Questions are also provided in the Evaluation Masters Booklet.

Evaluation Masters Booklet, pp. 137-138

436 Chapter 10

■ write an equation of a line that passes through a given point and is parallel or perpendicular to the graph of a given equation **(Lesson 10-6)**

Write an equation of the line that is perpendicular to the graph of $2x + y = 6$ and passes through $(2, 3)$.

$2x + y = 6$	$y = \frac{1}{2}x + b$
$y = -2x + 6$	$3 = \frac{1}{2}(2) + b$
$m = \frac{1}{2}$	$2 = b$

The equation is $y = \frac{1}{2}x + 2$.

Write an equation of the line that passes through a given point and is parallel to the graph of each equation.

29. $4x - y = 7;\ (2, -1)$ $y = 4x - 9$

30. $3x + 9y = 1;\ (3, 0)$ $y = -\frac{1}{3}x + 1$

Write an equation of the line that passes through a given point and is perpendicular to the graph of each equation.

31. $2x - 7y = 1;\ (-4, 0)$ $y = -\frac{7}{2}x - 14$

32. $8x - 3y = 7;\ (4, 5)$ $y = -\frac{3}{8}x + \frac{13}{2}$

■ find the coordinates of the midpoint of a line segment in the coordinate plane given the coordinates of the endpoints **(Lesson 10-7)**

The endpoints of a segment are $(11, 4)$ and $(9, 2)$. Find its midpoint.

$$(x, y) = \left(\frac{x_1 + x_2}{2}, \frac{y_1 + y_2}{2}\right)$$
$$= \left(\frac{11 + 9}{2}, \frac{4 + 2}{2}\right)$$
$$= (10, 3)$$

Find the coordinates of the midpoint of line segment AB.

33. $A(3, 5), B(9, -3)$ $(6, 1)$

34. $A(14, 4), B(2, 0)$ $(8, 2)$

35. $A(-6, 6), B(8, -11)$ $\left(1, -\frac{5}{2}\right)$

36. $A(2, 7), B(8, 4)$ $\left(5, \frac{11}{2}\right)$

37. $A(2, 5), B(4, 1)$ $(3, 3)$

39. $y = 45x - 10$, where x = time and y = distance

APPLICATIONS AND CONNECTIONS

38. **Skiing** A course for cross-country skiing is regulated so that the slope of any hill cannot be greater than 0.33. Suppose a hill rises 60 meters over a horizontal distance of 250 meters. Does the hill meet the requirement? **(Lesson 10-1)** yes

40. **Entertainment** Carolyn Parks owns stock in Star Gazer Motion Picture Company. Every other week, she graphs the closing value of a share of the stock. What is the midpoint between the highest and lowest values of the stock? **(Lessons 10-7 and 10-8)** $5.50

39. **Travel** Jon Erlanger is taking a long trip. In the first 2 hours he drives 80 miles. After that, he averages 45 miles per hour. Write an equation in slope-intercept form relating distance traveled and time. **(Lesson 10-2)**

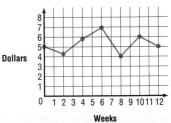

Determine the slope of the line passing through each pair of points.

1. $(9, 2), (3, -4)$ **1**

2. $(8, 3), (8, 1)$ **undefined**

Determine the slope and y-intercept of the graph of each equation.

3. $x - 8y = 3$ $\frac{1}{8}, -\frac{3}{8}$

4. $3x - 2y = 9$ $\frac{3}{2}, -\frac{9}{2}$

5. $\frac{1}{2}x + \frac{3}{4}y = 2$ $-\frac{2}{3}, \frac{8}{3}$

6. $y = 7$ **0, 7**

Write an equation in standard form of the line satisfying the given conditions.

7. passes through $(2, 5)$ and $(8, -3)$ $4x + 3y = 23$

8. passes through $(-2, -1)$ and $(6, -4)$ $3x + 8y = -14$

9. has slope of 2 and y-intercept = 3 $2x - y = -3$

10. has y-intercept = -4 and passes through $(5, -3)$ $x - 5y = 20$

11. slope = $\frac{3}{4}$ and passes through $(6, -2)$ $3x - 4y = 26$

Write an equation in slope-intercept form of the line satisfying the given conditions.

12. passes through $(4, -2)$ and the origin $y = -\frac{1}{2}x$

13. passes through $(-2, -5)$ and $(8, -3)$ $y = \frac{1}{5}x - \frac{23}{5}$

14. passes through $(6, 4)$ with y-intercept = -2 $y = x - 2$

15. slope = $-\frac{2}{3}$ and y-intercept = 5 $y = -\frac{2}{3}x + 5$

16. slope = 6 and passes through $(-3, -4)$ $y = 6x + 14$

17. parallel to $6x - y = 7$ and passes through $(-2, 8)$ $y = 6x + 20$

18. parallel to $3x + 7y = 4$ and passes through $(5, -2)$ $y = -\frac{3}{7}x + \frac{1}{7}$

19. perpendicular to $5x - 3y = 9$ and passes through the origin $y = -\frac{3}{5}x$

20. perpendicular to $x + 3y = 7$ and passes through $(5, 2)$ $y = 3x - 13$

Find the coordinates of the midpoint of the segment whose endpoints are given.

21. $(9, 3), (3, 6)$ $\left(6, \frac{9}{2}\right)$

22. $(-2, -7), (6, -5)$ $(2, -6)$

Graph each equation. **See Solutions Manual.**

23. $4x - 3y = 24$

24. $2x + 7y = 16$

25. Construction   Roberto drew a sketch of the antenna and guy wire support in his back yard. What is the slope of the guy wire? $\frac{7}{3}$

14 ft
|←6 ft→|

Bonus   The diameter of a circle has the endpoints $(8, 6)$ and $(2, -2)$. Find the center of the circle and at least two other points on the circle.
The center is at (5, 2); possible answers are (2, 6), (8, -2), and (9, 5).

Using the Chapter Test

This page may be used as a test or as a review. In addition, two multiple-choice tests and two free-response tests are provided in the Evaluation Masters Booklet. Chapter 10 Test, Form 1A is shown below.

Evaluation Masters Booklet, pp. 127-128

NAME _____ DATE _____

Chapter 10 Test, Form 1A

Write the letter for the correct answer in the blank at the right of each problem.

1. What is the slope of the line passing through $(1, 9)$ and $(-3, 16)$?
   A. $-\frac{7}{4}$ B. $-\frac{4}{7}$ C. $-\frac{25}{2}$ D. $-\frac{2}{25}$ 1. **A**

2. Find the value of r so that the line through $(8, r)$ and $(4, 5)$ has a slope of -4.
   A. 11   B. -11 C. 4   D. -4 2. **B**

3. Find an equation of the line through $(6, -3)$ with slope $\frac{2}{3}$.
   A. $-2x + 3y = 24$ B. $-2x + 3y = -21$ C. $3x - 2y = 24$ D. $3x - 2y = -21$ 3. **B**

4. Find an equation of the line through $(4, -5)$ and $(6, -9)$.
   A. $x + 2y = -6$ B. $x + 2y = -12$ C. $2x + y = 3$ D. $14x + 10y = 6$ 4. **C**

5. What is the x-intercept of the line with the equation $3x - 4y = 20$?
   A. 3   B. $\frac{3}{4}$ C. -5 D. $\frac{20}{3}$ 5. **D**

6. What is the slope of the graph of $4x + 5y = 10$?
   A. $-\frac{4}{5}$ B. 2   C. 4   D. -4 6. **A**

7. What is the y-intercept of the line with the equation $5x - \frac{1}{6}y = 3$?
   A. $\frac{1}{2}$ B. $-\frac{1}{2}$ C. 18   D. -18 7. **D**

8. Which equation is graphed below?
   A. $2y - x = 10$ B. $2x + y = -5$ C. $2x - y = 5$ D. $2y + x = -5$ 8. **C**

9. Which line is the graph of the equation $y = -3x + 1$?
   A. p B. q C. r D. s 9. **B**

NAME _____ DATE _____

Chapter 10 Test, Form 1A (continued)

10. What is the y-intercept of the line with slope $\frac{2}{3}$ and containing $(2, 7)$?
    A. $-\frac{8}{3}$ B. $\frac{17}{3}$ C. $6\frac{1}{3}$ D. $5\frac{1}{2}$ 10. **B**

11. Find an equation of the line containing $(2, -5)$ and $(6, 3)$.
    A. $y = \frac{1}{2}x - 6$ B. $y = \frac{1}{2}x$ C. $y = 2x + 12$ D. $y = 2x - 9$ 11. **D**

12. If line m has a slope of $-\frac{3}{8}$, then what is the slope of a line perpendicular to m?
    A. $\frac{3}{8}$ B. $\frac{3}{8}$ C. $\frac{8}{3}$ D. $-\frac{8}{3}$ 12. **C**

13. Find an equation of the line parallel to the graph of $4x + 2y = 8$ and containing $(-1, 5)$.
    A. $y = -2x + 9$ B. $y = 2x - 9$ C. $y = 2x + 7$ D. $y = -2x + 3$ 13. **D**

14. What are the coordinates of the midpoint of the line segment with endpoints $(-6, 2)$ and $(7, 10)$?
    A. $(8, 13)$ B. $\left(\frac{13}{2}, 4\right)$ C. $\left(\frac{1}{2}, 6\right)$ D. $\left(-2, \frac{17}{2}\right)$ 14. **C**

15. The center of a circle is $(-4, 7)$ and one endpoint of a diameter is $(2, -1)$. What is the other endpoint of the diameter?
    A. $(6, 15)$ B. $(-10, 16)$ C. $(-6, 13)$ D. $(-10, 15)$ 15. **D**

16. What is the equation of the line whose graph has a slope of $-\frac{2}{3}$ and a y-intercept of 4?
    A. $2x + 3y = 12$ B. $3y - 2x = 12$ C. $2x + 3y = 4$ D. $3y - 2x = 4$ 16. **A**

17. What is the equation of the line whose graph passes through the origin and has a slope of $\frac{1}{4}$?
    A. $y = 4x$ B. $y = \frac{1}{4}x$ C. $y = x + \frac{1}{4}$ D. $y + \frac{1}{4} = x$ 17. **B**

18. A highway is constructed so that it rises 0.75 feet for every 25 feet of horizontal distance. Find the grade (slope) of the hill expressed as a percent.
    A. 6%   B. 3%   C. 30%   D. 4%   18. **B**

19. To calculate the charge for a load of bricks, including delivery, the Redstone Brick Co. uses the equation $c = 0.42b + 25$, where c is the charge and b is the number of bricks. What is the delivery charge per load?
    A. $42   B. $67   C. $25   D. $17   19. **C**

20. Which type of graph shows how parts are related to a whole?
    A. bar graph   B. circle graph   C. line graph   D. pictograph   20. **B**

Bonus: For what value of k does $kx + 7y = 10$ have a slope of 3?   Bonus: **-21**

Test Generator Software is provided in both Apple and IBM versions. You may use this software to create your own tests, based on the needs of your students.

CHAPTER 11

Systems of Open Sentences

PREVIEWING THE CHAPTER

The chapter introduces students to systems of linear equations by having them solve systems by graphing and classify systems as consistent or inconsistent and independent or dependent. Then they learn to use algebraic methods including the substitution method and the elimination method with addition or subtraction and with multiplication and addition. Throughout this careful development, students attend to numerous and varied applications of the content. The chapter concludes with lessons in which students solve systems of inequalities by graphing.

Problem-Solving Strategy   Students learn to avoid unnecessary difficulties when solving problems by continually checking for hidden assumptions as they seek the solutions.

Lesson Objective Chart

Lesson (Pages)	Lesson Objectives	State/Local Objectives
11-1 (440-441)	**11-1:** Solve problems after checking for hidden assumptions.	
11-2 (442-446)	**11-2A:** Solve systems of equations by graphing.	
	11-2B: Determine whether a system of equations has one solution, no solution, or infinitely many solutions by graphing.	
11-3 (447-451)	**11-3:** Solve systems of equations by the substitution method.	
11-4 (452-456)	**11-4:** Solve systems of equations by the elimination method using addition or subtraction.	
11-5 (457-461)	**11-5:** Solve systems of equations by the elimination method using multiplication and addition.	
11-6 (463-467)	**11-6:** Solve systems of inequalities by graphing.	

ORGANIZING THE CHAPTER

You may want to refer to the **Course Planning Calendar** on page T36.

Lesson (Pages)	Pacing Chart (days) Course			Reteaching	Practice	Enrichment	Evaluation	Technology	Lab Manual	Mixed Problem Solving	Applications	Cooperative Learning Activity	Multicultural	Transparencies
	I	II	III											
11-1 (440-441)	1.5	1	1		p. 84								p. 56	11-1
11-2 (442-446)	1.5	1.5	1.5	p. 75	p. 85	p. 75	Quiz A, p. 149	p. 26				p. 41		11-2
11-3 (447-451)	1.5	1.5	1.5	p. 76	p. 86	p. 76	Quiz B, p. 149 Mid-Chapter Test, p. 153				p. 26			11-3
11-4 (452-456)	1.5	1	1	p. 77	p. 87	p. 77								11-4
11-5 (457-461)	1.5	1.5	1	p. 78	p. 88	p. 78	Quiz C, p. 150			p. 11				11-5
11-6 (463-467)	1.5	1.5	1	p. 79	p. 89	p. 79	Quiz D, p. 150	p. 11	pp. 37-38					11-6
Review (468-470)	1	1	1	Multiple Choice Tests, Forms 1A and 1B, pp. 141-144 Free Response Tests, Forms 2A and 2B, pp. 145-148										
Test (471)	1	1	1	Cumulative Review, pp. 151-152 Standardized Test Practice Questions, p. 154										

Lesson Planning Guide — **Blackline Masters Booklets** — *Activities*

Course I: Chapters 1-13; Course II: Chapters 1-14: Course III: Chapters 1-15

Other Chapter Resources

Student Edition

Cooperative Learning Activity, p. 441
Mid-Chapter Review, p. 456
Technology, p. 462
History Connection, p. 467
Algebraic Skills Review, p. 663
  (ex. 37-52)

Teacher Resource Package

Activity Masters Booklet
  Mixed Problem Solving, p. 11
  Applications, p. 26
  Cooperative Learning Activity, p. 41
  Multicultural Activity, p. 56

Technology Masters Booklet
  Scientific Calculator Activity, p. 11
  Graphing Calculator Activity, p. 26

Lab Manual
  Lab Activity, pp. 37-38

Other Supplements

Transparency for Chapter Opener
Problem-of-the-Week Activity
  Cards, 26-27
Video Algebra, 39-44

Software

Algebra 1 Test and Review
  Generator Software
  Available for Apple and IBM.

ENHANCING THE CHAPTER

Cooperative Learning

Establishing Accountability and Monitoring Behavior

It is important for the success of a group-learning session that students recognize their individual responsibility to the whole group since the purpose of a cooperative-learning group is to enhance the learning of each and every member. It is neither fair nor productive when only a few members of the group do all the work. One way you can encourage every-member participation is to make positive comments about various members' contributions to the group while you are monitoring the session. You also can encourage participation by asking a reluctant participant to paraphrase what another member has just said, by asking a member if they agree with a statement made by another member and to explain why they do or don't. Any intervention during your monitoring should not disrupt but enhance the group's efforts. While monitoring, you also can keep a written record of your observations that will provide you with a useful guide for planning future activities, for assigning roles to different students, for defining additional goals to be achieved, and for conducting conferences with individual students or their parents.

Technology

Included in this chapter is a graphing calculator feature. It deals with solving systems of equations graphically. Students will solve systems of equations on a graphing calculator and will then be able to see what is happening when we find a solution to a system of equations. It is another way of solving systems of equations and will be related to solving the systems algebraically. Students can then use this method and their graphing calculator to either solve systems or to check their work when they solve systems of equations algebraically.

Critical Thinking

Those who approach critical thinking from a theoretical base often make it sound far more bewildering and complicated than it is. Critical thinking is not unlike anything else we do; that is, if we do it once, and then continue to do it, it becomes a natural part of our existence. For example, you do not have to understand the theory of how an automobile operates to learn how to drive, and after you drive for awhile, you will make dozens of critical decisions without being aware of it, even on a short trip. To help students develop their critical-thinking skills, establish an environment where it becomes natural for them to expect additional questions from you, such as, "Can you explain why ...", "What would happen next if ...", "What other ways could have been used to ...", and so on.

Cooperative Learning, p. 41

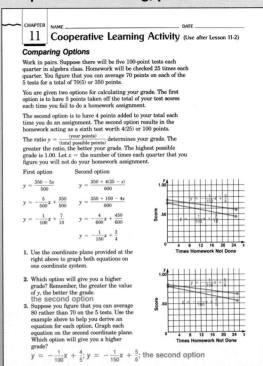

Technology, p. 11

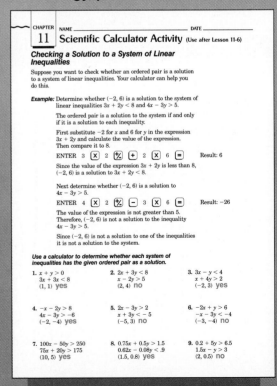

Problem of the Week Activity

The card shown below is one of two available for this chapter. It can be used as a class or small group activity.

Activity Card

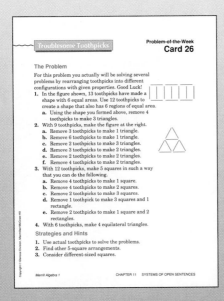

Manipulatives and Models

The following materials may be used as models or manipulatives in Chapter 11.

paper and scissors (Lesson 11-4)

Outside Resources

Books/Periodicals

Abbott, Edwin A. *Flatland*. Emerson Book, Inc.

Brianza, David. *Beginning Technical Mathematics Made Easy*. TAB Books, Inc,.

Films/Videotapes/Videodiscs

Strategies for Solving Word Problems in Algebra - Basic Operations, Guidance Association

Strategies for Solving Word Problems in Algebra - Formula Problems, Guidance Association

Software

Escape from Algebra, Milliken Publishing

Homework Helper - Math Word Problems, Spinnaker/Springboard

Multicultural

Multicultural Activity, p. 56

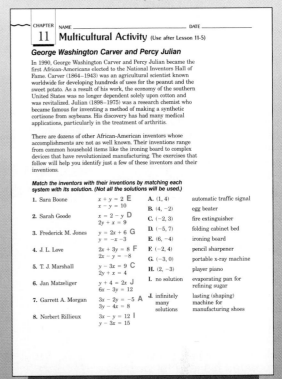

Lab Manual

Lab Activity, pp. 37-38

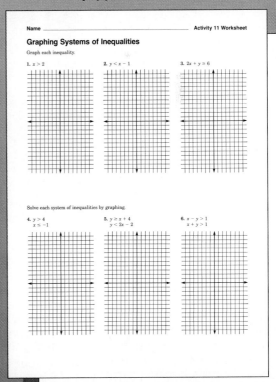

Using the Chapter Opener

Transparency 11-0 is available in the Transparency Package. It provides a full-color visual and motivational activity that you can use to engage students in the mathematical content of the chapter.

Background Information

Charles Dodgson had many flaws. One of his shoulders was higher than the other, he was deaf in one ear, he had a crooked smile, and his blue eyes were not level. He walked stiffly erect with a jerky gait and stuttered so badly that his upper lip trembled when he spoke. But Dodgson enjoyed games of all sorts, including chess, croquet, backgammon, and billiards. As a result, he invented many mathematical games, word puzzles, and secret codes, and authored two of America's best-loved books, in which he incorporated his love for puzzles and mathematics.

In this chapter, you will:
- Solve systems of equations and inequalities by graphing.
- Solve systems of equations algebraically.
- Solve problems after checking for hidden assumptions.

Chapter Project

Materials: paper, pencil, *Alice in Wonderland, Through the Looking Glass,* or other books by Lewis Carroll

Organize students into cooperative groups of analysts and writers. Have each group select at least one chapter of one of Lewis Carroll's books. Instruct members of each group to analyze and discuss each passage of their selected chapter for the purpose of identifying the hidden mathematical or scientific assumptions within. For example, how does the following passage compare with modern measurements of the center of Earth? "I must be getting somewhere near the centre of the earth. Let me see: that would be four thousand miles down, I think . . .''

Or, how does Alice's expanding and shrinking reflect Dodgson's views of the universe expanding or diminishing? Have each group record its analysis of passages from its selected chapter and present it to the class for further discussion. Have groups try writing their own passages.

11 Systems of Open Sentences

APPLICATION IN LITERATURE

Charles Lutwidge Dodgson (1832–1898) is better known as Lewis Carroll, the author of *Alice in Wonderland* and *Through the Looking Glass.* Dodgson, an English mathematician, weaved logic, mathematics, and science into his children's tales in ways that often appeared nonsensical. Look at the passage below. What is the hidden assumption?

> ". . . Let me see: four times five is twelve, and four times six is thirteen, and four times seven is—oh dear! I shall never get to twenty at that rate."

If you continue the progression described above, you should assume that it ends at 4 times 12, since multiplication tables taught during the time of Mr. Dodgson ended with twelves. Based on the examples in the passage, 4 times 12 must be 19, which is why the speaker exclaimed that twenty could not be reached "at that rate."

Dodgson also used straightforward mathematical problems in his books. Consider this passage from *Through the Looking Glass.*

> "Tweedledum said to Tweedledee: 'The sum of your weight and twice mine is 361 pounds.' Tweedledee said to Tweedledum: 'Contrariwise, the sum of your weight and twice mine is 362 pounds.'"

Do you know how much each one weighs?

Tweedledum, 120 lb;
Tweedledee, 121 lb

ALGEBRA IN ACTION

What two equations could you use to represent the statements made by Tweedledum and Tweedledee? Can you think of some methods that you could use to find numbers that are solutions to *both* equations? **See margin.**

"Contrariwise," continued Tweedledee, "if it was so, it might be; and if it were so, it would be; but as it isn't, it ain't. That's logic."

Lesson	Connections (C) and Applications (A)	Examples	Exercises
11-2	C: Geometry	5	41-42, 50
	A: Gardening		44
	Sales		45
	Ballooning		46
	Boating		49
11-3	C: Number Theory	4	35-37
	A: Metallurgy	3	
	Sports		42
	Finance		43
	Chemistry		44
	Sales		45, 48
11-4	C: Number Theory	2	31-32
	Statistics		36
	A: Uniform Motion	3	40
	Conferences		38
	Testing		39
	Aviation		44
11-5	C: Number Theory		27-28
	A: Banking	2	
	Uniform Motion	3	33, 35
	Sales		34, 36
	Gardening		39
11-6	A: Agriculture	3	
	Sales		47-48, 50, 55
	Painting		49

439

11-1 Lesson Notes

11-1 Problem-Solving Strategy: Hidden Assumptions

Lesson Resources

- Practice Master 11-1

 Transparency 11-1 contains the 5-Minute Check and a teaching aid for this lesson.

INTRODUCING THE LESSON

5-Minute Check

(over Chapter 10)

State the slopes of the lines parallel and perpendicular to the graph of each equation.

1. $4r = 2p - 7$ $-\frac{1}{2}, 2$

2. $t = 3m - 7$ $3, -\frac{1}{3}$

3. $5x - y = 7$ $5, -\frac{1}{5}$

Find the coordinates of the midpoint of the line segment whose endpoints are given.

4. (9, 5), (17, 3)   (13, 4)

5. (11, 4), (9, 2)   (10, 3)

Motivating the Lesson

Ask students to define the term "assumption" in their own words. Have students identify assumptions they made in the past that turned out to be false. For example, some students may have entered Algebra 1 with certain assumptions that have proven to be erroneous.

TEACHING THE LESSON

Chalkboard Example

For the Example

Sarah bought 16 rare coins at a flea market. She later learned one coin was a fake. Since it contains less gold, the fake coin is lighter than the other coins. Sarah intends on using a balance scale to find the fake coin. How many times will she need to measure the mass of coins before being able to identify the fake coin?   **4; She needs to weigh the coins in groups of 8, 4, 2, and then 1.**

Objective
11-1

After studying this lesson, you should be able to:

- solve problems after checking for hidden assumptions.

Sometimes we make problem solving more difficult than it is by incorporating hidden assumptions into the process. You can avoid this by asking yourself the following questions.

1. What *exactly* does the problem say?
2. What does the problem *not* say?
3. What am I assuming that isn't found in the problem?
4. Does my answer make sense?

Ask yourself these questions as you work through the problem below.

Example

 *FYI···*

The Hilton Hotel in Las Vegas is the largest hotel in the United States. It has 3174 rooms.

Two women agree to share a hotel room and pay a total of $65 when they check in. Later, the clerk realizes that he should have applied a corporate discount and charged them $60. He sends a bellhop up with the $5 refund for the room. The bellhop doesn't carry coins, so he returns only $4 to the women and keeps $1. This means that each woman has paid $30.50 as her share of the room, or a total of $61. The bellhop kept the other $1 for a total of $62. What happened to the other $3?

In this problem, an incorrect relationship is suggested. Can you discover this relationship? Let's change the amount of the discount and compare the results to those given.

Amount Clerk Returns	Amount Returned to Women	Amount Kept by Bellhop	Room Cost Per Person	Total Room Cost Plus Bellhop's "Tip"
$5	$4	$1	$30.50	$61 + $1 = $62
$7	$6	$1	$29.50	$59 + $1 = $60
$9	$8	$1	$28.50	$57 + $1 = $58

If you go by the amounts in the last column, we could ask what happened to the $3, $5, or $7. But perhaps you now realize that there is no reason why the total room charge to the women plus the bellhop's "tip" should equal $65. That is the hidden assumption in this problem.

1. What happened to the other $3?

CHECKING FOR UNDERSTANDING

Communicating Mathematics

Read and study the lesson to answer each question.

1. What *exactly* did the problem in the example ask?

2. What did the problem *not* say?   See margin.

3. What relationship does exist between the numbers in this problem?   room charge − bellhop's "tip" = $60

RETEACHING THE LESSON

Present the following problem.

Sally ran a mile in 7 min 3 s. This was 13 seconds slower than her best time. What was her best time?   6 min 50 s

Students may assume that "slower" means the best time is more and add, rather than subtract. Encourage students to read verbal problems and not make assumptions because of key words.

Additional Answers

2. The total room charge plus the bellhop's "tip" should be equal to $65.

4. There could be two skiers each skiing on one ski; The skier may have fallen off the skis and they came down the hill by themselves; The skier may have taken off a ski just before getting to the tree, gone around the tree, and then put the ski back on.

Solve each problem. Try to eliminate any hidden assumptions.

4. As Barry prepared to ski down a hill, he noticed that there were some strange ski tracks nearby. One track went around a tree on the left side. The other track went around on the right side. Give five reasonable explanations as to how this could have happened. **Answers will vary; see margin for partial list.**

EXERCISES

Practice

Solve. Use any strategy.

Strategies
Look for a pattern.
Solve a simpler problem.
Act it out.
Guess and check.
Draw a diagram.
Make a chart.
Work backwards.

5. At Walnut Bluff High School, there are 2100 students. Three percent of the students wear one ring. Of the other 97 percent, half wear two rings, and half wear no rings. How many rings are worn by the students at Walnut Bluff? **2100 rings**

6. In how many ways can you receive change for a quarter if at least one coin is a dime? **6 ways**

7. The MB Construction Company is building a new apartment complex that will contain 1037 units. If the apartment numbers are 1, 2, 3, and so on, how many single digits will be needed for the numbers on the apartment doors in the complex? **3041 digits**

8. A firefighter spraying water on a fire stood on the middle rung of a ladder. The smoke lessened, so he moved up 3 rungs. When it got too hot, he backed down 5 rungs. Later, he moved up 7 rungs and stayed until the fire was out. Then he climbed the remaining 6 rungs and went into the building. How many rungs did the ladder have? **23 rungs**

COOPERATIVE LEARNING ACTIVITY

Work in groups of four. Each person must understand the solution and be able to explain it to any person in the class.

Chef Cook's four best recipes appear on different pages of her cookbook, *Chef Cook Cooks,* which has recipes on pages 5 through 420. The page numbers of the four recipes have no repeated digits. The page number of the onion soup recipe is a divisor of the other three page numbers. The chicken salad page number is composed partially of consecutive digits. It is also more than twice the beef wellington page number, which is exactly five times the devil's food cake page number.

On what pages can Chef Cook find her four favorite recipes?

onion soup, p. 6; devil's food cake, p. 18; beef wellington, p. 90; chicken salad, p. 372

LESSON 11-1   PROBLEM-SOLVING STRATEGY: HIDDEN ASSUMPTIONS   441

EXTENDING THE LESSON

Math Power: Reasoning

Justin, Chris, Meg, Carla, and Ryan took part in a race. Neither Justin nor Carla finished first or last. Justin, Meg, and Ryan were the first three finishers. Justin finished before Ryan but after Meg. In what order did the students finish the race? **Meg, Justin, Ryan, Carla, Chris**

Cooperative Learning Activity

This activity provides students with an opportunity to *learn* things together, not just do things together. You may wish to refer to pages T6 - T8 and page 6C for the various elements of cooperative groups and specific goals and strategies for using them.

Lesson Resources

- Reteaching Master 11-2
- Practice Master 11-2
- Enrichment Master 11-2
- Video Algebra, 39

 Transparency 11-2 contains the 5-Minute Check and a teaching aid for this lesson.

INTRODUCING THE LESSON

5-Minute Check

(over Chapter 10)

State the slope and y-intercept of the graph of each equation.

1. $2x - y = 1$ 2, −1
2. $y = 3x - 7$ 3, −7

Write an equation in slope-intercept form of the line that passes through each pair of points.

3. $(5, 2), (-7, -4)$ $y = \frac{1}{2}x - \frac{1}{2}$
4. $(-1, 7), (8, -2)$
   $y = -x + 6$
5. $(4, 1), (5, 2)$ $y = x - 3$

Motivating the Lesson

Have students graph the equations $y = 2x - 1$ and $y = 3x + 1$ on the same set of axes. Ask them to identify the coordinates of the point where the graphs intersect. $(-2, -5)$

TEACHING THE LESSON

Teaching Tip ①   Point out that since there are two variables, the solution, if it exists, will be an ordered pair or ordered pairs.

Teaching Tip ②   If necessary, review graphing linear equations using x- and y-intercepts or the slope-intercept method.

Teaching Tip ③   Explain that the graphs of these equations coincide.

Objectives

11-2A
11-2B

After studying this lesson, you should be able to:
- solve systems of equations by graphing, and
- determine whether a system of equations has one solution, no solution, or infinitely many solutions by graphing.

Application

The Southside High School basketball team held a raffle to earn money for a trip to an out-of-state basketball tournament. Tickets for the raffle were sold for either $5 or $2. The team sold a total of 500 tickets for a total of $1450. How many $5 tickets and how many $2 tickets did the team sell?

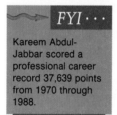

To solve this problem, let x = the number of $5 tickets, and let y = the number of $2 tickets. Then $5x$ = the amount of money collected from the sale of the $5 tickets and $2y$ = the amount of money collected from the sale of the $2 tickets. You can write two equations to represent this situation.

Number of $5 tickets	plus	number of $2 tickets	is 500.
x	+	y	= 500

Money from $5 tickets	plus	money from $2 tickets	is $1450.
5x	+	2y	= 1450

The equations $x + y = 500$ and $5x + 2y = 1450$ together are called a **system of equations**. The solution to this problem is the ordered pair of numbers that satisfies both of these equations.   **Teaching Tip ①**

One method for solving a system of equations is to graph the equations on the same coordinate plane. The coordinates of the point where the graphs intersect is the solution.

Example 1

FYI · · ·

Kareem Abdul-Jabbar scored a professional career record 37,639 points from 1970 through 1988.

Graph the equations $x + y = 500$ and $5x + 2y = 1450$ on the same coordinate plane. Then find the solution of the system of equations to answer the problem given above.   Teaching Tip ②

The graphs intersect at the point (150, 350).

Check:

$x + y = 500$	$5x + 2y = 1450$
$150 + 350 \overset{?}{=} 500$	$5(150) + 2(350) \overset{?}{=} 1450$
$500 = 500$ ✓	$1450 = 1450$ ✓

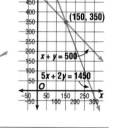

The solution of the system of equations $x + y = 500$ and $5x + 2y = 1450$ is (150, 350). Therefore, the basketball team sold 150 of the $5 tickets and 350 of the $2 tickets.

ALTERNATE TEACHING STRATEGIES

Using Questioning

Two lines are inconsistent but share the same slope. What do you know about the lines?   **They are parallel.**

Using Logical Reasoning

How could the graph of two different equations be shown by only one line?   **If the equations coincide, or have the same slope and intercepts, then their graph will be only one line.**

Example 2

Graph the equations $y = x - 4$ and $x + \frac{1}{2}y = \frac{5}{2}$ to find the solution of the system of equations.

The graphs intersect at the point $(3, -1)$.

Check:

$y = x - 4$ $x + \frac{1}{2}y = \frac{5}{2}$

$-1 \overset{?}{=} 3 - 4$ $3 + \frac{1}{2}(-1) \overset{?}{=} \frac{5}{2}$

$-1 = -1$ ✔ $\frac{5}{2} = \frac{5}{2}$ ✔

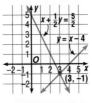

The solution is $(3, -1)$.

A system of equations that has exactly one solution is said to be consistent and independent.

A system of two linear equations has exactly one ordered pair as its solution when the graphs of the equations intersect at exactly one point. It is also possible for the two graphs to be parallel lines or to be on the same line. When the graphs are parallel lines, then the system of equations does not have a solution. When the graphs are the same line, the system of equations has infinitely many solutions.

Example 3

Graph the equations $x + y = 3$ and $x + y = 4$. Then determine the number of solutions to the system of equations.

The graphs of the equations are parallel lines. Since they do not intersect, there is no solution to this system of equations. Notice that the two lines have the same slope but different y-intercepts.

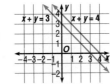

A system of equations that has no solution is said to be inconsistent.

Example 4

Graph the equations $2x + y = 3$ and $4x + 2y = 6$. Then determine the number of solutions to the system of equations.

Each equation has the same graph. Thus, any ordered pair on the graph will satisfy both equations. Therefore, there are infinitely many solutions to this system of equations. Notice that the graphs have the same slope and intercepts. **Teaching Tip** ③

A system of equations that has infinitely many solutions is said to be consistent and dependent.

The chart at the top of the next page summarizes the possible solutions to systems of linear equations.

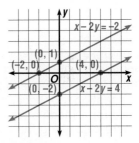
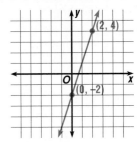

Description of Graph	Number of Solutions	Special Terminology
intersecting lines	exactly one	consistent and independent
parallel lines	none	inconsistent
same line	infinitely many	consistent and dependent

Example 5

CONNECTION
Geometry

The points $A(-8, -3)$, $B(2, 1)$, $C(1, -6)$, and $D(-4, -8)$ are vertices of a quadrilateral. What is the point of intersection of the two diagonals?

Draw quadrilateral $ABCD$ with diagonals AC and BD. The diagonals appear to intersect at the point $(-2, -5)$. To check this, find the equations of lines AC and BD and verify that $(-2, -5)$ is a solution of both equations. First, find the slope of each line using $m = \frac{y_2 - y_1}{x_2 - x_1}$.

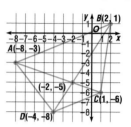

Equation for $\overline{AC}$

$m = \frac{-3 - (-6)}{-8 - 1}$

$= \frac{3}{-9}$ or $-\frac{1}{3}$

Equation for $\overline{BD}$

$m = \frac{1 - (-8)}{2 - (-4)}$

$= \frac{9}{6}$ or $\frac{3}{2}$

Then use the slope-intercept form, $y = mx + b$.

$y = -\frac{1}{3}x + b$ $y = \frac{3}{2}x + b$

$-6 = -\frac{1}{3}(1) + b$ $1 = \frac{3}{2}(2) + b$

$-\frac{17}{3} = b$ $-2 = b$

$y = -\frac{1}{3}x - \frac{17}{3}$ $y = \frac{3}{2}x - 2$

Check that $(-2, -5)$ is a solution to both equations.

$-5 \stackrel{?}{=} -\frac{1}{3}(-2) - \frac{17}{3}$ $-5 \stackrel{?}{=} \frac{3}{2}(-2) - 2$

$-5 = -5$ ✓ $-5 = -5$ ✓   The solution checks.

CHECKING FOR UNDERSTANDING

Communicating Mathematics

Complete.

1. If a system of two linear equations has no solution, then the graphs of the two equations must be ___?___ lines. **parallel**

2. If a system of two linear equations has exactly one solution, then the graphs of the two equations must be ___?___ lines. **intersecting**

3. If a system of two linear equations has infinitely many solutions, then the lines have the same slope and ___?___. **x- and y-intercepts**

4. Write a system of linear equations that has $(2, 1)$ as its only solution. **Answers will vary; a typical answer is $x + y = 3$ and $x - y = 1$.**

444   CHAPTER 11   SYSTEMS OF OPEN SENTENCES

State the ordered pair for the point of intersection of each pair of lines.

5. a and b (6, 3)

6. a and c (−3, 3)

7. a and d (1, 3)

8. b and c (0, 0)

9. b and d (2, 1)

10. c and d (5, −5)

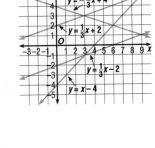

State the slope and y-intercept of the graph of each equation. Then determine whether the system of equations has one solution, no solution, or infinitely many solutions. **See margin for slope and y-intercept.**

Teaching Tip ④

11. $x + y = 6$
$x - y = 2$ **one**

12. $x + y = 6$
$3x + 3y = 3$
no solution

13. $x + 2y = 5$
$3x - 15 = -6y$
infinitely many

14. $2x + 3y = 5$
$-6x + 15 = 9y$
infinitely many

15. $3x - 8y = 4$
$6x - 42 = 16y$
no solution

16. $y = -3x$
$6y - x = -38$ **one**

EXERCISES

Practice

A

Use the graphs at the right to determine whether each system has one solution, no solution, or infinitely many solutions. If the system has one solution, name it.

17. $x + 3y = 12$
$x - 3y = -6$
one, (3, 3)

18. $x - 3y = 6$
$x - y = 4$
one, (3, −1)

19. $x - 3y = 6$
$x + 3y = 12$
one, (9, 1)

20. $x - 3y = -6$
$x - 3y = 6$
no solution

21. $x + 3y = 12$
$x - y = 4$
one, (6, 2)

22. $x - y = 4$
$x - 3y = -6$
one, (9, 5)

Graph each system of equations. Then determine whether the system has one solution, no solution, or infinitely many solutions. If the system has one solution, name it. 26. no solution   27. infinitely many   34. no solution

23. $y = -x$ (0, 0)
$y = 2x$

24. $x + y = 8$ (5, 3)
$x - y = 2$

25. $y = -3x$ (2, −6)
$4x + y = 2$

B

26. $x + 2y = 5$
$2x + 4y = 2$

27. $2x + 3y = 4$
$-4x - 6y = -8$

28. $3x - y = 4$ (0, −4)
$6x + 2y = -8$

29. $x - y = 2$ (3, 1)
$3y + 2x = 9$

30. $y = x + 3$ (−1, 2)
$3y + x = 5$

31. $2x + 3y = -17$
$y = x - 4$ (−1, −5)

32. $x + 2y = 0$ (−6, 3)
$y + 3 = -x$

33. $3x + y = -8$ (−3, 1)
$x + 6y = 3$

34. $x + 2y = 6$
$2y - 8 = -x$

LESSON 11-2   GRAPHING SYSTEMS OF EQUATIONS   445

Additional Answers

11. $m = -1, b = 6; m = 1,$
$b = -2$

12. $m = -1, b = 6; m = -1,$
$b = 1$

13. $m = -\frac{1}{2}, b = \frac{5}{2}; m = -\frac{1}{2},$
$b = \frac{5}{2}$

14. $m = -\frac{2}{3}, b = \frac{5}{3}; m = -\frac{2}{3},$
$b = \frac{5}{3}$

15. $m = \frac{3}{8}, b = -\frac{1}{2}; m = \frac{3}{8},$
$b = -\frac{21}{8}$

16. $m = -3, b = 0; m = \frac{1}{6},$
$b = -\frac{19}{3}$

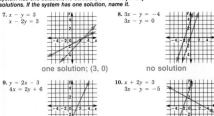

Graph each system of equations. Then determine whether the system has one solution, no solution, or infinitely many solutions. If the system has one solution, name it.

35. $x + 2y = -9$ $(1, -5)$ **36.** $4x + 3y = 24$ $(3, 4)$ **37.** $12x - y = -21$
$x - y = 6$ $10x - 16y = -34$ $\frac{1}{2}x + \frac{2}{3}y = -3$
                                                                          $(-2, -3)$

38. $\frac{1}{2}x + \frac{1}{3}y = 6$ $(8, 6)$ **39.** $\frac{2}{3}x + \frac{1}{4}y = 4$ infinitely   **40.** $3.4x + 6.3y = 4.4$
$y = \frac{1}{2}x + 2$ $x = -\frac{3}{8}y + 6$ many $2.1x + 3.7y = 3.1$
                                                                          $(5, -2)$

 CONNECTION GEOMETRY

41. The graphs of the equations $2x + y = 8$, $-x + 2y = 6$, and $7x + y = 3$ contain the sides of a triangle. Find the coordinates of the vertices of the triangle. $(0, 3), (2, 4), (-1, 10)$

42. The graphs of the equations $y = 2$, $3x + 2y = 1$, and $3x - 4y = -29$ contain the sides of a triangle. Find the measure of the area of the triangle. (*Hint:* Use the formula $A = \frac{1}{2}bh$.) **9**

Critical Thinking

43. The solution to the system of equations $Ax + y = 5$ and $Ax + By = 7$ is $(-1, 2)$. What are the values of A and B? $A = -3, B = 2$

Applications

44. **Gardening** The perimeter of a rectangular garden is 40 meters. The length of the garden is 1 meter less than twice its width. What are the dimensions of this garden? **13 m by 7 m**

45. **Sales** A cab ride costs $1.70 plus $0.10 per tenth of a mile traveled if you use the Blue Cab Company. The cost is $1.55 plus $0.15 per tenth of a mile traveled if you use the Red Cab Company. For what distance will the cab rides cost the same? **0.3 mile**

46. **Ballooning** A hot-air balloon is 10 meters above the ground rising at a rate of 15 meters per minute. Another balloon is 150 meters above the ground descending at a rate of 20 meters per minute.
   a. After how long will the balloons be at the same height? **4 min**
   b. What is that height? **70 m**

Mixed Review

47. Replace __?__ with $<$, $>$, or $=$ to make the sentence $\frac{7}{8}$ __?__ $\frac{29}{33}$ true. (Lesson 2-3). $<$

48. Simplify $(m^2n)(am)(an^2)$. (Lesson 6-2) $a^2m^3n^3$

49. **Boating** The rate of the current of a river is 5 miles per hour. A boat travels downstream 78 miles and returns in 32 hours. What is the rate of the boat in still water? (Lesson 8-7) **8 mph**

50. **Geometry** The center of a circle is at $(-2, 3)$. One endpoint of a diameter is at $(3, 9)$. Find the other endpoint of this diameter. (Lesson 10-8) $(-7, -3)$

EXTENDING THE LESSON

Math Power: Connections

The graph of the equations $y = 2$, $3x + 2y = 1$, and $3x - 4y = -29$ contain the sides of a triangle. Find the measure of the area of this triangle. (*Hint:* Use the formula $A = \frac{1}{2}bh$.) **9**

NAME _____ DATE _____
11-2 | **Enrichment Worksheet**

Graphing A Trip

The distance formula, $d = rt$, is used to solve many types of problems. If you graph an equation such as $d = 50t$, the graph is a model for a car going at 50 mi/h. The time the car travels is t; the distance in miles the car covers is d. The slope of the line is the speed.

Suppose you drive to a nearby town and return. You average 50 mi/h on the trip out but only 25 mi/h on the trip home. The round trip takes 5 hours. How far away is the town?

The graph at the rights represents your trip. Notice that the return trip is shown with a negative slope because you are driving in the opposite direction.

Solve each problem.

1. Estimate the answer to the problem in the above example. About how far away is the town?
   about 80 miles

2. Graph this trip and solve the problem. An airplane has enough fuel for 3 hours of safe flying. On the trip out the pilot averages 200 mi/h flying against a headwind. On the trip back, the pilot averages 250 mi/h. How long a trip out can the pilot make?
   about $1\frac{2}{3}$ hours and 330 miles

3. Graph this trip and solve the problem. You drive to a town 100 miles away. On the trip out you average 25 mi/h. On the trip back you average 50 mi/h. How many hours do you spend driving?
   6 hours

4. Graph this trip and solve the problem. You drive at an average speed of 50 mi/h to a discount shopping plaza, spend 2 hours shopping, and then return at an average speed of 25 mi/h. The entire trip takes 8 hours. How far away is the shopping plaza? **100 miles**

11-3 Substitution

Objective
11-3

After studying this lesson, you should be able to:
■ solve systems of equations by the substitution method.

Application

Kiyo wants to build a rectangular corral for her horse using picket fencing. To make the best use of the available land, the length of the corral must be three times its width. If Kiyo has 210 meters of fencing and wants to use it all, what are the dimensions of her corral?

Let y = the length of the corral and let x = its width. You know that the length must be three times the width. Also, the perimeter must be 210 meters since Kiyo has that much fencing. This information can be described by the following system of equations.

$$y = 3x$$
$$2y + 2x = 210$$

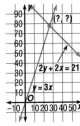

You could try to solve this system of equations by graphing, as shown at the right. Notice that the *exact* coordinates of the point where the lines intersect cannot be easily determined from this graph. The exact solution of this system of equations can be found by using algebraic methods. One such method is called **substitution**.

In the system $y = 3x$ and $2y + 2x = 210$, you know that y is equal to $3x$. Since y must have the same value in *both* equations, you can substitute $3x$ for y in the equation $2y + 2x = 210$.

$$2y + 2x = 210$$
$$2(3x) + 2x = 210 \qquad \text{\textit{Substitute 3x for y so the equation}}$$
$$8x = 210 \qquad \text{\textit{will have only one variable.}}$$
$$x = 26.25$$

Now find the value of y by substituting 26.25 for x in $y = 3x$.

FYI···

The world's horse population is estimated to be around 75 million.

$$y = 3x$$
$$y = 3(26.25) \qquad \text{\textit{You could also substitute 26.25 for x in 2y + 2x = 210.}}$$
$$y = 78.75$$

Check:
$$y = 3x \qquad\qquad 2y + 2x = 210$$
$$78.75 \overset{?}{=} 3(26.25) \qquad 2(78.75) + 2(26.25) \overset{?}{=} 210$$
$$78.75 = 78.75 ✓ \qquad\qquad 210 = 210 ✓$$

The solution of the system of equations is (26.25, 78.75). Therefore, the dimensions of Kiyo's corral are 78.75 meters by 26.25 meters.

LESSON 11-3 SUBSTITUTION 447

ALTERNATE TEACHING STRATEGIES

Using Problem Solving

Determine whether the graphs of the equations $x - y = 8$, $4x + y = 17$, and $2x + 5y = -5$ intersect at the same point. If so, name the point of intersection. **yes, (5, −3)**

Using Logical Reasoning

A palindromic number is one that is unchanged if its digits are reversed. Find a palindromic number for which the sum of the digits is 5. **Answers will vary. Possible answers include 212, 10,301, and 1,011,101.**

11-3 Lesson Notes

Lesson Resources
- Reteaching Master 11-3
- Practice Master 11-3
- Enrichment Master 11-3
- Video Algebra, 40, 42, 43
- Transparency 11-3 contains the 5-Minute Check and a teaching aid for this lesson.

INTRODUCING THE LESSON

5-Minute Check
(over Lesson 11-2)

Graph each pair of equations. Then state the solution of each system of equations.

1. $x + y = 3$, $y = x + 3$ **(0, 3)**
2. $y = x$, $x + y = 4$ **(2, 2)**
3. $y = -x$, $y = 2x$ **(0, 0)**

4. **If two distinct lines intersect, how many solutions exist?** one

5. **Under what conditions will two distinct lines in the same plane not have a solution?** when the lines are parallel

Motivating the Lesson

Review solving equations with the following activity. Let $y = 3$. Find the value of x in each equation by substituting 3 for y and solving for x.
1. $y - x = 6$ **−3**
2. $4x - y = 9$ **3**
3. $2y - 3x = 6$ **0**

Chalkboard Examples

For Example 1

Use substitution to solve each system of equations.

a. $y = 2x$ and $2x + 5y = -12$
$(-1, -2)$

b. $2y = -3x$ and $4x + y = 5$
$(2, -3)$

c. $x + y = 6$ and $3x + y = 15$
$\left(\frac{9}{2}, \frac{3}{2}\right)$

For Example 2

Use substitution to solve each system of equations.

a. $\frac{5}{2}x + 3y = 7$ and
$5x + 6y = 9$ no solution

b. $3x + 4y = 7$ and
$\frac{3}{2}x + 2y = 11$ no solution

For Example 3

a. **Solve Example 3 for the same data except that the 1000 grams of alloy is to be 35% copper.** 600 g, 400 g

b. **Solve Example 3 for the same data except that the 1000 grams of alloy is to be 38% copper.** 480 g, 520 g

Teaching Tip ❶ When an equation contains fractions, some students may find it easier to eliminate the fractions first. This can be done by multiplying each side of the equation by the LCM of the denominators.

Teaching Tip ❷ Emphasize that there are no ordered pairs that satisfy the system of equations. The solution set is the empty set, Ø. The system is inconsistent.

Example 1

Use substitution to solve the system of equations $x + 6y = 1$ and $3x - 10y = 31$.

Solve the first equation for x since the coefficient of x is 1.

$$x + 6y = 1$$
$$x = 1 - 6y$$

Next find the value of y by substituting $1 - 6y$ for x in the second equation.

$$3x - 10y = 31$$
$$3(1 - 6y) - 10y = 31$$
$$3 - 18y - 10y = 31$$
$$-28y = 28$$
$$y = -1$$

Then substitute -1 for y in either of the original equations and find the value of x. *Choose the equation that is easier for you to solve.*

$$x + 6y = 1$$
$$x + 6(-1) = 1$$
$$x - 6 = 1$$
$$x = 7$$

The solution of this system is $(7, -1)$. *Check this result.*

Example 2

Use substitution to solve the system of equations $\frac{3}{2}x - y = 3$ and $3x - 2y = 12$.

Solve the first equation for y since the coefficient of y is -1. **Teaching Tip ❶**

$$\frac{3}{2}x - y = 3$$
$$-y = -\frac{3}{2}x + 3$$
$$y = \frac{3}{2}x - 3$$

Then find the value of x by substituting $\frac{3}{2}x - 3$ for y in the second equation.

$$3x - 2y = 12$$
$$3x - 2\left(\frac{3}{2}x - 3\right) = 12$$
$$3x - 3x + 6 = 12$$
$$6 = 12$$

Teaching Tip ❷
The statement $6 = 12$ is false. This means that there are no ordered pairs that are solutions to both equations. Compare the slope-intercept forms of the equations, which are $y = \frac{3}{2}x - 3$ and $y = \frac{3}{2}x - 6$. Notice that these lines have the same slope but different y-intercepts. Thus, the lines are parallel and the system of equations has no solution.

Example 3

APPLICATION

Metallurgy

A metal alloy is 25% copper. Another metal alloy is 50% copper. How much of each alloy should be used to make 1000 grams of a metal alloy that is 45% copper?

EXPLORE   Let a = the number of grams of the 25% copper alloy.
Let b = the number of grams of the 50% copper alloy.

448   CHAPTER 11   SYSTEMS OF OPEN SENTENCES

	25% Copper	50% Copper	45% Copper
Total Grams	a	b	1000
Grams of Copper	$0.25a$	$0.50b$	$0.45(1000)$

PLAN   The system of equations is $a + b = 1000$ and $0.25a + 0.50b = 0.45(1000)$. Use substitution to solve this system.

SOLVE   Since $a + b = 1000$, $a = 1000 - b$.

$$0.25a + 0.50b = 0.45(1000)$$ **Teaching Tip ③**
$$0.25(1000 - b) + 0.50b = 450$$ *Substitute $1000 - b$ for a.*
$$250 - 0.25b + 0.50b = 450$$ *Solve for b.*
$$0.25b = 200$$
$$b = 800$$

$$a + b = 1000$$
$$a + 800 = 1000$$ *Substitute 800 for b.*
$$a = 200$$ *Solve for a.*

200 grams of the 25% copper alloy and 800 grams of the 50% copper alloy should be used.

EXAMINE   The 45% copper alloy contains $0.25(200) + 0.50(800) = 50 + 400$, or 450 grams of copper. Since $0.45(1000) = 450$, the answer is correct.

Teaching Tip ④

The sum of the digits of a two-digit number is 9. The number is 6 times the units digit. Find the number.   Teaching Tip ⑤

Let t = the tens digit and let u = the units digit of the number. Then any two-digit number can be represented as $10t + u$.

Since the sum of the digits is 9, one equation is $t + u = 9$. Since the number is 6 times its unit digit, another equation is $10t + u = 6u$. Use substitution to solve this system.

Since $t + u = 9$, $t = 9 - u$.

$$10t + u = 6u$$
$$10(9 - u) + u = 6u$$ *Substitute $9 - u$ for t.*
$$90 - 10u + u = 6u$$ *Solve for u.*
$$90 = 15u$$
$$6 = u$$

$$t + u = 9$$ *Substitute 6 for u.*
$$t + 6 = 9$$
$$t = 3$$ *Solve for t.*

The number is $10(3) + 6$, or 36. *Check this result.*

Example 4

CONNECTION

Number Theory

Reteaching Masters Booklet, p. 76

Chalkboard Example

For Example 4

Use a system of equations to solve each problem.

a. The sum of the digits of a two-digit number is 12. The number is 13 times the tens digit. Find the number.   **39**

b. The sum of the digits of a two-digit number is 8. The number is 11 times the tens digit. Find the number.   **44**

Teaching Tip ③   You may choose to rewrite this equation without decimals.
$$25a + 50b = 45,000$$

Teaching Tip ④   A digit is one of the numerals 0 through 9. A two-digit number means a whole number that can be named using two digits.

Teaching Tip ⑤   A review of the decimal system may be needed.
$$623 = 6 \times 10^2 + 2 \times 10^1 + 3 \times 10^0$$
$$tu = t \times 10^1 + u \times 10^0$$

RETEACHING THE LESSON

Give the class the following system of equations and have half the class use substitution by solving equation 1 for y and the other half of the class use substitution by solving equation 2 for x.
$$3x - 2y = 2$$
$$x + 4y = 10$$ **(2, 2)**

Discuss whether it matters which equation is substituted into which equation and how to look for the "best" way.

Checking for Understanding

Exercises 1-16 are designed to help you assess understanding through reading, writing, and speaking. You should work through Exercises 1-4 with your students, and then monitor their work on Exercises 5-16.

Error Analysis

When working a "digit problem," carefully explain the difference between the terms "digit" and "number." Have students read the problem word for word and translate into mathematics. Example: tens digit = T
units digit = U
the number = $10T + U$
A digit has no value, but a number has a value.

Closing the Lesson

Speaking Activity Have students explain how to solve a system of equations using the substitution method.

Practice Masters Booklet, p. 86

CHECKING FOR UNDERSTANDING

Communicating Mathematics

Read and study the lesson to answer each question.

1. To solve the system of equations $y = -5x + 1$ and $2x + 3y = 7$, why can you substitute $-5x + 1$ for y in the second equation? See margin.

2. In Example 3, what is the system of equations if a 30% copper alloy and a 70% copper alloy is used to make 1000 grams of the 45% copper alloy? $a + b = 1000$ and $0.30a + 0.70b = 0.45(1000)$

3. How many two-digit whole numbers are there such that the sum of the digits of the number is 9? 9 numbers

4. Explain why any 2-digit number can be represented by $10t + u$, where t is the tens digit and u is the ones digit. See margin.

Guided Practice

Solve each equation for x. Then, solve each equation for y. See margin.

5. $x + y = 5$

6. $2x + y = 3$

7. $2x + 3y = 6$

8. $3y - \frac{1}{2}x = 7$

9. $0.75x + 6 = -0.8y$

10. $\frac{2}{3}x - \frac{4}{5}y = 3$

For each system of equations, use the first equation to make a substitution in the second equation. Then solve the second equation. See margin.

11. $y = 3 + 2x$
$x + y = 7$

12. $y = 7 - x$
$2x - y = 8$

13. $y = x$
$5x = 12y$

14. $x = 5 - y$
$3y = 3x + 1$

15. $3x = -18 + 2y$
$x + 3y = 4$

16. $2x = 3 - y$
$2y = 12 - x$

EXERCISES

Practice

Use substitution to solve each system of equations. If the system *does not* have exactly one solution, state whether it has no solution or infinitely many solutions. 22. infinitely many   25. no solution

17. $y = 3x$ $(-3, -9)$
$x + 2y = -21$

18. $y = 2x$ $\left(\frac{8}{5}, \frac{16}{5}\right)$
$x + 2y = 8$

19. $x = 2y$ $\left(3, \frac{3}{2}\right)$
$4x + 2y = 15$

20. $3x + y = 6$ $(2, 0)$
$y + 2 = x$

21. $2x - y = -4$ $(13, 30)$
$-3x + y = -9$

22. $x = 3 - 2y$
$2x + 4y = 6$

23. $2x + 3y = 5$ $\left(\frac{12}{5}, \frac{1}{15}\right)$
$4x - 9y = 9$

24. $x - 3y = 3$ $\left(4, \frac{1}{3}\right)$
$2x + 9y = 11$

25. $9x + 6y = 14$
$3x + 2y = 11$

26. $3x + y = 2$ $\left(\frac{1}{2}, \frac{1}{2}\right)$
$4x - 2y = 1$

27. $3x + 5y = 2x$ $(0, 0)$
$x + 3y = y$

28. $x - 2y = 5$ $(-9, -7)$
$3x - 5y = 8$

29. $2x + 3 = 3y$ $(3, 3)$
$4x - 3y = 3$

30. $3x - 2y = -3$ $(5, 9)$
$25x + 10y = 215$

31. $0.5x - 2y = 17$
$2x + y = 104$
$(50, 4)$

32. $3x + 2y = 18$ $(4, 3)$
$-\frac{1}{4}x - \frac{2}{3}y = -3$

33. $8x + 6y = 44$ $(4, 2)$
$\frac{1}{4}x - 2y = -3$

34. $0.3x + 0.2y = 0.5$
$0.5x - 0.3y = 0.2$
$(1, 1)$

450   CHAPTER 11   SYSTEMS OF OPEN SENTENCES

Additional Answers

1. From the first equation, you know that y is equal to $-5x + 1$, and y must have the same value in both equations.

4. The tens digit, t, is the number of tens and the ones digit, u, is the number of ones. Any two-digit number can be written as 10 times its number of tens plus its number of ones, or $10(t) + u$.

5. $x = 5 - y; y = 5 - x$

6. $x = \frac{3}{2} - \frac{1}{2}y; y = 3 - 2x$

7. $x = 3 - \frac{3}{2}y; y = 2 - \frac{2}{3}x$

8. $x = 6y - 14; y = \frac{7}{3} + \frac{1}{6}x$

9. $x = -\frac{0.8}{0.75}y - 8;$
$y = -\frac{0.75}{0.8}x - 7.5$

10. $x = \frac{9}{2} + \frac{6}{5}y; y = \frac{5}{6}x - \frac{15}{4}$

Use a system of equations and substitution to solve each problem.

35. A two-digit number is 6 times its units digit. Find the number if the sum of its digits is 6. **24**

36. A two-digit number is 2 more than 8 times the sum of its digits. Find the number if its tens digit is 6 more than its units digit. **82**

37. A two-digit number is 7 times its unit digit. If 18 is added to the number, its digits are reversed. Find the number. **35**

▶**C** **Use substitution to solve each system of equations. Write each solution as an ordered triple of the form (x, y, z). 40. (14, 27, −6)**

38. $x + y + z = -54$
$x = -6y$
$z = 14y$ **(36, −6, −84)**

39. $2x + 3y - z = 17$
$y = -3z - 7$
$2x = z + 2$ **(−1, 5, −4)**

40. $12x - y + 7z = 99$
$x + 2z = 2$
$y + 3z = 9$

Critical Thinking

41. If 36 is subtracted from a certain two-digit positive integer, then its digits are reversed. Find all integers for which this is true.
40, 51, 62, 73, 84, 95

Applications

42. **Sports** Eric is preparing to run in the Bay Marathon. One day, he ran and walked a total of 16 miles. If he ran one mile more than twice as far as he walked, how many miles did he run? **5 miles**

43. **Finance** Fina invests $4000, part of it at 10% annual interest and the rest at 12% annual interest. If she earned $460 in interest at the end of one year, how much did Fina invest at each rate?

43. **$1000 at 10% and $3000 at 12%**

44. **Chemistry** MX Labs needs to make 500 gallons of a 34% acid solution. The only solutions available are 25% acid and 50% acid. How many gallons of each solution should be mixed to make the 34% solution? **320 gallons of 25% solution and 180 gallons of 50% solution**

45. **Sales** Musicville had a sale on 500 assorted cassette tapes. Some tapes were sold for $10 while the rest were sold for $8. After all of the tapes were sold, the average price of a tape was $9.50. How many $8 tapes were sold? **125 tapes**

Mixed Review

46. Solve $|13 - 2y| < 9$ and graph its solution set. **(Lesson 5-6)**

47. Factor $x^3 + 2x^2 - 4x - 8$. **(Lesson 7-8)** $(x + 2)^2(x - 2)$ $\{y | 2 < y < 11\}$

48. **Sales** Amy works at Savemore Shoes. Her daily income is described by the formula $f(s) = 25 + 0.15s$, where s is the amount of her total sales for the day. If Amy earned $94 on Monday, what were her total sales that day? **(Lesson 9-6)** **$460**

49. Write the standard form of the equation of the line passing through $(-5, 1)$ and $(6, -2)$. **(Lesson 10-2)** $3x + 11y = -4$

50. Graph the equations $5x - 3y = 12$ and $2x - 5y = 1$. Then state the solution of the system of equations. **(Lesson 11-2)** **(3, 1)**

LESSON 11-3 SUBSTITUTION **451**

EXTENDING THE LESSON

Math Power: Connections

The sum of the digits of a three-digit number is 15. The tens digit exceeds the units digit by the same amount that the hundreds digit exceeds the tens digit. If the digits are reversed, the new number is 76 times the original hundreds digit. Find the original number. **654**

Additional Answers

11. $x + (3 + 2x) = 7; x = \frac{4}{3}$

12. $2x - (7 - x) = 8; x = 5$

13. $5x = 12x; x = 0$

14. $3y = 3(5 - y) + 1; y = \frac{8}{3}$

15. $\left(-6 + \frac{2}{3}y\right) + 3y = 4; y = \frac{30}{11}$

16. $2y = 12 - \left(\frac{3}{2} - \frac{1}{2}y\right); y = 7$

Lesson Resources

- Reteaching Master 11-4
- Practice Master 11-4
- Enrichment Master 11-4
- Video Algebra, 41-43

 Transparency 11-4 contains the 5-Minute Check and a teaching aid for this lesson.

INTRODUCING THE LESSON

 5-Minute Check

(over Lesson 11-3)

Solve each equation for x. Then, solve each equation for y.

1. $y + 1 = x$ $x = y + 1$, $y = x - 1$
2. $2x + 3y = 6$ $x = \frac{1}{2}(6 - 3y)$, $y = \frac{1}{3}(6 - 2x)$
3. $y + 2x = 3$ $x = \frac{1}{2}(3 - y)$, $y = 3 - 2x$
4. **The sum of the digits of a two-digit number is 13. Twice the tens digit is two less than 5 times the units digit. Find the number.**   94
5. **A two-digit number is 6 times its units digit. The sum of its digits is 3. Find the number.** 12

Motivating the Lesson

Tell students that you are thinking of two numbers whose sum is 30 and whose difference is 10. Ask them to identify the numbers. (20, 10) Have student volunteers make up additional problems like this one for the class to solve.

TEACHING THE LESSON

Teaching Tip ① To convince students that elimination is the easier way to solve this system of equations, first have them solve it using substitution.

11-4 Elimination Using Addition and Subtraction

Objective
11-4

After studying this lesson, you should be able to:
- solve systems of equations by the elimination method using addition or subtraction.

Application

FYI · · ·

The world's largest amusement park is Disney World, located on 28,000 acres in Central Florida.

Winona and Larry each had a birthday party at Water World last weekend. The cost of admission to Water World was $137.50 for the 13 children and 2 adults at Winona's party. The admission was $103.50 for the 9 children and 2 adults at Larry's party. What was the price of admission to Water World for an adult and for a child?

Let a = the price of admission for one adult, and let c = the price of admission for one child. Then the information in this problem can be represented by the following system of equations.

$$2a + 13c = 137.50$$
$$2a + 9c = 103.50$$

Teaching Tip ① You could solve this system by first solving either of the equations for either a or c and then using substitution. However, a simpler method is to subtract one equation from the other since the coefficients of the variable a are the same. This method is called **elimination** because the subtraction eliminates one of the variables.

$$\begin{array}{r} 2a + 13c = 137.50 \\ (-)\ 2a +\ \ 9c = 103.50 \\ \hline 4c =\ \ 34 \\ c = 8.5 \end{array}$$

Write the equations in column form and subtract.

Notice that the variable a is eliminated.

Now substitute 8.5 for c in either equation and find the value of a.

$$2a + 9c = 103.50$$
$$2a + 9(8.5) = 103.50 \quad \text{\textit{Substitute 8.5 for c.}}$$
$$2a + 76.50 = 103.50$$
$$2a = 27$$
$$a = 13.5$$

Check:

$$2a + 13c = 137.50 \qquad\qquad 2a + 9c = 103.50$$
$$2(13.5) + 13(8.5) \stackrel{?}{=} 137.50 \qquad 2(13.5) + 9(8.5) \stackrel{?}{=} 103.50$$
$$137.5 = 137.50 \ ✓ \qquad\qquad 103.5 = 103.50 \ ✓$$

ALTERNATE TEACHING STRATEGIES

Using Questioning

Can you give an example of a system of equations in which both variables would be eliminated by addition? What is the solution of your system of equations? Answers will vary. The solution will either be no solution (for inconsistent systems) or infinitely many solutions (for consistent and dependent systems).

The solution of this system of equations is (13.5, 8.5). Thus, the cost of admission to Water World is $13.50 for an adult and $8.50 for a child.

In some systems of equations, the coefficients of terms containing the same variable are additive inverses. For these systems, the elimination method can be applied by adding the equations.

Example 1

Use elimination to solve the system of equations $x - 4y = 6$ and $3x + 4y = 10$.

Since the coefficients of the y-terms, -4 and 4, are additive inverses, you can solve the system by adding the equations.

$$
\begin{array}{ll}
x - 4y = 6 & \text{\textit{Write the equations in column form and add.}} \\
\underline{(+)\ 3x + 4y = 10} & \\
\quad 4x \quad\ = 16 & \text{\textit{Notice that the variable y is eliminated.}} \\
\quad\ x = 4 &
\end{array}
$$

Now substitute 4 for x in either equation and find the value of y.

$$
\begin{aligned}
x - 4y &= 6 \\
4 - 4y &= 6 \\
-4y &= 2 \\
y &= -\frac{1}{2}
\end{aligned}
$$

The solution of the system is $\left(4, -\frac{1}{2}\right)$. *Check this result.*

Example 2

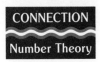
CONNECTION
Number Theory

The sum of two numbers is 42. Their difference is 6. Find the numbers.

Let x = the greater number.
Let y = the lesser number.

Since the sum of the numbers is 42, one equation is $x + y = 42$. Since the difference of the numbers is 6, another equation is $x - y = 6$. Use elimination to solve this system.

$$
\begin{array}{ll}
x + y = 42 & \\
\underline{(+)\ x - y = 6} & \text{\textit{Since the coefficients of the y-terms are}} \\
\quad 2x \quad\ = 48 & \text{\textit{additive inverses, use elimination by addition.}} \\
\quad\ x = 24 &
\end{array}
$$

$$
\begin{array}{ll}
x + y = 42 & \\
24 + y = 42 & \text{\textit{Substitute 24 for x.}} \\
\quad\ y = 18 & \text{\textit{Solve for y.}}
\end{array}
$$

The numbers are 24 and 18. *Check this result.*

LESSON 11-4 ELIMINATION USING ADDITION AND SUBTRACTION 453

Example 3

APPLICATION
Uniform Motion

A boat is rowed 24 miles downstream in 4 hours. In order to make the return trip upstream in the same amount of time, the rate of the boat in still water was doubled. Find the rate of the current and the rate of the boat in still water on the downstream trip.

EXPLORE Let b = the rate of the boat in still water on the downstream trip. Let c = the rate of the current. Then $2b$ = the rate of the boat in still water on the upstream trip.

Use the formula rate × time = distance, or $rt = d$.

	r	t	d	$rt = d$
Downstream	$b + c$	4	24	$4(b + c) = 24$
Upstream	$2b - c$	4	24	$4(2b - c) = 24$

Teaching Tip ②

PLAN

$4(b + c) = 24 \rightarrow b + c = 6$ *Divide each side of*
$4(2b - c) = 24 \rightarrow 2b - c = 6$ *both equations by 4.*

SOLVE

$$\begin{array}{r} b + c = 6 \\ (+)\ 2b - c = 6 \\ \hline 3b = 12 \\ b = 4 \end{array}$$

Since the coefficients of the c-terms are additive inverses, use elimination by addition.

$b + c = 6$ *Substitute 4 for b.*
$4 + c = 6$ *Solve for c.*
$c = 2$

The rate of the current is 2 miles per hour and the rate of the boat in still water on the downstream trip is 4 miles per hour.

EXAMINE The rate of the boat on the downstream trip is $4 + 2$ or 6 miles per hour. Its rate on the upstream trip is $2(4) - 2$ or 6 miles per hour. Since these rates are the same, the answer is correct.

CHECKING FOR UNDERSTANDING

Communicating Mathematics

Read and study the lesson to answer each question.

1. When is it easier to solve a system of equations by elimination using subtraction? **When the coefficients of either the *x*-terms or the *y*-terms are the same.**

2. When is it easier to solve a system of equations by elimination using addition? **When the coefficients of either the *x*-terms or the *y*-terms are additive inverses of each other.**

3. In Example 2, would you get the same answer if you let y = the greater number and x = the lesser number? Explain. **Yes, the numbers are the same but the solution is (18, 24) and not (24, 18).**

4. What is the result when you add $2x - 5y = 23$ and $-2x + 5y = 12$? What does the result tell you about the system of equations? **The result is $0 = 35$, which is false. Thus, the system has no solution.**

454 CHAPTER 11 SYSTEMS OF OPEN SENTENCES

RETEACHING THE LESSON

Let paper rectangles represent the coefficients of *x*, circles represent the coefficients of *y*, and squares represent constants. Use red for negatives and black for positives. Solve the system $x - 2y = 5$ and $2x + 2y = 7$.

Since there are 3 rectangles after adding, separate the squares into groups of 3. Since there are 4 groups, $x = 4$. Substitute 4 for x in either equation and solve for y.

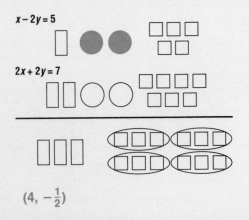

$x - 2y = 5$

$2x + 2y = 7$

$\left(4, -\frac{1}{2}\right)$

State whether addition, subtraction, both, or neither could be used to solve each system of equations. Then solve the system.

5. $3a + b = 6$
$4a + b = 7$
subtraction, $(1, 3)$

6. $m + 3n = 5$
$n + 2m = 3$
neither, $\left(\frac{4}{5}, \frac{7}{5}\right)$

7. $3x + y = 12$
$3y - 3x = 6$
addition, $\left(\frac{5}{2}, \frac{9}{2}\right)$

8. $5x + y = 9$
$y - 5x = 7$
both, $\left(\frac{1}{5}, 8\right)$

For each system of equations, first eliminate y. Then solve the system.

See margin.

9. $x + y = -3$
$2x + y = 6$

10. $x + y = 6$
$2x - y = 6$

11. $5x - 2y = 23$
$5x + 2y = 17$

12. $2x = 4 - 3y$
$3y - x = 11$

EXERCISES

Use elimination to solve each system of equations.

13. $x + y = 7$ $(8, -1)$
$x - y = 9$

14. $r - s = -5$ $(10, 15)$
$r + s = 25$

15. $2x - y = 32$ $(23, 14)$
$2x + y = 60$

16. $x - y = 3$ $(3, 0)$
$y + x = 3$

17. $-n + m = 6$ $\left(\frac{11}{2}, -\frac{1}{2}\right)$
$m + n = 5$

18. $x + y = 8$ $\left(\frac{14}{3}, \frac{10}{3}\right)$
$2x - y = 6$

19. $x + 2y = 8$ $\left(-1, \frac{9}{2}\right)$
$3x + 2y = 6$

20. $3x + 1 = -7y$ $\left(\frac{1}{3}, -\frac{2}{7}\right)$
$6x + 7y = 0$

21. $3x = 13 - y$ $(3, 4)$
$2x - y = 2$
$(8, -2)$

22. $2x - 3y = -4$ $(1, 2)$
$x = 7 - 3y$

23. $5s + 4t = 12$ $\left(2, \frac{1}{2}\right)$
$3s = 4 + 4t$

24. $12x - 9y = 114$
$7y + 12x = 82$

25. $4x - \frac{1}{3}y = 8$ $\left(\frac{14}{9}, -\frac{16}{3}\right)$
$5x + \frac{1}{3}y = 6$

26. $\frac{3}{4}x + \frac{1}{5}y = 5$ $(0, 25)$
$\frac{3}{4}x - \frac{1}{5}y = -5$

27. $\frac{2}{3}x - \frac{1}{2}y = 14$ $(24, 4)$
$\frac{5}{6}x - \frac{1}{2}y = 18$

28. $9x + 2y = 26$ $\left(\frac{26}{7}, -\frac{26}{7}\right)$
$1.5x - 2y = 13$

29. $3x + 0.2y = 7$ $(2, 5)$
$3x = 0.4y + 4$

30. $0.6m - 0.2n = 0.9$
$0.3m = 0.9 - 0.2n$
$(2, 1.5)$

Use a system of equations and elimination to solve each problem.

31. Find two numbers whose sum is 64 and whose difference is 42. **11, 53**

32. The units digit of a two-digit number exceeds twice the tens digit by 1. Find the number if the sum of its digits is 7. **25**

Use elimination twice to solve each system of equations. Write each answer as an ordered triple of the form (x, y, z).

33. $x - y + 2z = 8$
$2x + y + z = 13$
$4x - 3z = 7$ $(4, 2, 3)$

34. $-3x + y - z = 6$
$3x - 2y + 2z = -9$
$-y - 3z = 1$ $(-1, 2, -1)$

35. $5x - 2y + z = 0$
$2x - y + z = -3$
$3x + 4y = 18$
$(2, 3, -4)$

36. **Statistics** The mean of two numbers is 28. Find the numbers if 3 times one of the numbers equals half the other number. **8, 48**

37. Find the values of A and B if $(11, -5)$ is the only solution to the system of equations $Ax + By = 7$ and $Ax + (1 - 2B)y = 47$. $A = 2$, $B = 3$

LESSON 11-4 ELIMINATION USING ADDITION AND SUBTRACTION **455**

Additional Answers

9. $-x = -9$; $(9, -12)$
10. $3x = 12$; $(4, 2)$
11. $10x = 40$; $\left(4, -\frac{3}{2}\right)$
12. $3x = -7$; $\left(-\frac{7}{3}, \frac{26}{9}\right)$

Applications

Teaching Tip ③

38. **Conferences** Last year, 2713 teachers attended a technology conference. If there were 163 more men than women at the conference, how many men and how many women attended?

39. **Testing** Jerrod received a total score of 1340 on the Scholastic Aptitude Test (SAT). His math score was 400 points less than twice his verbal score. What was his math score and his verbal score?

40. **Uniform Motion** In still water, a speedboat travels 5 times faster than the current of the river. If the speedboat can travel 48 miles upstream and then back in 5 hours, find the rate of the current. **4 mph**

38. 1438 men and 1275 women   39. math: 760 points, verbal: 580 points

Mixed Review

41. Translate *the sum of y and the cube of n is equal to twice x* into an equation. **(Lesson 1-7)** $y + n^3 = 2x$

42. Solve $12m^2 + 3 = -20m$. Check your solution. **(Lesson 7-10)** $-\frac{1}{6}, -\frac{3}{2}$

43. Determine the domain, range, and inverse for {(5, 1), (−3, 2), (4, 2), (5, 0), (2, 2)}. **(Lesson 9-2) See margin.**

44. **Aviation** An airplane passing over Sacramento at an elevation of 37,000 feet begins its descent to land at Reno, 140 miles away. If the elevation of Reno is 4500 feet, what should be the approximate slope of descent? **(Lesson 10-1)** **4.4% or $\frac{11}{250}$**

45. Use substitution to solve the system of equations $y = -2x + 8$ and $3x - y = 17$. **(Lesson 11-3) (5, −2)**

MID-CHAPTER REVIEW

1. 376 teams are playing in a single-elimination basketball tournament. If a team loses one game, it is out of the tournament. How many games must be played before the winning team can be determined? **(Lesson 11-1) 375 games**

Graph each system of equations. Then determine if the system has one solution, no solution, or infinitely many solutions. If the system has one solution, name it. **(Lesson 11-2)**

2. $x - y = 3$ **(1, −2)**
   $3x + y = 1$

3. $2x - 3y = 7$
   $3y = 7 + 2x$
   no solution

4. $4x + y = 12$
   $x = 3 - \frac{1}{4}y$
   infinitely many

5. $2x - y = 3$
   $\frac{2}{3}x = y - 1$
   (3, 3)

Use substitution to solve each system of equations. **(Lesson 11-3)**

6. $y = 5x$ **(2, 10)**
   $x + 2y = 22$

7. $x = 2y + 3$ **(1, −1)**
   $3x + 4y = -1$

8. $2y - x = -5$
   $4y - 3x = -1$
   (−9, −7)

9. $3x + 2y = 18$
   $\frac{1}{4}x + \frac{2}{3}y = 3$
   (4, 3)

10. **Uniform Motion** Odina walks from her house to a friend's house in 1 hour. She can travel the same distance on her bicycle in 15 minutes. If she rides 6 miles per hour faster than she can walk, what is her speed on the bicycle? **(Lesson 11-3) 8 mph**

456 CHAPTER 11 SYSTEMS OF OPEN SENTENCES

EXTENDING THE LESSON

Math Power: Connections

The graphs of the equations $x - y = 1$, $x + y = 3$, and $-x + 5y = 19$ contain the sides of a triangle. Write the equation of the line that passes through the midpoint of the shortest side of the triangle and the vertex opposite the shortest side.
$x - 2y = -4$

Mid-Chapter Review

The Mid-Chapter Review provides students with a brief review of the concepts and skills in Lessons 11-1 through 11-4. Lesson numbers are given at the end of problems or instruction lines so students may review concepts not yet mastered.

Elimination Using Multiplication

Objective
11-5

After studying this lesson, you should be able to:
- solve systems of equations by the elimination method using multiplication and addition.

Application

A-1 Car Rental rents compact cars for a fixed amount per day plus a fixed amount for each mile driven. Benito Sanchez rented a car from A-1 for 6 days, drove it 550 miles, and spent $337. Lisa McGuire rented the same car for 3 days, drove it 350 miles, and spent $185. What are the charge per day and charge per mile driven, excluding gas, insurance, and taxes?

Let d = the charge per day for renting the car, and let m = the charge per mile driven. Then the information in this problem can be represented by the following system of equations.

$$6d + 550m = 337$$
$$3d + 350m = 185$$

Neither of the variables in this system can be eliminated by simply adding or subtracting the equations. Substitution could be used but the computations would not be easy. A simpler method is to multiply one of the equations by some number so that adding or subtracting eliminates one of the variables. For this system, multiply the second equation by -2 and add.

$$\begin{array}{ll} 6d + 550m = 337 \\ 3d + 350m = 185 \end{array} \xrightarrow{\text{Multiply by } -2.}$$

$$\begin{array}{r} 6d + 550m = 337 \\ (+) -6d - 700m = -370 \\ \hline -150m = -33 \\ m = 0.22 \end{array}$$

$$6d + 550m = 337$$
$$6d + 550(0.22) = 337 \qquad \textit{Substitute 0.22 for m.}$$
$$6d + 121 = 337 \qquad \textit{Solve for d.}$$
$$6d = 216$$
$$d = 36$$

Check:

$$\begin{array}{ll} 6d + 550m = 337 & 3d + 350m = 185 \\ 6(36) + 550(0.22) \stackrel{?}{=} 337 & 3(36) + 350(0.22) \stackrel{?}{=} 185 \\ 337 = 337 \ \checkmark & 185 = 185 \ \checkmark \end{array}$$

The solution to the system is $(36, 0.22)$. Thus, the charge per day is $36 and the charge per mile driven is $0.22 for this compact car.

For some systems of equations, it is necessary to multiply *each* equation by a different number in order to solve the system by elimination. This can be accomplished in several ways, depending on which of the variables you choose to eliminate.

LESSON 11-5 ELIMINATION USING MULTIPLICATION **457**

ALTERNATE TEACHING STRATEGIES

Using Problem Solving

Sue is $\frac{1}{5}$ of the way across a bridge on her bicycle when she sees a car approaching the bridge. The speed of the car is 55 mph. How fast should Sue bicycle if she wishes to turn around and reach the same end of the bridge at the same time as the car?
11 mph

Using Logical Reasoning

If the graph of one of the equations in a system is a vertical or horizontal line, what method would you use to solve the system? **Answers will vary; however, substitution is the easiest.**

Teaching Tip ① Emphasize that there are many other combinations of multipliers that can be used. You may want to have students suggest other multipliers.

Example 1

Use elimination to solve the system of equations $3x + 4y = -25$ and $2x - 3y = 6$ in two different ways.

Method 1 You can eliminate the variable x by multiplying the first equation by 2 and the second equation by −3 and then adding the resulting equations. **Teaching Tip** ①

$3x + 4y = -25$ Multiply by 2. $6x + 8y = -50$

$2x - 3y = 6$ Multiply by −3. $(+)\ -6x + 9y = -18$
$$17y = -68$$
$$y = -4$$

Now find x using one of the original equations.

$3x + 4y = -25$
$3x + 4(-4) = -25$ *Substitute −4 for y.*
$3x - 16 = -25$ *Solve for x.*
$3x = -9$
$x = -3$

The solution of the system is $(-3, -4)$.

Method 2 You can also solve this system by eliminating the variable y. Multiply the first equation by 3 and the second equation by 4. Then add.

$3x + 4y = -25$ Multiply by 3. $9x + 12y = -75$

$2x - 3y = 6$ Multiply by 4. $(+)\ 8x - 12y = 24$
$$17x = -51$$
$$x = -3$$

Now find y.

$3x + 4y = -25$
$3(-3) + 4y = -25$ *Substitute −3 for x.*
$-9 + 4y = -25$ *Solve for y.*
$4y = -16$
$y = -4$

The solution is $(-3, -4)$, which matches the result obtained above.

Example 2

APPLICATION

Banking

A bank teller accidentally reversed the digits in the amount of a check and overpaid a customer by $36. If the sum of the digits in the two-digit amount was 10, what was the actual amount of the check?

EXPLORE   Let t = the tens digit of the amount of the check.
Let u = the units digit.
The actual amount of the check can be represented by $10t + u$.
The amount paid by the teller can be represented by $10u + t$.
Why?

PLAN   Since the sum of the digits is 10, one equation is $t + u = 10$.
Since the teller overpaid the customer by $36, another equation is $(10u + t) - (10t + u) = 36$, or $-9t + 9u = 36$.

SOLVE

$$t + u = 10$$
$$-9t + 9u = 36$$

→ Multiply by 9. →

$$9t + 9u = 90$$
$$(+) -9t + 9u = 36$$
$$\overline{\hspace{1.5cm} 18u = 126}$$
$$u = 7$$

$$t + u = 10$$
$$t + 7 = 10 \quad \textit{Substitute 7 for u.}$$
$$t = 3 \quad \textit{Solve for t.}$$

The actual amount of the check was 10(3) + 7, or $37.
Check this result.

Example 3

A coal barge on the Ohio River travels 24 miles upstream in 3 hours. The return trip takes the barge only 2 hours. Find the rate of the barge in still water.

EXPLORE   Let b = the rate of the barge in still water.
Let c = the rate of the current.

PLAN   Use the formula $rt = d$ to write a system of equations.
Then solve the system to find the value of b.

	r	t	d	$rt = d$
Downstream	$b + c$	2	24	$2b + 2c = 24$
Upstream	$b - c$	3	24	$3b - 3c = 24$

Teaching Tip ❷

SOLVE

$$3b - 3c = 24$$ → Multiply by 2. → $$6b - 6c = 48$$

$$2b + 2c = 24$$ → Multiply by 3. → $$(+) \; 6b + 6c = 72$$
$$\overline{\hspace{1cm} 12b \hspace{1cm} = 120}$$
$$b = 10$$

The rate of the barge in still water is 10 miles per hour.
Find the value of c for this system and then check the solution.

CHECKING FOR UNDERSTANDING

Communicating Mathematics

Read and study the lesson to answer each question.

1. Are $5x - 7y = 3$ and $-15x + 21y = -9$ equivalent equations? **yes**

2. When using elimination to solve a system of equations, why might you need to multiply each equation by a different number? **In order to make either the x-term or y-term coefficients additive inverses.**

3. Write a system of equations where you can eliminate the variable y by multiplying one equation by 3 and then adding the equations. **Answers will vary; a typical answer is $x - y = 1$ and $x + 3y = 1$.**

LESSON 11-5 ELIMINATION USING MULTIPLICATION 459

RETEACHING THE LESSON

Have students go through a list of systems of equations and write which process would be best to use in order to solve (substitution, elimination using addition or subtraction, or elimination using multiplication). If elimination using multiplication is the process, have students use it to solve the problem.

Reteaching Masters Booklet, p. 78

Chapter 11   459

Checking for Understanding

Exercises 1-11 are designed to help you assess understanding through reading, writing, and speaking. You should work through Exercises 1-3 with your students, and then monitor their work on Exercises 4-11.

Closing the Lesson

Speaking Activity Ask students to describe how to solve a system of equations by the elimination method using multiplication and addition.

APPLYING THE LESSON

Homework Exercises

Assignment Guide
Basic: 12-28, 32-34, 38-41
Average: 15-29, 32-41
Enriched: 18-41

Practice Masters Booklet, p. 88

Guided Practice Explain the steps you would follow to eliminate the variable *x* in each system of equations. Then solve the system. **See margin.**

4. $x + 2y = 5$
$3x + y = 7$

5. $4x + y = 8$
$x - 7y = 2$

6. $y + x = 9$
$2y - x = 1$

7. $2x + y = 6$
$3x - 7y = 9$

For each system of equations, use multiplication and then addition to eliminate the variable *y*. Then solve the system. **See margin.**

8. $x + 8y = 3$
$4x - 2y = 7$

9. $4x - y = 4$
$x + 2y = 3$

10. $3y - 8x = 9$
$y - x = 2$

11. $5y - 4x = 2$
$2y + x = 6$

EXERCISES

Practice Use elimination to solve each system of equations.

12. $x - 5y = 0$ (5, 1)
$2x - 3y = 7$

13. $x + 4y = 30$ $\left(\frac{2}{3}, \frac{22}{3}\right)$
$2x - y = -6$

14. $9x + 8y = 7$ $\left(\frac{7}{9}, 0\right)$
$18x - 15y = 14$

15. $-5x + 8y = 21$ $\left(\frac{3}{5}, 3\right)$
$10x + 3y = 15$

16. $5x + 3y = 12$ (3, -1)
$4x - 5y = 17$

17. $4x + 3y = 19$
$3x - 4y = 8$ (4, 1)

18. $7x + 2y = 3(x + 16)$
$x + 16 = 5y + 3x$
(13, -2)

19. $2x - y = 36$ (4, -28)
$3x - 0.5y = 26$

20. $x - 0.5y = 1$
$0.4x + y = -2$
(0, -2)

21. $\frac{1}{3}x - y = -1$
$\frac{1}{5}x - \frac{2}{5}y = -1$ ($-9, -2$)

22. $\frac{1}{2}x - \frac{2}{3}y = \frac{7}{3}$
$\frac{3}{2}x + 2y = -25$ ($-6, -8$)

23. $\frac{2x + y}{3} = 15$
$\frac{3x - y}{5} = 1$ (10, 25)

24. $x + y = 600$
$0.06x + 0.08y = 46$
(100, 500)

25. $x + y = 20$ (4, 16)
$0.4x + 0.15y = 4$

26. $0.25(x + 4y) = 3.5$
$0.5x - 0.25y = 1$
$\left(\frac{10}{3}, \frac{8}{3}\right)$

CONNECTION
Number Theory

Use a system of equations and elimination to solve each problem.

27. The sum of the digits of a two-digit number is 7. If the digits are reversed, the new number is 3 less than 4 times the original number. Find the number. **16**

28. The ratio of the tens digit to the units digit of a two-digit number is 1:4. If the digits are reversed, the sum of the new number and the original number is 110. Find the number. **28**

Use elimination to solve each system of equations.

29. $\frac{2}{x + 7} - \frac{1}{y - 3} = 0$
$\frac{1}{x - 5} - \frac{3}{y + 6} = 0$ (11, 12)

30. $\frac{1}{x} + \frac{1}{y} = 7$ $\left(\frac{1}{5}, \frac{1}{2}\right)$
$\frac{2}{x} + \frac{3}{y} = 16$

31. $\frac{1}{x + y} = 2$ $\left(\frac{1}{3}, \frac{1}{6}\right)$
$\frac{1}{x - y} = \frac{1}{y}$

Critical Thinking 32. Explain how the elimination or substitution methods show that a system of equations is inconsistent or that a system of equations is consistent and dependent. **See margin.**

Additional Answers

4. Multiply the first equation by -3, then add; $\left(\frac{9}{5}, \frac{8}{5}\right)$.

5. Multiply the second equation by -4, then add; (2, 0)

6. Add; $\left(\frac{17}{3}, \frac{10}{3}\right)$.

7. Multiply the first equation by 3, multiply the second equation by -2, then add; (3, 0).

8. Multiply the second equation by 4, then add; $\left(\frac{31}{17}, \frac{5}{34}\right)$.

9. Multiply the first equation by 2, then add; $\left(\frac{11}{9}, \frac{8}{9}\right)$.

10. Multiply the second equation by -3, then add; $\left(-\frac{3}{5}, \frac{7}{5}\right)$.

11. Multiply the first equation by 2, multiply the second equation by -5, then add; (2, 2).

33. **Uniform Motion** A riverboat traveled 48 miles downstream in 2 hours. The return trip upstream took 2 hours and 40 minutes.
    a. Find the rate of the riverboat in still water. **21 mph**
    b. Find the rate of the current. **3 mph**

34. **Sales** The concession stand sells hot dogs and soda during Beck High School football games. John bought 6 hot dogs and 4 sodas and paid $6.70. Jessica bought 4 hot dogs and 3 sodas and paid $4.65.
    a. What is the price of a hot dog? **$0.75**
    b. What is the price of a soda? **$0.55**

35. **Uniform Motion** Traveling against the wind, a plane flies 2100 miles from Chicago to San Diego in 4 hours and 40 minutes. The return trip, traveling with a wind that is twice as fast, takes 4 hours. Find the rate of the plane in still air. **475 mph**

36. **Sales** The Beach Resort is offering two weekend specials. One includes a 2-night stay with 3 meals and costs $195. The other includes a 3-night stay with 5 meals and costs $300.
    a. What is the cost of a 1-night stay? **$75**
    b. What is the cost per meal? **$15**

Computer

Teaching Tip ③

37. The BASIC program at the right finds the solution of the following system of equations.
    $$ax + by = c$$
    $$dx + ey = f$$
    The formulas for the solution of this system are as follows.
    $$x = \frac{ce - bf}{ae - bd}, \quad y = \frac{af - cd}{ae - bd}$$

    Use the program to solve each system.

```
10 PRINT "ENTER THE COEFFICIENTS."
20 INPUT A,B,C,D,E,F
30 IF A*E-B*D=0 THEN 80
40 LET X = (C*E-B*F)/(A*E-B*D)
50 LET Y = (A*F-C*D)/(A*E-B*D)
60 PRINT "(";X;" , ";Y;") IS A
   SOLUTION."
70 GOTO 10
80 IF C*E-B*F=0 OR A*F-C*D=0
   THEN 110
90 PRINT "NO SOLUTION."
100 GOTO 10
110 PRINT "INFINITE NUMBER OF
    SOLUTIONS."
120 GOTO 10
130 END
```

    a. $5x + 5y = 16$
       $2x + 2y = 5$ **no solution**

    b. $7x - 3y = 5$ **infinite**
       $14x - 6y = 10$ **solutions**

    c. $x - 2y = 5$
       $3x - 5y = 8$ $(-9, -7)$

    d. $6x + 3y = 0$ **infinite**
       $4x + 2y = 0$ **solutions**

Mixed Review

38. Solve $\frac{1}{3}a + 3 = \frac{1}{2}a$. Check your solution. **(Lesson 3-7) 18**

39. **Gardening** Ms. Salgado has a rectangular garden that is 12 feet longer than it is wide. In order to surround the garden with railroad ties, she must reduce each side of the garden by 1 foot. In all, she reduced the area of the garden by 55 square feet. What were the original dimensions of her garden? **(Lesson 6-8) 34 ft by 22 ft**

40. Divide $\frac{m + 4}{m^2 + 4m + 4}$ by $\frac{m^2 - 16}{4m + 8}$. **(Lesson 8-3)** $\frac{4}{(m + 2)(m - 4)}$

41. Use elimination to solve the system of equations $x - 2y = 12$ and $-3x + 2y = 16$. **(Lesson 11-4)** $(-14, -13)$

LESSON 11-5 ELIMINATION USING MULTIPLICATION 461

EXTENDING THE LESSON

Math Power: Connections

The graphs of the equations $5x + 4y = 18$, $2x + 9y = 59$, and $3x - 5y = -4$ contain the sides of a triangle. Determine the vertices of the triangle. $(-2, 7)$, $(2, 2)$, $(7, 5)$

Additional Answer

32. When using either method, if you ever reach an equation such as $0 = 3$, which is always false, then the system is inconsistent. If you ever reach an equation such as $0 = 0$, which is always true, then the system is consistent and dependent.

Chapter 11, Quiz C, (Lessons 11-4 through 11-5), is available in the Evaluation Masters Booklet, p. 150.

Teaching Tip ③ Point out to students that Cramer's Rule is used in this program. Discuss the sequence of lines executed for the exercises. Combine the use of the program with the graphing calculator method in the Technology Feature.

Enrichment Masters Booklet, p. 78

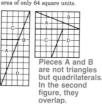
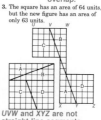

11-5 **Enrichment Worksheet**

NAME _____ DATE _____

Geometric Vanishing Acts

Puzzles of this type use a "trick" drawing. It appears that rearranging the pieces of each figure causes one or more squares to disappear.

Make figures of your own on graph paper. Then explain the "trick" in each puzzle.

1. The rectangle has an area of 65 square units, but the square has an area of only 64 square units.

Pieces A and B are not triangles but quadrilaterals. In the second figure, they overlap.

2. The square has an area of 64 square units, but the rectangle has an area of only 63 square units.

The triangle C actually has a height of $1\frac{1}{7}$ units, so the rectangle is really $9\frac{1}{7}$ units high.

3. The square has an area of 64 units, but the new figure has an area of only 63 units.

UVW and XYZ are not straight line segments. Thus, some "unit squares" of the second figure are not squares at all.

4. Rearranging the square on the left causes a 2-unit "hole" to appear.

Piece A is a quadrilateral, not a triangle. Thus, in the second figure, the tops of pieces B and C overlap the portions of piece A.

Objective This optional page shows how the graphing calculator can be used to perform mathematical computations and to enhance and extend mathematical concepts.

Teaching Suggestions

Point out to students that you will get the same answer by solving the system of equations algebraically as you will by solving the system of equations graphically. You may want to solve a pair of equations algebraically to demonstrate this fact. This is an important connection for your students.

Also point out that many times you may not be able to find an *exact* solution to a system of equations. You can trace to a point and it may not be the exact solution. It can, however, be an approximation. The key is knowing when the approximation is an appropriate solution.

You may want to experiment with the zoom features of your calculator. It can help you illustrate the exact solution point. If you graph some of the exercises in the standard viewing window and use trace and zoom, students will see the difficulty in trying to find an exact solution. The TI-81 has a ZOOM key, and there are a number of ways to zoom. You can also zoom in on the Casio by pressing [SHIFT] [×].

Zooming will "blow up" the area you are looking at. To zoom, simply trace to the intersection point of the equations and zoom in. If you decide to do this, check the range. It will automatically change.

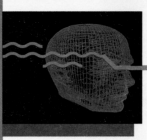

Technology

Solving Systems of Equations

BASIC
▶ **Graphing calculators**
Graphing software
Spreadsheets

Your graphing calculator can help you determine if a solution of a system of equations exists and, if it does, the calculator can help you find it. Using the trace function, you can move to the intersection of two lines and read the x- and y-values of the point of intersection.

Example

Graph the system $3x + y = 8$ and $x + y = 4$. Then find its solution.

For the TI-81

Set your calculator for the standard viewing window of $[-10, 10]$ by $[-10, 10]$. Then enter the equations and graph. You must first solve each equation for y.

$3x + y = 8 \rightarrow y = -3x + 8$
$x + y = 4 \rightarrow y = -x + 4$

[Y=] [(-)] 3 [X|T] [+] 8 [ENTER]

[(-)] [X|T] [+] 4 [GRAPH]

For the Casio

Set your calculator for the default viewing window. Then enter the equations and graph.

[Graph] [(-)] 3 [ALPHA] [X] [+] 8 [:]

[Graph] [(-)] [ALPHA] [X] [+] 4 [EXE]

Trace along the graph to the point of intersection. Use the [TRACE] and arrow keys. On the Casio, use the [X–Y] key to show the y-value. The solution is $(2, 2)$.

EXERCISES

Graph each pair of equations and use the trace key to find the solution. For the TI-81, use the viewing window $[-5, 5]$ by $[-5, 5]$. For the Casio, use the viewing window $[-4.7, 4.7]$ by $[-3.1, 3.1]$.

1. $y = 3x - 3$ $(1, 0)$
   $y = -3x + 3$

2. $y = 2$ $(-1, 2)$
   $y = 3x + 5$

3. $y = 2x - 4$ $(3, 2)$
   $y = -4x + 14$

4. $y = x$ $(-2, -2)$
   $y = 4x + 6$

5. $y = -0.8x + 1.28$
   $y = 0.4x - 1.24$
   $(2.1, -0.4)$

6. $y = 0.4x + 0.6$
   $y = -0.1x + 0.3$
   $(-1, -0.2)$

Graphing Systems of Inequalities

Objective 11-6

After studying this lesson, you should be able to:

■ solve systems of inequalities by graphing.

Consider the system of inequalities shown below.

$y \geq x + 2$
$y \leq -2x - 1$

The solution of the system is the set of all ordered pairs that satisfy *both* inequalities. This solution can be determined by graphing each inequality in the same coordinate plane as shown below.

Refer to Lesson 9-7 to review graphing inequalities in two variables.

Recall that the graph of each inequality is called a *half-plane*. The intersection of the two half-planes represents the solution to the system of inequalities. This solution is a region that contains the graphs of an infinite number of ordered pairs. The graphs of $y = x + 2$ and $y = -2x - 1$ are the boundaries of the region and are included in the graph of the system.

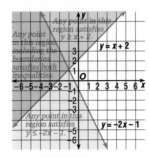

Example 1

Solve each system of inequalities by graphing.

a. $y > x - 3$ and $y \leq -1$

The solution is the ordered pairs in the intersection of the graphs of $y > x - 3$ and $y \leq -1$. This region is shaded in green at the right. The graphs of $y = -1$ and $y = x - 3$ are the boundaries of this region. The graph of $y = x - 3$ is a dashed line and is *not* included in the graph of the system.

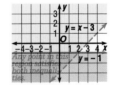

b. $x - 2y \leq -4$ and $4y < 2x - 4$

The graphs of $x - 2y = -4$ and $4y = 2x - 4$ are parallel lines. Because the two regions have no points in common, the system of inequalities has no solutions.

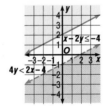

Lesson Resources

- Reteaching Master 11-6
- Practice Master 11-6
- Enrichment Master 11-6
- Video Algebra, 44
 Transparency 11-6 contains the 5-Minute Check and a teaching aid for this lesson.

INTRODUCING THE LESSON

🕐 5-Minute Check
(over Lesson 11-5)

Use elimination to solve each system of equations.

1. $\frac{1}{3}x - \frac{5}{6}y = -6$
   $4x + 7y = 30$ $(-3, 6)$
2. $2a + b = 19$
   $3a - 2b = -3$ $(5, 9)$
3. $x - y = 6$
   $x + y = 5$ $\left(\frac{11}{2}, -\frac{1}{2}\right)$
4. $x + y = 8$
   $2x - y = -6$ $\left(\frac{2}{3}, \frac{22}{3}\right)$
5. $y = 2x$
   $2x + y = 10$ $\left(\frac{5}{2}, 5\right)$

Motivating the Lesson

Open the lesson with a review of the methods for graphing a linear equation and a linear inequality. Review the method for testing an ordered pair on one side of the boundary line of the equation to determine which side of the graph to shade.

ALTERNATE TEACHING STRATEGIES

Using Problem Solving

Write a system of inequalities of the graph below.

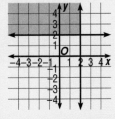

$x \leq 2, y \geq 2$

Chalkboard Examples

For Example 1

Solve the system by graphing.

a. $y < -2x + 4$ and $y > 3x - 4$

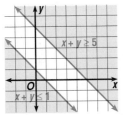

The solution is the intersection of the shaded regions.

b. $x + y \geq 5$ and $x + y \leq 1$

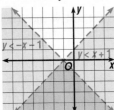

The system has no solution.

For Example 2

Solve the inequality $|x + 1| < -y$ by graphing.

This is equivalent to the system $y < x + 1$ and $y < -x - 1$.

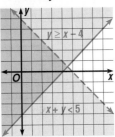

The solution is the intersection of the shaded regions.

For Example 3

Solve the following system of inequalities by graphing.
$x + y < 5$ and $y \geq x - 4$

The solution is the intersection of the shaded regions.

The solution to an inequality that contains an absolute value expression can also be determined by graphing. To do this, write the absolute value inequality as a system of inequalities that does not contain absolute value expressions.

Example 2

Solve the inequality $y \geq |x|$ by graphing.

The inequality $y \geq |x|$ is equivalent to the system of inequalities $y \geq x$ and $y \leq -x$. The solution is the set of all ordered pairs whose graphs are in the intersection of the graphs of these two inequalities. This region is shown in green at the right. The parts of the graphs of $y = x$ and $y = -x$ that are boundaries of this region are included in the graph of the system.

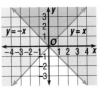

Example 3

APPLICATION
Agriculture

To ensure a growing season of sufficient length, Mr. Hobson has at most 16 days left to plant his corn and soybean crops. He can plant corn at a rate of 10 acres per day and soybeans at a rate of 15 acres per day. If he has at most 200 acres available, how many acres of each type of crop can he plant?

Let c = the number of days that corn will be planted.
Let s = the number of days that soybeans will be planted.
Since both c and s represent a number of days, neither can be a negative number. Thus, $c \geq 0$ and $s \geq 0$.

Then the following system of inequalities can be used to represent the conditions of this problem.

$c + s \leq 16$
$10c + 15s \leq 200$, where $c \geq 0$ and $s \geq 0$

The solution is the set of all ordered pairs whose graphs are in the intersection of the graphs of these inequalities. This region is shown in tan at the right. Only the portion of the region in the first quadrant is used since $c \geq 0$ and $s \geq 0$.

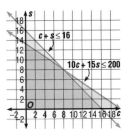

Any point in this region is a possible solution. For example, since $(7, 8)$ is a point in the region, Mr. Hobson could plant corn for 7 days and soybeans for 8 days. In this case, he would use 15 days to plant $10(7)$ or 70 acres of corn and $15(8)$ or 120 acres of soybeans.

CHECKING FOR UNDERSTANDING

Communicating Mathematics

Read and study the lesson to answer each question.

1. If a system of inequalities has a solution, how many ordered pairs will be contained in the region that is the solution? **an infinite number**

2. What are the equations of the four lines that are the boundaries of the region in Example 3? $c + s = 16$, $10c + 15s = 200$, $c = 0$, $s = 0$

3. Write a system of inequalities that has no solutions. **Answers will vary; a typical answer is $x + y < 1$ and $x + y > 2$.**

Guided Practice

State whether each ordered pair is a solution of the system of inequalities $x \le 3$ and $y > 6$.

4. $(3, 7)$ **yes**

5. $(-2, 6)$ **no**

6. $(7, 8)$ **no**

7. $(0, 8)$ **yes**

State which region in the graph at the right is the solution of each system of inequalities.

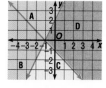

8. $y \ge 2x + 2$
   $y \le -x - 1$ **B**

9. $y \ge 2x + 2$
   $y \ge -x - 1$ **A**

10. $y \le 2x + 2$
    $y \le -x - 1$ **C**

11. $y \le 2x + 2$
    $y \ge -x - 1$ **D**

EXERCISES

Practice

Solve each system of inequalities by graphing. **See Solutions Manual.**

 A

12. $x > 3$
    $y < 6$

13. $y > 0$
    $x \le 0$

14. $y > 2$
    $y > -x + 2$

15. $y < -2$
    $y - x > 1$

16. $x \le 2$
    $y - 3 \ge 5$

17. $x \ge 1$
    $y + x \le 3$

18. $|y| < x$

19. $|x| \ge y$

 B

20. $y \ge 2x + 1$
    $y \le -x + 1$

21. $y \le x + 3$
    $y \ge x + 2$

22. $y \ge 3x$
    $3y \le 5x$

23. $y \ge x - 3$
    $y \ge -x - 1$

24. $y - x < 1$
    $y - x > 3$

25. $2y + x < 4$
    $3x - y > 6$

26. $y + 2 < x$
    $2y - 3 > 2x$

27. $x + 2y \le 7$
    $3x - 4y < 1$

28. $|y| + 1 < x$

29. $|y| > x + 3$

30. $|y - 4| > x$

31. $|2y + 4| \le x$

Determine whether the point of intersection of the two boundaries is part of the solution set for each system of inequalities.

32. $y < -x$
    $x \ge 6$ **no**

33. $y + 4 \le 8$
    $2y \le x$ **yes**

34. $x + 3y \ge 4$
    $2x - y < 5$ **no**

RETEACHING THE LESSON

Have students use the graph to determine whether each point is a solution of the system of inequalities.

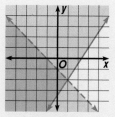

1. $(3, 0)$ **no**
2. $(-3, 0)$ **yes**
3. $(-1, -5)$ **yes**
4. $(1, -2)$ **no**
5. $(-4, 3)$ **no**
6. $(-3, -3)$ **yes**

Write a system of inequalities for the graph and check the answers by substituting into the inequalities.

$y < -x - 1$, $y \ge \frac{3}{2}x - \frac{7}{2}$

NAME _____ DATE _____

11-6 Reteaching Worksheet

Graphing Systems of Inequalities

The solution of a system of inequalities is the set of all ordered pairs that satisfy both inequalities. To find the solution of the system

$y > x + 2$
$y \le -2x - 1$,

graph each inequality. The graph of each inequality is called a **half-plane**. The intersection of the half-planes represents the solution of the system. The graphs of $y = x + 2$ and $y = -2x - 1$ are the boundaries of the region.

An inequality containing an absolute value expression can be graphed by graphing an equivalent system of two inequalities.

Solve each system of inequalities by graphing.

1. $y \ge 2x$
   $y \ge -1$

2. $5x - 2y < 6$
   $y > -x + 1$

3. $|y| > x$

4. $-x + y \le 6$
   $x + y \le 2$

5. Write a system of inequalities for the graph at the right.
   $x + y \le 2$
   $x > 1$

47.

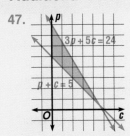

Answers will vary. Possible solutions: 1 lb of cashews, 6 lb of peanuts; 3 lb of cashews, 3 lb of peanuts; 4 lb of cashews, 1 lb of peanuts

48.

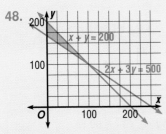

Answers will vary. Possible solutions: 25 students, 175 others; 50 students, 140 others; 100 students, 100 others

Practice Masters Booklet, p. 89

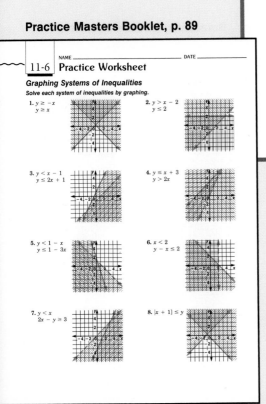

Write a system of inequalities for each graph.

35.

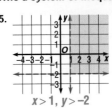

$x > 1, \ y > -2$

36.

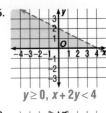

$y \geq 0, \ x + 2y < 4$

37.

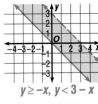

$y \geq -x, \ y < 3 - x$

38.

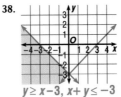

$y \geq x - 3, \ x + y \leq -3$

39.

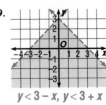

$y < 3 - x, \ y < 3 + x$

40.

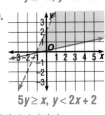

$5y \geq x, \ y < 2x + 2$

 41.

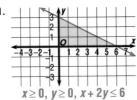

$x \geq 0, \ y \geq 0, \ x + 2y \leq 6$

42.

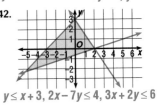

$y \leq x + 3, \ 2x - 7y \leq 4, \ 3x + 2y \leq 6$

Solve each system of inequalities by graphing. **See Solutions Manual.**

43. $x - y \leq 3$
$x + y \leq 1$
$y \geq 0$

44. $x + 4y < 4$
$5x - 8y < -8$
$3x - 2y \geq -16$

45. $x < 3$
$5y > x$
$x + 3y < 9$
$2x - y < -9$

Critical Thinking

46. Write an absolute value inequality for the graph at the right. (*Hint:* Find the equations for the four boundaries of this region.) $|x| + |y| \leq 2$

Applications

Graph a system of inequalities to solve each problem.

47. **Sales** Abby plans to spend at most $24 to buy cashews and peanuts for her Fourth of July party. The Nut Shoppe sells peanuts for $3 a pound and cashews for $5 a pound. If Abby needs to have at least 5 pounds of nuts for the party, how many of each type can she buy? List three possible solutions. **See margin.**

48. **Sales** The Debate Team needed to earn at least $500 to attend a national competition. The members decided to hold a raffle. They sold tickets at a price of $2 for students and $3 for everyone else. If they were allowed to sell at most 200 raffle tickets, how many of each type of ticket must the members sell to make enough money for the trip? List three possible solutions. **See margin.**

49. Painting A painter has exactly 32 units of yellow dye and 54 units of blue dye. She plans to mix the dyes to make two shades of green. Each gallon of the lighter shade of green requires 4 units of yellow dye and 1 unit of blue dye. Each gallon of the darker shade of green requires 1 unit of yellow dye and 6 units of blue dye. How many gallons of each shade of green can she mix? List three possible solutions. **See margin.**

Mixed Review

50. Sales The price of a suit was marked down $37.50. If the original price was $125, what was the rate of discount? **(Lesson 4-2)** 30%

51. Factor $-16 + 9x^2$. **(Lesson 7-6)** $(4 + 3x)(-4 + 3x)$

52. Add $\frac{x}{x^2 + 2x + 1} + \frac{1}{x + 1}$. **(Lesson 8-7)** $\frac{2x + 1}{(x + 1)^2}$

53. Solve $4y = 3 + 2x$ if the domain is $\{-2, -1, 0, 1, 3\}$. **(Lesson 9-3)** **See margin.**

54. Write an equation in slope-intercept form for the line that passes through $(-4, 3)$ and $(6, -5)$. **(Lesson 10-5)** $y = -\frac{4}{5}x - \frac{1}{5}$

55. Sales Joey sold 30 peaches from his fruit stand for a total of $7.50. He sold small ones for 20 cents each and large ones for 35 cents each. How many of each kind did he sell? **(Lesson 11-5)**
20 small and 10 large

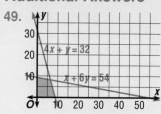

Additional Answers

49.

Answers will vary. Possible solutions: 2 light, 8 dark; 6 light, 8 dark; 7 light, 4 dark

53. $\left\{ \left(-2, -\frac{1}{4}\right), \left(-1, \frac{1}{4}\right), \left(0, \frac{3}{4}\right), \left(1, \frac{5}{4}\right), \left(3, \frac{9}{4}\right) \right\}$

HISTORY CONNECTION

The *K'iu-ch'ang Suan-shu*

The *K'iu-ch'ang Suan-shu*, or *Arithmetic in Nine Sections*, is the greatest of the ancient Chinese books on mathematics. A mathematician named Ch'ang Ts'ang is thought to have collected and edited these writings of the ancients around 213 B.C. The titles of its nine chapters are as follows.

1. **Squaring the Farm**, surveying
2. **Calculating the Cereals**, percentage and proportions
3. **Calculating the Shares**, partnership and the rule of three
4. **Finding Length**, sides of figures and square and cube roots
5. **Finding Volumes**
6. **Allegation**, motion problems
7. **Excess and Deficiency**, rule of false position
8. **Equations**, systems of linear equations
9. **Right Triangles**, Pythagorean Theorem, trigonometry

This work indicates that Chinese mathematicians were among the pioneers in establishing the early science of mathematics.

LESSON 11-6 GRAPHING SYSTEMS OF INEQUALITIES 467

EXTENDING THE LESSON

Math Power: Reasoning
Solve the system of inequalities.
$x + 4y \leq 13 \qquad x + 2y \geq -5$
$x - 5y \leq 16 \qquad 2x - y \geq -10$
$x + y \leq 4$

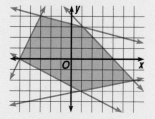

History Connection
The History Connection features introduce students to persons or cultures who were involved in the development of mathematics. You may want students to further research Chinese mathematicians.

Enrichment Masters Booklet, p. 79

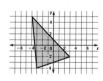

NAME _____ DATE _____
11-6 **Enrichment Worksheet**

Describing Regions

The shaded region inside the triangle can be described with a system of three inequalities.

$y < -x + 1$
$y > \frac{1}{3}x - 3$
$y > -9x - 31$

Write systems of inequalities to describe each region. You may first need to divide a region into triangles or quadrilaterals.

1.

$y < \frac{5}{2}x + 12$
$y < -\frac{5}{2}x + 12$
$y < 2$

2.

$y > -x - 2 \quad y < x + 2$
$y > x - 2 \quad y < -x + 2$
$y < 5 \quad y > -5$

3.

top: $y < \frac{3}{2}x + 7, y < -\frac{3}{2}x + 7, y > 4$
middle: $y < 4, y > 0, y > -\frac{4}{3}x - 4,$
$y > \frac{4}{3}x - 4$
bottom left: $y < 4x + 12, y > \frac{1}{2}x - 2,$
$y < 0, x < 0$
bottom right: $y < -4x + 12,$
$y > -\frac{1}{2}x - 2, y < 0, x < 0$

Chapter 11 467

The Chapter Summary and Review begins with an alphabetical listing of the new terms that were presented in the chapter. Have students define each term and provide an example of it, if appropriate.

The Skills and Concepts presented in the chapter are reviewed using a side-by-side format. Encourage students to refer to the Objectives and Examples on the left as they complete the Review Exercises on the right.

The Chapter Summary and Review ends with exercises that review Applications and Connections.

CHAPTER

 11 SUMMARY AND REVIEW

VOCABULARY

Upon completing this chapter, you should be familiar with the following terms:

system of equations	**442**	**452**	elimination
substitution	**447**	**463**	system of inequalities

SKILLS AND CONCEPTS

OBJECTIVES AND EXAMPLES	REVIEW EXERCISES

Upon completing this chapter, you should be able to:

■ solve systems of equations by graphing **(Lesson 11-2)**

Graph $y = x$ and $y = 2 - x$. Then find the solution.

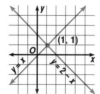

Use these exercises to review and prepare for the chapter test.

Graph each system of equations. Then find the solution to the system of equations.

1. $x + y = 6$
   $x - y = 2$ **(4, 2)**

2. $y = 2x - 7$
   $x + y = 11$ **(6, 5)**

3. $5x - 3y = 11$
   $2x + 3y = -25$ **(-2, -7)**

■ determine whether a system of equations has one solution, no solution, or infinitely many solutions by graphing **(Lesson 11-2)**

Graph $3x + y = -4$ and $6x + 2y = -8$. Then determine the number of solutions.

There are infinitely many solutions.

Graph each pair of equations. Then determine whether the system of equations has one solution, no solution, or infinitely many solutions. If the system has one solution, state it.

4. $x - y = 9$
   $x + y = 11$ **one, (10, 1)**

5. $9x + 2 = 3y$
   $y - 3x = 8$ **no solution**

6. $2x - 3y = 4$
   $6y = 4x - 8$ **infinitely many**

7. $3x - y = 8$
   $3x = 4 - y$ **one, (2, -2)**

■ solve systems of equations by the substitution method **(Lesson 11-3)**

Use substitution to solve the system of equations $y = x - 1$ and $4x - y = 19$.

$$
\begin{array}{l|l}
4x - y = 19 & y = x - 1 \\
4x - (x - 1) = 19 & = 6 - 1 \\
3x + 1 = 19 & = 5 \\
3x = 18 & \\
x = 6 & \\
\end{array}
$$

The solution is $(6, 5)$.

Use substitution to solve each system of equations.

8. $x = 2y$
   $x + y = 6$ $(4, 2)$

9. $2m + n = 1$
   $m - n = 8$ $(3, -5)$

10. $3a - 2b = -4$
    $3a + b = 2$ $(0, 2)$

11. $3x - y = 1$
    $2x + 4y = 3$ $\left(\frac{1}{2}, \frac{1}{2}\right)$

■ solve systems of equations by the elimination method using addition or subtraction **(Lesson 11-4)**

Use elimination to solve the system of equations $2m - n = 4$ and $m + n = 2$.

$$
\begin{array}{l|l}
2m - n = 4 & m + n = 2 \\
\underline{(+)\ m + n = 2} & 2 + n = 2 \\
3m \quad = 6 & n = 0 \\
m = 2 & \\
\end{array}
$$

The solution is $(2, 0)$.

Use elimination to solve each system of equations.

12. $x + 2y = 6$
    $x - 3y = -4$ $(2, 2)$

13. $2m - n = 5$
    $2m + n = 3$ $(2, -1)$

14. $3x - y = 11$
    $x + y = 5$ $(4, 1)$

15. $2s + 6r = 32$
    $6r - 9s = 21$ $(5, 1)$

■ solve systems of equations by the elimination method using multiplication and addition **(Lesson 11-5)**

Use elimination to solve the system of equations $3x - 4y = 7$ and $2x + y = 1$.

$$
\begin{array}{ll}
3x - 4y = 7 & 3x - 4y = 7 \\
2x + y = 1 \quad \boxed{\times 4} \Rightarrow & \underline{(+)\ 8x + 4y = 4} \\
& 11x \quad = 11 \\
2x + y = 1 & x = 1 \\
2(1) + y = 1 & \\
y = -1 & \\
\end{array}
$$

The solution is $(1, -1)$.

Use elimination to solve each system of equations.

16. $x - 2y = 5$
    $3x - 5y = 8$ $(-9, -7)$

17. $2x + 3y = 8$
    $x - y = 2$ $\left(\frac{14}{5}, \frac{4}{5}\right)$

18. $6x + 7y = 5$
    $2x - 3y = 7$ $(2, -1)$

19. $5m + 2n = -8$
    $4m + 3n = 2$ $(-4, 6)$

Alternate Review Strategy

To provide a brief in-class review, you may wish to read the following questions to the class and require a verbal or written response.

1. Graph the pair of equations. Then state the solution of the system of equations.
   $x + y = 8$
   $x - y = 2$ **(5, 3)**

2. Graph the pair of equations. Then determine whether the system has one solution, no solution, or infinitely many solutions. If the system has one solution, state it.
   $x + y = 4$
   $x + y = 9$ **no solution**

3. Use substitution to solve the system of equations.
   $x = 2y$
   $4x + 2y = 15$ $\left(3, \frac{3}{2}\right)$

4. Use elimination to solve the system of equations.
   $3t = 13 - p$
   $2t - p = 2$ **(4, 3)**

5. Use elimination to solve the system of equations.
   $2x + y = 3(x - 5)$
   $x + 5 = 4y + 2x$ **(13, -2)**

The Cumulative Review shown below can be used to review skills and concepts presented thus far in the text. Standardized Test Practice Questions are also provided in the Evaluation Masters Booklet.

Evaluation Masters Booklet, pp. 151-152

OBJECTIVES AND EXAMPLES	REVIEW EXERCISES

■ solve systems of inequalities by graphing (Lesson 11-6)

Solve the system of inequalities $x \ge -3$ and $y \le x + 2$ by graphing.

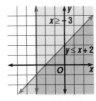

Solve each system of inequalities by graphing. **See Solutions Manual.**

20. $y > -x - 1$
    $y \le 2x + 1$

21. $2r + s < 9$
    $r + 11s < -6$

22. $|x + 2| \ge y$

APPLICATIONS AND CONNECTIONS

Solve the problem below. Try to eliminate any hidden assumptions.   (Lesson 11-1)

23. Copy the array of dots at the right onto a piece of paper. Without lifting your pencil from the paper, draw four straight line segments through the 9 dots.

Use a system of equations to solve each problem.   28. \$2000 at 6%, \$8000 at 8%

24. **Number Theory**   A two-digit number is 7 times its units digit. If 18 is added to the number, its digits are reversed. Find the original number. **(Lesson 11-3) 35**

25. **Geometry**   The difference between the length and width of a rectangle is 7 cm. Find the dimensions of the rectangle if its perimeter is 50 cm. **(Lesson 11-4) 16 cm by 9 cm**

26. **Uniform Motion**   Two trains start toward each other on parallel tracks at the same time from towns 450 miles apart. One train travels 6 miles per hour faster than the other train. What is the rate of each train if they meet in 5 hours? **(Lesson 11-3) 42 mph, 48 mph**

27. **Sales**   Mr. Ayala bought 5 shirts and 3 ties at the Clothes Outlet for \$102. Mr. Gilmore bought 8 shirts and 3 ties for \$147. What is the price of a shirt and the price of a tie at the Clothes Outlet?   **(Lesson 11-4) \$15, \$9**

28. **Finance**   Last year, Jodi invested \$10,000, part at 6% annual interest and the rest at 8% annual interest. If she received \$760 in interest at the end of the year, how much did she invest at each rate?   **(Lesson 11-5)**

29. **Uniform Motion**   A speedboat travels 60 miles with the current in 3 hours. The return trip against the current takes 4 hours. What is the rate of the speedboat in still water and the rate of the current?   **(Lesson 11-5)** $\frac{35}{2}$ mph, $\frac{5}{2}$ mph

Graph each system of equations. Then determine whether the system has one solution, no solution, or infinitely many solutions. If the system has one solution, name it.

1. $y = x + 2$
   $y = 2x + 7$ one, $(-5, -3)$

2. $x + 2y = 11$
   $x = 14 - 2y$ no solution

3. $2x + 5y = 16$
   $5x - 2y = 11$ one, $(3, 2)$

4. $3x + y = 5$
   $2y - 10 = -6x$ infinitely many

Use substitution or elimination to solve each system of equations.

5. $y = 7 - x$
   $x - y = -3$ $(2, 5)$

6. $x = 2y - 7$
   $y - 3x = -9$ $(5, 6)$

7. $x + y = 8$
   $x - y = 2$ $(5, 3)$

8. $3x - y = 11$
   $x + 2y = -36$ $(-2, -17)$

9. $3x + y = 10$
   $3x - 2y = 16$ $(4, -2)$

10. $5x - 3y = 12$
    $-2x + 3y = -3$ $(3, 1)$

11. $2x + 5y = 12$
    $x - 6y = -11$ $(1, 2)$

12. $x + y = 6$
    $3x - 3y = 13$ $\left(\frac{31}{6}, \frac{5}{6}\right)$

13. $3x + \frac{1}{3}y = 10$
    $2x - \frac{5}{3}y = 35$ $(5, -15)$

14. $8x - 6y = 14$
    $6x - 9y = 15$ $(1, -1)$

Solve each system of inequalities by graphing. See Solutions Manual.

15. $y \leq -3$
    $y > -x + 2$

16. $x \leq 2y$
    $2x + 3y \leq 7$

17. **Number Theory** The units digit of a two-digit number exceeds twice the tens digit by 1. Find the number if the sum of its digits is 10. **37**

18. **Uniform Motion** Marisel rode her bicycle against the wind for 1 hour and traveled 15 km. She returned the same distance with the wind in 36 minutes. What was the rate of the wind? **5 km per hour**

19. **Sales** Mr. Salvatore mixed nuts that cost $3.90 per pound with nuts that cost $4.30 per pound. He now has a mixture of 50 pounds of nuts that costs $4.20 per pound. How many pounds of each type of nut did he use? **12.5 lb of the $3.90, 37.5 lb of the $4.30**

20. **Automobiles** A gas station attendant is making 1000 gallons of antifreeze that is 48% alcohol. He has some antifreeze that is 40% alcohol and some that is 60% alcohol. How much of each type of antifreeze should he use? **600 gallons of 40%, 400 gallons of 60%**

Bonus

Number Theory The sum of the digits of a three-digit number is 20. The tens digit exceeds twice the units digit by 1. The hundreds digit is one less than twice the units digit. Find the number. **794**

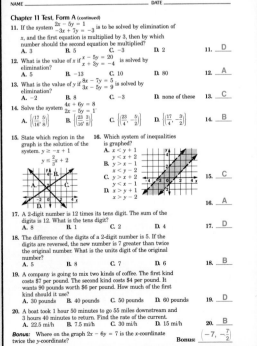

NAME _____ DATE _____

Chapter 11 Test, Form 1A

Write the letter for the correct answer in the blank at the right of each problem.

Use the graph to answer problems 1–4.

1. Which pair of lines is the graph of the system of equations $x + 2y = -1$, $2x + 3y = 0$?
   A. ℓ and m B. n and m
   C. ℓ and n D. ℓ and p 1. A

2. The number of solutions of the system of equations represented by lines n and p is
   A. exactly one. B. none. C. exactly two. D. infinitely many. 2. B

3. The equation for line p and the equation $y = 3x - 2$ form a system of equations. The number of solutions is
   A. exactly. B. none. C. exactly two. D. infinitely many. 3. D

4. Which ordered pair is the solution of the system of equations represented by lines ℓ and n?
   A. $(3, -2)$ B. $(0, 3)$ C. $(0, -1)$ D. $(-1, 0)$ 4. D

5. If the system $\begin{array}{l}y = x - 3 \\ \frac{1}{2}x + \frac{1}{3}y = 2\end{array}$ is graphed, in which quadrant will the solution lie?
   A. I B. II C. III D. IV 5. A

6. One of the two equations in a system of equations is $3y - x = 4$. In which quadrant would it be impossible to have a solution?
   A. I B. II C. III D. IV 6. D

7. If the system $\begin{array}{l}x + 2y = 15 \\ 5x + y = 21\end{array}$ is to be solved by substitution, which expression can be replaced for x in the second equation?
   A. $15 - 2y$ B. $21 - 5x$ C. $\frac{15 - x}{2}$ D. $\frac{21 - y}{5}$ 7. A

8. Solve the system $\begin{array}{l}x = 2y + 3 \\ 4x - 5y = 9\end{array}$ by substitution.
   A. $\{(2, 7)\}$ B. $\{(1, -1)\}$ C. $\{(5, 1)\}$ D. none of these 8. B

9. If the system $\begin{array}{l}x + 7y = 16 \\ 3x - 7y = 4\end{array}$ is solved by elimination, what is the value of x?
   A. 3 B. 4 C. 5 D. -6 9. C

10. Half the perimeter of a garden is 18 feet. The garden is 8 feet longer than it is wide. If $w =$ the width in feet and $\ell =$ the length in feet, which system must be true?
    A. $\begin{array}{l}\frac{1}{2}(\ell + w) = 18 \\ \ell = w + 8\end{array}$ B. $\begin{array}{l}\frac{1}{2}(\ell + w) = 18 \\ w = \ell + 8\end{array}$
    C. $\begin{array}{l}\ell + w = 8 \\ \ell - w = 18\end{array}$ D. $\begin{array}{l}\ell - w = 8 \\ \ell + w = 18\end{array}$ 10. D

NAME _____ DATE _____

Chapter 11 Test, Form A (continued)

11. If the system $\begin{array}{l}2x - 5y = 1 \\ -3x + 7y = -3\end{array}$ is to be solved by elimination of x, and the first equation is multiplied by 3, then by which number should the second equation be multiplied?
    A. 3 B. 5 C. -3 D. 2 11. D

12. What is the value of x if $\begin{array}{l}x - 5y = 20 \\ x + 3y = -4\end{array}$ is solved by elimination?
    A. 5 B. -13 C. 10 D. 80 12. A

13. What is the value of y if $\begin{array}{l}8x - 7y = 5 \\ 3x - 5y = 9\end{array}$ is solved by elimination?
    A. -2 B. 8 C. -3 D. none of these 13. C

14. Solve the system $\begin{array}{l}4x + 6y = 8 \\ 2x - 5y = 1\end{array}$
    A. $\left\{\left(\frac{17}{16}, \frac{5}{8}\right)\right\}$ B. $\left\{\left(\frac{23}{16}, \frac{3}{8}\right)\right\}$ C. $\left\{\left(\frac{23}{4}, -\frac{5}{2}\right)\right\}$ D. $\left\{\left(\frac{17}{4}, -\frac{3}{2}\right)\right\}$ 14. B

15. State which region in the graph is the solution of the system. $\begin{array}{l}y \geq -x + 1 \\ y \leq \frac{2}{3}x + 2\end{array}$ 15. C

16. Which system of inequalities is graphed?
    A. $\begin{array}{l}x < y + 1 \\ y < x + 2\end{array}$
    B. $\begin{array}{l}y > x - 1 \\ x < y - 2\end{array}$
    C. $\begin{array}{l}y > x + 2 \\ y < x - 1\end{array}$
    D. $\begin{array}{l}x > y + 1 \\ x > y - 2\end{array}$ 16. A

17. A 2-digit number is 12 times its tens digit. The sum of the digits is 12. What is the tens digit?
    A. 8 B. 1 C. 2 D. 4 17. D

18. The difference of the digits of a 2-digit number is 5. If the digits are reversed, the new number is 7 greater than twice the original number. What is the units digit of the original number?
    A. 5 B. 8 C. 7 D. 6 18. B

19. A company is going to mix two kinds of coffee. The first kind costs $7 per pound. The second kind costs $4 per pound. It wants 90 pounds worth $6 per pound. How much of the first kind should it use?
    A. 30 pounds B. 40 pounds C. 50 pounds D. 60 pounds 19. D

20. A boat took 1 hour 50 minutes to go 55 miles downstream and 3 hours 40 minutes to return. Find the rate of the current.
    A. 22.5 mi/h B. 7.5 mi/h C. 30 mi/h D. 15 mi/h 20. B

Bonus: Where on the graph $2x - 6y = 7$ is the x-coordinate twice the y-coordinate? Bonus: $\left(-7, -\frac{7}{2}\right)$

12 Radical Expressions

PREVIEWING THE CHAPTER

The focus of this chapter is on radicals. Students first learn to simplify rational square roots and find approximate values for square roots. Then they use the Pythagorean Theorem to find the length of one side of a triangle given the lengths of the other two sides. Irrational numbers are introduced, and students simplify square roots and radical expressions, including those involving addition and subtraction. Students apply what they now know to solve radical equations. The chapter concludes with the students using the Pythagorean Theorem to develop the distance formula.

Problem-Solving Strategy   Students learn to read and interpret information presented in a table or chart to solve problems.

Lesson Objective Chart

Lesson (Pages)	Lesson Objectives	State/Local Objectives
12-1 (474-476)	**12-1:** Solve problems by using a table.	
12-2 (477-481)	**12-2A:** Simplify rational square roots.	
	12-2B: Find approximate values for square roots.	
12-3 (482-486)	**12-3:** Use the Pythagorean Theorem.	
12-4 (487-491)	**12-4:** Identify irrational numbers.	
12-5 (492-496)	**12-5A:** Simplify square roots.	
	12-5B: Simplify radical expressions that contain variables.	
12-6 (497-500)	**12-6:** Simplify radical expressions involving addition and subtraction.	
12-7 (501-504)	**12-7:** Solve radical equations.	
12-8 (506-509)	**12-8:** Find the distance between two points in the coordinate plane.	

ORGANIZING THE CHAPTER

You may want to refer to the **Course Planning Calendar** on page T36.

Lesson Planning Guide

Lesson (Pages)	Pacing Chart (days) Course I	II	III	Reteaching	Practice	Enrichment	Evaluation	Technology	Lab Manual	Mixed Problem Solving	Applications	Cooperative Learning Activity	Multicultural	Transparencies
12-1 (474-476)	1	1	1		p. 90									12-1
12-2 (477-481)	1.5	1	1	p. 80	p. 91	p. 80	Quiz A, p. 163	p. 12			p. 27			12-2
12-3 (482-486)	1.5	1.5	1	p. 81	p. 92	p. 81			pp. 39-40	p. 12				12-3
12-4 (487-491)	1.5	1	1	p. 82	p. 93	p. 82	Quiz B, p. 163 Mid-Chapter Test, p. 167						p. 57	12-4
12-5 (492-496)	1.5	1.5	1	p. 83	p. 94	p. 83								12-5
12-6 (497-500)	1	1	1	p. 84	p. 95	p. 84	Quiz C, p. 164					p. 42		12-6
12-7 (501-504)	1	1	1	p. 85	p. 96	p. 85								12-7
12-8 (506-509)	1	1	1	p. 86	p. 97	p. 86	Quiz D, p. 164	p. 27						12-8
Review (510-512)	1	1	1	Multiple Choice Tests, Forms 1A and 1B, pp. 155-158 Free Response Tests, Forms 2A and 2B, pp. 159-162										
Test (513)	1	1	1	Cumulative Review, pp. 165-166 Standardized Test Practice Questions, p. 168										

Course I: Chapters 1-13; Course II: Chapters 1-14; Course III: Chapters 1-15

Other Chapter Resources

Student Edition

Cooperative Learning Activity, p. 476
History Connection, p. 481
Application, p. 486
Mid-Chapter Review, p. 491
Technology p. 505
Algebraic Skills Review, p. 662
  (ex. 1-73)

Teacher Resource Package

Activity Masters Booklet
  Mixed Problem Solving, p. 12
  Applications, p. 27
  Cooperative Learning Activity, p. 42
  Multicultural Activity, p. 57
Technology Masters Booklet
  Scientific Calculator Activity, p. 12
  Graphing Calculator Activity, p. 27
Lab Manual
  Lab Activity, pp. 39-40

Other Supplements

Transparency for Chapter Opener
Problem-of-the-Week Activity
  Cards, 28-29
Video Algebra, 47-52

Software

Algebra 1 Test and Review
  Generator Software
  Available for Apple and IBM.

Cooperative Learning

Providing Task Assistance

When monitoring cooperative-learning groups as they do their work, you should resist temptation to intervene any more often than is absolutely necessary. Even when intervening, your role should be more that of an enhancer rather than an answerer. For example, when a group appears to be stuck, say something such as, "Let's do a little brainstorming about ..." or "What do you think would happen if you tried ...", and give a hint to get them moving again. Even when it may be necessary to clarify instructions or review procedures and strategies, encourage the group to work their way through the problem by recalling a specific instruction you gave before the session began and then ask, "Now, who remembers what we said you should do next?" When students themselves seek assistance, they should first discuss among themselves and agree on the question that they want answered. The member whose role is *asker* should then address the question to you. You should respond only to the specific question, using terms relevant to the task, and then have one or more other members of the group paraphrase your answer to make sure that it is understood.

Technology

The Technology Feature after Lesson 12-7 shows how to use the *Mathematical Exploration Toolkit* to solve equations involving square roots. Students can focus on choosing the appropriate steps to change the form of the equations. The computer will perform the simplifying and calculating operations. As when solving radical equations by hand, all solutions must be checked. MET provides a way to test solutions in the original equation. MET has an automatic SOLVEFOR command. Used along with the command SSTEPS, students can inspect the steps the computer uses to solve equations. Some equations must be simplified before SOLVEFOR can find solutions.

Critical Thinking

Frequent use of the term "higher" to describe the levels of analysis, synthesis, and evaluation in Bloom's taxonomy can lead one to make the false assumption that students must master content at the levels of knowledge, comprehension, and application before they can move on to these higher levels. Students who may have difficulty memorizing certain facts often exhibit, in a proper environment, the creative ability to analyze and identify patterns in these facts or find parallel models and new applications. The higher levels of Bloom's taxonomy should provide guideposts for planning interesting and challenging activities in mathematics that engage the intellect of *all* students, not just those identified as having special talents.

Cooperative Learning, p. 42

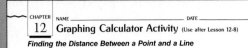

CHAPTER 12 — Cooperative Learning Activity (Use after Lesson 12-6)

Matching Radicals

Work in pairs. Cut out the rectangles drawn below. Simplify each radical expression that can be simplified, and match it to another equivalent expression. If you do this correctly, each rectangle will match one and only one rectangle.

Technology, p. 27

CHAPTER 12 — Graphing Calculator Activity (Use after Lesson 12-8)

Finding the Distance Between a Point and a Line

The following example uses a graphing calculator to find the distance between a point and a line.

Example: Find the distance between the point $(11, -1)$ and the line $y = 2x - 3$.

a. **Set the range.** Choose any range that is convenient.

b. **Graph** the point and the line.

c. Write the equation of the line through the given point that is perpendicular to the given line. The slope of the line $y = 2x - 3$ is 2. The slope of the line perpendicular to it must be $-\frac{1}{2}$ (so that the product of the two slopes is -1). Use the point-slope form of a linear equation.

Then an equation of the line through $(11, -1)$ that is perpendicular to the given line is $y + 1 = -\frac{1}{2}(x - 11)$, or $y = -\frac{1}{2}x + 4\frac{1}{2}$.

d. **Graph** $y = -0.5x + 4.5$.

e. **Trace** the coordinates of the intersection of the two lines (round to the nearest whole number). The intersection point is $(3, 3)$.

f. Use the distance formula to find the distance between the intersection point and the given point (round to the nearest tenth). This is the distance between the given point and the given line.

$$\text{distance} = \sqrt{(11 - 3)^2 + (-1 - 3)^2} = \sqrt{64 + 16}$$
$$= \sqrt{80} \approx 8.9$$

Use a graphing calculator and follow the procedure above to find the distance between the given point and the line. Make a sketch of the calculator display. Give the equations of the two lines that you use.

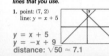

1. point: $(7, 2)$
   line: $y = x + 5$

   $y = x + 5$
   $y = -x + 9$
   distance: $\sqrt{50} \approx 7.1$

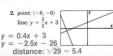

2. point: $(-8, -6)$
   line: $y = \frac{2}{5}x + 3$

   $y = 0.4x + 3$
   $y = -2.5x - 26$
   distance: $\sqrt{29} \approx 5.4$

Problem of the Week Activity

The card shown below is one of two available for this chapter. It can be used as a class or small group activity.

Activity Card

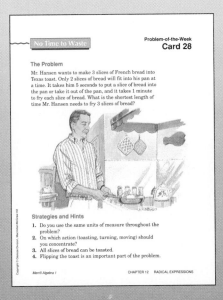

No Time to Waste

Problem-of-the-Week
Card 28

The Problem

Mr. Hansen wants to make 3 slices of French bread into Texas toast. Only 2 slices of bread will fit into his pan at a time. It takes him 5 seconds to put a slice of bread into the pan or take it out of the pan, and it takes 1 minute to fry each slice of bread. What is the shortest length of time Mr. Hansen needs to fry 3 slices of bread?

Strategies and Hints

1. Do you use the same units of measure throughout the problem?
2. On which action (toasting, turning, moving) should you concentrate?
3. All slices of bread can be toasted.
4. Flipping the toast is an important part of the problem.

Merrill Algebra 1   CHAPTER 12   RADICAL EXPRESSIONS

Manipulatives and Models

The following materials may be used as models or manipulatives in Chapter 12.

- newspapers or magazines (Lesson 12-1)
- tag board (Lesson 12-1)
- scientific calculator (all Lessons)
- geoboard (Lesson 12-3)

Outside Resources

Books/Periodicals

Ekeland, Ivar. *Mathematics and the Unexpected*. The University of Chicago Press.

Lushbaugh, Warren. *Polyominoes*. Charles Scribner's Sons.

Films/Videotapes/Videodiscs

Formulas in Mathematics, International Film Bureau

Linear Functions — Rate of Change of a Linear Function, Great Plains Instructional TV Library

Software

SEMCalc, Sunburst Communications, Inc.

TV-Solver, Universal

Mathematical Exploration Toolkit, IBM

Multicultural

Multicultural Activity, p. 57

CHAPTER 12   NAME _____ DATE _____

Multicultural Activities (Use after Lesson 12-4)

Ramanujan

Srinivasa Ramanujan (1887–1920)—considered by many to be India's greatest mathematician—made an astonishing number of contributions to mathematics in his brief lifetime. One of his many accomplishments was his rediscovery of a method for calculating a rational decimal approximation for the irrational number π. Using a mathematical structure called the **continued fraction**, he arrived at this formula.

$$\frac{\pi}{4} = \cfrac{1}{1 + \cfrac{1^2}{2 + \cfrac{3^2}{2 + \cfrac{5^2}{2 + \cfrac{7^2}{2 + \cfrac{9^2}{2 + \dots}}}}}}$$

The fraction follows this pattern to infinity.

In view of Ramanujan's lack of access to mathematical literature, it is remarkable how much of western mathematics he was able to reconstruct entirely on his own.

In 1987, mathematicians were able to calculate an approximation of π accurate to more than 100 million decimal places. Although present-day computer technology made their achievement possible, it is interesting to note that the method they used was essentially the same as the one rediscovered by Ramanujan nearly 75 years before!

Not all continued fractions are infinite. If a continued fraction is finite, it represents a rational number. Can you rewrite each of these continued fractions as a rational number in lowest terms? (*Hint:* Remember that a fraction bar acts as a grouping symbol.)

1. $\cfrac{1}{1 + \cfrac{1}{\cfrac{2}{3}}}$

2. $\cfrac{1}{1 + \cfrac{1}{\cfrac{4}{7}}}$

3. $\cfrac{1}{2 + \cfrac{1}{\cfrac{5}{12}}}$

4. $\cfrac{1}{2 + \cfrac{1}{\cfrac{13}{30}}}$

5. Another formula for evaluating π is given by the following infinite product.

$$\frac{\pi}{2} = \frac{2}{1} \cdot \frac{2}{3} \cdot \frac{4}{3} \cdot \frac{4}{5} \cdot \frac{6}{5} \cdot \frac{6}{7} \cdot \frac{8}{7} \cdot \frac{8}{9} \cdots$$

What pattern does this infinite product follow? **Answers will vary.**

Lab Manual

Lab Activity, pp. 39-40

Name _____   Activity 12 Worksheet

The Pythagorean Theorem

1. Cut three squares from graph paper with sides of length 3, 4, and 5. What is the area of each square?

Write an equation to show that the sum of the areas of two of the squares is equal to the area of the third square.

2. Place the three squares on a sheet of paper so that their sides form a triangle. What type of triangle is it?

Write an equation to show the relationship among the squares of the sides of the triangle. Let a and b represent the length of the legs and c the length of the hypotenuse.

3. Find the squares of the numbers from 1 to 30. Use your calculator.

$1^2 =$ _____ $7^2 =$ _____ $13^2 =$ _____ $19^2 =$ _____ $25^2 =$ _____

$2^2 =$ _____ $8^2 =$ _____ $14^2 =$ _____ $20^2 =$ _____ $26^2 =$ _____

$3^2 =$ _____ $9^2 =$ _____ $15^2 =$ _____ $21^2 =$ _____ $27^2 =$ _____

$4^2 =$ _____ $10^2 =$ _____ $16^2 =$ _____ $22^2 =$ _____ $28^2 =$ _____

$5^2 =$ _____ $11^2 =$ _____ $17^2 =$ _____ $23^2 =$ _____ $29^2 =$ _____

$6^2 =$ _____ $12^2 =$ _____ $18^2 =$ _____ $24^2 =$ _____ $30^2 =$ _____

4. Find four sets of three squares each such that the sum of two of the squares equals the third.

5. Find the length of the hypotenuse of the right triangle given the lengths of its other sides. Use a calculator.

a. 15 feet, 36 feet _____

b. 7.5 meters, 10 meters _____

c. 8 inches, 9 inches _____

Using the Chapter Opener

Transparency 12-0 is available in the Transparency Package. It provides a full-color visual and motivational activity that you can use to engage students in the mathematical content of the chapter.

Background Information

Spirals of the nautilus and the horns of a ram provide examples of the Pythagorean Theorem at work in nature. Other spirals in nature provide opportunities to present Fibonacci numbers. Starting with the number one, the Fibonacci sequence adds the preceding two numbers to get the next number, 1, 1, 2, 3, 5, 8, 13, 21, 34, and so on. Florets in the head of a daisy compose two opposing sets of rotating spirals; 21 in the clockwise direction of most daisies, and 34 counterclockwise. This 21:34 ratio is made up of two adjacent numbers in the Fibonacci sequence. Scales of pine cones have a 5:8 ratio.

In this chapter, you will:
- Find exact and approximate values for square roots.
- Simplify radical expressions.
- Solve radical equations.
- Solve problems that can be represented by radical equations.
- Solve problems by using tables.

Chapter Project

Materials: paper, pencil, selected plants, spiralled shells, magazines

Organize students into cooperative groups of analysts. Instruct each group to collect actual examples of spirals in nature, or photographs and drawings of such spirals from magazines. Have them include single-direction spirals such as in the horns of a ram, plus examples of opposing spirals as in daisies, pine cones, and

pineapples. Assign each group the task of counting the spirals of their samples and finding the ratios of opposing numbers of spirals to see if the ratios are made up of adjacent Fibonacci numbers. Then, have each group select at least one of its samples of spirals in nature and draw the spirals as right triangles winding

around a central point. Caution each group to be precise in its measurements and to apply the Pythagorean Theorem. Ask them to extend their spiral construction beyond that in the chapter opener. Finally, instruct each group to prepare a display and report results to the class.

Radical Expressions

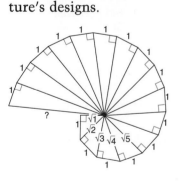

Have you ever noticed that Mother Nature is a very skilled designer? Just look around and you can find many examples of mathematics in nature's designs.

APPLICATION IN NATURE

The shell of a chambered nautilus is one of the many examples of mathematics occurring in nature's designs. This shell takes on its spiral shape because of the nautilus's growth pattern and the formation of small chambers of increasing size to accommodate this growth. The growth pattern of the nautilus can be studied by looking at the size and shape of the shell's spiral.

One method for studying the spiral is to use a set of right triangles winding around a point to represent the shape of the spiral. These right triangles are drawn so that the sides used to represent the spiral all have the same length, one unit, as shown in the figure below. Notice that each triangle has the same apex (top point). The longest side of each right triangle, called the *hypotenuse*, is also one of the shorter sides of the next triangle in the set. This design is called a "spiral of square roots" because of the relationship between the lengths of the sides of the right triangles.

The shell of the chambered nautilus is just one example of naturally occurring spirals. The next time you see a daisy, a sunflower, or a pineapple, see if you can find the spirals that are a part of their design.

ALGEBRA IN ACTION

Look at the triangle with sides 1, $\sqrt{1}$, and $\sqrt{2}$ in the figure at the left. Notice that $1^2 + (\sqrt{1})^2 = (\sqrt{2})^2$ since $(\sqrt{1})^2 = 1$ and $(\sqrt{2})^2 = 2$. Similarly, in the next few triangles, $1^2 + (\sqrt{2})^2 = (\sqrt{3})^2$, $1^2 + (\sqrt{3})^2 = (\sqrt{4})^2$, and $1^2 + (\sqrt{4})^2 = (\sqrt{5})^2$. This relationship between the measures of the sides of the right triangles is the basis for the *Pythagorean Theorem*. If you continue in this manner, what will be the measure of the side labeled ? in the figure? $\sqrt{17}$

473

Lesson	Connections (C) and Applications (A)	Examples	Exercises
12-1	C: Statistics	1	
12-2	C: Geometry		46-48, 52
	A: Plumbing	4	
	Law Enforcement		54
	Physics		55
	Electricity		56
	Aviation		59
12-3	C: Geometry		35-38
	Statistics		44
	A: Construction	4	41, 43
	Sailing		40
	Baseball		42
	Chemistry		47
12-4	C: Geometry		38-43
	A: Electricity	4	46
	Weather		47
	Physics		49
	Construction		52
12-5	C: Geometry	6	54, 61
	A: Physics		56
	Travel		57
	Electricity		63
12-6	C: Geometry	3, 5	33-35
	A: Construction		42-43
	Car Rental		46
12-7	C: Number Theory	2	14-17, 36-38
	Geometry		54
	A: Science		46
	Physics		47
	Recreation		48
	Gardening		50
12-8	C: Geometry	1	23-25
	A: Telecommunications		30-31
	Aviation		36

Lesson Resources

• Practice Master 12-1

 Transparency 12-1 contains the 5-Minute Check and a teaching aid for this lesson.

INTRODUCING THE LESSON

 5-Minute Check

(over Chapter 11)

Solve each system of equations.

1. $3x + 5y = 11$
   $2x + 3y = 7$ (2, 1)
2. $x + y = 8$
   $2x - 3y = -9$ (3, 5)
3. $3x + 3y = 6$
   $2x - y = 1$ (1, 1)
4. $r - s = -5$
   $r + s = 25$ (10, 15)
5. $-3x + 2y = 16$
   $x - 2y = -12$ (−2, 5)

Motivating the Lesson

Write the following subjects on the chalkboard: Spanish, French, Home Economics, and Industrial Technology. Poll the students to determine how many students took each of these subjects in 7th grade, in 8th grade, and in 9th grade. Ask students to represent the results of the poll in a table.

TEACHING THE LESSON

Teaching Tip ① Discuss the importance of a title and column headings on a table. Develop the idea that these labels identify the type of information being presented in the table.

12-1 Problem-Solving Strategy: Use a Table

Objective
12-1

After studying this lesson, you should be able to:
- solve problems by using a table.

One important problem-solving strategy that you have already used is to make a table or chart. In some situations, the information from a problem has already been organized in a table. In order to solve the problem, you must be able to read and interpret this information.

Example

CONNECTION
Statistics

FYI · · ·

Women received the right to vote with the passage of the 19th Amendment to the Constitution, August 26, 1920.

The Guessright Poll Company set up a survey to determine the voter's preference for mayor during various months prior to the election. A sample of 1000 people from the city's population of 550,000 was taken every other month. The results of the surveys are shown in the chart below. Based on this information, determine the following.   **Teaching Tip ①**

a. Which candidate gained the most votes from April to October?

b. In which month was the difference in votes between the two leading candidates the least?

Preference for Mayor				
Candidate	**Month**			
	April	**June**	**Aug.**	**Oct.**
Alvarez	223	286	294	347
Lewis	167	202	387	399
Rinehart	287	268	168	157
Others	209	152	64	31
Undecided	114	92	87	66

a. To determine which candidate gained the most votes from April to October, look at the totals in those columns of the table. Notice that only candidates Alvarez and Lewis had more votes in October than in April. Alvarez had $347 - 223$ or 124 more votes. Lewis had $399 - 167$ or 232 more votes. Therefore, Lewis gained the most votes from April to October.

b. To determine in which month the difference in votes between the leading candidates was the least, first look at each column to determine the leading candidates. Then, find each difference and compare.

April		June		August		October	
Rinehart	287	Alvarez	286	Lewis	387	Lewis	399
Alvarez	−223	Rinehart	−268	Alvarez	−294	Alvarez	−347
Difference	64		18		93		52

Therefore, June was the month in which the difference in votes between the two leading candidates was the least.

ALTERNATE TEACHING STRATEGIES

Using Manipulatives

Have students find examples of tables in newspapers and magazines. Ask students to mount each table found on a piece of tag board. Underneath the table, students should identify the type of information it presents.

Using Cooperative Groups

Divide the class into 4 or 5 small groups. Have each group identify some topic about which they would like to poll class members. Possible topics include course selections, favorite activities, and places of employment. After students gather data, have each group compile their findings in a table.

In mathematics, numerical values, especially those involving approximations, are often presented in tables or charts. For example, on page 644 of this text, there is a table of squares and approximate *square roots* of integers from 1 to 100. You may need to use the information in this table to solve problems in this chapter.

CHECKING FOR UNDERSTANDING

Communicating Mathematics

Read and study the lesson to answer each question.

1. In the example on page 474, during which month was the difference in votes between the two leading candidates the greatest? **August**

2. Name another problem-solving strategy that can be used with the strategy described in this lesson. **look for a pattern, list possibilities, guess and check**

Guided Practice

3. The table below shows the normal precipitation, in inches, for selected cities in the United States. Use this information to answer the following questions.

City	Jan.	Feb.	Mar.	Apr.	May	Jun.	July	Aug.	Sep.	Oct.	Nov.	Dec.
Albuquerque, NM	0.30	0.39	0.47	0.48	0.53	0.50	1.39	1.34	0.77	0.79	0.29	0.52
Boston, MA	3.69	3.54	4.01	3.49	3.47	3.19	2.74	3.46	3.16	3.02	4.51	4.24
Chicago, IL	1.85	1.59	2.73	3.75	3.41	3.95	4.09	3.14	3.00	2.62	2.20	2.11
Houston, TX	3.57	3.54	2.68	3.54	5.10	4.52	4.12	4.35	4.65	4.05	4.03	4.04
Mobile, AL	4.71	4.76	7.07	5.59	4.52	6.09	8.86	6.93	6.59	2.55	3.39	5.92
San Francisco, CA	4.37	3.04	2.54	1.59	0.41	0.13	0.01	0.03	0.16	0.98	2.29	3.98

a. Which city had the most precipitation in November? **Boston**

b. What is the driest month in Houston? **March**

c. What is the greatest monthly precipitation for any of the six cities? What month is it? What city is it? **8.86 in., July, Mobile**

d. What is the least difference between the greatest and the least monthly precipitation for any one month? What is the month? **3.26 in., October**

4. Each number below represents the age, in years, of U. S. presidents on their first inaugurations.

57 61 57 57 58 57 61 54 68 51 49 64 50 48
65 52 56 46 54 49 50 47 55 55 54 42 51 56
55 51 54 51 60 62 43 55 56 61 52 69 64

a. Organize this information into a table with the headings *Age at First Inauguration* and *Number of Times*. Then use the information in this table to answer questions b-e. **See margin for table.**

b. How many different ages are given? **21**

c. What was the difference in age between the youngest and oldest president? **27 years**

d. Which age(s) occurred most frequently? **51, 54, 55, 57**

e. How many presidents were in their 60s on their first inauguration? **10**

FYI · · ·

Theodore Roosevelt became the youngest man ever to become president of the United States when President William McKinley was assassinated in September of 1901. Roosevelt was 42.

RETEACHING THE LESSON

Investigate the patterns of the ones' digits for powers of the whole numbers 1 to 9. Assign a digit from 2 to 9 to each group of 3 students. **Answers for the first four powers are shown below.**

power	1	2	3	4	5	6	7	8	9
1	1	2	3	4	5	6	7	8	9
2	1	4	9	6	5	6	9	4	1
3	1	8	7	4	5	6	3	2	9
4	1	6	1	6	5	6	1	6	1

Chalkboard Example

For the Example

Use the table from the Example to answer each question.

a. What percent of the voters did not prefer Alvarez, Lewis, or Rinehart in the October poll? **9.7%**

b. During what month(s) did the preferred candidate for mayor stay the same? **Oct.**

c. Which candidate had the least change in number of votes from April to October? **Undecided lost 48 votes. (Alvarez gained 124.)**

EVALUATING THE LESSON

Checking for Understanding

Exercises 1-4 are designed to help you assess understanding through reading, writing, and speaking. You should work through Exercises 1-2 with your students, and then monitor their work on Exercises 3-4.

Closing the Lesson

Writing Activity Have students write a letter to an elementary school child which describes the steps to follow when making a table.

Additional Answer

4a.

Age at First Inaug.	No. of Times	Age at First Inaug.	No. of Times
42	1	56	3
43	1	57	4
44	0	58	1
45	0	59	0
46	1	60	1
47	1	61	3
48	1	62	1
49	2	63	0
50	2	64	1
51	4	65	1
52	2	66	0
53	0	67	0
54	4	68	1
55	4	69	1

Homework Exercises

Assignment Guide

Basic: 5-10
Average: 5-10
Enriched: 5-10

EXERCISES

Practice

Strategies

Look for a pattern.
Solve a simpler problem.
Act it out.
Guess and check.
Draw a diagram.
Make a chart.
Work backwards.

Solve. Use any strategy.

5. A vending machine dispenses products that each cost 50¢. It accepts quarters, dimes, and nickels only. How many different combinations of coins must the machine be programmed to accept? **10**

6. To determine a grade point average, four points are given for an A, three for a B, two for a C, one for a D, and zero for an F. If Greg has a total of 13 points for 5 classes, what combinations of grades could he receive? **AAADF, AABCF, AABDD, AACCD, ABBBF, ABBCD, ABCCC, BBBBD, BBBCC**

7. What is the next number in the sequence below? (*Hint:* This sequence involves powers of 3.) **3, for the units digit of 7^3**

$$0, 1, 8, 7, 4, 5, 6, \underline{}$$

8. In the figure at the right, exactly two line segments can be moved to make four squares. Which two segments should be moved?

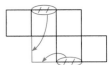

9. A woman was born in the 19th century. In a certain year, the square of her age was equal to the year. How old was she in 1885? **79**

10. In a six-team baseball tournament, the teams must play each other exactly one time. How many games will be played in this tournament? **15 games**

COOPERATIVE LEARNING ACTIVITY

Work in groups of three. Each person in the group should understand the solution and be able to explain it to any person in the class.

The large rectangle, shown in blue at the right, has been divided into eleven squares of various sizes. The sides of the smallest square, shown in red, are 9 cm long. What are the dimensions of the large rectangle? **176 cm by 177 cm**

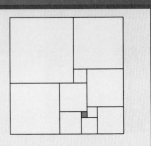

476 CHAPTER 12 RADICAL EXPRESSIONS

EXTENDING THE LESSON

Math Power: Communication

Have students write three questions about the information shown in the table on page 474. Then have students exchange papers and answer each other's questions.

Cooperative Learning Activity

This activity provides students with an opportunity to *learn* things together, not just do things together. You may wish to refer to pages T6 - T8 and page 6C for the various elements of cooperative groups and specific goals and strategies for using them.

12-2 Square Roots

Objectives

After studying this lesson, you should be able to:

12-2A ▪ simplify rational square roots, and

12-2B ▪ find approximate values for square roots.

Application

The Cutright Tile Co. has donated 144 tiles to the Southside Community Center to be used to cover the floor of a square patio. If each of the tiles is 18 inches by 18 inches, what are the dimensions of the largest patio that can be covered?

To solve this problem, determine how many tiles will be on each side of this patio. Find a number whose square is 144. Since $12^2 = 144$, the square patio will have 12 tiles on each side. Each side of this patio will be 12(18) or 216 inches long. Thus, the dimensions of the largest square patio are 216 inches by 216 inches or 18 feet by 18 feet.

In the problem, you needed a number whose square was 144. Recall that **squaring** a number means using that number as a factor two times.

Teaching Tip ❶

$$8^2 = 8 \cdot 8 = 64$$
$$(-8)^2 = (-8)(-8) = 64$$

8^2 is read "eight squared" and means eight is used as a factor two times.
-8 is used as a factor two times.

Finding a square root of 64 is the same as finding a number whose square is 64.

The opposite of squaring a number is finding its **square root**. To find a square root of 64, you must find two *equal* factors whose product is 64.

$$x^2 = x \cdot x = 64$$

Since 8 times 8 is 64, one square root of 64 is 8. Since -8 times -8 is also 64, another square root of 64 is -8. In the problem above, 12 is a square root of 144. Another square root of 144 is -12, but it was not considered as a solution to the tile problem. *Why?*

Definition of Square Root	If $x^2 = y$, then x is a square root of y.

The square root of a negative number is not defined for the sets of numbers covered thus far in this text.

An expression like $\sqrt{64}$ is called a **radical expression**. The symbol $\sqrt{}$ is a **radical sign**. It indicates the *nonnegative* or **principal** square root of the expression under the radical sign. The expression under the radical sign is called the **radicand**.

radical sign → $\sqrt{64}$ ← radicand

± means positive or negative.

$\sqrt{64} = 8$ $\quad$ $\sqrt{64}$ indicates the *principal* square root of 64.
$-\sqrt{64} = -8$ $\quad$ $-\sqrt{64}$ indicates the *negative* square root of 64.
$\pm\sqrt{64} = \pm 8$ $\quad$ $\pm\sqrt{64}$ indicates *both* square roots of 64.
$\quad$ *This is read "plus or minus the square root of 64."*

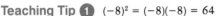

LESSON 12-2 SQUARE ROOTS 477

ALTERNATE TEACHING STRATEGIES

Using Logical Reasoning

What numbers equal their own square roots? **0, 1**

Using a Calculator

Use a calculator to simplify. Round to the nearest thousandth.

$$\frac{\sqrt{2.43} + \sqrt{69.25} - \sqrt{242}}{\frac{2\sqrt{72}}{3}} \quad -1.003$$

12-2 Lesson Notes

Lesson Resources

- Reteaching Master 12-2
- Practice Master 12-2
- Enrichment Master 12-2
- Technology Master, p. 12
- Activity Master, p. 27
- Video Algebra, 47

Transparency 12-2 contains the 5-Minute Check and a teaching aid for this lesson.

INTRODUCING THE LESSON

🕐 5-Minute Check

(over Chapter 11)

Solve each system of equations.

1. $x = 2y$
   $x + y = 6$ **(4, 2)**
2. $y = 3x$
   $x + 2y = -21$ **(-3, -9)**
3. $2x - y = 3x$
   $2x + y = 3y$ **(0, 0)**

Use a system of equations to solve each problem.

4. The tens digit of a two-digit number is twice the units digit. If the digits are reversed, the new number is 18 less than the original number. Find the original number. **42**

5. A speedboat travels 75 miles with the current in 3 hours. The return trip takes 5 hours. What is the rate of the current? **5 mph**

Motivating the Lesson

Open the lesson by allowing the students to experiment with the square root key on their calculators. Encourage students to experiment with both positive and negative numbers. Ask the students to define "square root" in their own words.

TEACHING THE LESSON

Teaching Tip ❶ Remind students that $-x^2$ means $-(x^2)$, not $(-x)^2$. Thus, parentheses are necessary to indicate the square of a negative number.

Chapter 12 477

Chalkboard Examples

For Example 1
Find each square root.

a. $\sqrt{49}$ 7

b. $\sqrt{121}$ 11

c. $\sqrt{144}$ 12

d. $\pm\sqrt{0.04}$ ± 0.2

e. $\pm\sqrt{1.69}$ ± 1.3

For Example 2
Find each square root.

a. $\sqrt{441}$ 21

b. $\sqrt{1024}$ 32

c. $\sqrt{\dfrac{25}{81}}$ $\dfrac{5}{9}$

For Example 3
Use a calculator to find each square root. Round decimal answers to the nearest hundredth.

a. $-\sqrt{46.5}$ -6.82

b. $-\sqrt{84.3}$ -9.18

Teaching Tip ② Encourage students to check square roots by squaring.

Teaching Tip ③ Before introducing this example, have students find square roots of numbers when given the prime factorizations. Point out that to find the square root of a power, divide the exponent by 2. For example,
$\sqrt{2^4 \times 3^4 \times 5^2} = 2^2 \times 3^2 \times 5$,
or 180.

Teaching Tip ④ Emphasize that $(2^3)^2 = 2^6$ and therefore $\sqrt{2^6} = 2^3$.

Example 1

Find each square root.

a. $\sqrt{81}$

Since $9^2 = 81$, you know that $\sqrt{81} = 9$.

b. $\pm\sqrt{0.09}$

Since $(0.3)^2 = 0.09$, you know that $\pm\sqrt{0.09} = \pm 0.3$. **Teaching Tip ②**

You may sometimes need to use prime factorization to find a square root of a number.

Example 2

Find each square root. **Teaching Tip ③**

a. $-\sqrt{576}$ **Teaching Tip ④**

$576 = 2^6 \cdot 3^2$ *Find the prime factorization of 576.*
$\quad\;\; = (2^3 \cdot 3)^2$
$\quad\;\; = 24^2$

Since $24^2 = 576$, you know that $-\sqrt{576} = -24$.

b. $\sqrt{\dfrac{256}{2025}}$

$\dfrac{256}{2025} = \dfrac{2^8}{3^4 \cdot 5^2}$ *Find the prime factorizations of 256 and 2025.*

$\quad\quad\;\; = \left(\dfrac{2^4}{3^2 \cdot 5}\right)^2$

$\quad\quad\;\; = \left(\dfrac{16}{45}\right)^2$

Since $\left(\dfrac{16}{45}\right)^2 = \dfrac{256}{2025}$, you know that $\sqrt{\dfrac{256}{2025}} = \dfrac{16}{45}$.

When will the square root of a whole number not be an integer?

Some calculators have a *square root key* labeled $\sqrt{}$ or $\sqrt{x}$. When you press this key, the number in the display is replaced by its principal square root. If a principal square root is *not* a whole number, then most calculators will round the result and display as many decimal places as they can handle.

Example 3

Find $\sqrt{2209}$ and $\pm\sqrt{1236}$. If the principal square root is *not* a whole number, round the result to the nearest hundredth.

a. Enter: 2209 $\boxed{\sqrt{x}}$ 47

Therefore, $\sqrt{2209} = 47$.

b. Enter: 1236 $\boxed{\sqrt{x}}$ 35.1567917

Therefore, $\pm\sqrt{1236}$ to the nearest hundredth is ± 35.16.

To check this result, compare $(35.16)^2$ to 1236.

In Example 3, you could also write $\pm\sqrt{1236} \approx \pm 35.16$. The symbol $\approx$ means *is approximately equal to*.

Example 4

APPLICATION

Plumbing

In order to allow for the proper flow of water, the opening of a circular pipe from a hot water heater must have an area of 0.785 square inches. Use the formula for the area of a circle, $A = \pi r^2$, to find the radius of the opening of the pipe. Use 3.14 for π.

$$A = \pi r^2$$

$$0.785 \approx 3.14r^2 \qquad \textit{Substitute 0.785 for A and 3.14 for } \pi.$$

$$\frac{0.785}{3.14} \approx \frac{3.14r^2}{3.14} \qquad \textit{Divide each side by 3.14.}$$

$$0.25 \approx r^2$$

$$0.5 \approx r \qquad \textit{Since 0.25 = (0.5)}^2\textit{, 0.5 is the square root of 0.25.}$$

Therefore, the radius of the opening of the pipe should be about 0.5 inches.

2. Because $2(2) = 4$ and $(-2)(-2) = 4$.   3. See margin.

CHECKING FOR UNDERSTANDING

Communicating Mathematics

Read and study the lesson to answer each question.

1. What are the radicand and principal square root of $\sqrt{25}$? **25, 5**

2. Why are both 2 and -2 square roots of 4?

3. Choose any positive number and enter it on a calculator. Then press the square root key, followed by the x^2 key. What is the result? Why?

4. Choose any negative number and enter it on a calculator. Then press the square root key. What is the result? Why? **Error message is given; the square root of a negative number is not a real number.**

Guided Practice

State the square of each number.

5. 12 **144**   6. -20 **400**   7. 0.3 **0.09**   8. $\frac{4}{7}$ **$\frac{16}{49}$**   9. $-\frac{11}{4}$ **$\frac{121}{16}$**

Simplify.

10. $\sqrt{121}$ **11**   11. $-\sqrt{81}$ **-9**   12. $\pm\sqrt{\frac{81}{64}}$ **$\pm\frac{9}{8}$**   13. $\sqrt{0.0016}$ **0.04**

Use a calculator to find each square root. Round answers to the nearest hundredth.

14. $\sqrt{85}$ **9.22**   15. $-\sqrt{149}$ **-12.21**   16. $\pm\sqrt{206}$ **±14.35**   17. $\sqrt{60.3}$ **7.77**

EXERCISES

Practice

Find the principal square root of each number.

18. 169 **13**   19. 256 **16**   20. $\frac{81}{121}$ **$\frac{9}{11}$**   21. $\frac{36}{196}$ **$\frac{6}{14}$ or $\frac{3}{7}$**

22. $\frac{400}{225}$ **$\frac{20}{15}$ or $\frac{4}{3}$**   23. 0.0025 **0.05**   24. 0.0289 **0.17**   25. 3.24 **1.8**

LESSON 12-2 SQUARE ROOTS 479

RETEACHING THE LESSON

Find the diameter to the nearest tenth of an inch of a round pizza that is the same size as a:

a. 6″ by 8″ pizza. **7.8″**

b. 10″ square pizza. **11.3″**

c. 10″ by 14″ pizza. **13.4″**

What size square pizza is as big as a:

a. 4″ by 18″ pizza? **8.5″**

b. 12″ round pizza? **10.6″**

Additional Answer

3. The result is the positive number entered; taking the square root and squaring are inverse operations.

Chalkboard Example

For Example 4

Suppose the opening of the pipe described in Example 4 was 0.07065 square inches. Find the radius of the opening of this pipe.   0.15

EVALUATING THE LESSON

Checking for Understanding

Exercises 1-17 are designed to help you assess understanding through reading, writing, and speaking. You should work through Exercises 1-4 with your students, and then monitor their work on Exercises 5-17.

Error Analysis

Students sometimes mistake the radical sign $\sqrt{}$ to mean square root, but $\sqrt{}$ means only the *principal* or nonnegative square root. From the equation $x^2 = y^2$, it does not follow that $x = y$, only that $|x| = |y|$ or $x = \pm y$.

Reteaching Masters Booklet, p. 80

NAME _____ DATE _____

12-2 Reteaching Worksheet

Square Roots

An expression such as $\sqrt{81}$ is called a **radical expression**. The symbol $\sqrt{}$ is a **radical sign**. It indicates the nonnegative or **principal square root** of the **radicand**, the expression under the radical sign.

Example 1: Simplify $-\sqrt{36}$.
Since $6^2 = 36$, $-\sqrt{36} = -6$.

Example 2: Simplify $\sqrt{784}$.
$784 = 2^4 \cdot 7^2$ *Find the prime factorization of 784.*
$= (2^2 \cdot 7)^2$
$= 28^2$
Since $28^2 = 784$, $\sqrt{784} = 28$.

A calculator can find square roots and display as many decimal places as its display screen allows.

Find the principal square root of each number.

1. 81 **9**   2. $\frac{25}{16}$ **$\frac{5}{4}$**   3. 0.0049 **0.07**   4. 1.44 **1.2**

Simplify.

5. $\sqrt{81}$ **9**   6. $-\sqrt{25}$ **-5**   7. $\pm\sqrt{64}$ **±8**   8. $\sqrt{3600}$ **60**

9. $-\sqrt{\frac{16}{25}}$ **$-\frac{4}{5}$**   10. $-\sqrt{\frac{9}{49}}$ **$-\frac{3}{7}$**   11. $\pm\sqrt{\frac{169}{625}}$ **$\pm\frac{13}{25}$**   12. $\sqrt{\frac{9}{81}}$ **$\frac{1}{3}$**

13. $\sqrt{841}$ **29**   14. $-\sqrt{1156}$ **-34**   15. $\sqrt{0.0289}$ **0.17**   16. $-\sqrt{5.76}$ **-2.4**

Use a calculator to find each square root. Round answers to the nearest thousandth.

17. $\sqrt{7.5}$ **2.739**   18. $\sqrt{47}$ **6.856**   19. $\sqrt{35}$ **5.916**   20. $\sqrt{101}$ **10.050**

Closing the Lesson

Speaking Activity Have students explain how to use prime factorizations to find the square root of a number.

APPLYING THE LESSON

Homework Exercises

Chapter 12, Quiz A, (Lessons 12-1 through 12-2), is available in the Evaluation Masters Booklet, p. 163.

Practice Masters Booklet, p. 91

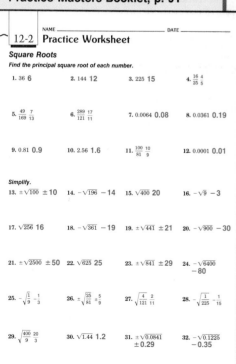

 Simplify.

26. $\pm\sqrt{144}$ ±12 **27.** $-\sqrt{100}$ -10 **28.** $\sqrt{529}$ 23

29. $\sqrt{484}$ 22   **30.** $-\sqrt{676}$ -26 **31.** $\pm\sqrt{961}$ ±31

32. $\pm\sqrt{1764}$ ±42 **33.** $\sqrt{2025}$ 45   **34.** $\sqrt{0.0729}$ 0.27

35. $-\sqrt{10.24}$ -3.2 **36.** $-\sqrt{\frac{169}{121}}$ $-\frac{13}{11}$ **37.** $\pm\sqrt{\frac{144}{1521}}$ $\pm\frac{12}{39}$

Use a calculator to find each square root. Round answers to the nearest thousandth.

38. $\sqrt{115.7}$ 10.756   **39.** $-\sqrt{175.6}$ -13.251 **40.** $\pm\sqrt{155.1}$ ±12.454 **41.** $\sqrt{531.4}$ 23.052

42. $-\sqrt{0.61}$ -0.781 **43.** $\sqrt{2.314}$ 1.521   **44.** $\sqrt{0.00462}$ 0.068   **45.** $\pm\sqrt{0.00932}$ ±0.097

Find the length of the side of each square. The area is given. Round answers to the nearest hundredth.

46.

32.49 ft²

5.70 ft

47.

129 in²

11.36 in.

48.

1400 cm²

37.42 cm

 Simplify.

49. $\sqrt{\sqrt{81}}$ 3   **50.** $\sqrt{\sqrt{625}}$ 5   **51.** $\sqrt{\sqrt{\sqrt{256}}}$ 2

52. The volume of a rectangular solid is 100 cm³. Its height is the product of its length and width. If the base of the solid is a square, find the dimensions of the solid. Use a calculator as needed. Round decimal answers to the nearest hundredth.
3.16 cm by 3.16 cm by 10 cm

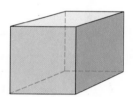

Critical Thinking 53. Choose any negative number and enter it on a calculator. Then press the x² key, followed by the square root key. What is the result? Why? **The absolute value of the number appears; calculators provide the principal square root.**

Applications 54. **Law Enforcement** The approximate speed s, in miles per hour, of a car traveling on a dry concrete road if it skidded d feet after its brakes were applied, is given by the formula $s = \sqrt{24d}$. What was the approximate speed of a car that skidded 150 feet on a dry concrete road after the brakes were applied? **60 miles per hour**

480 CHAPTER 12 RADICAL EXPRESSIONS

55. **Physics** For an object moving in a circular path, its acceleration, a, toward the center is given by the formula $a = \dfrac{v^2}{r}$. In this formula, v is the velocity of the object and r is the radius of the circular path. Find the velocity, in meters per second, of an object moving in a circular path with radius 20 meters, if its acceleration toward the center is 17 meters per second squared. Round your answer to the nearest tenth of a unit. **18.4 meters per second**

56. **Electricity** The power P, in watts, of a circuit is given by the formula $P = I^2R$. In this formula, I is the current in amperes and R is the resistance in ohms. Find the current in a circuit that produces 1200 watts of power if the resistance is 5 ohms. Round your answer to the nearest tenth of an ampere. **15.5 amperes**

Mixed Review

57. Eight is 20% of what number? **(Lesson 4-2)** 40

58. Factor $20a^2c^2 + 60a^2c + 45a^2$. **(Lesson 7-7)** $5a^2(2c + 3)^2$

59. **Aviation** An airplane can fly at a rate of 600 mph in calm air. It can fly 2413 miles with the wind in the same time it can fly 2147 miles against the wind. What is the speed of the wind? **(Lesson 8-9)** 35 mph

60. Graph $4x - 3y = 24$. **(Lesson 9-4)** See margin.

61. Write an equation in slope-intercept form of the line that passes through $(6, 3)$ and $(-2, 4)$. **(Lesson 10-5)** $y = -\dfrac{1}{8}x + \dfrac{15}{4}$

62. Solve the system $y - x > 1$ and $y + 2x \le 10$ by graphing. **(Lesson 11-6)** See margin.

HISTORY CONNECTION

Jaime Escalante

Jaime Escalante is the teacher at Garfield High School in Los Angeles, California on whom the movie *Stand and Deliver* is based. Escalante left a comfortable career in industry to teach mathematics in an economically depressed area of Los Angeles. When he joined the staff at Garfield, his junior class students were having trouble with fractions and percentages. Before the end of their senior year, 18 of these students would pass the most difficult mathematics exam given to high-school seniors, the National Advanced Placement Calculus Exam. Escalante believed that "math is the great equalizer," so he showed his students the misery into which a lack of education would lead them and raised their expectations of what was ahead of them. As a result, his students went on to colleges and universities, many with college credit and scholarships.

EXTENDING THE LESSON

Math Power:
Problem Solving
Simplify.

$\sqrt{\sqrt{\sqrt{256}}}$ 2

History Connection

The History Connection features introduce students to persons or cultures who were involved in the development of mathematics. You may want students to further research Escalante.

Additional Answers

60.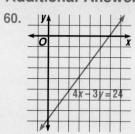
$4x - 3y = 24$

62.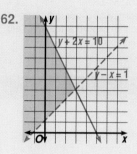
$y + 2x = 10$
$y - x = 1$

Enrichment Masters Booklet, p. 80

NAME _____ DATE _____

12-2 Enrichment Worksheet

Reading Algebra: The Discovery of Irrational Numbers

The following paragraph describes an important part of the history of mathematics. The questions below will help you understand the reading.

At first the Greek mathematicians believed that the lengths of line segments could be compared using natural numbers alone. In particular, for a square with a side of length n, there should be some natural number m to represent the diagonal of the square. The Pythagorean geometers proved that the square on the diagonal is exactly twice the square on the side.

From this it follows that we should have $m^2 = 2n^2$, and therefore $\left(\dfrac{m}{n}\right)^2 = 2$. By an ingenious geometric argument, they showed that no such rational number $\dfrac{m}{n}$ exists. The recognition of this fact made it evident that many theorems of geometry for which the Pythagoreans thought they had satisfactory proofs were without logical foundation.

Solve each problem.

1. What is a natural number? How is it different from a rational number? (Use a glossary if you need help.)
   Natural numbers are the positive integers: 1, 2, 3, ... Rational numbers can be written as the ratio $\dfrac{m}{n}$ of two integers, $n \ne 0$.

2. Draw a figure to show a square with side n and diagonal m.

3. The figure below shows a square and "the square on the diagonal." Draw a figure showing both the "square on the diagonal" and the "square on the side."

4. The paragraph says that there is no solution for $\left(\dfrac{m}{n}\right)^2 = 2$ if $\dfrac{m}{n}$ must be a rational number. For what type of number does the equation have a solution?
   irrational numbers; The solution is $\sqrt{2}$.

5. Does the paragraph *prove* that the diagonal of a square cannot be expressed as a rational number? Explain your answer.
   No, it refers to "an ingenious argument," but does not give the argument.

6. What do you suppose the Pythagoreans did about the "lost" theorems—the theorems that suddenly lacked proofs?
   Possible answer: They attempted to prove the theorems using new arguments.

Lesson Resources
- Reteaching Master 12-3
- Practice Master 12-3
- Enrichment Master 12-3
- Lab Manual, pp. 39-40
- Activity Master, p. 12
- Video Algebra, 51-52

 Transparency 12-3 contains the 5-Minute Check and a teaching aid for this lesson.

INTRODUCING THE LESSON

 **5-Minute Check**

(over Lesson 12-2)

Simplify.

1. $\pm\sqrt{144}$ ± 12
2. $\sqrt{0.0081}$ 0.09
3. $\sqrt{1764}$ 42
4. $\sqrt{484}$ 22
5. $\sqrt{289}$ 17

Motivating the Lesson

Open this lesson by measuring the length and width of the classroom. Then have students measure the length of a diagonal that cuts across the room. Write the three measurements on the board. Challenge students to determine a relationship among the numbers.

TEACHING THE LESSON

Teaching Tip 1 Point out to the students that if c is the measure of the longest side of a triangle and $c^2 \neq a^2 + b^2$, then the triangle is not a right triangle. This is called the converse of the Pythagorean Theorem.

12-3 The Pythagorean Theorem

Objective
12-3

After studying this lesson, you should be able to:
- use the Pythagorean Theorem.

Application

FYI · · ·

Before 1845, the bases on a baseball field were arranged in the shape of a U. Before 1859, umpires sat in a padded rocking chair behind the catcher.

A baseball scout uses many different tests to determine whether or not to draft a particular player. One test for catchers is to see how quickly they can throw a ball from home plate to second base. The scout must know the distance between the two bases in case a player cannot be tested on a baseball diamond. This distance can be found by separating the baseball diamond into two right triangles, as shown at the left.

The side opposite the right angle in a right triangle is called the **hypotenuse.** This side is *always* the longest side of a right triangle. The other two sides are called the **legs** of the right triangle.

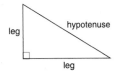

For the baseball diamond above, the distance from home plate to second base is equal to the length of the hypotenuse of the right triangle. The distance from home plate to first base and the distance from first base to second base are the lengths of the legs. On a baseball diamond, the distance from one base to the next is 90 feet.

To find the length of the hypotenuse, given the lengths of the legs, you can use a formula developed by the Greek mathematician, Pythagoras.

The Pythagorean Theorem Teaching Tip 1	In a right triangle, if a and b are the measures of the legs and c is the measure of the hypotenuse, then $$c^2 = a^2 + b^2.$$

For the baseball diamond, $a = 90$ and $b = 90$. You can use the Pythagorean Theorem to find the distance from home plate to second base.

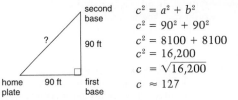

$c^2 = a^2 + b^2$
$c^2 = 90^2 + 90^2$ *$a = 90$ and $b = 90$*
$c^2 = 8100 + 8100$
$c^2 = 16{,}200$
$c = \sqrt{16{,}200}$ *Use a calculator to approximate $\sqrt{16{,}200}$ to the nearest unit.*
$c \approx 127$

The distance from home plate to second base is approximately 127 feet.

ALTERNATE TEACHING STRATEGIES

Using Connections

An isosceles triangle has at least two sides of equal length. Can an isosceles triangle be a right triangle? **yes**

An equilateral triangle has three sides of equal length. Can an equilateral triangle be a right triangle? **no**

A geometric model can also be used to illustrate the Pythagorean Theorem, as shown below. **Teaching Tip** ②

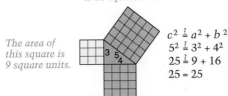

The area of this square is 25 square units.

The area of this square is 9 square units.

The area of this square is 16 square units.

$c^2 \stackrel{?}{=} a^2 + b^2$
$5^2 \stackrel{?}{=} 3^2 + 4^2$
$25 \stackrel{?}{=} 9 + 16$
$25 = 25$

You can use the Pythagorean Theorem to find the length of any side of a right triangle when the lengths of the other two sides are known.

Example 1

Find the length of the hypotenuse of a right triangle if $a = 15$ and $b = 8$.

$c^2 = a^2 + b^2$
$c^2 = 15^2 + 8^2$ *$a = 15$ and $b = 8$*
$c^2 = 225 + 64$
$c^2 = 289$
$c = 17$

The length of the hypotenuse is 17 units.

Example 2

Find the length of the other leg of a right triangle, to the nearest hundredth, if $a = 6$ and $c = 14$.

$c^2 = a^2 + b^2$
$14^2 = 6^2 + b^2$ *$a = 6$ and $c = 14$*
$196 = 36 + b^2$
$b^2 = 160$
$b = \sqrt{160}$ *Use a calculator to approximate $\sqrt{160}$*
$b \approx 12.65$ *to the nearest hundredth.*

The length of the leg, to the nearest hundredth, is 12.65 units.

The following statement, which is based on the Pythagorean Theorem, can be used to determine whether a triangle is a right triangle.

> If c is the measure of the longest side of a triangle and
> $c^2 \neq a^2 + b^2$, then the triangle is *not* a right triangle.

LESSON 12-3   THE PYTHAGOREAN THEOREM   483

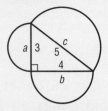

Since $A = \pi r^2$ is the formula for the area of a circle, $A = \frac{1}{2}(\pi r^2)$ or $A = \frac{1}{2}\pi r^2$ is the formula for the area of a semicircle. Use this formula to illustrate the Pythagorean Theorem using semicircles. The sides of the right triangle have lengths 3, 4, and 5 units.

area of semicircle with diameter 5 units = area of semicircle with diameter 3 units + area of semicircle with diameter 4 units

$\frac{1}{2}\pi\left(\frac{5}{2}\right)^2 = \frac{1}{2}\pi\left(\frac{3}{2}\right)^2 + \frac{1}{2}\pi(2)^2$

$\frac{25}{8}\pi = \frac{9}{8}\pi + 2\pi$

$\frac{25}{8}\pi = \frac{25}{8}\pi$

Chalkboard Examples

For Example 1

In the following exercises, c is the measure of the hypotenuse of a right triangle. Find each missing measure.

a. $a = 12$, $b = 16$, $c = ?$ **20**

b. $a = 11$, $b = \sqrt{23}$, $c = ?$ **12**

c. $a = 5$, $b = 7$, $c = ?$ $\sqrt{74}$ **or 8.60**

For Example 2

In the following exercises, c is the measure of the hypotenuse of a right triangle. Find each missing measure.

a. $a = 4$, $c = 10$, $b = ?$ $\sqrt{84}$ **or 9.17**

b. $a = 5$, $c = 6$, $b = ?$ $\sqrt{11}$ **or 3.32**

c. $c = 10$, $b = 7$, $a = ?$ $\sqrt{51}$ **or 7.14**

Example 3

The measures of the sides of a triangle are 5, 7, and 9. Determine whether this triangle is a right triangle.

Since the measure of the longest side is 9, let $c = 9$, $a = 5$, and $b = 7$. Then determine whether $c^2 = a^2 + b^2$.

$9^2 \overset{?}{=} 5^2 + 7^2$
$81 \overset{?}{=} 25 + 49$
$81 \neq 74$ Since $c^2 \neq a^2 + b^2$, the triangle is *not* a right triangle.

Example 4

APPLICATION
Construction

The walls of the Downtown Recreation Center are being covered with paneling. The doorway into one room is 0.9 m wide and 2.5 m high. What is the longest rectangular panel that can be taken through this doorway?

EXPLORE   The panel needs to be taken through the doorway diagonally. Let $c =$ the length of the diagonal, as shown at the right.

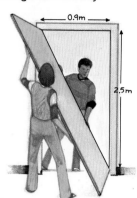

PLAN   Use the Pythagorean Theorem to find c. Let $a = 0.9$ and $b = 2.5$.

$c^2 = (0.9)^2 + (2.5)^2$

SOLVE $c^2 = 0.81 + 6.25$
$c^2 = 7.06$
$c = \sqrt{7.06}$ *Use a calculator to approximate $\sqrt{7.06}$.*
$c \approx 2.66$

The diagonal is about 2.66 meters long. Since space is needed to slide the panel through the doorway, the panel should be slightly less than 2.66 meters long.

EXAMINE   Check the solution by substituting 2.66 for c in the Pythagorean Theorem.

$$c^2 = a^2 + b^2$$
$$(2.66)^2 \overset{?}{=} (0.9)^2 + (2.5)^2$$
$$7.0756 \approx 7.06 \ \checkmark$$

CHECKING FOR UNDERSTANDING

Communicating Mathematics

Read and study the lesson to answer each question.

1. What is the name of the longest side of a right triangle? **hypotenuse**
2. State the Pythagorean Theorem in your own words. **See students' work.**
3. If you know the lengths of the three sides of a triangle, how can you determine if the triangle is a right triangle? **See margin.**

Guided Practice   State whether each sentence is *true* or *false*.

4. $3^2 + 4^2 = 5^2$ **true**   5. $9^2 + 10^2 = 11^2$ **false**   6. $6^2 + 8^2 = 9^2$ **false**

484   CHAPTER 12   RADICAL EXPRESSIONS

RETEACHING THE LESSON

Supply a geoboard to each pair of students. Stretch rubber bands over the pegs to form right triangles. Find the lengths of all sides. Demonstrate how to find the lengths $\sqrt{2}$, $\sqrt{3}$, $\sqrt{5}$, $\sqrt{10}$, $\sqrt{13}$, $3\sqrt{2}$. Form a square with an area of 2 square units.

Solve each equation. Assume each variable represents a positive number.

7. $6^2 + 8^2 = c^2$ **10** **8.** $5^2 + 12^2 = c^2$ **13** **9.** $a^2 + 15^2 = 17^2$ **8**

10. $a^2 + 24^2 = 25^2$ **7** **11.** $12^2 + b^2 = 20^2$ **16** **12.** $10^2 + b^2 = 26^2$ **24**

If c is the measure of the hypotenuse of a right triangle, find each missing measure.

13. $a = 9, b = 12, c = ?$ **15** **14.** $a = \sqrt{7}, b = \sqrt{9}, c = ?$ **4**

15. $b = \sqrt{30}, c = \sqrt{34}, a = ?$ **2** **16.** $a = \sqrt{11}, c = \sqrt{47}, b = ?$ **6**

EXERCISES   24. $\sqrt{27} \approx 5.20$ 25. $\sqrt{28} \approx 5.29$ 26. $\sqrt{67} \approx 8.19$ 28. $\sqrt{145} \approx 12.04$

Practice

If c is the measure of the hypotenuse of a right triangle, find each missing measure. Round answers to the nearest hundredth.

  A

17. $a = 16, b = 30, c = ?$ **34** **18.** $a = 11, c = 61, b = ?$ **60**

19. $b = 21, c = 29, a = ?$ **20** **20.** $a = \sqrt{13}, b = 6, c = ?$ **7**

21. $a = \sqrt{11}, c = 6, b = ?$ **5** **22.** $b = 13, c = \sqrt{233}, a = ?$ **8**

B

23. $a = 6, b = 3, c = ?$ $\sqrt{45} \approx 6.71$ **24.** $a = 4, b = \sqrt{11}, c = ?$

25. $a = 15, c = \sqrt{253}, b = ?$ **26.** $b = \sqrt{77}, c = 12, a = ?$

27. $b = 10, c = 11, a = ?$ $\sqrt{21} \approx 4.58$ **28.** $a = 12, c = 17, b = ?$

The measures of the sides of a triangle are given. Determine whether each triangle is a right triangle.

29. 9, 16, 20 **no** **30.** 9, 40, 41 **yes** **31.** 45, 60, 75 **yes**

32. 12, 11, 15 **no** **33.** 18, $\sqrt{24}$, 30 **no** **34.** 15, $\sqrt{31}$, 16 **yes**

C
CONNECTION
Geometry

For each problem, make a drawing. Then use an equation to solve the problem. Round answers to the nearest hundredth.

35. Find the length of the diagonal of a square if its area is 98 cm². **14 cm**

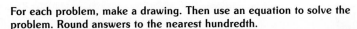

36. Find the length of the diagonal of a cube if each side of the cube is 5 inches long. $\sqrt{75}$ **in. or about 8.66 in.**

37. The area of a rectangle is 40 square meters. Find the length of a diagonal of the rectangle if its length is 2 meters less than twice its width. $\sqrt{89}$ **m or about 9.43 m**

38. Exactly two right triangles will be formed when what figure is cut along one of its diagonals? **rectangle**

Critical Thinking

39. Mary hikes 7 km north, 5 km west, and then 5 km north again. How far is Mary from the starting point of her hike? **13 km**

Applications

For Exercises 40–42, make a drawing. Then use an equation to solve the problem. Round answers to the nearest hundredth.

40. Baseball The person on third base fields the ball directly on the third-base line 20 feet beyond third base. How far must she throw the ball to reach first base? (*Hint:* The distance between bases is 90 feet.)
$\sqrt{20,200}$ ft or about 142.13 ft

LESSON 12-3 THE PYTHAGOREAN THEOREM **485**

Additional Answer

3. If the square of the length of the longest side equals the sum of the squares of the lengths of the other sides, then the triangle is a right triangle.

EVALUATING THE LESSON

Checking for Understanding

Exercises 1-16 are designed to help you assess understanding through reading, writing, and speaking. You should work through Exercises 1-3 with your students, and then monitor their work on Exercises 4-16.

Closing the Lesson

Writing Activity At the end of class, have students write down the key points to consider in using the Pythagorean Theorem.

APPLYING THE LESSON

Homework Exercises

Assignment Guide

Basic: 17-34, 39-41, 44-48
Average: 20-36, 39-48
Enriched: 23-48

Practice Masters Booklet, p. 92

NAME _____ DATE _____

12-3 Practice Worksheet

The Pythagorean Theorem

If c is the measure of the hypotenuse of a right triangle, find each missing measure. Round answers to the nearest hundredth.

1. $a = 3, b = 4, c = $ ___5___   **2.** $a = 6, c = 10, b = $ ___8___

3. $b = 12, c = 13, a = $ ___5___   **4.** $a = 6, c = 12, b = $ $\sqrt{108} \approx 10.39$

5. $a = 8, b = 6, c = $ ___10___   **6.** $a = 5, c = 13, b = $ ___12___

7. $b = 0.8, c = 1.0, a = $ ___0.6___   **8.** $a = 11, b = 4, c = $ $\sqrt{137} \approx 11.70$

9. $a = \sqrt{12}, b = 6, c = $ $\sqrt{48} \approx 6.93$ **10.** $b = 11, c = \sqrt{289}, a = $ $\sqrt{168} \approx 12.96$

11. $a = 19, b = \sqrt{39}, c = $ ___20___   **12.** $a = \sqrt{6}, b = \sqrt{19}, c = $ ___5___

The measures of the sides of a triangle are given. Determine whether each triangle is a right triangle.

13. 20, 21, 29 **yes**   **14.** 15, 30, 34 **no**

15. 9, $\sqrt{40}$, 11 **yes**   **16.** 21, 72, 75 **yes**

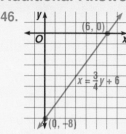

41. **Construction** James wants to position a 16-foot ladder so that the top of the ladder is 15 feet above the base of an outside wall of his house. How far should the bottom of the ladder be placed from the base of the wall? $\sqrt{31}$ ft or about 5.57 ft

42. **Sailing** A rope from the top of a mast on a sailboat is attached to a point 2 meters from the base of the mast. If the rope is 8 meters long, how high is the mast? $\sqrt{60}$ m or about 7.75 m

43. **Construction** A wire is run from the top of a 52-meter tower to the top of a 12-meter tower and then to the base of the 52-meter tower. If the two towers are 9 meters apart, how much wire is needed? **56 meters**

Mixed Review

44. **Statistics** Find the mean for the following set of data: 1, 14, 4, 8, 8, 7.35, 2.9, 12.75. **(Lesson 2-7)** 7.25

45. Find $\dfrac{2x^2 + 11x + 15}{2x^2 - 5x - 3} \div \dfrac{x^2 + 7x + 12}{x^2 + x - 12}$. **(Lesson 8-3)** $\dfrac{2x + 5}{2x + 1}$

46. Graph $x = \dfrac{3}{4}y + 6$ using the x- and y-intercepts. **(Lesson 10-4)** *See margin.*

47. **Chemistry** One solution is 50% glycol and another is 30% glycol. How much of each should be mixed to make a 100-gallon solution that is 45% glycol? **(Lesson 11-3)** 75 gal of 50%, 25 gal of 30%

48. Find $\pm \sqrt{4356}$. **(Lesson 12-2)** ± 66

APPLICATION

Escape Velocity

The minimum velocity v that a spacecraft must have to escape the gravitational force of a planet can be calculated using the formula $v = \sqrt{\dfrac{2GM}{r}}$, where G is a gravitational constant, M is the mass of the planet, and r is the radius of the planet.

Earth's mass is 5.98×10^{24} kg, its radius is 6.37×10^6 m, and $G = 6.67 \times 10^{-11}$ N-m²/kg². Compute the escape velocity for Earth.

$v = \sqrt{\dfrac{2GM}{r}}$ $G = 6.67 \times 10^{-11}, M = 5.98 \times 10^{24}, r = 6.37 \times 10^6$

$= \sqrt{\dfrac{2(6.67 \times 10^{-11})(5.98 \times 10^{24})}{6.37 \times 10^6}}$

$= \sqrt{\dfrac{7.97732 \times 10^{14}}{6.37 \times 10^6}}$

$= \sqrt{1.2523265 \times 10^8} \approx 1.12 \times 10^4$

The escape velocity for Earth is about 1.12×10^4 meters per second.

EXTENDING THE LESSON

Math Power: Connections

The length of a rectangle is 2 feet less than twice its width. Each diagonal is 34 feet. What are the dimensions of the rectangle? **16 ft, 30 ft**

Application

Point out that the gravitational constant is given in N-m²/kg². The abbreviation N stands for newton. One newton of force acting on a mass of one kilogram causes acceleration of one meter per second per second.

Real Numbers

Objective
12-4

After studying this lesson, you should be able to:
- identify irrational numbers.

Application

FYI · · ·

The symbol for a radical probably comes from an old European lowercase letter *r*, an abbreviation for the Latin word *radix*, meaning root.

Drew is building a storage shed in his backyard. The shed needs to have 120 square feet of floor space in order to store all of his equipment. Is it possible for Drew to build the shed with a square floor that has an area of *exactly* 120 square feet?

In order to build the storage shed with a square floor, Drew needs to know the length of each side of the square. Let s = the measure of the side of the square floor.

$$s^2 = 120 \qquad \text{\textit{The floor is to have an area of 120 ft}}^2.$$
$$s = \sqrt{120} \qquad \text{\textit{Use a calculator to find }}\sqrt{120}.$$
$$s = 10.9544511 \ldots$$

If the area of the square floor is to be exactly 120 square feet, then the length of each side must be exactly 10.9544511 . . . feet! Based on your knowledge of measurement and measuring devices, do you think that it is possible for Drew to build this floor?

SHED PLAN

The number $\sqrt{120} = 10.9544511\ldots$ is not a repeating or terminating decimal. Therefore, it is *not* a member of any of the sets of numbers you have encountered so far. These sets of numbers are listed below.

Natural numbers, **N**   {1, 2, 3, 4, . . .}   *Natural numbers are also called* <u>counting numbers</u>.

Whole numbers, **W**   {0, 1, 2, 3, 4, . . .}

Integers, **Z**   {. . ., −2, −1, 0, 1, 2, 3, 4, . . .}

Rational numbers, **Q** $\left\{\text{all numbers that can be expressed in the form } \frac{a}{b}, \text{ where } a \text{ and } b \text{ are integers and } b \neq 0\right\}$

Recall that repeating or terminating decimals name rational numbers since they can be represented as quotients of integers. The square roots of *perfect squares* also name rational numbers. For example, $\sqrt{0.16}$ names a rational number since it is equivalent to the rational number 0.4.

Numbers such as $\sqrt{120}$ are the square roots of numbers that are *not* perfect squares. Some other examples are shown below. What do you notice about these numbers?

None of these decimals terminate.

Teaching Tip ❶

$$\sqrt{2} = 1.414213\ldots \qquad \sqrt{3} = 1.732050\ldots \qquad \sqrt{7} = 2.645751\ldots$$

These numbers are *not* rational numbers since they are not repeating or terminating decimals. They are called **irrational numbers**. The set of irrational numbers is often denoted by the capital letter **I**.

LESSON 12-4   REAL NUMBERS   487

ALTERNATE TEACHING STRATEGIES

Using Questioning
1. Are all integers real numbers?   **yes**
2. Are all rational numbers real numbers?   **yes**
3. Are all real numbers irrational numbers?   **no**
4. Are any integers irrational numbers?   **no**

Using Problem Solving
Use >, <, or = to indicate the correct relationship between each pair of values.
1. 12, $\sqrt{152}$ **<**
2. −18, −$\sqrt{298}$ **<**
3. 14$\sqrt{5}$, 11$\sqrt{7}$ **>**
4. 16$\sqrt{3}$, $\sqrt{768}$ **=**
5. 12, $\sqrt{10}$ $\sqrt{14}$ **>**

Lesson Resources
- Reteaching Master 12-4
- Practice Master 12-4
- Enrichment Master 12-4
- Activity Master, p. 57
- Video Algebra, 47

 Transparency 12-4 contains the 5-Minute Check and a teaching aid for this lesson.

INTRODUCING THE LESSON

5-Minute Check
(over Lesson 12-3)
1. Find the length of the hypotenuse of a right triangle if the legs have measures of 5 and 7. $\sqrt{74}$
2. Find the measure of the leg of a right triangle if the other leg is 24 and the hypotenuse is 25.   **7**

The measures of three sides of a triangle are given. Determine whether each triangle is a right triangle.

3. 12, 13, 15   **no**
4. 6, 8, 10   **yes**
5. 9, 16, 20   **no**

Motivating the Lesson
Open the lesson with a review of repeating and terminating decimals. Ask students to express the following fractions as decimals: $\frac{7}{11}, \frac{5}{16}, \frac{14}{21}$. $0.\overline{63}$, 0.3125, 0.6

TEACHING THE LESSON

Teaching Tip ❶   Point out that irrational numbers are real numbers that cannot be expressed in the form $\frac{a}{b}$.

Chalkboard Examples

For Example 1

Name the set or sets of numbers to which each number belongs. Use N for natural numbers, W for whole numbers, Z for integers, Q for rational numbers and I for irrational numbers.

a. -9 Z, Q

b. $0.101101110\ldots$ I

c. $\sqrt{81}$ N, W, Z, Q

d. $0.33333\ldots$ Q

For Example 2

Use a calculator to find an approximate value for each expression.

a. $\sqrt{83}$ 9.110

b. $\sqrt{95}$ 9.747

For Example 3

Determine whether each square root is rational or irrational. If it is irrational, find two consecutive integers between which its graph lies on the number line.

a. $\sqrt{576}$ rational, 24

b. $\sqrt{480}$ irrational, between 21 and 22

c. $\sqrt{500}$ irrational, between 22 and 23

Teaching Tip ②   Any point on the number line can be assigned a value from the set of real numbers. Between any two real numbers there exists another real number.

Teaching Tip ③   Emphasize that the values for $\sqrt{n}$ in the table on page 644 are the decimal equivalent of each square root rounded to the nearest thousandth.

Definition of Irrational Numbers	Irrational numbers are numbers that *cannot* be expressed in the form $\frac{a}{b}$ where a and b are integers and $b \neq 0$.

Example 1

Name the set or sets of numbers to which each number belongs.

a. **0.8888 . . .**   This repeating decimal is a rational number since it is equivalent to $\frac{8}{9}$. This number can also be expressed as $0.\overline{8}$.

b. **3.141592 . . .**   This decimal is an irrational number since it does not repeat or terminate. Decimal approximations are often used for such numbers. $\pi \approx 3.14$

c. **$-\sqrt{9}$**   Since $-\sqrt{9} = -3$, this number is an integer and a rational number.

You have graphed rational numbers on number lines. Yet, if you graphed *all* of the rational numbers, the number line would still not be complete. The irrational numbers complete the number line. The set of irrational numbers together with the set of rational numbers form the set of **real numbers, R.** The graph of all real numbers is the entire number line.

Teaching Tip ②

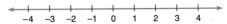

This is illustrated by the completeness property.

Completeness Property for Points on the Number Line	Each real number corresponds to exactly one point on the number line. Each point on the number line corresponds to exactly one real number.

Teaching Tip ③   You can use a calculator, computer, or table of square roots, like the one on page 644, to find approximate square roots. These values can be used to approximate the graphs of square roots.

Example 2

Use a calculator to find an approximate value for $\sqrt{54}$. Then graph $\sqrt{54}$ on the number line.

Enter: 54 $\boxed{\sqrt{x}}$ 7.34846923

An approximate value for $\sqrt{54}$ is 7.348.

Example 3

Is $\sqrt{8556}$ an irrational number? If it is, then name two consecutive integers between which its graph lies on the number line.

The value of $\sqrt{8556}$ is approximately 92.498649. It is irrational. This value can be found by using a calculator, computer, or table of square roots. The graph of $\sqrt{8556}$ lies between 92 and 93 on the number line.

Example 4

APPLICATION

Electricity

The voltage, V, in a circuit is given by the formula $V = \sqrt{PR}$. In this formula, V is in volts, P is the power in watts, and R is the resistance in ohms. An electrician has a circuit that produces 1800 watts of power. She wants the voltage in the circuit to be at most 110 volts. Should she design the circuit with a resistance of 6.4 ohms or 6.7 ohms?

For this circuit, $P = 1800$ and $V = 110$. To determine which resistance to use, you can use a calculator to evaluate $\sqrt{1800R}$ for $R = 6.4$ and for $R = 6.7$ to find out which one will produce at most 110 volts.

Evaluate $\sqrt{1800R}$ for $R = 6.4$.

Enter: 1800 $\boxed{\times}$ 6.4 $\boxed{=}$ $\boxed{\sqrt{x}}$ 107.331263

Evaluate $\sqrt{1800R}$ for $R = 6.7$.

Enter: 1800 $\boxed{\times}$ 6.7 $\boxed{=}$ $\boxed{\sqrt{x}}$ 109.818031

She can design the circuit with *either* resistance. If she wants the voltage in the circuit to be as close to 110 volts as possible, then she should design the circuit with a resistance of 6.7 ohms.

---

1. The measure must be a perfect square.   2. See margin for explanation; no.

CHECKING FOR UNDERSTANDING

Communicating Mathematics

Read and study the lesson to answer each question.

1. What must be true about the measure of the area of a square if the measure of its side is a natural number?

2. Explain the difference between the rational and irrational numbers. Are there any numbers that are both rational *and* irrational?

3. The graph of which set of numbers is the entire number line?
   real numbers

Determine whether each statement is *true* or *false*.

4. Every integer is also a real number.   true

5. Every rational number is also an irrational number.   false

6. Every real number is also a rational number.   false

7. Every natural number is also a whole number.   true

Guided Practice

Name the set or sets of numbers to which each real number belongs. Use N for natural numbers, W for whole numbers, Z for integers, Q for rational numbers, and I for irrational numbers.

8. $-\frac{1}{2}$ Q   9. $\frac{6}{3}$ N, W, Z, Q   10. 0 W, Z, Q   11. 0.3333 . . . Q

12. $\sqrt{11}$ I   13. $\sqrt{36}$ N, W, Z, Q   14. 0.6125 Q   15. 0.53694 . . . I

Find an approximation, to the nearest hundredth, for each square root.

16. $\sqrt{11}$ 3.32   17. $\sqrt{40}$ 6.32   18. $\sqrt{91}$ 9.54   19. $-\sqrt{89}$ −9.43

RETEACHING THE LESSON

Have students convert repeating decimals to ratios of integers. For example, consider
$x = 0.3636 \ldots$ or $0.\overline{36}$.
$100x = 36.3636 \ldots$
$-\quad x = \quad 0.3636 \ldots$
$99x = 36.0000 \ldots$
$x = \frac{36}{99}$ or $\frac{4}{11}$
This method cannot be used with nonrepeating decimals. They are irrational numbers.

Additional Answer

2. Rational numbers can be named by terminating or repeating decimals and irrational numbers cannot.

12-4 | NAME _____ DATE _____
Reteaching Worksheet

Real Numbers

The chart below illustrates the various kinds of real numbers.

Counting or Natural Numbers, N	$\{1, 2, 3, 4, \ldots\}$
Whole Numbers, W	$\{0, 1, 2, 3, 4, \ldots\}$
Integers, Z	$\{\ldots, -3, -2, -1, 0, 1, 2, 3, \ldots\}$
Rational Numbers, Q	{all numbers that can be expressed in the form $\frac{a}{b}$, where a and b are integers and $b \neq 0$}
Irrational Numbers, I	{numbers that cannot be expressed in the form $\frac{a}{b}$, where a and b are integers and $b \neq 0$}
Real Numbers, R	{rational numbers and irrational numbers}

Every real number can be graphed on the number line.

Completeness Property for Points on the Number Line
Each real number corresponds to exactly one point on the number line. Each point on the number line corresponds to exactly one real number.

Example: Use a calculator to find an approximate value for $\sqrt{23}$. Then graph $\sqrt{23}$ on the number line.

ENTER 23 $\boxed{\sqrt{x}}$ Result: 4.7958315 $\sqrt{23}$
An approximate value is 4.796.   -4 -3 -2 -1 0 1 2 3 4 5 6

State whether each number is *rational* or *irrational*.

1. 4.86868 . . .   2. 3.14   3. 1.010110111 . . .
   rational   rational   irrational
4. 5.637637 . . .   5. −0.515151 . . .   6. 1.19293949 . . .
   rational   rational   irrational

Find an approximation, to the nearest hundredth, for each square root. Then graph the square root on the number line below. −4.58

7. $\sqrt{15}$ 3.87   8. $\sqrt{84}$ 9.17   9. $\sqrt{60}$ 7.75   10. $-\sqrt{21}$ 11. $-\sqrt{40}$
                                                                                          −6.32

$-\sqrt{40}$ $-\sqrt{21}$ $\sqrt{15}$ $\sqrt{60}$ $\sqrt{84}$
-10 -9 -8 -7 -6 -5 -4 -3 -2 -1 0 1 2 3 4 5 6 7 8 9 10

490 Chapter 12

Closing the Lesson

Speaking Activity Have students give examples of natural numbers, whole numbers, integers, rational numbers, and irrational numbers.

APPLYING THE LESSON

Homework Exercises

Assignment Guide
Basic: 20-40, 44-46, 48-52
Average: 23-41, 44-52
Enriched: 26-52
All: Mid-Chapter Review, 1-11

Chapter 12, Quiz B, (Lessons 12-3 through 12-4), is available in the Evaluation Masters Booklet, p. 163.

Practice Masters Booklet, p. 93

NAME _____ DATE _____

Practice Worksheet

Real Numbers

State whether each decimal represents a rational, or an irrational, number.

1. 3.1201200120001... irrational	2. 0.$\overline{23}$ rational	3. 3.12 rational
4. 0.3333... rational	5. 0.852 rational	6. 2.040506... irrational
7. 6.114 rational	8. 2.1010010001... irrational	9. 0.5625 rational
10. 2.4 rational	11. 0.846153846153... rational	12. 37.65 rational

Find an approximation, to the nearest hundredth, for each square root. Then graph the square root on the number line provided.

13. $\sqrt{8} \approx 2.83$
14. $-\sqrt{12} \approx -3.46$
15. $\sqrt{24} \approx 4.90$
16. $-\sqrt{2} \approx -1.41$

Determine whether each number is rational, or irrational. If it is irrational, find two consecutive integers between which its graph lies on the number line.

17. $\sqrt{300}$ irrational; 17, 18
18. $\sqrt{520}$ irrational; 22, 23
19. $\sqrt{961}$ rational; 31

Find the area of each rectangle. Round answers to the nearest hundredth. (Hint: Use the Pythagorean Theorem.)

20. 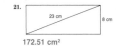 14 in. / 7 in.
84.87 in²

21. 23 cm / 8 cm
172.51 cm²

EXERCISES

Practice

State whether each decimal represents a rational or an irrational number.

20. 1.23123412 . . . I   21. 0.4444 . . . Q   22. 4.3434343 . . . Q
23. 4.34334333 . . . I   24. 7.6567876 . . . I   25. 1.24$\overline{37}$ Q

B

Find an approximation, to the nearest hundredth, for each square root. Then graph the square root on a number line.

26. $\sqrt{7}$ 2.65   27. $\sqrt{20}$ 4.47   28. $-\sqrt{50}$ −7.07   29. $-\sqrt{66}$ −8.12
30. $\sqrt{84}$ 9.17   31. $-\sqrt{31}$ −5.57   32. $-\sqrt{98}$ −9.90   33. $\sqrt{107}$ 10.34

Determine whether each number is rational or irrational. If it is irrational, find two consecutive integers between which its graph lies on the number line.

34. $\sqrt{6436}$ I; 80,81 35. $\sqrt{9025}$ Q; 95   36. $\sqrt{3840}$ I; 61,62 37. $\sqrt{7511}$
                                                                            I; 86,87

CONNECTION
Geometry

Find the area of each rectangle. Round answers to the nearest hundredth. (*Hint:* Use the Pythagorean Theorem.)

38. 16 cm / 8 cm

39. 27 ft / 18 ft

110.85 cm²   362.24 ft²

CONNECTION
Geometry

Solve each problem. Round answers to the nearest tenth.

40. The area of a square is 549 square inches. How many additional square inches of area would result in a new square whose sides have integral lengths? **27 square inches**

C

41. The length of a rectangle is three times its width. What are the dimensions of the rectangle if its area is 186 ft²? **7.9 ft by 23.7 ft**

42. A square is inscribed in a circle as shown at the right. If the radius of the circle is 3 cm, find the perimeter of the square. **17.0 cm**

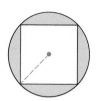

43. What is the area of the shaded region in the figure at the right? Use 3.14 for π. **10.3 cm²**

Critical Thinking

Find all numbers of the form $\sqrt{n}$ such that n is a natural number and the graph of $\sqrt{n}$ lies between each pair of numbers on the number line.

44. 3 and 4 $\sqrt{10}$, $\sqrt{11}$, $\sqrt{12}$,$\sqrt{13}$,   45. 5.25 and 5.5 $\sqrt{28}$, $\sqrt{29}$, $\sqrt{30}$
                   $\sqrt{14}$, $\sqrt{15}$

Applications

46. **Electricity** A circuit is designed with two resistance settings R, 4.6 ohms and 5.2 ohms, and two power settings P, 1200 watts and 1500 watts. Which settings can be used so that the voltage of the circuit is between 75 volts and 85 volts? Use $V = \sqrt{PR}$.
5.2 ohms and 1200 watts or 4.6 ohms and 1500 watts

47. Weather The time, t, in hours, that a storm will last is given by the formula $t = \sqrt{\frac{d^3}{216}}$, where d is the diameter of the storm in miles. Suppose the umpires at a baseball game declared a rain delay at 10:00 P.M. The storm causing the rain delay has a diameter of 12 miles. If it takes 20 minutes to get the field ready after the rain has stopped, can the game be restarted before 1:00 A.M.?
No, since rain will end at about 12:50 A.M.

Mixed Review

48. Multiply $(3x - 0.5)(3x + 0.5)$. **(Lesson 6-9)** $9x^2 - 0.25$

49. Physics Solve the motion formula $F = \frac{GMn}{d^2}$ for d. **(Lesson 8-10)** $d = \pm\sqrt{\frac{GMn}{F}}$

50. Determine the slope and y-intercept of the graph of $7x - 3y = 10$. **(Lesson 10-3)** $m = \frac{7}{3}, b = -\frac{10}{3}$

51. Use elimination to solve the system of equations $3x + 4y = 7$ and $3x - 4y = 8$. **(Lesson 11-4)** $\left(\frac{5}{2}, -\frac{1}{8}\right)$

52. Construction Lorena needs to run a wire from the top of a telephone pole to a stake on the ground 10 meters from the base of the pole. Lorena only has 16 meters of wire to use. Does she have enough wire if the pole is 14 meters tall? **(Lesson 12-3)** No, she needs about 17.2 m of wire.

MID-CHAPTER REVIEW

The following high temperatures were recorded in Cleveland during a cold spell that lasted 30 days. **(Lesson 12-1)**

29°F	26°F	17°F	12°F	5°F	4°F	25°F	17°F	23°F	18°F
2°F	12°F	27°F	16°F	27°F	16°F	30°F	6°F	16°F	5°F
0°F	5°F	29°F	18°F	16°F	22°F	29°F	8°F	23°F	24°F

1. Organize this information into a table with headings *Temperature in Degrees Fahrenheit* and *Number of Days*. Then use the table to answer the following questions. **See margin.**

2. Which high temperature occurs the greatest number of times? **16°F**

3. How many days was the high temperature in the range 10–19? **10 days**

Simplify. **(Lesson 12-2)**

4. $-\sqrt{441}$ −21 **5.** $\sqrt{10.89}$ 3.3 **6.** $\pm\sqrt{0.0841}$ ±0.29 **7.** $\sqrt{\frac{576}{729}}$ $\frac{8}{9}$

If c is the measure of the hypotenuse of a right triangle, find each missing measure. **(Lesson 12-3)**

8. $a = 21, b = 28, c = ?$ **35** **9.** $a = 0.5, c = 1.3, b = ?$ **1.2** **10.** $b = \sqrt{17}, c = 9, a = ?$ **8**

11. Can the measures of the sides of a right triangle be 24, 30, and 36? **(Lesson 12-3)** **no**

EXTENDING THE LESSON

Math Power: Connections

The area of a triangle is 38 m². If the base is twice the height, what is the base of the triangle?
$\left(\text{Use the formula } A = \frac{1}{2}bh.\right)$
$2\sqrt{38}$ m or 12.4 m

Mid-Chapter Review

The Mid-Chapter Review provides students with a brief review of the concepts and skills in Lessons 12-1 through 12-4. Lesson numbers are given at the end of problems or instruction lines so students may review concepts not yet mastered.

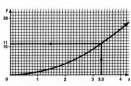

Lesson Resources

- Reteaching Master 12-5
- Practice Master 12-5
- Enrichment Master 12-5
- Video Algebra, 47-48

 Transparency 12-5 contains the 5-Minute Check and a teaching aid for this lesson.

INTRODUCING THE LESSON

🕐 5-Minute Check

(over Lesson 12-4)

1. **Name the set of numbers to which $\sqrt{7}$ belongs.** I
2. **Name the set of numbers to which $\sqrt{0.04}$ belongs.** Q
3. **Use a calculator to determine an approximate value for $\sqrt{179}$. Round the answer to the nearest thousandth.** 13.379
4. **Use a calculator to determine between which two integers $-\sqrt{184}$ lies.** $-13, -14$
5. **Use a calculator to determine between which two integers $\sqrt{500}$ lies.** 22, 23

Motivating the Lesson

You may want to open this lesson with a review of prime numbers and what it means to write the prime factorization of a number. You may want to use the Sieve of Eratostenes to develop primes less than 100. Absolute value should also be reviewed.

TEACHING THE LESSON

Teaching Tip ① Point out that to simplify a square root with a variable, absolute value symbols are necessary when the variable has an even exponent and the exponent of the square root is odd. For example, in $\sqrt{x^4} = x^2$, since x is squared in the answer, it will automatically be positive. In $\sqrt{x^6} = x^3$, in order to guarantee that x^3 is positive, $|x^3|$ is necessary instead of x^3.

Objectives

12-5A
12-5B

After studying this lesson, you should be able to:
- simplify square roots, and
- simplify radical expressions that contain variables.

A radical expression is in *simplest form* if the radicand has no perfect square factors other than one. The following property can be used to simplify square roots.

Product Property of Square Roots	For any numbers a and b, where $a \geq 0$ and $b \geq 0$, $\sqrt{ab} = \sqrt{a} \cdot \sqrt{b}$.

The product property of square roots and prime factorization can be used to simplify radical expressions in which the radicand is not a perfect square.

Example 1

Simplify $\sqrt{375}$.

$$\sqrt{375} = \sqrt{3} \cdot \sqrt{5} \cdot \sqrt{5} \cdot \sqrt{5} \quad \textit{Prime factorization of 375}$$
$$= \sqrt{3} \cdot \sqrt{5} \cdot \sqrt{5^2} \quad \textit{Product property of square roots}$$
$$= \sqrt{3 \cdot 5} \cdot 5$$
$$= 5\sqrt{15}$$

When finding the principal square root of an expression containing variables, be sure that the result is not negative. Consider the expression $\sqrt{x^2}$. Its simplest form is not x since, for example, $\sqrt{(-3)^2} \neq -3$. For radical expressions like $\sqrt{x^2}$, use absolute value to ensure nonnegative results.

Teaching Tip ①

$$\sqrt{x^2} = |x| \qquad \sqrt{x^3} = x\sqrt{x} \qquad \sqrt{x^4} = x^2 \qquad \sqrt{x^6} = |x^3|$$

For $\sqrt{x^3}$, absolute value is not used since x cannot be negative. If x were negative, then x^3 would be negative and $\sqrt{x^3}$ would not be defined. Why is absolute value not used for $\sqrt{x^4}$?

Example 2

Simplify $\sqrt{200m^2y^3}$.

$$\sqrt{200m^2y^3} = \sqrt{2 \cdot 2 \cdot 2 \cdot 5 \cdot 5 \cdot m \cdot m \cdot y \cdot y \cdot y} \quad \textit{Prime factorization}$$
$$= \sqrt{2} \cdot \sqrt{2^2} \cdot \sqrt{5^2} \cdot \sqrt{m^2} \cdot \sqrt{y} \cdot \sqrt{y^2} \quad \textit{Product property of square roots}$$
$$= \sqrt{2} \cdot 2 \cdot 5 \cdot |m| \cdot \sqrt{y} \cdot y \quad \textit{The absolute value of m ensures a nonnegative result. Why is the absolute value not indicated for y?}$$
$$= 10|m|y\sqrt{2y}$$

ALTERNATE TEACHING STRATEGIES

Using Discussion

Find values of a and b so that it is necessary to use absolute value in the expression $\sqrt{x^a} = |x^b|$. $a = 2, b = 1$; $a = 6, b = 3$; $a = 10, b = 5$; and so on.

Using Logical Reasoning

Find values for m and n so that m and n are not perfect squares but $\frac{\sqrt{m}}{\sqrt{n}}$ is a perfect square. **Answers will vary.** Some typical answers are $m = 50$ and $n = 2$, or $m = 12$ and $n = 3$.

The product property can also be used to multiply square roots.

Example 3 Simplify $\sqrt{10} \cdot \sqrt{20}$.

$\sqrt{10} \cdot \sqrt{20} = \sqrt{10 \cdot 20}$ *Product property of square roots*

$= \sqrt{10^2 \cdot 2}$

$= \sqrt{10^2} \cdot \sqrt{2}$ or $10\sqrt{2}$

You can divide square roots and simplify radical expressions that involve division by using the quotient property of square roots.

Quotient Property of Square Roots	For any numbers a and b, where $a \geq 0$ and $b > 0$, $$\sqrt{\frac{a}{b}} = \frac{\sqrt{a}}{\sqrt{b}}.$$

A fraction containing radicals is in simplest form if no radicals are left in the denominator.

Example 4 Simplify $\dfrac{\sqrt{72}}{\sqrt{6}}$. **Teaching Tip ②**

$\dfrac{\sqrt{72}}{\sqrt{6}} = \sqrt{\dfrac{72}{6}}$ *Quotient property of square roots*

$= \sqrt{12}$

$= \sqrt{2^2 \cdot 3}$ *Prime factorization*

$= \sqrt{2^2} \cdot \sqrt{3}$ or $2\sqrt{3}$

The next example illustrates a method for simplifying radical expressions called **rationalizing the denominator**. This method may be used to eliminate radicals from the denominator of a fraction.

Example 5 Simplify $\dfrac{\sqrt{32}}{\sqrt{3}}$.

$\dfrac{\sqrt{32}}{\sqrt{3}} = \dfrac{\sqrt{32}}{\sqrt{3}} \cdot \dfrac{\sqrt{3}}{\sqrt{3}}$ *Notice that $\dfrac{\sqrt{3}}{\sqrt{3}} = 1$.* **Teaching Tip ③**

$= \dfrac{\sqrt{32 \cdot 3}}{\sqrt{3 \cdot 3}}$

$= \dfrac{\sqrt{16 \cdot 2 \cdot 3}}{\sqrt{3^2}}$

$= \dfrac{\sqrt{16} \cdot \sqrt{2} \cdot \sqrt{3}}{3}$ *Do you see why $\dfrac{\sqrt{3}}{\sqrt{3}}$ was used?* **Teaching Tip ④**

$= \dfrac{4\sqrt{6}}{3}$

Teaching Tip ② Point out the different situations in Examples 4 and 5. In Example 4, the denominator is a factor of the numerator; in Example 5, it is not.

Teaching Tip ③ Guide students into understanding why $\dfrac{\sqrt{3}}{\sqrt{3}}$ is used. Ask what can be done to make the denominator, $\sqrt{3}$, a perfect square. Then ask if it is possible to multiply the denominator by $\sqrt{3}$ without changing the value of the fraction. Emphasize that multiplication by $\dfrac{\sqrt{3}}{\sqrt{3}}$ results in an equivalent expression since $\dfrac{\sqrt{3}}{\sqrt{3}} = 1$.

Teaching Tip ④ Explain that the goal in multiplying by $\dfrac{\sqrt{3}}{\sqrt{3}}$ was to make the radicand in the denominator a perfect square, thus simplifying the expression.

Teaching Tip ⑤ Stress that the product of these binomials is the difference of squares.

Example 6

CONNECTION

Geometry

The ratio of the measures of the legs of a right triangle is 2:1. Find the ratio of the measure of the shorter leg to the measure of the hypotenuse of the triangle.

Let a = the measure of the shorter leg of the right triangle.
Let b = the measure of the longer leg.
Then $\dfrac{b}{a} = \dfrac{2}{1}$ or $b = 2a$.

By the Pythagorean Theorem, $c^2 = a^2 + b^2$. Therefore, $c = \sqrt{a^2 + b^2}$ and the ratio of the shorter leg to the hypotenuse is $\dfrac{a}{\sqrt{a^2 + b^2}}$.

$\dfrac{a}{\sqrt{a^2 + b^2}} = \dfrac{a}{\sqrt{a^2 + (2a)^2}}$ *Substitute 2a for b.*

$= \dfrac{a}{\sqrt{5a^2}}$ *$a^2 + (2a)^2 = a^2 + 4a^2 = 5a^2$*

$= \dfrac{a}{\sqrt{5} \cdot \sqrt{a^2}}$

$= \dfrac{a}{\sqrt{5} \cdot a} \cdot \dfrac{\sqrt{5}}{\sqrt{5}}$ *a must be positive, so absolute value does not need to be indicated for a.*

$= \dfrac{\sqrt{5}}{5}$

The ratio of the measure of the shorter leg to the measure of the hypotenuse is $\dfrac{\sqrt{5}}{5}$ to 1 or about 0.45 to 1.

Binomials of the form $a\sqrt{b} + c\sqrt{d}$ and $a\sqrt{b} - c\sqrt{d}$ are **conjugates** of each other. For example, $8 + \sqrt{2}$ and $8 - \sqrt{2}$ are conjugates. Conjugates are useful for simplifying radical expressions because their product is always a rational number with no radicals.

$(\sqrt{2})^2 = \sqrt{2} \cdot \sqrt{2}$
$= \sqrt{2 \cdot 2}$
$= \sqrt{2^2}$
$= 2$

$(8 + \sqrt{2})(8 - \sqrt{2}) = 8^2 - (\sqrt{2})^2$ *Use the pattern $(a - b)(a + b) = a^2 - b^2$ to simplify the product.*
$= 64 - 2$
$= 62$

Conjugates are often used to rationalize the denominators of fractions containing square roots.

Example 7

Simplify $\dfrac{3}{3 - \sqrt{5}}$.

To rationalize the denominator, multiply both the numerator and denominator of the fraction by the conjugate of $3 - \sqrt{5}$, which is $3 + \sqrt{5}$.

$\dfrac{3}{3 - \sqrt{5}} = \dfrac{3}{3 - \sqrt{5}} \cdot \dfrac{3 + \sqrt{5}}{3 + \sqrt{5}}$ *Notice that $\dfrac{3 + \sqrt{5}}{3 + \sqrt{5}} = 1$.*

$= \dfrac{3(3) + 3\sqrt{5}}{3^2 - (\sqrt{5})^2}$ *Use the distributive property to multiply numerators. Use the pattern $(a - b)(a + b) = a^2 - b^2$ to multiply denominators.* **Teaching Tip ⑤**

$= \dfrac{9 + 3\sqrt{5}}{9 - 5}$

$= \dfrac{9 + 3\sqrt{5}}{4}$

RETEACHING THE LESSON

To convince students that rationalizing the denominator produces equivalent results, have them find approximate values of the following expressions.

$\dfrac{2}{\sqrt{3}}$ $\dfrac{2 \cdot \sqrt{3}}{\sqrt{3} \cdot \sqrt{3}}$ $\dfrac{2\sqrt{3}}{3}$

The values should all be about 1.1547.

When simplifying radical expressions, check the following conditions to determine if you have the expression in simplest form.

Simplified Form for Radicals	A radical expression is in simplest form when the following three conditions have been met. 1. No radicands have perfect square factors other than one. 2. No radicands contain fractions. 3. No radicals appear in the denominator of a fraction.

CHECKING FOR UNDERSTANDING

Communicating Mathematics

Read and study the lesson to answer each question. 1, 3. See margin.

1. State the product property of square roots in your own words.

2. Why are absolute values sometimes needed when simplifying radical expressions containing variables? **to ensure nonnegative results**

3. What do you do when you rationalize a denominator?

4. What is the conjugate of $5 - 9\sqrt{2}$? $5 + 9\sqrt{2}$

Guided Practice

Simplify.

5. $\sqrt{20}$ $2\sqrt{5}$ 6. $\sqrt{18}$ $3\sqrt{2}$ 7. $\sqrt{48}$ $4\sqrt{3}$ 8. $\frac{\sqrt{42}}{\sqrt{6}}$ $\sqrt{7}$ 9. $\frac{\sqrt{20}}{\sqrt{5}}$ 2

State the conjugate of each expression. Then multiply the expression by its conjugate. **See margin.**

10. $3 + \sqrt{2}$ 11. $\sqrt{5} - 7$ 12. $\sqrt{3} - \sqrt{7}$ 13. $2\sqrt{8} + 3\sqrt{5}$

State the fraction by which each expression should be multiplied to rationalize the denominator.

14. $\frac{3}{\sqrt{5}}$ $\frac{\sqrt{5}}{\sqrt{5}}$ 15. $\frac{2\sqrt{3}}{\sqrt{8}}$ $\frac{\sqrt{2}}{\sqrt{2}}$ 16. $\sqrt{\frac{8}{7}}$ $\frac{\sqrt{7}}{\sqrt{7}}$ 17. $\frac{2\sqrt{5}}{4 - \sqrt{3}}$ $\frac{4 + \sqrt{3}}{4 + \sqrt{3}}$

EXERCISES

Practice

Simplify. Use absolute value symbols when necessary. 30–37. See margin.

18. $\sqrt{75}$ $5\sqrt{3}$ 19. $\sqrt{45}$ $3\sqrt{5}$ 20. $\sqrt{80}$ $4\sqrt{5}$ 21. $\sqrt{72}$ $6\sqrt{2}$

22. $\sqrt{98}$ $7\sqrt{2}$ 23. $\sqrt{280}$ $2\sqrt{70}$ 24. $\sqrt{500}$ $10\sqrt{5}$ 25. $\sqrt{1000}$ $10\sqrt{10}$

26. $\frac{\sqrt{7}}{\sqrt{3}}$ $\frac{\sqrt{21}}{3}$ 27. $\frac{\sqrt{5}}{\sqrt{10}}$ $\frac{\sqrt{2}}{2}$ 28. $\sqrt{\frac{3}{7}}$ $\frac{\sqrt{21}}{7}$ 29. $\sqrt{\frac{11}{32}}$ $\frac{\sqrt{22}}{8}$

30. $\sqrt{10} \cdot \sqrt{30}$ 31. $2\sqrt{5} \cdot \sqrt{5}$ 32. $5\sqrt{10} \cdot 3\sqrt{10}$ 33. $7\sqrt{30} \cdot 2\sqrt{6}$

34. $\sqrt{\frac{2}{3}} \cdot \sqrt{\frac{5}{2}}$ 35. $\sqrt{\frac{1}{6}} \cdot \sqrt{\frac{6}{11}}$ 36. $\sqrt{32x^2}$ 37. $\sqrt{40b^4}$

Additional Answers

1. The square root of the product of two or more positive numbers is equal to the product of their square roots.

3. Multiply the numerator and denominator of a fraction by the same number so that a radical is not left in the denominator.

10. $3 - \sqrt{2}$; 7
11. $\sqrt{5} + 7$; -44

12. $\sqrt{3} + \sqrt{7}$; -4
13. $2\sqrt{8} - 3\sqrt{5}$; -13
30. $10\sqrt{3}$
31. 10
32. 150
33. $84\sqrt{5}$
34. $\frac{\sqrt{15}}{3}$
35. $\frac{\sqrt{11}}{11}$
36. $4|x|\sqrt{2}$
37. $2b^2\sqrt{10}$

EVALUATING THE LESSON

Checking for Understanding

Exercises 1-17 are designed to help you assess understanding through reading, writing, and speaking. You should work through Exercises 1-4 with your students, and then monitor their work on Exercises 5-17.

Error Analysis

Students may make errors when squaring the product of a rational and an irrational number. For example, they may incorrectly evaluate $(3\sqrt{2})(3\sqrt{2})$ as $9 \cdot 4$ or $3 \cdot 2$. Point out that the rational numbers and the irrational numbers should be squared separately and their product should be found.

Assignment Guide

Basic: 18-49, 55-56, 58-63
Average: 24-52, 55-63
Enriched: 26-63

Practice Masters Booklet, p. 94

12-5 NAME ____ DATE ____
Practice Worksheet

Simplifying Square Roots
Simplify. Use absolute value symbols when necessary.

1. $\sqrt{20}$ $2\sqrt{5}$ 2. $\sqrt{40}$ $2\sqrt{10}$ 3. $\sqrt{99}$ $3\sqrt{11}$ 4. $\sqrt{108}$ $6\sqrt{3}$

5. $\sqrt{420}$ $2\sqrt{105}$ 6. $\sqrt{275}$ $5\sqrt{11}$ 7. $\sqrt{640}$ $8\sqrt{10}$ 8. $\sqrt{704}$ $8\sqrt{11}$

9. $\sqrt{1250}$ $25\sqrt{2}$ 10. $\frac{\sqrt{5}}{\sqrt{3}}$ $\frac{\sqrt{15}}{3}$ 11. $\frac{\sqrt{1}}{\sqrt{6}}$ $\frac{\sqrt{6}}{6}$ 12. $\frac{\sqrt{6}}{\sqrt{7}}$ $\frac{\sqrt{42}}{7}$

13. $\sqrt{\frac{1}{5}}$ $\frac{\sqrt{5}}{5}$ 14. $\sqrt{\frac{5}{32}}$ $\frac{\sqrt{10}}{8}$ 15. $\sqrt{5} \cdot \sqrt{60}$ $10\sqrt{3}$ 16. $3\sqrt{5} \cdot \sqrt{5}$ 15

17. $\sqrt{6} \cdot 4\sqrt{24}$ 48 18. $11\sqrt{14} \cdot 2\sqrt{7}$ $154\sqrt{2}$ 19. $\sqrt{\frac{3}{4}} \cdot \sqrt{\frac{4}{5}}$ $\frac{\sqrt{15}}{5}$ 20. $\sqrt{\frac{1}{7}} \cdot \sqrt{\frac{7}{11}}$ $\frac{\sqrt{11}}{11}$

21. $\sqrt{16b^4}$ $4b^2$ 22. $\sqrt{81c^5d^4}$ $9c^2d^2\sqrt{c}$ 23. $\sqrt{124y^6w^7}$ $2|y^3| \cdot w^3\sqrt{31w}$ 24. $\sqrt{\frac{18}{x^2}}$ $\frac{3\sqrt{2x}}{x^3}$

25. $\frac{3}{5 - \sqrt{2}}$ $\frac{15 + 3\sqrt{2}}{23}$ 26. $\frac{5}{\sqrt{7} + \sqrt{3}}$ $\frac{5\sqrt{7} - 5\sqrt{3}}{4}$ 27. $\frac{6x}{5 + \sqrt{x}}$ $\frac{30x - 6x\sqrt{x}}{x - 25}$ 28. $\frac{3\sqrt{7}}{-1 - \sqrt{27}}$ $\frac{9\sqrt{21} - 3\sqrt{7}}{26}$

Closing the Lesson

Writing Activity Have students summarize this section by writing a list of the key points that they learned.

APPLYING THE LESSON

Homework Exercises

See assignment guide on page 495.

Additional Answers

38. $3|ab|\sqrt{6}$
39. $4|x|y\sqrt{5y}$
40. $2|m|y^2\sqrt{15}$
41. $7x^2y^3\sqrt{3xy}$
42. $\dfrac{\sqrt{6b}}{6}$
43. $\dfrac{3\sqrt{3}}{|r|}$
44. $\dfrac{n^2\sqrt{5mn}}{2|m^3|}$
45. $\dfrac{|x|\sqrt{3xy}}{2|y^3|}$
46. $\dfrac{6-\sqrt{3}}{33}$
47. $\dfrac{5\sqrt{5}+45}{-38}$
48. $12\sqrt{6}+12\sqrt{5}$

Enrichment Masters Booklet, p. 83

NAME _____ DATE _____

12-5 Enrichment Worksheet

Rational Exponents

You have developed the following properties of powers when a is a positive real number and m and n are integers:

$a^m \cdot a^n = a^{m+n}$ $(ab)^m = a^m b^m$ $a^0 = 1$
$(a^m)^n = a^{mn}$ $\dfrac{a^m}{a^n} = a^{m-n}$ $a^{-n} = \dfrac{1}{a^n}$

Exponents need not be restricted to integers. We can define rational exponents so that operations involving them will be governed by the properties for integer exponents.

$\left(a^{\frac{1}{2}}\right)^2 = a^{\frac{1}{2}\cdot 2} = a$ $\left(a^{\frac{1}{3}}\right)^3 = a^{\frac{1}{3}\cdot 3}$ $\left(a^{\frac{1}{n}}\right)^n = a^{\frac{1}{n}\cdot n} = a$
$a^{\frac{1}{2}}$ squared is a. $a^{\frac{1}{3}}$ cubed is a. $a^{\frac{1}{n}}$ to the n power is a.
$a^{\frac{1}{2}}$ is a square root of a. $a^{\frac{1}{3}}$ is a cube root of a. $a^{\frac{1}{n}}$ is an nth root of a.
$a^{\frac{1}{2}} = \sqrt{a}$ $a^{\frac{1}{3}} = \sqrt[3]{a}$ $a^{\frac{1}{n}} = \sqrt[n]{a}$

Now let us investigate the meaning of $a^{\frac{m}{n}}$.

$a^{\frac{m}{n}} = a^{m\cdot\frac{1}{n}}(a^m)^{\frac{1}{n}} = \sqrt[n]{a^m}$ $a^{\frac{m}{n}} = a^{\frac{1}{n}\cdot m} = \left(a^{\frac{1}{n}}\right)^m = (\sqrt[n]{a})^m$
Therefore, $a^{\frac{m}{n}} = \sqrt[n]{a^m}$ or $(\sqrt[n]{a})^m$

Example 1: Write $\sqrt[4]{a^3}$ in exponential form.   **Example 2:** Write $a^{\frac{2}{3}}$ in radical form.
$\sqrt[4]{a^3} = a^{\frac{3}{4}}$ $a^{\frac{2}{3}} = \sqrt[3]{a^2}$

Example 3: Divide: $\dfrac{a^{\frac{3}{4}}}{a^{\frac{1}{4}}}$
$\dfrac{a^{\frac{3}{4}}}{a^{\frac{1}{4}}} = a^{\frac{3}{4}-\frac{1}{4}} = a^{\frac{2}{4}} = a^{\frac{1}{2}}$ or $\sqrt{a}$

Write each expression in radical form.
1. $b^{\frac{3}{2}}$ $\sqrt{b^3}$ 2. $3c^{\frac{1}{3}}$ $3\sqrt[3]{c}$ 3. $(3c)^{\frac{1}{2}}$ $\sqrt{3c}$

Write each expression in exponential form.
4. $\sqrt[4]{b^3}$ $b^{\frac{3}{4}}$ 5. $\sqrt{4a^3}$ $(4a^3)^{\frac{1}{2}} = 2a^{\frac{3}{2}}$ 6. $2\cdot\sqrt[3]{b^2}$ $2b^{\frac{2}{3}}$

Perform the operation indicated. Answers should show positive exponents only.
7. $(a^3b^{\frac{1}{4}})^2$ $a^6b^{\frac{1}{2}}$ 8. $\dfrac{-8a^{\frac{3}{4}}}{2a^{\frac{1}{2}}}$ $-4a^{\frac{1}{4}}$ 9. $\left(\dfrac{b^{\frac{1}{2}}}{b^{-\frac{3}{4}}}\right)^3$ $b^{\frac{7}{2}}$
10. $\sqrt[3]{a^3}\cdot\sqrt{a}$ a^2 11. $(a^{\frac{3}{2}}b^{-\frac{1}{3}})^{-\frac{1}{2}}$ $\dfrac{b^{\frac{1}{6}}}{a}$ 12. $-2a^{\frac{1}{6}}b^{\frac{1}{3}}(5a^{\frac{1}{3}}b^{-\frac{3}{3}})$
$-10a^{\frac{5}{6}}$
$\dfrac{-10a^{\frac{5}{6}}}{b^{\frac{2}{3}}}$

Simplify. Use absolute value symbols when necessary. 38–53. See margin.

38. $\sqrt{54a^2b^2}$ 39. $\sqrt{80x^2y^3}$ 40. $\sqrt{60m^2y^4}$ 41. $\sqrt{147x^5y^7}$

42. $\sqrt{\dfrac{b}{6}}$ 43. $\sqrt{\dfrac{27}{r^2}}$ 44. $\sqrt{\dfrac{5n^5}{4m^5}}$ 45. $\dfrac{\sqrt{9x^5y}}{\sqrt{12x^2y^6}}$

46. $\dfrac{1}{6+\sqrt{3}}$ 47. $\dfrac{10}{\sqrt{5}-9}$ 48. $\dfrac{12}{\sqrt{6}-\sqrt{5}}$ 49. $\dfrac{9b}{6+\sqrt{b}}$

C 50. $\dfrac{2\sqrt{5}}{-4+\sqrt{8}}$ 51. $\dfrac{2\sqrt{7}}{3\sqrt{5}+5\sqrt{3}}$ 52. $\dfrac{3\sqrt{2}-\sqrt{7}}{2\sqrt{3}-5\sqrt{2}}$ 53. $\dfrac{\sqrt{a}-\sqrt{b}}{\sqrt{a}+\sqrt{b}}$

CONNECTION
Geometry

54. Find the length of the diagonal of a square whose area is $48s^3$ square feet. **$4s\sqrt{6s}$ feet**

Critical Thinking

55. Is the sentence $\sqrt{a\cdot b} = \sqrt{a}\cdot\sqrt{b}$ true for negative numbers? Why or why not? **Square roots of negative numbers are not defined in the set of real numbers.**

Applications

56. **Physics** The period of a pendulum is the time in seconds that it takes the pendulum to make one complete swing back and forth. The formula for the period P of a pendulum is $P = 2\pi\sqrt{\dfrac{\ell}{32}}$, where ℓ is the length of the pendulum in feet. Suppose a clock sounds one "tick" after each complete swing back and forth of a 2-foot-long pendulum. How many ticks would the clock sound in one minute? Use 3.14 for π and round to the nearest whole number. **38 ticks**

57. **Travel** Lois rode her bike due west for 2 hours at a constant speed. She then rode due north for 3 hours at twice that speed.

   a. Write an expression, in simplest form, to represent how far Lois is from the starting point of her bike ride. Let s = the speed at which Lois rode due west. **$2s\sqrt{10}$ miles**

   b. Find this distance, to the nearest tenth of a mile, if her starting speed was 5 miles per hour. **31.62 miles**

Mixed Review

58. Write as an equation: *the square of the sum of a and b is equal to the product of the squares of a and b.* **(Lesson 1-7)** $(a+b)^2 = a^2b^2$

59. Factor $12r^2 - 16rs - 11s^2$. **(Lesson 7-5)** $(2r+s)(6r-11s)$

60. Is $\{(5, 4), (6, 1), (-2, 3), (0, 3)\}$ a function? Is the inverse of this relation a function? **(Lesson 9-5)** **yes; no**

61. **Geometry** If one endpoint of a line segment is at $(-4, 11)$ and the midpoint is at $(8, 3)$, find the coordinates of the other endpoint. **(Lesson 10-8)** $(20, -5)$

62. Graph the equations $x + y = 5$ and $x - 2y = -4$. Then find the solution to the system of equations. **(Lesson 11-2)** $(2, 3)$

63. **Electricity** The resistance R of a power circuit is 4.5 ohms. How much current I, in amperes, can the circuit generate if it can produce at most 1500 watts of power P? Use $I^2R = P$. **(Lesson 12-4)**
    about 18.26 amperes

EXTENDING THE LESSON

Math Power: Problem Solving

Simplify $\dfrac{2}{\sqrt{3}+\sqrt{5}+\sqrt{6}}$.
(Hint: Treat $\sqrt{3}+\sqrt{5}+\sqrt{6}$ as

$$\dfrac{4\sqrt{3}+2\sqrt{5}+\sqrt{6}-3\sqrt{10}}{14}$$

Additional Answers

49. $\dfrac{54b - 9b\sqrt{b}}{36 - b}$

50. $\dfrac{-2\sqrt{5} - \sqrt{10}}{2}$

51. $\dfrac{3\sqrt{35} - 5\sqrt{21}}{-15}$

52. $\dfrac{30 + 6\sqrt{6} - 2\sqrt{21} - 5\sqrt{14}}{-38}$

53. $\dfrac{a - 2\sqrt{ab} + b}{a - b}$

12-6 Adding and Subtracting Radical Expressions

Objective
12-6

After studying this lesson, you should be able to:
- simplify radical expressions involving addition and subtraction.

Radical expressions in which the radicands are alike can be added or subtracted in the same way that monomials are added or subtracted.

Monomials	Radical Expressions
$3x + 2x = (3 + 2)x = 5x$	$3\sqrt{2} + 2\sqrt{2} = (3 + 2)\sqrt{2} = 5\sqrt{2}$
$7y - 4y = (7 - 4)y = 3y$	$7\sqrt{5} - 4\sqrt{5} = (7 - 4)\sqrt{5} = 3\sqrt{5}$

Notice that the distributive property was used to simplify each radical expression. **Teaching Tip ❶**

Example 1

Simplify $3\sqrt{11} + 6\sqrt{11} - 2\sqrt{11}$.

$3\sqrt{11} + 6\sqrt{11} - 2\sqrt{11} = (3 + 6 - 2)\sqrt{11}$
$= 7\sqrt{11}$

Example 2

Simplify $9\sqrt{7} - 4\sqrt{2} + 3\sqrt{2} + 5\sqrt{7}$. **Teaching Tip ❷**

$9\sqrt{7} - 4\sqrt{2} + 3\sqrt{2} + 5\sqrt{7} = 9\sqrt{7} + 5\sqrt{7} - 4\sqrt{2} + 3\sqrt{2}$ *Commutative property*
$= (9 + 5)\sqrt{7} + (-4 + 3)\sqrt{2}$
$= 14\sqrt{7} - \sqrt{2}$

Example 3

Find the exact measure of the perimeter of the rectangle.

$p = 2\ell + 2w$
$= 2(2\sqrt{6} + \sqrt{3}) + 2(3\sqrt{3} - 2)$
$= 4\sqrt{6} + 2\sqrt{3} + 6\sqrt{3} - 4$
$= 4\sqrt{6} + (2 + 6)\sqrt{3} - 4$
$= 4\sqrt{6} + 8\sqrt{3} - 4$

$3\sqrt{3} - 2$

$2\sqrt{6} + \sqrt{3}$

The exact measure of the perimeter is $4\sqrt{6} + 8\sqrt{3} - 4$.

In Example 2, the expression $14\sqrt{7} - \sqrt{2}$ cannot be simplified further because the radicands are different, there are no common factors, and each radicand is in simplest form. The same is true for the expression $4\sqrt{6} + 8\sqrt{3} - 4$ in Example 3.

LESSON 12-6 ADDING AND SUBTRACTING RADICAL EXPRESSIONS   497

ALTERNATE TEACHING STRATEGIES

Using Questioning
Find values for a and b so that $\sqrt{a} + \sqrt{b} = 5\sqrt{2}$.
$a = 2$ and $b = 32$,
$a = 8$ and $b = 18$, or
$a = 0$ and $b = 50$

Using Problem Solving
Without using a calculator, determine whether $2\sqrt{2} + \sqrt{3}$ or $2\sqrt{6}$ has the greater value. $2\sqrt{6}$

12-6 Lesson Notes

Lesson Resources
- Reteaching Master 12-6
- Practice Master 12-6
- Enrichment Master 12-6
- Activity Master, p. 42
- Video Algebra, 49

 Transparency 12-6 contains the 5-Minute Check and a teaching aid for this lesson.

INTRODUCING THE LESSON

🕐 5-Minute Check
(over Lesson 12-5)

Simplify.
1. $\sqrt{75}$ $5\sqrt{3}$
2. $\sqrt{90}$ $3\sqrt{10}$
3. $\sqrt{48m^4}$ $4m^2\sqrt{3}$
4. $\sqrt{x^4y^4}$ x^2y^2
5. $\sqrt{a^3b^3}$ $ab\sqrt{ab}$

Motivating the Lesson
Open the lesson with a review of addition and subtraction of monomials. Ask students to simplify $4b + 7b$. $11b$ Then have them simplify $4b^2 + 7b + 2b$. $4b^2 + 9b$ Remind students that only like terms can be combined.

TEACHING THE LESSON

Teaching Tip ❶   If students can use the distributive property with ease, they should have no trouble adding and subtracting expressions with like radicands.

Teaching Tip ❷   Remind students that only when the radicands are alike can terms be added or subtracted.

Chalkboard Examples

For Example 1
Simplify $3\sqrt{5} + 4\sqrt{5} - 2\sqrt{5}$.
$5\sqrt{5}$

For Example 2
Simplify $6\sqrt{7} - 2\sqrt{7} - \sqrt{3} + 4\sqrt{3}$. $4\sqrt{7} + 3\sqrt{3}$

If each radical in a radical expression is not in simplest form, simplify them first. Then use the distributive property, whenever possible, to further simplify the expression.

Example 4

Simplify $7\sqrt{98} + 5\sqrt{32} - 2\sqrt{75}$.

$7\sqrt{98} + 5\sqrt{32} - 2\sqrt{75} = 7\sqrt{7^2 \cdot 2} + 5\sqrt{4^2 \cdot 2} - 2\sqrt{5^2 \cdot 3}$
$= 7(\sqrt{7^2} \cdot \sqrt{2}) + 5(\sqrt{4^2} \cdot \sqrt{2}) - 2(\sqrt{5^2} \cdot \sqrt{3})$
$= 7(7\sqrt{2}) + 5(4\sqrt{2}) - 2(5\sqrt{3})$
$= 49\sqrt{2} + 20\sqrt{2} - 10\sqrt{3}$
$= 69\sqrt{2} - 10\sqrt{3}$ *Distributive property*

Example 5

CONNECTION
Geometry

Teaching Tip ③

Find a decimal approximation for the area of the rectangle. Then find the exact measure of the area. Compare the decimal approximation of the exact measure to the original decimal approximation for the area to verify your results.

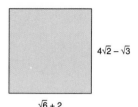

$4\sqrt{2} - \sqrt{3}$

$\sqrt{6} + 2$

$A = \ell w$
$= (4\sqrt{2} - \sqrt{3})(\sqrt{6} + 2)$

Use a calculator to find a decimal approximation for the area.

Enter: (4 × 2 √x − 3 √x) × (6 √x + 2) =

Display: `17.4633727`

The measure of the area is approximately 17.46.

Simplify $(4\sqrt{2} - \sqrt{3})(\sqrt{6} + 2)$ to find the exact measure of the area.

$(4\sqrt{2} - \sqrt{3})(\sqrt{6} + 2) = 4\sqrt{2} \cdot \sqrt{6} + 4\sqrt{2} \cdot 2 - \sqrt{3} \cdot \sqrt{6} - \sqrt{3} \cdot 2$ *Use FOIL.*
$= 4\sqrt{12} + 8\sqrt{2} - \sqrt{18} - 2\sqrt{3}$
$= 4\sqrt{2^2 \cdot 3} + 8\sqrt{2} - \sqrt{3^2 \cdot 2} - 2\sqrt{3}$
$= 4(2\sqrt{3}) + 8\sqrt{2} - 3\sqrt{2} - 2\sqrt{3}$
$= 8\sqrt{3} + 5\sqrt{2} - 2\sqrt{3}$
$= 6\sqrt{3} + 5\sqrt{2}$

The exact measure of the area is $6\sqrt{3} + 5\sqrt{2}$.

Now, use a calculator to find a decimal approximation for the measure of the area.

Enter: 6 × 3 √x + 5 × 2 √x =

Display: `17.4633727`

Since the approximations are equal, the results have been verified.

498   CHAPTER 12   RADICAL EXPRESSIONS

CHECKING FOR UNDERSTANDING

Communicating Mathematics

Read and study the lesson to answer each question.

1. What property do you use to simplify the sum or difference of radicals? **distributive property**

2. Why should you simplify each radical in a radical expression before adding or subtracting? **to determine if there are any like radicands.**

3. How can you use a calculator to verify that two radical expressions are equal? **Use the calculator to evaluate each expression and check that each gives the same decimal approximation.**

Guided Practice

Name the expressions in each group that have the same radicand.

4. $5\sqrt{3}$, $4\sqrt{6}$, $3\sqrt{3}$
5. $4\sqrt{2}$, $7\sqrt{2}$, $2\sqrt{7}$
6. $2\sqrt{10}$, $-5\sqrt{10}$, $10\sqrt{5}$

Name the expressions in each group that will have the same radicand after each expression is written in simplest form.

7. $5\sqrt{14}$, $-3\sqrt{7}$, $2\sqrt{28}$
8. $3\sqrt{20}$, $3\sqrt{5}$, $5\sqrt{6}$
9. $\sqrt{18}$, $\sqrt{24}$, $\sqrt{12}$, $\sqrt{28}$ **none**
10. $3\sqrt{32}$, $2\sqrt{48}$, $\sqrt{50}$, $7\sqrt{200}$

Simplify.

11. $8\sqrt{6} + 3\sqrt{6}$ $11\sqrt{6}$
12. $4\sqrt{3} - 7\sqrt{3}$ $-3\sqrt{3}$
13. $3\sqrt{5} - 5\sqrt{3}$ in simplest form
14. $25\sqrt{13} + \sqrt{13}$ $26\sqrt{13}$
15. $18\sqrt{2x} + 3\sqrt{2x}$ $21\sqrt{2x}$
16. $3\sqrt{5m} - 5\sqrt{5m}$ $-2\sqrt{5m}$

17-32. Exact and approximate values are given.   21. $13\sqrt{3} + \sqrt{2}$; 23.93

EXERCISES
22. $4\sqrt{6} - 6\sqrt{2} + 5\sqrt{7}$; 14.54   28. $-2\sqrt{5} - 6\sqrt{6}$; -19.17

Practice

Simplify. Then use a calculator to verify your answer.

17. $4\sqrt{3} + 7\sqrt{3} - 2\sqrt{3}$ $9\sqrt{3}$; 15.59
18. $2\sqrt{11} - 6\sqrt{11} - 3\sqrt{11}$ $-7\sqrt{11}$; -23.22
19. $5\sqrt{5} + 3\sqrt{5} - 18\sqrt{5}$ $-10\sqrt{5}$; -22.36
20. $\sqrt{6} + 2\sqrt{2} + \sqrt{10}$ $\sqrt{6} + 2\sqrt{2} + \sqrt{10}$; 8.44
21. $8\sqrt{3} - 2\sqrt{2} + 3\sqrt{2} + 5\sqrt{3}$
22. $4\sqrt{6} + \sqrt{7} - 6\sqrt{2} + 4\sqrt{7}$

23. $2\sqrt{3} + \sqrt{12}$ $4\sqrt{3}$; 6.93
24. $3\sqrt{7} - 2\sqrt{28} - \sqrt{7}$; -2.65
25. $2\sqrt{50} - 3\sqrt{32}$ $-2\sqrt{2}$; -2.83
26. $3\sqrt{27} + 5\sqrt{48}$ $29\sqrt{3}$; 50.23
27. $\sqrt{18} + \sqrt{108} + \sqrt{50}$ $8\sqrt{2} + 6\sqrt{3}$; 21.71
28. $2\sqrt{20} - 3\sqrt{24} - \sqrt{180}$
29. $\sqrt{7} + \sqrt{\frac{1}{7}}$ $\frac{8}{7}\sqrt{7}$; 3.02
30. $\sqrt{10} - \sqrt{\frac{2}{5}}$ $\frac{4}{5}\sqrt{10}$; 2.53
31. $3\sqrt{3} - \sqrt{45} + 3\sqrt{\frac{1}{3}}$ $4\sqrt{3} - 3\sqrt{5}$; 0.22
32. $6\sqrt{\frac{7}{4}} + 3\sqrt{28} - 10\sqrt{\frac{1}{7}}$ $\frac{53\sqrt{7}}{7}$, 20.03

LESSON 12-6 ADDING AND SUBTRACTING RADICAL EXPRESSIONS 499

Checking for Understanding

Exercises 1-16 are designed to help you assess understanding through reading, writing, and speaking. You should work through Exercises 1-3 with your students, and then monitor their work on Exercises 4-16.

Closing the Lesson

Speaking Activity Have students explain how addition and subtraction of monomials is similar to that of radical expressions.

APPLYING THE LESSON

Homework Exercises

Assignment Guide

Basic: 17-35, 40-42, 44-48
Average: 20-37, 40-48
Enriched: 23-48

Practice Masters Booklet, p. 95

Chapter 12, Quiz C, (Lessons 12-5 through 12-6), is available in the Evaluation Masters Booklet, p. 164.

CONNECTION Geometry

Find the exact measures of the perimeter and area, in simplest form, for each rectangle.

33.

$\sqrt{14} + \sqrt{7}$

$\sqrt{7}$

$4\sqrt{7} + 2\sqrt{14}; \ 7 + 7\sqrt{2}$

34.
$4\sqrt{7} - 2\sqrt{12}$

$\sqrt{3}$

$8\sqrt{7} - 6\sqrt{3}; \ 4\sqrt{21} - 12$

35.

$\sqrt{8} + \sqrt{27}$

$\sqrt{3} - \sqrt{2}$

$8\sqrt{3} + 2\sqrt{2}; \ 5 - \sqrt{6}$

C ▷ Simplify.

36. $(\sqrt{14} + \sqrt{35})(\sqrt{5} - \sqrt{2})$ $3\sqrt{7}$

37. $(2\sqrt{10} + 3\sqrt{15})(3\sqrt{3} - 2\sqrt{2})$ $19\sqrt{5}$

38. $(\sqrt{6} + \sqrt{8})(\sqrt{24} + \sqrt{2})$ $10\sqrt{3} + 16$

39. $(2\sqrt{10} - 3)(3\sqrt{5} + 5\sqrt{2})$ $15\sqrt{2} + 11\sqrt{5}$

Critical Thinking

40. Is the sum of two irrational numbers always an irrational number? Explain. **No; for example, $-\sqrt{2} + \sqrt{2} = 0$.**

41. Is the sentence $\sqrt{a + b} = \sqrt{a} + \sqrt{b}$ ever true? **Yes, if $a = 0$ and/or $b = 0$.**

Applications

42. Construction Akikta wants to build a wooden border around a square bulletin board that has an area of 44 square feet. The wood for the border can only be purchased in lengths that are an integral number of feet. What is the least number of feet of wood that Akikta can purchase to build the border? **27 feet**

43. Construction A wire is stretched from the top of a 10-foot pole to a stake in the ground and then to the base of the pole. If a total of 18 feet of wire is needed, how far is the stake from the pole? (*Hint:* In the figure, $a + b = 18$. So, $b = 18 - a$.) **6.2 or $6\frac{2}{9}$ ft**

b 10 ft

a

Mixed Review

44. Solve $\dfrac{2n + 1}{7} \ge \dfrac{n + 4}{5}$. **(Lesson 5-3)** $n \ge \dfrac{23}{3}$

45. Simplify $\dfrac{k^2 + 2k - 3}{k^2 + 6k + 5} \cdot \dfrac{k^2 - 1}{3k + 9}$. **(Lesson 8-7)** $\dfrac{k^2 - 2k + 1}{3k + 15}$

46. Car Rental The cost of a one-day car rental from Best Car Rental is $42.20 if you drive 110 miles, $55.50 if you drive 175 miles, and $62 if you drive 200 miles. Write an equation to describe this relationship and use it to determine the per-mile charge for a one-day rental. **(Lesson 9-8)** $y = 18 + 0.22x$; **$0.22 per mile**

47. Write an equation for the line that is perpendicular to the graph of $x - 4y = 16$ and that passes through $(-1, 1)$. **(Lesson 10-6)** $y = -4x - 3$

48. Simplify $\sqrt{1944}$. **(Lesson 12-5)** $18\sqrt{6}$

EXTENDING THE LESSON

Math Power: Connections

Simplify $\sqrt{\dfrac{a}{b}} + \sqrt{\dfrac{b}{a}}$. $\dfrac{(a + b)\sqrt{ab}}{ab}$

Enrichment Masters Booklet, p. 84

12-6 Enrichment Worksheet

NAME _____ DATE _____

The Wheel of Theodorus

The Greek mathematicians were intrigued by problems of representing different numbers and expressions using geometric constructions.

Theodorus, a Greek philosopher who lived about 425 B.C., is said to have discovered a way to construct the sequence $\sqrt{1}, \sqrt{2}, \sqrt{3}, \sqrt{4}, \ldots$.

The beginning of his construction is shown. You start with an isosceles right triangle with sides 1 unit long.

Use the figure above. Write each length as a radical expression in simplest form.

1. line segment AO $\sqrt{1}$
2. line segment BO $\sqrt{2}$
3. line segment CO $\sqrt{3}$
4. line segment CO $\sqrt{4}$

5. Describe how each new triangle is added to the figure.
   Draw a new side of length 1 at right angles to the last hypotenuse. Then draw the new hypotenuse.

6. The length of the hypotenuse of the first triangle is $\sqrt{2}$. For the second triangle, the length is $\sqrt{3}$. Write an expression for the length of the hypotenuse of the nth triangle.
   $\sqrt{n + 1}$

7. Show that the method of construction will always produce the next number in the sequence. *Hint:* Find an expression for the hypotenuse of the $(n + 1)$th triangle.
   $\sqrt{(\sqrt{n})^2 + (1)^2} = \sqrt{n + 1}$

8. In the space below, construct a Wheel of Theodorus. Start with a line segment 1 centimeter long. When does the Wheel start to overlap?
   after length $\sqrt{18}$

Radical Equations

Objective
12-7

After studying this lesson, you should be able to:
- solve radical equations.

Application

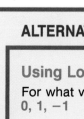

The speed, s, in miles per hour that a car travels when it skids d feet after the brakes are applied is given by the formula $s = \sqrt{30fd}$. In this formula, f is the coefficient of friction, which depends on the type and condition of the road. Mr. Robey told police he was traveling at about 30 miles per hour when he applied the brakes and skidded on a wet concrete road. The length of his skid marks was measured at 110 feet. If $f = 0.4$ for a wet concrete road, should Mr. Robey's car have skidded that far when he applied the brakes?

Use the formula $s = \sqrt{30fd}$ to find d when $s = 30$ and $f = 0.4$.

$$s = \sqrt{30fd}$$
$$30 = \sqrt{30(0.4)d} \quad \text{\textit{Substitute 30 for s and 0.4 for f.}}$$
$$30 = \sqrt{12d}$$

Equations like $30 = \sqrt{12d}$ that contain radicals with variables in the radicand are called **radical equations**. To solve these equations, first isolate the radical on one side of the equation. Then square each side of the equation to eliminate the radical. **Teaching Tip ①**

$$30 = \sqrt{12d}$$
$$30^2 = (\sqrt{12d})^2 \quad \text{\textit{Square each side to eliminate the radical.}}$$
$$900 = 12d$$
$$d = 75$$

Check:
$$30 = \sqrt{12d}$$
$$30 \stackrel{?}{=} \sqrt{12(75)}$$
$$30 \stackrel{?}{=} \sqrt{900}$$
$$30 = 30 \quad \checkmark$$

At 30 miles per hour, Mr. Robey's car should have skidded 75 feet after the brakes were applied and not 110 feet. Therefore, he was traveling faster than 30 miles per hour.

Consider the equation $x = 3$.

$$x = 3$$
$$x^2 = 9 \quad \text{\textit{Square each side.}}$$

The solutions are $x = 3$ *and* $x = -3$. Squaring each side of an equation does not necessarily produce results that satisfy the *original* equation. In this case, the solution -3 for $x^2 = 9$ is not a solution of the original equation $x = 3$. Therefore, you must check *all* solutions when you solve radical equations.

ALTERNATE TEACHING STRATEGIES

Using Logical Reasoning
For what values of a is $\sqrt{|a|} = |a|$?
$0, 1, -1$

Using Problem Solving
The square root of the product of 4 and a number is 26. Find the number. **169**

Lesson Resources
- Reteaching Master 12-7
- Practice Master 12-7
- Enrichment Master 12-7
- Video Algebra, 50

 Transparency 12-7 contains the 5-Minute Check and a teaching aid for this lesson.

INTRODUCING THE LESSON

🕐 5-Minute Check
(over Lesson 12-6)

Simplify. Use absolute value symbols when necessary.
1. $\sqrt{98c^2d^3}$ $7cd\sqrt{2d}$
2. $8\sqrt{11} + 5\sqrt{11} - 16\sqrt{11}$
   $-3\sqrt{11}$
3. $3\sqrt{5} + 2\sqrt{20}$ $7\sqrt{5}$
4. $\frac{\sqrt{21}}{\sqrt{3}}$ $\sqrt{7}$
5. $\sqrt{3}(\sqrt{6} + 2\sqrt{3})$ $3\sqrt{2} + 6$

Motivating the Lesson
Open the lesson by asking students to square both sides of the following equations.
1. $\sqrt{x} = 12$
2. $\sqrt{n} = 8$
3. $\sqrt{2y} = -11$

Ask students to describe the results. Develop the idea that squaring each side of the equation eliminates the radical.

TEACHING THE LESSON

Teaching Tip ① Emphasize the importance of isolating the radical by showing an example of what happens when students do not.

$$\sqrt{y} + 3 = 0$$
$$(\sqrt{y} + 3)^2 = 0$$
$$y + 6\sqrt{y} + 9 = 0$$

The radical still remains.

Example 1

Solve $\sqrt{3x - 14} + x = 6$ and check.

$$\sqrt{3x - 14} + x = 6$$
$$\sqrt{3x - 14} = 6 - x \qquad \text{Isolate the radical by subtracting x from each side.}$$
$$3x - 14 = (6 - x)^2 \qquad \text{Square each side of the equation.}$$
$$3x - 14 = 36 - 12x + x^2 \qquad \text{Recall that } (a - b)^2 = a^2 - 2ab + b^2.$$
$$0 = x^2 - 15x + 50$$
$$0 = (x - 5)(x - 10) \qquad \text{Factor.}$$

$x - 5 = 0$ or $x - 10 = 0$ *Zero product property*
$\quad x = 5 \qquad\qquad x = 10$

Check: $\sqrt{3x - 14} + x = 6$ **Teaching Tip ❷**

$\sqrt{3(5) - 14} + 5 \overset{?}{=} 6$	or	$\sqrt{3(10) - 14} + 10 \overset{?}{=} 6$
$\sqrt{15 - 14} + 5 \overset{?}{=} 6$		$\sqrt{30 - 14} + 10 \overset{?}{=} 6$
$\sqrt{1} + 5 \overset{?}{=} 6$		$\sqrt{16} + 10 \overset{?}{=} 6$
$1 + 5 = 6$ ✔		$4 + 10 \neq 6$

Notice that 10 does *not* satisfy the original equation. Therefore, 5 is the *only* solution of $\sqrt{3x - 14} + x = 6$.

Example 2

CONNECTION
Number Theory

The *geometric mean* of two numbers is a square root of their product. Thus, the geometric mean of numbers *a* and *b* is $\pm\sqrt{ab}$. Find two numbers that have a geometric mean of 6 given that one number is 5 more than the other.

EXPLORE   Let x = the lesser number.
Then $x + 5$ = the greater number.

PLAN $\pm\sqrt{x(x + 5)} = 6$ *The geometric mean of the numbers is 6.*
$\quad x(x + 5) = 36$ *Square each side.*

SOLVE $\quad x^2 + 5x = 36$
$x^2 + 5x - 36 = 0$
$(x + 9)(x - 4) = 0$ *Factor.*

$x + 9 = 0$ or $x - 4 = 0$ *Zero product property*
$\quad x = -9 \qquad\qquad x = 4$

If $x = -9$, then $x + 5 = -4$. If $x = 4$, then $x + 5 = 9$. Thus, the numbers are -9 and -4, or 4 and 9.

EXAMINE $\sqrt{-9(-4)} \overset{?}{=} 6$ $\sqrt{4(9)} \overset{?}{=} 6$
$\qquad\qquad \sqrt{36} = 6$ ✔ $\sqrt{36} = 6$ ✔

RETEACHING THE LESSON

Have students solve the following equation as an illustration of how combining like terms and factoring can be used together.

$$x + 2 = x\sqrt{3}$$
$$x - x\sqrt{3} = -2$$
$$x(1 - \sqrt{3}) = -2$$
$$x = \frac{-2}{1 - \sqrt{3}}$$
$$x = 1 + \sqrt{3}$$

CHECKING FOR UNDERSTANDING

Communicating Mathematics

Read and study the lesson to answer each question.

1. When solving a radical equation, what is the first thing you should do? **Isolate the radical.**
2. *True* or *false:* Squaring each side of an equation always results in an equivalent equation. **false**
3. Write a radical equation that has *no* solution. **Answers will vary; typical answers are $\sqrt{x} = -1$ and $\sqrt{2x} + 5 = 2$.**
4. Write an expression for the geometric mean of 5 and x. **$\pm\sqrt{5x}$**

Guided Practice

Square each side of the following equations.

5. $\sqrt{x} = 5$ $x = 25$ 6. $\sqrt{y + 1} = 3$ $y + 1 = 9$ 7. $11 = \sqrt{2a - 5}$
                                                                          $121 = 2a - 5$

Solve each equation. Check the solutions.

8. $\sqrt{y} = 3$ 9   9. $\sqrt{m} = -2$ **no real solution**   10. $-\sqrt{a} = -8$ 64

11. $\sqrt{5x} = 5$ 5   12. $\sqrt{-3a} = 6$ −12   13. $\sqrt{x - 3} = 6$ 39

Find the geometric mean of each pair of numbers.

14. 4, 9   **6**   15. 5, 20   **10**   16. 7, 10 $\sqrt{70}$ 17. 4, 8 $4\sqrt{2}$

EXERCISES

Practice

Solve each equation. Check the solutions.   26. **no real solution**   30. $\pm\frac{4}{3}\sqrt{3}$

18. $\sqrt{r} = 3\sqrt{5}$ **45**   19. $4\sqrt{7} = \sqrt{-m}$ **−112**   20. $\sqrt{b} - 5 = 0$ **25**

21. $\sqrt{2d} + 1 = 0$
   no real solution   22. $5 - \sqrt{3x} = 1$ $\frac{16}{3}$ 23. $2 + 3\sqrt{m} = 13$ $\frac{121}{9}$

24. $\sqrt{4x + 1} = 3$ **2**   25. $\sqrt{8s + 1} - 5 = 0$ **3**   26. $\sqrt{3b - 5} + 6 = 2$

27. $\sqrt{\frac{x}{4}} = 6$ **144**   28. $\sqrt{\frac{5k}{7}} - 8 = 2$ **140**   29. $5\sqrt{\frac{4a}{3}} - 2 = 0$ $\frac{3}{25}$

30. $4\sqrt{3m^2 - 15} = 4$ 31. $\sqrt{2z^2 - 121} = z$ **11**   32. $\sqrt{5x^2 - 7} = 2x$ $\sqrt{7}$

33. $\sqrt{x + 2} = x - 4$ **7**   34. $\sqrt{1 - 2x} = 1 + x$ **0**   35. $4 + \sqrt{x - 2} = x$ **6**

36. The geometric mean of a certain number and 4 is 26. Find the number. **169**
37. Find two numbers with a geometric mean of $\sqrt{24}$ given that one number is 2 more than the other. **−6, −4, or 4, 6**
38. Find two numbers with a geometric mean of 12 given that one number is 11 less than three times the other. **$-\frac{16}{3}$, −27 or 9, 16**

EVALUATING THE LESSON

Checking for Understanding
Exercises 1-17 are designed to help you assess understanding through reading, writing, and speaking. You should work through Exercises 1-4 with your students, and then monitor their work on Exercises 5-17.

Closing the Lesson
Writing Activity Have students work in groups of two or three on the chalkboard exercises for the last ten minutes of class. This will allow them to check each other's work and find out if they understand the material before class ends.

APPLYING THE LESSON

Homework Exercises

Assignment Guide
Basic: 18-38, 45-46, 49-54
Average: 21-41, 45-54
Enriched: 24-54

Practice Masters Booklet, p. 96

NAME _____   **DATE** _____

12-7 Practice Worksheet

Radical Equations

Solve each equation. Check the solutions.

1. $\sqrt{5x} = 10$ **20**   2. $\sqrt{4x} = 6$ **9**   3. $3\sqrt{5} = \sqrt{-n}$ **−45**

4. $\sqrt{p} - 9 = 0$ **81**   5. $\sqrt{3a} + 2 = 0$ **no solution**   6. $6 - \sqrt{2y} = -2$ **32**

7. $\sqrt{2x - 1} = 5$ **13**   8. $4 = \sqrt{3k - 2}$ **6**   9. $\sqrt{2x + 9} + 10 = 15$ **8**

10. $\sqrt{4x - 4} - 4 = 0$ **5**   11. $\sqrt{\frac{m}{3}} = 14$ **588**   12. $\sqrt{\frac{3s}{5}} - 4 = 2$ **60**

13. $6\sqrt{\frac{3x}{2}} - 3 = 0$ $\frac{1}{6}$ 14. $6 + \sqrt{\frac{5r}{6}} = -2$ **no solution**   15. $3\sqrt{4y^2 + 3} = 36$ $\pm\frac{1}{2}\sqrt{141}$

16. $\sqrt{2x^2 - 9} = x$ **3**   17. $\sqrt{x + 5} = x - 1$ **4**   18. $8\sqrt{4x^2 - 43} = 40$ $\pm\sqrt{17}$

Solve each equation. Check the solution. (*Hint:* You will need to square each side twice.)

39. $\sqrt{x + 16} = \sqrt{x} + 4$ **0** 40. $6 - \sqrt{x} = \sqrt{x - 12}$ 41. $\sqrt{x + 5} = 5 + \sqrt{x}$
16   **no real solution**

Solve each system of equations. 43. $\left(\frac{1}{4}, \frac{25}{36}\right)$

42. $3\sqrt{x} - 5\sqrt{y} = 9$ **(9, 0)** 43. $-4\sqrt{a} + 6\sqrt{b} = 3$ 44. $m = 4n$ **(16, 4)**
$2\sqrt{x} + 5\sqrt{y} = 6$ $-3\sqrt{a} + 3\sqrt{b} = 1$ $\sqrt{m} - 5\sqrt{n} = -6$

Critical Thinking

45. Find two numbers such that the square root of their sum is 5 and the square root of their product is 12. **16 and 9**

Applications

46. **Science** The horizontal distance you can see is related to your height above the ground by the formula $V = 3.5\sqrt{h}$. In this formula, V is the distance in kilometers that you can see horizontally and h is your height in meters above the ground. If you look out the window of an airplane on a cloudless day and can see for a distance of about 315 km, what is the altitude of the plane? **8100 m or 8.1 km**

47. **Physics** The time, in seconds, that it takes an object, initially at rest, to fall a distance of s meters is given by the formula $t = \sqrt{\dfrac{2s}{g}}$. In this formula, g is the acceleration due to gravity in meters per second squared. On the moon, a rock falls 7.2 meters in 3 seconds. What is the acceleration due to gravity on the moon? **1.6 m/s²**

48. **Recreation** The rangers at an aid station received a distress call from a group camping 60 miles east and 10 miles south of the station. A jeep sent to the campsite travels directly east for some number of miles and then turns and heads directly to the campsite. If the jeep traveled a total of 66 miles to get to the campsite, for how many miles did it travel due east? **$54\frac{2}{3}$ miles**

60 mi

10 mi

Mixed Review

49. Solve $8 = \dfrac{11t - 10}{7}$. **(Lesson 3-5) 6**

50. **Gardening** Mr. Schultz doubled the area of his rectangular garden by adding a strip of new soil of uniform width along each of the sides. If the dimensions of the original garden were 10 feet by 15 feet, how wide a strip of new soil did he add? **(Lesson 7-10) 2.5 feet**

51. Solve $6x + 5y = 11$ if the domain is $\{-4, -2, 0, 1, 5\}$. **(Lesson 9-3)**
See margin.

52. Determine the value of r so that the line that passes through $(r, 4)$ and $(3, -r)$ has a slope of $2r$. **(Lesson 10-1)** $-\frac{1}{2}, 4$

53. Use substitution to solve the system of equations $y = -2x + 10$ and $2x + 3y = 6$. **(Lesson 11-3) (6, −2)**

54. **Geometry** The measures of the sides of a triangle are $\sqrt{363}$, $\sqrt{27}$, and $2\sqrt{108}$. Find the measure of its perimeter. **(Lesson 12-6)**
$26\sqrt{3} \approx 45.03$

504 CHAPTER 12 RADICAL EXPRESSIONS

EXTENDING THE LESSON

**Math Power:
Problem Solving**

Five times the square root of a number is 6 less than the number. Find the number. **36**

Additional Answer

51. $\left\{(-4, 7), \left(-2, \frac{23}{5}\right), \left(0, \frac{11}{5}\right), (1, 1), \left(5, \frac{-19}{5}\right)\right\}$

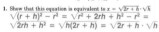

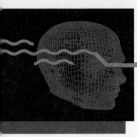

Technology

Solving Radical Equations

BASIC
Graphing calculators
► Graphing software
Spreadsheets

You can use the *Mathematics Exploration Toolkit* to solve equations involving square roots. The steps are as follows. First, isolate the radical on one side of the equation. Then raise both sides to the second power to remove the radical. The CALC commands below will be used.

ADD (add)   SUBTRACT (sub)   MULTIPLY (mult)
DIVIDE (div)   FACTOR (fac)   RAISETO (rai)
SIMPLIFY (simp)   STORE (sto)   SUBSTITUTE (subs)

To enter the square root symbol, type a &.

Example

Solve $\sqrt{x - 1} = x - 3$.

Enter	Result
&(x − 1) = x − 3	$\sqrt{x - 1} = x - 3$
sto a	saves the equation as a
rai 2	$(\sqrt{x - 1})^2 = (x - 3)^2$
simp	$x - 1 = x^2 - 6x + 9$
sub x−1	$x - 1 - (x - 1) = x^2 - 6x + 9 - (x - 1)$
simp	$0 = x^2 - 7x + 10$
fac	$0 = (x - 5)(x - 2)$

By inspection, the solutions are $x = 5$ or $x = 2$.

Check:
a	$\sqrt{x - 1} = x - 3$	
subs 5 x	$\sqrt{5 - 1} = 5 - 3$	
simp	$2 = 2$ ✔	
a	$\sqrt{x - 1} = x - 3$	
subs 2 x	$\sqrt{2 - 1} = 2 - 3$	
simp	$1 = -1$	

The only solution is 5.

EXERCISES

Use CALC to solve each equation. Check all solutions. Record the steps used to solve each equation.

1. $\sqrt{x} + 4 = 1$ no solution
2. $3 + \sqrt{2x} = 7$ 8
3. $\sqrt{3x - 8} = 5$ 11
4. $x - \sqrt{x + 1} = 1$ 3
5. $\sqrt{6 - x} = 4 - x$ 2
6. $\sqrt{2x + 6} = \sqrt{3x - 9}$ 15

TECHNOLOGY: SOLVING RADICAL EQUATIONS 505

Using Technology

Objective This optional page shows how graphing software can be used to perform mathematical computations and to enhance and extend mathematical concepts.

Teaching Suggestions

Some radical equations can be solved automatically with the SOLVEFOR command. Other equations require choosing appropriate steps to simplify the equation before the computer can solve it. You may wish to have students use the SOLVEFOR and SSTEPS commands to reveal the steps used by the computer to solve equations. Have students compare the steps they chose to those chosen by the computer and by other students. Point out to students that there are many effective ways to solve an equation. Encourage them to experiment with operations on equations.

INTRODUCING THE LESSON

🕐 5-Minute Check

(over Lesson 12-7)

Simplify.

1. $\sqrt{m} = 10$ 100
2. $\sqrt{r} = 12$ 144
3. $\sqrt{t} = ab$ **(ab)²**
4. $\sqrt{3p} = 6$ 12
5. $\sqrt{y - 2} = 0$ 2

Motivating the Lesson

Open the lesson with a review of the Pythagorean Theorem. Ask students to find the length of the leg of a right triangle if $a = 24$ and $c = 25$. $b = 7$ Develop the idea that the distance formula introduced in this lesson is a simplified version of the Pythagorean Theorem.

TEACHING THE LESSON

Teaching Tip ①   Encourage students to check the results. Point out that the negative result does not need to be omitted. It represents the y-coordinate of a point in the plane, not a distance.

Teaching Tip ②   You may wish to have students graph the points $(7, -3)$, $(5, -12)$, and $(5, 6)$ to better understand why it is reasonable for a to have two values.

Objective
12-8

After studying this lesson, you should be able to:

■ find the distance between two points in the coordinate plane.

Application

The Beck Corporation is having a fiber optic cable system installed between two new offices. Becktower I is 4 miles east and 5 miles north of Beck Central. Becktower II is 5 miles west and 2 miles north of Beck Central. How many miles of cable will be needed to connect the new offices?

To help solve this problem, the engineer in charge of the project drew a map on a grid, like the one shown at the right. The sides of each small square in the grid represent a distance of 1 mile. Since the distances are given from Beck Central, she placed it at the origin of the grid. Thus, Becktower I is located at the point $(4, 5)$ and Becktower II is located at the point $(-5, 2)$. The amount of cable needed is the length of the segment joining these two points. Let $d =$ the length of this side.

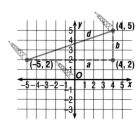

In the illustration above, notice that a right triangle can be formed by drawing lines parallel to the axes from points $(-5, 2)$ and $(4, 5)$. These lines intersect at the point $(4, 2)$. The measure, a, of the side that has $(-5, 2)$ as an endpoint is the difference of the x-coordinates, $4 - (-5)$, or 9. The measure, b, of the side that has $(4, 5)$ as an endpoint is the difference of the y-coordinates, $5 - 2$, or 3.

Now the Pythagorean Theorem can be used to find d, the distance from Becktower I to Becktower II. This is also the distance between the points $(-5, 2)$ and $(4, 5)$.

$c^2 = a^2 + b^2$ *Pythagorean Theorem*
$d^2 = 9^2 + 3^2$ *Substitute 9 for a, 3 for b, and d for c.*
$d^2 = 81 + 9$
$d^2 = 90$
$d = \sqrt{90}$ *In simplest form, $\sqrt{90} = 3\sqrt{10}$.*
$d \approx 9.49$

About 9.49 miles of cable will be needed to connect the two new offices.

The method used for finding the distance between $(-5, 2)$ and $(4, 5)$ can also be used to find the distance between *any* two points in the coordinate plane. The result can be described by the following formula.

ALTERNATE TEACHING STRATEGIES

Using Discussion

Why is it easy to find the distance between two points in the coordinate plane that form either a vertical or horizontal line segment?   **You can just subtract the coordinates that are different.**

<table>
<tr><td>

The Distance Formula

</td><td>

The distance, d, between any two points with coordinates (x_1, y_1) and (x_2, y_2) is given by the following formula.

$$d = \sqrt{(x_2 - x_1)^2 + (y_2 - y_1)^2}$$

</td></tr>
</table>

Example 1

CONNECTION
Geometry

If the diagonals of a trapezoid have the same length, then the trapezoid is isosceles. Find the lengths of the diagonals of the trapezoid with vertices $A(-2, 2)$, $B(10, 6)$, $C(9, 8)$ and $D(0, 5)$ to determine if it is isosceles.

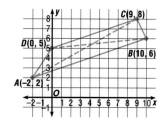

The diagonals of the trapezoid are segments AC and BD. Use the distance formula to compare the lengths of the segments.

AC is the measure of $\overline{AC}$ and BD is the measure of $\overline{BD}$.

For AC, let $x_2 = 9$, $x_1 = -2$, $y_2 = 8$, and $y_1 = 2$.

$$d = \sqrt{(x_2 - x_1)^2 + (y_2 - y_1)^2}$$
$$AC = \sqrt{[9 - (-2)]^2 + (8 - 2)^2}$$
$$= \sqrt{11^2 + 6^2}$$
$$= \sqrt{121 + 36}$$
$$= \sqrt{157}$$

For BD, let $x_2 = 0$, $x_1 = 10$, $y_2 = 5$, and $y_1 = 6$.

$$d = \sqrt{(x_2 - x_1)^2 + (y_2 - y_1)^2}$$
$$BD = \sqrt{(0 - 10)^2 + (5 - 6)^2}$$
$$= \sqrt{(-10)^2 + (-1)^2}$$
$$= \sqrt{100 + 1}$$
$$= \sqrt{101}$$

Since $\sqrt{157} \neq \sqrt{101}$, trapezoid $ABCD$ is not isosceles.

Example 2

Find the value of a if the distance between points $(5, a)$ and $(7, -3)$ is $\sqrt{85}$ units.

$$d = \sqrt{(x_2 - x_1)^2 + (y_2 - y_1)^2} \quad \text{*Let } x_2 = 7, x_1 = 5, y_2 = -3, \text{ and } y_1 = a.*$$
$$\sqrt{85} = \sqrt{(7 - 5)^2 + (-3 - a)^2}$$
$$\sqrt{85} = \sqrt{2^2 + (-3 - a)^2}$$
$$\sqrt{85} = \sqrt{4 + 9 + 6a + a^2}$$
$$\sqrt{85} = \sqrt{a^2 + 6a + 13}$$
$$85 = a^2 + 6a + 13 \qquad \text{*Square each side.*}$$
$$0 = a^2 + 6a - 72$$
$$0 = (a + 12)(a - 6) \qquad \text{*Factor.*}$$
$$a + 12 = 0 \quad \text{or} \quad a - 6 = 0$$
$$a = -12 \qquad\qquad a = 6 \quad \text{*You can check these answers by*}$$

Teaching Tip ❶–❷

The value of a is -12 or 6.
substituting -12 and 6 for a in the equation $\sqrt{85} = \sqrt{(7 - 5)^2 + (-3 - a)^2}$.

RETEACHING THE LESSON

1. Show that a triangle with vertices $A(-3, 4)$, $B(5, 2)$, and $C(-1, -5)$ is isosceles but not equilateral.
2. Show that a quadrilateral with vertices $A(1, 1)$, $B(4, -2)$, $C(1, -3)$, and $D(-2, 0)$ is a parallelogram.
3. Show that $(2, 3)$ is the center of a circle through $(5, 7)$, $(-1, -1)$, and $(-2, 0)$.

Checking for Understanding

Exercises 1-8 are designed to help you assess understanding through reading, writing, and speaking. You should work through Exercises 1-4 with your students, and then monitor their work on Exercises 5-8.

Error Analysis

Make sure when using the distance formula that students subtract the coordinates in corresponding order. For example, some students may substitute as follows:

$$d = \sqrt{(x_2 - x_1)^2 + (y_1 - y_2)^2}, \text{ or }$$
$$d = \sqrt{(x_1 - x_2)^2 + (y_2 - y_1)^2}$$

Closing the Lesson

Speaking Activity Have students identify the distance formula. Then ask them to describe the relationship between the distance formula and the Pythagorean Theorem.

Practice Masters Booklet, p. 97

508 Chapter 12

CHECKING FOR UNDERSTANDING

Communicating Mathematics

Read and study the lesson to answer each question. See margin.

1. Explain how the distance formula is actually an application of the Pythagorean Theorem.
2. When finding the distance between (18, 8) and (5, 7), do you have to choose 18 for x_1? Explain.
3. Explain how you can find the distance between (10, 3) and (2, 3) without using the distance formula.
4. Explain how you can find the distance between (−1, 5) and (−1, −2) without using the distance formula.

Guided Practice

Find the distance between each pair of points whose coordinates are given.

5. (3, 4), (6, 8) 5
6. (−4, 2), (4, 17) 17
7. (3, 7), (−2, −5) 13
8. (5, −1), (11, 7) 10

EXERCISES

Practice

Find the distance between each pair of points whose coordinates are given. Express answers in simplest form and as decimal approximations rounded to the nearest hundredth.

9. (2, 2), (5, −1) $3\sqrt{2}$ or 4.24
10. (−8, −4), (−3, −8) $\sqrt{41}$ or 6.40
11. (5, 4), (−3, 8) $4\sqrt{5}$ or 8.94
12. (2, 7), (10, −4) $\sqrt{185}$ or 13.60
13. (9, −2), (3, −6) $2\sqrt{13}$ or 7.21
14. (4, 2), $\left(6, -\frac{2}{3}\right)$ $\frac{10}{3}$ or 3.33

15. $\left(6, -\frac{2}{7}\right), \left(5, \frac{3}{7}\right)$ $\frac{\sqrt{74}}{7}$ or 1.23
16. $\left(\frac{4}{5}, -1\right), \left(2, -\frac{1}{2}\right)$ $\frac{13}{10}$ or 1.30
17. $(2\sqrt{5}, 9), (4\sqrt{5}, 3)$ $2\sqrt{14}$ or 7.48
18. $(3\sqrt{2}, 7)(5\sqrt{2}, 9)$ $2\sqrt{3}$ or 3.46

Find the value of *a* if the points whose coordinates are given are the indicated distance apart.

19. (4, 7), (a, 3); d = 5 7 or 1
20. (−3, a), (5, 2); d = 17 17 or −13
21. (a, 5), (−7, 3); d = $\sqrt{29}$ −2 or −12
22. (4, −2), (−5, a); d = $\sqrt{130}$ −9 or 5

Find the lengths of the diagonals of each trapezoid with the given vertices to determine whether it is isosceles. See Solutions Manual.

23. (0, 0), (7, 0), (7, 4), (1, 4) no
24. (1, 1), (5, 9), (2, 8), (0, 4) yes
25. Find the perimeter of the triangle with vertices A(2, −1), B(−2, 2), and C(−6, 14). $22 + 4\sqrt{10}$ or about 34.65 units

Find the distance between each pair of points whose coordinates are given. Express answers in simplest form.

26. $(\sqrt{8}, \sqrt{3}), (\sqrt{3}, -\sqrt{8})$ $\sqrt{22}$
27. $(-3\sqrt{6}, \sqrt{10}), (2\sqrt{5}, 6\sqrt{3})$ $8\sqrt{3}$

Additional Answers

1. Apply the Pythagorean Theorem to the right triangle with vertices (x_1, y_1), (x_2, y_1), and (x_2, y_2), where d, the distance between (x_1, y_1) and (x_2, y_2), is the measure of the hypotenuse.
2. No; you can use 18 for x_2 as long as you use 8 for y_2, 5 for x_1, and 7 for y_1.
3. The distance between them is the absolute value of the difference of their x-coordinates, |10 − 2| or 8 units.
4. The distance between them is the absolute value of the difference of their y-coordinates, |5 − (−2)| or 7 units.

28. Find the value of a if the distance between points $(a, 5)$ and $(3, -2a)$ is 5 units. **−1 or −$\frac{9}{5}$**

Critical Thinking

29. Show that the triangle with vertices $(3, -2)$, $(-3, 7)$, and $(-9, 3)$ is a right triangle. **See margin.**

Applications

30. **Telecommunications** Refer to the application at the beginning of this lesson. Suppose the Beck Corporation decides to build a distribution center 12 miles south of Beck Central. How many additional miles of cable will be needed to connect Beck Central, Becktower I, and Becktower II to the distribution center? **about 44.33 miles**

31. **Telecommunications** In order to set long distance rates, phone companies first superimpose an imaginary coordinate grid over the United States. Then the location of each exchange is represented by an ordered pair on the grid. The units on this grid are approximately equal to 0.316 miles. So, a distance of 3 units on the grid equals an actual distance of about 3(0.316) or 0.948 miles. Suppose the exchanges in two cities are (1583, 5622) and (7878, 9213). Find the actual distance between these cities, to the nearest mile. **2290 miles**

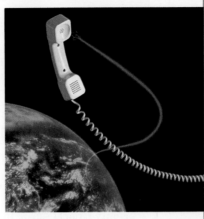

Computer

32. Use the BASIC program at the right to find the distance between each pair of points whose coordinates are given.

   a. $(5, -1)$, $(11, 7)$ **10**

   b. $(12, -2)$, $(-3, 5)$ **≈16.55**

   c. $\left(0.67, -4\right)$, $(3, -2)$ **≈3.07**

```
10 PRINT "ENTER COORDINATES OF
   POINT (X1, Y1)."
20 INPUT X1, Y1
30 PRINT "ENTER COORDINATES OF
   POINT (X2, Y2)."
40 INPUT X2, Y2
50 D = SQR((X2-X1)*(X2-X1) +
   (Y2-Y1)*(Y2-Y1))
60 PRINT "DISTANCE FROM ("; X1; ", ";
   Y1; ") TO ("; X2; ", "; Y2; ") IS ";
   D; " UNITS."
```

Mixed Review

33. Simplify $\frac{4m^2 - 6m - 4}{2m^2 - 8m + 8}$. **(Lesson 8-1)** $\frac{2m + 1}{m - 2}$

34. If $f(x) = 3x - 5$ and $g(x) = x^2 - x$, find $f[g(-2)]$. **(Lesson 9-5) 13**

35. Write the standard form of an equation of the line passing through $(8, 3)$ and $(5, -1)$. **(Lesson 10-2)** $4x - 3y = 23$

36. **Aviation** Flying with the wind, a plane travels 300 miles in 40 minutes. Flying against the wind, it travels 300 miles in 45 minutes. Find the air speed of the plane. **(Lesson 11-5) 425 mph**

37. Solve $\sqrt{x^2 + 3} = 3 - x$. **(Lesson 12-7) 1**

EXTENDING THE LESSON

Math Power: Connections

The endpoints of $\overline{AB}$ are $A(-2, 6)$ and $B(4, 2)$. The endpoints of $\overline{CD}$ are $C(3, 7)$ and $D(1, 4)$. Show that $\overline{CD}$ is a perpendicular bisector of $\overline{AB}$.

a. Find the midpoint of $\overline{AB}$.
   (1, 4)
   Since the midpoint of $\overline{AB}$ is point D, $\overline{CD}$ is a bisector of $\overline{AB}$.

b. Find the slopes of $\overline{AB}$ and $\overline{CD}$. slope of $\overline{AB} = -\frac{2}{3}$; slope of $\overline{CD} = \frac{3}{2}$; Since $\left(-\frac{2}{3}\right)\left(\frac{3}{2}\right) = -1$, $\overline{AB}$ and $\overline{CD}$ are perpendicular.
Therefore, $\overline{CD}$ is a perpendicular bisector of $\overline{AB}$.

Using the Chapter Summary and Review

The Chapter Summary and Review begins with an alphabetical listing of the new terms that were presented in the chapter. Have students define each term and provide an example of it, if appropriate.

The Skills and Concepts presented in the chapter are reviewed using a side-by-side format. Encourage students to refer to the Objectives and Examples on the left as they complete the Review Exercises on the right.

The Chapter Summary and Review ends with exercises that review Applications and Connections.

CHAPTER **12** SUMMARY AND REVIEW

VOCABULARY

Upon completing this chapter, you should be familiar with the following terms:

conjugate	**494**	**477**	radical expression
hypotenuse	**482**	**477**	radical sign
irrational numbers	**487**	**477**	radicand
legs	**482**	**493**	rationalizing the denominator
principal square root	**477**	**488**	real numbers
Pythagorean Theorem	**482**	**477**	square root
radical equation	**501**		

SKILLS AND CONCEPTS

OBJECTIVES AND EXAMPLES	REVIEW EXERCISES
Upon completing this chapter you should be able to:	Use these exercises to review and prepare for the chapter test.

- simplify rational square roots **(Lesson 12-2)**

$$\sqrt{1225} = \sqrt{5^2 \cdot 7^2}$$
$$= \sqrt{(5 \cdot 7)^2}$$
$$= \sqrt{35^2} \text{ or } 35$$

Simplify.

1. $\sqrt{169}$ **13**   2. $-\sqrt{784}$ **−28**

3. $-\sqrt{0.0289}$ **−0.17**   4. $\pm\sqrt{\frac{196}{225}}$ $\pm\frac{14}{15}$

- find approximate values for square roots **(Lesson 12-2)**

Find $\sqrt{167.3}$ to the nearest hundredth.

Using a calculator, $\sqrt{167.3} \approx 12.93$.

Use a calculator to find each square root. Round answers to the nearest hundredth.

5. $-\sqrt{61.7}$ **−7.85**   6. $\sqrt{191.6}$ **13.84**

7. $\pm\sqrt{23.04}$ **±4.8**   8. $\pm\sqrt{10.028}$ **±3.17**

- use the Pythagorean Theorem **(Lesson 12-3)**

Find the measure of the hypotenuse of a right triangle if $a = 15$ and $b = 20$.

$c^2 = a^2 + b^2$
$c^2 = 15^2 + 20^2$
$c^2 = 225 + 400$
$c^2 = 625$
$c = 25$

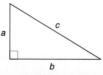

Use the Pythagorean Theorem to find each missing measure to the nearest hundredth.

9. $a = 30, b = 16, c = ?$ **34**

10. $a = 6, b = 10, c = ?$ $\sqrt{136} \approx 11.66$

11. $a = 10, c = 15, b = ?$ $\sqrt{125} \approx 11.18$

12. The measures of the sides of a triangle are 20, 21, and 29. Determine whether this triangle is a right triangle. **yes**

- identify irrational numbers
  (Lesson 12-4)

Identify $\sqrt{21.16}$ and $-17.121121112\ldots$ as rational or irrational numbers.

Since $\sqrt{21.16} = 4.6$, it is a rational number. Since $-17.121121112\ldots$ does not repeat or terminate, it is an irrational number.

Determine whether each number is rational or irrational.

13. $\sqrt{31.25}$ irrational

14. $\sqrt{0.1296}$ rational

15. $-8.10011001\ldots$ rational

16. $4.21222324\ldots$ irrational

- simplify square roots   **(Lesson 12-5)**

$$\sqrt{450} = \sqrt{2 \cdot 3 \cdot 3 \cdot 5 \cdot 5}$$
$$= \sqrt{2} \cdot \sqrt{3^2} \cdot \sqrt{5^2}$$
$$= \sqrt{2} \cdot 3 \cdot 5 \text{ or } 15\sqrt{2}$$

$$\frac{\sqrt{12}}{\sqrt{5}} = \frac{\sqrt{12}}{\sqrt{5}} \cdot \frac{\sqrt{5}}{\sqrt{5}}$$
$$= \frac{\sqrt{2 \cdot 2 \cdot 3 \cdot 5}}{\sqrt{5 \cdot 5}}$$
$$= \frac{\sqrt{2^2} \cdot \sqrt{3} \cdot \sqrt{5}}{\sqrt{5^2}} \text{ or } \frac{2\sqrt{15}}{5}$$

Simplify.

17. $\sqrt{108}$ $6\sqrt{3}$

18. $\sqrt{720}$ $12\sqrt{5}$

19. $2\sqrt{6} - \sqrt{48}$ $2\sqrt{6} - 4\sqrt{3}$

20. $\dfrac{\sqrt{5}}{\sqrt{55}}$ $\dfrac{\sqrt{11}}{11}$

21. $\sqrt{\dfrac{20}{7}}$ $\dfrac{2\sqrt{35}}{7}$

22. $\dfrac{9}{3+\sqrt{2}}$ $\dfrac{27 - 9\sqrt{2}}{7}$

- simplify radical expressions that contain variables   **(Lesson 12-5)**

$$\sqrt{343x^2y^3} = \sqrt{7 \cdot 7^2 \cdot x^2 \cdot y \cdot y^2}$$
$$= \sqrt{7^2} \cdot \sqrt{x^2} \cdot \sqrt{y^2} \cdot \sqrt{7} \cdot \sqrt{y}$$
$$= 7|x|y\sqrt{7y}$$

Simplify. Use absolute value symbols when necessary. 24. $2|a|b^2\sqrt{11b}$

23. $\sqrt{96x^4}$ $4x^2\sqrt{6}$

24. $\sqrt{44a^2b^5}$

25. $\sqrt{\dfrac{60}{y^2}}$ $\dfrac{2\sqrt{15}}{|y|}$

26. $\dfrac{\sqrt{3a^3b^4}}{\sqrt{8ab^{10}}}$ $\dfrac{a\sqrt{6}}{4|b^3|}$

- simplify radical expressions involving addition and subtraction   **(Lesson 12-6)**

$$\sqrt{6} - \sqrt{54} + 3\sqrt{12} + 5\sqrt{3}$$
$$= \sqrt{6} - \sqrt{3^2 \cdot 6} + 3\sqrt{2^2 \cdot 3} + 5\sqrt{3}$$
$$= \sqrt{6} - \sqrt{3^2} \cdot \sqrt{6} + 3(\sqrt{2^2} \cdot \sqrt{3}) + 5\sqrt{3}$$
$$= \sqrt{6} - 3\sqrt{6} + 3(2\sqrt{3}) + 5\sqrt{3}$$
$$= -2\sqrt{6} + 11\sqrt{3}$$

Simplify. Exact and approximate values are given.

27. $2\sqrt{13} + 8\sqrt{15} - 3\sqrt{15} + 3\sqrt{13}$
    $5\sqrt{13} + 5\sqrt{15}$; 37.39

28. $4\sqrt{27} + 6\sqrt{48}$ $36\sqrt{3}$; 62.35

29. $5\sqrt{18} - 3\sqrt{112} - 3\sqrt{98}$
    $-6\sqrt{2} - 12\sqrt{7}$; -40.23

30. $\sqrt{8} + \sqrt{\dfrac{1}{8}}$ $\dfrac{9\sqrt{2}}{4}$; 3.18

- solve radical equations   **(Lesson 12-7)**

$$\sqrt{5 - 4x} = 13$$
$$5 - 4x = 169$$
$$-4x = 164$$
$$x = -41$$

Solve each equation. Check the solutions.

31. $\sqrt{3x} = 6$ 12

32. $\sqrt{7x - 1} = 5$ $\dfrac{26}{7}$

33. $\sqrt{\dfrac{4a}{3}} - 2 = 0$ 3

34. $\sqrt{x + 4} = x - 8$ 12

Alternate Review Strategy

To provide a brief in-class review, you may wish to read the following questions to the class and require a verbal or written response.

1. Simplify $\pm\sqrt{31.36}$. ± 5.6
2. The measures of the sides of a triangle are 16, 30, and 34. Is this triangle a right triangle?   **yes**
3. Determine whether 7.634 is a rational or irrational number.   **rational**
4. Simplify $\sqrt{605}$. $11\sqrt{5}$
5. Simplify $2\sqrt{27} - 4\sqrt{12}$. $-2\sqrt{3}$
6. Solve and check.
   $\sqrt{2a^2 - 144} = a$ 12
7. Find the distance between a pair of points with the following coordinates: $(5, -1)$, $(11, 7)$.   10

The Cumulative Review shown below can be used to review skills and concepts presented thus far in the text. Standardized Test Practice Questions are also provided in the Evaluation Masters Booklet.

Evaluation Masters Booklet, pp. 165-166

■ find the distance between two points in the coordinate plane **(Lesson 12-8)**

Find the distance between the points $(-5, 1)$ and $(1, 5)$.

$$d = \sqrt{(x_2 - x_1)^2 + (y_2 - y_1)^2}$$
$$= \sqrt{(-5 - 1)^2 + (1 - 5)^2}$$
$$= \sqrt{(-6)^2 + (-4)^2}$$
$$= \sqrt{36 + 16} \text{ or } \sqrt{52} \approx 7.21$$

Find the distance between each pair of points whose coordinates are given.

35. $(9, -2), (1, 13)$ 17

36. $(4, 2), (7, -9)$ $\sqrt{130} \approx 11.40$

37. Find the value of a if the distance between the points $(5, -2)$ and $(a, -3)$ is $\sqrt{170}$ units.   18 or -8

APPLICATIONS AND CONNECTIONS

Use the information in the table shown below to answer each question.   **(Lesson 12-1)**

Number of Hits by Home Run Champions							
Year	1960	1965	1970	1975	1980	1985	1990
National League	41	52	45	38	48	37	40
American League	40	32	44	36	41	40	51

38. How many times did a home run champion hit less than 40 home runs?   4 times

39. In what year(s) did the American League champion hit more home runs than the National League champion?   1985, 1990

Solve each problem. Round answers to the nearest hundredth.

40. **Geometry** The measure of the area of a square is 108. What is the measure of a side of this square, rounded to the nearest hundredth? **(Lesson 12-2)** 10.39

41. **Geometry** The length of a rectangle is 1.1 cm and its width is 6.0 cm. Find the length of a diagonal of the rectangle. **(Lesson 12-3)** 6.1 cm

42. **Number Theory** Find two numbers with geometric mean 18 if one number is 3 more than twice the other. **(Lesson 12-7)** 12, 27 or $-13.5, -24$

43. **Geometry** Find the perimeter of the triangle with vertices $A(0, 0)$, $B(-3, 4)$, and $C(6, 8)$. **(Lesson 12-8)** 24.85 units

44. **Nature** An 18-foot tall tree is broken by the wind. The top of the tree falls and touches the ground 12 feet from its base. How many feet from the base of the tree did the break occur? **(Lesson 12-3)** 5 ft

45. **Law Enforcement** Lina told the police officer that she was traveling at 55 mph when she applied the brakes and skidded. The skid marks at the scene were 240 feet long. Should Lina's car have skidded that far if it was traveling at 55 mph? Use the formula $s = \sqrt{15d}$. **(Lesson 12-7)**

45. No, it should skid about 201.7 ft.

TEST

30, 32. See margin.

The table at the right shows American consumption of fresh fruits per capita in pounds. Use this information to answer the following questions.

Fruit	1965	1970	1975	1980	1985
Bananas	17.9	17.4	17.7	20.8	23.4
Apples	15.7	16.3	18.3	18.3	16.7
Grapes	3.8	2.5	2.9	3.3	6.6

1. What is the consistently most-popular fruit? bananas

2. In what year did the most-popular fruit change? 1975

3. Why do you think grapes have such low consumption? They weigh less.

Name the set or sets of numbers to which each of the following numbers belongs. Use N for natural numbers, W for whole numbers, Z for integers, Q for rational numbers, and I for irrational numbers.

4. $\sqrt{16}$ N, W, Z, Q   5. $-\sqrt{18}$ I   6. 4.565656 … Q   7. $\frac{3}{8}$ Q

Use the Pythagorean Theorem to find each missing measure to the nearest hundredth. 8. $2\sqrt{41} \approx 12.81$

8. $a = 8, b = 10, c = ?$ 9. $a = 12, c = 20, b = ?$ 16

10. $a = b, c = 12, b = ?$ $6\sqrt{2} \approx 8.49$

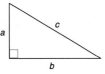

Simplify. Use absolute value symbols when necessary. Exact and approximate answers are given.

11. $\sqrt{40}$ $2\sqrt{10}$, 6.32   12. $\sqrt{72} \cdot \sqrt{48}$ $24\sqrt{6}$, 58.79   13. $\sqrt{54x^4y}$ $3x^2\sqrt{6y}$, $7.35x^2\sqrt{y}$

14. $\sqrt{45xy^3}$ $3|y|\sqrt{5xy}$, 6.71$|y|\sqrt{xy}$ 15. $\sqrt{\frac{32}{25}}$ $\frac{4}{5}\sqrt{2}$, 1.13   16. $\sqrt{\frac{3x^2}{4n^3}}$ $\frac{|x|\sqrt{3n}}{2n^2}$, $\frac{0.87|x|\sqrt{n}}{n^2}$

17. $\frac{7}{7+\sqrt{5}}$ $\frac{49-7\sqrt{5}}{44}$, 0.76   18. $3\sqrt{50} - 2\sqrt{8}$ $11\sqrt{2}$, 15.56   19. $\sqrt{6} + \sqrt{\frac{2}{3}}$ $\frac{4}{3}\sqrt{6}$, 3.27

20. $2\sqrt{27} + \sqrt{63} - 4\sqrt{3}$ $2\sqrt{3} + 3\sqrt{7}$, 11.4   21. $(4 + \sqrt{5})(4 - \sqrt{5})$ 11   22. $\sqrt{2}(\sqrt{18} + 4\sqrt{3})$ $6 + 4\sqrt{6}$, 15.80

Solve each equation. Check the solutions.

23. $\sqrt{t} + 5 = 3$ no real solution   24. $\sqrt{5x^2 - 9} = 2x$ 3   25. $\sqrt{4x + 1} = 5$ 6   26. $\sqrt{4x - 3} = 6 - x$ 3

Find the distance between each pair of points whose coordinates are given.

27. $(4, 7), (4, -2)$ 9   28. $(-9, 2), (3, -3)$ 13   29. $(-1, 1), (1, -5)$ $2\sqrt{10}$, 6.32

30. **Geometry** Find the measures of the perimeter and the area, in simplest form, for the rectangle shown at the right.

31. Find the value of a if the distance between the points $(8, 1), (5, a)$ is 5 units. 5 or -3

32. **Geometry** The length of a rectangle is 4 times its width. Find the dimensions of the rectangle if its area is 224 cm².

33. **Construction** Khoa wants a 12-foot ladder to reach a window 10 feet from the base of a wall. How far out from the base of the wall should he position the bottom of the ladder? $\sqrt{44}$ ft $\approx$ 6.63 ft

$2\sqrt{32} - 3\sqrt{6}$

$\sqrt{6}$

98,304$\sqrt{3}$ cm³,
Bonus 170,267.52 cm³
The diagonal of a cube is 96 cm long. What is the volume of the cube?

Test Generator Software is provided in both Apple and IBM versions. You may use this software to create your own tests, based on the needs of your students.

Additional Answers

30. $16\sqrt{2} - 4\sqrt{6}$, 12.83;
    $16\sqrt{3} - 18$, 9.71

32. $2\sqrt{14}$ cm by $8\sqrt{14}$ cm or 7.48 cm by 29.93 cm

---

Using the Chapter Test

This page may be used as a test or as a review. In addition, two multiple-choice tests and two free-response tests are provided in the Evaluation Masters Booklet. Chapter 12 Test, Form 1A is shown below.

Evaluation Masters Booklet, pp. 155-156

NAME _____ DATE _____

Chapter 12 Test, Form 1A

Write the letter for the correct answer in the blank at the right of each problem.

1. Simplify $\pm \sqrt{.0196}$.
   A. ± 1.4 B. ± 0.14 C. ± 0.014 D. ± 0.0014 1. B

2. Simplify $\sqrt{\frac{81}{256}}$.
   A. $\frac{9}{16}$ B. $\pm \frac{9}{16}$ C. $\frac{3}{4}$ D. $\pm \frac{3}{4}$ 2. A

3. Which number is irrational?
   A. $\sqrt{\frac{4}{9}}$ B. 9.737737773…
   C. 8.888…   D. They are all irrational.   3. B

4. Use a calculator to find $\sqrt{53.23}$ to the nearest hundredth.
   A. 8.00   B. 7.20   C. 7.29   D. 7.30   4. D

5. Simplify $6\sqrt{7} \cdot 2\sqrt{7}$.
   A. 56   B. 588   C. $12\sqrt{7}$ D. 84   5. D

6. Simplify $\sqrt{18n^3y^2}$.
   A. $3n|y|\sqrt{2n}$ B. $2|n|y\sqrt{3n}$ C. $3n|y|\sqrt{2n}$ D. $2n|y|\sqrt{3n}$ 6. A

7. The skid marks at the scene of an accident were 45 feet long. What was the speed of the car, to the nearest whole number, before the brakes were applied? Use the formula $s = \sqrt{24d}$, where s is the speed in miles per hour and d is the length of the skid marks in feet.
   A. 69 mi/h   B. 81 mi/h   C. 33 mi/h   D. 54 mi/h   7. C

8. Simplify $\sqrt{252}$.
   A. $7\sqrt{6}$ B. $7\sqrt{36}$ C. $6\sqrt{7}$ D. $36\sqrt{7}$ 8. C

9. The length of a rectangle is $\sqrt{12}$ and the width is $\sqrt{7} - \sqrt{6}$. What is the exact measure of the area in simplest form?
   A. $\sqrt{84} - \sqrt{72}$ B. $\sqrt{12}$ C. $2\sqrt{21} - 2\sqrt{18}$ D. $2\sqrt{21} - 2\sqrt{18}$ 9. C

10. Simplify $\sqrt{\frac{48}{y^2}}$.
    A. $4y\sqrt{3}$ B. $4|y|\sqrt{3}$ C. $\frac{4\sqrt{3}}{y}$ D. $\frac{4\sqrt{3}}{|y|}$ 10. D

11. Simplify $\sqrt{\frac{3}{16}} \cdot \sqrt{\frac{4}{3}}$.
    A. $\sqrt{\frac{1}{4}}$ B. $\frac{\sqrt{3}}{24}$ C. $\frac{1}{2}$ D. $\frac{1}{4}$ 11. C

12. Simplify. $\frac{3}{4 - \sqrt{13}}$
    A. $\frac{\sqrt{13}}{-3}$ B. $\frac{12 + 3\sqrt{13}}{29}$ C. $4 + \sqrt{13}$ D. $\frac{12 - 3\sqrt{13}}{29}$ 12. C

13. What is the product of $2\sqrt{7} + 3\sqrt{5}$ and its conjugate?
    A. $4\sqrt{7} - 9\sqrt{5}$ B. 73   C. -29 D. -17 13. D

NAME _____ DATE _____

Chapter 12 Test, Form 1A (continued)

14. Simplify $5\sqrt{7} - \sqrt{7}$.
    A. $4\sqrt{7}$ B. -35 C. 5   D. $-5\sqrt{7}$ 14. A

15. Which expression cannot be simplified?
    A. $5\sqrt{8} + 6\sqrt{2}$ B. $5\sqrt{10} + 3\sqrt{5}$
    C. $7\sqrt{48} + \sqrt{108}$ D. $\sqrt{52} + \sqrt{13}$ 15. B

16. Simplify $\sqrt{18} - \sqrt{54} + 2\sqrt{50}$.
    A. $13\sqrt{2} - 3\sqrt{6}$ B. $-4\sqrt{3} + 4\sqrt{5}$
    C. $-4\sqrt{3} - 4\sqrt{5}$ D. $8\sqrt{2} - 3\sqrt{6}$ 16. A

17. Simplify $\sqrt{15} + \sqrt{\frac{3}{5}}$.
    A. $\frac{2\sqrt{15}}{5}$ B. $\frac{6\sqrt{15}}{5}$ C. $2\sqrt{3}$ D. $\frac{\sqrt{15}}{5}$ 17. B

18. Solve $\sqrt{3n + 1} + 3 = 7$.
    A. $\{13\}$ B. $\{\frac{1}{3}\}$ C. $\{-1, \frac{1}{3}\}$ D. $\{5\}$ 18. D

19. Solve $\sqrt{3a + 28} = a$.
    A. $\{-4\}$ B. $\{7\}$ C. $\{7, -4\}$ D. no solution   19. B

20. Which equation has no real solution?
    A. $\sqrt{6x - 8} = -6$ B. $\sqrt{6x - 8} = 6$
    C. $\sqrt{6x - 8} = -6$ D. $\sqrt{6x - 8} = 6$ 20. C

21. The legs of a right triangle have lengths of a and b. The hypotenuse has a length of c. If $a = \sqrt{8}$ and $c = 9$, then what is the length of b?
    A. $\sqrt{17}$ B. $\sqrt{89}$ C. $\sqrt{73}$ D. 1   21. C

22. Which of the following are measures of three sides of a right triangle?
    A. 4, 7, 8   B. 10, 15, 20   C. 3, 7, 9   D. 9, 12, 15   22. D

23. What is the length of the diagonal of a rectangle with length of 12 meters and width of 5 meters?
    A. 169 meters   B. 13 meters   C. $\sqrt{17}$ meters   D. $\sqrt{119}$ meters   23. B

24. What is the distance between $(-3, 4)$ and $(2, 7)$?
    A. $\sqrt{34}$ B. $\sqrt{74}$ C. $2\sqrt{30}$ D. $\sqrt{10}$ 24. A

25. Numerical values, especially those involving approximations, are most often presented in
    A. circle graphs.   B. tables.
    C. bar graphs.   D. line graphs.   25. B

Bonus: Simplify $\sqrt{4x^2 + 12x + 9}$.   **Bonus:** $|2x + 3|$

CHAPTER

12 College Entrance Exam Preview

The test questions on these pages deal with coordinates and geometry. The figures shown may not be drawn to scale.

Directions: Choose the best answer. Write A, B, C, or D.

1. The midpoint of $\overline{AB}$ is M. If the coordinates of A are $(-3, 2)$ and the coordinates of M are $(-1, 5)$, what are the coordinates of B?
   B
   (A) (1, 10)   (B) (1, 8)
   (C) (0, 7)   (D) (-5, 8)

2.

$$\begin{array}{c} S \qquad\qquad T \\ \end{array}$$
   -2 -1 0 1 2 3 4

   The length of $\overline{ST}$ is

   (A) 5   (B) $4\frac{1}{2}$ (C) $5\frac{1}{2}$ (D) 6

3. What is the area of the shaded triangle in square units?
   B
   (A) 12   (B) $12\sqrt{3}$
   (C) $24\sqrt{3}$ (D) 24

4. Seven squares of the same size form a rectangle when placed side by side. The perimeter of the rectangle is 496. What is the area of each square?
   D
   (A) 72 ft²   (B) 324 ft²
   (C) 900 ft²   (D) 961 ft²

5. What is the total length of fencing needed to enclose a rectangular area 46 feet by 34 feet?
   D
   (A) 26 yards 1 foot
   (B) $26\frac{2}{3}$ yards
   (C) 52 yards 2 feet
   (D) $53\frac{1}{3}$ yards

6. The number of degrees in the smaller angle formed by the hands of a clock at 12:15 is
   B
   (A) 120   (B) $82\frac{1}{2}$ (C) $92\frac{1}{2}$ (D) 90

7. The length of each side of a square is $\frac{3}{5}x + 1$. The perimeter of the square is
   A
   (A) $\frac{12x + 20}{5}$ (B) $\frac{12x + 4}{5}$
   (C) $\frac{3x + 4}{5}$ (D) $\frac{3}{5}x + 16$

8. If a line passes through point $(0, 2)$ and has a slope of 4, what is the equation of the line?
   C
   (A) $x = 2y + 4$ (B) $x = 4y + 2$
   (C) $y = 4x + 2$ (D) $y = 2x + 4$

9. The larger circle has a diameter of b. The area of the shaded ring in square units is
   C

   (A) $b^2 - c^2$ (B) $\pi b^2 - \pi c^2$
   (C) $\frac{1}{4}\pi(b^2 - c^2)$ (D) $\frac{1}{2}(b^2 - c^2)$

10. If a circle of radius 10 meters has its radius decreased by 2 meters, by what percent is its area decreased?
    D
    (A) 20%   (B) 40%   (C) 80%   (D) 36%

11. What is the value of
B   x if the area of the
    triangle is $\frac{1}{4}$ the
    area of the square?

(A) $\sqrt{2}$ (B) $2\sqrt{2}$ (C) 4   (D) 8

12. The slope of the line passing through
A   the points (2, −5) and (−4, 7) is

(A) −2   (B) −1   (C) $\frac{-1}{2}$ (D) 2

13. The coordinates of the x-intercept of
D   the line with equation $3x + 4y = 12$ is

(A) (0, 3)   (B) (3, 0)

(C) (0, 4)   (D) (4, 0)

14. The area of the triangle formed by
A   the x-axis, the y-axis and the line
    $y = 2x − 3$ is

(A) $\frac{9}{4}$ (B) $\frac{9}{2}$ (C) 9   (D) 36

15. The area of the square is 64 and the
A   perimeter of each of the two
    congruent triangles is 20. What is the
    perimeter of the figure?

(A) 40   (B) 48   (C) 56   (D) 104

16. The ratio of the area of a circle to its
B   circumference is

(A) $\frac{2}{r}$ (B) $\frac{r}{2}$ (C) π (D) $\frac{\pi}{2r}$

17. Find the slope of the line that is
D   perpendicular to the line
    $2x − 3y = 12$.

(A) $\frac{2}{3}$ (B) $-\frac{2}{3}$ (C) $\frac{3}{2}$ (D) $-\frac{3}{2}$

18. What are the coordinates of the
A   intersection of the lines whose
    equations are $x − 2y = 6$ and
    $3x + 4y = 4$?

(A) (2, −2)   (B) (2, 2)
(C) (−2, 2)   (D) (−2, −2)

TEST TAKING TIP

Although most of the basic formulas that you need to answer the questions on a standardized test are usually given to you in the test booklet, it is a good idea to review the formulas beforehand.

The area of a circle with radius r is πr^2.

The area of a triangle is the product of $\frac{1}{2}$ the base and the height.

The perimeter of a rectangle is twice the sum of its length and width.

The circumference of a circle with radius r is $2\pi r$.

The coordinates of the midpoint, (x, y) of a line segment whose endpoints are at (x_1, y_1) and (x_2, y_2) are

$$(x, y) = \left(\frac{x_1 + x_2}{2}, \frac{y_1 + y_2}{2}\right).$$

CHAPTER 13

Quadratics

PREVIEWING THE CHAPTER

The chapter introduces students to quadratic equations by having them find the equation of the axis of symmetry and the coordinates of the vertex, and then using these to graph the quadratic equation and approximate the roots of the equation. Students next learn to solve a quadratic equation by completing the square and then generalize the method to develop and use the quadratic formula. Students then focus on the discriminant and note how it can be used to determine the number of real roots of an equation. The chapter concludes with a lesson on applications involving quadratic equations.

Problem-Solving Strategy Students learn to use the strategy of *identifying subgoals* to solve multi-step problems.

Lesson Objective Chart

Lesson (Pages)	Lesson Objectives	State/Local Objectives
13-1 (518-522)	**13-1A:** Find the equation of the axis of symmetry and the coordinates of the vertex of the graph of a quadratic function.	
	13-1B: Graph quadratic functions.	
13-2 (523-526)	**13-2:** Find the roots of a quadratic equation by graphing.	
13-3 (527-529)	**13-3:** Solve problems by identifying subgoals.	
13-4 (531-535)	**13-4:** Solve quadratic equations by completing the square.	
13-5 (536-540)	**13-5:** Solve quadratic equations by using the quadratic formula.	
13-6 (541-545)	**13-6:** Evaluate the discriminant of a quadratic equation to determine the nature of the roots of the equation.	
13-7 (546-549)	**13-7:** Solve problems that can be represented by quadratic equations.	
13-8 (550-553)	**13-8A:** Find the sum and product of the roots of a quadratic equation.	
	13-8B: Write a quadratic equation given its roots.	

ORGANIZING THE CHAPTER

You may want to refer to the **Course Planning Calendar** on page T36.

Lesson Planning Guide

Blackline Masters Booklets

Lesson (Pages)	Pacing Chart (days) Course I	II	III	Reteaching	Practice	Enrichment	Evaluation	Technology	Lab Manual	Mixed Problem Solving	Applications	Cooperative Learning Activity	Multicultural	Transparencies
13-1 (518-522)	1.5	1.5	1.5	p. 87	p. 98	p. 87		p. 28	pp. 41-42	p. 13				13-1
13-2 (523-526)	1	1	1	p. 88	p. 99	p. 88	Quiz A, p. 177							13-2
13-3 (527-529)	1.5	1	1		p. 100									13-3
13-4 (531-535)	1.5	1.5	1.5	p. 89	p. 101	p. 89	Quiz B, p. 177 Mid-Chapter Test, p. 181							13-4
13-5 (536-540)	1.5	1.5	1	p. 90	p. 102	p. 90		p. 13			p. 28			13-5
13-6 (541-545)	1.5	1.5	1	p. 91	p. 103	p. 91	Quiz C, p. 178					p. 43		13-6
13-7 (546-549)	1	1	1	p. 92	p. 104	p. 92							p. 58	13-7
13-8 (550-553)	1.5	1	1	p. 93	p. 105	p. 93	Quiz D, p. 178							13-8
Review (554-556)	1	1	1	Multiple Choice Tests, Forms 1A and 1B, pp. 169-172 Free Response Tests, Forms 2A and 2B, pp. 173-176										
Test (557)	1	1	1	Cumulative Review, pp. 179-180 Standardized Test Practice Questions, p. 182										

Course I: Chapters 1-13; Course II: Chapters 1-14; Course III: Chapters 1-15

Other Chapter Resources

Student Edition

Cooperative Learning Activity, p. 529
Technology, p. 530
Mid-Chapter Review, p. 540
History Connection, p. 549
Algebraic Skills Review,
   p. 662 (ex. 74-83),
   p. 663 (ex. 53-61)

Teacher Resource Package

Activity Masters Booklet
   Mixed Problem Solving, p. 13
   Applications, p. 28
   Cooperative Learning Activity, p. 43
   Multicultural Activity, p. 58
Technology Masters Booklet
   Scientific Calculator Activity, p. 13
   Graphing Calculator Activity, p. 28
Lab Manual
   Lab Activity, pp. 41-42

Other Supplements

Transparency for Chapter Opener
Problem-of-the-Week Activity
   Cards, 30-31
Video Algebra, 54-57

Software

Algebra 1 Test and Review
   Generator Software
   Available for Apple and IBM.

ENHANCING THE CHAPTER

Cooperative Learning

Intervening to Teach Cooperative-Learning Skills

In many of their other activities, both inside and outside of school, students are required to compete more often than to cooperate. Therefore, it may require some time and attention for students to develop positive group skills. Experienced researchers recommend that only a few of these skills be taught each semester. Each new skill should be clearly defined before the session begins and skills that were introduced earlier reviewed. Then, after the session begins, the teacher should monitor the groups and intervene when appropriate. Remember to intervene only when necessary and then in a positive manner. Once students recognize the need for the skill, they only need help with developing it. This involves the teacher including examples of expected behavior when the skill is first defined and then offering appropriate guidance and feedback as students practice the skill during their cooperative-learning sessions. After each session, you also should provide time for the students to discuss and assess their behaviors. To motivate the discussion, you can simply ask each group to list the two things they did better this time than the last time and the one thing they plan to do better the next time.

Technology

In this chapter, there is a feature on graphing quadratic equations. This section will help students to be able to recognize the graph of a quadratic function and its general shape, and it will also teach them how certain changes in a quadratic equation will affect the shape of the graph of a quadratic equation. This section will also help in solving quadratic equations by finding the point(s) where the graph crosses the x-axis (if there are any). This can be used to solve the quadratic equation, or it can be used to check their work if they solved the equation in a different way.

Critical Thinking

Opportunities should be provided for *all* students to develop their critical-thinking skills. Having them work with partners or in small, heterogeneous groups provides a support system as they endeavor to seek alternatives, move away from the obvious, produce a large number of ideas, take different approaches, embellish ideas, take a guess, build mental images, and develop the courage to expose oneself to failure and defend one's own ideas. Ample research shows that inspiring all students to think at a higher level gives dignity to their efforts in mathematics, leads them to remember concepts longer, and inspires them to develop a lifelong enthusiasm for learning.

Cooperative Learning, p. 43

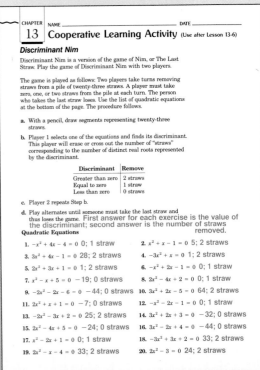

Technology, p. 13

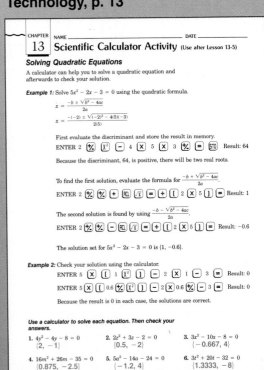

Problem of the Week Activity

'he card shown below is one of two available for this chapter. It can e used as a class or small group activity.

ctivity Card

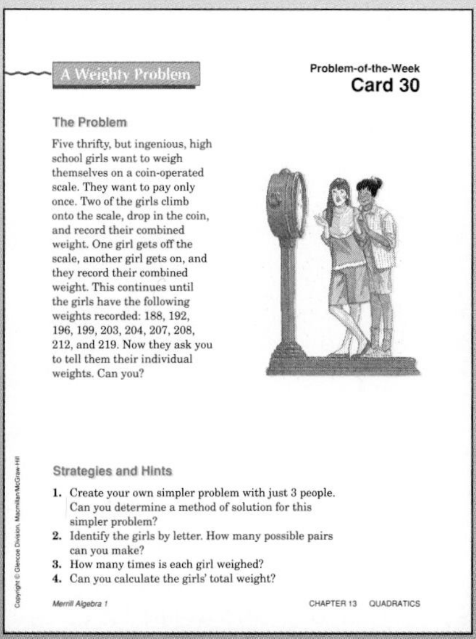

A Weighty Problem

Problem-of-the-Week
Card 30

The Problem

Five thrifty, but ingenious, high school girls want to weigh themselves on a coin-operated scale. They want to pay only once. Two of the girls climb onto the scale, drop in the coin, and record their combined weight. One girl gets off the scale, another girl gets on, and they record their combined weight. This continues until the girls have the following weights recorded: 188, 192, 196, 199, 203, 204, 207, 208, 212, and 219. Now they ask you to tell them their individual weights. Can you?

Strategies and Hints

1. Create your own simpler problem with just 3 people. Can you determine a method of solution for this simpler problem?
2. Identify the girls by letter. How many possible pairs can you make?
3. How many times is each girl weighed?
4. Can you calculate the girls' total weight?

Merrill Algebra 1 CHAPTER 13 QUADRATICS

Multicultural

Multicultural Activity, p. 58

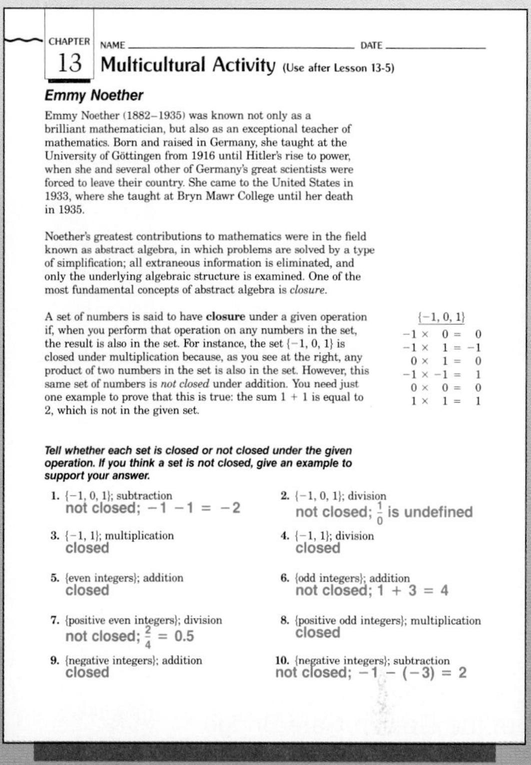

CHAPTER 13 NAME ____ DATE ____

Multicultural Activity (Use after Lesson 13-5)

Emmy Noether

Emmy Noether (1882–1935) was known not only as a brilliant mathematician, but also as an exceptional teacher of mathematics. Born and raised in Germany, she taught at the University of Göttingen from 1916 until Hitler's rise to power, when she and several other of Germany's great scientists were forced to leave their country. She came to the United States in 1933, where she taught at Bryn Mawr College until her death in 1935.

Noether's greatest contributions to mathematics were in the field known as abstract algebra, in which problems are solved by a type of simplification; all extraneous information is eliminated, and only the underlying algebraic structure is examined. One of the most fundamental concepts of abstract algebra is *closure*.

A set of numbers is said to have **closure** under a given operation if, when you perform that operation on any numbers in the set, the result is also in the set. For instance, the set {−1, 0, 1} is closed under multiplication because, as you see at the right, any product of two numbers in the set is also in the set. However, this same set of numbers is *not closed* under addition. You need just one example to prove that this is true: the sum 1 + 1 is equal to 2, which is not in the given set.

{−1, 0, 1}
$-1 \times 0 = 0$
$-1 \times 1 = -1$
$0 \times 1 = 0$
$-1 \times -1 = 1$
$0 \times 0 = 0$
$1 \times 1 = 1$

Tell whether each set is closed or not closed under the given operation. If you think a set is not closed, give an example to support your answer.

1. {−1, 0, 1}; subtraction
not closed; $-1 - 1 = -2$
2. {−1, 0, 1}; division
not closed; $\frac{1}{0}$ is undefined
3. {−1, 1}; multiplication
closed
4. {−1, 1}; division
closed
5. {even integers}; addition
closed
6. {odd integers}; addition
not closed; $1 + 3 = 4$
7. {positive even integers}; division
not closed; $\frac{2}{4} = 0.5$
8. {positive odd integers}; multiplication
closed
9. {negative integers}; addition
closed
10. {negative integers}; subtraction
not closed; $-1 - (-3) = 2$

Manipulatives and Models

'he following materials may be used as models or manipulatives in :hapter 13.

- Ping-Pong® ball (Lesson 13-2)
- string (Lesson 13-2)
- scientific calculator (Lessons 13-4 and 13-5)

Lab Manual

Lab Activity, pp. 41-42

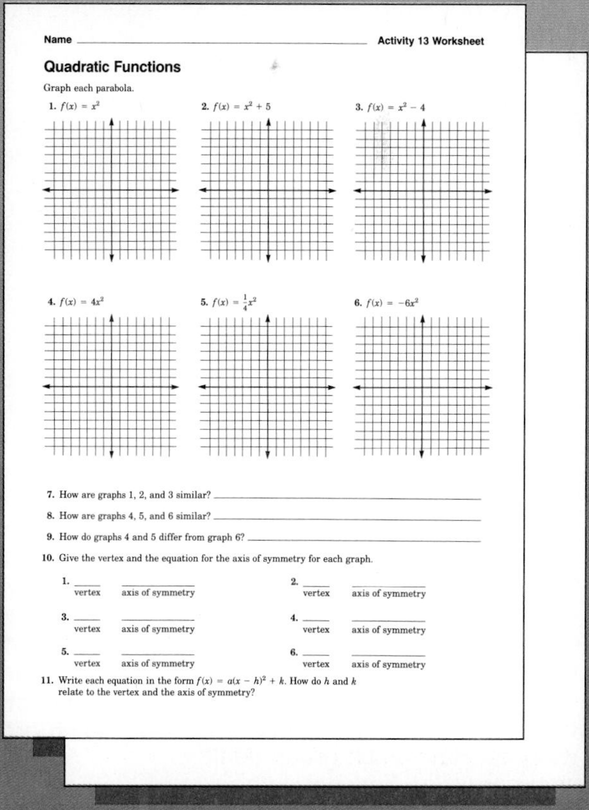

Name ____ Activity 13 Worksheet

Quadratic Functions

Graph each parabola.

1. $f(x) = x^2$
2. $f(x) = x^2 + 5$
3. $f(x) = x^2 - 4$
4. $f(x) = 4x^2$
5. $f(x) = \frac{1}{4}x^2$
6. $f(x) = -6x^2$
7. How are graphs 1, 2, and 3 similar? ____
8. How are graphs 4, 5, and 6 similar? ____
9. How do graphs 4 and 5 differ from graph 6? ____
10. Give the vertex and the equation for the axis of symmetry for each graph.
 1. ____ vertex ____ axis of symmetry
 2. ____ vertex ____ axis of symmetry
 3. ____ vertex ____ axis of symmetry
 4. ____ vertex ____ axis of symmetry
 5. ____ vertex ____ axis of symmetry
 6. ____ vertex ____ axis of symmetry
11. Write each equation in the form $f(x) = a(x - h)^2 + k$. How do h and k relate to the vertex and the axis of symmetry?

Outside Resources

;ooks/Periodicals

owenstein, Dyno. *Graphs, A First Book.* Franklin Watts, Inc.

1itchell, Robert and Donald Prickel. *Number Power 5 - Graphs, Tables, Schedules and Maps.* Contemporary Books, Inc.

ilms/Videotapes/Videodiscs

:ommon Generation of Conics, Educational Solutions, Inc.

Quadratic Functions Parts 1 and 2, MD Center for Public Broadcasting

oftware

;raphing Equations, Sunburst Communications, Inc.

:onic Sections, EduTech

Using the Chapter Opener

Transparency 13-0 is available in the Transparency Package. It provides a full-color visual and motivational activity that you can use to engage students in the mathematical content of the chapter.

Background Information

John August Roebling, a German-born American engineer, constructed the first truly modern suspension bridge. His grand success spanned Niagara Falls in 1855. He then undertook construction of the Brooklyn Bridge in 1867. Roebling had a tragic accident in 1869 and his son assumed responsibility for construction after his death. The Brooklyn Bridge was completed in 1883. The main span (the length between the two towers) of the Verrazano-Narrows Bridge in New York is the longest in the world at 4260 feet. The main span of the Golden Gate Bridge in San Francisco is 4200 feet.

In this chapter, you will:
- Graph quadratic functions.
- Solve quadratic equations.
- Determine the nature of the roots of a quadratic equation.
- Solve problems that can be represented by quadratic equations.
- Solve problems by identifying subgoals.

Chapter Project

Materials: pencil, white posterboard, light chain or string, lead fishing weights

Organize students into cooperative groups of prospective bridge builders. Instruct each group to bring to class a light chain or string, and twelve or more lead fishing weights. Have each group tie its chain or string between two stationary supports (desks, chairs, and so on) so that it hangs loosely in the form of a catenary curve. The distance between supports should equal the length of a posterboard. Have each group bring its posterboard up to the chain or string and draw the curve onto the posterboard. Then, instruct each group to tie its weights along the chain or string at equal intervals, as in a suspension bridge. Again, have each group draw the resulting parabolic curve onto its posterboard. Finally, have each group evaluate and report the difference between the first catenary curve and the second parabolic curve.

Quadratics

APPLICATION IN CONSTRUCTION

The longest bridge in the world is the Humber suspension bridge in Hull, England. Its main span is 1410 meters long, which is over 860 meters longer than the longest non-suspension bridge, the Quebec Railway cantilever bridge in Canada. In fact, there are 22 suspension bridges that are longer than the Quebec Railway bridge. Why can suspension bridges be built so much longer than other types of bridges? The answer lies in the shape of the cables connecting the towers on these bridges.

When you hang a cable between two supports and then attach weights at equal intervals along the cable, the curve of the cable has the shape of a *parabola*. The cable between two towers of a suspension bridge has a parabolic shape since the shorter cables attached to this cable are equally spaced between the towers. The weight of the bridge exerts tension on the cable, which in turn exerts an inward pull on the towers holding the cable. This method of distributing the bridge's weight allows for a greater distance between the supporting towers.

ALGEBRA IN ACTION

Another shape often used in construction is the *catenary*, which looks very much like a parabola. A cable has the shape of a catenary when it is hung loosely between two supports and *no* weights are attached.

catenary

parabola

Research the following structures to see if they have the shape of a catenary or the shape of a parabola.

a. Memorial Arch
   catenary

b. Golden Gate Bridge
   parabola

The suspension bridge is one of the oldest engineering forms. As early as the 4th century A.D., these bridges were built by using vines for cables and placing the roadway directly on the cables.

Lesson	Connections (C) and Applications (A)		Examples	Exercises
13-1	A:	Finance	2	44
		Physics		43
		Agriculture		45
		Consumerism		46
13-2	C:	Number Theory	2	20-21
		Statistics		39
	A:	Diving		37
		Physics		38
		Construction		43
13-3	C:	Number Theory		6
	A:	Manufacturing	1	
13-4	C:	Geometry		35, 43
		Number Theory		48
	A:	Construction	4	44
		Photography		45
		Travel		46
		Consumerism		47
13-5	A:	Physics	2	50, 56
		Finance		51
13-6	C:	Geometry	2	38, 51
	A:	Physics		43
		Consumerism		44
		Sales		46
		Business		48
13-7	C:	Geometry	1	34, 37
		Number Theory		25-26
	A:	Manufacturing	2	
		Construction		27
		Gardening		28
		Physics		29
		Framing		30
		Mowing		31
		Sales		32
		Work		35
13-8	A:	Physics	3	48, 55
		Finance		49
		Uniform Motion		53

517

13-1

Graphing Quadratic Functions

Lesson Resources

- Reteaching Master 13-1
- Practice Master 13-1
- Enrichment Master 13-1
- Technology Master, p. 28
- Lab Manual, pp. 41-42
- Activity Master, p. 13
- Video Algebra, p. 57

 Transparency 13-1 contains the 5-Minute Check and a teaching aid for this lesson.

INTRODUCING THE LESSON

 5-Minute Check

(over Chapter 12)

Simplify.

1. $-\sqrt{64}$ -8
2. $\sqrt{900}$ 30
3. $\sqrt{700}$ $10\sqrt{7}$
4. $\sqrt{99a^3b^7}$ $3ab^3\sqrt{11ab}$
5. $\sqrt{3} \cdot \sqrt{15}$ $3\sqrt{5}$

Motivating the Lesson

Ask students to describe a parabola. Have a volunteer draw this plane curve on the chalkboard. Ask students to identify common objects that have this shape. Possible examples include a satellite dish and an automobile headlight.

Objectives
13-1A
13-1B

After studying this lesson, you should be able to:
- find the equation of the axis of symmetry and the coordinates of the vertex of the graph of a quadratic function, and
- graph quadratic functions.

Application

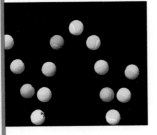

The path of an object when it is thrown or dropped is called the *trajectory* of the object. A bouncing object, like the tennis ball in the photo, will have a trajectory in a general shape called a **parabola.**

The path of this tennis ball, between its first and second bounces, is given by the equation $y = 6x - 0.5x^2$. In this equation, y is the height of the ball in inches, and x is the horizontal distance of the ball in inches, from the spot of its first bounce. A graph of this equation is shown at the right.

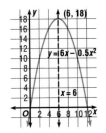

Equations such as $y = 6x - 0.5x^2$ and $y = x^2 - 4x + 1$ describe a type of function known as a **quadratic function.**

Definition of Quadratic Function	A quadratic function is a function that can be described by an equation of the form $y = ax^2 + bx + c$, where $a \neq 0$.

Graphs of quadratic functions have certain common characteristics. For instance, they all have the general shape of a parabola. The table and graph below can be used to illustrate other common characteristics of quadratic functions. Notice the matching values in the y-column of the table.

x	$x^2 - 4x + 1$	y
-1	$(-1)^2 - 4(-1) + 1$	6
0	$0^2 - 4(0) + 1$	1
1	$1^2 - 4(1) + 1$	-2
2	$2^2 - 4(2) + 1$	-3
3	$3^2 - 4(3) + 1$	-2
4	$4^2 - 4(4) + 1$	1
5	$5^2 - 4(5) + 1$	6

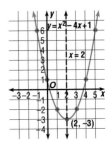

ALTERNATE TEACHING STRATEGIES

Using Discussion

Have students graph $y = x^2$, $y = x^2 - 4$, and $y = (x + 2)^2 + 5$. Ask students to identify the minimum points of each graph.
$(0, 0)$, $(0, -4)$, $(-2, 5)$
Have students predict the minimum point of $y = x^2 + 7$. $(0, 7)$

Using Problem Solving

Ask students to predict whether the graph of $y = \frac{1}{3}x^2$ will be narrower or wider than the graph of $y = x^2$. Then have students graph each equation to check the accuracy of their predictions.

Notice that in the y-column of the table, -3 does not have a matching value. Also, notice that -3 is the y-coordinate of the lowest point of the graph. The point $(2, -3)$ is the *lowest point*, or **minimum point**, of the graph of $y = x^2 - 4x + 1$. For the graph of $y = 6x - 0.5x^2$ on page 518, the point $(6, 18)$ is the *highest point*, or **maximum point**. The maximum point or minimum point of a parabola is also called the **vertex** of the parabola.

The graph of a quadratic function will have a minimum point or a maximum point but not both.

The vertical line containing the vertex of a parabola is called the **axis of symmetry** for the graph. Thus, the equation of the axis of symmetry for the graph of $y = x^2 - 4x + 1$ is $x = 2$.

Teaching Tip ➊

In general, the equation of the axis of symmetry for the graph of a quadratic function can be found by using the following rule.

Equation of the Axis of Symmetry	The equation of the axis of symmetry for the graph of $y = ax^2 + bx + c$, where $a \neq 0$, is $x = -\dfrac{b}{2a}$.

Example 1

Find the equation of the axis of symmetry and the coordinates of the vertex of the graph of $y = x^2 - x - 6$. Then use the information to draw the graph.

First, find the equation of the axis of symmetry.

$$x = -\frac{b}{2a}$$
$$= -\left(\frac{-1}{2 \cdot 1}\right) \quad \text{For } y = x^2 - x - 6, \\ a = 1 \text{ and } b = -1.$$
$$= \frac{1}{2}$$

Next, find the vertex. Since the equation of the axis of symmetry is $x = \frac{1}{2}$, the x-coordinate of the vertex must be $\frac{1}{2}$. You can find the y-coordinate by substituting $\frac{1}{2}$ for x in $y = x^2 - x - 6$.

$$y = \left(\frac{1}{2}\right)^2 - \frac{1}{2} - 6$$
$$= \frac{1}{4} - \frac{1}{2} - 6 \text{ or } -\frac{25}{4}$$

The point $\left(\frac{1}{2}, -\frac{25}{4}\right)$ is the vertex of the graph. *This point is a minimum.*

Finally, construct a table. For values of x, be sure to choose some integers greater than $\frac{1}{2}$ and some less than $\frac{1}{2}$. This insures that points on each side of the axis of symmetry are plotted.

x	$x^2 - x - 6$	y
-2	$(-2)^2 - (-2) - 6$	0
-1	$(-1)^2 - (-1) - 6$	-4
0	$0^2 - 0 - 6$	-6
1	$1^2 - 1 - 6$	-6
2	$2^2 - 2 - 6$	-4
3	$3^2 - 3 - 6$	0

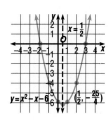

Teaching Tip ➊   The axis of symmetry is helpful for determining which elements of the domain to choose when graphing a function.

Chalkboard Example

For Example 1
Find the equation of the axis of symmetry and the coordinates of the vertex of the graph of each equation.

a. $y = x^2 - 4x - 5$
   $x = 2$; $(2, -9)$

b. $y = -x^2 + 2x - 1$
   $x = 1$; $(1, 0)$

c. $y = -x^2 - 6x + 10$
   $x = -3$; $(-3, 19)$

d. $y = x^2 + 8x + 13$
   $x = -4$; $(-4, -3)$

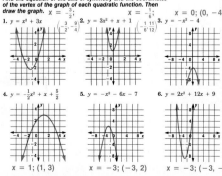

Look at the graph in Example 1. If this graph is folded along its axis of symmetry, the two halves of the graph would coincide. In other words, the two halves of the parabola are *symmetric* with respect to the axis of symmetry. This is true for the graph of any quadratic function.

In general, a graph of a quadratic function will have a minimum point and open *upward* when the coefficients of y and x^2 have the same sign. The graph will have a maximum point and open *downward* when the coefficients of y and x^2 have opposite signs. Also, the vertex of the graph *always* lies on the axis of symmetry.

Example 2

APPLICATION
Finance

A movie theater has seats for 1200 people and has been filled to capacity for almost every showing. Tickets currently cost $5.00 and the owner wants to increase this price. She estimates that for each $0.50 increase in the ticket price, 100 fewer people will attend each showing. Based on this estimate, what ticket price will maximize her income?

EXPLORE Let x = the number of $0.50 price increases.
Then, $5.00 + 0.50x$ = the ticket price, and
$1200 - 100x$ = the number of tickets sold for one showing.
Finally, let y = the income from one showing.

PLAN

Income	is	number of tickets sold	times	ticket price.

$$y = (1200 - 100x) \times (5.00 + 0.50x)$$
$$= 6000 + 600x - 500x - 50x^2$$
$$= -50x^2 + 100x + 6000$$

SOLVE Notice that the result is a quadratic function. Since the coefficients of y and x^2 have opposite signs, the graph of $y = -50x^2 + 100x + 6000$ has a *maximum* point. The x-coordinate of this maximum point will indicate the number of $0.50 price increases needed to maximize the income.

Since the vertex of the graph lies on the axis of symmetry, its x-coordinate is given by the equation of the axis of symmetry.

$$x = -\frac{b}{2a}$$
$$= -\left(\frac{100}{2(-50)}\right) \quad a = -50, \quad b = 100$$
$$= 1$$

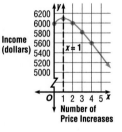

The equation of the axis of symmetry is x = 1.

The income is maximized when the owner makes one $0.50 price increase. Thus, the ticket price should be 5.00 + 0.50(1) or $5.50. *Examine this solution by trying other values of x in the income equation to see if the income can be greater than $[1200 - 100(1)] \cdot [5.00 + 0.50(1)]$ or $6050.*

520   CHAPTER 13   QUADRATICS

CHECKING FOR UNDERSTANDING

Communicating Mathematics

Complete.

1. The graphs of all quadratic functions have a general shape called a ___?___. **parabola**

2. The vertex of a parabola is the ___?___ point or the ___?___ point of the graph. **maximum, minimum**

3. The two halves of a parabola are ___?___ with respect to its axis of symmetry. **symmetric**

4. The graph of $y = ax^2 + 3x + 5$ has a maximum point if a is ___?___. **negative**

Guided Practice

State whether the graph of each quadratic function opens upward or downward.

5. $y = x^2 - 1$ **up**

6. $y = -x^2 + x + 1$ **down**

7. $y = -5x^2 - 3x + 2$ **down**

8. $y = 2x^2 + 5x - 2$ **up**

Find the equation of the axis of symmetry of the graph of each quadratic function. **9. $x = -\frac{1}{2}$**

9. $y = x^2 + x + 3$

10. $y = -x^2 + 4x + 5$
$x = 2$

11. $y = 3x^2 + 6x + 16$
$x = -1$

Find the coordinates of the vertex of the graph of each quadratic equation.

12. $y = x^2 + 6x + 8$
$(-3, -1)$

13. $y = -x^2 + 3x$ $\left(\frac{3}{2}, \frac{9}{4}\right)$

14. $y = 5x^2 - 20x + 37$
$(2, 17)$

EXERCISES

Practice

Find the equation of the axis of symmetry and the coordinates of the vertex of the graph of each quadratic function. **See margin.**

15. $y = -x^2 + 5x + 6$

16. $y = x^2 - 4x + 13$

17. $y = x^2 + 2x$

18. $y = -3x^2 + 4$

19. $y = 3x^2 + 24x + 80$

20. $y = -4x^2 + 8x + 13$

21–32. See margin.

Find the equation of the axis of symmetry and the coordinates of the vertex of the graph of each quadratic function. Then draw the graph.

21. $y = x^2 - 4x - 5$

22. $y = -x^2 + 4x + 5$

23. $y = -x^2 + 6x + 5$

24. $y = x^2 - x - 6$

25. $y = x^2 - 3$

26. $y = -x^2 + 7$

27. $y = 2x^2 + 3$

28. $y = \frac{1}{2}x^2 + 3x + \frac{9}{2}$

29. $y = \frac{1}{4}x^2 - 4x + \frac{15}{4}$

30. $y = -3x^2 - 6x + 4$

31. $y = -1(x - 2)^2 + 1$

32. $y = 3(x + 1)^2 - 20$

The axis of symmetry for a parabola is the y-axis. Given that each point below lies on the graph, find another point that also lies on the graph.

33. $(1, 1)$ $(-1, 1)$

34. $(-3, 17)$ $(3, 17)$

35. $(-4, 0)$ $(4, 0)$

LESSON 13-1 GRAPHING QUADRATIC FUNCTIONS 521

Additional Answers

For the graphs to Exercises 21-32, see the Solutions Manual.

21. $x = 2$; $(2, -9)$

22. $x = 2$; $(2, 9)$

23. $x = 3$; $(3, 14)$

24. $x = \frac{1}{2}$; $\left(\frac{1}{2}, -\frac{25}{4}\right)$

25. $x = 0$; $(0, -3)$

26. $x = 0$; $(0, 7)$

27. $x = 0$; $(0, 3)$

28. $x = -3$; $(-3, 0)$

29. $x = 8$; $\left(8, -\frac{49}{4}\right)$

30. $x = -1$; $(-1, 7)$

31. $x = 2$; $(2, 1)$

32. $x = -1$; $(-1, -20)$

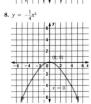

NAME _____ DATE _____

13-1 Practice Worksheet

Graphing Quadratic Functions

Find the equation of the axis of symmetry and the coordinates of the vertex of the graph of each quadratic function.

1. $y = x^2 - 2x - 8$
$x = 1$, $(1, -9)$

2. $y = -x^2 + x + 12$
$x = \frac{1}{2}$, $\left(\frac{1}{2}, \frac{49}{4}\right)$

3. $y = 8x^2 + 12x$
$x = \frac{3}{4}$, $\left(\frac{3}{4}, -\frac{9}{2}\right)$

4. $y = -2x^2 + x + 2$
$x = \frac{1}{4}$, $\left(\frac{1}{4}, \frac{17}{8}\right)$

Find the equation of the axis of symmetry and the coordinates of the vertex of the graph of each quadratic function. Then draw the graph.

5. $y = x^2 - 3x + 2$

6. $y = -x^2 - 2x + 3$

7. $y = x^2 - 2$

8. $y = -\frac{1}{4}x^2$

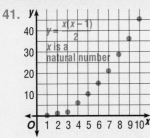
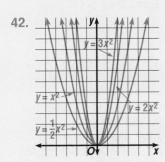
Match each graph with its equation.

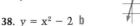

36. $y = x^2 + 2$ **c**   a. (0, 2)   b.   c. (0, 2)

37. $y = -x^2 + 2$ **a**

38. $y = x^2 - 2$ **b**   (0, -2)

39. The x-intercepts of the graph of a quadratic function are -5 and 2. What is the equation of the axis of symmetry for this graph? $x = \frac{-3}{2}$

40. The vertex of the graph of a quadratic function is $(6, 8)$. If one x-intercept of the graph is -1, what is the other x-intercept? **13**

41. The function $y = \frac{x(x - 1)}{2}$ describes the number of handshakes, y, that occur when x different people all shake each other's hands. Graph this function. **See margin.**

Critical Thinking

42. Draw the graphs of $y = \frac{1}{2}x^2$, $y = x^2$, $y = 2x^2$, and $y = 3x^2$ on the same set of axes. Then compare the graphs. **See margin.**

Applications

43. Physics The height h, in feet, that a certain arrow will reach t seconds after being shot directly upward is given by the formula $h = 112t - 16t^2$. What is the maximum height for this arrow? **196 ft**

44. Finance A bus company transports 900 people a day between Morse Rd. and High St. A one-way bus fare is $1.00. The owners estimate that for each $0.10 price increase, 60 passengers will be lost. What should the one-way fare be in order to maximize their income? **$1.25**

45. Agriculture At the beginning of the harvest season, a farmer has 20,000 pounds of potatoes for which the selling price is $9.50 per 100-pound lot. For each week that he waits there will be an additional 1000 pounds to sell, but the selling price will drop by $0.25 per 100 pounds per week. How many weeks should the farmer wait before selling his crop in order to have the greatest possible income? **9 weeks**

Mixed Review

46. Consumerism Julio is offered two payment plans when he buys a sofa. Under one plan, he pays $400 down and x dollars a month for 9 months. Under the other, he pays no money down and x + 25 dollars a month for 12 months. How much did Julio pay for the sofa? **(Lesson 3-6) $700**

47. Graph $3x - 2y \leq 6$. **(Lesson 9-6) See margin.**

48. Write an equation of the line that is parallel to the graph of $-5x + 6y = 12$ and passes through $(-2, -2)$. **(Lesson 10-6)** $-5x + 6y = -2$

49. Use elimination to solve the system of equations $2x + y = 5$ and $-2x + 3y = 7$. **(Lesson 11-4)** $(1, 3)$

50. Find two values for a if the distance between points $(8, 1)$ and $(5, a)$ is 5 units. **(Lesson 12-8)** $5, -3$

522   CHAPTER 13   QUADRATICS

EXTENDING THE LESSON

Math Power: Problem Solving

Graph the following pair of equations on the same coordinate plane. Then compare the graph of the second equation to that of the first equation.
$y = x^2$; $y = (x + 6)^2 - 8$
The second graph is 6 units to the left and 8 units below the first graph.

Additional Answer

47.

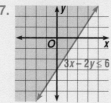

$3x - 2y \leq 6$

Solving Quadratic Equations by Graphing

Objective
13-2

After studying this lesson, you should be able to:
- find the roots of a quadratic equation by graphing.

Application

FYI···

The Chinese first used rockets and firelances in battle in 1100 A.D.

Tonio launched a toy rocket from a point 50 meters above ground level. The height above ground level h, in meters, of the rocket after t seconds is given by the formula $h = 50 + 45t - 5t^2$. How many seconds after the launch will his rocket hit the ground?

When Tonio's rocket hits the ground, the value of h will be 0. Thus, you can solve this problem by solving the quadratic equation $0 = 50 + 45t - 5t^2$. This equation can be solved by using factoring.

$$0 = 50 + 45t - 5t^2$$
$$0 = 5(10 + 9t - t^2)$$
$$0 = 5(10 - t)(1 + t)$$

$10 - t = 0$ or $1 + t = 0$ *Zero product property*
$10 = t$ $t = -1$

Since t represents time, t cannot be negative. Therefore, $t = -1$ is not a solution. Tonio's rocket will hit the ground 10 seconds after launch.

The solutions of the equation $0 = 50 + 45t - 5t^2$ are also called the **roots** of the equation. Notice that the roots, 10 and -1, of this equation are the x-intercepts of the graph of the *related quadratic function*, $h = 50 + 45t - 5t^2$. **Teaching Tip ❶**

x	50 + 45t − 5t²	y
−1	$50 + 45(-1) - 5(-1)^2$	0
0	$50 + 45(0) - 5(0)^2$	50
2	$50 + 45(2) - 5(2)^2$	120
4	$50 + 45(4) - 5(4)^2$	150
5	$50 + 45(5) - 5(5)^2$	150
7	$50 + 45(7) - 5(7)^2$	120
9	$50 + 45(9) - 5(9)^2$	50
10	$50 + 45(10) - 5(10)^2$	0

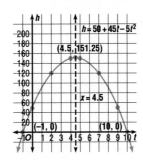

Real roots are roots that are real numbers.

In general, the real roots of any quadratic equation of the form $ax^2 + bx + c = 0$ are the x-intercepts of the graph of the related function $y = ax^2 + bx + c$.

You can always solve a quadratic equation by graphing the related function. However, you may only be able to find approximations of the roots by graphing.

LESSON 13-2 SOLVING QUADRATIC EQUATIONS BY GRAPHING **523**

ALTERNATE TEACHING STRATEGIES

Using Models

Introduce students to the Jordan Curve Theorem through the following activity. Have a volunteer come to the front of the class. Draw a line on the floor and have the students step over it one time, then two times, then three times. Ask the class what would occur if the student stepped over the line 17 times, 30 times, and so on. To end

up on the opposite side of the line, the student must cross it an odd number of times.

Lesson Resources

- Reteaching Master 13-2
- Practice Master 13-2
- Enrichment Master 13-2
- Video Algebra, 57

Transparency 13-2 contains the 5-Minute Check and a teaching aid for this lesson.

INTRODUCING THE LESSON

🕐 **5-Minute Check**
(over Lesson 13-1)

For the graph of each equation, determine whether it has a maximum or minimum point, identify the coordinates of the point, and identify the equation of the line of symmetry.

1. $y = x^2 - 4x + 7$
   minimum, (2, 3), x = 2
2. $y = x^2 + 8x + 11$
   minimum, (−4, −5), x = −4
3. $y = -x^2 + 5$
   maximum, (0, 5), x = 0
4. $y = -x^2 + 2x - 3$
   maximum, (1, −2), x = 1

Motivating the Lesson

Toss a Ping-pong® ball and ask students to describe a curve that approximates the shape of its trajectory. Attach a Ping-pong® ball to each end of a piece of string and have the string hang in a parabolic shape. Remind students that the curve is not a parabola but a catenary which is closely approximated by a parabola. Ask students to identify the axis of symmetry. Challenge them to determine if the axis of symmetry moves when the two Ping-pong® balls remain in the same place and a longer string is used. **Axis of symmetry does not move.**

TEACHING THE LESSON

Teaching Tip ❶ Explain that the x-intercepts are the zeros of the function.

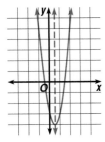
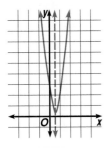
Example 1

Find the roots of $x^2 + 6x + 6 = 0$ by graphing the related function. If exact roots cannot be found, state the consecutive integers between which the roots are located.

The graph of the related function $y = x^2 + 6x + 6$ has a minimum point and opens upward since y and x^2 have the same sign.

axis of symmetry: $x = -\dfrac{b}{2a}$

               $= -\dfrac{6}{2(1)}$ or -3 *For $y = x^2 + 6x + 6$, $a = 1$ and $b = 6$.*

The equation of the axis of symmetry is $x = -3$. *Be sure to find the coordinates of the minimum point by finding the value of y when x is -3.*

x	$x^2 + 6x + 6$	y
−5	$(-5)^2 + 6(-5) + 6$	1
−4	$(-4)^2 + 6(-4) + 6$	−2
−3	$(-3)^2 + 6(-3) + 6$	−3
−2	$(-2)^2 + 6(-2) + 6$	−2
−1	$(-1)^2 + 6(-1) + 6$	1

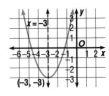

From the graph you can see that one root is between −5 and −4, and the other root is between −2 and −1.

Example 2

Find two real numbers whose sum is 4 and whose product is 5.

EXPLORE   Let x = one of the numbers.
          Then $4 - x$ = the other number.

PLAN   Since the product of the two numbers is 5, you know that $x(4 - x) = 5$.

$$x(4 - x) = 5$$
$$4x - x^2 = 5$$
$$0 = x^2 - 4x + 5$$

SOLVE   You can solve $0 = x^2 - 4x + 5$ by graphing the related function $y = x^2 - 4x + 5$. This graph opens upward and the equation of its axis of symmetry is $x = -\dfrac{-4}{2(1)}$, or $x = 2$.

x	$x^2 - 4x + 5$	y
0	$0^2 - 4(0) + 5$	5
1	$1^2 - 4(1) + 5$	2
2	$2^2 - 4(2) + 5$	1
3	$3^2 - 4(3) + 5$	2
4	$4^2 - 4(4) + 5$	5

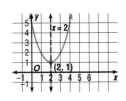

The graph has no x-intercepts since it does not cross the x-axis. This means the equation $x^2 - 4x + 5 = 0$ has no real roots. Thus, it is *not* possible for two real numbers to have a sum of 4 and a product of 5. *Examine this solution.*

RETEACHING THE LESSON

Give students a list of maximum and minimum points of a parabola and have them describe the number of roots of its equation and why.
Example: Minimum point is $(-1, -1)$. There are two roots because the minimum point is below the x-axis and the parabola will open up, therefore crossing the x-axis twice.

CHECKING FOR UNDERSTANDING

Communicating Mathematics

Read and study the lesson to answer each question.

1. What is the related function for the equation $x^2 - 5x + 6 = 0$?
   $y = x^2 - 5x + 6$
2. How can you find the real roots of a quadratic equation given the graph of its related function? **They are the x-intercepts of the graph.**

3. Can you always find the *exact* roots of a quadratic equation by graphing its related function? **no**

Guided Practice

State the roots of each quadratic equation whose related function is graphed below. **−1, 1**   **0, 2**   **no real roots**   **2**

4. 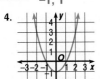   5.   6. 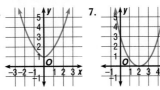   7.

Find the roots of each equation by graphing its related function. If exact roots cannot be found, state the consecutive integers between which the roots are located.

8. $x^2 - x - 12 = 0$ 9. $x^2 + 7x + 12 = 0$ 10. $x^2 - 9 = 0$
   −3, 4   **−3, −4**   **−3, 3**

EXERCISES

Practice

Find the roots of each equation by graphing its related function. If exact roots cannot be found, state the consecutive integers between which the roots are located.   **19. $2 < x < 3, -4 < x < -3$**

A

11. $x^2 - 10x = -21$ **3, 7**   12. $x^2 + 4x = 12$ **−6, 2**   13. $x^2 - 2x + 2 = 0$
                                                                     no real roots

14. $x^2 - 4x + 1 = 0$ 15. $x^2 - 8x + 16 = 0$ **4**   16. $3x^2 + 2x + 4 = 0$
   $0 < x < 1, 3 < x < 4$ **no real roots**

17. $x^2 + 6x = -7$ 18. $6x^2 - 13x = 15$ 19. $4x^2 = 35 - 4x$
   $-5 < x < -4, -2 < x < -1$ **$-1 < x < 0, 3$**

B

CONNECTION
Number Theory

20. Find two real numbers whose sum is 18 and whose product is 81. **9, 9**

21. Find two real numbers whose difference is 6 and whose product is 91.
    −13, −7; 7, 13

Match each equation with the graph of its related function.

22. $x^2 - 3x + 2 = 0$ **c**   a.   b.   c.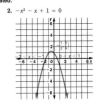

23. $x^2 + x - 2 = 0$ **b**

24. $x^2 - x - 2 = 0$ **a**

LESSON 13-2 SOLVING QUADRATIC EQUATIONS BY GRAPHING   **525**

Additional Answer

36. The value of the function changes from negative when $x = 1$ to positive when $x = 2$. To do this, the value of the function would have to be 0 for some value of x between 1 and 2. Thus, this value of x represents the x-intercept of the function and would therefore be a root of the related equation.

NAME _____ DATE _____

13-2 Enrichment Worksheet

Mechanical Constructions of Parabolas

A given line and a point determine a parabola. Here is one way to construct the curve.

Use a right triangle ABC (or a stiff piece of rectangular cardboard).

Place one leg of the triangle on the given line d. Fasten one end of a string with length BC at the given point F and the other end to the triangle at point B.

Put the tip of a pencil at point P and keep the string tight.

As you move the triangle along the line d, the point of your pencil will trace a parabola.

Draw the parabola determined by line d and point F.

1.
2.
3.
4.

5. Use your drawings to complete this conclusion. The greater the distance of point F from line d, the wider the opening of the parabola.

25–32. See Solutions Manual.
The roots of a quadratic equation are given. Graph the related quadratic function if it has the indicated maximum or minimum point.

25. roots: 2, 6
    minimum point: $(4, -2)$

26. roots: 0, -6
    maximum point: $(-3, 4)$

27. root: -5
    maximum point: $(-5, 0)$

28. roots: no real roots
    minimum point: $(-5, 1)$

29. roots: no real roots
    maximum point: $(3, -2)$

30. root: 2
    minimum point: $(2, 0)$

C 31. roots: $-6 < x < -5, -5, < x < -4$
    minimum point: $(-5, -1)$

32. roots: $-4 < x < -3, 1 < x < 2$
    maximum point: $(-1, 6)$

Locate the y-intercepts of each quadratic relation by graphing.

33. $x = 2y^2 - 8y + 7$
    $1 < y < 2, 2 < y < 3$

34. $x = y^2 - 2y + 3$
    no y-intercepts

35. $x = -\frac{3}{4}y^2 - 6y - 9$
    $-2, -6$

Critical Thinking

36. Suppose the value of a quadratic function is negative when $x = 1$ and positive when $x = 2$. Explain why it is reasonable to assume that the related equation has a root between 1 and 2. **See margin.**

Applications

37. **Diving**   Wendy is diving from a 10-meter platform. Her height h in meters above the water when she is x meters away from the platform is given by the formula $h = -x^2 + 2x + 10$. Approximately how far away from the platform is she when she enters the water? **between 4 meters and 5 meters**

38. **Physics**   The height h in feet of a ball t seconds after being tossed upward is given by the formula $h = 84t - 16t^2$.

    a. After how many seconds will the ball reach a height of 80 feet for the *second* time? **4 seconds**

    b. After how many seconds will it hit the ground? **5.25 seconds**

    c. What is its maximum height? **102.2 feet**

Mixed Review

39. **Statistics**   What is the average of $2b - 4$, $b + 5$, and $3b + 8$? **(Lesson 2-7)** $2b + 3$

40. Write an equation for the relation $\{(-2, 0), (-1, -3), (0, -4), (1, -3), (2, 0)\}$.   **(Lesson 9-7)** $y = x^2 - 4$

41. Determine the slope, y-intercept, and x-intercept of the graph of $2x - 3y = 13$.   **(Lesson 10-3)** $\frac{2}{3}; -\frac{13}{3}, \frac{13}{2}$

42. Simplify $\sqrt{720}$.   **(Lesson 12-5)** $12\sqrt{5}$

43. **Construction**   Muturi has 120 meters of fence to make a rectangular pen for his rabbits. If a shed is used as one side of the pen, what would be the maximum area for the pen?   **(Lesson 13-1)** 1800 m^2

526   CHAPTER 13   QUADRATICS

EXTENDING THE LESSON

Math Power: Connections

Write an equation for the problem described below. Let x represent the measure of the length of the rectangle. Determine the solution to the problem by graphing the related function.

The width of the rectangle is 4 ft less than the length. Find the length of the rectangle if the area is 8.5 ft².   **about 5.5 ft**

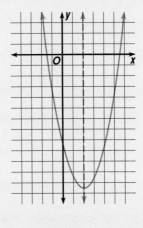

13-3 Problem-Solving Strategy: Identify Subgoals

**Objective
13-3**

After studying this lesson, you should be able to:

■ solve problems by identifying subgoals.

Sometimes finding the solution to a problem requires several steps. An important strategy for solving such problems is to *identify subgoals*. This strategy involves taking steps that will either produce part of the solution or make the problem easier to solve.

Example 1

APPLICATION

Manufacturing

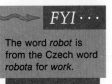

FYI · · ·

The word *robot* is from the Czech word *robota* for work.

Funtime Toys uses robots to assemble their Speedy cars. Three of the robots can assemble 10 cars in 21 minutes. If all the robots assemble cars at the same rate, how many cars can 14 robots assemble in 90 minutes?

Finding an equation to represent this problem will be easier if you develop the equation in steps rather than trying to write one directly from the given information.

Step 1 Determine the rates at which the cars are assembled when 3 robots are working and when 14 robots are working. These two rates can then be used to determine the rate of assembly when 1 robot is working.

$$\text{rate of assembly} = \frac{\text{number of cars assembled}}{\text{time needed to assemble cars}}$$

You know that 3 robots can assemble 10 cars in 21 minutes. Let x = the number of cars that 14 robots can assemble in 90 minutes.

$$\begin{array}{ll}
\text{rate of assembly} \\
\text{for 3 robots} = \frac{10}{21} & \text{rate of assembly} \\
& \text{for 14 robots} = \frac{x}{90} \\[2mm]
\text{rate of assembly} \\
\text{for 1 robot} = \frac{10}{21} \div 3 & \text{rate of assembly} \\
& \text{for 1 robot} = \frac{x}{90} \div 14 \\[2mm]
\qquad = \frac{10}{63} & \qquad = \frac{x}{1260}
\end{array}$$

Step 2 Since all of the robots assemble cars at the same rate, the two rates of assembly for 1 robot must be equal.

$$\frac{10}{63} = \frac{x}{1260}$$

$12600 = 63x$ *Means-extremes property*

$200 = x$

Therefore, 14 robots can assemble 200 cars in 90 minutes.

Step 3 Let's check our solution. There are about 5 times as many robots working for about 4 times as long. Hence, they should assemble about 5 · 4 or 20 times as many cars. Since 10 · 20 = 200, the solution checks.

ALTERNATE TEACHING STRATEGIES

Using Discussion

Develop the idea that there are often many ways of finding a solution to a problem. Encourage students to describe other methods of solving the problems presented in the examples.

Lesson Resources

- Practice Master 13-3
- Video Algebra, 54

 Transparency 13-3 contains the 5-Minute Check and a teaching aid for this lesson.

INTRODUCING THE LESSON

⏱ 5-Minute Check
(over Lesson 13-2)

Find the roots of each equation by graphing the related function.

1. $y = x^2 - 8x + 12$ **2, 6**
2. $x^2 + 6x + 9 = 0$ **−3**
3. $x^2 - 3x + 7 = 0$
   no real roots
4. $x^2 - 4x + 5 = 0$
   no real roots
5. $x^2 - 2x + 1 = 0$ **1**

Motivating the Lesson

Introduce the lesson by posing the following problem to the students: A high school class intends to hold a car wash to raise money for a class trip. The students estimate a team of 3 students can wash a car in 15 minutes. If 81 students participate in the fund raiser, about how many cars can they wash in 1 hour? Discuss with the class possible ways of solving the problem. Then have the students find the solution.
108 cars

TEACHING THE LESSON

Chalkboard Example

For Example 1
How many cars could 21 robots assemble in 1 hour?   **200**

EVALUATING THE LESSON

Checking for Understanding

Exercises 1-6 are designed to help you assess understanding through reading, writing, and speaking. You should work through Exercises 1-2 with your students, and then monitor their work on Exercises 3-6.

Closing the Lesson

Speaking Activity Ask students to explain how identification of subgoals can help find a solution to a problem.

Example 2 | **How many pairs of unit fractions have a sum of $\frac{1}{2}$?**

A unit fraction has 1 as its numerator and a positive integer as its denominator. The unit fractions are $\frac{1}{2}, \frac{1}{3}, \frac{1}{4}, \frac{1}{5}, \ldots$.

Suppose one of the fractions in the pair is $\frac{1}{3}$. You can use subtraction to find the other fraction. Since $\frac{1}{2} - \frac{1}{3} = \frac{1}{6}$, it follows that $\frac{1}{6} + \frac{1}{3} = \frac{1}{2}$. Therefore, the pair $\frac{1}{6}$ and $\frac{1}{3}$ is one solution.

Suppose one fraction in the pair is $\frac{1}{4}$. Since $\frac{1}{2} - \frac{1}{4} = \frac{1}{4}$, $\frac{1}{4} + \frac{1}{4} = \frac{1}{2}$. The pair $\frac{1}{4}$ and $\frac{1}{4}$ is a second solution.

Suppose one fraction in the pair is $\frac{1}{5}$. Since $\frac{1}{2} - \frac{1}{5} = \frac{3}{10}$ and $\frac{3}{10}$ is *not* a unit fraction, there is no unit fraction that can be added to $\frac{1}{5}$ to get $\frac{1}{2}$.

Are there any other pairs of unit fractions whose sum is $\frac{1}{2}$? Is so, one of the fractions must be greater than $\frac{1}{4}$ and the other less than $\frac{1}{4}$. *Why?*

Since $\frac{1}{3}$ and $\frac{1}{2}$ are the *only* unit fractions greater than $\frac{1}{4}$, the two solutions given above are the only pairs of unit fractions whose sum is $\frac{1}{2}$.

---

1. produce part of the solution or make the problem easier to solve

CHECKING FOR UNDERSTANDING

Communicating Mathematics

Read and study the lesson to answer each question.

1. The strategy described in this lesson involves taking steps that will result in one of two outcomes. What are these outcomes?

2. Name another strategy that can be used with the strategy described in this lesson. guess and check, look for a pattern, make a table, solve a simpler problem

Guided Practice

Solve each problem by identifying subgoals.

Strategies
Look for a pattern.
Solve a simpler problem.
Act it out.
Guess and check.
Draw a diagram.
Make a chart.
Work backwards.

3. Two dogs need to eat 3 pounds of dog food per week for proper nutrition. What is the maximum number of dogs that can eat 90 pounds of dog food for 6 weeks? 10 dogs

4. How many pairs of unit fractions have a sum of $\frac{1}{6}$? 5 pairs

5. How many whole numbers less than 200 have digits whose sum is 10? 19 numbers

6. **Number Theory** *Palindromes* are words or numbers that read the same backward or forward. For example, 11, 686, and 1881 are palindromes. How many numbers between 10 and 1000 are palindromes? 99

RETEACHING THE LESSON

Find the digit represented by each letter in the following division problem where each letter represents a different digit.

```
          X T X T
TDX) E D E I T X        I = 0
      E S X             T = 1
      ─────             S = 2
      S S I             D = 4
      T D X             X = 5
      ─────             N = 6
      E X T             E = 7
      E S X
      ─────
      S N X
      T D X
      ─────
      T S I
```

EXERCISES

Practice Solve. Use any strategy. 8. See margin.

7. Suppose the scoring in football is simplified to 7 points for a touchdown and 3 points for a field goal. What scores are impossible to achieve? 1, 2, 4, 5, 8, 11

8. Mr. Apple, Mr. Pear, Miss Peach, and Mrs. Berry are eating apples, pears, peaches, and berries, although none of them are eating the same fruit as their last name. Neither Mr. Pear nor Mrs. Berry is eating apples. If Mr. Apple and Mrs. Berry are eating pieces of fruit that have different first initials, who is eating what?

9. The three co-captains from West High School meet with the four co-captains from East High School for the coin toss. If each co-captain shakes hands with the referee and each opposing co-captain, how many handshakes occur? 19 handshakes

10. What is the next symbol in the following sequence? 88

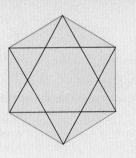

11. Babe Ruth hit 714 home runs over 22 seasons, from 1914 to 1935. He averaged 102 games per season. During what season would he have hit his 714th home run if he had averaged 162 games per season and hit home runs at the same rate? his 13th season

12. Jim is 17 times as old as his brother was when Jim was as old as his brother was when Jim was as old as his brother is now. If their father is less than 90 years old, how old are Jim and his brother?
Jim is 51 years old and his brother is 35.

COOPERATIVE LEARNING ACTIVITY

Work in groups of four. Each person in the group should understand the solution and be able to explain it to any person in the class.

The large hexagon, shown in blue at the right, has been divided into 16 regions of various shapes and sizes. How many rectangles and how many triangles can you find in this figure? (*Hint:* Number each of the regions. Then use the numbers to name the rectangles and triangles.) 5 rectangles and 50 triangles

LESSON 13-3 PROBLEM-SOLVING STRATEGY: IDENTIFY SUBGOALS 529

EXTENDING THE LESSON

Math Power: Problem Solving

Emily is $2\frac{1}{2}$ times as old as Sarah. In 5 years, five times Sarah's age will be equal to her grandfather, Sam's, age today. Sam is $\frac{3}{4}$ of a century old. How old are Emily, Sarah, and Sam today? Emily is 25, Sarah is 10, and Sam is 75.

Cooperative Learning Activity

This activity provides students with an opportunity to *learn* things together, not just do things together. You may wish to refer to pages T6 - T8 and page 6C for the various elements of cooperative groups and specific goals and strategies for using them.

Using Technology

Objective This optional page shows how the graphing calculator can be used to perform mathematical computations and to enhance and extend mathematical concepts.

Teaching Suggestions

Work through the example with students very carefully. For the graph of $(x + 2)^2 + 5$, try to get them to guess why the graph moved up or down or left or right. See if you can get them to see the connection between the vertex of the parabola and the numbers and their location in the equation. For the graph of $3x^2$, make sure they notice that it is narrower. Ask them what would happen if you multiplied x^2 by a number less than 1. It would be wider than the graph of x^2. Once again, try to get them to see the location of the number and how it affects the graph.

You can extend this lesson to solving quadratic equations by having students use the trace function to find the points where the graph crosses the x-axis. These values would solve the equation, and you could demonstrate this point by solving an equation algebraically. Students can then use graphing as a check in later lessons of this chapter.

Try to get students to suggest range values before they graph the equations. Ask them to guess what a good range would be to graph a certain function.

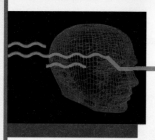

Technology
Solving Quadratic Equations

A graphing calculator is a powerful tool for studying functions. When a group of functions is graphed on the same axes, you can compare the graphs to make generalizations about types of functions. Then you can predict what a function will look like by studying the equation.

Example

Graph $y = x^2$, $y = 3x^2$, and $y = (x + 2)^2 + 5$ on the same set of axes. Use a range of $[-8, 6]$ by $[-4, 20]$.

For the TI-81

First, set the range.

[RANGE] [(-)] 8 [ENTER] 6 [ENTER] 1 [ENTER] [(-)] 4 [ENTER] 20 [ENTER] 1 [ENTER]

Enter $y = x^2$.   [Y=] [CLEAR] [X|T] [x^2] [ENTER]

Enter $y = 3x^2$.   [CLEAR] 3 [X|T] [x^2] [ENTER]

Enter $y = (x + 2)^2 + 5$ and graph.

[CLEAR] [(] [X|T] [+] 2 [)] [x^2] [+] 5 [GRAPH]

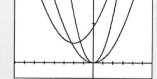

For the Casio

First, set the range.

[RANGE] [(-)] 8 [EXE] 6 [EXE] 1 [EXE] [(-)] 4 [EXE] 20 [EXE] 1 [EXE]

Graph $y = x^2$.   [Graph] [ALPHA] [x] [x^2] [EXE]

Graph $y = 3x^2$.   [Graph] 3 [ALPHA] [x] [x^2]

Graph $(x + 2)^2 + 5$.   [Graph] [(] [ALPHA] [x] [+] 2 [)] [x^2] [+] 5 [EXE]

Notice that the three graphs look very much alike. However, the graph of $y = 3x^2$ is narrower than the graph of $y = x^2$. The graph of $y = (x + 2)^2 + 5$ is translated 2 units to the left and 5 units upward.

EXERCISES

Use a graphing calculator to graph each pair of equations on the same set of axes. Then compare the graph of the second equation to the graph of the first equation. **1. 3 units above   2. 10 units to the right**

1. $y = x^2$; $y = x^2 + 3$

2. $y = x^2$; $y = (x - 10)^2$

3. $y = x^2$; $y = 0.25x^2$ **wider**

4. $y = x^2$; $y = (x + 4)^2 - 8$

4 units to the left, 8 units below

Solving Quadratic Equations by Completing the Square

Objective
13-4

After studying this lesson, you should be able to:

■ solve quadratic equations by completing the square.

Application

FYI · · ·

A photograph of a nautilus shell sold for $115,000 in April 1989.

Carlos Rodriguez is framing a picture. He begins with a square piece of matting and then cuts out a 6-inch by 6-inch square to accommodate the picture. If the area of the remaining matting is 28 square inches, how large was the original square piece of matting?

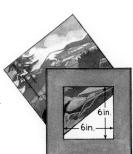

6 in.

6 in.

Let x = the length of a side of the original square piece of matting. The area of the cutout is 36 square inches. Then, $x^2 - 36 =$ the area of the matting after the 6-inch-by-6-inch square is cut out.

Since the area of the remaining matting is 28 square inches, you can solve the equation $x^2 - 36 = 28$ to find x. One method for solving this equation is shown below.

$x^2 - 36 = 28$
$\quad x^2 = 64$ *Add 36 to each side.*
$\quad x = \pm\sqrt{64}$ *Find the square root of each side.*
$\quad x = \pm 8$

Since -8 inches is not a reasonable solution, the length of a side of the original square piece of matting must be 8 inches. *Check this result.*

The method used for solving the equation $x^2 - 36 = 28$ can also be used to solve equations such as $x^2 - 4x + 4 = 3$.

Example 1

Solve $x^2 - 4x + 4 = 3$.

$x^2 - 4x + 4 = 3$
$\quad (x - 2)^2 = 3$ *$x^2 - 4x + 4$ is a perfect square trinomial.*
$\quad \sqrt{(x - 2)^2} = \sqrt{3}$ *Find the square root of each side.*
$\quad |x - 2| = \sqrt{3}$
$\quad x - 2 = \pm\sqrt{3}$ *Why is this true?* **Teaching Tip ❶**
$\quad x = 2 \pm\sqrt{3}$ *Add 2 to each side.*

The solution set is $\{2 + \sqrt{3}, 2 - \sqrt{3}\}$.

LESSON 13-4 SOLVING QUADRATIC EQUATIONS BY COMPLETING THE SQUARE   531

ALTERNATE TEACHING STRATEGIES

Using Discussion

How many roots does
$x^2 + bx + \left(\frac{b}{2}\right)^2 = 0$ have?
(Hint: Try some values for b.)   1

Lesson Resources

- Reteaching Master 13-4
- Practice Master 13-4
- Enrichment Master 13-4
- Video Algebra, 55
- Transparency 13-4 contains the 5-Minute Check and a teaching aid for this lesson.

INTRODUCING THE LESSON

🕐 5-Minute Check
(over Lesson 13-2)

Find the roots of each equation by graphing the related function.

1. $x^2 - 9 = 0$ $-3, 3$
2. $x^2 - 5x - 6 = 0$ $6, -1$
3. $x^2 - 4x + 5 = 0$ no roots
4. $x^2 - 8x + 16 = 0$ 4
5. $x^2 - x - 12 = 0$ $-3, 4$

Motivating the Lesson

Introduce the lesson with a review of factoring. Ask students to factor each of the following.
1. $x^2 + 4x + 4$ $(x + 2)^2$
2. $x^2 - 6x + 9$ $(x - 3)^2$
3. $n^2 + 10n + 25$ $(n + 5)^2$
4. $y^2 - 2y + 1$ $(y - 1)^2$

TEACHING THE LESSON

Teaching Tip ❶ Because $|x - 2| = \sqrt{3}$ means $x - 2 = \sqrt{3}$ or $x - 2 = -\sqrt{3}$, you may wish to refer students to solving open sentences containing absolute value on page 199.

Chalkboard Example

For Example 1
Solve $x^2 + 6x + 9 = 5$.
$\{-3 + \sqrt{5}, -3 - \sqrt{5}\}$

For Example 2

Find the value of c that makes each trinomial a perfect square.

a. $x^2 - 20x + c$ 100

b. $y^2 + y + c$ $\frac{1}{4}$

c. $m^2 - 3m + c$ $\frac{9}{4}$

For Example 3

Solve each equation by completing the square.

a. $x^2 - 6x + 8 = 0$ {2, 4}

b. $x^2 - 6x + 5 = 0$ {1, 5}

c. $m^2 + 4m - 9 = 0$
$\{-2 + \sqrt{13}, -2 - \sqrt{13}\}$

d. $x^2 - 6x + 7 = 0$
$\{3 + \sqrt{2}, 3 - \sqrt{2}\}$

Teaching Tip ②   Discuss this example thoroughly. Make sure students understand the third step of the solution. The number 9 is added because it completes the square for $x^2 + 6x$. That is, $\left(\frac{6}{2}\right)^2 = 9$.

Teaching Tip ③   You may wish to include the following steps:
$\sqrt{(x + 3)^2} = \sqrt{25}$
$|x + 3| = 5$

Teaching Tip ④   A calculator may be used to aid in checking the roots of an equation.

To use the method shown in Example 1, the quadratic expression on one side of the equation must be a perfect square. To make it a perfect square, a method called **completing the square** may be used.

Consider the pattern for squaring a binomial such as x + 6.

$(x + 6)^2 = x^2 + 2(6)(x) + 6^2$
$\qquad\quad = x^2 + 12x \quad + 36$

$\left(\frac{12}{2}\right)^2 \rightarrow 6^2$ *Notice that one-half of 12 is 6 and 6^2 is 36.*

To complete the square for a quadratic expression of the form $x^2 + bx$, you can follow the steps below.

Step 1	Find one-half of b, the coefficient of x.
Step 2	Square the result of Step 1.
Step 3	Add the result of Step 2 to $x^2 + bx$.

Example 2

Find the value of *c* that makes $x^2 + 14x + c$ a perfect square.

Step 1	Find one-half of 14.	$\frac{14}{2} = 7$
Step 2	Square the result of Step 1.	$7^2 = 49$
Step 3	Add the result of Step 2 to $x^2 + 14x$.	$x^2 + 14x + 49$

Thus, c = 49. Notice that $x^2 + 14x + 49 = (x + 7)^2$.

Example 3

Solve $x^2 + 6x - 16 = 0$ by completing the square. **Teaching Tip ②**

$x^2 + 6x - 16 = 0$ *Notice that $x^2 + 6x - 16$ is not a perfect square.*
$\quad\;\; x^2 + 6x = 16$ *Add 16 to each side. Then complete the square.*
$x^2 + 6x + 9 = 16 + 9$ *Since $\left(\frac{6}{2}\right)^2 = 9$, add 9 to each side.*
$\quad\;\;\; (x + 3)^2 = 25$ *Factor $x^2 + 6x + 9$.*
$\qquad\;\; x + 3 = \pm 5$ *Find the square root of each side.* **Teaching Tip ③**
$\qquad\qquad\;\; x = -3 \pm 5$ *Subtract 3 from each side.*

$x = -3 + 5$ or $x = -3 - 5$
$\quad = 2$ $\qquad\qquad\quad = -8$

The solution set is {2, −8}. *Check this result.* **Teaching Tip ④**

This method for solving quadratic equations cannot be used unless the coefficient of the first term is 1. To solve a quadratic equation where this coefficient is not 1, divide each term by the coefficient, as shown in Example 4.

Example 4

The Cartland Company wants to redesign the main conference room at its corporate headquarters. Because of the existing design of the building, the maximum length of the redesigned rectangular conference room can be 9 meters less than twice its maximum width. Find the dimensions, to the nearest tenth of a meter, for the largest possible conference room if its area is to be 390 square meters.

EXPLORE　Let w = the maximum width of the redesigned conference room. Then $2w - 9$ = the maximum length of the conference room.

PLAN

Length   times   width   equals   area.

$(2w \cdot 9)$　×　　w　　=　　390

SOLVE

$$2w^2 - 9w = 390$$

$$w^2 - \frac{9}{2}w = 195 \qquad \text{\textit{Divide each side by 2.}}$$

$$w^2 - \frac{9}{2}w + \frac{81}{16} = 195 + \frac{81}{16} \qquad \text{\textit{Complete the square.}}$$

$$\left(w - \frac{9}{4}\right)^2 = \frac{3201}{16}$$

$$w - \frac{9}{4} = \pm\frac{\sqrt{3201}}{4}$$

$$w = \frac{9 \pm \sqrt{3201}}{4}$$

The roots of $(2w - 9)w = 390$ are $\dfrac{9 + \sqrt{3201}}{4}$ and $\dfrac{9 - \sqrt{3201}}{4}$.

You can use a calculator to find decimal approximations for these numbers.

Enter: (9 + 3201 √x) ÷ 4 = `16.3943452`

Enter: (9 − 3201 √x) ÷ 4 = `-11.8943452`

The roots of the equation are approximately 16.4 and −11.9.

Since −11.9 meters is not a reasonable solution, the width must be 16.4 meters. Therefore, the dimensions of the redesigned conference room, rounded to the nearest tenth of a meter, are 16.4 meters by 2(16.4) − 9 or 23.8 meters.

EXAMINE　Since $23.8 \times 16.4 = 390.32$, the answer seems reasonable.

LESSON 13-4　SOLVING QUADRATIC EQUATIONS BY COMPLETING THE SQUARE　533

RETEACHING THE LESSON

Have students solve several quadratic equations that have either fractional or decimal coefficients by completing the square. Many students are confused by these type of quadratics and need extra practice.

Chapter 13　533

Checking for Understanding

Exercises 1-16 are designed to help you assess understanding through reading, writing, and speaking. You should work through Exercises 1-4 with your students, and then monitor their work on Exercises 5-16.

Error Analysis

Students need to first look at the coefficient of the first term to be sure it is 1. Make sure they divide *all* terms by that coefficient if it is not 1.

Example: $3x^2 - 7x = 3$

$x^2 - \frac{7}{3}x = 3$ $x^2 - \frac{7}{3}x = 1$

    no   yes

Practice Masters Booklet, p. 101

CHECKING FOR UNDERSTANDING

Communicating Mathematics

Read and study the lesson to answer each question.

1. What is the value of $\sqrt{x^2}$? $|x|$

2. What are the three steps used to complete the square for the expression $x^2 + bx$? **See margin.**

3. If you were solving the equation $3x^2 - 8x = 9$ by completing the square, what should be your first step? **Divide each side by 3.**

4. Which method for solving a quadratic equation always produces an *exact* solution, graphing or completing the square? **completing the square**

Guided Practice

State whether each trinomial is a perfect square.

5. $b^2 + 4b + 3$ no
6. $m^2 - 10m + 25$ yes
7. $r^2 - 8r - 16$ no

8. $d^2 + 11d + 121$ no
9. $h^2 - 13h + \frac{169}{4}$ yes
10. $4x^2 + 12x + 9$ yes

Find the value of c that makes each trinomial a perfect square.

11. $x^2 + 8x + c$ 16
12. $a^2 - 6a + c$ 9
13. $m^2 + 7m + c$ $\frac{49}{4}$

Solve each equation by completing the square.

14. $y^2 + 4y + 3 = 0$ $-1, -3$
15. $n^2 - 8n + 7 = 0$ 1, 7
16. $t^2 - 4t = 21$ 7, -3

EXERCISES

Practice

Find the value of c that makes each trinomial a perfect square.

17. $x^2 - 7x + c$ $\frac{49}{4}$
18. $a^2 + 5a + c$ $\frac{25}{4}$
19. $9x^2 - 18x + c$ 9

Solve each equation by completing the square. Leave irrational roots in simplest radical form. **28, 30–34. See margin.**

20. $r^2 + 14r - 10 = 5$ 1, -15
21. $y^2 + 7y + 10 = -2$ -3, -4
22. $x^2 - 5x + 2 = -2$ 4, 1

23. $4x^2 - 20x + 25 = 0$ $\frac{5}{2}$
24. $z^2 - 4z = 2$ $2 \pm \sqrt{6}$
25. $b^2 + 4 = 6b$ $3 \pm \sqrt{5}$

26. $y^2 - 8y = 4$ $4 \pm 2\sqrt{5}$
27. $x^2 - 10x = 23$ $5 \pm 4\sqrt{3}$
28. $2d^2 + 3d - 20 = 0$

29. $a^2 - \frac{7}{2}a + \frac{3}{2} = 0$ 3, $\frac{1}{2}$
30. $\frac{1}{2}q^2 - \frac{5}{4}q - 3 = 0$
31. $0.3x^2 + 0.1x = 0.2$

32. $r^2 + 0.25r = 0.5$
33. $2x^2 - 5x + 1 = 0$
34. $3x^2 - 7x - 3 = 0$

35. **Geometry** Find the dimensions of a rectangle whose perimeter is 37 yards and whose area is 78 square yards. **6.5 yd by 12 yd**

Additional Answers

2. *Step 1:* Find one-half of b;
Step 2: Square the result of Step 1;
Step 3: Add the result of Step 2 to $x^2 + bx$.

28. $\frac{5}{2}, -4$

30. $-\frac{3}{2}, 4$

31. $\frac{2}{3}, -1$

32. $-0.125 \pm \sqrt{0.515625}$

33. $\frac{5 \pm \sqrt{17}}{4}$

34. $\frac{7 \pm \sqrt{85}}{6}$

Find the value of c that makes each trinomial a perfect square.

36. $x^2 + cx + 64$ **16, −16**

37. $4x^2 + cx + 225$ **60, −60**

38. $cx^2 + 28x + 49$ **4**

39. $cx^2 − 18x + 36$ **$\frac{9}{4}$**

Solve each equation by completing the square. Leave irrational roots in simplest radical form.

40. $x^2 + 4x + c = 0$
$-2 \pm \sqrt{4-c}$

41. $x^2 + bx + c = 0$
$\dfrac{-b \pm \sqrt{b^2 - 4c}}{2}$

42. $x^2 + 4bx + b^2 = 0$
$b(-2 \pm \sqrt{3})$

Critical Thinking

43. **Geometry** Write the quadratic function $y = x^2 − 4x + 7$ in the form $y = (x − h)^2 + k$. Then graph the function. What is the relationship of the point (h, k) to the graph? **It is the vertex of the graph.**

Application

44. **Construction** The rectangular penguin pond at the Bay Park Zoo is 12 meters long by 8 meters wide. The zoo wants to double the area of the pond by increasing the length and width by the same amount. By how much should the length and width be increased? **4 meters**

45. **Photography** Sheila is placing a photograph behind a 12-inch-by-12-inch piece of matting. The photograph is to be positioned so that the matting is twice as wide at the top and bottom as it is at the sides. If the area of the photograph is to be 54 square inches, what are its dimensions? **9 in. by 6 in.**

| ← 12 in. → |
| 2x in. |
| x in.   12 in.   x in. |
| 2x in. |

46. **Travel** Two trains left the same station at the same time. One was traveling due north at a speed that was 10 mph faster than the other train, which was traveling due east. After one hour, the trains were 71 miles apart. How fast, to the nearest mile per hour, was each train traveling? (*Hint: Use the Pythagorean Theorem*) **45 mph, 55 mph**

Mixed Review

47. **Consumerism** Denise Williams has budgeted $150 to have business cards printed. A card printer charges $11 to set up each job and an additional $6 per box of 100 cards printed. What is the greatest number of cards Ms. Williams can have printed? **(Lesson 5-3)** **2300 cards**

48. **Number Theory** The tens digit of a two-digit number exceeds twice its units digit by 1. If the digits are reversed, the number is 4 more than 3 times the sum of the digits. Find the original number. **(Lesson 11-3)** **52**

49. Simplify $5\sqrt{72} + 2\sqrt{20} − 3\sqrt{5}$. **(Lesson 12-6)** **$30\sqrt{2} + \sqrt{5}$**

50. Locate the roots of $4x^2 − 12x + 3 = 0$ between two consecutive integers by graphing the related function. **(Lesson 13-2)** **$0 < x < 1, 2 < x < 3$**

51. Determine how many whole numbers less than 1000 have digits whose sum is 10. **(Lesson 13-3)** **63**

LESSON 13-4 SOLVING QUADRATIC EQUATIONS BY COMPLETING THE SQUARE **535**

EXTENDING THE LESSON

Math Power:
Problem Solving

Solve the equation for x in terms of a by completing the square. State the restrictions on a so that the equation will have real-number roots.

$ax^2 − 3x + 4 = 0$

$x = \dfrac{3 \pm \sqrt{9 − 16a}}{2a}$; $a \leq \dfrac{9}{16}$, $a \neq 0$

Closing the Lesson

Speaking Activity Have students explain how to use the completing the square method to solve $x^2 − 36 = 0$.

APPLYING THE LESSON

Homework Exercises

Assignment Guide
Basic: 17-37, 43-44, 47-51
Average: 21-39, 43-51
Enriched: 26-51

Chapter 13, Quiz B, (Lessons 13-3 through 13-4), is available in the Evaluation Masters Booklet, p. 177.

Enrichment Masters Booklet, p. 89

NAME _____ DATE _____

13-4 Enrichment Worksheet

Graphing Circles by Completing Squares

One use for completing the square is to graph circles. The general equation for a circle with center at the origin and radius r is $x^2 + y^2 = r^2$. An equation represents a circle if it can be transformed into the sum of two squares.

$x^2 − 6x + y^2 + 4y − 3 = 0$
$(x^2 − 6x +) + (y^2 + 4y +) = 3$
$(x^2 − 6x + 9) + (y^2 + 4y + 4) = 3 + 9 + 4$
$(x − 3)^2 + (y + 2)^2 = 4^2$

Notice that the center of the circle is at the point $(3, −2)$.

Transform each equation into the sum of two squares. Then graph the circle represented by the equation. Use the coordinate plane provided at the bottom of the page.

1. $x^2 − 14x + y^2 + 6y + 49 = 0$
   $(x − 7)^2 + (y + 3)^2 = 3^2$
2. $x^2 + y^2 − 8y − 9 = 0$
   $x^2 + (y − 4)^2 = 5^2$
3. $x^2 + 10x + y^2 + 21 = 0$
   $(x + 5)^2 + y^2 = 2^2$
4. $x^2 + y^2 + 10y + 16 = 0$
   $x^2 + (y + 5)^2 = 3^2$
5. $x^2 − 30x + y^2 + 209 = 0$
   $(x − 15)^2 + y^2 = 4^2$
6. $x^2 − 18x + y^2 − 12y + 116 = 0$
   $(x^2 − 9)^2 + (y − 6)^2 = 1^2$
7. $x^2 + 30x + y^2 − 4y + 193 = 0$
   $(x + 15)^2 + (y − 2)^2 = 6^2$
8. $x^2 + 38x + y^2 − 12y + 393 = 0$
   $(x + 19)^2 + (y − 6)^2 = 2^2$

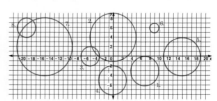

Lesson Resources

- Reteaching Master 13-5
- Practice Master 13-5
- Enrichment Master 13-5
- Technology Master, p. 13
- Activity Master, p. 28

 Transparency 13-5 contains the 5-Minute Check and a teaching aid for this lesson.

INTRODUCING THE LESSON

 5-Minute Check

(over Lesson 13-4)

Solve each equation by completing the square.

1. $r^2 + 8r + 7 = 0$ $-1, -7$
2. $b^2 - 4b = 21$ $7, -3$
3. $m^2 - 11m - 12 = 0$
    $12, -1$
4. $t^2 + 14t - 10 = 5$ $1, -15$
5. $b^2 - 6b + 8 = 0$ $2, 4$

Motivating the Lesson

Introduce the lesson with a review of the general form of a quadratic equation, $ax^2 + bx + c = 0$. Ask students to name a, b, and c for each quadratic equation.

1. $2x^2 - 4x + 3 = 0$ $2, -4, 3$
2. $x^2 + x - 5 = 0$ $1, 1, -5$
3. $7x^2 - 10x + 3 = 0$ $7, -10, 3$
4. $-3x^2 + 4x - 12 = 0$
    $-3, 4, -12$

13-5 Solving Quadratic Equations Using the Quadratic Formula

Objective
13-5

After studying this lesson, you should be able to:

- solve quadratic equations by using the quadratic formula.

Application

FYI · · ·

Captain Eugene A. Cernan and Dr. Harrison H. Schmitt spent 74 hours 59 minutes on the moon in December 1972.

The height H of an object t seconds after it is propelled upward is given by the formula $H = -\frac{1}{2}gt^2 + vt + h$. In this formula, v is the initial upward velocity of the object, h is its initial height, and g is the acceleration due to gravity. Suppose an astronaut on the moon throws a baseball with an initial upward velocity of 10 meters per second while letting go of the ball 2 meters above the ground. How much longer will the ball stay in the air than a baseball thrown on Earth under the exact same conditions? On Earth, g is 9.8 meters per second squared and on the moon, g is 1.6 meters per second squared.

On both Earth and the moon, $v = 10$ and $h = 2$. The value of H is 0 when the baseball hits the ground. Therefore, the two equations below can be used to describe this situation.

Baseball thrown on the moon

$$0 = -\frac{1}{2}(1.6)t^2 + 10t + 2$$

$$0 = -0.8t^2 + 10t + 2$$

Baseball thrown on Earth

$$0 = -\frac{1}{2}(9.8)t^2 + 10t + 2$$

$$0 = -4.9t^2 + 10t + 2$$

You could solve these equations by graphing the related functions, but that will produce only a rough approximation of the actual solution. You could also try solving the equations by completing the square, but that would not be a simple task. Another alternative is to develop a general formula for solving *any* quadratic equation. To do this, you begin with the general form, $ax^2 + bx + c = 0$, where $a \neq 0$.

$$ax^2 + bx + c = 0$$

$$x^2 + \frac{b}{a}x + \frac{c}{a} = 0 \qquad \textit{Divide by a so the coefficient of x}^2 \textit{ becomes 1.}$$

$$x^2 + \frac{b}{a}x = -\frac{c}{a} \qquad \textit{Subtract } \frac{c}{a} \textit{ from each side.}$$

Now complete the square.

$$x^2 + \frac{b}{a}x + \left(\frac{b}{2a}\right)^2 = -\frac{c}{a} + \left(\frac{b}{2a}\right)^2$$

$$\left(x + \frac{b}{2a}\right)^2 = -\frac{c}{a} + \frac{b^2}{4a^2} \qquad \textit{Factor the left side.}$$

$$\left(x + \frac{b}{2a}\right)^2 = \frac{b^2 - 4ac}{4a^2} \qquad \textit{Simplify the right side.}$$

ALTERNATE TEACHING STRATEGIES

Using Logical Reasoning

Find values for r, s, and t so that $\dfrac{r + s\sqrt{x}}{t}$ can be simplified. r, s, and t must have a common factor other than one.

Using Calculators

Use a calculator to find the roots of each equation rounded to the nearest hundredth.

a. $5.97x^2 - 17.1x + 2.54 = 0$
    $\{2.71, 0.16\}$
b. $1.9y^2 - 11.5y - 6.2 = 0$
    $\{6.55, -0.50\}$
c. $9.35t^2 + 1.97t - 7.42 = 0$
    $\{0.79, -1.00\}$

Finally, find the square root of each side and solve for x.

$$x + \frac{b}{2a} = \pm\sqrt{\frac{b^2 - 4ac}{4a^2}}$$

$$x + \frac{b}{2a} = \frac{\pm\sqrt{b^2 - 4ac}}{2a}$$ *Simplify the square root on the right side.*

$$x = \frac{\pm\sqrt{b^2 - 4ac}}{2a} - \frac{b}{2a}$$ *Subtract $\frac{b}{2a}$ from each side.*

$$x = \frac{-b \pm \sqrt{b^2 - 4ac}}{2a}$$ *The result is an expression for x.*

This result is called the **quadratic formula** and can be used to solve *any* quadratic equation. **Teaching Tip ❶**

The Quadratic Formula	The roots of a quadratic equation of the form $ax^2 + bx + c = 0$, where $a \neq 0$, are given by the formula $$x = \frac{-b \pm \sqrt{b^2 - 4ac}}{2a}.$$

Teaching Tip ❷ In order for the roots of $ax^2 + bx + c = 0$ to be real numbers, the value of $b^2 - 4ac$ must be nonnegative. If $b^2 - 4ac$ is negative, the $\sqrt{b^2 - 4ac}$ is not defined and the equation has no real roots.

Example 1

Use the quadratic formula to solve $x^2 - 8x - 4 = 0$.

$$x = \frac{-b \pm \sqrt{b^2 - 4ac}}{2a}$$

$$= \frac{-(-8) \pm \sqrt{(-8)^2 - 4(1)(-4)}}{2(1)}$$ *a = 1, b = −8, c = −4*

$$= \frac{8 \pm \sqrt{64 + 16}}{2}$$

$$= \frac{8 \pm \sqrt{80}}{2}$$ *$\sqrt{80} = \sqrt{16 \cdot 5}$ or $4\sqrt{5}$*

$$x = \frac{8 + 4\sqrt{5}}{2} \quad \text{or} \quad x = \frac{8 - 4\sqrt{5}}{2}$$

$$= 4 + 2\sqrt{5} \qquad\qquad = 4 - 2\sqrt{5}$$ *Check this result.*

The solution set is $\{4 + 2\sqrt{5}, 4 - 2\sqrt{5}\}$.

Teaching Tip ❶ Encourage students to memorize the quadratic formula. Emphasize that it can be used to solve any quadratic equation.

Teaching Tip ❷ Remind students that the square root of a negative number is not defined for the set of real numbers.

Chalkboard Example

For Example 1
Use the quadratic formula to solve each equation. Leave irrational roots in simplest radical form.

a. $x^2 + 6x + 8 = 0$ $\{-2, -4\}$

b. $x^2 - 2x - 15 = 0$ $\{-3, 5\}$

c. $2x^2 + 7x - 15 = 0$ $\left\{-5, \frac{3}{2}\right\}$

EVALUATING THE LESSON

Checking for Understanding

Exercises 1-19 are designed to help you assess understanding through reading, writing, and speaking. You should work through Exercises 1-4 with your students, and then monitor their work on Exercises 5-19.

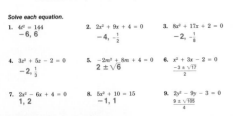

Example 2

APPLICATION

Physics

Solve the problem given at the beginning of the lesson by using the quadratic formula. Solve the equations $0 = -0.8t^2 + 10t + 2$ and $0 = -4.9t^2 + 10t + 2$. Round answers to the nearest tenth of a second.

You can use a calculator to help with the computations when using the quadratic formula.

Moon   For $0 = -0.8t^2 + 10t + 2$, $a = -0.8$, $b = 10$ and $c = 2$. First, evaluate $\sqrt{b^2 - 4ac}$, or $\sqrt{10^2 - 4(-0.8)(2)}$ and store the value.

Enter: (10 x^2 − 4 × 0.8 +/- × 2) √x STO

Display: 10.3150376

Next, find the value of $\frac{-b + \sqrt{b^2 - 4ac}}{2a}$. *Remember, you have stored the value of $\sqrt{b^2 - 4ac}$.*

Enter: (10 +/- + RCL) ÷ (2 × 0.8 +/-) =

Display: −0.19689848

Finally, find the value of $\frac{-b - \sqrt{b^2 - 4ac}}{2a}$.

Enter: (10 +/- − RCL) ÷ (2 × 0.8 +/-) =

Display: 12.6968985

The decimal approximations for the roots of $0 = -0.8t^2 + 10t + 2$ are −0.2 and 12.7. Thus, the ball will stay in the air for about 12.7 seconds when thrown on the moon. *−0.2 seconds is not an acceptable answer.*

Earth   By following the steps used above, you will find that the decimal approximations for the roots of the equation $0 = -4.9t^2 + 10t + 2$ are −0.2 and 2.2. Thus, the ball will stay in the air for about 2.2 seconds when thrown on Earth. *Again, −0.2 seconds is not an acceptable answer.*

Therefore, the ball thrown on the moon will stay in the air for 12.7 − 2.2 or about 10.5 seconds longer than the ball thrown on Earth.

CHECKING FOR UNDERSTANDING

Communicating Mathematics

Read and study the lesson to answer each question.

1. What method for solving quadratic equations was used to develop the quadratic formula? **completing the square**

2. What coefficient of a quadratic equation cannot equal 0 in the quadratic formula? $a \neq 0$

3. *True or false:* If $b^2 > 4ac$, then the quadratic equation $ax^2 + bx + c = 0$ has no real roots. **false**

4. What are the two roots of the quadratic equation $ax^2 + bx + c = 0$?
   $$\frac{-b + \sqrt{b^2 - 4ac}}{2a}, \frac{-b - \sqrt{b^2 - 4ac}}{2a}$$

RETEACHING THE LESSON

Have half the class solve a quadratic equation by using the quadratic formula and the other half of the class solve by completing the square. Compare answers and discuss which method was better to use for that problem. Given a new problem, exchange tasks for each half of the class. Solve and discuss.

State the values of *a*, *b*, and *c* for each quadratic equation.

5. $x^2 + 7x + 6 = 0$ 1, 7, 6
6. $2t^2 - t - 15 = 0$ 2, −1, −15
7. $2y^2 + 3 = -7y$ 2, 7, 3
8. $2x^2 = 98$ 2, 0, −98
9. $4a^2 + 8a = 0$ 4, 8, 0
10. $3k^2 + 11k = 4$ 3, 11, −4

Find the value of $b^2 - 4ac$ for each quadratic equation.

11. $x^2 + 5x - 6 = 0$ 49
12. $y^2 - 7y - 8 = 0$ 81
13. $m^2 - 2m = 35$ 144
14. $4n^2 - 20n = 0$ 400
15. $5t^2 = 125$ 2500
16. $3x^2 + 14x = 5$ 256

Solve each equation.

17. $m^2 + 4m + 2 = 0$
$-2 \pm \sqrt{2}$
18. $-4x^2 + 8x = -3$
$\frac{2 \pm \sqrt{2}}{7}$
19. $3k^2 + 2 = -8k$
$\frac{-4 \pm \sqrt{10}}{3}$

EXERCISES

Solve each equation. **See margin.**

 A

20. $x^2 + 7x + 6 = 0$
21. $r^2 + 10r + 9 = 0$
22. $-a^2 + 5a - 6 = 0$
23. $y^2 - 25 = 0$
24. $-2d^2 + 8d + 3 = 3$
25. $2r^2 + r - 15 = 0$
26. $3n^2 - 2n = 1$
27. $2y^2 + 3 = -7y$
28. $8t^2 + 10t + 3 = 0$

B
29. $z^2 - 13z - 32 = 0$
30. $y^2 - \frac{3y}{5} + \frac{2}{25} = 0$
31. $3x^2 - \frac{5}{4}x - \frac{1}{2} = 0$
32. $24x^2 - 2x - 15 = 0$
33. $21a^2 + 5a - 6 = 0$
34. $2x^2 = 0.7x + 0.3$
35. $-r^2 - 6r + 3 = 0$
36. $4b^2 + 20b + 23 = 0$
37. $-4y^2 + 13 = -16y$

Approximate the *x*-intercepts of the graph of each function to the nearest tenth. (*Hint:* the *x*-intercepts are the roots of the related equation.)

38. $y = x^2 - 6x + 1$ 5.8, 0.2
39. $y = 4x^2 + 8x - 1$ −2.1, 0.1
40. $y = 2x^2 - x - 2$ −0.8, 1.3
41. $y = 3x^2 - 5x + 1$ 0.2, 1.4

C
42. $y = 3.2x^2 - 5.6x - 7.1$ −0.8, 2.6
43. $y = 1.9x^2 + 6.5x + 2.7$
−0.5, −2.9

Write a quadratic equation that has the given roots. **See margin.**

44. $-1 \pm \sqrt{3}$
45. $\frac{-3 \pm \sqrt{5}}{2}$
46. $\frac{1 \pm \sqrt{33}}{4}$
47. $\frac{4 \pm \sqrt{7}}{3}$

48. If a quadratic equation can be solved by factoring, what can you say about the value of $b^2 - 4ac$? **It is a perfect square.**

49. If a quadratic equation has exactly one real root, what can you say about the value of $b^2 - 4ac$? **It is equal to 0.**

50. **Physics** Rafael is tossing rocks off the edge of a 10-meter-high cliff. He throws one rock with an initial upward velocity of 15 meters per second. Use the formula $H = -4.9t^2 + vt + h$ to answer each question. Round your answers to the nearest tenth of a second.
   a. When will the rock reach a height of 25 meters above the ground?
   b. When will the rock return to the height from which it was thrown?
   c. When will the rock hit the ground? **a. never, b. 3.1 sec c. 3.7 sec**

LESSON 13-5 SOLVING QUADRATIC EQUATIONS USING THE QUADRATIC FORMULA 539

Additional Answers

For Exercises 20–37, exact answers and decimal answers rounded to the nearest hundredth are given.
20. −1, −6
21. −1, −9
22. 2, 3
23. 5, −5
24. 0, 4
25. $\frac{5}{2}$, −3
26. 1, −$\frac{1}{3}$
27. −$\frac{1}{2}$, −3
28. −$\frac{1}{2}$, −$\frac{3}{4}$
29. $\frac{13 \pm 3\sqrt{33}}{2}$; 15.12, −2.12
30. $\frac{2}{5}$, $\frac{1}{5}$
31. $\frac{2}{3}$, −$\frac{1}{4}$
32. $\frac{5}{6}$, −$\frac{3}{4}$

Additional Answers

33. $\frac{3}{7}$, −$\frac{2}{3}$
34. 0.6, −0.25
35. $-3 \pm 2\sqrt{3}$; 0.46, −6.46
36. $\frac{-5 \pm \sqrt{2}}{2}$; −1.79, −3.21
37. $\frac{4 \pm \sqrt{29}}{2}$; 4.69, −0.69
44. $x^2 + 2x - 2 = 0$
45. $x^2 + 3x + 1 = 0$
46. $2x^2 - x - 4 = 0$
47. $3x^2 - 8x + 3 = 0$

Practice Masters Booklet, p. 102

NAME _____ DATE _____

13-5 | Practice Worksheet

Solving Quadratic Equations by Using the Quadratic Formula
Solve each equation.

1. $4m^2 + 3m = 1$
   $\frac{1}{4}$, −1
2. $3n^2 = 10n$
   0, $\frac{10}{3}$

3. $p^2 + 4p + 1 = 0$
   $-2 + \sqrt{3}, -2 - \sqrt{3}$
4. $q^2 - 5q + 2 = 0$
   $\frac{5 + \sqrt{17}}{2}, \frac{5 - \sqrt{17}}{2}$

5. $r^2 - 7r + 3 = 0$
   $\frac{7 + \sqrt{37}}{2}, \frac{7 - \sqrt{37}}{2}$
6. $a^2 + 6a + 3 = 0$
   $-3 + \sqrt{6}, -3 - \sqrt{6}$

7. $3y^2 + 2y - 3 = 0$
   $\frac{-1 + \sqrt{10}}{3}, \frac{-1 - \sqrt{10}}{3}$
8. $5z^2 - 3 = 0$
   $\frac{\sqrt{15}}{5}, -\frac{\sqrt{15}}{5}$

9. $x^2 + \frac{2}{3}x - \frac{15}{9} = 0$
   1, −$\frac{5}{3}$
10. $e^2 + \frac{5}{12}e = \frac{1}{4}$
   $\frac{1}{3}$, $\frac{3}{4}$

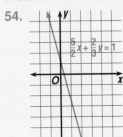
51. Finance   Elise received \$100 from her father on her birthday and placed it in a savings account. After 3 years, she has $100[(1 + r)^2 + (1 + r) + 1]$ dollars in the account, where r is the annual interest rate. Find this rate, to the nearest tenth of a percent, if Elise has \$325 in the account after 3 years.   **8.1%**

Mixed Review   **52.** Simplify $\frac{3}{4}a^2 + 5ab + \frac{1}{2}a^2$.   **(Lesson 1-6)** $\frac{5}{4}a^2 + 5ab$

53. Simplify $\frac{a^2}{a^2 - b^2} + \frac{a}{(a-b)^2}$.   **(Lesson 8-7)** $\frac{a^3 - a^2b + a^2 + ab}{(a+b)(a-b)^2}$

54. Graph $\frac{5}{2}x + \frac{2}{3}y = 1$.   **(Lesson 9-4) See margin.**

55. Write the standard form of the equation of the line passing through $(4, -1)$ and $(2, 5)$.   **(Lesson 10-2)** $3x + y = 11$

56. Physics   The time t, in seconds, it takes an object to drop d feet is given by the formula $4t = \sqrt{d}$. Jessica and Lu-Chan each dropped a stone at the same time, but Jessica dropped hers from a spot higher than Lu-Chan's. Lu-Chan's stone hit the ground 1 second before Jessica's. If Jessica's stone dropped 112 feet farther than Lu-Chan's, how long did it take her stone to hit the ground?   **(Lesson 12-7)** **4 seconds**

57. Solve $2x^2 - 6x - 5 = 0$ by completing the square.   **(Lesson 13-4)** $\frac{3 \pm \sqrt{19}}{2}$

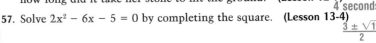

MID-CHAPTER REVIEW

Find an equation of the axis of symmetry and the coordinates of the vertex of the graph of each quadratic function.   (Lesson 13-1)

1. $y = x^2 - x - 12$
$x = \frac{1}{2}; \left(\frac{1}{2}, -\frac{49}{4}\right)$

2. $y = -2x^2 - 9$
$x = 0; (0, -9)$

3. $y = -3x^2 - 6x + 5$
$x = -1; (-1, 8)$

Find the roots of each equation by graphing its related function. If exact roots cannot be found, state the consecutive integers between which the roots are located.   (Lesson 13-2)

4. $x^2 + 6x + 10 = 0$
no real roots

5. $x^2 - 2x - 1 = 0$
$-1 < x < 0, 2 < x < 3$

6. $x^2 - 5x - 6 = 0$ **6, -1**

Solve each equation by completing the square.   (Lesson 13-4)

7. $x^2 - 6x + 7 = 0$ $3 \pm \sqrt{2}$

8. $2b^2 - b - 7 = 14$ $\frac{7}{2}, -3$

Solve each equation by using the quadratic formula.   (Lesson 13-5)

9. $y^2 + 8y + 15 = 0$ $-5, -3$

10. $p^2 + 5p + 3 = 0$ $\frac{-5 \pm \sqrt{13}}{2}$

11. Three painters can paint 4 houses in 5 days. How long would it take 5 painters to paint 18 houses if they all worked at the same rate?   **(Lesson 13-3) 13.5 days**

540   CHAPTER 13   QUADRATICS

EXTENDING THE LESSON

Math Power:
Problem Solving

Solve each equation. Express irrational roots in simplest radical form and in decimal form to the nearest hundredth.

1. $(2n - 3)^2 - 7 = 6n + 1$
$\frac{9 + \sqrt{77}}{4}$; 4.44, 0.06

2. $(3x + 2)^2 = (x - 1)^2 + 4$
$\frac{-7 + \sqrt{57}}{8}$; 0.07, -1.82

13-6 Using the Discriminant

Objective
13-6

After studying this lesson, you should be able to:
- evaluate the discriminant of a quadratic equation to determine the nature of the roots of the equation.

Application

Trevor and Mineku are mountain climbing on Sopher Peak. In order to climb one of the cliffs, Trevor must throw his grappling hook up onto a ledge that is 15 meters above him. If Trevor can throw the grappling hook with an initial velocity of at most 13 meters per second, can he throw the hook onto the ledge?

In Lesson 13-5, you learned that the height H of an object t seconds after it is propelled upward is given by the formula $H = -\frac{1}{2}gt^2 + vt + h$. For this problem, $v = 13$ and $g = 9.8$, since Trevor is on Earth. Since the ledge is 15 meters above Trevor, we can let $H = 15$ and $h = 0$. Thus, this problem can be represented by the following equation.

$$15 = -\frac{1}{2}(9.8)t^2 + 13t + 0$$

$$0 = -4.9t^2 + 13t - 15$$

To determine if Trevor will be able to throw the grappling hook onto the ledge, we can use the quadratic formula to solve this equation for t.

$$t = \frac{-b \pm \sqrt{b^2 - 4ac}}{2a} \qquad a = -4.9, b = 13, c = -15$$

$$= \frac{-13 \pm \sqrt{13^2 - 4(-4.9)(-15)}}{2(-4.9)}$$

$$= \frac{-13 \pm \sqrt{169 - 294}}{-9.8}$$

$$= \frac{-13 \pm \sqrt{-125}}{-9.8}$$

Notice that the number under the radical sign is negative. This indicates that the equation $0 = -4.9t^2 + 13t - 15$ has *no* real roots. Therefore, Trevor cannot throw the grappling hook up onto the ledge.

Teaching Tip ❶

In the quadratic formula, the expression under the radical sign, $b^2 - 4ac$, is called the **discriminant**. The value of the discriminant for a quadratic equation can give you information about the nature of the roots of the equation. In particular, the value of the discriminant is used to determine the number of real roots for a quadratic equation. Recall that the real roots of a quadratic equation are the x-intercepts of the graph of its related function.

There are three cases to consider: when the value of the discriminant is positive, when it is zero, and when it is negative.

LESSON 13-6 USING THE DISCRIMINANT 541

13-6 Lesson Notes

Lesson Resources
- Reteaching Master 13-6
- Practice Master 13-6
- Enrichment Master 13-6
- Activity Master, p. 43
- Video Algebra, 56

 Transparency 13-6 contains the 5-Minute Check and a teaching aid for this lesson.

INTRODUCING THE LESSON

🕐 **5-Minute Check**
(over Lesson 13-5)

State the values of a, b, and c for each quadratic equation.

1. $3k^2 + 11k = 4$ **3, 11, −4**
2. $3p^2 + 2 = -5p$ **3, 5, 2**
3. $2r^2 + 8r = 0$ **2, 8, 0**

Solve each equation.

4. $y^2 + 8y + 15 = 0$ **−3, −5**
5. $2p^2 = 98$ **±7**

Motivating the Lesson

Ask students to simplify the expression 8 ± 3. Develop the idea that the expression represents two numbers and it is the $\pm$ sign that generates the two results.

TEACHING THE LESSON

Teaching Tip ❶   Emphasize that the <u>discriminant</u> is $b^2 - 4ac$, not $\sqrt{b^2 - 4ac}$.

ALTERNATE TEACHING STRATEGIES

Using Logical Reasoning
Show that if a and c have different signs, then $ax^2 + bx + c = 0$ $(a \neq 0)$ has two real roots.   Since $ac < 0$, then $-4ac > 0$. Thus, $b^2 - 4ac > 0$ and $ax^2 + bx + c = 0$ has two real roots.

Using Problem Solving
Determine the values of k so that the equation $x^2 + kx + 36 = 0$ will have one real root.   **12, −12**

Case 1: Positive Discriminant

Solve $x^2 + 3x - 2 = 0$.

$$x = \frac{-b \pm \sqrt{b^2 - 4ac}}{2a}$$

$$= \frac{-3 \pm \sqrt{3^2 - 4(1)(-2)}}{2(1)} \quad \begin{array}{l} a = 1, b = 3, \\ c = -2 \end{array}$$

$$= \frac{-3 \pm \sqrt{9 + 8}}{2}$$

$$= \frac{-3 \pm \sqrt{17}}{2}$$

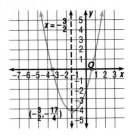

Notice that the graph of the related function $y = x^2 + 3x - 2$ has two distinct x-intercepts.

$x \approx -3.56$ or $x \approx 0.56$ **Teaching Tip ③**   **Teaching Tip ②**

In this case, $b^2 - 4ac > 0$ and there are two distinct real roots.

Case 2: Discriminant of Zero

Solve $x^2 - 8x + 16 = 0$.

$$x = \frac{-b \pm \sqrt{b^2 - 4ac}}{2a}$$

$$= \frac{-(-8) \pm \sqrt{(-8)^2 - 4(1)(16)}}{2(1)}$$

$$= \frac{8 \pm \sqrt{64 - 64}}{2}$$

$$= \frac{8 \pm 0}{2} \text{ or } 4$$

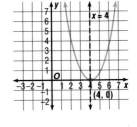

Notice that the graph of the related function $y = x^2 - 8x + 16$ has one distinct x-intercept.

In this case, $b^2 - 4ac = 0$ and there is exactly one distinct real root.

Notice that the x-intercept is the vertex of the parabola.

Case 3: Negative Discriminant

Solve $x^2 + 6x + 10 = 0$.

$$x = \frac{-b \pm \sqrt{b^2 - 4ac}}{2a}$$

$$= \frac{-6 \pm \sqrt{6^2 - 4(1)(10)}}{2(1)}$$

$$= \frac{-6 \pm \sqrt{36 - 40}}{2}$$

$$= \frac{-6 \pm \sqrt{-4}}{2}$$

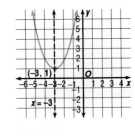

Notice that the graph of the related function $y = x^2 + 6x + 10$ has no x-intercepts.

In this case, $b^2 - 4ac < 0$ and there are no real roots since *no* real number can be the square root of a negative number.

Teaching Tip ④   The relationship between the value of the discriminant and the nature of the roots of a quadratic equation can be summarized as follows.

	Discriminant	Nature of Roots
Nature of Roots of a Quadratic Equation	$b^2 - 4ac > 0$	two distinct real roots
	$b^2 - 4ac = 0$	one distinct real root
	$b^2 - 4ac < 0$	no real roots

542   CHAPTER 13   QUADRATICS

Example 1

State the value of the discriminant of each equation. Then determine the nature of the roots of the equation.

a. $2x^2 + 10x + 11 = 0$

$$b^2 - 4ac = (10)^2 - 4(2)(11) \qquad a = 2, b = 10, c = 11$$
$$= 100 - 88$$
$$= 12$$

Since $b^2 - 4ac > 0$, then $2x^2 + 10x + 11 = 0$ has two distinct real roots.

b. $3x^2 + 4x + 2 = 0$

$$b^2 - 4ac = (4)^2 - 4(3)(2) \qquad a = 3, b = 4, c = 2$$
$$= 16 - 24$$
$$= -8$$

Since $b^2 - 4ac < 0$, then $3x^2 + 4x + 2 = 0$ has no real roots.

Example 2

CONNECTION
Geometry

Can a rectangle with a perimeter of 42 cm have an area of 110.25 cm²?

EXPLORE Let ℓ = the length of the rectangle.
Let w = the width of the rectangle.
To solve this problem, you need to determine if there are values of ℓ and w such that $2\ell + 2w = 42$ and $\ell w = 110.25$.

PLAN First solve $2\ell + 2w = 42$ for ℓ. Then substitute the expression for ℓ into $\ell w = 110.25$. A quadratic equation results that represents the area of a rectangle whose perimeter is 42 cm.

SOLVE
$$2\ell + 2w = 42$$
$$\ell + w = 21 \qquad \textit{Divide each side by 2.}$$
$$\ell = 21 - w$$

$$(21 - w)w = 110.25 \qquad \textit{Substitute } 21 - w \textit{ for } \ell.$$
$$21w - w^2 = 110.25$$
$$0 = w^2 - 21w + 110.25$$
$$0 = 4w^2 - 84w + 441 \qquad \textit{Multiply each side by 4.}$$

You could solve the equation $0 = 4w^2 - 84w + 441$. However, you *only* need to determine if the equation has *any* real roots. You can do this by evaluating the determinant.

$$b^2 - 4ac = (-84)^2 - 4(4)(441) \qquad a = 4, b = -84, c = 441$$
$$= 7056 - 7056$$
$$= 0$$

Since $b^2 - 4ac = 0$, then $0 = 4w^2 - 84w + 441$ has one distinct real root. Thus, there is a rectangle with a perimeter of 42 cm and an area of 110.25 cm². *Examine this solution.*

RETEACHING THE LESSON

Show the students various quadratic graphs and have them describe the discriminants. Then give them the equations for each of the graphs and have them find the discriminants and check to see if their descriptions were correct.

Chalkboard Examples

For Example 1

State the value of the discriminant for each equation. Then determine the nature of the roots of the equation.

a. $2x^2 - 11x + 13 = 0$
   17, two real distinct roots

b. $16x^2 + 24x + 9 = 0$
   0, one real distinct root

c. $3x^2 + 7x - 26 = 0$
   361, two real distinct roots

For Example 2

Determine if a rectangle with each of the following perimeters can have an area of 400 square inches.

a. 82 inches   yes

b. 80 inches   yes

c. 78 inches   no

Reteaching Masters Booklet, p. 91

Checking for Understanding

Exercises 1-10 are designed to help you assess understanding through reading, writing, and speaking. You should work through Exercises 1-4 with your students, and then monitor their work on Exercises 5-10.

Closing the Lesson

Writing Activity Have students summarize the relationship between the value of the discriminant and the nature of the roots of an equation in paragraph form.

Additional Answers

5. 25; 2 real roots
6. 49; 2 real roots
7. 0; 1 real root
8. −351; no real roots
9. −11; no real roots
10. 12; 2 real roots
11. 5; 2 real roots
12. 1.44; 2 real roots
13. 0; 1 real root
14. 0; 1 real root
15. −20; no real roots
16. $-\frac{61}{12}$; no real roots

Practice Masters Booklet, p. 103

NAME _____ DATE _____
| 13-6 | **Practice Worksheet** |

Using the Discriminant

State the value of the discriminant for each equation. Then determine the nature of the roots of the equation.

1. $x^2 - 5x + 4 = 0$
   9; two real roots
2. $3x^2 - 2x + 1 = 0$
   −8; no real roots

3. $z^2 - 4.6z + 5.29 = 0$
   0; one real root
4. $\frac{5}{2}c^2 - \frac{3}{10}e = 6$
   60.09; two real roots

Determine the nature of the roots of each equation. Then find all real roots. Express irrational roots in simplest radical form and in decimal form rounded to the nearest hundredth.

5. $p^2 - 8p + 7 = 0$
   two real roots; 1, 7
6. $2c^2 + 7c = 3$
   two real roots;
   $\frac{-7 + \sqrt{73}}{4}, \frac{-7 - \sqrt{73}}{4}$; 0.39, −3.89

7. $e^2 = 6e - 9$
   one real root; 3
8. $x^2 - x + 8 = 0$
   no real roots

9. $5k + 11 = 4k^2$
   two real roots;
   $\frac{5 + \sqrt{201}}{8}, \frac{5 - \sqrt{201}}{8}$; 2.40, −1.15
10. $4t^2 - 4t + 1 = 0$
    one real root; $\frac{1}{2}$

CHECKING FOR UNDERSTANDING

Communicating Mathematics

Complete.

1. In the quadratic formula, the expression ___?___ is the discriminant. $b^2 - 4ac$

2. A quadratic equation has two real roots when the discriminant is ___?___. **greater than zero**

3. If the discriminant of a quadratic equation is 0, then the ___?___ of the graph of the related function is its x-intercept. **vertex**

4. If a quadratic equation has two *irrational* roots, then the discriminant of the equation ___?___ a perfect square. **is not**

Guided Practice

State the value of the discriminant for each equation. Then determine the nature of the roots of the equation. **See margin.**

5. $x^2 + 3x - 4 = 0$
6. $m^2 + 5m - 6 = 0$
7. $s^2 + 8s + 16 = 0$
8. $2z^2 + 7z + 50 = 0$
9. $3x^2 + x + 1 = 0$
10. $2a^2 - 2a - 1 = 0$

EXERCISES

Practice

State the value of the discriminant for each equation. Then determine the nature of the roots of the equation. **See margin.**

11. $y^2 + 3y + 1 = 0$
12. $x^2 - 1.2x = 0$
13. $4a^2 + 10a = -6.25$
14. $\frac{4}{3}n^2 + 4n + 3 = 0$
15. $\frac{3}{2}m^2 + m = -\frac{7}{2}$
16. $2r^2 = \frac{1}{2}r - \frac{2}{3}$

Determine the nature of the roots of each equation. Then find all real roots. Express irrational roots in simplest radical form and in decimal form rounded to the nearest hundredth. **See margin.**

17. $y^2 - 4y + 1 = 0$
18. $k^2 + 6k + 10 = 0$
19. $r^2 + 4r - 12 = 0$
20. $h^2 - 16h + 64 = 0$
21. $2x^2 + 3x + 1 = 0$
22. $3y^2 + y - 1 = 0$
23. $6r^2 - 5r = 7$
24. $8p^2 + 1 = -7p$
25. $9y^2 = 6y - 1$
26. $0.3a^2 + 0.8a = -0.4$
27. $x^2 - \frac{5}{3}x = \frac{-2}{3}$
28. $\frac{1}{3}x^2 + 13\frac{1}{3} = 4x$
29. $5c^2 - 7c = 1$
30. $15a^2 + 2a + 16 = 0$
31. $11z^2 = z + 3$

Determine the number of x-intercepts of the graph of each function *without* graphing the function.

32. $y = x^2 + 5x + 3$ **2**
33. $y = x^2 + 4x + 7$ **0**
34. $y = 7x^2 - 3x - 1$ **2**
35. $y = 0.6x^2 + x - 1.8$ **2**
36. $y = \frac{3}{2}x^2 + 2x + \frac{5}{4}$ **0**
37. $y = 4x^2 - \frac{4}{3}x + \frac{1}{9}$ **1**

38. **Geometry** Can a rectangle with a perimeter of 56 meters have an area of 200 square meters? **no**

Additional Answers

17. $2 \pm \sqrt{3}$; 3.73, 0.27
18. no real roots
19. 2, −6
20. 8
21. $-\frac{1}{2}$, −1
22. $\frac{-1 \pm \sqrt{13}}{6}$; 0.43, −0.77
23. $\frac{5 \pm \sqrt{193}}{12}$; 1.57, −0.74
24. $\frac{-7 \pm \sqrt{17}}{16}$; −0.18, −0.70
25. $\frac{1}{3}$
26. $-2, -\frac{2}{3}$

27. $1, \frac{2}{3}$
28. no real roots
29. $\frac{7 \pm \sqrt{69}}{10}$; 1.53, −0.13
30. no real roots
31. $\frac{1 \pm \sqrt{133}}{22}$; 0.57, −0.48

Determine the values of k so that each quadratic equation has the indicated number of real roots.

39. $x^2 + kx + 36 = 0$; 1
  12, −12

40. $x^2 + 8x + k = 0$; 2
  $k < 16$

41. $kx^2 + 5x = 1$; 0
  $k < \dfrac{-25}{4}$

Critical Thinking

42. In the quadratic equation $ax^2 + bx + c = 0$, if $ac < 0$, what must be true about the nature of the roots of the equation? **always two real roots**

Applications

43. Physics The height h, in feet, of a certain rocket t seconds after blast-off is given by the formula $h = -16t^2 + 2320t + 125$.
  a. Approximately how long after blast-off will this rocket reach a height of 84,225 feet? **72.5 seconds**
  b. Is this the maximum height of the rocket? **yes**

44. Consumerism A grocer sells 50 loaves of bread a day at $1.15 per loaf. The grocer estimates that for each $0.05 price increase, 2 fewer loaves of bread will be sold each day. What price can she charge in order to have a daily income of $65? **not possible**

Computer

Teaching Tip ⑤

45. This BASIC program uses the quadratic discriminant to determine the nature of the roots of any quadratic equation. Real roots are computed by means of the quadratic formula.

Use the program to find and determine the roots of each quadratic equation.

```
10 INPUT "ENTER THE COEFFICIENTS
   OF AX^2 + BX + C = 0,";A,B,C
20 LET D = B^2-4*A*C
30 IF D < 0 THEN 110
40 LET X1 = (-B+SQR(D))/(2*A)
50 LET X2 = (-B-SQR(D))/(2*A)
60 IF D = 0 THEN 90
70 PRINT "THE TWO REAL DISTINCT
   ROOTS ARE ";X1;" AND ";X2;"."
80 GOTO 120
90 PRINT "THE ONE REAL DISTINCT
   ROOT IS ";X1;"."
100 GOTO 120
110 PRINT "THERE ARE NO REAL
    ROOTS."
120 END
```

  a. $3x^2 - 2x + 1 = 0$ **none**
  b. $4x^2 + 4x + 1 = 0$ $-\dfrac{1}{2}$
  c. $7x^2 + 2x - 5 = 0$ $-1, \dfrac{5}{7}$
  d. $x^2 - 11x + 10 = 0$ **10, 1**
  e. $2x^2 + x + 1 = 0$ **none**
  f. $x^2 - 6x = 0$ **0, 6**

Mixed Review

46. Sales Ruth paid $19.61 for a videotape. This included 6% sales tax. What was the cost of the videotape before taxes? **(Lesson 4-4)** **$18.50**

47. Is the inverse of $\{(-1, 3), (-1, 0), (2, -1)\}$ a function? **(Lesson 9-5)** **yes**

48. Business Jake's Garage charges $83 for a two-hour repair job and $185 for a five-hour repair job. Define variables and write an equation that Jake can use to bill customers for repair jobs of any length of time. **(Lesson 10-5)** **See margin.**

49. Solve the system $y < 3x$ and $x + 2y \geq -21$ by graphing. **(Lesson 11-6)**
  See margin.

50. Simplify $\sqrt{59.29}$. **(Lesson 12-2)** **7.7**

51. Geometry The perimeter of a rectangle is 8 m and its area is 2 m². Find its dimensions, to the nearest tenth of a meter. **(Lesson 13-5)**
  3.4 m by 0.6 m

Homework Exercises

Assignment Guide
Basic: 11-38, 42-43, 46-51
Average: 17-51
Enriched: 17-51

Chapter 13, Quiz C, (Lessons 13-5 through 13-6), is available in the Evaluation Masters Booklet, p. 178.

Teaching Tip ⑤ Challenge students to modify the program so that it will sort out and solve linear equations. As written, the program will end in an error if $A = 0$. These lines will allow linear equations to be entered and solved.

Additional Answer

49.

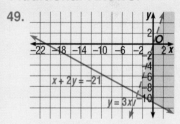

Enrichment Masters Booklet, p. 91

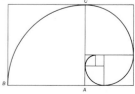

13-6 Enrichment Worksheet

Golden Rectangles

A **Golden Rectangle** has the property that its sides satisfy the following proportion.

$$\frac{a + b}{a} = \frac{a}{b}$$

Two quadratic equations can be written from the proportion. These are sometimes called **golden quadratic equations**.

1. In the proportion, let $a = 1$. Use cross-multiplication to write a quadratic equation.
$b^2 + b - 1 = 0$

2. Solve the equation in problem 1 for b.
$b = \dfrac{-1 + \sqrt{5}}{2}$

3. In the proportion, let $b = 1$. Write a quadratic equation in a.
$a^2 - a - 1 = 0$

4. Solve the equation in problem 3 for a.
$a = \dfrac{1 + \sqrt{5}}{2}$

5. Explain why $\frac{1}{2}(\sqrt{5} + 1)$ and $\frac{1}{2}(\sqrt{5} - 1)$ are called Golden Ratios.
They are the ratios of the sides in a Golden Rectangle. The first is the ratio of the long side to the short side; the second is short side: long side.

Another property of Golden Rectangles is that a square drawn inside a Golden Rectangle creates another, smaller Golden Rectangle.

In the design at the right, opposite vertices of each square have been connected with quarters of circles.

For example, the arc from point B to point C is created by putting the point of a compass at point A. The radius of the arc is the length BA.

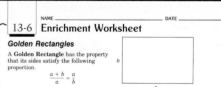

6. On a separate sheet of paper, draw a larger version of the design. Start with a Golden Rectangle with a long side of 10 inches.
The short side should be about $6\frac{3}{16}$ inches.

EXTENDING THE LESSON

Math Power: Problem Solving

Determine the values of k so that the equation $kx^2 + 5x - 1 = 0$ will have no real roots. $k < -\dfrac{25}{4}$

Additional Answers

48. Let h = the number of hours for the repair job and c = the total charge.
$c = 34h + 15$

INTRODUCING THE LESSON

 5-Minute Check

(over Lesson 13-6)

Determine the nature of the roots of each equation.

1. $3x^2 - 5x - 7 = 0$
   2 real roots
2. $t^2 - 8t + 16 = 0$
   1 real root
3. $9y^2 + 16 = 0$
   no real roots
4. $12x^2 - 7 = 0$ **2 real roots**
5. $5t^2 + 8t + 4 = 0$
   no real roots

Motivating the Lesson

Introduce the lesson by posing the following question: If the constant term of a quadratic equation is zero, what is known about its roots? **One root is 0.**

TEACHING THE LESSON

Teaching Tip ❶ Point out that the equation could be solved for *w*.

Teaching Tip ❷ The length of each side of the piece of sheet metal is about 18.8 cm. Thus, the dimensions of the pan are about 14.8 cm × 14.8 cm × 2 cm.

Chalkboard Example

For Example 1
Find the dimensions of a rectangle if the area is 63 cm² and the perimeter is 32 cm.
$63 = w(16 - w)$; **7 cm, 9 cm**

13-7 Application: Solving Quadratic Equations

Objective
13-7

After studying this lesson, you should be able to:
- solve problems that can be represented by quadratic equations.

You have studied a variety of methods for solving quadratic equations. The table below summarizes these methods.

Method	Can be Used	Comments
graphing	always	Not always exact; use only when an approximate solution is sufficient.
factoring	sometimes	Use if constant term is 0 or factors are easily determined.
completing the square	always	Useful for equations of the form $x^2 + bx + c = 0$ where b is an even number.
quadratic formula	always	Other methods may be easier to use, but this method always gives exact values.

You can use these methods to solve problems that can be represented by quadratic equations.

Example 1

CONNECTION
Geometry

The perimeter of a rectangle is 60 cm. Find the dimensions of the rectangle if its area is 221 cm².

EXPLORE   Let ℓ = the measure of the length of the rectangle.
Let w = the measure of its width.
Since the perimeter of the rectangle is 60 cm, $2\ell + 2w = 60$.
Since the area of the rectangle is 221 cm², $221 = \ell w$.

PLAN   First solve $2\ell + 2w = 60$ for ℓ.

$$2\ell + 2w = 60$$
$$\ell + w = 30 \quad \text{\textit{Divide each side by 2.}}$$
$$\ell = 30 - w \quad \textbf{Teaching Tip ❶}$$

SOLVE   Then substitute $30 - w$ for ℓ in $221 = \ell w$ and solve.

$$221 = (30 - w)w$$
$$221 = 30w - w^2$$
$$w^2 - 30w + 221 = 0$$
$$(w - 13)(w - 17) = 0 \quad \text{\textit{Factor.}}$$
$$w - 13 = 0 \quad \text{or} \quad w - 17 = 0$$
$$w = 13 \qquad\qquad w = 17$$

ALTERNATE TEACHING STRATEGIES

Using Problem Solving

Solve the equation by an appropriate method.
$(2x + 5)(x - 2) = 3x(6 - x) - 10$
$0, \frac{17}{5}$

If $w = 13$, then $\ell = 30 - 13$ or 17.
If $w = 17$, then $\ell = 30 - 17$ or 13.
Thus, the dimensions of the rectangle are 13 cm and 17 cm.

EXAMINE If the dimension of the rectangle are 13 cm and 17 cm, then its perimeter is $2(13) + 2(17)$ or 60 cm and its area is $13(17)$ or 221 cm². Thus, the solution is correct.

Example 2

APPLICATION
Manufacturing

A pan is to be formed by cutting 2 cm-by-2 cm squares from each corner of a square piece of sheet metal and then folding the sides. If the volume of the pan is to be 441 cm², what are the dimensions of the original piece of sheet metal?

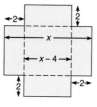

Let x = the measure of a side of the square piece of sheet metal. Then $x - 4$ = the measure of a side of the square base of the pan.

You can use the formula for the volume of a rectangular solid, $\ell wh = V$, to write an equation to represent the problem.

$(x - 4)(x - 4)(2) = 441$ *$\ell = x - 4$, $w = x - 4$, $h = 2$, $V = 441$*
$2x^2 - 16x + 32 = 441$
$2x^2 - 16x - 409 = 0$

$x = \dfrac{16 \pm \sqrt{(-16)^2 - 4(2)(-409)}}{2(2)}$ *Use the quadratic formula with $a = 2$, $b = -16$, and $c = -409$.*

$= \dfrac{16 \pm \sqrt{256 + 3272}}{4}$

$x = \dfrac{16 + \sqrt{3528}}{4}$ or $x = \dfrac{16 - \sqrt{3528}}{4}$ *Use a calculator to approximate each root to the nearest tenth.*
≈ 18.8 ≈ -10.8

Teaching Tip ❷

The length of each side of the piece of sheet metal should be about 18.8 cm since the length cannot be −10.8 cm. The volume of this pan is $(18.8 - 4)(18.8 - 4)(2)$ or 438.08 cm³. Thus, the answer appears reasonable.

CHECKING FOR UNDERSTANDING

Communicating Mathematics

Read and study the lesson to answer each question.

1. Name four methods for solving quadratic equations. **graphing, factoring, completing the square, using quadratic formula**
2. Which of the four methods does not always find an exact solution? **graphing**
3. In Example 2, what would be the dimensions of the original piece of sheet metal if the squares measured 1 cm on a side instead of 2 cm? **23 cm by 23 cm**

LESSON 13-7 APPLICATION: SOLVING QUADRATIC EQUATIONS 547

RETEACHING THE LESSON

Have the students solve the following geometry problem: The hypotenuse of a right triangle is 29 meters long. The length of one leg is 1 meter shorter than the length of the other leg. Find the lengths of the legs.
20 m and 21 m

Chalkboard Example

For Example 2

A box is to be formed by cutting squares measuring 4 inches on a side from a square piece of cardboard and then folding the sides. If the volume of the box is to be 576 in², what is the original size of the cardboard?
$576 = (x - 8)(x - 8)(4)$; **The length of each side is 20 in.**

EVALUATING THE LESSON

Checking for Understanding

Exercises 1-15 are designed to help you assess understanding through reading, writing, and speaking. You should work through Exercises 1-3 with your students, and then monitor their work on Exercises 4-15.

Error Analysis

When using the quadratic formula, watch that students don't simplify a radical expression incorrectly.
Example: $\dfrac{-4 \pm \sqrt{2}}{2} \neq -2 \pm \sqrt{2}$

Reteaching Masters Booklet, p. 92

13-7 NAME _____ DATE _____
Reteaching Worksheet

Application: Solving Quadratic Equations

You have studied a variety of methods for solving quadratic equations. The table below summarizes these methods.

Method	Can be Used	Comments
Graphing	always	Not always exact; use only when an approximate solution is sufficient
Factoring	sometimes	Use if constant term is 0 or factors are easily determined.
Completing the Square	always	Useful for equations of the form $x^2 + bx + c = 0$ where b is even.
Quadratic Formula	always	Other methods may be easier, but this method *always* works.

Solve each quadratic equation by an appropriate method. Express irrational roots in simplest radical form and in decimal form rounded to the nearest hundreth.

1. $x^2 + 2x - 3 = 0$
   -3, 1
2. $h^2 - 8h + 16 = 0$
   4
3. $6x^2 + 4x - 1 = 0$
   $\dfrac{-2 \pm \sqrt{10}}{6}$; 0.19, -0.86
4. $x^2 + 6x - 9 = 0$
   $-3 \pm 3\sqrt{2}$; 1.24; -7.24

Solve each problem. Approximate any irrational solutions to the nearest tenth.

5. Find two integers whose sum is 16 and whose product is 48.
   12, 4
6. Find two integers whose difference is 5 and whose product is 84.
   12, 7
7. A rectangle has a perimeter of 14.6 cm and an area of 11.5 cm². Find the dimensions of the rectangle.
   2.3 cm and 5 cm
8. The perimeter of a rectangle is 4.5 m. The length is twice the width. The area is 1.125 m². Find its dimensions.
   1.5 m and 0.75 m

Closing the Lesson

Speaking Activity Quadratic equations can be solved by many methods. Ask the students to describe the disadvantages of the following methods.
1. **graphing** not always exact
2. **factoring** sometimes factors cannot be easily determined
3. **completing the square** b should be an even number in equations of the form $x^2 + bx + c = 0$ or this process is not efficient

---

APPLYING THE LESSON

Homework Exercises

Assignment Guide
Basic: 16-30, 33-38
Average: 20-38
Enriched: 20-38

Additional Answers

4. factoring
5. factoring or quadratic formula
6. quadratic formula or completing the square
7. quadratic formula
8. factoring or quadratic formula
9. quadratic formula or completing the square

Practice Masters Booklet, p. 104

13-7	**Practice Worksheet**

NAME _____ DATE _____

Application: Solving Quadratic Equations
Solve each quadratic equation by an appropriate method. Express irrational roots in simplest radical form and in decimal form rounded to the nearest hundredth.

1. $x^2 + 5x - 14 = 0$
   2, −7
2. $2r^2 + 5r + 2 = 0$
   $-\frac{1}{2}$, −2

3. $1 = 3c^2 - 5c$
   $\frac{5 + \sqrt{37}}{6}, \frac{5 - \sqrt{37}}{6}$; 1.85, −0.18
4. $y^2 + 8y - 6 = 0$
   $-4 + \sqrt{22}, -4 - \sqrt{22}$; 0.69, −8.69

5. $\frac{1}{8}d^2 - 1 = -5d$
   $-20 + 2\sqrt{102}, -20 - 2\sqrt{102}$; 0.20, −40.20
6. $0.25z^2 + z + 1 = 0$
   −2

Solve each problem.

7. The perimeter of a rectangle is 32 cm. Find the dimensions of the rectangle if its area is 63 cm². length, 9 cm; width, 7 cm
8. Find two integers whose difference is 7 and whose product is 18. 2, 9

Guided Practice

See margin.

State the method that is most appropriate for solving each equation.

4. $x^2 - 12x + 27 = 0$
5. $2m^2 + 19m + 9 = 0$
6. $a^2 - 12a - 4 = 0$
7. $3r^2 - 7r = 5$
8. $3x^2 - 2x = 5$
9. $y^2 + 4y = 9$

Solve each quadratic equation by an appropriate method. See margin.

10. $x^2 - 8x - 20 = 0$
11. $y^2 + 10y - 2 = 0$
12. $r^2 + 13r = -42$
13. $3x^2 - 7x - 6 = 0$
14. $2a^2 + 4a + 1 = 0$
15. $3z^2 - 7z = 3$

EXERCISES

Practice

Solve each quadratic equation by an appropriate method. Express irrational roots in simplest radical form and in decimal form rounded to the nearest hundredth. **See margin.**

Teaching Tip ③

16. $3h^2 - 5h - 2 = 0$
17. $2k^2 + k - 5 = 0$
18. $2y^2 - 4y + 3 = 0$
19. $3z^2 = 5z - 1$
20. $2m^2 + 4m = 5$
21. $x^2 - 1.1x = 0.6$
22. $x^2 - \frac{17}{20}x + \frac{3}{20} = 0$
23. $\frac{1}{4}y^2 = y + \frac{1}{2}$
24. $0.7a^2 - 2.8a = 7$
   5 and 7

CONNECTION

Number Theory

25. Find two integers whose sum is 12 and whose squares differ by 24.
26. The sum of a number and its reciprocal is $\frac{10}{3}$. Find the number. 3 or $\frac{1}{3}$

Applications

Solve each problem. Approximate any irrational solutions to the nearest tenth.

27. **Construction** A box is to be formed from a rectangular piece of sheet metal by cutting squares measuring 5 inches on a side and then folding the sides. The piece of sheet metal is twice as long as it is wide. If the volume of the box is to be 1760 in³, what are the dimensions of the original piece of sheet metal? 21 in. by 42 in.

28. **Gardening** Gene Knight has a rectangular flower garden that measures 15 meters by 20 meters. He wishes to build a concrete walk of uniform width around the garden. His budget for the project allows him to buy enough concrete to cover an area of 74 square meters. How wide can he build the walk? 1 m

29. **Physics** Janice tosses a softball directly upward with an initial velocity of 100 feet per second. Use the formula $h = vt - 16t^2$ to answer each question.
   a. When will the ball reach a height of 84 feet? 1 s, 5.25 s
   b. When will the ball hit the ground? 6.25 s

30. **Framing** Miguel wants to make a square picture frame that is 5 cm wide. The frame is to be designed so that the area available for a picture is two-thirds of the total area of the picture and the frame. What will be the dimensions of this frame? 54.5 cm by 54.5 cm

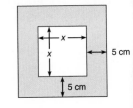

Additional Answers

10. 10, −2
11. $-5 \pm 3\sqrt{3}$; 0.20; −10.20
12. −7, −6
13. $-\frac{2}{3}$, 3
14. $\frac{-2 \pm \sqrt{2}}{2}$; −0.29, −1.71
15. $\frac{7 \pm \sqrt{85}}{6}$; 2.70, −0.37
16. $-\frac{1}{3}$, 2

17. $\frac{-1 \pm \sqrt{41}}{4}$; 1.35, −1.85
18. no real roots
19. $\frac{5 \pm \sqrt{13}}{6}$; 1.43, 0.23
20. $\frac{-2 \pm \sqrt{14}}{2}$; 0.87, −2.87
21. 1.5, −0.4
22. $\frac{1}{4}, \frac{3}{5}$
23. $2 \pm \sqrt{6}$; 4.45, −0.45
24. $2 \pm \sqrt{14}$; 5.74, −1.74

31. **Mowing** Lisa, Nicole, and Amber are to mow a rectangular lawn that measures 100 feet by 120 feet. Lisa is going to mow one-third of the lawn by mowing a strip of uniform width around the outer edge of the lawn. What are the dimensions of the lawn still to be mowed? **80 ft by 100 ft**

32. **Sales** The Computer Club bought a $68 graphics software package for club use. If there had been 1 more student in the club, then cost per member to buy the software would have been $0.25 less. How many students are in the club? **16 students**

Critical Thinking

33. Write a proportion to represent the following statement: *The ratio of 1 to a positive number is equal to the ratio of the number to 1 minus the number.* Then solve the proportion to find the number. Express your answer in simplest radical form and in decimal form rounded to the nearest thousandth. *This number is called the golden ratio.*
See margin.

Mixed Review

34. **Geometry** The area of a square is $4x^2 - 28x + 49$ cm². What is the value of x if the perimeter of the square is 60 cm? **(Lesson 7-10) 11**

35. **Work** . Pipe A can fill a tank in 4 hours and pipe B can fill the tank in 8 hours. With the tank empty, pipe A is turned on, and one hour later, pipe B is turned on. How long will pipe B run before the tank is full? Use $rt = w$. **(Lesson 8-9) 2 hours**

36. Use substitution to solve the system of equations $5x + 6y = 74$ and $2x - 3y = 8$. **(Lesson 11-3) (10, 4)**

37. **Geometry** The measures of the sides of a triangle are 0.9, 1.6, and 2.0. Is this triangle a right triangle? **(Lesson 12-3) no**

38. Find the discriminant of $5b^2 = 1 + 6b$. Determine the nature of the roots of the equation. **(Lesson 13-6) 56; 2 real roots**

∼∼∼∼ HISTORY CONNECTION ∼∼∼∼

Muhammed ibn Musa al Khwarizmi

Just where did this thing called "algebra" come from? Around 825 A.D., an Arab mathematician, Al-Khwarizmi, wrote about a practical form of mathematics for everyday people, for use in trade and commerce, law, surveying, and construction. The word *algebra* is taken from the title of his work, *Hisab al-jabr w'al muqabalah*, which mainly dealt with solving linear equations. The title has been translated as *The Science of Restoring and Cancelling*. This probably refers to the process of adding a number to each side of an equation (restoring) and dividing each side of an equation by a number (cancelling). Al-Khwarizmi also solved quadratic equations by completing the square. Although he was not the first person to do this, his work became very important in shaping the way we solve these types of equations today. For these reasons, Al-Khwarizmi is often called "The Father of Algebra."

LESSON 13-7 APPLICATION: SOLVING QUADRATIC EQUATIONS 549

EXTENDING THE LESSON

Math Power: Connections

An equation to approximate the stopping distance for an automobile is $d = \dfrac{x^2}{20} + \dfrac{11}{10}x$, where x is the rate in miles per hour and d is the stopping distance in feet. What is the maximum safe speed when the stopping distance is 50 feet?
about 22.5 mph

History Connection

The History Connection features introduce students to persons or cultures who were involved in the development of mathematics.
You may want students to further research Al-Khwarizmi.

INTRODUCING THE LESSON

🕐 5-Minute Check

(over Lesson 13-7)

Solve.

1. $x^2 - \left(\frac{5}{4}\right)x + \frac{3}{8} = 0$ $\left\{\frac{3}{4}, \frac{1}{2}\right\}$
2. $15n^2 + 16n - 15 = 0$ $\left\{-\frac{5}{3}, \frac{3}{5}\right\}$
3. $r^2 + 13r = -42$ $\{-7, -6\}$
4. Find two numbers whose sum is 25 and whose product is 154.   **11 and 14**
5. Find two consecutive odd integers whose product is 483.   **21 and 23, −23 and −21**

Motivating the Lesson

Ask students to find the sum and the product of 9 and 18. Challenge the students to identify a relationship between the sum, product, and original numbers. Adding the digits of either the sum, product, or 18 totals 9.

TEACHING THE LESSON

Chalkboard Example

For Example 1

Find a quadratic equation having the given roots.

a. $2 + \sqrt{3}, 2 - \sqrt{3}$
   $x^2 - 4x + 1 = 0$

b. $4 + \sqrt{2}, 4 - \sqrt{2}$
   $x^2 - 8x + 14 = 0$

c. $3 + \sqrt{11}, 3 - \sqrt{11}$
   $x^2 - 6x - 2 = 0$

13-8 The Sum and Product of Roots

Objectives

After studying this lesson, you should be able to:

13-8A ■ find the sum and product of the roots of a quadratic equation, and

13-8B ■ write a quadratic equation given its roots.

Engineers, scientists, and mathematicians are often asked to find an equation that can be used to describe a certain situation or problem. Sometimes, the results of the problem are known and an equation can be found that fits these results. Finding this equation is just like finding an equation given the roots of the equation.

Suppose the roots of a quadratic equation are known to be −3 and 8.

If x = −3, then x + 3 = 0.   If x = 8, then x − 8 = 0.

The quadratic equation $(x + 3)(x - 8) = 0$, or $x^2 - 5x - 24 = 0$, has roots −3 and 8. *Why?*

Suppose you find the sum and the product of the roots of this quadratic equation.

Sum of roots: −3 + 8 = 5   **Product of roots:** −3 · 8 = −24

Now look at the equation again. What do you notice?

product of roots ──┐ *The product of the roots is the constant term.*
                   ↓
$x^2 - 5x - 24 = 0$
       ↑
opposite of sum ──┘ *The opposite of the sum of the roots is the*
    of roots   *coefficient of x.*

This relationship between the roots and coefficients is true for all quadratic equations. Suppose the two roots are r_1 and r_2. Then the quadratic equation is $(x - r_1)(x - r_2) = 0$. Multiplying the binomials results in the equation $x^2 - (r_1 + r_2)x + r_1r_2 = 0$. Notice that the coefficient of x, $-(r_1 + r_2)$, is the opposite of the sum of the roots. Also, the constant term, r_1r_2, is the product of the roots.

Example 1

Use the sum and the product of roots to find a quadratic equation whose roots are $1 + \sqrt{5}$ and $1 - \sqrt{5}$.

Opposite of the sum of roots

$= -[(1 + \sqrt{5}) + (1 - \sqrt{5})]$
$= -[(1 + 1) + (\sqrt{5} - \sqrt{5})]$
$= -2$

Product of roots

$= (1 + \sqrt{5})(1 - \sqrt{5})$
$= 1 - \sqrt{5} + \sqrt{5} - 5$
$= -4$

ALTERNATE TEACHING STRATEGIES

Using Logical Reasoning

Find k such that 3 is a root of the equation $x^2 + kx - 21 = 0$.
Let r = the second root of the equation. Then, since the product of the roots is $\frac{c}{a}$, $3r = -\frac{21}{1}$. So r = −7.
Since the sum of the roots is $-\frac{b}{a}$,
$3 + (-7) = -\frac{k}{1}$. Thus, k = 4.

The opposite of the sum of the roots, -2, is the coefficient of x. The product of the roots, -4, is the constant term. Thus, a quadratic equation whose roots are $1 + \sqrt{5}$ and $1 - \sqrt{5}$ is $x^2 - 2x - 4 = 0$.

Now consider the quadratic equation of the form $ax^2 + bx + c = 0$, where $a \neq 0$. Dividing each side by a results in the equation $x^2 + \frac{b}{a}x + \frac{c}{a} = 0$. By comparing this equation to the equation $x^2 - (r_1 + r_2)x + r_1r_2 = 0$, the following rule may be derived.

Sum and Product of Roots of a Quadratic Equation	For a quadratic equation of the form $ax^2 + bx + c = 0$, where $a \neq 0$, the sum of the roots of the equation is $-\frac{b}{a}$ and the product of the roots of the equation is $\frac{c}{a}$.

Example 2

Are $\frac{3}{2}$ and $-\frac{4}{3}$ roots of $6x^2 - x - 12 = 0$?

If $\frac{3}{2}$ and $-\frac{4}{3}$ are the roots, then their sum must be equal to $-\frac{b}{a}$ and their product must be equal to $\frac{c}{a}$.

Sum of Roots

$\frac{3}{2} + \left(-\frac{4}{3}\right) = \frac{9}{6} - \frac{8}{6}$

$= \frac{1}{6}$

Product of Roots

$\frac{3}{2}\left(-\frac{4}{3}\right) = -2$

Since $-\frac{b}{a} = -\left(\frac{-1}{6}\right)$ or $\frac{1}{6}$ and $\frac{c}{a} = \frac{-12}{6}$ or -2, $\frac{3}{2}$ and $-\frac{4}{3}$ are roots of the equation. **Teaching Tip ❶**

Example 3

APPLICATION
Physics

A research engineer proposes that the height h, in feet, of a rocket t seconds after blast-off is given by the formula $h = -16t^2 + 256t + 3124$. If the altitude of the rocket was 4500 feet after 5.5 seconds and after 10.5 seconds, is the proposed equation correct?

For the proposed equation to be correct, 5.5 and 10.5 must be the roots of the equation $4500 = -16t^2 + 256t + 3124$, or $16t^2 - 256t + 1376 = 0$. Rather than solving this equation to determine if 5.5 and 10.5 are the roots, you can check their sum and their product.

For $16t^2 - 256t + 1376 = 0$, $-\frac{b}{a} = \frac{-(-256)}{16}$ or 16 and $\frac{c}{a} = \frac{1376}{16}$ or 86.

Sum of Roots

$5.5 + 10.5 = 16$

Product of Roots

$5.5(10.5) = 57.75$

Since $57.75 \neq 86$, 5.5 and 10.5 are *not* roots of the proposed equation. Therefore, the proposed equation is not correct.

LESSON 13-8   THE SUM AND PRODUCT OF ROOTS   **551**

RETEACHING THE LESSON

Have students solve the following problems using what they know about roots:

1. If -3 is one root of $2r^2 + br - 3 = 0$, find the other root and the value of b.
$r = \frac{1}{2}, b = 5$

2. If 3 is one root of $3z^2 - bz - 3 = 0$, find the other root and the value of b.
$r = -\frac{1}{3}, b = 8$

Chalkboard Examples

For Example 2
State whether the given numbers are roots of each equation.

a. 2, 3; $x^2 + 5x + 6 = 0$ **no**

b. 5, 5; $x^2 - 10x + 25 = 0$ **yes**

c. $\frac{1}{2}, -\frac{1}{2}; 4x^2 - 1 = 0$ **yes**

For Example 3
Find a quadratic equation having the given roots.

a. $\frac{5}{2}$, 1 $2x^2 - 7x + 5 = 0$

b. $-2, \frac{1}{3}$ $3x^2 + 5x - 2 = 0$

c. $\frac{3}{5}$, 4 $5x^2 - 23x + 12 = 0$

d. $\frac{1}{2}, -\frac{1}{4}$ $8x^2 - 2x - 1 = 0$

Teaching Tip ❶   Remind students that the roots can also be verified by substituting them into the equation and evaluating. However, the method shown in the example is less time consuming.

Reteaching Masters Booklet, p. 93

NAME _____   DATE _____
13-8 Reteaching Worksheet

The Sum and Product of Roots

You can find the general form of a quadratic equation given its roots.

Finding Quadratic Equations
To find a quadratic equation of the general form $x^2 + bx + c = 0$ given its roots:
1. The coefficient of x is the opposite of the sum of the roots.
2. The constant term is the product of the roots.

The method of the sum and the product of roots for finding quadratic equations is especially useful when the roots involve radicals.

Sum and Product of Roots
Given the quadratic equation $ax^2 + bx + c = 0$, where $a \neq 0$, the sum of the roots of the equation is $-\frac{b}{a}$ and the product of the roots of the equation is $\frac{c}{a}$.

Example: Use the sum and the product of roots to find a quadratic equation whose roots are $2 + \sqrt{3}$ and $2 - \sqrt{3}$.

opposite of the sum of roots
$= -[(2 + \sqrt{3}) + (2 - \sqrt{3})]$
$= -4$ (coefficient of x)

product of roots
$= (2 + \sqrt{3})(2 - \sqrt{3})$
$= 1$ (constant term)

Thus, a quadratic equation whose roots are $2 + \sqrt{3}$ and $2 - \sqrt{3}$ is $x^2 - 4x + 1 = 0$.

Find the sum and the product of the roots of each equation.

1. $2h^2 + 6h - 8 = 0$ $-3; -4$
2. $4y^2 + 8y + 8 = 0$ $-2; 2$
3. $x^2 - 3x + 12 = 0$ $3; 12$
4. $n^2 + 12n + 32 = 0$ $-12; 32$
5. $\frac{1}{2}x^2 - \frac{3}{2}x + 8 = 0$ $3; 16$
6. $z^2 - \frac{3}{4}z + \frac{3}{8} = 0$ $\frac{3}{4}; \frac{3}{8}$

Write a quadratic equation having the given roots.

7. 1, 6
$x^2 - 7x + 6 = 0$
8. 8, -4
$x^2 - 4x - 32 = 0$
9. 4, 1
$x^2 - 5x + 4 = 0$
10. 2, 3
$x^2 - 5x + 6 = 0$
11. -4, 9
$x^2 - 5x - 36 = 0$
12. -3, 5
$x^2 - 2x - 15 = 0$
13. $1 + \sqrt{7}, 1 - \sqrt{7}$
$x^2 - 2x - 6 = 0$
14. $-10 + \sqrt{5}, -10 - \sqrt{5}$
$x^2 + 20x + 95 = 0$
15. $\sqrt{6}, -\sqrt{6}$
$x^2 - 6 = 0$

Chapter 13   551

Checking for Understanding

Exercises 1-17 are designed to help you assess understanding through reading, writing, and speaking. You should work through Exercises 1-3 with your students, and then monitor their work on Exercises 4-17.

Closing the Lesson

Writing Activity Have students write the steps to follow to find a quadratic equation in the general form when given its roots.

APPLYING THE LESSON

Homework Exercises

Assignment Guide
Basic: 18-40, 46-48, 50-55
Average: 22-43, 46-55
Enriched: 24-55

Additional Answers

14. $x^2 - 7x + 10 = 0$
15. $x^2 + 5x - 6 = 0$
16. $3x^2 - 23x + 14 = 0$
17. $x^2 + 0.3x - 0.18 = 0$
18. $-15, 54$
19. $5, -24$

Practice Masters Booklet, p. 105

NAME _____ DATE _____

13-8 | **Practice Worksheet**

The Sum and Product of Roots
Find the sum and the product of each equation.

1. $x^2 + 6x - 16 = 0$
   $-6; -16$
2. $y^2 - 4y - 5 = 0$
   $4; -5$

3. $a^2 + 5a + 4 = 0$
   $-5; 4$
4. $b^2 - 9b + 14 = 0$
   $9; 14$

5. $2z^2 + 5z + 2 = 0$
   $-\frac{5}{2}; 1$
6. $3w^2 - 5w - 2 = 0$
   $\frac{5}{3}, -\frac{2}{3}$

7. $\frac{3}{4}v^2 - \frac{1}{4}v - \frac{1}{2} = 0$
   $\frac{1}{3}; -\frac{2}{3}$
8. $4r^2 - 4r - 3 = 0$
   $1; -\frac{3}{4}$

Write a quadratic equation having the given roots.

9. $2, -4$
   $x^2 + 2x - 8 = 0$
10. $1, -6$
   $x^2 + 5x - 6 = 0$

11. $\frac{1}{2}, -2$
   $2x^2 + 3x - 2 = 0$
12. $-\frac{1}{4}, 3$
   $4x^2 - 11x - 3 = 0$

13. $2 + \sqrt{3}, 2 - \sqrt{3}$
   $x^2 - 4x + 1 = 0$
14. $5 + \sqrt{2}, 5 - \sqrt{2}$
   $x^2 - 10x + 23 = 0$

CHECKING FOR UNDERSTANDING

Communicating Mathematics

Read and study the lesson to answer each question.

1. For the equation $x^2 + bx + c = 0$, how is b related to the roots of the equation? **It is the opposite of the sum of the roots.**

2. For the equation $x^2 + bx + c = 0$, how is c related to the roots of the equation? **It is the product of the roots.**

3. If r and s are roots of a quadratic equation, what is the factored form of the equation? **$(x - r)(x - s) = 0$**

Guided Practice

State the sum and the product of the roots of each equation.

4. $x^2 - 5x + 6 = 0$ **5, 6**
5. $3m^2 + 6m - 3 = 0$ **$-2, -1$**
6. $4t^2 + 8t + 3 = 0$ **$-2, \frac{3}{4}$**
7. $6a^2 - 13a = 15$ **$\frac{13}{6}, -\frac{5}{2}$**

State whether each pair of numbers are the roots of each equation.

8. $-6, 3; y^2 + 3y - 18 = 0$ **yes**
9. $2, 3; n^2 + 5n - 6 = 0$ **no**
10. $-1, 7; b^2 - 8b = -7$ **no**
11. $\frac{-1}{3}, \frac{1}{2}; x^2 - \frac{1}{6}x - \frac{1}{6} = 0$ **yes**
12. $1 + \sqrt{7}, 1 - \sqrt{7}; r^2 - 2r - 6 = 0$ **yes**
13. $4 + \sqrt{3}, 4 - \sqrt{3}; x^2 + 8x = -13$ **no**

Write a quadratic equation having the given roots. **See margin.**

14. $5, 2$
15. $1, -6$
16. $\frac{2}{3}, 7$
17. $0.3, -0.6$

EXERCISES

Practice

Find the sum and the product of the roots of each equation. **See margin.**

18. $y^2 + 15y + 54 = 0$
19. $a^2 - 5a - 24 = 0$
20. $6x^2 + 31x + 35 = 0$
21. $z^2 + \frac{13}{2}z - \frac{9}{4} = 0$
22. $\frac{1}{2}m^2 - \frac{3}{2}m + 4 = 0$
23. $2c^2 - \frac{2}{3}c = \frac{1}{6}$
24. $12x^2 - 4x = 9$
25. $6k^2 - 0.02 = 0.4k$
26. $2y^2 - 6 = -y\sqrt{2}$

Write a quadratic equation having the given roots. **See margin.**

27. $4, 7$
28. $6, -5$
29. $1, -10$
30. $-2, -17$
31. $\frac{5}{2}, 2$
32. $\frac{-3}{4}, 8$
33. $\frac{2}{3}, \frac{-3}{2}$
34. $-1.4, -2.2$
35. $\sqrt{2}, -\sqrt{2}$
36. $\sqrt{3}, \sqrt{3}$
37. $2 + \sqrt{3}, 2 - \sqrt{3}$
38. $-4 + \sqrt{10}, -4 - \sqrt{10}$
39. $3 + \sqrt{5}, 5 + \sqrt{3}$
40. $\frac{2 - \sqrt{11}}{3}, \frac{2 + \sqrt{11}}{3}$

Additional Answers

20. $-\frac{31}{6}, \frac{35}{6}$
21. $-\frac{13}{2}, -\frac{9}{4}$
22. $3, 8$
23. $\frac{1}{3}, -\frac{1}{12}$
24. $\frac{1}{3}, -\frac{3}{4}$
25. $\frac{1}{15}, -\frac{1}{300}$
26. $-\frac{\sqrt{2}}{2}, -3$
27. $x^2 - 11x + 28 = 0$
28. $x^2 - x - 30 = 0$
29. $x^2 + 9x - 10 = 0$

30. $x^2 + 19x + 34 = 0$
31. $2x^2 - 9x + 10 = 0$
32. $4x^2 - 29x - 24 = 0$
33. $6x^2 + 5x - 6 = 0$
34. $x^2 + 3.6x + 3.08 = 0$
35. $x^2 - 2 = 0$
36. $x^2 - 2x\sqrt{3} + 3 = 0$
37. $x^2 - 4x + 1 = 0$
38. $x^2 + 8x + 6 = 0$
39. $x^2 - (8 + \sqrt{3} + \sqrt{5})x + (15 + 5\sqrt{5} + 3\sqrt{3} + \sqrt{15})$
40. $9x^2 - 12x - 7 = 0$

C Find the value of k such that indicated number is a root of the given equation.

41. 3; $x^2 + kx - 21 = 0$ **4**

42. 1; $x^2 + kx + 5 = 0$ **−6**

43. -5; $x^2 + 12x + k = 0$ **35**

44. 3; $x^2 + 6x - k = 0$ **27**

45. Write the general form of the quadratic equation with roots q and r.
$x^2 - (q + r)x + qr = 0$

Critical Thinking Show that the following statements are true for the equation $ax^2 + bx + c = 0$. (*Hint:* Use the roots from the quadratic formula.) See margin.

46. The sum of the roots is $-\dfrac{b}{a}$.

47. The product of the roots is $\dfrac{c}{a}$.

48. **72 feet per second**

Applications

48. **Physics** A rocket is launched from a height of 50 feet. The rocket reaches a height of 122 feet at 1.5 seconds and at 3 seconds. Was the initial velocity of this rocket 72 feet per second or 80 feet per second? Use the formula $H = -16t^2 + vt + h$.

49. **Finance** A theater has seats for 500 people. To increase income, the owner plans to raise the price of tickets which is now $6.00. She estimates that if p is the number of $0.50 price increases, then the expression $3000 + 100p - 12.5p^2$ represents her income. If the maximum income actually occurs when the ticket price is $8.00, is this expression for the income correct? **yes**

Mixed Review

50. Find $\left(\dfrac{5}{7}a^2 - \dfrac{3}{4}a + \dfrac{1}{2}\right) - \left(\dfrac{3}{7}a^2 + \dfrac{1}{2}a - \dfrac{1}{2}\right)$. (Lesson 6-6) $\dfrac{2}{7}a^2 - \dfrac{5}{4}a + 1$

51. Simplify $\dfrac{n^2 - 4}{n^2 - 4n - 12} \div (n - 2)$. (Lesson 8-4) $\dfrac{1}{n - 6}$

52. Draw a mapping of the relation shown at the right. Then write the relation and its inverse as sets of ordered pairs. (Lesson 9-2) See margin.

x	2	6	7	8
y	−2	5	3	−2

53. **Uniform Motion** When Neil was 2 miles upstream from camp on a canoe trip, he passed a log floating downstream with the current. He paddled upstream for 1 more hour and then returned to camp just as the log arrived. What was the rate of the current? (Lesson 11-5) **1 mph**

54. Solve $\sqrt{3x - 5} + x = 11$ and check. (Lesson 12-7) **7**

55. **Physics** The height h, in meters, that Andreina is above the water t seconds after beginning her dive is given by the formula $h = -5t^2 + 6t + 10$. After how many seconds will Andreina hit the water, rounded to the nearest tenth of a second? (Lesson 13-7) **2.1 seconds**

LESSON 13-8 THE SUM AND PRODUCT OF ROOTS 553

EXTENDING THE LESSON

Math Power: Problem Solving

The general form of a cubic, or third degree, equation is given as
$x^3 - (r_1 + r_2 + r_3)x^2 + (r_1r_2 + r_1r_3 + r_2r_3)x - (r_1r_2r_3) = 0$,
where r_1, r_2, and r_3 are the roots of the equation. Find the cubic equation whose roots are -1, 3, and 7. $x^3 - 9x^2 + 11x + 21 = 0$

Additional Answers

46. $\dfrac{-b + \sqrt{b^2 - 4ac}}{2a} + \dfrac{-b - \sqrt{b^2 - 4ac}}{2a} = -\dfrac{2b}{2a} = -\dfrac{b}{a}$

47. $\dfrac{-b + \sqrt{b^2 - 4ac}}{2a} \cdot \dfrac{-b - \sqrt{b^2 - 4ac}}{2a} = \dfrac{b^2 - (b^2 - 4ac)}{4a^2} = \dfrac{4ac}{4a^2} = \dfrac{c}{a}$

Chapter 13, Quiz D, (Lessons 13-7 through 13-8), is available in the Evaluation Masters Booklet, p. 178.

Additional Answer

52.

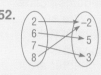

$\{(2, -2), (6, 5), (7, 3), (8, -2)\}$;
$\{(-2, 2), (5, 6), (3, 7), (-2, 8)\}$

Enrichment Masters Booklet, p. 93

13-8 **Enrichment Worksheet**

NAME _____ DATE _____

Curious Circles

Two circles can be arranged in four ways: one circle can be inside the other, they can be separate, they can overlap, or they can coincide.

In how many ways can a given number of circles be either separate or inside each other? (The situations in which the circles overlap or coincide are not counted here.)

Here is the answer for 3 circles. There are 4 different possibilities.

Solve each problem. Make drawings to show your answers.

1. Show the different ways in which 2 circles can be separate or inside each other. How many ways are there? **two ways**

2. Show the different ways for 4 circles. How many ways are there? **nine ways**

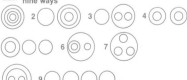

3. Use your answer for Exercise 2 to show that the number of ways for 5 circles is at least 18. see below

4. Find the number of ways for 5 circles. Show your drawings on a separate sheet of paper. **20 ways**

3. First, draw an extra circle next to each of the ways for 4 circles. Then draw a circle around each of the ways for 4 circles.

Additional Answers

5.

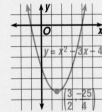

6.

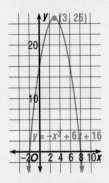

VOCABULARY

Upon completing this chapter, you should be familiar with the following terms:

axis of symmetry	519	518	parabola
completing the square	532	537	quadratic formula
discriminant	541	518	quadratic function
maximum point	519	523	root
minimum point	519	519	vertex

SKILLS AND CONCEPTS

OBJECTIVES AND EXAMPLES	REVIEW EXERCISES

Upon completing this chapter you should be able to:

■ find the equation of the axis of symmetry and the coordinates of the vertex of the graph of a quadratic function   (Lesson 13-1)

For the graph of $y = x^2 - 8x + 12$, the equation of the axis of symmetry is $x = -\frac{-8}{2(1)}$ or $x = 4$.

Since $4^2 - 8(4) + 12 = -4$, the graph has a minimum point at $(4, -4)$.

Find the equation of the axis of symmetry and the coordinates of the vertex of the graph of each quadratic function.

1. $y = x^2 - 3x - 4$ $x = \frac{3}{2}$; $\left(\frac{3}{2}, -\frac{25}{4}\right)$
2. $y = -x^2 + 6x + 16$ $x = 3$; $(3, 25)$
3. $y = -2x^2 + 9x - 9$ $x = \frac{9}{4}$; $\left(\frac{9}{4}, \frac{9}{8}\right)$
4. $y = 3x^2 + 6x - 17$ $x = -1$; $(-1, -20)$

■ graph a quadratic function (Lesson 13-1)

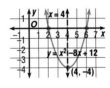

Using the results from Exercises 1–4, graph each quadratic function. See margin.

5. $y = x^2 - 3x - 4$
6. $y = -x^2 + 6x + 16$
7. $y = -2x^2 + 9x - 9$
8. $y = 3x^2 + 6x - 17$

■ find the roots of a quadratic equation by graphing   (Lesson 13-2)

Based on the graph of $y = x^2 - 8x + 12$ shown above, the roots of the equation $x^2 - 8x + 12 = 0$ are 2 and 6.

Find the roots of each equation by graphing its related function.

9. $x^2 - x - 12 = 0$ $-3, 4$
10. $x^2 + 6x + 9 = 0$ -3
11. $x^2 + 4x - 3 = 0$ $-5 < x < -4, 0 < x < 1$
12. $2x^2 - 5x + 4 = 0$ no real roots

Additional Answers

7.

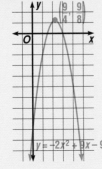

8.

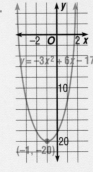

Alternate Review Strategy

To provide a brief in-class review, you may wish to read the following questions to the class and require a verbal response.

■ solve quadratic equations by completing the square   **(Lesson 13-4)**

$y^2 + 6y + 2 = 0$

$\quad y^2 + 6y = -2$

$y^2 + 6y + 9 = -2 + 9$

$\quad (y + 3)^2 = 7$

$\quad\quad y + 3 = \pm\sqrt{7}$

$\quad\quad\quad y = -3 \pm \sqrt{7}$

The roots are $-3 + \sqrt{7}$ and $-3 - \sqrt{7}$.

Find the value of c that makes each trinomial a perfect square.

13. $x^2 + 8x + c$ **16**

14. $r^2 - 5r + c$ $\frac{25}{4}$

Solve each equation by completing the square. **See margin.**

15. $x^2 - 16x + 32 = 0$

16. $m^2 - 7m = 5$

17. $4a^2 + 16a + 15 = 0$

1. Find the equation of the axis of symmetry and the coordinates of the vertex of the graph of $y = x^2 - 8x + 10$.   **$x = 4$, $(4, -6)$**

2. Find the roots of $x^2 + 3x - 18 = 0$ by graphing its related function.   **$-6, 3$**

3. Find the value of c that makes the trinomial a perfect square. $x^2 - 20x + c$ **100**

■ solve quadratic equations by using the quadratic formula   **(Lesson 13-5)**

Solve $2x^2 + 7x - 15 = 0$.

$x = \dfrac{-7 \pm \sqrt{(7)^2 - 4(2)(-15)}}{2(2)}$

$\quad = \dfrac{-7 \pm \sqrt{169}}{4}$

$x = \dfrac{-7 + 13}{4}$ or $x = \dfrac{-7 - 13}{4}$

$\quad = \dfrac{3}{2}$ $\quad\quad\quad = -5$

Solve each equation by using the quadratic formula.

18. $x^2 - 8x = 20$ **10, -2**

19. $5b^2 + 9b + 3 = 0$ $\dfrac{-9 \pm \sqrt{21}}{10}$; **$-0.44, -1.36$**

20. $9k^2 - 1 = 12k$ $\dfrac{2 \pm \sqrt{5}}{3}$; **1.41, -0.08**

21. $2m^2 = \dfrac{17}{6}m - 1$ $\dfrac{3}{4}, \dfrac{2}{3}$

22. $3s^2 - 7s - 2 = 0$ $\dfrac{7 \pm \sqrt{73}}{6}$; **2.59, -0.26**

4. Solve by using the quadratic formula. $y^2 + 8y + 15 = 0$ **$-3, -5$**

5. Use the discriminant to determine the nature of the roots of the equation. $y^2 + 3y + 1 = 0$ **2 real roots**

■ evaluate the discriminant of a quadratic equation to determine the nature of the roots of the equation   **(Lesson 13-6)**

The discriminant of $3x^2 - 8x - 40 = 0$ is $(-8)^2 - 4(3)(-40)$ or 544. Thus, the equation has 2 real roots.

Use the discriminant to determine the nature of the roots of each equation.

23. $9k^2 - 13k + 4 = 0$ **2 real roots**

24. $7x^2 - 6x + 5 = 0$ **no real roots**

25. $9a^2 + 25 = 30a$ **1 real root**

26. $4p^2 + 4p = 15$ **2 real roots**

6. Find two numbers that differ by 7 and have a product of 144.   **9 and 16, -16 and -9**

7. Find a quadratic equation having the roots 6, 1.   **$x^2 - 7x + 6 = 0$**

■ solve problems that can be represented by quadratic equations   **(Lesson 13-7)**

A rectangle has a perimeter of 38 in. and an area of 84 in². Find the dimensions of this rectangle.

Since $2\ell + 2w = 38$, $2\ell = 38 - 2w$ or $\ell = 19 - w$. Since $\ell w = 84$, $(19 - w)w = 84$ or $0 = w^2 - 19w + 84$. The roots of this equation are 7 and 12. Therefore, the dimensions are 7 in. and 12 in.

Solve.

27. Find two integers whose sum is 21 and whose product is 90.   **6, 15**

28. The length of a rectangular garden is 8 feet more than its width. A walkway 3 feet wide surrounds the outside of the garden. If the total area of the walkway alone is 288 square feet, what are the dimensions of the garden?   **17 ft by 25 ft**

Additional Answers

For Exercises 15-17, exact answers and decimal answers rounded to the nearest hundredth are given.

15. $8 \pm 4\sqrt{2}$; **13.66, 2.34**

16. $\dfrac{7 \pm \sqrt{69}}{2}$; **7.65, -0.65**

17. $-\dfrac{3}{2}, -\dfrac{5}{2}$

The Cumulative Review shown below can be used to review skills and concepts presented thus far in the text. Standardized Test Practice Questions are also provided in the Evaluation Masters Booklet.

Evaluation Masters Booklet, pp. 179-180

■ find the sum and product of the roots of a quadratic equation **(Lesson 13-8)**

For the equation $3x^2 + 8x + 9 = 0$, the sum of the roots is $-\frac{b}{a} = \frac{-8}{3}$, and the product of the roots is $\frac{c}{a} = \frac{9}{3}$ or 3.

Find the sum and product of the roots of each equation.

29. $y^2 + 8y - 14 = 0$ $-8, -14$

30. $4a^2 - 6a + 11 = 0$ $\frac{3}{2}, \frac{11}{4}$

31. $2x^2 - x = 6$ $\frac{1}{2}, -3$

■ write a quadratic equation given its roots **(Lesson 13-8)**

Find a quadratic equation whose roots are 2 and $\frac{5}{3}$.

Sum of roots: $2 + \frac{5}{3} = \frac{11}{3}$ $-\frac{b}{a} = \frac{11}{3}$

Product of roots: $2 \cdot \frac{5}{3} = \frac{10}{3}$ $\frac{c}{a} = \frac{10}{3}$

The equation is $3x^2 - 11x + 10 = 0$.

Find a quadratic equation having the given roots.

32. $1, -8$ $x^2 + 7x - 8 = 0$

33. $\frac{3}{2}, -4$ $2x^2 + 5x - 12 = 0$

34. $3 + \sqrt{5}, 3 - \sqrt{5}$ $x^2 - 6x + 4 = 0$

NAME _____ DATE _____

~~**Cumulative Review**~~ (Chapters 1-13)

1. Write a mathematical expression for the product of 8 and the square of a number.
   1. $8n^2$

2. State the property shown in $(ab)c = a(bc)$
   2. Assoc., Mult.

3. Find $-7 - (-13)$.
   3. 6

4. Solve $3.8 = b + 7.2$.
   4. -3.4

5. Simplify $-5(4) + (-6)(-2)$.
   5. -8

6. Find three consecutive odd integers such that 8 more than twice the first integer is equal to 19 less than three times the third integer.
   6. 15, 17, 19

7. Graph the solution set of $m \geq -4\frac{1}{2}$ on a number line.
   7. (number line) $-6 -4 -2\ 0\ 2\ 4\ 6$

8. Solve $\frac{4}{3}z < -\frac{3}{5}$.
   8. $z < -\frac{9}{20}$

9. Express 0.00056×10^7 in scientific notation.
   9. 5.6×10^3

10. A price decreased from \$85 to \$72.25. Find the percent of decrease.
    10. 15%

11. Simplify $7x^2(x + 3) - 2x(x^2 + 1) + 6(2x^3 + x^2 - 3)$.
    11. $17x^3 + 27x^2 - 2x - 18$

12. A certain triangle has two congruent sides. The third side is 2 inches shorter than either of the congruent sides. If the perimeter of the triangle is 28 inches, what are the lengths of the congruent sides?
    12. 10 inches

Factor, if possible.

13. $15y^3 + 5y^2 - 30ay^2$
    13. $5y^2(3y + 1 - 6a)$

14. $16a^2 - 24ab + 9b^2$
    14. $(4a - 3b)^2$

Solve each equation.

15. $(x + 3)(x - 4) = 0$
    15. $-3, 4$

16. $4r^2 - 7r + 3 = 0$
    16. $\frac{3}{4}, 1$

17. Simplify $\frac{m^2 - 1}{2 - m - m^2}$.
    17. $\frac{m + 1}{m + 2}$

18. Solve $4x = 5 + y$ if the domain is $\{-3, -1, 1, 5\}$.
    18. $\{(-3, -17), (-1, -9), (1, -1), (5, 15)\}$

19. Given $f(x) = 12x^2 - 5x - 3$, find $f(-2)$.
    19. 55

20. Write an equation for the relationship between the variables in the chart at the right.

x	0	2	4	6
y	4	8	12	16

    20. $y = 2x + 4$

21. Determine the value of r so that the line through $(1, 3)$ and $(6, r)$ has slope of $-\frac{2}{5}$.
    21. 1

NAME _____ DATE _____

Cumulative Review (Chapters 1-13)

22. Graph $4x + 2y = 1$ using the slope-intercept method.
    22. (graph)

23. Write an equation for the line that is parallel to the graph of $2y - 6x = 3$ and passes through $(-3, 2)$. Use slope-intercept form.
    23. $y = 3x + 11$

24. Use substitution to solve the system of equations $x + y = 2$ and $2x - y = 1$.
    24. $(1, 1)$

25. Use elimination to solve the system of equations $2x + 2y = -4$ and $7x + 4y = 1$.
    25. $(3, -5)$

26. Mrs. Walton invests \$5000, part of it at 11% annual interest and the rest at 13% annual interest. If she receives \$610 interest at the end of one year, how much did she invest at each rate?
    26. \$2000 at 11% \$3000 at 13%

27. State whether $0.\overline{46}$ represents a rational number or an irrational number.
    27. rational

28. Simplify $2\sqrt{8} + 2\sqrt{12} - 3\sqrt{2}$.
    28. $\sqrt{2} + 4\sqrt{3}$

29. Find the distance between the pair of points with coordinates $(7, -1)$ and $(-4, -2)$.
    29. $\sqrt{122}$ or 11.05

30. Find the equation of the axis of symmetry and the coordinates of the maximum or minimum point for the graph of $y = x^2 + x - 12$.
    30. $x = -\frac{1}{2}$; Min. pt.: $\left(-\frac{1}{2}, -12\frac{1}{4}\right)$

31. Use the quadratic formula to solve $x^2 + 3x + 1 = 0$.
    31. $\frac{-3 \pm \sqrt{5}}{2}$

32. Solve $2y^2 - 7y = 4$ by an appropriate method.
    32. $-\frac{1}{2}, 4$

33. Solve $\frac{1}{2}x^2 - \frac{1}{2}x - 10 = 0$ by completing the square.
    33. $-4, 5$

APPLICATIONS AND CONNECTIONS

35. **Number Theory** How many numbers between 1000 and 10,000 are palindromes? **(Lesson 13-3)** 90

36. **Geometry** The area of a certain square is one-half the area of the rectangle formed if the length of one side of the square is increased by 2 cm and the length of an adjacent side is increased by 3 cm. What are the dimensions of the square? **(Lesson 13-7)** 6 cm by 6 cm

37. **Sales** A helicopter service transports passengers to an island during vacation season. Each day, 500 people are transported for a round trip fare of \$20. The owner has decided to increase the fare. A survey has shown that for each \$1 increase in fare, 20 less people will use the service. What fare will maximize the owner's income? **(Lesson 13-1)** \$22.50

38. **Physics** The height h, in feet, of a rocket t seconds after blast-off is given by the formula $h = 1440t - 16t^2$.
    a. After how many seconds will the rocket reach a height of 25,000 ft?
    b. After how many seconds will the rocket reach a height of 35,000 ft?
    c. After how many seconds will the rocket hit the ground?
    (Lesson 13-6) a. ≈ 23.5 sec., ≈ 66.5 sec.
    b. never   c. 90 seconds

Find the equation of the axis of symmetry and the coordinates of the vertex of the graph of each quadratic function.

1. $y = 4x^2 - 8x - 17$ $x = 1; (1, -21)$

2. $y = -3x^2 + 12x + 34$ $x = 2; (2, 46)$

Find the roots of each equation by graphing its related function. If exact roots cannot be found, state the consecutive integers between which the roots are located.

3. $x^2 + x - 2 = 0$ $-2, 1$

4. $x^2 - 8x + 11 = 0$ $1 < x < 2, 6 < x < 7$

5. Solve $m^2 - 8m - 4 = 0$ by completing the square. $4 \pm 2\sqrt{5}; 8.47, -0.47$

6. Solve $2k^2 - 9k + 8 = 0$ by using the quadratic formula. $\frac{9 \pm \sqrt{17}}{4}; 3.28, 1.22$

Solve each quadratic equation by an appropriate method. Express irrational roots in simplest radical form and in decimal form rounded to the nearest hundredth.

7. $2x^2 - 5x - 12 = 0$ $4, -\frac{3}{2}$

8. $m^2 + 18m + 75 = 0$ $-9 \pm \sqrt{6}; -6.55, -11.45$

9. $3y^2 - 2y - 4 = 0$ $\frac{1 \pm \sqrt{13}}{3}; 1.54, -0.87$

10. $3k^2 + 2k = 5$ $1, -\frac{5}{3}$

11. $6n^2 + 7n = 20$ $\frac{4}{3}, -\frac{5}{2}$

12. $2x^2 - 10 = 3x$ $\frac{3 \pm \sqrt{89}}{4}; 3.11, -1.61$

13. $7a^2 + \frac{23}{3}a + 2 = 0$ $-\frac{3}{7}, -\frac{2}{3}$

14. $x^2 - 4.4x + 4.2 = 0$ $1.4, 3$

Use the discriminant to determine the nature of the roots of each equation.

15. $3y^2 - y - 10 = 0$ **2 real roots**

16. $4b^2 + 12b + 9 = 0$ **1 real root**

17. $3m^2 - 9m + 7 = 0$ **no real roots**

18. $y^2 + y\sqrt{3} - 5 = 0$ **2 real roots**

19. Find the sum and the product of the roots of $3m^2 - 15m + 41 = 0$. $5, \frac{41}{3}$

Find a quadratic equation having the given roots.

20. $-2, \frac{5}{4}$ $4x^2 + 3x - 10 = 0$

21. $6 + \sqrt{3}, 6 - \sqrt{3}$ $x^2 - 12x + 33 = 0$

22. **Geometry** A rectangle has a perimeter of 44 cm and area of 105 cm². Find its dimensions. **7 cm by 15 cm**

23. **Number Theory** Find two real numbers whose sum is 22 and whose product is 125. **No such real numbers exist.**

24. **Construction** A rectangular piece of sheet metal is 3 times as long as it is wide. Squares measuring 2 cm on a side are cut from each corner and the sides are folded up in order to make a box. If the volume of the box needs to be 512 cm³, what must be the dimensions of the piece of sheet metal? **12 cm by 36 cm**

25. **Diving** Greg is diving off a 3-meter springboard. His height h, in meters, above the water when he is x meters away from the board is given by the formula $y = -x^2 + 3x + 3$. What is the maximum height Greg will reach on a dive? About how far away from the board is he when he enters the water? **5.25 m, 3.8 m**

Bonus Find the coordinates of the vertex of the graph of the equation $y = ax^2 + bx + c$, where $a \neq 0$. $\left(-\frac{b}{2a}, \frac{4ac - b^2}{4a}\right)$

Using the Chapter Test

This page may be used as a test or as a review. In addition, two multiple-choice tests and two free-response tests are provided in the Evaluation Masters Booklet. Chapter 13 Test, Form 1A is shown below.

Evaluation Masters Booklet, pp. 169-170

NAME _____ DATE _____

Chapter 13 Test, Form 1A

Write the letter for the correct answer in the blank at the right of each problem.

1. What is the equation of the axis of symmetry and the coordinates of the vertex of the graph of $y = 2x^2 - 12x + 6$?
   A. $x = -3; (-3, 60)$ B. $x = 3; (3, -12)$
   C. $x = -3; (-3, 78)$ D. $x = 3; (3, 6)$ .... 1. __B__

2. Find the equation of the axis of symmetry for the graph of $y = -4x^2 + 5x + 1$, and state whether the axis of symmetry contains the maximum point or the minimum point of the graph.
   A. $x = -\frac{5}{8}$; maximum   B. $x = -\frac{5}{8}$; minimum
   C. $x = \frac{5}{8}$; maximum   D. $x = \frac{5}{8}$; minimum .... 2. __C__

3. What are the coordinates of the vertex of the graph of $y = -2x^2 - 8$?
   A. $(-2, -16)$ B. $(-2, 8)$ C. $(2, -16)$ D. $(0, -8)$ .... 3. __D__

4. If a quadratic equation has exactly one real root, then which of the following could be the graph of the related function?

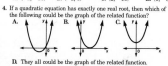

   D. They all could be the graph of the related function. .... 4. __B__

5. If the roots of $x^2 + 4x + 1 = 0$ are located by graphing the related function, between which pairs of integers does a root of the equation lie?
   A. -4 and -3 B. -2 and -1 C. 0 and 1 D. 2 and 3 .... 5. __A__

6. What value of c makes $x^2 - 5x + c$ a perfect square?
   A. $-\frac{5}{2}$ B. $\frac{25}{2}$ C. $\frac{25}{4}$ D. -5 .... 6. __C__

7. If $2n^2 - 6n = 3$ is to be solved by completing the square, what would be the best thing to do first?
   A. Add $6n$ to each side.   B. Divide each side by 2.
   C. Add 9 to each side.   D. Subtract 3 from each side. .... 7. __B__

8. Five snowplows can plow 20 city blocks in 6 hours. If all the snowplows work at the same rate, how many city blocks can 12 snowplows plow in 8 hours?
   A. 64 B. 80 C. 72 D. 37 .... 8. __A__

9. Solve $(x + 5)^2 = 10$.
   A. $\{\pm\sqrt{10}\}$ B. $\{\pm\sqrt{5}\}$ C. $\{-5 \pm \sqrt{10}\}$ D. $\{10 \pm \sqrt{5}\}$ .... 9. __C__

NAME _____ DATE _____

Chapter 13 Test, Form 1A (continued)

10. Solve $3x^2 + 4x - 1 = 0$.
    A. $\left[\frac{-2 \pm 2\sqrt{7}}{3}\right]$ B. $\left[\frac{-4 \pm \sqrt{7}}{6}\right]$ C. $\left[-1, \frac{1}{3}\right]$ D. $\left[\frac{-2 \pm \sqrt{7}}{3}\right]$ .... 10. __D__

11. Solve $2y^2 - 5 = 1$.
    A. $\{\pm\sqrt{3}\}$ B. $\left[\frac{5 \pm \sqrt{17}}{4}\right]$ C. $\left[\frac{5 \pm \sqrt{33}}{4}\right]$ D. $\{9\}$ .... 11. __A__

12. Solve $x^2 + 5x - 6 = 0$.
    A. $\{6, -1\}$ B. $\{-6, 1\}$ C. $\{-3, -2\}$ D. $\{3, 2\}$ .... 12. __B__

13. What is the value of the discriminant of the equation $3x^2 - 2x - 5 = 0$?
    A. 64 B. 8 C. -56 D. $\sqrt{-56}$ .... 13. __A__

14. If the value of the discriminant is 0, then the quadratic equation has
    A. one real root.   B. two rational roots.
    C. no real roots.   D. two irrational roots. .... 14. __A__

15. Which equation has no real roots?
    A. $x^2 - 10x + 5 = 0$ B. $x^2 - 5x - 10 = 0$
    C. $x^2 - 10x - 5 = 0$ D. $x^2 - 5x + 10 = 0$ .... 15. __D__

16. Which method is easiest for solving the equation $3n^2 - 81n = 0$?
    A. graphing   B. factoring
    C. completing the square   D. quadratic formula .... 16. __B__

17. The perimeter of a rectangle is 49 cm. Its area is 117 cm². If x represents the width of the rectangle in centimeters, which equation must be true?
    A. $x(49 - x) = 117$ B. $x(x - 49) = 117$
    C. $x\left(\frac{49}{2} - x\right) = 117$ D. $x\left(x - \frac{49}{2}\right) = 117$ .... 17. __C__

18. A rectangular piece of sheet metal is 4 inches longer than it is wide. Squares measuring 2 inches on a side are cut from each corner and the sides are folded to form a box. The volume of the box is 154 cubic inches. What is the width of the original piece of sheet metal?
    A. 7 inches B. 9 inches C. 11 inches D. 15 inches .... 18. __C__

19. What are the sum and product of the roots of the equation $4x^2 - x - 6 = 0$?
    A. $\frac{1}{4}, \frac{3}{2}$ B. $-\frac{1}{4}, \frac{3}{2}$ C. $\frac{1}{4}, -\frac{3}{2}$ D. $-\frac{1}{4}, -\frac{3}{2}$ .... 19. __C__

20. Which is an equation with roots of $-\frac{1}{2}$ and $\frac{2}{3}$?
    A. $6x^2 + 2x + 1 = 0$ B. $6x^2 - 2x - 1 = 0$
    C. $6x^2 - 2x + 1 = 0$ D. $6x^2 - x - 2 = 0$ .... 20. __D__

Bonus: Solve the equation $x + 5 + \frac{4}{x} = 0$. Bonus: $\{-1, -4\}$

Test Generator Software is provided in both Apple and IBM versions. You may use this software to create your own tests, based on the needs of your students.

CHAPTER 14

Statistics and Probability

PREVIEWING THE CHAPTER

The chapter reviews and extends students' knowledge of statistics and probability. Students display and interpret data on line plots, stem-and-leaf plots, box-and-whisker plots, and scatter plots. They calculate and interpret the mean, median, and mode (measures of central tendency) and the range, upper and lower quartiles, and interquartile range (measures of variation) of sets of data. After understanding the distinction between probability and odds of simple events, students conduct and interpret probability experiments involving both simple and compound events.

Problem-Solving Strategy   Students learn to use *solve a simpler but related problem* as a strategy for solving problems that otherwise would involve long and cumbersome calculations.

Lesson Objective Chart

Lesson (Pages)	Lesson Objectives	State/Local Objectives
14-1 (560-564)	**14-1A:** Interpret numerical data from a table.	
	14-1B: Display and interpret statistical data on a line plot.	
14-2 (565-569)	**14-2:** Display and interpret data on a stem-and-leaf plot.	
14-3 (570-574)	**14-3:** Calculate and interpret the mean, median, and mode of a set of data.	
14-4 (575-578)	**14-4:** Calculate and interpret the range, quartiles, and the interquartile range of a set of data.	
14-5 (579-582)	**14-5:** Display and interpret data on a box-and-whisker plot.	
14-6 (583-587)	**14-6:** Graph and interpret pairs of numbers on a scatter plot.	
14-7 (589-593)	**14-7A:** Find the probability of a simple event.	
	14-7B: Find the odds of a simple event.	
14-8 (594-597)	**14-8:** Conduct and interpret probability experiments.	
14-9 (598-599)	**14-9:** Solve problems by first solving a simpler but related problem.	
14-10 (600-603)	**14-10:** Find the probability of a compound event.	

ORGANIZING THE CHAPTER

You may want to refer to the **Course Planning Calendar** on page T36.

Lesson (Pages)	Course I	Course II	Course III	Reteaching	Practice	Enrichment	Evaluation	Technology	Lab Manual	Mixed Problem Solving	Applications	Cooperative Learning Activity	Multicultural	Transparencies
14-1 (560-564)	–	1	1	p. 94	p. 106	p. 94								14-1
14-2 (565-569)	–	1.5	1	p. 95	p. 107	p. 95								14-2
14-3 (570-574)	–	1	1	p. 96	p. 108	p. 96	Quiz A, p. 191		pp. 43-44					14-3
14-4 (575-578)	–	1	1	p. 97	p. 109	p. 97								14-4
14-5 (579-582)	–	1	1	p. 98	p. 110	p. 98	Mid-Chapter Test, p. 195							14-5
14-6 (583-587)	–	1.5	1	p. 99	p. 111	p. 99	Quiz B, p. 191	p. 29			p. 29			14-6
14-7 (589-593)	–	1	1	p. 100	p. 112	p. 100		p. 14						14-7
14-8 (594-597)	–	1	1	p. 101	p. 113	p. 101	Quiz C, p. 192					p. 44		14-8
14-9 (598-599)	–	1	1		p. 114								p. 59	14-9
14-10 (600-603)	–	1	1	p. 102	p. 115	p. 102	Quiz D, p. 192		pp. 45-46	p. 14				14-10
Review (604-606)	–	1	1	Multiple Choice Tests, Forms 1A and 1B, pp. 183-186 Free Response Tests, Forms 2A and 2B, pp. 187-190										
Test (607)	–	1	1	Cumulative Review, pp. 193-194 Standardized Test Practice Questions, p. 196										

Blackline Masters Booklets — Activities — *Lesson Planning Guide* — Pacing Chart (days)

Course I: Chapters 1-13; Course II: Chapters 1-14; Course III: Chapters 1-15

Other Chapter Resources

Student Edition
Mid-Chapter Review, p. 587
Technology, p. 588
History Connection, p. 593
Cooperative Learning Activity, p. 599

Teacher Resource Package
Activity Masters Booklet
 Mixed Problem Solving, p. 14
 Applications, p. 29
 Cooperative Learning Activity, p. 44
 Multicultural Activity, p. 59
Technology Masters Booklet
 Scientific Calculator Activity, p. 14
 Graphing Calculator Activity, p. 29
Lab Manual
 Lab Activity, pp. 43-44

Other Supplements
Transparency for Chapter Opener
Problem-of-the-Week Activity
 Cards, 32-34
Video Algebra, 61-63

Software
Algebra 1 Test and Review
 Generator Software
 Available for Apple and IBM.

ENHANCING THE CHAPTER

Cooperative Learning

Providing Closure to the Lesson

After each session, ample time should be provided for students to summarize what they have learned. To reinforce their understanding of the academic content acquired during the session, groups should review the major points covered and discuss any additional questions that they may have about the content. Class discussions can be a proper forum for this review. For example, select a number of one group to discuss with the class what his or her group concluded and how they reached these conclusions. Encourage the reporter to be thorough by asking for specific examples or additional details about various points. Do not immediately accept or reject the report, but involve the rest of the class by asking members of other groups if they agree or disagree with the conclusions reached by the reporter's group and if any group used different procedures to arrive at the same conclusions. You can also ask groups to relate this content to content learned earlier and to provide examples of different settings or applications where the content could be utilized. Such sharing of ideas and methods will ensure a greater retention of the academic content learned during the group activities.

Technology

This chapter includes a feature on regression lines. This feature teaches the students how to graph a linear regression problem and looks at how the calculator graphed the line that "best fits" the data. This can be used to show students how to interpret some of the data that they learned to classify in previous sections. It also graphs a regression line from a scatter plot of data.

Critical Thinking

Critical thinking often involves looking for the less obvious. For example, suppose each time a person tosses a coin, the result is heads at least 75% of the time. Why? To say that the coin is not perfectly balanced is an obvious answer. Suppose that when anyone else tosses the same coin, the results are always close to 50% heads. Now, what is a possible explanation? When students brainstorm with the goal of finding less obvious but reasonable explanations, they are engaging and exercising their higher-level thinking skills. You might want to have students look for news articles where the implied conclusion is not the only conclusion that could be supported by the data offered and present a report for a class discussion.

Cooperative Learning, p. 44

CHAPTER 14   NAME _____   DATE _____

Cooperative Learning Activity (Use after Lesson 14-8)

The Monte Carlo Approach to Probability

The Monte Carlo method is a way of solving probability problems using random number generators. These generators involve, in their simplest form, such procedures as tossing coins or rolling dice.

Work in small groups. Read the situation given in the following. Then use the procedure described.

Situation: The Oat-O Cereal company offers one prize in each cereal box. There are six different prizes available. There are equal numbers of each of the six prizes, and the chance of getting any of the six prizes is the same. You are to predict about how many cereal boxes you would have to buy to get all six prizes. **Answers will vary.**

Procedure:

Step 1. Use the numbers on a die to represent each of the six different prizes. For example, a 1 on the die represents Prize A, a 2 on the die represents Prize B, and so on. Each roll of the die represents one cereal box. In a trial, the die is rolled repeatedly until every number is turned up at least once.

Step 2 For each trial, keep track of the die rolls as shown in the example, writing down the results of each roll and the number of rolls it takes to achieve all six numbers.

Example:

Trial	Results of Rolls	Number of rolls
1	5, 1, 2, 2, 6, 4, 1, 4, 6, 6, 1, 2, 4, 3	14
2	6, 2, 3, 5, 4, 5, 5, 6, 6, 1	10
3	5, 1, 5, 4, 6, 6, 3, 4, 6, 1, 1, 5, 6, 5, 2	15

Step 3. Perform 100 trials to ensure a reliable estimate.

Step 4. Find the mean length of a trial as follows. Divide the total number of rolls in all the trials (total number of cereal boxes) by the total number of trials.

The theoretical value is 14.7, found by using mathematical probability theory. The more trials that you perform, the closer that your mean will be to the theoretical mean.

Technology, p. 29

CHAPTER 14   NAME _____   DATE _____

Graphing Calculator Activity (Use after Lesson 14-6)

Scatter Plots

The median age of the U.S. population from 1960 to 1980 and projected by the U.S. Bureau of the Census to the year 2020 is given by the chart at the right.

A graphing calculator can be used to make a scatter plot of the data.

Year	Median Age
1960	29.4
1970	27.9
1980	30.0
1990	33.0
2000	36.4
2010	38.9
2020	40.2

a. **Specify** The statistical drawing mode. (This varies with calculators.)

b. **Set the range** for x and y. Choose any convenient range.

c. **Input** the data as (x, y) points. (This varies with calculators.)

d. **Graph** the points.

As the scatter plot shows, after the year 1970, there is a positive association between the variables. Based on this plot, can you predict the approximate median age of the U.S. population in the year 2030? What is your prediction? **yes; about 42.4 years**

Use a graphing calculator to make a scatter plot of the data below. First plot the average cost of a public college. Then plot the average cost of a private college over the same time period.

Average Cost of 4-year college		
Year	Public	Private
1980	804	3617
1981	909	4113
1982	1031	4639
1983	1148	5093
1984	1228	5556
1985	1318	6121
1986	1414	6658
1987	1490	7200
1988	1578	8004
1989	1694	8737

1. Is there a positive, negative, or no association between the variables? **public: positive private: positive**

2. Are public or private college costs about the same? **no**

3. Which college cost is increasing at a higher rate? **the private college**

4. Predict the average cost of a 4-year public college in the year 1992. **$1983** Do the same for a private college. **$10,127**

Problem of the Week Activity

The card shown below is one of three available for this chapter. It can be used as a class or small group activity.

Activity Card

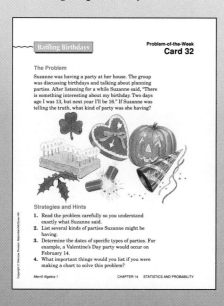

Baffling Birthdays

Problem-of-the-Week
Card 32

The Problem

Suzanne was having a party at her house. The group was discussing birthdays and talking about planning parties. After listening for a while Suzanne said, "There is something interesting about my birthday. Two days ago I was 13, but next year I'll be 16." If Suzanne was telling the truth, what kind of party was she having?

Strategies and Hints

1. Read the problem carefully so you understand exactly what Suzanne said.
2. List several kinds of parties Suzanne might be having.
3. Determine the dates of specific types of parties. For example, a Valentine's Day party would occur on February 14.
4. What important things would you list if you were making a chart to solve this problem?

Merrill Algebra 1   CHAPTER 14   STATISTICS AND PROBABILITY

Manipulatives and Models

The following materials may be used as models or manipulatives in Chapter 14.

- newspapers (Lesson 14-1)
- coins (Lesson 14-8)
- dice (Lesson 14-8)

Outside Resources

Books/Periodicals

Hollander, Myles and Frank Proschan. *The Statistical Exorcist - Dispelling Statistics Anxiety.* Marcel Dekker, Inc.

McGervey, John D. *Probabilities in Everyday Life.* Nelson-Hall.

Films/Videotapes/Videodiscs

Statistics at a Glance, Media Guild

Inferential Statistics I and II, Media Guild

Software

Principles of Statistics, Studyware Corporation

Interpreting Graphs, Conduit Educational Software

Data Insights, Sunburst Communications, Inc.

Multicultural

Multicultural Activity, p. 59

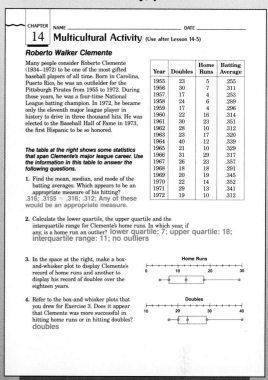

CHAPTER **14** NAME _____ DATE _____

Multicultural Activity (Use after Lesson 14-5)

Roberto Walker Clemente

Many people consider Roberto Clemente (1934–1972) to be one of the most gifted baseball players of all time. Born in Carolina, Puerto Rico, he was an outfielder for the Pittsburgh Pirates from 1955 to 1972. During those years, he was a four-time National League batting champion. In 1972, he became only the eleventh major league player in history to drive in three thousand hits. He was elected to the Baseball Hall of Fame in 1973, the first Hispanic to be so honored.

Year	Doubles	Home Runs	Batting Average
1955	23	5	.255
1956	30	7	.311
1957	17	4	.253
1958	24	6	.289
1959	17	4	.296
1960	22	16	.314
1961	30	23	.351
1962	28	10	.312
1963	23	17	.320
1964	40	12	.339
1965	21	10	.329
1966	31	29	.317
1967	26	23	.357
1968	18	18	.291
1969	20	19	.345
1970	22	14	.352
1971	29	13	.341
1972	19	10	.312

The table at the right shows some statistics that span Clemente's major league career. Use the information in this table to answer the following questions.

1. Find the mean, median, and mode of the batting averages. Which appears to be an appropriate measure of his hitting?
.316; .3155 ≈ .316; .312; Any of these would be an appropriate measure.

2. Calculate the lower quartile, the upper quartile and the interquartile range for Clemente's home runs. In which year, if any, is a home run an outlier? lower quartile: 7; upper quartile: 18; interquartile range: 11; no outliers

3. In the space at the right, make a box-and-whisker plot to display Clemente's record of home runs and another to display his record of doubles over the eighteen years.

Home Runs

4. Refer to the box-and whisker plots that you drew for Exercise 3. Does it appear that Clemente was more successful in hitting home runs or in hitting doubles? doubles

Doubles

Lab Manual

Lab Activity, pp. 43-44

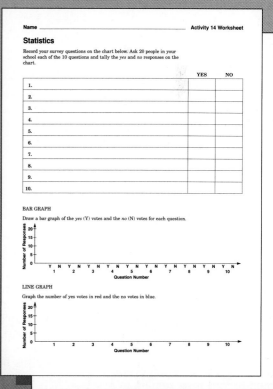

Name _____ Activity 14 Worksheet

Statistics

Record your survey questions on the chart below. Ask 20 people in your school each of the 10 questions and tally the *yes* and *no* responses on the chart.

	YES	NO
1.		
2.		
3.		
4.		
5.		
6.		
7.		
8.		
9.		
10.		

BAR GRAPH

Draw a bar graph of the *yes* (Y) votes and the *no* (N) votes for each question.

LINE GRAPH

Graph the number of yes votes in red and the no votes in blue.

Transparency 14-0 is available in the Transparency Package. It provides a full-color visual and motivational activity that you can use to engage students in the mathematical content of the chapter.

Background Information

There is an interesting probability question dealing with births that has become known as the "birthday problem." For a large group of people, it is difficult to find the probability that two of them have the same birthday, but it is fairly simple to find the probability that all the people have different birthdays. The calculations show that if there are 23 people in the group, the probability is slightly less than 50% that they all have different birthdays. This means the probability is slightly more than 50% that at least two people have the same birthday! In fact, for a group of 50 people, the probability is about 97% that at least two people will have the same birthday!

CHAPTER OBJECTIVES

In this chapter, you will:

- Display data on line plots, stem-and-leaf plots, and box-and-whisker plots.
- Find the mean, median, mode, range, and interquartile range of a set of data.
- Draw scatter plots for sets of data.
- Find the probability and odds of events.

Chapter Project

Materials: paper, pencil, ruler

Organize students into cooperative groups. Assign each group the task of gathering information on the gender of the first two children for 50 families. Different groups should not ask the same family for this information. Then, each group should record their results in a table like the one shown at the right, and compare their probabilities to the actual probabilities of 0.25 for 2 boys, 0 girls, 0.50 for 1 boy and 1 girl, and 0.25 for 0 boys and 2 girls.

After the groups report their results to the class, compile the results into a table, calculate the probabilities for all the families involved, and compare the results to the actual probabilities. At this time, you might wish to discuss how the information from the entire class should produce better results since a greater number of families is being used.

14 Statistics and Probability

APPLICATION IN PROBABILITY

Probability is a way to measure the chances that something will occur in relation to the possible alternatives. For example, the probability that a woman gives birth to a boy is $\frac{1}{2}$. But this probability is *not* a guarantee. A couple might have four children and all are boys, or they might have six children and all are girls.

Now you might think that a couple with six girls would not expect to have another girl if they decided to have a seventh child. In fact, the probability that the seventh child is a girl is still $\frac{1}{2}$, since the gender of this child is not affected by the gender of the previous six children.

What if you know that a family has seven children and six of them are girls? Is the probability that the seventh child is a girl still $\frac{1}{2}$? There are eight possibilities: all seven children are girls, or either the first, second, third, fourth, fifth, sixth, or seventh child is a boy. Since in only one of these cases the seventh child is a girl, the probability is $\frac{1}{8}$.

ALGEBRA IN ACTION

Complete the chart below to find each probability for the given conditions and number of children.

The study of probability arose from our desire to estimate the chance that the outcome of an event, like the toss of a coin, the roll of a die, or the birth of a child, will occur in a certain way.

Conditions	Number of Children					
	2	3	4	5	6	7
All children are girls given that you know all but the last child are girls.	$\frac{1}{2}$	$\frac{1}{2}$	$?\frac{1}{2}$	$?\frac{1}{2}$	$?\frac{1}{2}$	$\frac{1}{2}$
All children are girls given that you know all but one child are girls.	$\frac{1}{3}$	$\frac{1}{4}$	$?\frac{1}{5}$	$?\frac{1}{6}$	$?\frac{1}{7}$	$\frac{1}{8}$
All children are girls.	$\frac{1}{4}$	$\frac{1}{8}$	$?\frac{1}{16}$	$?\frac{1}{32}$	$?\frac{1}{64}$	$\frac{1}{128}$

559

Children	Number of Times (N)	Probability (N ÷ 50)
2 boys, 0 girls		
1 boy, 1 girl		
0 boys, 2 girls		

Lesson	Connections (C) and Applications (A)	Examples	Exercises
14-1	A: Transportation	2	18
	Meteorology		15
	History		16
	Consumerism		17
	Manufacturing		20
14-2	C: Statistics		22
	A: Income	2	
	School		15, 20
	Work		16
	Sports		14, 17
	Stock Market		18
	Housing		19
	Travel		24
14-3	C: Num. Theory		29
	A: Meteorology	1	
	Sports	3, 5	19, 21, 23, 26
	Exercise		20
	School		22
	Geography		24
	Business		25, 27
	Physics		32
14-4	C: Geometry		27
	A: Finance	3	
	School		22
	Foods		23
	Entertainment		24
	Consumerism		29
14-5	A: Fundraising	1	
	Travel		16
	Weather		17
	Sports		18, 19
	Consumerism		20
	Health		21
14-6	C: Geometry		24
	A: Finance		15
	Weather		16
	Sports		17-18
	School		19
	Aviation		22
14-7	C: Num. Theory		36
	A: Weather	4	
	Entertainment		38, 40
	Consumerism		39
	Finance		41
	Recreation		43
14-8	C: Num. Theory		14
	A: Civics	1	
	Baseball		9
	Employment		10
14-10	A: Entertainment		11
	Law		12
	Finance		13
	Construction		15

Statistics and Line Plots

Lesson Resources

- Reteaching Master 14-1
- Practice Master 14-1
- Enrichment Master 14-1
- Video Algebra, 61

 Transparency 14-1 contains the 5-Minute Check and a teaching aid for this lesson.

INTRODUCING THE LESSON

🕐 5-Minute Check

(over Chapter 13)

Solve each equation.

1. $n^2 + \frac{1}{6}n - \frac{1}{6} = 0$ $\left\{ \frac{1}{3}, -\frac{1}{2} \right\}$

2. $t^2 - 14t + 49 = 0$ $\{7\}$

3. $y^2 + 5y = 0$ $\{-5, 0\}$

4. Find two numbers whose sum is 35 and whose product is 300. **15 and 20**

5. Find two numbers that differ by 7 and have a product of 144. **9 and 16, −16 and −9**

Motivating the Lesson

Ask students what factors would be important to them if buying a car. Ask them how they would obtain information about these factors. Write the following data on the chalkboard:

Fuel Economy	Model A	Model B	Model C
EPA estimate city/highway	19/29	18/26	19/24
195-mile trip	29	27	25

Have students interpret this data to identify the model that gets the best fuel economy in expressway driving. Ask students to identify the car that has the lowest miles per gallon average for overall performance.

Objectives
14-1A
14-1B

After studying this lesson, you should be able to:
- interpret numerical data from a table, and
- display and interpret statistical data on a line plot.

The study of statistics is sometimes called data analysis.

Teaching Tip ❶

Each day when you read newspapers or magazines, watch television, or listen to the radio, you are bombarded with numerical information about the national economy, sports, politics, and so on. Interpreting this numerical information, or **data**, is important to your understanding of the world around you. A branch of mathematics called **statistics** helps provide you with methods for collecting, organizing, and interpreting data.

Statistical data can be organized and presented in numerous ways. One of the most common ways is to use a table or chart. The chart at the right shows the hourly wages earned by the principal wage earner in ten families.

Using tables or charts like the one at the right should enable you to more easily analyze the given data.

Family	Hourly Wage
A	$8.00
B	$10.50
C	$20.25
D	$9.40
E	$11.00
F	$13.75
G	$8.50
H	$10.50
I	$9.00
J	$11.00

Example 1

Use the information in the chart above to answer each question.

a. What are the maximum and minimum hourly wages of the principal wage earner for the ten families?

The principal wage earner in Family C makes $20.25 per hour. This is the maximum hourly wage of all the families.

The principal wage earner in Family A makes $8.00 per hour. This is the minimum hourly wage of the ten families.

b. What percent of the families have a principal wage earner that makes less than $10.00 per hour?

The principal wage earners in Family A ($8.00), Family D ($9.40), Family G ($8.50), and Family I ($9.00) each make less than $10.00 per hour. Thus, 4 out of 10, or 40%, of the families have a principal wage earner that makes less than $10.00 per hour.

In some instances, statistical data can be presented on a number line. Numerical information displayed on a number line is called a **line plot**. For example, the data in the table above can be presented in a line plot.

560 CHAPTER 14 STATISTICS AND PROBABILITY

ALTERNATE TEACHING STRATEGIES

Using Discussion

In a recent phone poll, phone numbers were selected randomly from the phone book and the person who answered was asked for his or her choice for mayor in the upcoming election. 48% of the respondants named Candidate A, 42% named Candidate B, and 10% had no opinion.

Discuss whether these results are representative of the general population.

From Example 1, you know that the data in the chart range from $8.00 per hour to $20.25 per hour. In order to represent each hourly wage on a number line, the scale used must include these values. A *"w"* is used to represent each hourly wage. When more than one *"w"* has the same location on the number line, additional *"w"*'s are placed one above the other. A line plot for the hourly wages is shown below.

Note that some data values are located between integer values on the number line.

Teaching Tips 2 3

| Example 2 | | |

FYI · · ·

The busiest foreign airport was Heathrow in London with 39,905,200 arriving and departing passengers in 1989.

The number of passengers arriving at and departing from the ten busiest airports in the United States for a one-year period are listed below.

Airport	Passengers	Airport	Passengers
Chicago (O'Hare)	59,130,007	San Francisco	29,939,835
Dallas/Ft. Worth	47,579,046	Denver	27,568,003
Los Angeles	44,967,221	Miami	23,385,010
Atlanta	43,312,285	New York (LGA)	23,158,317
New York (JFK)	30,323,077	Honolulu	22,617,340

a. **Make a line plot of the data.**

The numbers in the table are too large to represent easily on a number line. Change each number to represent every 1,000,000 passengers arriving and departing, and round to the nearest whole number. For example, since 59,130,007 = 59.130007 × 1,000,000, you would plot an "x" at 59 to represent O'Hare.

b. **Determine how many airports had approximately 25,000,000 passengers arrive and depart during the year.**

Four airports, Denver, Miami, New York (LGA), and Honolulu, had approximately 25,000,000 passengers arrive and depart during the year.

c. **Determine if any airport had a much greater number of passengers arrive and depart than the other airports.**

Based on the line plot, it appears that O'Hare Airport had a much greater number of passengers arriving and departing.

The data in the table in Example 2 were collected by checking airport records. Data can also be collected by taking actual measurements, by conducting surveys or polls, or by using questionnaires.

When you study and analyze data to draw conclusions, it is important that you know how the data were obtained. For example, would you want to draw conclusions about the favorite subject at your entire school based on the results of a survey of seniors only? Why or why not?

LESSON 14-1 STATISTICS AND LINE PLOTS 561

Checking for Understanding

Exercises 1-8 are designed to help you assess understanding through reading, writing, and speaking. You should work through Exercises 1-3 with your students, and then monitor their work on Exercises 4-8.

Error Analysis

In order to answer questions using a line plot, the scales should be accurate enough to read right off the plot. They should also be as precise as possible.
Example:

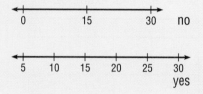

no

yes

Closing the Lesson

Speaking Activity Ask students to compare how data is presented in a table with its presentation on a line plot.

Reteaching Masters Booklet, p. 94

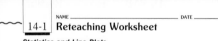

CHECKING FOR UNDERSTANDING

Communicating Mathematics

Read and study the lesson to answer each question.

1. What is the name for the numerical information used in statistics? **data**

2. Why do you think tables and charts are useful for presenting statistical data? **Answers will vary. A typical answer is that the information is easier to read and interpret when presented in a table.**

3. What are some other ways you could survey some of the students at your school in order to draw conclusions about the favorite subject at your school? **See margin.**

4-7. See margin.

Guided Practice **State the scale you would use to make a line plot for the following data.**

4. 4.2, 5.3, 7.6, 9.6, 7.3, 6.7

5. 30, 30, 40, 40, 10, 20, 50, 40

6. 123, 234, 789, 456, 111, 420, 397, 334

7. 7895, 3785, 9987, 1672, 4444, 6754, 5550, 3197, 7965, 10,615

8. The following table lists the percent of 18-year-olds with high school diplomas for each of 9 years.

Year	1950	1955	1960	1965	1970	1975	1980	1985	1990
Percent	56	65	72	71	77	74	72	74	72

a. What was the lowest percent of 18-year-olds with high school diplomas? **56%**

b. In what year did the highest percent occur? **1970**

c. In how many years was the percent with diplomas less than 74%? **6 years**

d. During how many of the 5-year intervals did the percent increase? **4**

e. What was the greatest decrease over a 5-year interval for the percent with diplomas? **3%, from 1970–1975**

f. Make a line plot of the data. **See margin.**

EXERCISES

Practice
A

9. Use the line plot at the right to answer each question.

a. What was the highest score on the test? **50**

b. What was the lowest score on the test? **22**

c. How many students took the test? **30 students**

d. How many students scored in the 40s? **9 students**

e. What score was received by the most students? **26**

Class Scores on a Science Test

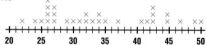

RETEACHING THE LESSON

Have students obtain data from the newspaper that would be good to use on a line plot. Have them cut out the data, make a line plot, and then present it to the class.

Additional Answers

3. Answers will vary; possible answers are taking every 10th students from an alphabetical listing and randomly choosing a student out of each class during the first class of the day.

4. from 4 to 10, intervals of 1

5. from 10 to 50, intervals of 10

6. from 100 to 800, intervals of 100

---

10. The high temperatures in degrees Fahrenheit for 50 cities in 1989 are listed below.

94	103	82	90	95	94	96	103	108	90	98	101	96
95	103	92	92	107	91	98	99	94	98	102	99	91
97	97	100	99	96	100	104	94	118	95	92	110	96
98	106	100	92	91	102	94	97	96	87	91		

a. Organize the data into a table with the headings **High Temperature** and **Number of Cities.** See Solutions Manual.

b. What was the highest high temperature for any of the cities? 118°F

c. What was the lowest high temperature for any of the cities? 82°F

d. Which temperature(s) occurred most frequently? 94°F, 96°F

e. Which temperature(s) between 90°F and 110°F are not in the table?

f. How many cities had a high temperature of 100°F? 3 cities

g. How many cities had a high temperature of at least 100°F? 15 cities

h. How many cities had a high temperature of at most 95°F? 20 cities

e. 93°F, 105°F, 109°F

11. Each number below represents the age of a United States president on his first inauguration.

57	61	57	57	58	57	61
54	68	51	49	64	50	48
65	52	56	46	54	49	50
47	55	55	54	42	51	56
55	51	54	51	60	62	43
55	56	61	52	69	64	

a. Make a line plot of the ages of United States presidents on their first inauguration. See margin.

b. How many ages are given? 41

c. Do any of the ages appear clustered? If so, which ones? yes; 54–57

12. The players with the most runs batted in (RBI) for the National League (1969–1990) are listed below.

a. Make a line plot of the data. See margin.

b. What was the greatest number of RBIs during a season? 149

c. What was the least number of RBIs during a season? 91

d. What was the most frequent number of RBIs during a season?

e. How many of the players had from 119 to 129 RBIs? 13

d. 121, 125

Year	Name	RBI	Year	Name	RBI
1969	Willie McCovey	126	1981	Mike Schmidt	91
1970	Johnny Bench	148	1982	Dale Murphy	109
1971	Joe Torre	137		Al Oliver	
1972	Johnny Bench	125	1983	Dale Murphy	121
1973	Willie Stargell	119	1984	Mike Schmidt	106
1974	Johnny Bench	129		Gary Carter	
1975	Greg Luzinski	120	1985	Dave Parker	125
1976	George Foster	121	1986	Mike Schmidt	119
1977	George Foster	149	1987	Andre Dawson	137
1978	George Foster	120	1988	Will Clark	109
1979	Dave Winfield	118	1989	Kevin Mitchell	125
1980	Mike Schmidt	121	1990	Matt Williams	122

LESSON 14-1 STATISTICS AND LINE PLOTS 563

Additional Answers

7. from 1000 to 11,000, intervals of 1000

8f.

11a.

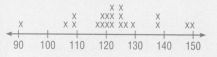

13b. No; the number of hours of television watched for Ms. Lee's students is more spread out while the number of hours watched for Mr. Jebson's students is more clustered between 15 and 30 hours.

15.

17.

NAME _____ DATE _____

14-1 Enrichment Worksheet

The Digits of π

The number π (pi) is the ratio of the circumference of a circle to its diameter. It is a nonrepeating and nonterminating decimal. No block of the digits of π ever repeats. Here are the first 201 digits of π including 200 digits that follow the decimal point.

3.14159	26535	89793	23846
69399	37510	58209	74944
86280	34825	34211	70679
09384	46095	50582	23172
84102	70193	85211	05559
26433	83279	50288	41971
59230	78164	06286	20899
82148	08651	32823	06647
53594	08128	34111	74502
64462	29489	54930	38196

Solve each problem.

1. If each of the digits appeared with equal frequency, how many times would each digit appear in the first 200 places following the decimal point? **20**

2. Complete this frequency distribution table for the first 200 digits of π that follow the decimal point.

Digit	Frequency (Tally Marks)	Frequency (Number)	Cumulative Frequency
0	𝍷𝍷𝍷 𝍷𝍷𝍷 𝍷𝍷𝍷 𝍷𝍷𝍷	19	19
1	𝍷𝍷𝍷 𝍷𝍷𝍷 𝍷𝍷𝍷 𝍷𝍷𝍷	20	39
2	𝍷𝍷𝍷 𝍷𝍷𝍷 𝍷𝍷𝍷 𝍷𝍷𝍷 𝍷𝍷𝍷	24	63
3	𝍷𝍷𝍷 𝍷𝍷𝍷 𝍷𝍷𝍷 𝍷𝍷𝍷	20	83
4	𝍷𝍷𝍷 𝍷𝍷𝍷 𝍷𝍷𝍷 𝍷𝍷𝍷 𝍷𝍷	22	105
5	𝍷𝍷𝍷 𝍷𝍷𝍷 𝍷𝍷𝍷 𝍷𝍷𝍷	20	125
6	𝍷𝍷𝍷 𝍷𝍷𝍷 𝍷	16	141
7	𝍷𝍷𝍷 𝍷𝍷𝍷 𝍷𝍷	12	153
8	𝍷𝍷𝍷 𝍷𝍷𝍷 𝍷𝍷𝍷 𝍷𝍷𝍷 𝍷𝍷𝍷	24	177
9	𝍷𝍷𝍷 𝍷𝍷𝍷 𝍷𝍷𝍷 𝍷𝍷𝍷	23	200

3. Explain how the cumulative frequency column can be used to check a project like this one. **The last number should be 200, the number of items being counted.**

4. Which digit(s) appears most often? **2 and 8**

5. Which digit(s) appears least often? **7**

13. Ms. Lee and Mr. Jebson each asked 15 students from their algebra classes how many hours of television they watched last week. The results are shown in the line plot at the right. Use this plot to answer each question.

Number of Hours Watching Television

× – Ms. Lee's students
● – Mr. Jebson's students

a. Which group of 15 students watched the most television? **Mr. Jebson's**

b. Does the pattern for the number of hours watching television appear to be the same for both groups? Explain. **See margin.**

Critical Thinking

14. Use the line plot for Exercise 13. Find the average number of hours that the students in Ms. Lee's class and Mr. Jebson's class watched television. Do the values support your answer to Exercise 13? **Mr. Jebson's, 21 hours; Ms. Lee's, 18 hours; answers will vary.**

Applications

15. Meteorology Make a line plot of the data about the high temperatures for 50 cities in 1989 used in Exercise 10. Which temperatures occurred exactly four times? **See margin; 91°F, 92°F, 98°F.**

16. History Refer to the data on the ages of presidents used for Exercise 11. Organize the data into a table with the headings **Age on First Inauguration** and **Number of Times.** Under **Age on First Inauguration,** group the data by fives, starting with 41–45. In which of these five-year interval(s) did the most ages occur? **See Solutions Manual; 51–55.**

17. Consumerism The cost per cup, in cents, of 28 different liquid laundry detergents are listed below. Make a line plot of the data. Then determine how many detergents cost at most 17¢ per cup. **See margin; 15.**

28	17	16	18	19	21	26
15	19	19	16	14	21	12
26	17	30	17	13	18	14
22	10	12	19	9	15	12

Mixed Review

18. Travel Paula wants to reach Urbanville at 10 A.M. If she drives at 36 miles per hour, she would reach Urbanville at 11 A.M. But if she drives at 54 miles per hour, she would arrive at 9 A.M. At what speed should she drive to reach Urbanville exactly at 10 A.M.? **(Lesson 4-7) 43.2 mph**

19. Given $f(x) = x^2 - 2x$ and $g(x) = 1 - 3x$, find $g[f(a)]$. **(Lesson 9-5)** $-3a^2 + 6a + 1$

20. Manufacturing At the end of January, Don's Sporting Equipment had manufactured 450 tennis racket covers. At the end of May, the company had manufactured a total of 3250 tennis racket covers. Assuming that the planned production of tennis racket covers can be represented by a straight line, determine how many will be manufactured by the end of the year. **(Lesson 10-5) 8150 covers**

21. Find the geometric mean of 12 and 27. **(Lesson 12-7) 18**

22. Find a quadratic equation whose roots are $\frac{7}{3}$ and -3. **(Lesson 13-8)** $3x^2 + 2x - 21 = 0$

EXTENDING THE LESSON

Math Power: Problem Solving

The enrollment per class in each of the three high schools in Brunswick is given in the table. Using the enrollment for each high school as separate sets of data, make a line plot that differentiates between each set.

	9th	10th	11th	12th
North	500	450	432	405
Central	648	640	563	552
South	425	405	372	354

```
        N N
  S S  S S  N      N      CC        CC
  +--+--+--+--+--+--+--+--+--+--+--+--+--+
 350   400   450   500   550   600   650
```

14-2 Stem-and-Leaf Plots

Objective
14-2

After studying this lesson, you should be able to:
- display and interpret data on a stem-and-leaf plot.

Application

Mr. Juarez wants to study the distribution of the scores for a 100-point unit exam given in his first-period biology class. The scores of the 35 students in the class are listed below.

82 77 49 84 44 98 93 71 76 65 89 95 78 69 89 64
88 54 96 87 92 80 44 85 93 89 55 62 79 90 86 75
74 99 62

He can organize and display the scores in a compact way using a **stem-and-leaf plot**.

A stem may have one or more digits. A leaf always has just one digit.

In a stem-and-leaf plot, the greatest common place value of the data is used to form the *stems*. The numbers in the next greatest common place-value position are then used to form the *leaves*. In the list above, the greatest place value is tens. Thus, the number 82 would have stem 8 and leaf 2.

To make the stem-and-leaf plot, first make a vertical list of the stems. Since the test scores range from 44 to 99, the stems range from 4 to 9. Then, plot each number by placing the units digit (leaf) to the right of its correct stem. Thus, the score 82 is plotted by placing leaf 2 to the right of stem 8. The complete stem-and-leaf plot is shown at the right.

Stem	Leaf
4	9 4 4
5	4 5
6	5 9 4 2 2
7	7 1 6 8 9 5 4
8	2 4 9 9 8 7 0 5 9 6
9	8 3 5 6 2 3 0 9

8|2 represents a score of 82.

A second stem-and-leaf plot can be made to arrange the leaves in numerical order from least to greatest as shown at the right. This will make it easier for Mr. Juarez to analyze the data.

Stem	Leaf
4	4 4 9
5	4 5
6	2 2 4 5 9
7	1 4 5 6 7 8 9
8	0 2 4 5 6 7 8 9 9 9
9	0 2 3 3 5 6 8 9

Example 1

Use the information in the stem-and-leaf plots above to answer each question.

a. What were the highest and lowest scores on the test? 99 and 44

b. Which test score occurred most frequently? 89 (3 times)

c. In which 10-point interval did the most students score?
80–89 (10 students)

d. How many students received a score of 70 or better? 25 students

ALTERNATE TEACHING STRATEGIES

Using Cooperative Groups

Divide the class into 4 or 5 small groups. Tell each group they are to poll at least 20 individuals regarding the number of hours a week they watch TV. Assign each group a particular age range for the individuals they are to poll. For example, one group might poll persons between the ages of 10 and 14 while another group polls persons between the ages of 20 and 24. Have each group summarize their data in a stem-and-leaf plot. Display the plots to the class to determine whether a relationship exists between age and amount of time watching TV.

Lesson Resources

- Reteaching Master 14-2
- Practice Master 14-2
- Enrichment Master 14-2
- Video Algebra, 61

 Transparency 14-2 contains the 5-Minute Check and a teaching aid for this lesson.

INTRODUCING THE LESSON

5-Minute Check
(over Lesson 14-1)

True or *False.*

1. A line plot helps you to see the distribution and clustering of data. **True**

2. A line plot would be more useful than a table when reviewing your test grades in algebra over the past semester. **False**

Use the line plot below to answer the questions.

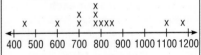

3. What was the greatest attendance? just under 1200

4. What appears to be the average attendance, rounded to the nearest hundred? 800

5. From the information shown, can we determine any information regarding an increase or decrease in attendance over the 12-game period? no

Motivating the Lesson

Have students examine the line plots in the previous lesson to determine the amount of data entries they show. Develop the idea that line plots are suitable for presenting a limited amount of data within a short range. Ask students if a line plot is suitable for presenting 100 data elements with a range of 150 between the minimum and maximum points.

Chalkboard Examples

For Example 1

Make a stem-and-leaf plot of history test scores given, arranging the leaves in numerical order. Then, answer each question.

65, 82, 73, 91, 95, 86, 78, 69, 80, 88

Stem	Leaf
6	5 9
7	3 8
8	0 2 6 8
9	1 5

a. In which interval did most students score? **80-89**

b. What were the highest and lowest scores? **95, 65**

For Example 2

The enrollment of several small colleges in the Center City area are listed below. Make a back-to-back stem-and-leaf plot of enrollments comparing rounded values and truncated values. Then answer each question.

Miller Business School - 1342
Capital College - 1685
Para-Professional
Institute - 1013
Parke College - 2350
State Community - 3781
Fashion Institute - 1096
College of Art and
Design - 1960
Franklin Community
College - 3243

Rounded	Stem	Truncated
7 3 1 0	1	0 0 3 6 9
4 0	2	3
8 2	3	2 7

a. What range of student enrollment is represented on the rounded side by 2|4? **2350 - 2449**

b. What range of student enrollment is represented on the truncated side by 1|9? **1900 - 1999**

Sometimes the data for a stem-and-leaf plot are numbers that have more than two digits. Before plotting these numbers, they may need to be rounded or *truncated* to determine each stem and leaf. Suppose you wanted to plot 356 using the hundreds digit for the stem.

Rounded	Truncated
Round 356 to 360. Thus, you would plot 356 using stem 3 and leaf 6. What would be the stem and leaf of 499? *5 and 0*	To truncate means to cut off, so truncate 356 as 350. Thus, you would plot 356 using stem 3 and leaf 5. What would be the stem and leaf of 499? *4 and 9*

A *back-to-back stem-and-leaf plot* is sometimes used to compare two sets of data or rounded and truncated values of the same set of data. In a back-to-back plot, the same stem is used for the leaves of both plots.

Example 2

APPLICATION
Income

The average annual pay for workers in selected states are listed below. Make a back-to-back stem-and-leaf plot of the average annual pay comparing rounded values and truncated values. Then answer each question.

State	Avg. Annual Pay	State	Avg. Annual Pay
Alaska	$28,033	Michigan	$24,193
California	$24,126	Minnesota	$21,481
Colorado	$21,472	New Jersey	$25,748
Connecticut	$26,234	New York	$26,347
Delaware	$21,977	Ohio	$21,501
Illinois	$23,608	Pennsylvania	$21,485
Maryland	$22,515	Texas	$21,130
Massachusetts	$24,143	Virginia	$21,053

Since the data range from $21,053 to $28,033, the stems range from 21 to 28 for both plots.

Rounded	Stem	Truncated
5 5 5 5 1 1	21	0 1 4 4 4 5 9
5 0	22	5
6	23	6
2 1 1	24	1 1 1
7	25	7
3 2	26	2 3
	27	
0	28	0

Teaching Tip ❶

Using rounded data, 28|0 represents $27,950 to $28,049.

Using truncated data, 28|0 represents $28,000 to $28,099.

a. What does 21|5 represent in each plot?
It represents $21,450 to $21,549 for rounded data and $21,500 to $21,599 for truncated data.

b. What is the difference between the highest and lowest average annual pay? about $6900 for rounded data and $7000 for truncated data

c. Did more of the states have average annual pay above or below $25,000? below $25,000

d. Does there appear to be any significant difference between the two stem-and-leaf plots? no

RETEACHING THE LESSON

Have students make a stem-and-leaf plot of the data on the ages of United States presidents on their first inauguration in Exercise 11 on page 563. Have students discuss the differences in the two types of plots and analyze which plot is better to use for certain circumstances.

Stem	Leaf
4	2 3 6 7 8 9 9
5	0 0 1 1 1 1 2 2 4
	4 4 4 5 5 5 5 6 6
	6 7 7 7 7 8
6	0 1 1 1 2 4 4 5 8
	9

5|1 = 51 years old

CHECKING FOR UNDERSTANDING

Communicating Mathematics

Read and study the lesson to answer each question. **1–3. See margin.**

1. Suppose a student in Mr. Juarez's biology class received a score of 100. How would this score be represented in the stem-and-leaf plot?

2. If the number 53.7 is plotted using stem 5 and leaf 3, how would the number 99.8 be plotted?

3. If the number 6373 is plotted using stem 63 and leaf 7, how would the number 6498 be plotted?

4. In what situations is a back-to-back stem-and-leaf plot used? **to compare two sets of data**

Guided Practice

Write the stems that would be used for a plot of each set of data. **See margin.**

5. 23, 46, 54, 13, 28, 54, 37

6. 8, 13, 21, 73, 101, 49, 52, 33

7. 24.5, 26.1, 25.8, 19.1, 23.2, 24.1, 23.7, 22.9

8. 236, 450, 748, 254, 755, 347, 97, 396

Suppose two digits of each number are to be used in a stem-and-leaf plot. Find the rounded and the truncated values for each number.

9. 456,876 **46, 45** 10. 34,591 **35, 34** 11. 4321 **43, 43** 12. 1,234,567 **12, 12**

13. Use the stem-and-leaf plot below to answer each question.

a. What was the highest temperature recorded? **85°F**

b. What was the lowest temperature recorded? **49°F**

c. On how many days was the high temperature in the 70s? **11 days**

d. What temperature(s) occurred most frequently? **77°F**

Daily High Temperature in April

Stem	Leaf
8	0 2 2 5
7	0 3 3 4 5 7 7 7 8 9 9
6	1 2 3 5 5 6 7 8 8 9
5	4 7 8 8
4	9 4|9 = 49°F

EXERCISES

Applications

14. **Football** The stem-and-leaf plot below gives the number of catches of the NFL's leading pass receiver for each season through 1990.

a. What was the greatest number of catches during a season? **106**

b. What was the least number of catches during a season? **60**

c. How many seasons are listed? **31**

d. What number of catches occurred most frequently? **71, 73**

e. How many times did the leading pass receiver have at least 90 catches? **9**

Stem	Leaf
6	0 1 2 6 7
7	1 1 1 2 2 3 3 3 4 5 8
8	0 2 6 8 8 9
9	0 1 2 2 5
10	0 0 1 6

9|2 represents 92 catches.

Additional Answers

1. Add stem 10 and leaf 0 to its right (10|0) in the plot.

2. Use stem 9 and leaf 9 since the data is truncated in the plot.

3. The plot of 6498 cannot be determined since the example does not show whether the data is being rounded or truncated.

5. 1, 2, 3, 4, 5

6. 0, 1, 2, 3, 4, 5, 6, 7, 8, 9, 10

7. 19, 20, 21, 22, 23, 24, 25, 26

8. 0, 1, 2, 3, 4, 5, 6, 7

14-2 Reteaching Worksheet

NAME _____ DATE _____

Stem-and-Leaf Plots

Mrs. Corrigan interviewed some students who were willing to help her with some typing. The number of words typed per minute by each student is listed below.

20   19   18   16   17   17   14

This data can be organized on a **stem-and-leaf plot**. The greatest common place value of each piece of data is used to form the **stem**. The next greatest place value is used to form the **leaves**.

Stem	Leaf
1	9 8 6 7 7 4
2	0

1|8 represents a rate of 18 words per minute.

Data with more than two digits may be rounded 13.5 ⇒ 14 or truncated 13.5 ⇒ 13.

The rounded and truncated values of the data at the right can be compared in a back-to-back stem-and-leaf plot.

61.5	51.9	60.0
46.0	38.5	39.1
56.2	33.0	61.5
65.4	51.0	52.3

Rounded	Stem	Truncated
9 9 3	3	3 8 9
6	4	6
6 2 2 1	5	1 1 2 6
5 2 2 0	6	0 1 1 5

In a back-to-back stem-and-leaf plot, the same stem is used for the leaves of both plots.

Solve each problem.

1. The stem-and-leaf plot at the right shows the height, in feet, of buildings in San Francisco that are over 500 ft tall.

   a. How tall is the tallest building? **850 ft**

   b. What is the height of the shortest building that is taller than 500 ft? **520 ft**

   c. What building height occurs most frequently? **570 ft**

Stem	Leaf
5	2 3 3 4 5 6 7 7 7
6	
7	8
8	5

5|6 represents a height of 560 feet.

2. Lori sells tickets at a movie theater. Her sales for week 1 were $173, $194, $160, $182, $183, and $247. Sales for week 2 were $137, $182, $151, $193, $199, and $194.

   a. Make a stem-and-leaf plot of two weeks' sales. Round the data to the nearest $10.

   b. What is the most amount of money made in one day during the two week period? **$247**

Stem	Leaf
1	3 5 6 7 8 8 8 9 9 9 9
2	4

1|6 represents $160-$169.

---

15. **School** Each number below represents the age of a student in Ms. Nichols' evening calculus class at DeAnzio Community College.

22 17 25 24 19 27 33 16 35 26 20 18 24
33 18 19 48 36 19 23 55 18 18 19 27 18
19 25 17 32 19 45 19 20 30

   a. Make a stem-and-leaf plot of the data. **See margin.**

   b. How many people attend Ms. Nichols' class? **35 people**

   c. What is the difference in ages between the oldest and youngest person in class? **39 years**

   d. What is the most common age for a student in the class? **19 years**

   e. Which age group is most widely represented in the class? **teens**

   f. How many of Ms. Nichols' students are older than 25 years old? **12 students**

16. **Work** The stem-and-leaf plot below gives the average weekly earnings in 1990 for various occupations.

   a. What were the highest weekly earnings? **$740–$749**

   b. What were the lowest weekly earnings? **$260–$269**

   c. How many occupations have weekly earnings of at least $500? **6**

   d. What range does 5|1 represent? **$510–$519**

   e. Have the leaf values in this data been truncated or rounded? **truncated**

Stem	Leaf
2	6 7
3	1 2 8 9
4	1 3 6 8 8 8 9
5	0 1 6
6	
7	1 2 4

3|8 represents $380–$389.

17. **Auto Racing** Each number below represents the average speed, in miles per hour, of the winning car in the last 31 Indianapolis 500s.

139 139 140 143 147 151 144
151 153 157 156 158 163 159
159 149 149 161 161 159 143
139 162 162 164 153 171 162
145 168 186

   a. Make a stem-and-leaf plot of this data. **See margin.**

   b. In what speed range were most of the winning cars? **150–159 mph**

18. **Stock Market** Each number below represents shares of CCXY stock traded each day over a 28-day period.

924 832 154 523 932 128 324 643 329 364 293
843 734 231 435 276 832 876 924 833 435 555
498 349 467 856 647 165

   a. Make a stem-and-leaf plot of the data. Round numbers of shares to the nearest ten. **See margin.**

   b. What is the difference between the greatest and least number of shares traded during this period? **804 shares**

   c. How many times were less than 400 shares of stock traded? **10 times**

   d. What 10-share range of stocks traded occurred most frequently? **825–834 shares**

19. **Housing** The following table lists the median price, in thousands of dollars, of existing single-family homes in various cities in the U.S. for 1990.

City	Price	City	Price	City	Price
Atlanta	85	Honolulu	290	Omaha	65
Baltimore	104	Indianapolis	73	Orlando	80
Boston	182	Kansas City	74	Philadelphia	98
Chicago	112	Knoxville	74	Phoenix	82
Cleveland	77	Las Vegas	89	Pittsburgh	69
Dallas	94	Los Angeles	212	St. Louis	83
Denver	85	Milwaukee	82	San Francisco	262
Detroit	76	New Orleans	68	Seattle	136
Hartford	157	New York	174	Washington, D.C.	145

a. Make a stem-and-leaf plot of the data. **See margin.**

b. What is the difference in price of homes in the most and least expensive cities? **$225,000**

c. In what price range are most of the homes for these cities? **$80,000–$89,000**

20. **Education** The table below lists the average Scholastic Aptitude Test (SAT) scores for males and females for certain years between 1967 and 1989.

Year	1967	1970	1975	1977	1980	1982	1985	1987	1989
Males	977	968	932	928	919	924	936	935	934
Females	935	926	880	872	863	864	877	878	875

a. Make a back-to-back stem-and-leaf plot of the SAT scores for males and females. **See margin.**

b. What information about the relationship between the SAT scores of males and females does it present? **See margin.**

Critical Thinking

21. The height, in inches, of the students in a health class are 65, 63, 68, 66, 72, 61, 62, 63, 59, 58, 61, 74, 65, 63, 71, 60, 62, 63, 71, 70, 59, 66, 61, 62, 68, 69, 64, 63, 70, 61, 68, and 67. If the stems 5, 6, and 7 are used in a stem-and-leaf plot, the distribution of heights would not be easy to analyze. How could you change the stems so the data is displayed in a way that is easier to analyze? **See margin.**

Mixed Review

22. **Statistics** Carita's bowling scores for the first four games of a five-game series are $b + 2$, $b + 3$, $b - 2$, and $b - 1$. What must her score be for the last game to have an average of $b + 2$? **(Lesson 3-7)** $b + 8$

23. Simplify $\dfrac{12x^4 + 12x^3 - 9x^2}{12x^3 + 18x^2 - 12x}$. **(Lesson 8-1)** $\dfrac{x(2x + 3)}{2(x + 2)}$

24. **Travel** While driving to Fullerton, Mrs. Sumner travels at an average speed of 40 mph. On the return trip, she travels at an average speed of 56 mph and saves two hours of travel time. How far does Mrs. Sumner live from Fullerton? **(Lesson 11-5)** **280 miles**

25. Find the distance between the points (10, 8) and (2, −3). **(Lesson 12-8)** $\sqrt{185} \approx 13.6$

26. Solve $\frac{1}{2}t^2 - 2t - \frac{3}{2} = 0$ by completing the square. **(Lesson 13-4)** $2 \pm \sqrt{7}$

27. Make a line plot of the data on the heights of the students in health class given in Exercise 21. What was the most common height for the students in this class? **(Lesson 14-1)** **See margin; 63 in.**

EXTENDING THE LESSON

Math Power: Reasoning

The following table shows the percent of households in two major cities that own the appliances listed. Explain why a stem-and-leaf plot of the data would not be an adequate representation.

Appliance	City A	City B
TV	88	94
Dishwasher	28	43

Even though a back-to-back stem-and-leaf plot would distinguish between the data for City A and City B, it would not distinguish between the data for TVs and dishwashers.

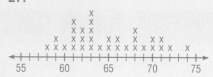

14-3

14-3 Measures of Central Tendency

Lesson Resources

- Reteaching Master 14-3
- Practice Master 14-3
- Enrichment Master 14-3
- Lab Manual, pp. 43-44
- Video Algebra, 61

 Transparency 14-3 contains the 5-Minute Check and a teaching aid for this lesson.

INTRODUCING THE LESSON

 5-Minute Check

(over Lesson 14-2)

1. **Use a stem-and-leaf plot to represent the following test data: 56, 75, 73, 89, 92, 87, 64, and 82.**

Stem	Leaf
5	6
6	4
7	3 5
8	2 7 9
9	2

2. **Based on the plot above, in what interval did the most grades fall?** 80-89

3. **Suppose the data in a given situation is: 125, 128, 134, 158, 164, 144, 168, 172, and 165. What stems would you use to represent the data?** 12, 13, 14, 15, 16, 17

Motivating the Lesson

Reports in newspapers and on TV often refer to the "average": the "average" American makes $25,865 a year, the "average" cost of housing is $9,600 per year, and so on. Ask students how average is determined. Is it determined in the same manner in all types of situations?

TEACHING THE LESSON

Teaching Tip ❶ You may wish to suggest that students use a calculator to aid in computation.

Objective
14-3

After studying this lesson, you should be able to:
- calculate and interpret the mean, median, and mode of a set of data.

Application

As part of its grand opening celebration, Zumpone's World of Sports is giving away two tickets to next year's Super Bowl to the person who correctly guesses the winning score of this year's Super Bowl.

In order to make the best possible guess, Jason has decided to study the results of previous Super Bowls. He lists the winning scores of the first 25 Super Bowls in a stem-and-leaf plot as shown at the right. Based on this information, what should be Jason's guess for the winning score?

Stem	Leaf
1	4 6 6 6
2	0 0 1 3 4 4 6 7 7 7
3	1 2 3 5 5 8 8 9
4	2 6
5	5

2|1 represents 21 points.

In analyzing statistical data, it is useful to have a number that describes a set of data. In the problem above, Jason wants to find a number that best describes all of the data. Numbers known as *measures of central tendency* are often used to describe sets of data since they represent centralized or *middle* values of the data. Three measures of central tendency are called the **mean, median,** and **mode**.

The mean of a set of data is a number that represents an average of the numbers in the set.

Definition of Mean	The mean of a set of data is the sum of the numbers in the set divided by the number of numbers in the set.

Example 1

APPLICATION
Meteorology

The high temperatures for a week during January in Milwaukee were 19°, 21°, 18°, 17°, 18°, 22°, 46°. Find the mean high temperature for that week.

$$\text{mean} = \frac{19 + 21 + 18 + 17 + 18 + 22 + 46}{7}$$

$$= \frac{161}{7}$$

$$= 23$$

The mean is the sum of the 7 numbers divided by 7.

Teaching Tip ❶

The mean, or average, high temperature for the week was 23°.

Teaching Tip ❷

Notice in Example 1 that the mean high temperature, 23°, is greater than all of the daily high temperatures except one, 46°. Thus, 23° does not appear to be the best number to use to describe this set of data. Extremely low or high values, like 46°, affect the mean a great deal. In such cases, the mean becomes less representative of the values in a set of data.

570 CHAPTER 14 STATISTICS AND PROBABILITY

ALTERNATE TEACHING STRATEGIES

Using Applications

Use statistics regarding the school enrollment, one of the school's athletic teams, or a professional sports team to determine the mean, median, and mode of a set of data. Make a chart to share the statistics and measures of central tendency with the class.

The second measure of central tendency is the median.

Definition of Median	The median of a set of data is the middle number when the numbers in the set are arranged in numerical order.

Example 2

Teaching Tip 3

Find the median high temperature for the high temperatures given in Example 1.

First arrange the temperatures in order from least to greatest.

17° 18° 18° 19° 21° 22° 46°

Since there are seven temperatures, the middle one is the fourth value, 19°. Thus, the median high temperature for the week is 19°. *The median is not affected by the extremely high temperature, 46°.*

If a set of data contains an even number of elements, then the median of the set is the value halfway between the two middle elements.

Teaching Tip 4

Example 3

APPLICATION

Baseball

FYI · · ·

The major league record for the highest batting average in a season is held by Rogers Hornsby who hit 0.424 for the St. Louis in 1924.

The batting averages for 10 players on a baseball team are 0.234, 0.253, 0.312, 0.333, 0.286, 0.240, 0.183, 0.222, 0.297, and 0.275. Find the median batting average for these players.

Arrange the batting averages in ascending order.

0.183 0.222 0.234 0.240 0.253 0.275 0.286 0.297 0.312 0.333

Since there are an even number of batting averages, 10, the median is halfway between the two middle values, 0.253 and 0.275.

$$\frac{0.253 + 0.275}{2} = 0.264 \qquad \textit{Find the mean of the two middle values.}$$

The median batting average for the 10 players is 0.264.

Notice in Examples 2 and 3 that the number of values greater than the median is the same as the number of values less than the median.

The third measure of central tendency is the mode.

Definition of Mode	The mode of a set of data is the number that occurs most often in the set.

Example 4

Find the mode of the high temperatures given in Example 1.

In the set of temperatures 19°, 21°, 18°, 17°, 18°, 22°, 46°, the temperature 18° occurs twice. Thus, 18° is the mode of the high temperatures for the week. *The mode is not affected by the extremely high temperature.*

LESSON 14-3 MEASURES OF CENTRAL TENDENCY 571

Chalkboard Examples

For Example 1

The heights of players on South High School's basketball team are 72″, 74″, 70″, 77″, 75″, and 70″. Find the mean height. 73″

For Example 2

Find the median height for the basketball players given in Chalkboard Example 1. 73″

For Example 3

The tuition costs for ten private schools in Ohio are $7568, $8650, $9225, $5880, $6720, $8840, $7820, $8260, $8432, and $8990. Find the median tuition costs. $8346

For Example 4

Find the mode of the heights of basketball players described in Chalkboard Example 1. 70″

Teaching Tip 3 Emphasize that data must be arranged in numerical order, either from greatest to least value or from least to greatest value, in order to find the median.

Teaching Tip 4 When there are an even number of elements in a set of data, the median is found by determining the mean of the two middle elements.

Sets of data with two modes are called bimodal.

If no number in a set of data occurs more often than the other numbers, then the set has no mode. It is also possible for a set of data to have more than one mode. For example, the set of data {2, 3, 3, 4, 6, 6} has two modes, 3 and 6.

Based on the results of Examples 1, 2, and 4, the set of data {19°, 21°, 18°, 17°, 18°, 22°, 46°} has mean 23°, median 19°, and mode 18°. These examples show that the mean, median, and mode are not always the same value.

Example 5

APPLICATION
Sports

Refer to the problem presented at the beginning of the lesson. Find the median, mode, and mean for the winning scores to determine what Jason's guess should be for the winning score this year.

The stem-and-leaf plot for the 25 scores is shown below.

Median Since there are 25 values, the median is the 13th value. Counting from the top down, you will find that this value is 27. Thus, the median score is 27.

Mode Note that for stem 1, there are three leaves with a value of 6. Also, for stem 2, there are three leaves with a value of 7. Thus, the scores have two modes, 16 and 27.

Stem	Leaf
1	4 6 6 6
2	0 0 1 3 4 4 6 7 7 7
3	1 2 3 5 5 8 8 9
4	2 6
5	5

2|1 represents 21 points.

Mean Add the 25 scores and then divide by 25. Since the sum of the 25 scores is 725, the mean score is $\frac{725}{25}$ or 29.

Since the median and one of the modes of the scores is 27, it appears that a good guess for the winning score is 27 points.

CHECKING FOR UNDERSTANDING

Communicating Mathematics

Complete.

1. Measures of central tendency represent ___?___ values of a set of data. **middle**

2. If the numbers in a set of data are arranged in numerical order, then the ___?___ of a set is the middle number. **median**

3. Extremely high or low values affect the ___?___ of a set of data. **mean**

4. If all the numbers in a set of data occur the same number of times, then the set has no ___?___. **mode**

Guided Practice

Find the mean, median, and mode for each set of data.

5. 4, 6, 12, 5, 8 **7; 6; no mode**

6. 9, 9, 9, 9, 8 **8.8; 9; 9**

7. 7, 19, 9, 4, 7, 2 **8; 7; 7**

8. 300, 34, 40, 50, 60 **96.8; 50; no mode**

9. 23, 23, 23, 12, 12, 12 **17.5; 17.5; 12, 23**

10. 10, 3, 17, 1, 8, 6, 12, 15 **9; 9; no mode**

EXERCISES

Practice Find the median and mode of the data shown in each line plot.

11.

4; 2

12.

46; 35, 63

Find the median and mode of the data shown in each stem-and-leaf plot.

13.

Stem	Leaf
7	3 5
8	2 2 4
9	0 4 7 9
10	5 8
11	4 6 9|4 = 94

94; 82

14.

Stem	Leaf
5	3 6 8
6	5 8
7	0 3 7 7 9
8	1 4 8 8 9
9	9 6|8 = 68

77; 77, 88

15.

Stem	Leaf
19	3 5 5
20	2 2 5 8
21	5 8 8 9 9 9
22	0 1 7 8 9
	21|5 = 215

218; 219

B List six numbers that satisfy each set of conditions. 16-17. See students' work.

16. The mean is 50, the median is 40, and the mode is 20.

17. The mean is 70, the median is 75, and the modes are 65 and 100.

18. The mean of a set of ten numbers is 5. When the greatest number in the set is eliminated, the mean of the new set of numbers is 4. What number was eliminated from the original set of numbers? 14

Applications

19. Football Michael Anderson of the West High Bears averages 137.6 yards rushing per game for the first five games of the season. He rushes for 155 yards in the sixth game. What is his new rushing average?
140.5 yards

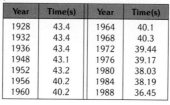

20. Advertising A magazine ad shows 5 videotape cameras for sale. The prices given are $499, $895, $679, $1195, and $1400. Find the mean and median price of the cameras.
$933.60; $895

21. Basketball In a girl's basketball game between Lincoln High School and Taft High School, the Taft players' individual scores were 12, 4, 5, 3, 11, 23, 4, 6, 7, and 8. Find the mean, median, and mode of the individual points. 8.3, 6.5, 4

22. School Patty's scores on the 25-point quizzes in her English class are 20, 21, 18, 21, 22, 22, 24, 21, 20, 19, and 23. Find the mean, median, and mode of her quiz scores. 21, 21, 21

23. Sports One of the events in the Winter Olympics is the Men's 500-meter Speed Skating. The winning times for this event are shown at the right. Find the mean, median, and mode of the times.
40.61, 40.2, 43.4

Year	Time(s)	Year	Time(s)
1928	43.4	1964	40.1
1932	43.4	1968	40.3
1936	43.4	1972	39.44
1948	43.1	1976	39.17
1952	43.2	1980	38.03
1956	40.2	1984	38.19
1960	40.2	1988	36.45

LESSON 14-3 MEASURES OF CENTRAL TENDENCY **573**

Additional Answers

29.

33.

Stem	Leaf (rounded)
36	5
37	
38	0 2
39	2 4
40	1 2 2 3
41	
42	
43	1 2 4 4 4

$39|2 = 39.15$ to 39.24 seconds

NAME _____ DATE _____

14-3 Enrichment Worksheet

Other Kinds of Means

There are many different kinds of means besides the arithmetic mean. A mean for a set of numbers has these two properties:

a. It typifies or represents the set.

b. If is not less than the least number and it is not greater than the greatest number.

Here are the formulas for the arithmetic mean and three other means.

Arithmetic Mean
Add the numbers in the set. Then divide the sum by n, the number of elements in the set.
$$\frac{x_1 + x_2 + x_3 + \dots + x_n}{n}$$

Geometric Mean
Multiply all the numbers in the set. Then find the nth root of their product.
$$\sqrt[n]{x_1 \cdot x_2 \cdot x_3 \cdot \dots \cdot x_n}$$

Harmonic Mean
Divide the number of elements in the set by the sum of the reciprocals of the numbers.
$$\frac{n}{\frac{1}{x_1} + \frac{1}{x_2} + \frac{1}{x_3} + \dots + \frac{1}{x_n}}$$

Quadratic Mean
Add the squares of the numbers. Divide their sum by the number in the set. Then, take the square root.
$$\sqrt{\frac{x_1^2 + x_2^2 + x_3^2 + \dots + x_n^2}{n}}$$

Find the four different means for each set of numbers.

1. 10, 100
$A = 55$ $G = 31.62$
$H = 18.18$ $Q = 71.06$

2. 50, 60
$A = 55$ $G = 54.77$
$H = 54.55$ $Q = 55.23$

3. 1, 2, 3, 4, 5,
$A = 3$ $G = 2.61$
$H = 2.19$ $Q = 3.32$

4. 2, 2, 4, 4
$A = 3$ $G = 2.83$
$H = 2.67$ $Q = 3.16$

5. Use the results of Exercises 1 to 4 to compare the relative sizes of the four types of means.
From least to greatest, the means are the harmonic, geometric, arithmetic, and quadratic means.

24. **Geography** The areas in square miles of the 20 largest natural U. S. lakes are given below. Find the mean, median, and mode of these areas.

31,700 1697 242 700 22,300 451 374 432 23,000 207
1000 1361 315 625 9,910 215 458 360 7,550 435

5166.6, 541.5, no mode

25. **Work** Each number below represents the number of days that each employee of the Simpson Corporation was absent during 1990. Find the mean, median, and mode of the number of days. 4.45; 4; 3, 5

0 10 8 5 8 9 3 3 2 9 7 0 4 2 4 6 2
9 13 3 1 5 5 7 2 6 5 3 4 7 1 1 5 3
3   1 4 5 1 2

26. **Diving** Participants in diving events have each of their dives rated by 7 judges using a scale from 0 to 10. A diver's score is computed by eliminating the highest and lowest ratings of the judges and then finding the mean of the remaining five scores. This rating is then multiplied by a number that represents the difficulty of the dive attempted. Wendy received ratings of 8.2, 9.0, 7.3, 8.2, 7.7, 8.6, and 8.3 on a dive with difficulty 3.3. What was her score? 27.06

27. **Business** Of the 42 employees at Speedy Pizza, sixteen make $4.75 an hour, four earn $5.50 an hour, three earn $6.85 an hour, six earn $4.85 an hour, and thirteen earn $5.25 an hour. Find the mean, median, and mode of the hourly wages. $5.14, $4.85, $4.75

Critical Thinking

28. The annual salaries of the 12 employees at CompuSoftware Inc. are $38,500, $34,000, $27,500, $38,500, $63,500, $125,000, $31,500, $30,000, $38,500, $31,500, $92,500, and $31,000.

a. If you are the personnel director, would you quote the median, mean, or mode as the "average" salary of the employees when interviewing a job applicant? Why? The mean; it is higher.

b. If the employees were trying to justify a pay raise to the management, would they quote the median, mean, or mode as their "average" salary? Why? The median; it is lower, and half of the employees make less than this amount.

Mixed Review

29. **Number Theory** Draw a Venn diagram to find the intersection of {letters in the word *statistics*} and {letters in the words *data analysis*}. (Lesson 2-1) See margin.

30. Factor $24x^2 - 61xy + 35y^2$. (Lesson 7-8) $(8x - 7y)(3x - 5y)$

31. Write an equation in standard form of the line with slope of -3 that passes through $(3, 7)$. (Lesson 10-2) $3x + y = 16$

32. **Physics** An object is fired upward from the top of tower. Its height h, in feet, above the ground t seconds after firing is given by the formula $h = -16t^2 + 96t + 125$. a. 3 seconds

a. How long after firing does the object reach its maximum height?

b. What is this maximum height? (Lesson 13-1) 269 feet

33. Make a stem-and-leaf plot for the winning times in the Men's 500-meter Speed Skating event using the data given in Exercise 23. (Lesson 14-2) See margin.

574 CHAPTER 14 STATISTICS AND PROBABILITY

EXTENDING THE LESSON

Math Power:
Problem Solving

Find the mean, median, and mode of the hourly wages of 20 workers. Ten workers earn $4.75 per hour, one earns $5.50 per hour, one earns $6.75 per hour, two earn $4.80 per hour, and six earn $5.25 per hour.

mean = $5.04, median = $4.78, mode = $4.75

14-4 Measures of Variation

Objective
14-4

After studying this lesson, you should be able to:

■ calculate and interpret the range, quartiles, and the interquartile range of a set of data.

Application

Pacquita Colón and Larry Nielson are two candidates for promotion to manager of sales at Fitright Shoes. In order to determine who should be promoted, the owner, Mr. Tarsel, looked at each person's quarterly sales record for the last two years.

Quarterly Sales (thousands of dollars)							
Ms. Colón	30.8	29.9	30.0	31.0	30.1	30.5	30.7	31.0
Mr. Nielson	31.0	28.1	30.2	33.2	31.8	29.8	28.9	31.0

After studying the data, Mr. Tarsel found that the mean of the quarterly sales was $30,500, the median was $30,600, and the mode was $31,000 for both Ms. Colón and Mr. Nielson. If he was to decide between the two, Mr. Tarsel needed to find more numbers to describe this data.

The example above shows that measures of central tendency may not give an accurate enough description of a set of data. Often, *measures of variation* are also used to help describe the *spread* of the data. One of the most commonly used measures of variation is the **range**.

Definition of Range

> The range of a set of data is the difference between the greatest and the least values of the set.

Example 1

Use the information in the table above to determine the range in the quarterly sales for Ms. Colón and Mr. Nielson during the last two years.

Ms. Colón's greatest quarterly sales were $31,000 and her least were $29,900. Therefore, the range is $31,000 − $29,900 or $1100.

Mr. Nielson's greatest quarterly sales were $33,200 and his least were $28,100. Therefore, the range is $33,200 − $28,100 or $5100.

Based on this analysis, Ms. Colón's sales are much more consistent, a quality Mr. Tarsel values. Therefore, Ms. Colón is promoted.

Teaching Tip ❶

Another commonly used measure of variation is called the **interquartile range**. In a set of data, the *quartiles* are values that divide the data into four equal parts. The median of a set of data divides the data in half. The **upper quartile (UQ)** divides the upper half into two equal parts. The **lower quartile (LQ)** divides the lower half into two equal parts. The difference between the upper and lower quartile is the interquartile range.

LESSON 14-4 MEASURES OF VARIATION **575**

ALTERNATE TEACHING STRATEGIES

Using Reasoning
Use the set of data 12, 24, 18, 17, 10, and 22.
1. Find the median. **17.5**
2. Find the median of all values less than the median. **12**
3. Find the median of all values greater than the median. **22**
4. Comment on what the three "medians" do to the original set.
   They divide the set into four parts.

14-4 Lesson Notes

Lesson Resources
- Reteaching Master 14-4
- Practice Master 14-4
- Enrichment Master 14-4
- Video Algebra, 61
- Transparency 14-4 contains the 5-Minute Check and a teaching aid for this lesson.

INTRODUCING THE LESSON

🕐 **5-Minute Check**
(over Lesson 14-3)

For Exercises 1-4, use the following set of data: 12, 24, 18, 17, 10, 22, and 16.

1. Make a stem-and-leaf plot of the data.

Stem	Leaf
1	0 2 6 7 8
2	2 4

2. Find the mean. **17**
3. Find the median. **17**
4. Find the mode. **none**

5. **Determine the mean of the following set of data: 14.6, 8.3, 9.7, 16.1, 12.3, 18.4, 15.3, 17.3.** **14**

Motivating the Lesson
Have students find the mean, median, and mode of the following temperatures that occurred in Phoenix, Arizona over a 7-day period: 83, 84, 95, 85, 85, 80, and 48. Ask students to identify a temperature that deviates greatly from these measures of central tendency. Introduce the idea that in this lesson, students will learn about measures that can be used to determine variations that occur in a given set of data. **mean = 80, median = 84, mode = 85; 48**

TEACHING THE LESSON

Teaching Tip ❶ The median is a quartile.

Chapter 14 575

Definition of Interquartile Range	The difference between the upper quartile and the lower quartile of a set of data is called the interquartile range. It represents the middle half, or 50%, of the data in the set.

Example 2

The Birch Corporation held its annual golf tournament for its employees. The scores for 18 holes were 88, 91, 102, 80, 115, 99, 101, 103, 139, 105, 99, 95, 76, 105, and 112. Find the median, upper and lower quartiles, and the interquartile range for these scores.

First, order the 15 scores. Then, find the median.

76 80 88 91 95 99 99 **101** 102 103 105 105 112 115 139
↑
median

The lower quartile is the median of the lower half of the data and the upper quartile is the median of the upper half.

76 80 88 **91** 95 99 99 **101** 102 103 105 **105** 112 115 139
lower quartile   median   upper quartile

The interquartile range is 105 − 91 or 14. Therefore, the middle half, or 50%, of the golf scores vary by 14. **Teaching Tip ❷**

An outlier will not affect the median, LQ, or UQ, but it will affect the mean.

In Example 2, one score, 139, is much greater than the others. In a set of data, a value that is much higher or much lower than the rest of the data is called an **outlier**. An outlier is defined as any element of the set of data that is at least 1.5 interquartile ranges above the upper quartile or below the lower quartile.

$(1.5)(14) = 21$
$105 + 21 = 126$
$91 - 21 = 70$

To determine if 139 or any of the other scores from Example 2 is an outlier, first multiply 1.5 times the interquartile range, 14. Then add this product to the UQ, 105, and subtract it from the LQ, 91. These values give the boundaries for determining outliers. Since 139 > 126, the score 139 is an outlier. This is the only outlier. *Why?*

Example 3

APPLICATION Finance

The stem-and-leaf plot at the right represents the number of shares of the 20 most active stocks that were bought and sold on the New York Stock Exchange during 1989.

Stem	Leaf
1	[2 2 7
2	3 [3 3] 4 4 5 6] [6 8 8 9
3	[0 1] 4 6
4	0 6]

4|0 represents 400,000,000 shares.

a. The brackets group the values in the lower half and the values in the upper half. What do the boxes contain?
   values used to find the lower and upper quartiles

b. Find the interquartile range.
   The median is 26. LQ = $\frac{23 + 23}{2}$ or 23 and UQ = $\frac{30 + 31}{2}$ or 30.5. The interquartile range is 30.5 − 23 or 7.5.

576 CHAPTER 14 STATISTICS AND PROBABILITY

RETEACHING THE LESSON

Using the stem-and-leaf plot on page 567, Exercise 13, find the range, median, upper and lower quartiles, and interquartile range.
range = 36°, median = 79.5°, UQ = 77°, LQ = 63°, interquartile range = 14°

c. Find any outliers.

$$30.5 + (1.5)(7.5) = 30.5 + 11.25 \qquad\qquad 23 - (1.5)(7.5) = 23 - 11.25$$
$$= 41.75 \qquad\qquad\qquad\qquad\qquad = 11.75$$

Since $46 > 41.75$, 46 is an outlier.

CHECKING FOR UNDERSTANDING

Communicating Mathematics

Read and study the lesson to answer each question.

1. The range is the difference between which two values in a set of data? **greatest value and least value**

2. Quartiles divide a set of data into how many equal parts? **4**

3. What measure of central tendency is affected by an outlier? **mean**

4. Which would you expect to have a greater interquartile range, the set consisting of the weights of each student in your school or the set consisting of the heights of each of these students? **set of weights**

Guided Practice

Find the range for each set of data.

5. 12, 17, 16, 23, 18 **11**

6. 56, 45, 37, 43, 10, 34 **46**

7. 77, 78, 68, 96, 99, 84, 65 **34**

8. 30, 90, 40, 70, 50, 100, 80, 60 **70**

9. 3, 3.2, 6, 45, 7, 26, 2, 3.4, 4, 5.3, 5, 78, 8, 1, 5 **77**

Find the median and upper and lower quartiles for each set of data.

10. 12, 17, 16, 23, 18 **17; 20.5; 14**

11. 56, 45, 37, 43, 10, 34 **40; 45; 34**

12. 77, 78, 68, 96, 99, 84, 65 **78; 96; 68**

13. 30, 90, 40, 70, 50, 100, 80, 60 **65; 85; 45**

14. 3, 3.2, 6, 45, 7, 26, 1, 3.4, 4, 5.3, 5, 78, 8, 21, 5 **5.3; 21; 3.4**

EXERCISES

Practice

Find the range, median, upper and lower quartiles, and interquartile range for each set of data.

15. 85, 77, 58, 69, 62, 73, 55, 82, 67, 77, 59, 92, 75, 69, 76 **37; 73, 77, 62; 15**

16. 1050, 1175, 835, 1075, 1025, 1145, 1100, 1125, 975, 1005, 1125, 1095, 1075, 1055 **340; 1075, 1125, 1025; 100**

17. 211, 225, 205, 207, 208, 213, 180, 200, 210, 229, 199, 206, 212, 208, 220, 197, 211, 204, 206, 212 **49; 208, 212, 204.5; 7.5**

18.
Stem	Leaf
0	0 2 3
1	1 7 9
2	2 3 5 6
3	3 4 4 5 9
4	0 7 8 8

$2|2 = 22$

48; 26, 39, 17; 22

19.
Stem	Leaf
7	3 4 7 8
8	0 0 3 5 7
9	4 6 8
10	0 1 8
11	1 9

$9|4 = 9.4$

4.6; 8.7, 10.05, 7.9; 2.15

20.
Stem	Leaf
25	0 3 7 9
26	1 3 4 5 5 6
27	1 5 6 6 9
28	1 2 3 5 8
29	2 5 6 9

$27|5 = 2750$

490; 2755, 2840, 2635; 205

APPLYING THE LESSON

Homework Exercises

See assignment guide on page 577.

Enrichment Masters Booklet, p. 97

Critical Thinking

21. Give an example of a set of 11 numbers that has range 60, median 50, and interquartile range 15. Does this set have an outlier?
    See students' work.

Applications

22. **School**   Art and Gina's test scores in algebra are given below.
    Art: 87, 54, 78, 97, 65, 82, 75, 68, 82, 73, 66, 75
    Gina: 70, 80, 57, 100, 73, 74, 65, 77, 91, 69, 71, 76

    a. Find the range and interquartile range for each set of scores.

    b. Identify any outliers.

    c. Which one had the more consistent scores? **See margin.**

23. **Foods**   The stem-and-leaf plot at the right represents the cost per cup of various brands of coffee.

Stem	Leaf
0	6 6 6 6 8 9 9 9 9
1	0 2 3 4 5 7 7 8 8
2	4 8 9
3	0 2

    $1|2 = \$0.12$

    a. Find the range and interquartile range for the costs. **\$0.26, \$0.09**

    b. Identify any outliers. **\$0.32**

24. **Entertainment**   The total rental sales of the all-time top 20 movies, as of January 1990, are listed below.

    Rental Sales (in millions of dollars)

Title	Total Rentals	Title	Total Rentals
Back to the Future	104.4	Indiana Jones and the Last Crusade	115.5
Batman	150.5		
Beverly Hills Cop	108.0	Indiana Jones and the Temple of Doom	109.0
Close Encounters of the Third Kind	82.8	Jaws	129.6
The Empire Strikes Back	141.6	Raiders of the Lost Ark	115.6
		Rain Man	86.0
E.T.	228.6	Return of the Jedi	168.0
The Exorcist	89.0	Star Wars	193.5
Grease	96.3	Superman	82.8
Ghostbusters	130.2	Tootsie	96.3
The Godfather	86.3	Three Men and a Baby	81.3

    a. Find the range, quartiles, and interquartile range for the rentals. **\$147,300,000; \$87,650,000, \$108,500,000, \$135,900,000; \$48,250,000**

    b. Identify any outliers. **E.T. at \$228,600,000**

Mixed Review

25. Solve $-5 < 4 - 3x < 13$. Graph the solution set.   **(Lesson 5-5)**
    $-3 < x < 3$

26. Write the inverse of the relation $\{(-3, 3), (2, -2), (-1, 1), (0, 0), (1, -1)\}$. **(Lesson 9-2)** $\{(3, -3), (-2, 2), (1, -1), (0, 0), (-1, 1)\}$

27. **Geometry**   The radius r, in inches, of a sphere with surface area S in^2 is given by the formula $r = \frac{1}{2}\sqrt{\frac{S}{\pi}}$, where $\pi \approx \frac{22}{7}$. Find the radius of a sphere with surface area 440 in^2.   **(Lesson 12-1)** $\sqrt{35} \approx 5.92$ in.

28. Solve $35x^2 - 11x = 6$ using the quadratic formula.   **(Lesson 13-5)** $\frac{3}{5}, -\frac{2}{7}$

29. **Consumerism**   The prices of six different models of printers in a computer store are \$299, \$369, \$525, \$359, \$228, and \$398. Find the mean and median prices for the printers.   **(Lesson 14-3)** \$363; \$364

EXTENDING THE LESSON

Math Power: Reasoning

A set of data contains 7 elements. The median is 8900, the interquartile range is 1200, and there is one outlier above the upper quartile. Find a set of data that satisfies all the conditions.   **Answers will vary.** Compile the student responses to investigate how different the data might be.

Additional Answers

22a. Art: range - 43, interquartile range - 15; Gina: range - 43, interquartile range - 9
22b. Gina's score of 100
22c. Gina had more consistent scores since she had the smaller interquartile range.

Objective
14-5

After studying this lesson, you should be able to:

■ display and interpret data on a box-and-whisker plot.

Box-and-whisker plots are sometimes called box plots.

When analyzing a set of data, it is often helpful to draw a graphical representation of the data. One such graph, which shows the quartiles and *extreme* values of the data, is called a **box-and-whisker plot.**

In Lesson 14-2, we discussed the following 35 scores for an exam given to Mr. Juarez's first-period biology class.

82, 77, 49, 84, 44, 98, 93, 71, 76, 64, 89, 95, 78, 69, 89, 65, 88, 54, 96, 87, 92, 80, 44, 85, 93, 89, 55, 62, 79, 90, 86, 75, 74, 99, 62

Suppose Mr. Juarez wants to display this data in a box-and-whisker plot. Since the quartiles must be determined before drawing a box-and-whisker plot, he must first arrange the data in numerical order or make a stem-and-leaf plot. The stem-and-leaf plot that we made in Lesson 14-2 is shown below.

Stem	Leaf
4	[4 4 9
5	4 5
6	2 2 4 5̄ 9
7	1 4 5 6 7 8 9]
8	0 [2 4 5 6 7 8 9 9 9̄
9	0 2 3 3 5 6 8 9]

8|2 represents a score of 82.

The median for this set of data is 80. The lower quartile is 65 and the upper quartile is 89. The *extreme values* are the least value (LV), 44, and the greatest value (GV), 99.

The number line may be drawn horizontally or vertically.

To make the box-and-whisker plot, first draw a number line. Assign a scale to the number line that includes the extreme values. Plot dots to represent the extreme values (LV and GV), the upper and lower quartiles (LQ and GQ), and the median (M).

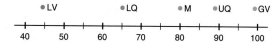

Draw a box around the interquartile range. Mark the median by a vertical line through its point in the box. The median line will not always divide the box into equal parts. Draw a segment from the lower quartile to the least value and one from the upper quartile to the greatest value. These segments are the *whiskers* of the plot.

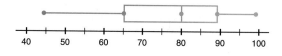

ALTERNATE TEACHING STRATEGIES

Using Problem Solving

Seven students collected cans for a recycling project. Three students each collected 10 cans, one student collected 20 cans, and the balance of the students collected 30 cans each. Make a box-and-whisker plot for this data. Identify the median, LQ, UQ, and lower and upper extremes.

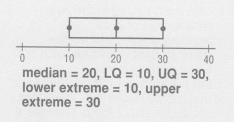

median = 20, LQ = 10, UQ = 30, lower extreme = 10, upper extreme = 30

Lesson Resources

• Reteaching Master 14-5
• Practice Master 14-5
• Enrichment Master 14-5
• Video Algebra, 61

 Transparency 14-5 contains the 5-Minute Check and a teaching aid for this lesson.

INTRODUCING THE LESSON

🕐 **5-Minute Check**
(over Lesson 14-4)

Given the data 32, 45, 67, 93, 82, 55, 58, 45, 13, and 54.

1. **Show the data in a stem-and-leaf plot.**

Stem	Leaf
1	3
2	
3	2
4	5 5
5	4 5 8
6	7
7	
8	2
9	3

2. **Find the median.** 54.5
3. **Find the upper and lower quartiles.**
   UQ = 67, LQ = 45
4. **Find the interquartile range.**
   22

Motivating the Lesson

Reinforce student understanding of the terms *median, upper quartile,* and *lower quartile* by the following activity. Tell students that they represent a set of data arranged in ascending height. Have them determine which of the class members represents the median. Then ask students to identify the class member who represents the upper quartile and the class member who represents the lower quartile.

Teaching Tip ❶ The interquartile range is 57.5 − 42.5 or 15. The 1.5 interquartile range above and below the quartiles is found by multiplying 1.5 times 15. Any value (1.5)(15) or 22.5 points above the UQ or 22.5 below the LQ is an outlier. In this case, 57.5 + 22.5 = 80. Since 81 > 80, it is an outlier.

Chalkboard Example

For the Example

Organize the given information in a stem-and-leaf plot. Then, use the stem-and-leaf plot to draw a box-and-whisker plot. Identify the extreme values and quartiles.
26, 42, 57, 12, 38, 63, 45, 18

Stem	Leaf	Box Plot
1	2 8	10 --
2	6	20 --
3	8	30 --
4	2 5	40 --
5	7	50 --
6	3	60 --

lower extreme = 12, upper extreme = 63, median = 40, UQ = 51, LQ = 22

Reteaching Masters Booklet, p. 98

NAME _____ DATE _____
14-5 | Reteaching Worksheet

Box-and-Whisker Plots

A box-and-whisker plot displays the extremes, the quartiles, and the median for a set of data. It may be drawn horizontally or vertically.

Data: 3, 7, 9, 14, 16, 19, 19, 25

Stem	Leaf
0	3 7 9
1	4 6 9 9
2	5

1|6 represents 16.

Interquartile range is 19 − 8, or 11.

Box-and-Whisker Plot:
Lower extreme is 3.
Lower quartile is 8.
Median is 15.
Upper quartile is 19.
Upper extreme is 25.

Study the box at the right. Note the dots marking the extremes, the quartiles, and the median.

Answer each question for the indicated box-and-whisker plot.

1. What are the upper and lower extremes? 4; 16
2. What is the median? 12
3. What are the upper and lower quartiles? 15; 10
4. What is the interquartile range? 5

Use the data given to complete the following. Data: 19, 49, 73, 30, 32, 46, 51, 30

5. Graph the data on a stem-and-leaf plot.

Stem	Leaf
1	9
3	0 0 2
4	6 9
5	1
7	3

4|6 represents 46.

6. Transfer the data to a vertical box-and-whisker plot.

7. What are the extremes? 19; 73
8. What is the interquartile range? 20
9. Why are the whiskers unequal? The difference between the LQ and the LV is less than the difference between the GV and the UQ.
10. How is an outlier determined? Are there any outlier values? Multiply 1.5 times the interquartile range, 20. Then add this product to the UQ, 50, and subtract it from the LQ, 30. There are no outliers.

Even though the whiskers are different lengths, each whisker contains at least one-fourth of the data while the box contains at least one-half of the data.

Now check for outliers. The interquartile range of these scores is 89 − 65 or 24. **Teaching Tip** ❶

$$65 - (1.5)(24) = 65 - 36 \qquad 89 + (1.5)(24) = 89 + 36$$
$$= 29 \qquad\qquad\qquad = 125$$

Since none of the test scores is above 125 or below 29, there are no outliers.

If a set of data contains outliers, then a box-and-whisker plot can be altered to show them. This is shown in the following example.

Example

APPLICATION
Fundraising

Twelve members of the Beck High School Pep Club are selling programs at the football game. The number of programs sold by each person is listed below.

George	51	Anthony	27	Kendra	55	Eddie	54
Vinette	69	Marlene	60	Carmen	39	Jason	46
Tomás	46	Kohana	53	Danny	81	Nashoba	23

a. **Make a box-and-whisker plot of this data.**

First arrange the data in numerical order.

$$[23\ 27\ \boxed{39\ 46}\ 46\ 51]\ [53\ 54\ \boxed{55\ 60}\ 69\ 81]$$

The extreme values are 23 and 81. The median is $\frac{51 + 53}{2}$ or 52. The lower quartile is $\frac{39 + 46}{2}$ or 42.5. The upper quartile is $\frac{55 + 60}{2}$ or 57.5. Thus, the interquartile range is 57.5 − 42.5 or 15.

Now check for outliers.

$$57.5 + (1.5)(15) = 57.5 + 22.5 \qquad 42.5 - (1.5)(15) = 42.5 - 22.5$$
$$= 80 \qquad\qquad\qquad = 20$$

Since 81 > 80, the value 81 is an outlier.

The box-and-whisker plot for this set of data is shown at the right. A point is plotted for 69 since it is the last value that is not an outlier. The whisker is drawn to this point as shown. Outliers are plotted as isolated points.

b. **Analyze the box-and-whisker plot to determine if any of the members did an exceptional job selling programs.**

Based on this plot, Danny did an exceptionally good job selling programs.

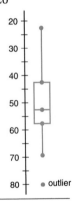

RETEACHING THE LESSON

Give each row of students a different set of data for a box-and-whiskers plot. Have every student draw their own plot on an overhead transparency. Put the plots on the overhead so that the class can see them. Ask questions about the plot to see if it was drawn correctly. Discuss problems and good points of the plots.

CHECKING FOR UNDERSTANDING

Communicating Mathematics

Read and study the lesson to answer each question.

1. Explain how to determine the scale of the number line in a box-and-whisker plot. **The scale must be large enough to include the least and greatest values.**

2. The two whiskers in a box-and-whisker plot connect what values? **least value and lower quartile; greatest value and upper quartile**

3. What percent of the data is included in the box of a box-and-whisker plot? **50%**

4. What information about a set of data can you determine from its box-and-whisker plot? **Answers may vary; typical answers may include quartiles, interquartile range, and outliers.**

Guided Practice

Answer each question for the indicated box-and-whisker plot. 8. 90 and 120

5. What percent of the data is between 120 and 130? **25%**

6. What is the median? **95**

7. What is the least value in this set of data? **85**

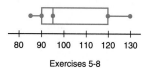

8. Between what two values of the data is the middle 50% of the data?

9. What is the upper quartile? **90**

10. What is the greatest number in this set of data? **90**

11. What percent of the data is between 50 and 90? **75%**

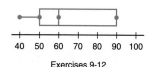

Exercises 5-8

12. Why does this plot have only one whisker? **The upper quartile and greatest value are the same.**

EXERCISES

Practice

A

Compare box-and-whisker plots X and Y to answer each question.

13. Which plot has the lesser median? **X**

14. Which plot has the greater range? **Y**

15. Which plot has the lesser interquartile range? **Y**

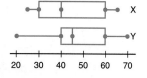

Applications

16. **Travel** Speeds of the fastest train runs in the U.S. and Canada are given below in miles per hour. Make a box-and-whisker plot of the data. **See margin.**

| 93.5 | 82.5 | 89.3 | 83.8 | 81.8 | 86.8 |
| 90.8 | 84.9 | 95.0 | 83.1 | 83.2 | 88.2 |

LESSON 14-5 BOX-AND-WHISKER PLOTS **581**

Additional Answer

16.

EVALUATING THE LESSON

Checking for Understanding

Exercises 1-12 are designed to help you assess understanding through reading, writing, and speaking. You should work through Exercises 1-4 with your students, and then monitor their work on Exercises 5-12.

Closing the Lesson

Speaking Activity Ask students to describe the steps to follow when making a box-and-whisker plot.

APPLYING THE LESSON

Homework Exercises

Assignment Guide
Basic: 13-20, 22-28
Average: 16-28
Enriched: 16-28

Practice Masters Booklet, p. 110

14-5 Practice Worksheet

NAME _____ DATE _____

Box-and-Whisker Plots

Compare box-and-whisker plots A and B to answer each question.

1. What is the median of each set of data? **Both are 70.**

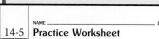

2. Which plot has the lesser range? **A**

3. Which plot has the greater interquartile range? **B**

4. What is the upper quartile of each set of data? **A: 80; B: 85**

5. What is the lower quartile of each set of data? **A: 65; B: 60**

6. What is the least value in plot A? **50**

7. What is the greatest value in plot B? **100**

8. Which plot illustrates the larger range of data? **B**

9. What percent of the data in plot B is between 60 and 85? **50%**

10. What percent of the data in plot A is greater than 80? **25%**

11. What percent of the data in plot A is less than 65? **25%**

12. The numbers below represent forty eighteen-hole scores of a golfer at Crystal Springs Golf Club. Make a box-and-whisker plot of this data in the space provided.

88	80	80	77	84	74	80	79	83	77
75	75	78	79	77	81	72	85	75	76
78	76	77	72	75	70	78	77	72	79
78	75	79	77	77	73	77	78	82	86

13. What is the median score? **77**

14. What percent of the scores were lower than 80? **75%**

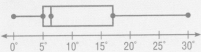
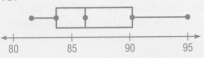

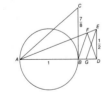
17. **Weather** The following high temperatures were recorded during a two-week cold spell in St. Louis. Make a box-and-whisker plot of the temperatures. **See margin.**

   20° 2° 12° 5° 4° 16° 17° 7° 6° 16° 5° 0° 5° 30°

18. **Basketball** The numbers below represent the 20 highest points-scored-per-game averages for a season in the NBA from 1947 to 1990. Make a box-and-whisker plot of this data. **See margin.**

   35.0 33.5 32.5 37.9 31.2 38.4 34.5 34.7 32.9 44.8
   31.7 37.1 36.5 34.0 50.4 32.3 33.6 34.8 33.1 35.6

19. **Baseball** The stem-and-leaf plot at the right shows the number of home runs hit by the home run leaders in the National League in 1990. Make a box-and-whisker plot of the data. **See margin.**

Stem	Leaf
2	2 3 3 4 4 4 4 5 5 6
	7 7 8
3	2 2 3 3 5 7
4	0 3|3 = 33

20. **Consumerism** Ten light bulbs were purchased from each of two different manufacturers, A and B. The bulbs were tested to determine how many hours of light they would provide. The results are given below.

   A: 290, 300, 497, 395, 450, 360, 740, 500, 520, 370
   B: 400, 410, 460, 450, 350, 495, 375, 405, 485, 520

   a. Make a box-and-whisker plot comparing the data. **See Solutions Manual.**

   b. Based on this plot, from which manufacturer would you buy your light bulbs? Explain. **See margin.**

21. **Health** The table below shows the number of years of life expected for men and women born in various years from 1920 to 1989. Make a box-and-whisker plot for the men's data and for the women's data. Then compare the plots. **See Solutions Manual.**

Year	Men	Women	Year	Men	Women	Year	Men	Women
1920	53.6	54.6	1960	66.6	73.1	1980	70.0	77.5
1930	58.1	61.6	1965	66.8	73.7	1985	71.2	78.2
1940	60.8	65.2	1970	67.1	74.7	1989	71.8	78.5
1950	65.6	71.1	1975	68.8	76.6			

Critical Thinking

22. Name a set of data with ten numbers for which its box-and-whisker plot would have no whiskers. **Answers will vary; typical answer might be 10, 10, 10, 20, 25, 25, 30, 40, 40, 40.**

Mixed Review

23. Solve $29 - 3a = 2(3a - 4) + 3$. **(Lesson 6-7)** $\frac{34}{9}$

24. Graph $2x - y = 6$. **(Lesson 9-4) See Solutions Manual.**

25. Solve the system $x + y = 4$ and $3x - 5y = 60$. **(Lesson 11-3)** $(10, -6)$

26. Simplify $\frac{1}{7 - \sqrt{3}}$. **(Lesson 12-5)** $\frac{7 + \sqrt{3}}{46}$

27. Find the discriminant and determine the nature of the roots of $3n^2 - n - 5 = 0$. **(Lesson 13-6) 61, 2 real roots**

28. Use the information from Exercise 16 to find the range, quartiles and interquartile range of the 20 highest points-scored-per-game averages in the NBA. Identify any outliers. **19.2; 33.0, 34.6, 36.8; 3.8; 44.8, 50.4**

EXTENDING THE LESSON

Math Power: Connections

Have students do research to find the median ages of men and women at the time of their first marriage for the decades of 1900 and 1990. Have students determine the mean, mode, quartiles, range, interquartile range, and any outliers for each set of data and display the data using box-and-whisker plots. Then compare the plots.

Scatter Plots

Objective
14-6

After studying this lesson, you should be able to:
■ graph and interpret pairs of numbers on a scatter plot.

Application

FYI ···

A branch of statistics called *regression analysis* deals with finding functions that approximate the relationship between sets of data.

Each student in Ms. Suber's sociology class was given the assignment of conducting a survey and interpreting the results. Jenelle decided to conduct a survey to determine whether there was a relationship between the amount of time spent studying for an exam and the grade earned on the exam. To do this, she asked 15 classmates in her history class to record the amount of time that they studied for an upcoming exam. Then she recorded their test scores. She organized the results in the table shown at the right.

Based on this information, can she conclude that there is a relationship between study time and exam scores?

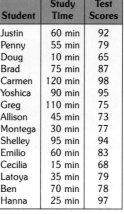

Student	Study Time	Test Scores
Justin	60 min	92
Penny	55 min	79
Doug	10 min	65
Brad	75 min	87
Carmen	120 min	98
Yoshica	90 min	95
Greg	110 min	75
Allison	45 min	73
Montega	30 min	77
Shelley	95 min	94
Emilio	60 min	83
Cecilia	15 min	68
Latoya	35 min	79
Ben	70 min	78
Hanna	25 min	97

In order to determine if there is a relationship, Jenelle needs to compare study times and test scores. One way to do this is to display the information in a graph called a **scatter plot**. In a scatter plot, the two sets of data are plotted as ordered pairs in the coordinate plane. Place the data for time studies on the horizontal axis, and the data for the test scores on the vertical axis. For example, the information about Justin is plotted as the point (60, 92).

a. Describe the point with the box around it.

It represents a study time of 75 minutes with a resulting test score of 87.

b. Who studied quite a bit and had a fairly low test score?

Greg

c. Who did not study much and had a fairly high test score?

Hanna

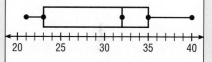

d. Does the scatter plot show a relationship between study time and test scores?

In general, the scatter plot seems to show that a higher grade is directly related to the amount of time spent studying.

LESSON 14-6   SCATTER PLOTS   583

ALTERNATE TEACHING STRATEGIES

Using Applications

State which value is determined by the other value.

1. miles per gallon and speed traveled
miles per gallon by speed

2. hourly wage and weekly pay
weekly pay by hourly wage

Lesson Resources

- Reteaching Master 14-6
- Practice Master 14-6
- Enrichment Master 14-6
- Technology Master p. 29
- Activity Master, p. 29

 Transparency 14-6 contains the 5-Minute Check and a teaching aid for this lesson.

INTRODUCING THE LESSON

🕐 5-Minute Check
(over Lesson 14-5)

Use the box-and-whisker plot shown to answer the following questions.

```
20    25    30    35    40
```

1. What is the lower extreme?
21
2. What is the range? 19
3. What is the median? 32
4. What is the upper quartile?
35
5. What is the interquartile range? 12

Motivating the Lesson

A local football team has gained the following yards in its first seven games. Have students analyze the data to identify a pattern.

GAME	YARDAGE
1	348
2	350
3	300
4	295
5	280
6	250
7	225

The yardage per game is decreasing.

Develop the idea that neither a stem-and-leaf plot nor a box-and-whisker plot would show this pattern.

Chalkboard Examples

For Example 1

The table below lists the number of shots attempted and the number of shots made by each of eleven members of a basketball team. Make a scatter plot of the data and answer the questions below.

Player	Shots Attempted	Shots Made
A	240	160
B	200	120
C	135	50
D	80	50
E	75	70
F	35	20
G	20	10
H	12	5
I	9	7
J	5	5
K	2	0

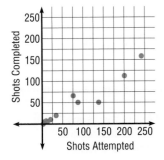

a. **Do the points graphed seem to fall on a line?** Yes, with the exception of a few, the points formed appear to form a line slanting upward.

b. **Is there a negative, positive, or no association between the variables?** positive

For Example 2

Use the scatter plot from Chalkboard Example 1 to answer the following question.
Does there appear to be any association between the number of shots attempted and the number of shots completed?
Yes, the plot seems to indicate that as the number of shots attempted increases so does the number of shots completed.

When data is displayed in a scatter plot, usually the purpose is to determine if there is a pattern, or association, between the variables on the graph. If an association does exist, it may be *negative* or *positive*. In the application on the previous page, if you could draw a line that is suggested by the points in the scatter plot, it would have a positive slope. Thus, the association between study time and test scores is said to be positive.

Example 1

The scatter plot below compares the number of hours per week people watched television to the number of hours per week they spent doing some physical activity. Does there appear to be any association between time spent watching television and physical activity?

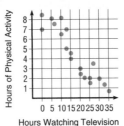

The plot seems to indicate that the greater the amount of time spent watching television, the less the amount of time spent doing physical activity. Thus, there appears to be a *negative* association between watching television and physical activity.

Example 2

Each week, Ms. Suber gives a 50-point quiz in her sociology class. The scatter plots below compare the week the quizzes were taken to the quiz scores of two students, Mike and Melanie. Does there appear to be any association between the week they took the quiz and their quiz score?

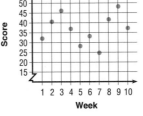 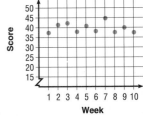

In the scatter plot on the left, the points are very spread out. There appears to be no association between the week Mike took the quiz and his score. In the scatter plot on the right, there appears to be an association between the week Melanie took the quiz and her score. However, it is impossible to tell whether this association is positive or negative.

Even when a scatter plot shows no association between two sets of data, the plot can still be used to answer questions about the data. For example, you can use the scatter plot in Example 2 to determine how many weeks Mike scored over 40 points.

CHECKING FOR UNDERSTANDING

Communicating Mathematics

Read and study the lesson to answer each question. 1-2. See margin.

1. Describe how to draw a scatter plot for two sets of data.

2. How do you determine from a scatter plot whether there appears to be any association between the two sets of data plotted?

3. *True* or *false:* If two sets of data do not show a positive association in a scatter plot, then they will show a negative association. **false**

4. In Example 2, suppose there was a positive association between the week Mike took the quiz and his quiz score. What would this tell you about Mike's quiz scores? **They were improving with time.**

Guided Practice

Determine whether a scatter plot of the data for the following would show positive, negative, or no association between the variables.

5. amount of money earned and spent **positive**

6. heights of sons and fathers **positive**

7. speed of car and miles per gallon **negative or positive**

8. age of car and its value **negative**

9. your height and month of birth **none**

10. playing time and points scored **positive**

EXERCISES

Practice

Which graphs show an association between the variables? If there is an association, is it positive, negative, or not possible to tell?

A

11.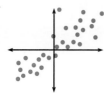
positive

12.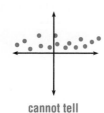
cannot tell

13.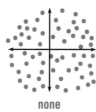
none

B

14. Collect data from your classmates on the number of hours per week they watch television and the number of hours per week they spend studying. Make a scatter plot of the data. **Answers will vary. See students' work.**

Applications

15. **Finance** The table below shows the annual income and the number of years of college education for eleven people.

Income (thousands)	$23	$20	$25	$47	$19	$48	$35	$10	$39	$26	$36
College Education (years)	3	2	4	6	2.5	7.5	6.5	1	5.5	4.5	4

a. Make a scatter plot of the data. **See Solutions Manual.**

b. Based on this plot, how does the number of years of college affect income? **See Solutions Manual.**

LESSON 14-6 SCATTER PLOTS 585

Additional Answers

1. Place data from one set on the horizontal axis and data for the other set on the vertical axis. Then plot corresponding elements in the sets as ordered pairs.

2. If the distribution of points resembles a line, then there may be an association between the two sets of data plotted.

16. **Weather**   The maximum and minimum monthly temperatures in July of ten cities are given in the table below.

    a. Make a scatter plot of the data. **See Solutions Manual.**

    b. Which city has the highest maximum and minimum temperatures? **Norfolk, VA**

    c. Which city has the lowest minimum and maximum temperatures? **Portland, ME**

    d. Is there a cluster of points in the plot? If so, explain why. **See margin.**

City	Maximum	Minimum
Hartford, CT	85	62
Baltimore, MD	87	67
Boston, MA	82	65
Portland, ME	79	57
Concord, NH	83	56
Albany, NY	83	60
New York, NY	84	69
Burlington, VT	81	59
Norfolk, VA	90	70
Huntington, WV	86	65

a. See Solutions Manual.
b-e. See margin.

17. **Hockey**   The number of points scored and assists made by members of the 1990 Stanley Cup Champion Edmonton Oilers is given in the table.

    a. Make a scatter plot of the data.

    b. Does the scatter plot show a positive or negative association?

    c. Could you predict the number of assists a player would have if you were given the number of goals for that player?

    d. Do you think that the position of a player affects the number of points scored by that player?

    e. Do you think that the amount of time played affects the number of points scored by a player?

Player	Goals	Assists
Messier	45	84
Kurri	33	60
Anderson	34	38
Klima	30	33
Tikkanen	30	33
Simpson	29	32
MacTarish	21	22
Smith	7	34
Lowe	7	26
Murphy	10	19
Lamb	12	16
Gelinas	17	8
Gregg	4	20
Muni	5	12

18. **Golf**   The earnings of the leading money winners on the PGA and LPGA golf tours from 1978–1989 are given in the table below.

Year	PGA Earnings (in thousands)	LPGA Earnings (in thousands)	Year	PGA Earnings (in thousands)	LPGA Earnings (in thousands)
1978	362	190	1984	476	267
1979	463	216	1985	542	416
1980	531	231	1986	653	492
1981	376	207	1987	926	466
1982	446	310	1988	1148	347
1983	427	291	1989	1395	654

    a. Make a scatter plot of each set of data, using the year as the first variable. **See Solutions Manual.**

    b. What do the scatter plots indicate? **See margin.**

19. **School**   The table below shows the typing speeds of 12 students.

Typing Speed (wpm)	33	45	46	20	40	30	38	22	52	44	42	55
Experience (weeks)	4	7	8	1	6	3	5	2	9	6	7	10

    a. Make a scatter plot of this data. **See Solutions Manual.**

    b. Draw a line that "fits" the data in the scatter plot. Find an equation of the line. **See Solutions Manual.**

    c. Use the equation to predict the typing speed of a student after a 12-week course. **See margin.**

Additional Answers

16d. Yes, due to the geographical location of these cities.

17b. positive

17c. Yes; you could estimate the number of assists by using the points in the scatter plot.

17d. Yes; some players have more opportunities to score points because of the position they play for the team.

17e. Yes since more playing time provides a player with more opportunities to score points.

18b. Earnings for the leading money winners for the PGA and LPGA are both increasing with time.

19c. about 66 words per minute

20. Use the data from Exercise 18 to make a scatter plot comparing LPGA and PGA earnings from 1978 to 1989. What does the association between the variables in this scatter plot indicate? **See margin.**

21. Write an algebraic expression for *25 less than six times the square of a number.* **(Lesson 1-1)** $6x^2 - 25$

22. **Aviation** The top flying speed of an open cockpit biplane is 120 mph. At this speed, a 420-mile trip flying with the wind takes the same amount of time as a 300-mile trip flying against the wind. What is the speed of the wind? **(Lesson 8-9)** 20 mph

23. Graph $5x + 2 = 7y$. **(Lesson 10-4)** See margin.

24. **Geometry** Find the dimensions of a rectangle with a perimeter of 15.4 cm and an area of 14.4 cm²? **(Lesson 13-7)** 3.2 cm by 4.5 cm

25. Use the data from Exercise 18 to make a box-and-whisker plot for the earnings of the leading money winner on the PGA tour from 1978 to 1989. **(Lesson 14-5)** See margin.

MID-CHAPTER REVIEW

The table below shows the normal seasonal precipitation, in inches, for selected cities in the U.S. Use this data to complete Exercises 1–6.

Season	Albuquerque	Boston	Chicago	Denver	Houston	Kansas City	New Orleans	San Francisco
Winter	1.3	11.8	5.5	2.4	9.2	4.1	14.9	10.5
Spring	1.4	10.1	11.0	5.9	12.9	10.2	14.2	1.9
Summer	3.7	9.8	10.5	4.6	11.9	10.0	18.6	0.3
Fall	1.8	12.5	6.5	2.6	10.8	4.8	12.1	7.1
Totals	8.2	44.2	33.5	15.5	44.8	29.1	59.8	19.8

1. What are the greatest and the least seasonal precipitation for any of the cities? **(Lesson 14-1)** 18.6 in., summer, New Orleans; 0.3 in., summer, San Francisco

2. Make a line plot of the winter precipitation for the eight cities. **(Lesson 14-1)**

3. Make a stem-and-leaf plot of the fall precipitation for the eight cities. **(Lesson 14-2)**

4. Find the mean, median, and mode of the spring precipitation for the eight cities. **(Lesson 14-3)** 8.45 in., 10.15 in., no mode

5. Find the range, quartiles, and interquartile range of the summer precipitation in the eight cities. Identify any outliers. **(Lesson 14-4)** 18.3 in.; 4.15 in., 9.9 in.; 11.2 in.; 7.05 in.; no outliers

6. Make a box-and-whisker plot of the total precipitation for the eight cities. **(Lesson 14-5)**

7. Make a scatter plot of the following data. **(Lesson 14-6)**

Miles Driven	200	322	250	290	310	135	60	150	180	70	315	175
Fuel Used (gallons)	7.5	14	11	10	10	5	2.3	5	6.2	3	11	6.5

2, 3, 6, 7. See Solutions Manual.

EXTENDING THE LESSON

Math Power: Reasoning

The daily high temperatures in Seattle were recorded for the month of November, 1990. The data is shown in the form of a scatter plot with the horizontal scale representing the day of the month and the vertical scale representing the temperature.
For the questions at the right, answers will vary. Typical answers are given.

1. What information can be determined from the plot?
   any weather trends that occurred during the month

2. What information cannot be determined from the plot?
   how the daily temperatures in 1990 compared with average temperatures over an extended period of time

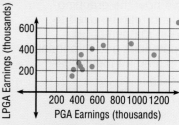
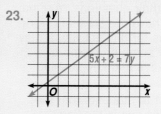
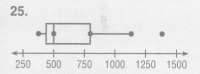

Using Technology

Objective This optional page shows how the graphing calculator can be used to perform mathematical computations and to enhance and extend mathematical concepts.

Teaching Suggestions

One of the most frustrating things about this lesson may be finding the keys on the calculator. Have patience with your students. Take the time to help them locate keys and answer their questions. You may want to have the students work in groups for this activity. It may head off some problems of finding keys and key-pushing errors.

Point out to students that the regression line is the line that "best fits" the data. There are points above and points below the line, or the line is in the "middle" of the points. Also explain to students that the closer the data points are to the line the better the fit of the line.

To have students grasp the idea of regression lines, have them graph what they think will be the regression line in the problems before the calculator graphs it. Then compare their guesses with the actual regression line. This can help them with their estimation skills.

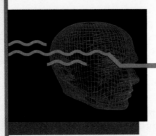

Technology
Regression Lines

BASIC
▶ **Graphing calculators**
Graphing software
Spreadsheets

Is the number of police officers related to the number of crimes? Is the amount of time spent studying related to test scores? Each of these relationships involves two variables. Therefore, they can be denoted with ordered pairs of the form (x, y). The ordered pairs of data can be graphed on a coordinate system as points. If the points lie on the same line or close to a line, they are said to be *linearly related*. A **regression line** is a line that best fits data that are linearly related.

Example

Graph the ordered pairs of data in the table and draw a regression line.

x	−8	−6	2	4	−1
y	−4	3	−1	5	9

	T1-81	*Casio*
1. Set the range values as desired.	(Possible choice: [−10, 10] by [−5, 15].)	
2. Clear the graphics screen.	[2nd] [DRAW] 1 [ENTER]	[Cls] [EXE]
3. Set the mode and clear the statistical memories.	[2nd] [STAT] [◄] 2 [ENTER] [2nd] [STAT] [◄] [ENTER]	[SHIFT] [MODE] [÷] [SHIFT] [Scl] [EXE]
4. Enter the data.	[(-)] 8 [ENTER] [(-)] 4 [ENTER] [(-)] 6 [ENTER] 3 [ENTER] 2 [ENTER] [(-)] 1 [ENTER] 4 [ENTER] 5 [ENTER] [(-)] 1 [ENTER] 9 [ENTER]	[(-)] 8 [SHIFT] [,] [(-)] 4 [DT] [(-)] 6 [SHIFT] [,] 3 [DT] 2 [SHIFT] [,] [(-)] 1 [DT] 4 [SHIFT] [,] 5 [DT] [(-)] 1 [SHIFT] [,] 9 [DT]
5. Graph the regression line and scatter plot.	[2nd] [STAT] [►] 2 [ENTER] [2nd] [STAT] 2 [ENTER] [Y=] [VARS] [►] [►] 4 [ENTER] [GRAPH] [2nd] [STAT] [►] 2 [ENTER]	[GRAPH] [SHIFT] [LINE] 1 [EXE]

EXERCISES

Graph each set of data and draw a regression line. See margin.

1.
x	−2	−1	2	3	4	7
y	1	−3	−2	5	2	6

2.
x	−3	−3	−2	−1	1	2
y	6	3	5	1	−1	−1

Additional Answers

1.
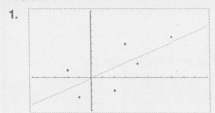

2.
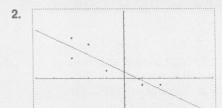

14-7 Probability and Odds

Objectives
14-7A
14-7B

After studying this lesson, you should be able to:
- find the probability of a simple event, and
- find the odds of a simple event.

Application

Denise is one of 32 students entered in the Paradise Valley Chess Club's annual tournament. Of the 32 students, 7 are freshmen, 6 are sophomores, 9 are juniors, and 10 are seniors. If Denise is a junior, how likely is it that her first opponent is also a junior?

The probability of an event may be written as a percent, a fraction, or a decimal.

We do not know who Denise's first opponent will be. When we are uncertain about the occurrence of an event, we can measure the chances of its happening with **probability**. The probability of an event is a ratio that tells how likely it is that an event will take place. The numerator is the number of favorable outcomes and the denominator is the number of possible outcomes. For example, suppose you want to know the probability of getting a 2 on one roll of a die. When you roll a die, there are six possible outcomes. Of these outcomes, only one is favorable, a 2. Therefore, the probability is $\frac{1}{6}$. We write $P(2)$ to represent *the probability of getting a 2 on one roll of a die.*

Definition of Probability	$P(\text{event}) = \dfrac{\text{number of favorable outcomes}}{\text{number of possible outcomes}}$

Example 1

Determine the probability that Denise's first opponent in the chess tournament is a junior to answer the problem presented above.

Since there are 32 students, Denise has 31 possible opponents. Since she is a junior, there are only 8 juniors left to be her first opponent.

$$P(\text{junior}) = \frac{\text{number of juniors}}{\text{total number of opponents}} \quad \text{\small number of favorable outcomes}$$
$$\quad \text{\small number of possible outcomes}$$

$$= \frac{8}{31}$$

The probability that Denise's first opponent is a junior is $\frac{8}{31}$.

Example 2

Diego has a collection of tapes that he plays regularly. He has 10 rock tapes, 5 jazz tapes, and 8 country tapes. If Diego chooses a tape at random, what is the probability that he will choose a jazz tape?

$$P(\text{jazz tape}) = \frac{\text{number of jazz tapes}}{\text{total number of tapes}} \quad \text{\small number of favorable outcomes}$$
$$\quad \text{\small number of possible outcomes}$$

$$= \frac{5}{23}$$

The probability that Diego chooses a jazz tape is $\frac{5}{23}$.

LESSON 14-7 PROBABILITY AND ODDS **589**

ALTERNATE TEACHING STRATEGIES

Using Discussion
Develop student understanding of probability and odds by asking the following questions.
1. What is the meaning of the word "random"?
2. What are examples of situations that have a probability of 0? of 1?

3. Suppose the odds of an event occurring are 3:2. What is the probability that the event occurs? $\frac{3}{5}$

14-7 Lesson Notes

Lesson Resources
- Reteaching Master 14-7
- Practice Master 14-7
- Enrichment Master 14-7
- Technology Master, p. 14
 Transparency 14-7 contains the 5-Minute Check and a teaching aid for this lesson.

INTRODUCING THE LESSON

5-Minute Check
(over Lesson 14-6)

Use the scatter plot shown below to answer the questions.

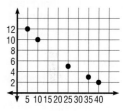

1. **What ordered pairs are represented?** {(5, 12), (10, 10), (25, 5), (35, 3), (40, 2)}
2. **Does the plot indicate a negative, positive, or no association?** negative

Motivating the Lesson
Introduce the lesson by asking the following questions:
1. Suppose a student is to be randomly selected from among the members of the class. What is the probability that you will be selected?
2. Suppose the class was divided in half and a student was to be selected from each half of the class. How would this affect the probability that you will be selected?

Chalkboard Examples

For Example 1

Lynn collects stamps from different countries. He has five from Canada, two from France, one from Russia, four from Great Britain, and one from Germany. If he accidentally loses one stamp, what is the probability that it is the stamp from Russia? $\frac{1}{13}$

For Example 2

Grace has a collection of jerseys from college campuses that she has visited. Two jerseys come from colleges in Indiana, three from California, one from Ohio, one from Washington, D.C., and three from New York. If she grabs a jersey without looking, what is the probability that she will grab one from Indiana? $\frac{1}{5}$

For Example 3

The door prize at a party with 25 people is given by writing numbers 1 through 25 on the bottom of the paper plates used.

a. **What is the probability that an individual had the winning plate?** $\frac{1}{25}$

b. **What are the odds of winning the door prize?** **1:24**

c. **What are the odds of not winning the door prize?** **24:1**

For Example 4

The probability that Jim Jackson will make his next free throw is 75% or $\frac{3}{4}$. Find the odds that he will not make his next free throw. **1:3**

FYI···

A description of probability was first presented by the French mathematician Pierre-Simon Laplace in 1795.

Some outcomes have an equal chance of occurring. We say that such outcomes are **equally likely**.

What are the possible values for the probability of an event? Consider the following cases.

1. Suppose it is impossible for an event to occur. This means that there are no favorable outcomes. Thus, the probability of an impossible event must be 0.

2. Suppose an event is certain to occur. This means that every possible outcome is a favorable outcome. Thus, the probability of a certain event must be 1.

3. Suppose an event is neither impossible nor certain. This means that the number of favorable outcomes is greater than 0 but less than the number of possible outcomes. Thus, the probability of this event must be greater than 0 and less than 1.

Based on these three cases, we can conclude that the probability of any event is always a value between 0 and 1, inclusive. This can be expressed as $0 \le P(\text{event}) \le 1$.

Another way to measure the chance of an event's occurring is with **odds**. The odds of an event is the ratio that compares the number of ways an event can occur to the number of ways it *cannot* occur.

Definition of Odds	The odds of an event occurring is the ratio of the number of ways the event can occur (successes) to the number of ways the event cannot occur (failures).

Odds = number of successes : number of failures

Example 3

The Southside Youth Center is having a raffle to make money for a new gymnasium. The Ryder family bought 10 raffle tickets, two for each family member. If 1000 raffle tickets are sold, what are the odds that a member of the Ryder family will win the raffle?

The Ryder family has 10 of the 1000 tickets. Thus, there are $1000 - 10$ or 990 tickets that will not be winning tickets for the Ryder family.

Odds of winning = number of chances of drawing winning ticket : number of chances of drawing other tickets

= 10:990 or 1:99   *This is read "1 to 99."*

Example 4

APPLICATION

Weather

The Channel 8 weather forecaster states that the probability of rain tomorrow is 40% or $\frac{2}{5}$. Find the odds that it will not rain tomorrow.

If the probability of rain tomorrow is $\frac{2}{5}$, then the number of failures (rain) is 2, while the total number of outcomes is 5. This means that the number of successes (no rain) must be $5 - 2$ or 3.

Odds of no rain = number of successes : number of failures

= 3:2   *This is read "3 to 2."*

CHECKING FOR UNDERSTANDING

Communicating Mathematics

Read and study the lesson to answer each question. **1-2. See margin.**

1. Give three examples of events that have *equally likely* outcomes.

2. Suppose you roll a die. Give examples of an impossible event and a certain event.

3. If the odds that an event will occur are 3:5, what are the odds that the event will *not* occur? **5:3**

4. Nick says that the probability of getting heads in one toss of a coin is 1 out of 2. Felicia says that the odds of getting heads in one toss of a coin are 1 to 1. Who is correct? **They both are.**

Guided Practice

The probability of an event can be graphed on a number line like the one shown below. Copy the number line and then graph the probability of each event. **5, 6, 10. Answers may vary.**

$$0 \qquad \frac{1}{2} \qquad 1$$

Impossible   Unlikely   50-50 Chance   Likely   Certain

5. It will rain today.
6. You will pass your next test.
7. This is an algebra book. **1**
8. A coin will land tails up. $\frac{1}{2}$
9. Today is Friday. $\frac{1}{7}$
10. You will go skiing tomorrow.

Determine if each event described below has equally likely outcomes.

11. tossing a fair coin **yes**
12. passing a test **no**
13. winning a golf game **no**
14. rolling a die **yes**
15. winning a lottery **yes**
16. choosing a soft drink at random from a machine **yes**

EXERCISES

Practice

A

Find the probability of each outcome if a die is rolled.

17. a 3 $\frac{1}{6}$
18. a number less than 1   **0**
19. an even number $\frac{1}{2}$
20. a number greater than 1 $\frac{5}{6}$

Find the odds of each outcome if a die is rolled.

21. a multiple of 3   **1:2**
22. a number greater than 3   **1:1**
23. not a 2   **5:1**
24. a number less than 5   **2:1**

B

A card is selected at random from a deck of 52 cards.

25. What is the probability of selecting a black card? $\frac{1}{2}$

26. What is the probability of selecting a king? $\frac{1}{13}$

27. What are the odds of selecting a club? **1:3**

28. What are the odds of *not* selecting a red 7? **25:1**

29. What is the probability of selecting a club *or* an ace? $\frac{4}{13}$

RETEACHING THE LESSON

Working in pairs, have one student give an experiment and ask the probability of a certain event happening. The other student finds the probability and then asks the first student the probability of another event happening in that same experiment, and so on. Have students record their questions and answers.

Additional Answers

1. Answers will vary; typical answers are rolling a die, tossing a coin, and choosing a marble at random from a bag.

2. Answers will vary; typical answer for an impossible event is getting a 7 and for a certain event is getting a number less than 7.

14-7   **Reteaching Worksheet**

NAME _____   DATE _____

Probability and Odds

The **probability** of an event is a ratio that tells how likely it is that the event will take place.

Definition of Probability
$P(\text{event}) = \dfrac{\text{number of favorable outcomes}}{\text{number of possible outcomes}}$

Example 1: Mr. Babcock picks 5 of the 25 students in his algebra class at random for a special project. What is the probability of being picked?

$$P(\text{being picked}) = \frac{\text{number of students picked}}{\text{total number of students}}$$

The probability of being picked is $\frac{5}{25}$ or $\frac{1}{5}$.

The probability of any event has a value from 0 to 1. If the probability of an event is 0, it is impossible for the event to occur. An event that is certain to occur has a probability of 1. This can be expressed as $0 \le P(\text{event}) \le 1$.

The **odds** of an event occurring is the ratio of the number of ways an event can occur (successes) to the number of ways the event cannot occur (failures).

Definition of Odds
$\text{Odds} = \dfrac{\text{number of successes}}{\text{number of failures}}$

Example 2: Find the odds that a member of Mr. Babcock's class will be picked for the special project.

Number of successes: 5   Number of failures: 20
Odds of being picked = number of successes : number of failures
= 5 : 20, or 1 : 4

Solve each problem.

1. There were 2 colas, 1 ginger ale, 5 cherry sodas, and 4 root beers in the cooler. What is the probability of pulling out a cola? $\frac{1}{6}$

2. It will rain 8 times in November and snow 3 times. The other days it will be sunny. What is the probability of sun? the odds of sun? $\frac{19}{30}$; 19 : 11

There is a bowl of money at the carnival. The bowl contains 50 quarters, 75 dimes, 100 nickels, and 125 pennies.

3. If one coin is chosen, what is the probability that a quarter will be chosen? $\frac{1}{7}$

4. What would be the odds of choosing a quarter if all the dimes were removed first? 2 : 9

5. What are the odds that a dime will not be chosen? 11 : 3

6. What are the odds of choosing a penny? 5 : 9

30. If the probability that an event will occur is $\frac{2}{3}$, what are the odds that the event will occur? **2:1**

31. If the probability that an event will occur is $\frac{3}{7}$, what are the odds that the event will *not* occur? **4:3**

32. If the odds that an event will occur are 8:5, what is the probability that the event will occur? $\frac{8}{13}$

33. If the odds that an event does *not* occur are 9:14, what is the probability that the event does occur? $\frac{14}{23}$

34. The number of males and females enrolled in each grade at Oak Grove High School is given in the table below. You are conducting a survey on reading habits for the school newspaper by selecting students at random.

    a. What is the probability that a student chosen is a female? $\frac{107}{207}$

Grade	9th	10th	11th	12th
Male	130	150	100	120
Female	150	100	110	175

    b. What is the probability that a student chosen is a male in the 9th grade? $\frac{26}{207}$

    c. What are the odds that a student chosen is in the 10th grade? **50:157**

    d. If a student from the 11th grade is selected, is it more likely that the student is a male or a female? **female**

35. What is the probability that a number chosen at random from the domain {0, 1, 2, 3, 4, 5, 6, 7, 8, 9} will satisfy the inequality $2x + 3 < 17$? **0.7**

CONNECTION

Number Theory

36. If a three-digit number is selected at random from the set of all three-digit numbers, what are the odds that all three of the digits will be prime numbers? **16:209**

Critical Thinking

37. A butterfly lands on one of the six squares of the T-shaped figure shown and then randomly moves to an adjacent square. What is the probability that the butterfly ends up on the red square? $\frac{1}{4}$

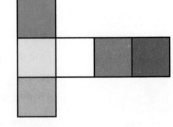

Applications

38. **Entertainment** A reception is scheduled for an open area of Spring Grove Park, and a tent has been ordered in case of rain. Weather reports indicate a 50% chance of rain on the day of the reception. Whether or not it rains, there is a 50% chance the tent will not arrive in time for the reception due to traffic problems. What is the probability the people at the reception will get wet? **0.25**

39. **Consumerism** A shipment of 100 clocks was just received by The Clock Shoppe. There is a 4% probability that one of the clocks was damaged during shipment, even though the package does not give any indication that the clock is damaged. If Alison buys one of these clocks, what are the odds that she is buying a damaged clock? **1:24**

592 CHAPTER 14 STATISTICS AND PROBABILITY

Practice Masters Booklet, p. 112

NAME _____ DATE _____

14-7 **Practice Worksheet**

Probability and Odds

Find the probability of each outcome if a die is rolled.

1. a 1 $\frac{1}{6}$

2. a number less than 3 $\frac{1}{3}$

3. an odd number $\frac{1}{2}$

4. a number greater than 6 **0**

5. an even number less than 6 $\frac{1}{3}$

6. a number greater than 0 **1**

Find the odds of each outcome if a die is rolled.

7. a multiple of 2 **1 : 1**

8. a number less than 2 **1 : 5**

9. a factor of 6 **2 : 1**

10. a 5 **1 : 5**

11. not a 1 **5 : 1**

12. a number greater than 5 **1 : 5**

A card is selected at random from a deck of 52 cards.

13. What is the probability of selecting a red card? $\frac{1}{2}$

14. What is the probability of selecting an ace? $\frac{1}{13}$

15. What are the odds of selecting a diamond? **1 : 3**

16. What are the odds of not selecting a black 2? **25 : 1**

The number of male and female doctors in Camron are listed by age in the table at the right. Use this data to answer the following questions.

17. What is the probability that a doctor chosen is in the 45–54 age group? $\frac{1}{6}$

18. What is the probability that a doctor chosen is a female? $\frac{31}{132}$

19. What are the odds that a doctor chosen is a female under 35 years? **3 : 19**

20. What are the odds that a doctor chosen is a male between the ages of 35 and 54 years? **5 : 7**

Camron Doctors		
Age	Male	Female
Under 35	29	18
35–44	36	8
45–54	19	3
55–64	17	2

592 Chapter 14

40. **Entertainment** The freshman class of Perry High School is planning an end-of-the-year dance. The dance committee decides to award door prizes. They want the odds of winning a prize to be 1:5. If they plan for 180 tickets to be sold for the dance, how many prizes will be needed? **30**

Mixed Review

41. **Finance** Dolores earned $340 in 4 days by mowing lawns and doing yardwork. At that rate, how long will it take her to earn $935? **(Lesson 4-8)** **11 days**

42. Solve the inequality $|x - 1| < y$ by graphing. **(Lesson 11-6)** See margin.

43. **Recreation** Frank is competing in a kite-flying contest. At the time of the judging, he lets out 250 feet of string. The judge standing directly below Frank's kite is 70 feet away from Frank. How high is Frank's kite? **(Lesson 12-3)** **240 feet**

no real roots

44. Locate the real roots of $x^2 - 8x + 18 = 0$ by graphing. **(Lesson 13-2)**

45. The table below shows the heights and weights of each of 12 players on a pro basketball team. **(Lesson 14-6)**

Height (inches)	75	82	75	74	80	80	75	79	80	78	76	81
Weight (pounds)	180	235	184	185	230	205	185	230	221	195	205	215

a. Make a scatter plot of this data.
b. Describe the association between height and weight. **See margin.**

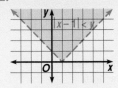
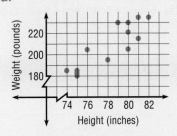

HISTORY CONNECTION

Graunt and Bernoulli

Statistical methods have been developed in only the last 350 years, largely as a result of researchers in other fields needing better methods for analyzing data. John Graunt, for example, collected records of births and deaths in London. He published his findings in *Natural and Political Observations* in 1662. Graunt, a merchant, was one of the first to study population in this way.

Probability has also only recently been studied by mathematicians. Jacob Bernoulli (1654–1705) is considered to be the founder of probability. He wrote *The Art of Conjecturing*, which was published in 1713, eight years after his death. This book showed how probability theory can be applied to a great number of collected statistical data.

EXTENDING THE LESSON

Math Power: Connections

Twenty-one Little League Baseball teams each played seven games. The stem-and-leaf plot at the right shows the sum of the runs scored by each team in the seven games. Use this to answer each question.

1. What is the probability that a team scored 98 runs? $\frac{1}{7}$

Stem	Leaf
6	0 2 3
7	1 5 8 9
8	2 4 5 7 9
9	5 7 8 8 8
10	1 4 6 7

$7|5 = 75$

2. What is the probability that a team scored less than 80 runs? $\frac{1}{3}$

3. What are the odds in favor of a team scoring more than 100 runs? **4:17**

Lesson Resources

- Reteaching Master 14-8
- Practice Master 14-8
- Enrichment Master 14-8
- Activity Master, p. 44
- Video Algebra, 62-63

 Transparency 14-8 contains the 5-Minute Check and a teaching aid for this lesson.

INTRODUCING THE LESSON

 5-Minute Check

(over Lesson 14-7)

A card is drawn from a standard deck of 52 cards. What is the probability that:

1. the card is black? $\frac{1}{2}$

2. the card is a king? $\frac{1}{13}$

A number is selected at random from the set {1, 2, 3, 4, 5, 6, 7, 8, 9, 10}. What is the probability that:

3. the number is even? $\frac{1}{2}$

4. the number is prime? $\frac{2}{5}$

5. The odds of an event not occurring are 7:3. What is the probability that the event will occur? $\frac{3}{10}$

Motivating the Lesson

A jar of mixed nuts is advertised as containing less than 50% peanuts. You open a jar and use a teaspoon to take out a sample. All eight of the nuts on the spoon are peanuts. What conclusions can be drawn regarding the advertisement? Is one trial sufficient to draw any conclusions about the percent of peanuts in the jar? What factor might have affected the results of the trial?

14-8 Empirical Probability

Objective
14-8

After studying this lesson, you should be able to:
- conduct and interpret probability experiments.

Application

Mike wanted to know what was the most popular color for cars in his town. He decided to conduct an experiment by looking at cars at two intersections. The number of cars of each color was counted and recorded in the table below.

Color	Intersection 1	Intersection 2	Total
Blue	21	19	40
Brown	16	19	35
Red	12	15	27
Black	9	15	24
White	8	7	15
Green	4	5	9
Totals	70	80	150

Using the results of his experiment, Mike computed the following probabilities.

$$P(\text{red car}) = \frac{\text{number of red cars}}{\text{total number of cars}} = \frac{27}{150} \text{ or } 18\%$$

$$P(\text{brown car}) = \frac{35}{150} \text{ or } 23.\overline{3}\% \qquad P(\text{blue car}) = \frac{40}{150} \text{ or } 26.\overline{6}\%$$

$$P(\text{black car}) = \frac{24}{150} \text{ or } 16\% \qquad P(\text{green car}) = \frac{9}{150} \text{ or } 6\%$$

$$P(\text{white car}) = \frac{15}{150} \text{ or } 10\%$$

Based on these results, which color car would you most likely see in Mike's town? Which color car would you least likely see?

Probability calculated by making observations or conducting experiments, like the one Mike did, is called **emperical probability.** Empirical probabilities are not exact, since the results may vary when the experiment is repeated. For example, Mike's result might have been different if he had chosen two different intersections or even if he had counted cars at the same intersections on a different day. One way to make an empirical probability more accurate is to gather a lot of data.

As the number of trials in an experiment increases, the empirical probability will get closer to the probability that is expected. For example, suppose you are tossing a fair coin to determine the probability of getting

ALTERNATE TEACHING STRATEGIES

Using Manipulatives

If you toss a coin, theoretically, what should the chances of getting heads be? the chances of getting tails? Conduct an experiment by tossing a coin 50 times. Record the results. Compare the experimental results with the theoretical results discussed above.   **0.5; 0.5; Students should find that the experimental results closely approximate the theoretical results.**

A coin or die is called *fair* if each of its outcomes are equally likely.

a tail. Then the more times you toss the coin, the closer your empirical probability should get to the expected probability of $\frac{1}{2}$.

One important use of empirical probability involves making predictions about a large group of people based on the results of a poll or survey. This technique, called *sampling,* is used when it is impractical or impossible to question every member of the group.

Example

Mrs. Roberts gave her civics class the assignment of determining the candidate for student body president preferred by students in the upcoming election. The class randomly chose 150 students and asked who they preferred, Jane or Troy. Use the results of the survey, shown at the right, to answer each question.

Preference for Student Body President		
Students	Jane	Troy
Male	38	42
Female	54	16

a. If a female student is chosen at random, what is the probability that she prefers Jane?

The poll included 54 + 16 or 70 females. Since 54 of 70 females preferred Jane, the probability is $\frac{54}{70}$ or about 0.77.

b. A student selected at random prefers Jane. What is the probability that this student is male?

In the poll, 38 + 54 or 92 students preferred Jane. Since 38 of the 92 were male, the probability is $\frac{38}{92}$ or about 0.41.

c. If a student is chosen at random, what is the probability that the student favors Troy?

Of the 150 students polled, 42 + 16 or 58 students preferred Troy. Thus, the probability is $\frac{58}{150}$ or about 0.39.

CHECKING FOR UNDERSTANDING

Communicating Mathematics

Read and study the lesson to answer each question.

1. What is empirical probability? Probability calculated by making observations or performing experiments.
2. If you toss a fair coin ten times, should the result always be 5 heads and 5 tails? Why? No; the empirical probability is only an approximation of the probability that is expected.
3. Suppose you roll a die ten times and get a 6 all ten times. Can you say this die is *not* fair? Why or why not? No; it is possible to get a 6 each time in ten rolls of a fair die. More trials are needed to determine whether or not this die is fair.

LESSON 14-8 EMPIRICAL PROBABILITY 595

RETEACHING THE LESSON

Divide the class into four groups. Have each group throw one die. Have group 1 throw it 25 times, group 2 throw it 50 times, and so on up to 100. Have each group record their data and find the probability of three different events. Compare their answers and also the actual answers for these events happening. Discuss.

Speaking Activity A die is thrown twice. What is the probability that the sum of the two resulting numbers is 12? Explain how you arrived at your answer. $\frac{1}{36}$

APPLYING THE LESSON

Homework Exercises

Assignment Guide
Basic: 5-6, 8-10, 12-16
Average: 6-16
Enriched: 6-16

Chapter 14, Quiz C, (Lessons 14-7 through 14-8), is available in the Evaluation Masters Booklet, p. 192.

Practice Masters Booklet, p. 113

NAME _____ DATE _____

14-8 **Practice Worksheet**

Empirical Probability

1. Toss two coins at least 50 times.

a. Record the number of heads and tails.
Answers may vary. See students' work.

b. What is the probability of tossing two tails? $\frac{1}{4}$, or 0.25

c. What is the probability of tossing at least one tail? $\frac{3}{4}$, or 0.75

d. What is the probability of tossing exactly one tail? $\frac{1}{2}$, or 0.5

e. What result occurred most often? Is this what you would have expected? Why or why not? Answers will vary.

2. Toss three dice at least 50 times.

a. Record the sums of the faces.
Answers will vary. See students' work.

b. What is the probability of a sum of 4? $\frac{1}{18}$, or 0.06

c. What is the probability of a sum less than 6? $\frac{1}{6}$, or 0.17

d. Which sum occurred most often? Is this what you would have expected? Why or why not? Answers will vary.

e. Which sum occurred least often? Is this what you would have expected? Why or Why not? Answers will vary.

Guided Practice

4. Ten students in Mr. Howard's algebra class believe that a coin is not fair. To test this assumption, each one tossed the coin 30 times and recorded results as shown in the table below. **Teaching Tip ❶**

Student	1	2	3	4	5	6	7	8	9	10
Number of Heads	21	22	18	20	21	21	19	22	18	19
Number of Tails	9	8	12	10	9	9	11	8	12	11

a. Find P(heads) for each of the ten students. **See margin.**

b. Based on this data, does the coin appear to be fair? **no**

c. Give an estimate for P(head) for this coin. (*Hint:* you could use the mean, median, or mode of this data.) **Answers will vary.**

d. How can you get a better estimate of P(heads) for this coin?

Do more trials.

EXERCISES

Practice

Teaching Tip ❷

5. Roll two dice at least 100 times. **5-7. Answers will vary.**

a. Record the sums of the faces. **Expected answers are given.**

b. What is the probability of a sum of 3? $\frac{2}{36} \approx 0.056$

c. What is the probability of a sum of 7? $\frac{6}{36} \approx 0.167$

d. What is the probability of a sum less than 5? $\frac{6}{36} \approx 0.167$

e. What is the probability of a sum greater than 6? $\frac{21}{36} \approx 0.583$

f. Which sum occurred most often? Is this what you would have expected? Why or why not?

g. Which sum occurred least often? Is this what you would have expected? Why or why not?

B **6.** Toss three coins at least 100 times.

a. Record the number of heads and tails.

b. What is the probability of tossing three heads? **0.125**

c. What is the probability of tossing exactly one tail? **0.375**

d. What is the probability of tossing at least two tails? **0.5**

e. What is the probability of tossing at most two heads? **0.875**

f. What result occurred most often? Is this what you would have expected? Why or why not?

g. What result occurred least often? Is this what you would have expected? Why or why not?

C **7.** From a deck of 52 cards, remove the ace to 10 from one suit. Shuffle the 42 cards and then deal out one card. Record the result, replace the card, and shuffle again. Repeat the experiment 100 times. **a.** $\frac{1}{42} \approx 0.02$

a. What is the probability of getting the same card twice in a row?

b. What is the probability of getting the same card three times in a row? $\left(\frac{1}{42}\right)^2 \approx 0.0006$

c. What is the probability of getting an ace, then a two, then a three, and so on until the tenth card drawn is a ten? 1.1×10^{-11}

Critical Thinking **8.** In a survey done by Yogurt and Stuff, 415 of the 700 people interviewed said they liked blueberry frozen yogurt, 269 people said they liked chocolate swirl frozen yogurt, and 124 people said they liked both flavors. Based on this survey, what is the probability that a person dislikes both of these flavors? **0.2**

Additional Answer

4a. For each probability, decimal answers are rounded to the nearest hundredth.

$\frac{7}{10}$, 0.7; $\frac{11}{15}$, 0.73; $\frac{3}{5}$, 0.6; $\frac{2}{3}$, 0.67; $\frac{7}{10}$, 0.7; $\frac{7}{10}$, 0.7; $\frac{19}{30}$, 0.63; $\frac{11}{15}$, 0.73; $\frac{3}{5}$, 0.6; $\frac{19}{30}$, 0.63

9. Baseball Of the 12 National League baseball stadiums, 6 have natural grass. Of the 14 American League baseball stadiums, 10 have natural grass. If a game on television is being played at a stadium with natural grass, what are the odds that it is an American League stadium? **5:3**

10. Employment The table below gives the employment status of the students at Monroe High School. Based on this data, find the probability that a student selected at random who works after school is a senior and the probability that a senior selected at random works after school. Should these probabilities be equal? $\frac{18}{59} \approx 0.31$; $\frac{72}{100} = 0.72$; **not necessarily**

Employment	Freshman	Sophomore	Junior	Senior
Does not work	115	76	45	28
Works after school	45	54	65	72

11. The BASIC program at the right simulates a random experiment in which an outcome is chosen (with replacement) from among equally likely outcomes. First enter the number of outcomes. Then enter the number of trials to be run. In the example below, there were 5 equally likely outcomes. The experiment was run for 200 trials.

```
10 INPUT "ENTER THE NUMBER
   OF EQUALLY LIKELY
   OUTCOMES: ";N
20 INPUT "ENTER THE NUMBER
   TRIALS: ";K
30 FOR X = 1 TO K
40 LET P = INT(N * RND(1) + 1)
50 LET F(P) = F(P) + 1
60 NEXT X
70 PRINT
80 PRINT "OUTCOME",
   "FREQUENCY"
90 FOR I = 1 TO N
100 PRINT I, F(I)
110 NEXT I
120 END
```

OUTCOME	FREQUENCY
1	37
2	41
3	39
4	44
5	39

a. Use the program to simulate tossing a coin for 50 trials and for 400 trials. **Use N = 2; see students' work.**

b. Use the program to simulate rolling a die for 100 trials and for 500 trials. **Use N = 6; see students' work.**

12. Write an equation for the relation $\{(-4, 3), (-2, 2), (0, 1), (2, 0), (4, -1)\}$. **(Lesson 9-7)** $y = 1 - \frac{1}{2}x$

13. Determine the value of r so that the line passing through $(2, r)$ and $(5, 1)$ has a slope of $-\frac{5}{3}$. **(Lesson 10-1)** **6**

14. Number Theory If the digits of a two-digit positive integer are reversed, the result is 6 less than twice the original number. Find all such integers for which this is true. **(Lesson 11-5)** **24**

15. Simplify $8\sqrt{50} + 5\sqrt{72} - 2\sqrt{98}$. **(Lesson 12-6)** $56\sqrt{2} \approx 79.20$

16. If a card is selected at random from a deck of 52 cards, what are the odds that it is not a face card? **(Lesson 14-7)** **10:3**

LESSON 14-8 EMPIRICAL PROBABILITY 597

EXTENDING THE LESSON

Math Power: Problem Solving

One-hundred fifty students from the 2162-student body at North High School were computer selected at random to participate in an educational study. The breakdown of students selected is shown in the table at the right. Use the table to find each probability.

	9th	10th	11th	12th
Male	22	23	15	18
Female	13	26	13	20

1. the probability of selecting a 9th-grade female $\frac{13}{150}$ or 0.087

2. the probability of selecting an 11th-grader $\frac{28}{150}$ or 0.187

3. the probability of selecting a male student $\frac{78}{150}$ or 0.52

Enrichment Masters Booklet, p. 101

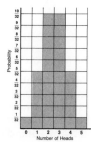

NAME _____ DATE _____

14-8 **Enrichment Worksheet**

Histograms for Probability

When a bar graph is used to picture a frequency distribution of data, such as in a coin-tossing experiment, the graph is called a histogram.

Make a histogram to show the probabilities of getting different numbers of heads in each coin-tossing experiment.

1. A coin is tossed 2 times.   2. A coin is tossed 3 times.

3. A coin is tossed 4 times.   4. A coin is tossed 5 times.

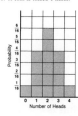

5. Describe the shape the histogram is approaching as the number of coin tosses increases. **Answers will vary. The histogram approaches a bell-shaped curve.**

Chapter 14   597

14-9 Lesson Notes

Lesson Resources

- Practice Master 14-9
- Activity Master, p. 59

Transparency 14-9 contains the 5-Minute Check and a teaching aid for this lesson.

INTRODUCING THE LESSON

⏱ 5-Minute Check
(over Lesson 14-8)

1. When a pair of dice are tossed, what sum should occur most frequently? **7**
2. A box contains 5 red marbles and 6 blue marbles. What is the probability that a marble selected at random is red? $\frac{5}{11}$
3. A coin is tossed twice. What is the probability that the result is two heads? $\frac{1}{4}$

Motivating the Lesson

Write the following sequence of numbers on the chalkboard:

7, 5, 8, 4, 9, ___, ___, ___.

Ask students to identify the relationship between the first and second numbers, between the second and third numbers, and between the third and fourth numbers. Have students continue the pattern to fill in the blanks. **3, 10, 2**

Develop the idea that before the missing numbers could be identified, the relationships between previous numbers had to be determined.

14-9 Problem-Solving Strategy: Solve a Simpler Problem

Objective
14-9

After studying this lesson, you should be able to:
- solve problems by first solving a simpler but related problem.

An important strategy for solving complicated or unfamiliar problems is to solve a simpler problem. This strategy involves setting aside the original problem and solving a simpler or more familiar case. The same methods that are used to solve the simpler problem can then be applied to the original problem.

Example

Find the sum of the first 1000 natural numbers.

EXPLORE   The first 1000 natural numbers are the numbers 1 through 1000, inclusive. Thus, we want to find the following sum.

$$S = 1 + 2 + 3 + \ldots + 998 + 999 + 1000$$

PLAN   This problem can be solved by actually adding all of the numbers, but this would be very tedious, even if a calculator is used. Let's consider a simpler version of the problem: finding the sum of the first ten natural numbers.

$$S = 1 + 2 + 3 + 4 + 5 + 6 + 7 + 8 + 9 + 10$$

Notice that pairs of addends have a sum of 11.

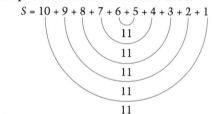

$$S = 10 + 9 + 8 + 7 + 6 + 5 + 4 + 3 + 2 + 1$$

11
11
11
11
11

Each sum is 11. Since there are $10 \div 2$ or 5 such sums, the sum of the first ten natural numbers is $5 \cdot 11$ or 55.

SOLVE   Now use this method to solve the original problem.

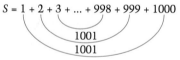

$$S = 1 + 2 + 3 + \ldots + 998 + 999 + 1000$$

1001
1001

Each sum is 1001. Since there are $1000 \div 2$ or 500 such sums, the sum of the first 1000 natural numbers is $500 \cdot 1001$ or 500,500.

598   CHAPTER 14   STATISTICS AND PROBABILITY

TEACHING THE LESSON

Chalkboard Example

For the Example

Harry bought 10 notebooks and pens for $12.20. A pen cost $0.10 less than a notebook. What is the cost of each item? How many of each did he buy? pen: $1.19; notebook: $1.29; 10 pens, 3 notebooks

---

RETEACHING THE LESSON

Using a simpler problem, find how many diagonals there are in a convex polygon with 50 sides.
1175 diagonals

1. So that the methods used for solving the simpler problem can then be used to solve the original problem.

CHECKING FOR UNDERSTANDING

Communicating Mathematics

Read and study the lesson to answer each question.

1. Why do you use the solve-a-simpler-problem strategy?

2. What other problem-solving strategy was also used in the example? **look for a pattern**

Guided Practice

Solve each problem by solving a simpler problem.

3. A total of 3001 digits was used to print all of the page numbers (beginning with 1) of the Northern College yearbook. How many pages are in this yearbook? **1027 pages**

4. How many line segments are needed to connect 1001 points if each pair of points must be connected by a line segment? **500,500 line segments**

EXERCISES

Practice

Solve. Use any strategy.

5. While hiking with his dog, cat, and bird, Jesse came to a rope bridge. He can only carry one animal at a time across the bridge. He cannot leave the dog and cat together or the cat and bird together since they will fight. Can he get all the animals across the bridge without having any fights among the animals? If so, explain how. **See margin.**

6. Numero Uno says, "I'm thinking of a three-digit number that is both a perfect square and a perfect cube. What is my number?" **729**

7. Alice bought a dozen peaches and pears for $3.78. A peach cost 3¢ more than a pear. What is the cost of each type of fruit? How many of each type did she buy? **10 peaches at 32¢ each and 2 pears at 29¢ each or 2 peaches at 34¢ each and 10 pears at 31¢ each**

8. Complete.
   1, 1, 2, 4, 7, 13, 24, _?_, _?_, _?_, 274, 504 **44, 81, 149**

9. If a hen and a half can lay an egg and a half in a day and a half, how many hens are needed to lay a dozen eggs in one day? **12 hens**

~ COOPERATIVE LEARNING ACTIVITY ~

Work in groups of five. Each person in the group should understand the solution and be able to explain it to any person in the class.

Design a pair of dice with the following restrictions.

1. The dice must be shaped like regular dice, with 6 sides.
2. You must be able to get a sum of 1, 2, 3, 4, 5, 6, 7, 8, 9, 10, 11, or 12 when the dice are rolled.
3. Each of the sums must have the same probability of occurring.

Describe your dice.

One die has sides 0, 0, 0, 6, 6, 6; the other has sides 1, 2, 3, 4, 5, 6.

EXTENDING THE LESSON

Math Power: Problem Solving

A street vendor sells a can of soda for one-half the price of a hot dog. During a lunch hour, the vendor sold twice as many sodas as hot dogs to take in $51.00. How much does each item cost? How many of each item were sold? **soda: $0.75, hot dog: $1.50; 34 sodas, 17 hot dogs**

EVALUATING THE LESSON

Checking for Understanding

Exercises 1-4 are designed to help you assess understanding through reading, writing, and speaking. You should work through Exercises 1-2 with your students, and then monitor their work on Exercises 3-4.

Closing the Lesson

Speaking Activity Have students explain how they would solve Guided Practice Exercise 3 by solving a simpler but related problem.

APPLYING THE LESSON

Homework Exercises

Assignment Guide
Basic: 5-9
Average: 5-9
Enriched: 5-9

Practice Masters Booklet, p. 114

14-9 | **Practice Worksheet**

NAME _____ DATE _____

Problem-Solving: Solve a Simpler Problem

Solve each problem by solving a simpler but related problem.

1. Find the sum of the first 1000 odd numbers. **1,000,000**

2. An ant is crawling up a greased pole that is 11 m high. Each day it crawls 2 m and at night slips back 50 cm. At this rate, how many days will it take the ant to reach the top of the pole? **7 days**

3. How many different squares are there in a rectangular grid that measures 2 by 2? 4 by 2? 6 by 2? 20 by 2? **5; 11; 17; 59**

4. A four-sided polygon has two diagonals. A five-sided polygon has five diagonals. How many diagonals does a ten-sided polygon have? **35 diagonals**

5. A ball is dropped from a height of 20 m and always rebounds $\frac{1}{4}$ of the distance from the previous fall. How far does it rebound the fifth time? $\frac{5}{256}$ m

Additional Answer

5. Take the cat across first. Then go back, pick up either the dog or the bird, and take it across the bridge. Now, go back with the cat, leave it, pick up the remaining animal, and take it across. Finally, go back, pick up the cat again, and take it across.

Lesson Resources

- Reteaching Master 14-10
- Practice Master 14-10
- Enrichment Master 14-10
- Activity Master, p. 14
- Lab Manual, pp. 45-46

 Transparency 14-10 contains the 5-Minute Check and a teaching aid for this lesson.

INTRODUCING THE LESSON

 ### 5-Minute Check
(over Lesson 14-8)

All the diamonds have been removed from a standard deck of playing cards. If a card is drawn from the remaining cards, what is the probability that the card:

1. is a club? $\frac{1}{3}$

2. is an ace? $\frac{1}{13}$

3. has a point value lower than 5? $\frac{9}{39}$

4. is a face card? $\frac{12}{39}$

5. is either a jack or king? $\frac{6}{39}$

Motivating the Lesson

A car manufacturer offers a sedan and hatchback model. Either model can be bought with or without a sunroof. All of the car models can be purchased in either blue, white, red, or black. Determine all the possible combinations of car options by making a list. How many combinations are there? **16**

TEACHING THE LESSON

Teaching Tip ❶ You may wish to explain that these events are independent. The occurrence of Gwen selecting a particular skirt does not affect her selection of a blouse.

14-10 Compound Events

Objective 14-10

After studying this lesson, you should be able to:
- find the probability of a compound event.

Application

Gwen has three skirts that she wears to school: 1 blue, 1 yellow, and 1 red. She also has 4 blouses that she can wear with any of the skirts: 1 yellow, 1 white, 1 striped, and 1 tan. Maria owns the same blue skirt and white blouse as Gwen, and she is wearing that outfit today. If Gwen chose one of her skirt-blouse outfits at random, what is the probability she and Maria are wearing the same outfit?

In order to calculate this probability, you need to know how many different skirt-blouse outfits are possible for Gwen. One method for finding all of the outfits is by using a *tree diagram*. **Teaching Tip ❶**

Notice that the number of possible outfits is the product of the number of skirts (3) and the number of blouses (4).

In the tree diagram shown, each skirt color is given at the left. The four blouse possibilities branch from each skirt color. Then, each of the possible outfits is shown at the right. Since there are 12 possible outcomes, Gwen has 12 possible outfits to wear.

The colored lines in the tree diagram show the blue skirt, white blouse outfit.

Since Gwen chose her outfit randomly, you can assume each skirt-blouse outfit is equally likely. Therefore, the probability that Maria and Gwen are wearing the same blue skirt and white blouse is $\frac{1}{12}$ or about 0.083.

Skirt	Blouse	Outcome
blue	yellow	blue, yellow
	white	blue, white
	striped	blue, striped
	tan	blue, tan
yellow	yellow	yellow, yellow
	white	yellow, white
	striped	yellow, striped
	tan	yellow, tan
red	yellow	red, yellow
	white	red, white
	striped	red, striped
	tan	red, tan

The problem above is an example of finding the probability of a **compound event**. A compound event consists of two or more *simple events*. Gwen's choice of a skirt is a simple event, and her choice of a blouse is a simple event. Gwen's choice of a skirt and a blouse is a compound event.

Example 1

Use the tree diagram above to answer each question.

a. What is the probability Gwen and Maria are wearing the same skirt?

Since 4 of the 12 outfits use the blue skirt, the probability is $\frac{4}{12}$ or about 0.33.

ALTERNATE TEACHING STRATEGIES

Using Connections

Suppose a tree diagram is created so that it represents the probabilities rather than the possible outcomes. What arithmetic operation would be used to determine the probability of a compound event? **multiplication**

b. What is the probability Gwen and Maria are wearing the same blouse?

Since 3 of the 12 outfits use the white blouse, the probability is $\frac{3}{12}$ or 0.25.

Example 2

Sean and Aaron have enough money to order a large pizza with 3 different toppings. Their four favorite toppings are pepperoni (P), mushrooms (M), olives (O), and red peppers (R). After a few minutes of arguing, they decide that one topping must be pepperoni. If they choose the other 2 toppings at random, what is the probability they will also choose olives?

1st Choice	2nd Choice	3rd Choice	Outcomes

pepperoni
- mushrooms
  - olives —— PMO ✔
  - red peppers —— PMR
- olives
  - mushrooms —— POM ✔
  - red peppers —— POR ✔
- red peppers
  - mushrooms —— PRM
  - olives —— PRO ✔

There are six ways Sean and Aaron can choose the other 2 toppings. In four cases, the pizza chosen will have olives as a topping. Thus, the probability they will also choose olives is $\frac{4}{6}$ or about 0.67.

Example 3

Ralph had three questions remaining in the true-false section of his biology final. Because he was almost out of time, Ralph had to guess the answer to each of these questions. If the answers are true, false, true, what is the probability that Ralph answered at least two of the last three questions correctly?

1st Question	2nd Question	3rd Question	Outcome

T
- T
  - T —— TTT ✔
  - F —— TTF
- F
  - T —— TFT ✔
  - F —— TFF ✔

F
- T
  - T —— FTT
  - F —— FTF
- F
  - T —— FFT ✔
  - F —— FFF

There are eight possible outcomes. In four cases, Ralph answers two or three of the questions correctly. Therefore, the probability that he answers at least two of the last three questions correctly is $\frac{4}{8}$ or 0.5.

LESSON 14-10 COMPOUND EVENTS 601

RETEACHING THE LESSON

Have students draw a tree diagram for various compound event problems. Once this step is mastered, the problem of finding the probability of a compound event is simplified.

Checking for Understanding

Exercises 1-3 are designed to help you assess understanding through reading, writing, and speaking. You should work through Exercises 1-2 with your students, and then monitor their work on Exercise 3.

Closing the Lesson

Speaking Activity Gary has one blue coat, one gray coat, one pair of gray slacks, one pair of blue slacks, one white shirt, one gray shirt, and one red shirt. Ask students to explain why the probability of Gary choosing the gray slacks and the blue coat is $\frac{1}{4}$ or 0.25.

APPLYING THE LESSON

Homework Exercises

Assignment Guide
Basic: 4-8, 10-11, 13-17
Average: 6-17
Enriched: 7-17

Practice Masters Booklet, p. 115

CHECKING FOR UNDERSTANDING

Communicating Mathematics

Read and study the lesson to answer each question.

1. Refer to the problem at the beginning of the lesson. How many possible outfits does Gwen have if she buys **a.** a beige skirt, **b.** a beige blouse, or **c.** a beige skirt and beige blouse? **16, 15, 20**

2. What is the difference between a simple event and a compound event?
See margin.

Guided Practice

3. An automobile dealer has cars available with the combinations of colors, engines, and transmissions indicated in the tree diagram shown. A car is selected at random.

a. What is the probability of selecting a car with manual transmission? **0.5**

b. What is the probability of selecting a blue car with manual transmission? **0.25**

c. What is the probability of selecting a car with a 4-cylinder engine and a manual transmission? **0.25**

d. What is the probability of selecting a blue car with a 6-cylinder engine and an automatic transmission? **0.125**

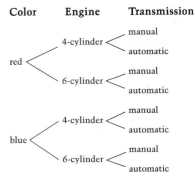

EXERCISES

Practice

4. Draw a tree diagram to show the possibilities for boys and girls in a family of 4 children. Assume that the probabilities for girls and boys being born are the same.

A

a. What is the probability the family has exactly 4 girls? $\frac{1}{16} = 0.0625$

b. What is the probability the family has 2 boys and 2 girls in any order? $\frac{3}{8} = 0.375$

5. Use a tree diagram to find the probability of getting at least one tail when four fair coins are tossed. $\frac{15}{16} = 0.9375$

6. Compare and contrast the tree diagram used for Exercise 5 with the one used for Exercise 4. **See margin.**

B

7. Box A contains one blue and one green marble. Box B contains one green and one red marble. Box C contains one white and one green marble. A marble is drawn at random from each box.

a. What is the probability that all of the marbles are green? **0.125**

b. What is the probability that exactly two marbles are green? **0.375**

c. What is the probability that at least one marble is not green? **0.875**

Additional Answers

2. A compound event consists of two or more simple events. Tossing a coin is a simple event while tossing two coins is a compound event.

6. Answers may vary; typical answer is that the overall tree diagrams are the same.

16. Answers will vary. P(heads) should be approximately $\frac{1}{2}$ or 0.50. If not, then the results do not necessarily imply that the coin is not fair because of the low number of trials. More trials must be done in order to determine whether or not the coin is fair.

8. With each shrimp, salmon, or crab dinner at the Seafood Palace, you may have soup or salad. With shrimp, you may have broccoli or a baked potato. With salmon, you may have rice or broccoli. With crab, you may have rice, broccoli, or a potato. If all combinations are equally likely, find the probability of an order containing each item.

   a. salmon $\frac{2}{7}$
              b. soup $\frac{1}{2}$
   c. rice $\frac{2}{7}$
              d. shrimp and rice 0
   e. salad and broccoli $\frac{3}{14}$
        f. crab, soup, and rice $\frac{1}{14}$

9. Two men and three women are each waiting for a job interview. There is only enough time to interview two people before lunch.

   a. What is the probability that both people are women? $\frac{3}{10} = 0.3$
   b. What is the probability at least one person is a woman? $\frac{9}{10} = 0.9$
   c. Which is more likely, one of the people is a woman and the other is a man, or both people are either men or women? **man and woman**

Critical Thinking

10. After each football game, 80% of the students at the game go to pick up pizza while the others go home. After picking up the pizza, 40% of the students go home while the rest go to a friend's house. If Kelly goes to the game, what is the probability she will go to a friend's house that night? **48%**

Applications

11. **Entertainment** In order to raise money for a trip to the opera, the music club has set up a lottery using two-digit numbers. The first digit will be a numeral from 1 to 4. The second digit will be a numeral from 3 to 8. One of the digits in Trudy's lottery number is 2, but she can't remember which digit. If only one two-digit lottery number is drawn, what is the probability that Trudy will win? $\frac{1}{4} = 0.25$

12. **Law** A three-judge panel is being used to settle a dispute. Both sides in the dispute have decided that a majority decision will be upheld. If each judge will render a favorable decision based on the evidence presented two-thirds of the time, what is the probability that the correct side will win the dispute? $\frac{20}{27} \approx 0.741$

Mixed Review

13. **Finance** A selling price of $145,000 for a home included a 6.5% commission for the real estate agent. How much money did the owners receive from this sale? **(Lesson 4-4)** **$135,575**

14. Simplify $\frac{4}{5-p} - \frac{3}{p-5}$. **(Lesson 8-7)** $\frac{7}{5-p}$

15. **Construction** Janet's family room has an area rug that is 9 feet by 12 feet. A strip of floor of equal width is uncovered along all edges of the rug. Janet wants to place ceramic tiles on this part of the floor. If the area of the uncovered floor is 270 ft², what is the width of the space to be tiled? **(Lesson 13-5)** **4.5 ft**

16. Toss a coin 50 times. Then determine $P(\text{heads})$ for this coin. Are the results what you expected? If not, does this imply that the coin is not fair. Explain. **(Lesson 14-8)** **See margin.**

17. Solve by solving a simpler problem. **(Lesson 14-9)**

   Determine the number of diagonals of a convex polygon with 100 sides. **4950 diagonals**

EXTENDING THE LESSON

Math Power: Connections

A four-sided (tetrahedral) die has faces numbered 1, 2, 5, 6. If the die is tossed twice, what is the probability that the sum of the numbers facing down is 7? $\frac{1}{4}$

Chapter 14, Quiz D, (Lessons 14-9 through 14-10), is available in the Evaluation Masters Booklet, p. 192.

Enrichment Masters Booklet, p. 102

NAME _____ DATE _____

14-10 Enrichment Worksheet

Conditional Probability

The probability of an event given the occurrence of another event is called **conditional probability**. The conditional probability of event A given event B is denoted $P(A|B)$.

Example: Suppose a pair of dice is rolled. It is known that the sum is greater than seven. Find the probability that the dice match.

There are 15 sums greater than seven and there are 36 possible pairs altogether.

$P(B) = \frac{15}{36}$

There are three matching pairs greater than seven, (4, 4), (5, 5), and (6, 6).

$P(A \text{ and } B) = \frac{3}{36}$

$P(A|B) = \frac{P(A \text{ and } B)}{P(B)}$

$= \frac{\frac{3}{36}}{\frac{15}{36}}$ or $\frac{1}{5}$

The conditional probability is $\frac{1}{5}$.

A card is drawn from a standard deck of 52 cards and is found to be red. Given that event, find each of the following probabilities.

1. $P(\text{heart})$ $\frac{1}{2}$
2. $P(\text{ace})$ $\frac{1}{13}$
3. $P(\text{face card})$ $\frac{3}{13}$
4. $P(\text{jack or ten})$ $\frac{2}{13}$
5. $P(\text{six of spades})$ 0
6. $P(\text{six of hearts})$ $\frac{1}{26}$

A sports survey taken at Stirers High School shows that 48% of the respondents liked soccer, 66% liked basketball, and 38% liked hockey. Also, 30% liked soccer and basketball, 22% liked basketball and hockey and 28% liked soccer and hockey. Finally, 12% liked all three sports.

7. Find the probability that Meg likes soccer if she likes basketball. $\frac{5}{11}$
8. Find the probability that Juan likes basketball if he likes soccer. $\frac{5}{8}$
9. Find the probability that Mieko likes hockey if she likes basketball. $\frac{1}{3}$
10. Find the probability that Greg likes hockey if he likes soccer. $\frac{7}{12}$

The Chapter Summary and Review begins with an alphabetical listing of the new terms that were presented in the chapter. Have students define each term and provide an example of it, if appropriate.

The Skills and Concepts presented in the chapter are reviewed using a side-by-side format. Encourage students to refer to the Objectives and Examples on the left as they complete the Review Exercises on the right.

The Chapter Summary and Review ends with exercises that review Applications and Connections.

Additional Answers

3. Percents are rounded to the nearest tenth. Exxon: 4.0%, Ford Motor: 3.9%, General Electric: 7.1%, General Motors: 3.3%, IBM: 6.0%, Mobil: 3.0%, Philip Morris: 7.4%; Philip Morris; no

4.

5.

CHAPTER 14 SUMMARY AND REVIEW

VOCABULARY

Upon completing this chapter, you should be familiar with the following terms:

box-and-whisker plot	579	570	mode
compound event	600	589	probability
data	560	590	odds
equally likely events	590	576	outlier
experimental probability	594	575	range
interquartile range	575	583	scatter plot
line plot	560	560	statistics
lower quartile	575	565	stem-and-leaf plot
mean	570	575	upper quartile
median	570		

SKILLS AND CONCEPTS

OBJECTIVES AND EXAMPLES	REVIEW EXERCISES

Upon completing this chapter you should be able to:

- interpret numerical data from a table or chart **(Lesson 14-1)**

Company	Sales	Income
Exxon	87	3.5
Ford Motor	97	3.8
General Electric	55	3.9
General Motors	127	4.2
IBM	63	3.8
Mobil	60	1.8
Philip Morris	39	2.9

Which one had the greatest sales? GM

- display and interpret statistical data on a line plot **(Lesson 14-1)**

Use the data in the table above to make a line plot of sales.

Use these exercises to review and prepare for the chapter test.

Use the data in the table at the left to answer each question. Sales and income are given in billions of dollars.

1. Which company had the least sales? **Philip Morris**
2. Which company had the least income? **Mobil**
3. For each company, determine income as a percent of sales (income ÷ sales). Which one had the greatest income as a percent of sales? Was it the company with the greatest income? **See margin.**

Make a line plot for each set of data.

4. 78, 74, 86, 88, 99, 63, 85, 85, 85
5. 134, 167, 137, 138, 120, 134, 145, 155, 152, 159, 164, 135, 144, 156

4-5. See margin.

Additional Answers

6.

Stem	Leaf
4	0 1 2 2 4
5	0 5 6
6	2 5 6 9
7	6 8
8	3

6|2 = $62

7.

Rounded	Stem	Truncated
8 6 5 1	3	1 4 6 8
4 3	4	2 4 9
8 7 6 0	5	6 6 8
8	6	7

rounded data: 3|1 = 4250-4349
truncated data: 3|1 = 4300-4399

- display and interpret data on a
stem-and-leaf plot **(Lesson 14-2)**

Use the data in the table on the previous
page to make a stem-and-leaf plot of
income in 1989.

Stem	Leaf	
1	8	2|9 represents
2	9	2.9 billion
3	5 8 8 9	dollars.
4	2	

- calculate and interpret the mean,
median, and mode of a set of
data **(Lesson 14-3)**

Find the mean, median, and mode of 4,
5, 6, 6, 10, 9, 14, 16, 16, 16, 30.

mean: The sum of the 11 values is 132.

$\frac{132}{11} = 12$

median: 6th value = 9

mode: 16

- calculate and interpret the range,
quartiles, and the interquartile range of
a set of data **(Lesson 14-4)**

Find the range, upper and lower
quartiles, and interquartile range of the
data for Lesson 14-3.

range: 30 − 4 = 26
lower quartile: 3rd value = 6
upper quartile: 9th value = 16
interquartile range: 16 − 6 = 10

- display and interpret data on a
box-and-whisker plot **(Lesson 14-5)**

Make a box-and-whisker plot of the data
for Lesson 14-3.

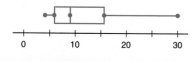

---

6. The prices for 15 different types of
athletic shoes are listed below. Make a
stem-and-leaf plot of the prices. How
many of the prices are between $40
and $50 inclusive? **See margin.**
$42 $44 $76 $56 $78 $62 $65 $69
$55 $66 $42 $83 $50 $40 $41

7. Make a back-to-back stem-and-leaf
plot of the following data comparing
rounded and truncated values. **See margin.**
4267, 5679, 3623, 6791, 3471, 3124,
5629, 4444, 3812, 5814, 4967

---

8. Find the mean, median, and mode of
6.8, 8.4, 6.2, 5.7, 5.6, 7.1, 9.9, 1.5,
7.1, 5.4, 3.4. **6.1; 6.2; 7.1**

9. The stem-and-leaf plot below shows
points scored by losing teams in the
first 25 Super Bowls. Find the mean,
median, and mode of the scores.

Stem	Leaf	**12.92; 10; 10**
0	3 6 7 7 7 7 9	
1	0 0 0 0 0 0 3 4 4 6 6 7 7 9 9	
2	0 1	
3	1	3|1 represents 31 points.

10. Use the data in Exercise 9 to find the
range, quartiles, and interquartile
range of points scored by losing teams
in the first 25 Super Bowls. **28; 8, 10, 17; 9**

11. The average annual snowfall, in inches,
for 12 northeastern cities are listed
below. Find the interquartile range
for this data. Identify any outliers.
111.5   70.7   59.8   68.6   63.8   254.8
 64.3   82.3   91.7   88.9   110.5   77.1
34.7, 254.8 in.

12. Use the data in Exercise 9 to make a
box-and-whisker plot of points scored
by losing teams in the first 25 Super
Bowls. **12-13. See margin.**

13. The number of calories in a serving of
french fries at 13 restaurants are 250,
240, 220, 348, 199, 200, 125, 230,
274, 239, 212, 240, and 327. Make a
box-and-whisker plot of this data.

Alternate Review Strategy

To provide a brief in-class review,
you may wish to read the
following questions to the class
and require a verbal or written
response.

1. Find the mean, median, and
mode of 7.7, 3.6, 6.6, 5.1, 5.3,
8.2, 6.7, 5.4, 4.8, 7.7, 7.1, 6.2,
7.5
**mean = 6.3, median = 6.6,
mode = 7.7**

2. Find the range, the upper and
lower quartiles, and the
interquartile range for the
following data:
78, 96, 65, 84, 99, 68, 77.
**range = 34, UQ = 96,
LQ = 68, IQ = 28**

3. Make a box-and-whisker plot
for the values 60, 50, 45, 55,
40, 75, 65, 60, 50.

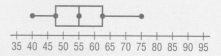

4. If one of the first 100 positive
integers is selected at random,
what is the probability that the
number is *not* prime?
$\frac{74}{100} = 0.74$

5. Two coins are tossed 50
times. The coins both land on
tails 14 times. What is the
probability that neither coin
landed on tails? $\frac{36}{50}$ or **0.72**

6. A bag contains a red marble
and a white marble. Another
bag contains a blue marble
and a red marble. A third bag
holds a red marble and a
black marble. If a marble is
drawn at random from each of
the bags, what is the
probability that all three
marbles are red? $\frac{1}{8}$ or **0.125**

Additional Answers

12.

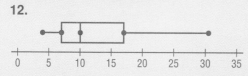

13.

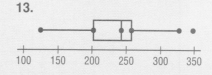

The Cumulative Review shown below can be used to review skills and concepts presented thus far in the text. Standardized Test Practice Questions are also provided in the Evaluation Masters Booklet.

Evaluation Masters Booklet, pp. 193-194

NAME _____ DATE _____

Cumulative Review (Chapters 1–14)

1. Solve $12\frac{1}{2} - 9\frac{2}{3}$.
   1. _____ $2\frac{5}{6}$

2. Find $-23 + 15$.
   2. _____ -8

3. Solve $7.8 = 0.3y - 2.1$.
   3. _____ 33

4. Solve the inequality $2x - 2 \le -2$ or $2x - 2 \ge 2$. Then graph the solution set.
   4. _____ $x \le 0$ or $x \ge 2$
   -4 -3 -2 -1 0 1 2 3 4

5. Simplify $(2r^2t)(-4r^4t^3)$.
   5. _____ $-8r^6t^4$

6. Justina is 3 times as old as her sister. The sum of their ages is 12. How old is Justina?
   6. _____ 9 years

7. Martha weighs 95 pounds and Patrick weighs 114 pounds. They are seated at opposite ends of a seesaw. Martha and Patrick are 11 feet apart, and the seesaw is balanced. How far is Patrick from the fulcrum?
   7. _____ 5 ft

8. Find $(2x^2y - 3xy + 4y^3) - (4xy - 3y^3 + x^2y)$.
   8. _____ $x^2y - 7xy + 7y^3$

9. Find $(3m - 2n)(3m + 2n)$.
   9. _____ $9m^2 - 4n^2$

Factor, if possible.

10. $12c - 8d - 15rc + 10rd$
    10. _____ $(4 - 5r)(3c - 2d)$

11. $3a^2 - 13a + 12$
    11. _____ $(3a - 4)(a - 3)$

12. Solve $14q^2 - 21 = -35q$.
    12. _____ $\frac{1}{2}, -3$

13. When one integer is added to the square of the next consecutive integer, the sum is 131. Find the integers.
    13. _____ 10 and 11, or −13 and −12

14. Solve $2a = 4b - 6$ for b.
    14. _____ $b = \frac{1}{2}a + \frac{3}{2}$

15. Write an equation for the relationship between the variables in the chart.

x	−3	−1	1	3
y	2	1	0	−1

   15. _____ $y = -\frac{1}{2}x + \frac{1}{2}$

16. Determine the slope of the line passing through $(3, -2)$ and $(1, 1)$.
    16. _____ $-\frac{3}{2}$

NAME _____ DATE _____

Cumulative Review (Chapters 1–14)

17. Write an equation in slope-intercept form for the line with a slope of 4 and passing through $(-2, 1)$.
    17. _____ $y = 4x + 9$

18. Write an equation for the line that is perpendicular to the graph of $y - 3x = 2$ and passes through $(0, 6)$.
    18. _____ $y = -\frac{1}{3}x + 6$

19. Solve the system of equations $x + y = -5$ and $3x - 2y = 10$.
    19. _____ $(0, -5)$

Simplify.

20. $-\sqrt{\frac{81}{100}}$
    20. _____ $-\frac{9}{10}$

21. $\frac{\sqrt{40}}{\sqrt{7}}$
    21. _____ $\frac{2\sqrt{70}}{7}$

22. $\sqrt{20} - \sqrt{45} + \sqrt{72}$
    22. _____ $-\sqrt{5} + 6\sqrt{2}$

23. Determine the number of real roots for $r^2 + 5r - 3 = 0$ by using the discriminant. Find all real roots.
    23. _____ 2 real roots $\frac{-5 \pm \sqrt{37}}{2}$

24. Solve $z^2 - 10z + 16 = 0$ by an appropriate method.
    24. _____ $2, 8$

25. Find a quadratic equation having the roots 2 and −6.
    25. _____ $x^2 + 4x - 12 = 0$

26. Find $\frac{a^2}{a - b} \cdot \frac{a^2 - b^2}{a}$.
    26. _____ $a^2(a + b)$

27. Find $(2x^2 + 3x - 5) \div (x - 3)$.
    27. _____ $2x + 9 + \frac{22}{x - 3}$

28. Find $\frac{2}{3k - 1} + \frac{k}{k + 3}$.
    28. _____ $\frac{3k^2 + k + 6}{(3k - 1)(k + 3)}$

29. Solve $\frac{7}{x^2 - 5x} + \frac{3}{5 - x} = \frac{4}{x}$.
    29. _____ $\frac{27}{7}$

30. The speed of the current in a river is 5 mi/h. A boat travels 26 miles downstream in 2 hours and returns in $8\frac{2}{3}$ hours. What is the speed of the boat in still water?
    30. _____ 8 mi/h

31. Find the mean, median, and mode for the data listed below.
    5, 4, 2, 9, 5, 10, 15, 12
    31. _____ mean: 7.75 median: 7 mode: 5

A card is selected at random from a standard deck of 52 cards.

32. Find the probability of selecting a face card.
    32. _____ $\frac{3}{13}$

33. Find the odds in favor of selecting a black face card.
    33. _____ $3:23$

- Graph and interpret pairs of numbers on a scatter plot **(Lesson 14-6)**

  This scatter plot shows a negative association since the line suggested by the points would have a negative slope.

14. Draw a scatter plot of the data on income and sales for the top U.S. companies given in the table on page 604. Let the horizontal axis be sales. What type of association, if any, is shown between sales and income? **See margin.**

- find the probability of a simple event **(Lesson 14-7)**

  If a soccer team consists of 8 seniors, 7 juniors, 3 sophomores, and 2 freshmen, then the probability that a player chosen at random is a senior is $\frac{8}{20}$ or 0.4.

15. For the soccer team listed at the left, find the probability that a player chosen at random is not a junior or a freshman. $\frac{11}{20} = 0.55$ 16. $\frac{25}{100} = 0.25$

16. If one of the first 100 positive integers is selected at random, what is the probability that the number is prime?

- find the odds of a simple event **(Lesson 14-7)**

  On the soccer team given above, the odds that a player chosen at random is *not* a junior are 13:7.

17. If the odds that an event occurs are 9:4, what is the probability that the event occurs? $\frac{9}{13} \approx 0.692$

18. What are the odds that one of the 30 people at Terry's birthday party will not win one of the 8 door prizes? **11:4**

- conduct and interpret probability experiments **(Lesson 14-8)**

  Two dice are rolled 100 times. If the sum 11 appears 8 times, then $P(\text{sum of } 11) = \frac{8}{100}$ or 0.08.

Toss two coins 100 times. Record the results and use them to answer each question. Answers will vary. Approx. answers are given.

19. What is the probability of tossing exactly one head? $\frac{1}{2} = 0.5$

20. What is the probability of tossing at least one head? $\frac{3}{4} = 0.75$

- find the probability of a compound event **(Lesson 14-10)**

  Marcus guesses on two multiple-choice questions on a quiz. If each question has four possible answers, then the probability that he answers both questions incorrectly is $\frac{9}{16}$ or 0.5625.

21. Matthew has 2 brown and 4 black socks in his dresser. While dressing one morning, he pulled out 2 socks without looking. What is the probability that he chose a matching pair?

22. Each day, Angie takes one of 4 ferries from Lehigh to Port City. Find the probability that Angie takes a different ferry on two consecutive days. $\frac{3}{4} = 0.75$

   21. $\frac{7}{15} \approx 0.46\overline{6}$

---

23. Solve by solving a simpler problem. **(Lesson 14-9)**

   There are 208 baseball teams in the state playoff. If a team loses, it is eliminated and plays no more games. How many games will be needed to decide the state champion? **207 games**

Additional Answer

14.
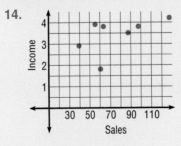

The numbers below represent the mean number of students per teacher in the 50 states in 1988.

18.7 17.0 18.2 15.7 22.7 17.8 13.1 16.4 13.3 17.1 18.5 21.1 16.0
20.6 17.1 17.8 15.8 15.2 17.8 18.2 14.6 16.8 13.7 19.8 17.0 14.6
18.4 15.9 15.8 15.0 20.3 16.2 13.6 18.5 14.9 17.5 15.4 17.6
16.5 18.4 15.9 14.6 17.2 15.4 19.3 24.5 13.6 16.1 20.4 15.1

1. Make a stem-and-leaf plot of the ratios. **See Solutions Manual.**
2. How many of the ratios were in the 17s? **10**
3. Find the median and the mode of the ratios. **16.9; 14.6, 17.8**
4. What is the range of the ratios? **11.4**
5. Find the upper and lower quartiles and the interquartile range of the ratios. **18.4, 15.4, 3.0**
6. Identify any outliers in the ratios. **24.5**

The table at the right shows the shots attempted and the shots made for 10 players on the Patriots basketball team during the first five games of the season.

Basketball Player	A	B	C	D	E	F	G	H	I	J
Shots Attempted	60	25	35	12	80	4	15	42	11	22
Shots Made	25	10	15	4	36	1	6	16	4	8

7. Make a line plot of the shots attempted. **See margin.**
8. What are the greatest number and the least number of shots made? **36, 1**
9. Find the mean number of shots attempted and shots made. **30.6, 12.5**
10. Find the quartiles and interquartile range of the shots attempted. **12, 23.5, 42; 30**
11. Make a box-and-whisker plot of the shots attempted. **See margin.**
12. Draw a scatter plot of the data. Let the horizontal axis be *Shots Attempted*. Does this plot show positive, negative, or no association? **See margin.**

During a 20-song sequence on a popular radio station, 8 soft rock, 7 hard rock, and 5 rap songs are played at random. You tune in to the station.

13. What is the probability that a hard rock song is playing? $\frac{7}{20} = 0.35$
14. What are the odds that a rap song is playing? **1:3**

The table at the right shows how registered voters voted on Issue 12 in the 4th District.

Vote	Yes	No	Did Not Vote
Men	165	140	185
Women	205	105	200

15. $\frac{385}{1000} = 0.385$

15. If a voter is chosen at random, what is the probability that the person did not vote?
16. If a man who voted is chosen at random, what are the odds that he voted yes? **33:28**
17. If a person who voted no is chosen at random, what is the probability that the person is a woman? $\frac{3}{7} \approx 0.43$
18. If the odds that it will rain are 3:7, find the probability of rain. $\frac{3}{10} = 0.3$
19. If the probability of rain is 0.45, find the odds that it will not rain. **0.55:0.45 or 11:9**

Bonus   If a couple has four children, are they more likely to have two boys and two girls or three of one gender and one of the other?

Additional Answers

7.

11.

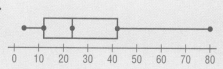

12.

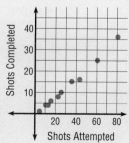

15

Trigonometry

PREVIEWING THE CHAPTER

The chapter introduces right-triangle trigonometry. Students begin with a review of angles and their properties. The relationship between the sides of a 30°-60°-90° triangle are studied and used to find the measures of two sides given the measure of the third side. Relationships between similar triangles are studied, and students use the similarity properties to find the measures of corresponding parts of similar triangles. This background leads to the study of the sine, cosine, and tangent ratios associated with an acute angle in a right triangle.

Problem-Solving Strategy Students learn to *make and use models* such as a simple sketch, a scale drawing, or a three-dimensional manipulative as an aid in solving problems.

Lesson Objective Chart

Lesson (Pages)	Lesson Objectives	State/Local Objectives
15-1 (610-614)	**15-1A:** Find the complement and the supplement of an angle.	
	15-1B: Find the measure of the third angle of a triangle given the measure of the other two angles.	
15-2 (615-616)	**15-2:** Solve problems by making models.	
15-3 (617-621)	**15-3:** Find the measures of the sides of a 30° - 60° right triangle given the measure of one side.	
15-4 (622-625)	**15-4:** Find the unknown measures of the sides of two similar triangles.	
15-5 (626-631)	**15-5A:** Compute the sine, cosine, and tangent of an acute angle of a right triangle given the measures of its sides.	
	15-5B: Find the measure of an acute angle of a right triangle given a trigonometric value or the lengths of two of the sides.	
15-6 (632-636)	**15-6A:** Use trigonometric ratios to solve verbal problems.	
	15-6B: Use trigonometric ratios to solve right triangles.	

ORGANIZING THE CHAPTER

You may want to refer to the **Course Planning Calendar** on page T36.

Lesson Planning Guide / Blackline Masters Booklets

Lesson (Pages)	Course I	Course II	Course III	Reteaching	Practice	Enrichment	Evaluation	Technology	Lab Manual	Mixed Problem Solving	Applications	Cooperative Learning Activity	Multicultural	Transparencies
15-1 (610-614)	–	–	1	p. 103	p. 116	p. 103							p. 60	15-1
15-2 (615-616)	–	–	1		p. 117		Quiz A, p. 205							15-2
15-3 (617-621)	–	–	1	p. 104	p. 118	p. 104	Quiz B, p. 205 Mid-Chapter Test, p. 209			p. 15				15-3
15-4 (622-625)	–	–	1	p. 105	p. 119	p. 105	Quiz C, p. 206				p. 30			15-4
15-5 (626-631)	–	–	1.5	p. 106	p. 120	p. 106		p. 15						15-5
15-6 (632-636)	–	–	1.5	p. 107	p. 121	p. 107	Quiz D, p. 206	p. 30	pp. 47-48			p. 45		15-6
Review (638-640)	–	–	1	Multiple Choice Tests, Forms 1A and 1B, pp. 197-200 Free Response Tests, Forms 2A and 2B, pp. 201-204 Cumulative Review, pp. 207-208 Standardized Test Practice Questions, p. 210									
Test (641)	–	–	1										

Course I: Chapters 1-13; Course II: Chapters 1-14; Course III: Chapters 1-15

Other Chapter Resources

Student Edition
Cooperative Learning Activity, p. 616
Mid-Chapter Review, p. 621
History Connection, p. 636
Technology, p. 637

Teacher Resource Package
Activity Masters Booklet
    Mixed Problem Solving, p. 15
    Applications, p. 30
    Cooperative Learning Activity, p. 45
    Multicultural Activity, p. 60
Technology Masters Booklet
    Scientific Calculator Activity, p. 15
    Graphing Calculator Activity, p. 30
Lab Manual
    Lab Activity, pp. 47-48

Other Supplements
Transparency for Chapter Opener
Problem-of-the-Week Activity
    Cards, 35-36
Video Algebra, 59-60

Software
Algebra 1 Test and Review
    Generator Software
    Available for Apple and IBM.

ENHANCING THE CHAPTER

Cooperative Learning

Assessing How Well the Group Functioned

To ensure improved performance in cooperative-learning sessions, it is important to process what students have learned about group skills after each session. Whole-class discussions can be a valuable way to do this since groups can learn from the experiences of other groups. Such discussions should concentrate on how well the groups functioned during the session, what things were done well, and what things could be improved. To begin the processing, select one member from a group to discuss with the class one or two things that they did well during the session. Encourage the reporter to provide details and examples. Ask about specific actions taken by group members that helped, such as encouraging each other to participate, keeping one another focused on the task, paraphrasing or expanding on contributions, and so on. If you wish, you can also ask a reporter to discuss something that the group could have done better or would like to work harder on. The reporter need not use names but should be as specific as possible. The emphasis should be on improving the effectiveness of students in cooperating with and assisting other members of this group. This sharing of ideas and experiences will promote improved group behavior in future sessions.

Technology

This chapter includes a feature on graphing trigonometric functions. This feature will help students understand the concept of trigonometric functions, and it will help them see a relationship between these functions and their graphs. It will also help them make a connection between trigonometric values and where those values lie on a graph. Finally, it will help students make the connection between right triangle trigonometry and the graphs of trigonometric functions.

Critical Thinking

Students will live and work in a world that provides them with easy access to powerful personal computers and software programs with interactive processes for finding and understanding solutions to business problems. Such programs require the user to employ higher-level thinking skills for successful implementation. As part of their preparation for this world, students should be given opportunities not only to answer but also to ask "What if" questions. Use the word problems in the text to provide opportunities for students to create new conditions, including reversals where instead of finding the solution, the student gives a different solution and asks how the conditions must be changed to achieve the given results.

Cooperative Learning, p. 45

CHAPTER 15 — Cooperative Learning Activity (Use after Lesson 15-6)

High-Rise Danger

Work in pairs to solve the following mystery.

There has been an attempted murder. A shot was fired through the intended victim's second story window. The bullet missed the occupant and was found embedded in the back wall of the room. It was fired from one of the windows of a high-rise apartment building across the street. In the figure at the right, distances are not shown in the proportion, but they are listed in the chart below.

Description of Distance	Label	Distance in Feet
From the bullet hole in the wall to the floor	CE	1
From the bullet hole in the window to the floor	BD	5
From the floor to the street	DG	12
From the back wall to the window wall	DE	10
From the window wall to the high rise	FG	80

In the high rise, each window is 6 feet tall. The second floor window sill is 14 feet above street level, the third floor window sill is 24 feet above the street level, the fourth is 34 feet above street level, and so on.

1. You are the detective assigned to the case. From which floor was the shot fired? fifth floor

2. Suppose the window was open when the shot was fired. You do not have a bullet hole in the window, but the bullet when it hit the wall formed an angle measuring 8° with the floor. From which floor of the high rise was the shot fired? third floor

3. Suppose the window was open and the angle of the bullet with the floor could not be determined. The intended victim's window sill was 2 feet from the floor and the window is 5 feet tall. Find those floors of the high rise from which the bullet could have been fired. third, fourth, fifth, sixth, and seventh floors

Technology, p. 15

CHAPTER 15 — Scientific Calculator Activity (Use after Lesson 15-5)

The Trigonometric Function Keys

Calculators simplify the use of trigonometric functions by eliminating the need for trigonometry tables. The trigonometric function keys can be used to find the value of a trigonometric function of a specific angle. Remember that most calculators can work in either degree or radian measure, and you need to put the calculator in the correct mode for your computations. In the examples, assume that the calculator is in the degree mode.

Example 1: Find sin 30°.

ENTER 30 [SIN]   Result: 0.5

The [COS] and [TAN] keys are used in the same manner.

Given the value of a trigonometric function, it is possible to find the measure of an angle corresponding to that value. For the cosine, your key may look like one of the following (the sine and tangent keys will be similar).

[COS⁻¹] or [INV] [COS]

Example 2: Find x, if cos x = 0.866025.

ENTER 0.866025 [INV] [COS]   Result: 30°
or
ENTER 0.866025 [COS⁻¹]   Result: 30°

Use a calculator to find each value.

1. sin 30° 0.5
2. tan 75° 3.7320508
3. cos 45° 0.7071068
4. sin 45° 0.7071068
5. tan 45° 1
6. cos 60° 0.5
7. sin 81° 0.9876883
8. tan 12° 0.2125566
9. cos 9° 0.9876883

Find the measure of each angle to the nearest degree.

10. x, if sin x = 0.866025 60°
11. x, if cos x = 0.951057 18°
12. y, if cos y = 0.939693 20°
13. x, if tan x = 2.4751 68°
14. x, if tan x = 0.726543 36°
15. y, if sin y = 0.573576 35°
16. x, if sin x = 0.766044 50°
17. x, if cos x = 0.970296 14°
18. y, if cos y = 0.766044 40°
19. x if tan x = 57.28996 89°

20. Use some of the values you obtained above to make a conjecture about relationships between trigonometric functions. Answers will vary. Sample answer: If sin x = cos y, then x + y = 90°.

Problem of the Week Activity

The card shown below is one of two available for this chapter. It can be used as a class or small group activity.

Activity Card

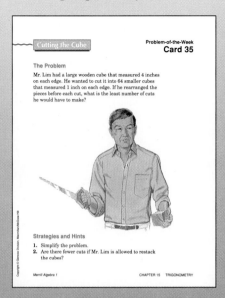

Cutting the Cube

Problem-of-the-Week
Card 35

The Problem

Mr. Lim had a large wooden cube that measured 4 inches on each edge. He wanted to cut it into 64 smaller cubes that measured 1 inch on each edge. If he rearranged the pieces before each cut, what is the least number of cuts he would have to make?

Strategies and Hints

1. Simplify the problem.
2. Are there fewer cuts if Mr. Lim is allowed to restack the cubes?

Merrill Algebra 1   CHAPTER 15   TRIGONOMETRY

Manipulatives and Models

The following materials may be used as models or manipulatives in Chapter 15.

- paper (Lessons 15-1 and 15-2)
- construction paper (Lesson 15-3)
- cardboard (Lesson 15-3)
- string (Lesson 15-3)
- tape (Lesson 15-3)
- protractor (Lessons 15-3 and 15-6)
- weight (Lesson 15-6)

Outside Resources

Books/Periodicals

Thompson, J.E. *Trigonometry for the Practical Worker.* Van Nostrand

Simon Seymour. *The Optical Illusion Book.* William Morrow and Company.

Films/Videotapes/Videodiscs

Trigonometry, Educational Solutions, Inc.

Modeling the Universe, Pyramid Films

Software

Escape, Sunburst Communication, Inc.

Trigonometry of the Right Triangle, Micro Computer Workshop

Multicultural

Multicultural Activity, p. 60

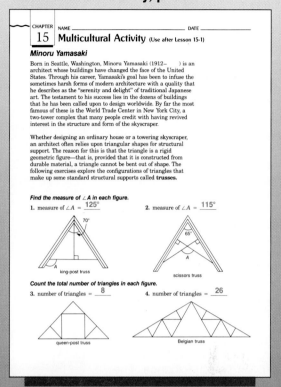

CHAPTER **15** **Multicultural Activity** (Use after Lesson 15-1)

NAME _____ DATE _____

Minoru Yamasaki

Born in Seattle, Washington, Minoru Yamasaki (1912–   ) is an architect whose buildings have changed the face of the United States. Through his career, Yamasaki's goal has been to infuse the sometimes harsh forms of modern architecture with a quality that he describes as the "serenity and delight" of traditional Japanese art. The testament to his success lies in the dozens of buildings that he has been called upon to design worldwide. By far the most famous of these is the World Trade Center in New York City, a two-tower complex that many people credit with having revived interest in the structure and form of the skyscraper.

Whether designing an ordinary house or a towering skyscraper, an architect often relies upon triangular shapes for structural support. The reason for this is that the triangle is a rigid geometric figure—that is, provided that it is constructed from durable material, a triangle cannot be bent out of shape. The following exercises explore the configurations of triangles that make up some standard structural supports called **trusses**.

Find the measure of ∠A in each figure.

1. measure of ∠A = 125°

   70°

   A

   king-post truss

2. measure of ∠A = 115°

   65°

   A

   scissors truss

Count the total number of triangles in each figure.

3. number of triangles = 8

   queen-post truss

4. number of triangles = 26

   Belgian truss

Lab Manual

Lab Activity, pp. 47-48

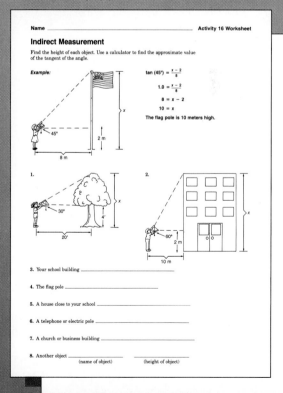

Name _____   Activity 16 Worksheet

Indirect Measurement

Find the height of each object. Use a calculator to find the approximate value of the tangent of the angle.

Example:

45°

8 m

2 m

x

$\tan(45°) = \frac{x-2}{8}$

$1.0 = \frac{x-2}{8}$

$8 = x - 2$

$10 = x$

The flag pole is 10 meters high.

1.

30°

20′

4′

x

2.

60°

10 m

2 m

x

3. Your school building _____

4. The flag pole _____

5. A house close to your school _____

6. A telephone or electric pole _____

7. A church or business building _____

8. Another object _____
   (name of object)   (height of object)

Using the Chapter Opener

Transparency 15-0 is available in the Transparency Package. It provides a full-color visual and motivational activity that you can use to engage students in the mathematical content of the chapter.

Background Information

Light *refracts* when it moves from one substance to another. This is because light travels at different speeds in different substances. The amount of refraction is determined by comparing the angles of incidence and refraction of a light ray as it moves between the substances. For a light ray entering a substance in which it travels more slowly, its angle of refraction is smaller than its angle of incidence. Similarly, for a light ray entering a substance in which it travels more quickly, its angle of refraction is larger than its angle of incidence. The property of a substance that determines the speed of light in that substance is its *optical density*.

CHAPTER OBJECTIVES

In this chapter, you will:
- Find the complement and supplement of an angle.
- Use proportions to find the missing measures for similar triangles.
- Find the sine, cosine, and tangent of an acute angle of a right triangle given the measure of its sides.
- Use trigonometric ratios to solve problems.
- Solve problems by making a model.

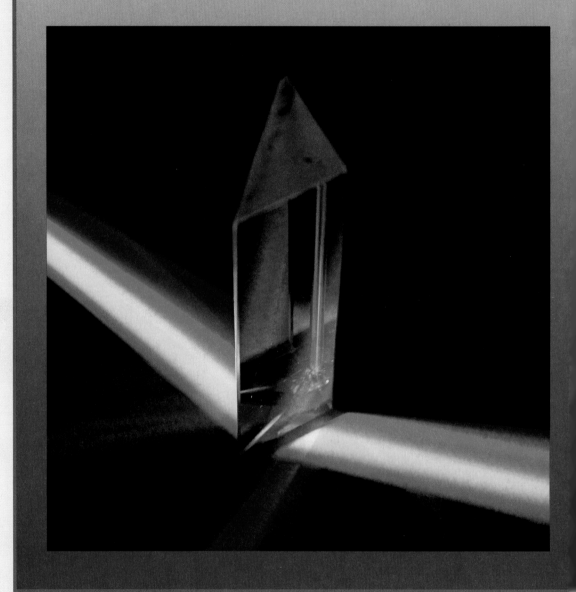

Chapter Project

Materials: paper, pencil, library resources

Organize the students into cooperative groups. Assign each group the task of researching and reporting on at least one of the following questions concerning the refraction of light.

- What is total internal refraction?
- What causes mirages to appear along highways during the summer?
- Why does an object like a spoon or pencil appear broken when placed in a glass of water?
- Why does sunlight reach you before the sun is above the horizon in the morning and after the sun has set in the evening?
- Why do the colors in white light separate when the light passes through a prism?
- What causes a rainbow?

As part of the report, have each group give a short presentation of their research to the class.

15 Trigonometry

Lesson	Connections (C) and Applications (A)	Examples	Exercises
15-1	A: Football		64
	Billiards		65
	Mountain		66
	Climbing		
15-3	A: Recreation	3	
	Construction	4	43
	Architecture		42
15-4	C: Statistics		30
	A: Construction		22
	Surveying		23
	Cinemato-		24
	graphy		
15-5	C: Statistics		47
	A: Transportation	4	
	Physics	5	39, 41
	Meteorology		40
15-6	A: Forestry	2	
	Fishing	3	
	Construction	4	
	Space Travel		27
	Archaeology		28
	Law Enforce-		29
	ment		
	Navigation		30

APPLICATION IN OPTICS

Light will change direction, or bend, as it moves from one substance to another, such as from air to water. This bending of light at the boundary of two substances is called *refraction*. The amount of refraction depends on the angle at which the light falls on the boundary of the two substances.

Consider a light ray, or *incident ray*, that falls on the boundary between two substances. Once the ray enters the new substance, it is then a *refracted ray*. The relationship between the angle of incidence, i, and the angle of refraction, r, was discovered by the Dutch scientist Willebrord Snell (1591–1626) and is called *Snell's Law*.

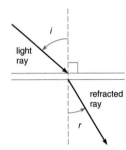

$$n = \frac{\sin i}{\sin r}$$

In this equation, n is called the *index of refraction* and is constant for any light ray traveling from one substance to another. The abbreviation sin represents the *sine* of an angle, a ratio that you will learn about in this chapter.

When you place part of your leg in a pool, why does it look like the leg "bends" at the surface of the water? The answer is that light traveling from the water to your eyes "bends" when it hits the surface of the water.

ALGEBRA IN ACTION

Copy and complete the chart below. Which has the smallest index of refraction? **water to glass**

Substances	sin i	sin r	Index of Refraction
air to water	0.8660	0.6508	? 1.33
air to glass	0.5000	0.3107	? 1.61
air to diamond	0.7071	0.2924	? 2.42
water to glass	0.2588	0.2135	? 1.21
water to diamond	0.7760	0.4210	? 1.82
glass to diamond	0.9659	0.6428	? 1.50

609

INTRODUCING THE LESSON

 5-Minute Check

(over Chapter 14)

1. If the odds in favor of an event of occurring are 8:3, what is the probability of the event occurring? $\frac{8}{11}$

2. If the probability of an event occurring is $\frac{3}{7}$, what are the odds that it will not occur? 4:3

3. A card is selected at random from a deck of 52 cards. What are the odds in favor of selecting a diamond? 1:3

4. What is the probability that a family with three children has two girls and one boy in any order? Assume that the probability a girl is born is the same as the probability a boy is born. $\frac{3}{8}$ or 0.375

5. Find the probability that a family with four children has four boys. Assume that the probability a boy is born is the same as the probability a girl is born. $\frac{1}{16}$ or 0.0625

Motivating the Lesson

Draw the following angles on the chalkboard. Ask students to name each angle in two ways.

1. $\angle XYZ$ $\angle Y$

2. $\angle MNP$ $\angle N$

3. $\angle RST$ $\angle S$

4. $\angle BCD$ $\angle C$

15-1 Angles and Triangles

Objectives

After studying this lesson, you should be able to:

15-1A ■ find the complement and the supplement of an angle, and

15-1B ■ find the measure of the third angle of a triangle given the measure of the other two angles.

Application

On fourth down in a football game, the team with the ball usually punts. How far will the football go? The distance depends not only on the strength of the punter, but also on the angle at which the ball is kicked. If the angle is too small, the ball will fall short. If the angle is too large, the ball will go very high but not far.

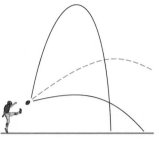

In this lesson, you will learn about different angle measures and their applications to practical problems.

A *protractor* can be used to measure angles as shown below.

Teaching Tip ❶

The symbol for angle is ∠.

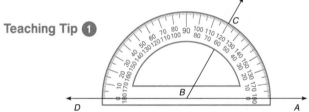

Angle *ABC* (denoted ∠*ABC*) measures 60°. However, where ray *BC* intersects the curve of the protractor, there are two readings, 60° and 120°. The measure of ∠*DBC* is 120°. What is the sum of the measures of ∠*ABC* and ∠*DBC*?

Supplementary Angles	Two angles are supplementary if the sum of their measures is 180°.

Example 1

The measure of an angle is four times the measure of its supplement. Find the measure of each angle.

Let x = the lesser measure.
Then 4x = the greater measure.

$x + 4x = 180$ *The sum of the measures is 180°.*
$\qquad 5x = 180$
$\qquad\ x = 36$

The measures are 36° and 4 · 36° or 144°. *Check this result.*

ALTERNATE TEACHING STRATEGIES

Using Logical Reasoning

Can a triangle contain supplementary angles? Can a triangle contain complementary angles? Explain your answer.

No, a triangle cannot contain supplementary angles because the sum of measures of two supplementary angles is 180° which is the sum of degree measures of the three angles in a triangle. A

triangle can contain complementary angles since the sum of their degree measures is only 90°.

Complementary Angles	Two angles are complementary if the sum of their measures is 90°.

Example 2

The measure of an angle is 26° greater than its complement. Find the measure of each angle.

Let x = the lesser measure.
Then x + 26 = the greater measure.

$x + (x + 26) = 90$ *The sum of the measures is 90°.*
$2x + 26 = 90$
$2x = 64$
$x = 32$

The measures are 32° and 32° + 26° or 58°. *Check this result.*

What is the sum of the measures of the three angles of a triangle? Use a protractor to measure the angles of each triangle below. Then find the sum of the measures of each triangle.

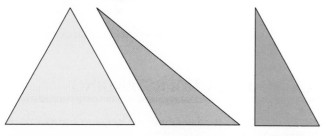

What did you discover? In each case, your sum should be approximately 180°.

Sum of the Angles of a Triangle	The sum of measures of the angles in any triangle is 180°.

In an equilateral triangle, each angle has the same measure. We say that the angles are **congruent**. The sides of an equilateral triangle are also congruent.

Example 3
Teaching Tip ❷ ❸

What is the measure of the angles of an equilateral triangle?

Let x = the measure of each angle.

$x + x + x = 180$
$3x = 180$
$x = 60$

Each angle measures 60°.

Teaching Tip ❶ When discussing the introduction to this lesson, point out to students that angle *ABC* is the supplement of angle *DBC* and vice versa.

Chalkboard Examples

For Example 1
The measure of an angle is 20° less than three times its supplement. Find the measure of each angle. 130°, 50°

For Example 2
An angle measures 42° less than its complement. Find the measure of each angle. 24°, 66°

For Example 3
a. **Find the measure of the third angle of a triangle if the other two angles measure 32° and 82°.** 66°

b. **Find the measure of the third angle of a triangle if the other two angles measure 15° and 113°.** 52°

Teaching Tip ❷ It may be necessary to review with students the properties of the special triangles in Examples 3 and 4.

Teaching Tip ❸ Remind students that congruent means equal measures.

Chalkboard Examples

For Example 4

What are the measures of the base angles of an isosceles triangle in which the vertex angle measures 20°? 80°

For Example 5

The measures of the angles of a triangular vegetable garden are given as $x°$, $x°$, and $2x°$. What are the measures of each angle?
45°, 45°, 90°

EVALUATING THE LESSON

Checking for Understanding

Exercises 1-21 are designed to help you assess understanding through reading, writing, and speaking. You should work through Exercises 1-3 with your students, and then monitor their work on Exercises 4-21.

Additional Answer

1. A compliment is an expression of praise. A complement is something that completes or fills. The word complement has mathematical meaning.

Reteaching Masters Booklet, p. 103

NAME ______________________ DATE ____________

15-1 Reteaching Worksheet

Reading Algebra: Related Meanings of Words

Many of our English words have Latin roots. Knowing the Latin derivation of a nonmathematical definition of an English word may help you understand and remember a mathematical definition of the same word.

The word *complement* is derived from the Latin word *complēre* which means *to make full* or *to complete*. Study how each meaning of *complement* is related to the meaning of its Latin root.

General meaning: Something that completes, or makes up a whole

Grammatical meaning: A word or words used after a verb to complete a predicate construction

Musical meaning: An interval in music that completes a given octave

Nautical meaning: All of the officers and crew of a ship

In geometry, one angle is a *complement* of another angle if the sum of the two angles is 90°. Think of two complementary angles as making a *full* or *complete* right angle.

Look up the meanings of the Latin roots of the following words, as well as two definitions of each word: one nonmathematical, the other mathematical. Tell how the meaning of the Latin root might help you remember the mathematical definition of the word.

Answers will vary. Sample answers are given.

1. Supplement supplēre: to complete, supply; something added to extend or strengthen the whole; the angle that when added to a given angle makes 180°; Think of extending one ray of a 90° angle to produce a straight line of 180°. The resulting two right angles are supplementary.
2. Acute acūtes: sharp; Having a sharp point or tip; Designating an angle less than 90°; Associate acute angles with sharply pointed angles.
3. Congruent congruens; meeting together, agreeing; Corresponding in character or kind; coinciding exactly when superimposed; Remember that when one of two congruent triangles is laid on top of the other, their corresponding sides and angles coincide.

Example 4 **In an isosceles triangle, at least two angles have the same measure. What are the measures of the base angles of an isosceles triangle in which the vertex angle measures 40°?**

In an isosceles triangle, the base angles are equal.
Let x = the measure of each base angle.

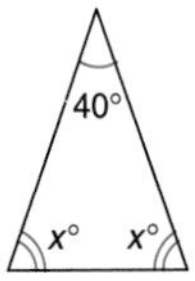

$$\begin{aligned} x + x + 40 &= 180 \\ 2x + 40 &= 180 \\ 2x &= 140 \\ x &= 70 \end{aligned}$$

The base angles each measure 70°.

Example 5 **The measures of the angles of a triangular vegetable garden are given as $x°$, $3x°$, and $4x°$. What are the measures of each angle?**

The sum of the measures of the angles of a triangle is 180°.

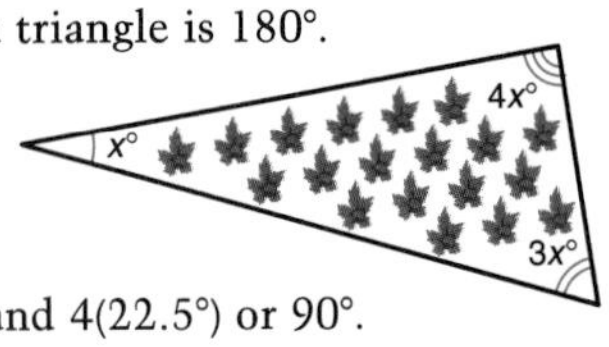

$$\begin{aligned} x + 3x + 4x &= 180 \\ 8x &= 180 \\ x &= 22.5 \end{aligned}$$

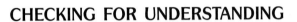

The measures are 22.5°, 3(22.5°) or 67.5°, and 4(22.5°) or 90°.

CHECKING FOR UNDERSTANDING

Communicating Mathematics

Read and study the lesson to answer each question. 1. See margin.

1. The words *compliment* and *complement* sound very much alike. What are their meanings? Which word has the mathematical meaning?
2. Three types of triangles are right, obtuse, and acute. A right triangle has one angle with measure equal to 90°, an obtuse triangle has one angle with measure greater than 90°, and an acute triangle has all angles with measures less than 90°. In the diagram on page 611, identify each triangle as right, obtuse, or acute. left: acute; center: obtuse; right: right
3. Can a right triangle have two 90° angles? Explain. See margin.

Guided Practice

Find the complement of each angle measure.

4. 42° 48°
5. 13° 77°
6. 45° 45°
7. 24° 66°
8. 11° 79°
9. 76° 14°
10. $3x°$ $(90 - 3x)°$
11. $(2x + 40)°$ $(50 - 2x)°$
12. $(x - 7)°$ $(97 - x)°$

Find the supplement of each angle measure.

13. 130° 50°
14. 65° 115°
15. 87° 93°
16. 90° 90°
17. 32° 148°
18. 156° 24°
19. $y°$ $(180 - y)°$
20. $6m°$ $(180 - 6m)°$
21. $(x - 20)°$ $(200 - x)°$

RETEACHING THE LESSON

The following activity can be used to illustrate that the sum of the measures of the angles in a triangle is 180°. Have each student make a paper triangle (the more varied the types of triangles, the better the concept is illustrated.) Have each student tear off the corners of the triangle and place them side-by-side with the vertices touching. Students should see that the corners form a 180° angle.

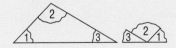

EXERCISES

Practice

 Find both the complement and the supplement of each angle measure.

31–37. See margin.

22. 42° 48°, 138° **23.** 87° 3°, 93° **24.** 125° none, 55° **25.** 160° none, 20°

26. 90° 0°, 90° **27.** 68° 22°, 112° **28.** 21° 69°, 159° **29.** 174° none, 6°

30. 99° none, 81° **31.** $a°$ **32.** $3y°$ **33.** $(x + 30)°$

34. $(x - 38)°$ **35.** $5x°$ **36.** $(90 - x)°$ **37.** $(180 - y)°$

Find the measure of the third angle of each triangle in which the measures of two angles of the triangle are given.

38. 16°, 42° 122° **39.** 40°, 70° 70° **40.** 50°, 45° 85°

41. 90°, 30° 60° **42.** 89°, 90° 1° **43.** 63°, 12° 105°

 44. 43°, 118° 19° **45.** 4°, 38° 138° **46.** $x°, y°$ $(180 - x - y)°$

47. $x°, (x + 20)°$ $(160 - 2x)°$ **48.** $y°, (y - 10)°$ $(190 - 2y)°$ **49.** $m°, (2m + 1)°$ $(179 - 3m)°$

50. One of the congruent angles of an isosceles triangle measures 37°. Find the measures of the other angles. 37°, 106°

51. The measures of the angles of a certain triangle are consecutive even integers. Find their measures. 58°, 60°, 62°

52. An angle measures 38° less than its complement. Find the measures of the two angles. 26°, 64°

53. One of the angles of a triangle measures 53°. Another angle measures 37°. What is the measure of the third angle? 90°

54. One angle of a triangle measures 10° more than the second. The measure of the third angle is twice the sum of the first two angles. Find the measure of each angle. 25°, 35°, 120°

55. One of the two complementary angles measures 30° more than three times the other. Find the measure of each angle. 15°, 75°

56. Find the measure of an angle that is 10° more than its complement. 50°

57. Find the measure of an angle that is 30° less than its supplement. 75°

58. Find the measure of an angle that is one-half the measure of its complement. 30°

59. Find the measure of an angle that is one-half the measure of its supplement. 60°

60. The measures of the angles of a triangle are given as $x°$, $2x°$, and $3x°$. What are the measures of each angle? 30°, 60°, 90°

61. The measures of the angles of a triangle are given as $x°$, $(x + 5)°$, and $(2x + 3)°$. What are the measures of each angle? 43°, 48°, 89°

62. The measures of the angles of a triangle are given as $6x°$, $(x - 3)°$, and $(3x + 7)°$. What are the measures of each angle? 105.6°, 14.6°, 59.8°

LESSON 15-1 ANGLES AND TRIANGLES 613

Additional Answers

3. No; the sum of the measures of the angles of a triangle is 180°. Since the measure of each angle is greater than 0°, having two 90° angles would result in a sum that is greater than 180°.

31. $(90 - a)°, (180 - a)°$
32. $(90 - 3y)°, (180 - 3y)°$
33. $(60 - x)°, (150 - x)°$
34. $(128 - x)°, (218 - x)°$
35. $(90 - 5x)°, (180 - 5x)°$
36. $x°, (90 + x)°$
37. $(y - 90)°, y°$

Additional Answer

63. 1080°; an octagon can be divided into six triangles by drawing the five diagonals from a single vertex of the octagon. The sum of the measures of the angles of these triangles, which is 6 · 180° or 1080°, is equal to the sum of the measures of the interior angles of the octagon.

Critical Thinking

63. Using the fact that the sum of the measures of the angles of any triangle is 180°, determine the sum of the measures of the interior angles of an octagon. Justify your answer. **See margin.**

Applications

64. **Football** A punter for Darien High School punts a football into the air at an angle of 40° from the horizontal (the ground). At what angle measure from the vertical is the ball punted? **50°**

65. **Billiards** In billiards, the ball bounces off the cushion at the same angle at which it hits. If it strikes the cushion at 30° and rebounds at 30°, what is the measure of the angle between the two paths of the ball? **120°**

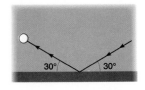

66. **Mountain Climbing** *Rapelling* is a technique used by climbers to make a difficult descent. Climbers back to the edge and spring off. To avoid slipping, the climber's legs should remain perpendicular to the side of the ledge. The ledge at the right is 50° off the vertical. What is the measure of the climber's angle with the vertical? **40°**

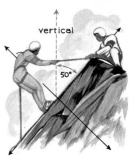

Mixed Review

67. Write *R is the product of a and m decreased by z* as an equation. **(Lesson 1-7)** $R = am - z$

68. Simplify $(5a^2b^2c)(-7a^3)$. **(Lesson 6-1)** $-35a^5b^2c$

69. Write a system of inequalities for the graph at the right. **(Lesson 11-6)**

$x \leq 2, y \geq 2$

70. Find the distance between $(-3, 5)$ and $(2, 7)$. **(Lesson 12-8)** $\sqrt{29}$ or 5.385

71. Find the equation of the axis of symmetry and the coordinates of the maximum or minimum point of the graph of $y = -5x^2 + 15x + 23$. **(Lesson 13-1)** $x = \frac{3}{2}, \left(\frac{3}{2}, \frac{137}{4}\right)$

72. Find the sum and product of the roots of $b^2 + 12b - 28 = 0$. **(Lesson 13-8)** $-12, -28$

73. Bill, Raul, and Joe are in a bicycle race. If each boy has an equal chance of winning, find the probability that Raul finishes last. **(Lesson 14-10)** $\frac{1}{3} = 0.\overline{3}$

EXTENDING THE LESSON

Math Power: Reasoning

Show that when the measure of a given angle is added to twice the measure of the complement of the angle, the result equals the measure of the supplement of the angle.

Let a = the measure of the angle. Then, $90 - a$ = the measure of its complement and $180 - a$ = the measure of its supplement.

$a + 2(90 - a) = a + 180 - 2a,$
$= 180 - a$

Enrichment Masters Booklet, p. 103

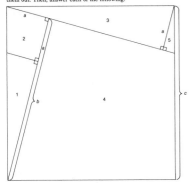

NAME _____ DATE _____

15-1 Enrichment Worksheet

Pythagorean Theorem

Glue the figures in the square below on hard paper and cut them out. Then, answer each of the following.

1. What is the area of the large square? c^2 square units

2. Form two separate squares from the six figures. **See students' work.**

3. What is the area of each of the smaller squares? a^2 square units, b^2 square units

4. What is the relationship between the three squares? $a^2 + b^2 = c^2$

5. Does $a^2 + b^2 = c^2$? yes

Problem-Solving Strategy: Make a Model

Objective
15-2

After studying this lesson, you should be able to:
■ solve problems by making models.

Models are often useful in solving problems. A model can be a simple sketch, a precise scale drawing, or a three-dimensional object. In this chapter, you will make models of angles and triangular shapes.

Example

A landscaping plan suggests that 6 square concrete tiles be placed in a garden. At least one side of each tile is to be matched evenly with a side of another tile. If the tiles are one foot long on each side and the perimeter of the area to be covered by the tiles is 14 feet, what are some possible arrangements of the tiles?

This problem can be solved by cutting 6 congruent squares from a piece of paper. Arrange these squares until you find a pattern with a perimeter of 14 units. Some possible patterns are shown below.

perimeter = 10 units   perimeter = 12 units   perimeter = 14 units

perimeter = 12 units   perimeter = 12 units   perimeter = 14 units

Two possible configurations are  and .

CHECKING FOR UNDERSTANDING

Communicating Mathematics

Read and study the lesson to answer each question. 1, 3. See margin.

1. What other models could you use to solve the tile problem?

2. The following diagrams are all variations of the same pattern.

Can you find a pattern with a perimeter of 14 units that is different than the ones already given? **See Solutions Manual.**

3. How could an interior decorator use models to design ways to arrange furniture in a room?

RETEACHING THE LESSON

A different landscaping plan uses 6 triangular concrete tiles. At least one side of each tile is to be matched evenly with a side of another tile. The tiles are one foot long on each side and the perimeter of the area to be covered by the tiles is 6 feet. Show how configurations fit the requirements by arranging 6 congruent triangles cut from a piece of paper.

Additional Answers

1. Answers will vary; typical answers are sketches of the six squares or cardboard squares from some board game.

3. Answers will vary; typical answer is that pieces of paper or cardboard that represent pieces of furniture can be moved around on a scale drawing of the room.

15-2 Lesson Notes

Lesson Resources
• Practice Master 15-2
 Transparency 15-2 contains the 5-Minute Check and a teaching aid for this lesson.

INTRODUCING THE LESSON

5-Minute Check
(over Lesson 15-1)

Find the measure of the third angle of each triangle in which the measure of two angles of the triangle are given.

1. 15°, 86°   79°
2. 22°, 110°   48°
3. 66°, 52°   62°
4. 73°, 19°   88°
5. 31°, 115°   34°

Motivating the Lesson

Ask students if they have ever made a scale model of an object such as a car or airplane. Discuss the relationship between the model pieces and the actual parts of the object. Ask the students who have made such models to identify the ratio used to make the model, such as 1 inch on the model represented 3 feet on the actual object. Pose questions to the class based on the scales identified.

TEACHING THE LESSON

Chalkboard Example

For the Example

Suppose 8 square concrete tiles were used in the garden. If the perimeter of the area covered by the tiles is 16 feet, what are some arrangements of the tiles?

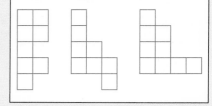

Checking for Understanding

Exercises 1-6 are designed to help you assess understanding through reading, writing, and speaking. You should work through Exercises 1-3 with your students, and then monitor their work on Exercises 4-6.

Closing the Lesson

Speaking Activity Ask students to explain how making a model can help find a solution to a problem.

APPLYING THE LESSON

Homework Exercises

Assignment Guide
Basic: 7-9
Average: 7-9
Enriched: 7-9

Chapter 15, Quiz A, (Lessons 15-1 through 15-2), is available in the Evaluation Masters Booklet, p. 205.

Practice Masters Booklet, p. 117

15-2 **Practice Worksheet**

NAME _____ DATE _____

Problem-Solving: Make a Model
Solve. Make a model.

1. Six tiles are put together to form a hexagon. Each tile is in the shape of an equilateral triangle. If each side of the equilateral triangles is 8 centimeters long, what is the perimeter of the hexagon?
48 cm

2. A square garden that measures 6 meters on each side is bordered by a brick walk 2 meters wide. What is the area of the garden and the walk?
100 m²

3. A 12-inch piece of rubber tubing is cut into three pieces. The first piece is 3 inches longer than the third piece. The second piece is twice the sum of the other two pieces. How long is the second piece?
8 in.

4. A rectangular yard measures 50 meters by 25 meters. If posts to support a fence are to be placed 5 meters apart around the perimeter of the yard, how many posts are needed?
30 posts

5. The dimensions of a rectangular floor are 15 feet by 10 feet. How many 1-inch square tiles are needed to cover the floor?
21,600 tiles

6. A concrete slab that measures 2 feet by 1 foot costs $2.50. How much would it cost to use slabs such as these to construct a 3-foot-wide walk around a rectangular swimming pool that measures 25 feet by 20 feet?
$382.50

Guided Practice

Solve. Make a model.

4. Two tiles are put together to form a pentagon. One tile is in the shape of a square, and the other is in the shape of an equilateral triangle. If one side of the triangle is 10 centimeters long, what is the perimeter of the pentagon? **50 cm**

5. A painting is 12 inches by 20 inches. The painting is bordered by a mat that is 3 inches wide. The frame around the mat is 2 inches wide. What is the area of the picture, including the frame and mat? **660 in²**

6. In the Centerville Community Softball League tournament, the losing team from each game is out of the tournament and the winning team goes on to play another winning team until a first-place team is determined. If 16 teams enter the tournament, how many games will be played? **15 games**

EXERCISES

Practice

Solve. Use any strategy.

7. Hong and Dora each have a bag of marbles. If Hong gave Dora one marble, they would each have the same number of marbles. However, if Dora would give Hong one marble, Hong would have twice as many marbles as Dora. How many marbles does each one have? **Hong: 7, Dora: 5**

8. The six faces of a wooden cube are painted orange, and then the cube is cut into 64 one-inch cubes.
   a. How many of the smaller cubes have exactly 3 painted faces? **8 cubes**
   b. How many of the smaller cubes have exactly 2 painted faces? **24 cubes**
   c. How many have exactly 1 painted face? **24 cubes**
   d. How many have no painted faces? **8 cubes**

9. Mr. Zerman went shopping. In the first store he spent half of his money plus an additional dollar. At the second store he spent half of his remaining money plus another dollar. This pattern continued until he left the fifth store with no money left. How much money did he have before he started shopping? **$62**

COOPERATIVE LEARNING ACTIVITY

Work in groups of three. Each person must understand the solution and be able to explain it to any person in the class.

There are 8 small boxes identical in color, size, and shape. Seven of the boxes each contain an inexpensive costume ring and therefore have the same weight. One box contains a valuable diamond ring and weighs slightly more than the other boxes. You cannot open the boxes, but you can use a balance scale. How can you be sure to pick the box with the diamond ring, if you can only use the balance scale two times? **See margin.**

EXTENDING THE LESSON

Math Power: Connections

Interior designers often make models of rooms to show various ways of arranging furniture. Use colored paper and a piece of cardboard to show two possible ways of rearranging the objects in your algebra classroom.

Answer for Cooperative Learning Activity

Place 3 boxes on each side of the scale. If both sides weigh the same, weigh the remaining 2 boxes to determine which contains the ring. If one side weighs more, keep those 3 boxes and set the others aside. Place one box on each side of the scale. If one box weighs more, then it contains the ring. Otherwise, the box not weighed contains the ring.

15-3 30°–60° Right Triangles

Objective 15-3

After studying this lesson, you should be able to:

■ find the measures of the sides of a 30°–60° right triangle given the measure of one side.

Application

The two poles at the end of the swing set at the right form a triangle with the ground. You can use a special right triangle to find the height of the swing set.

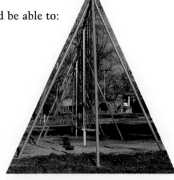

Teaching Tips ❶ ❷

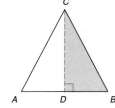

The hypotenuse of a right triangle is the side opposite the right angle.

Examine the equilateral triangle shown at the left. What is the measure of ∠B?

Line segment CD (denoted $\overline{CD}$) can be drawn perpendicular to $\overline{AB}$. CD bisects ∠ACB. What is the measure of ∠DCB?

Triangle CDB is a special triangle called a **30°–60° right triangle**.

$\overline{CD}$ bisects $\overline{AB}$. Since the measure of $\overline{DB}$ is one-half the measure of $\overline{AB}$, it is also one-half the measure of the hypotenuse, $\overline{BC}$. *Why?*

In a 30°–60° right triangle, the measure of the hypotenuse is twice the measure of the side opposite the 30° angle.

Lower case letters are often used to designate the measures of the sides of a triangle. For example, the measure of the side opposite angle R is r.

Example 1

For each 30°–60° right triangle, find the indicated measures.

a. Find the measure of $\overline{MK}$ in △RMK.

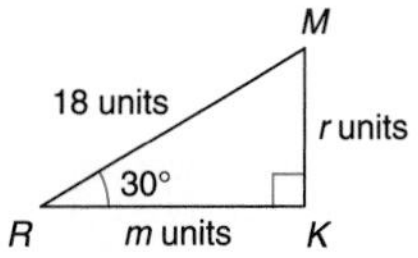

$r = \frac{1}{2}k$ *The measure of the hypotenuse is k.*

$= \frac{1}{2}(18)$

$= 9$

Thus, $\overline{MK}$ is 9 units long.

b. Find the measure of $\overline{PQ}$ in △PQR.

$r = 2q$ *The measure of the side opposite*
$= 2(6)$ *the 30° angle is 6.*
$= 12$

Thus, $\overline{PQ}$ is 12 units long.

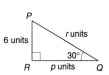

LESSON 15-3 30°–60° RIGHT TRIANGLES **617**

ALTERNATE TEACHING STRATEGIES

Using Logical Reasoning

Can the lengths of the sides of a 30°-60° right triangle be whole numbers? Why or why not? **No, because the measure of the side opposite the 60° angle is √3 times the measure of the leg adjacent to the 60° angle.**

Using Models

The angle formed where two walls meet is usually a 90° angle. Have students use string, tape, and a protractor to make a model of a 30°-60° right triangle with the corner of a room forming the 90° angle.

Lesson Resources

- Reteaching Master 15-3
- Practice Master 15-3
- Enrichment Master 15-3

 Transparency 15-3 contains the 5-Minute Check and a teaching aid for this lesson.

INTRODUCING THE LESSON

5-Minute Check
(over Lesson 15-1)

Find the complement and supplement of each angle measure.

1. 24°   66°, 156°
2. 67°   23°, 113°
3. 55°   35°, 125°
4. 80°   10°, 100°
5. 34°   56°, 146°

Motivating the Lesson

Draw the following triangles on the chalkboard. Ask students to name all the sides and angles in each triangle.

1. 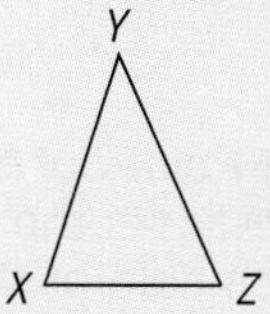
$\overline{XY}$, $\overline{YZ}$, $\overline{XZ}$
∠X, ∠Y, ∠Z

2. 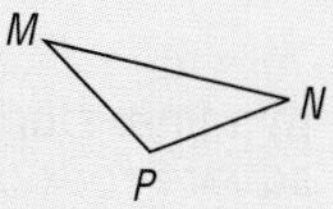
$\overline{MN}$, $\overline{NP}$, $\overline{PM}$
∠M, ∠N, ∠P

TEACHING THE LESSON

Teaching Tip ❶ Emphasize that CD denotes line segment CD. Also, point out that lower case letters are used to denote the measure of the side opposite a given angle.

Teaching Tip ❷ Review with students the meaning of *bisect*.

Chalkboard Examples

For Example 1

Find the measure of $\overline{BC}$ in △ABC.

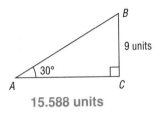

For Example 2

Find the length of $\overline{AC}$ in △ABC.

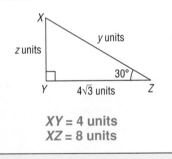

15.588 units

For Example 3

Find the length of $\overline{XY}$ and $\overline{XZ}$ in △XYZ.

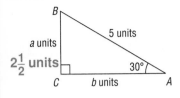

$XY = 4$ units
$XZ = 8$ units

Teaching Tip ❸ Point out that this final step represents the square root of each side of the equation $b^2 = 3a^2$.

In triangle *ABC* (denoted △*ABC*), *a* represents the measure of the side opposite the 30° angle. The Pythagorean Theorem can be used to find *b*, the measure of the side opposite the 60° angle.

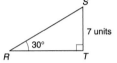

$$a^2 + b^2 = c^2 \qquad \textit{Pythagorean Theorem}$$
$$a^2 + b^2 = (2a)^2 \qquad \textit{Replace c with 2a.}$$
$$a^2 + b^2 = 4a^2$$
$$b^2 = 4a^2 - a^2 \quad \textit{Solve for b.}$$
$$b^2 = 3a^2$$
$$b = a\sqrt{3} \qquad \textbf{Teaching Tip ❸}$$

The measures of the sides of a 30°–60° right triangle are summarized as follows.

30°–60° Right Triangle	In a **30°–60° right triangle**, if *a* is the measure of the side opposite the 30° angle, then 2*a* is the measure of the hypotenuse, and $a\sqrt{3}$ is the measure of the side opposite the 60° angle.

Example 2

For each 30°–60° right triangle, find the length of the indicated side.

a. Find the measure of $\overline{RT}$ in △*RST*.

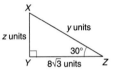

$$s = r\sqrt{3} \qquad \textit{The measure of the side}$$
$$= 7\sqrt{3} \qquad \textit{opposite the 30° angle is r.}$$
$$\approx 12.124$$

Thus, $\overline{RT}$ is approximately 12.124 units long.

b. Find the measures of $\overline{XY}$ and $\overline{XZ}$ in △*XYZ*.

$$x = z\sqrt{3}$$
$$8\sqrt{3} = z\sqrt{3}$$
$$8 = z \qquad \textit{Divide each side by } \sqrt{3}.$$

Since $y = 2z$, then $y = 2(8)$ or 16. Thus, $\overline{XY}$ is 8 units long, and $\overline{XZ}$ is 16 units long.

Example 3

APPLICATION

Recreation

Suppose each pole holding up the swing set on page 617 is 10 feet long. What is the height of the swing set?

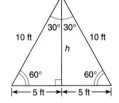

Draw a model of the problem. Look at one of the right triangles. The hypotenuse is 10 feet long, and the side opposite the 30° angle is 5 feet long. The height is the length of the side opposite the 60° angle.

$$h = 5\sqrt{3}$$
$$\approx 8.66$$

The height of the swing is about 8.66 feet, or 8 ft 8 in.

Example 4

APPLICATION

Construction

FYI · · ·

Trusses are also used in many kinds of machinery, such as cranes and lifts, and in aircraft wings and fuselages.

In construction, a truss is often used to support the weight of a roof. An architect designs a building so that the rafters form an angle of 30° with the span. If the rafters are 14 feet long, how high is the vertical support and how wide is the span?

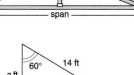

The truss forms two congruent right triangles. Draw a model of one triangle to find the measures.

Let a be the measure of the side opposite the 30° angle.
Let b be the measure of the side opposite the 60° angle.

$a = \frac{1}{2}(14)$ $b = 7\sqrt{3}$
$= 7$ ≈ 12.124

The vertical support is 7 feet. Since b represents half the span, the span is about 2(12.124) or 24.25 feet.

CHECKING FOR UNDERSTANDING

Communicating Mathematics

Read and study the lesson to answer each question.

1. In a 30°–60° right triangle, the ratio of the measures of the sides is $1:\sqrt{3}:2$. Will the ratio stay the same no matter how large the 30°–60° right triangle is? Justify your answer. **yes**

2. What is the length of the other leg of the triangle at the right? **2x cm**

3. What is the length of the hypotenuse of the triangle at the right? **4x cm**

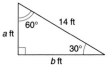

Guided Practice

The length of the hypotenuse of a 30°–60° right triangle is given. Find the length of the side opposite the 30° angle in each triangle.

4. 8 m **4 m**   5. 16 cm **8 cm**   6. 13 mm **6.5 mm** 7. 9 mi **4.5 mi**

8. $4\frac{1}{2}$ in. **$2\frac{1}{4}$ in.**   9. $3\frac{3}{8}$ in. **$1\frac{11}{16}$ in.**   10. 16.36 m   11. 4.63 cm
                                                   8.18 m   **2.315 cm**

The length of the side opposite the 60° angle in a 30°–60° right triangle is given. Find the length of the other two sides.

12. $4\sqrt{3}$ ft   13. $2\sqrt{3}$ cm   14. $8\sqrt{3}$ m   15. $\sqrt{3}$ mi
    4 ft, 8 ft   **2 cm, 4 cm**   **8 m, 16 m**   **1 mi, 2 mi**

EXERCISES

Practice

The length of the side opposite the 30° angle in a 30°–60° right triangle is given. Find the length of the hypotenuse in each triangle. **18. 8.7 mm**

16. 7 m **14 m**   17. 6.2 cm **12.4 cm** 18. 4.35 mm   19. $4\frac{1}{2}$ mi **9 mi**

20. $6\frac{3}{8}$ in. **$12\frac{3}{4}$ in.**   21. 13 m **26 m**   22. 3.86 cm   23. $7\frac{3}{4}$ in. **$15\frac{1}{2}$ in.**
                                                   7.72 cm

RETEACHING THE LESSON

Find the area of a regular hexagon that has sides of length 10 inches. Hint: Draw line segments from the center to the vertices of the hexagon and find the area of one triangle.
The area is $150\sqrt{3}$ in² or about 259.81 in².

Chalkboard Example

For Example 4
Find the length of $\overline{XY}$ and $\overline{XZ}$ in $\triangle XYZ$.

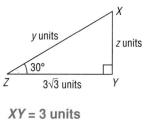

$XY = 3$ units
$XZ = 6$ units

EVALUATING THE LESSON

Checking for Understanding

Exercises 1-15 are designed to help you assess understanding through reading, writing, and speaking. You should work through Exercises 1-3 with your students, and then monitor their work on Exercises 4-15.

Assignment Guide

Average: 20-38, 41-50
Enriched: 22-50
All: Mid-Chapter Review, 1-11

Reteaching Masters Booklet, p. 104

Error Analysis

Students sometimes confuse the two methods most commonly used to represent the lengths of the sides of a 30° - 60° right triangle.

Method 1: Let x = measure of side opposite 30° angle. Then $2x$ = measure of hypotenuse.

Method 2: Let x = hypotenuse. Then $\frac{x}{2}$ = measure of side opposite 30° angle. To prevent errors, encourage students to consistently use one of the methods.

Closing the Lesson

Writing Activity Have students write a brief paragraph explaining how to find the measures of the sides of a 30° - 60° right triangle given the measure of one side.

APPLYING THE LESSON

Homework Exercises

See assignment guide on page 619.

Practice Masters Booklet, p. 118

 Find the missing length in each triangle.

24.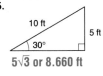
8 cm, 4 cm, 30°
$4\sqrt{3}$ or 6.928 cm

25.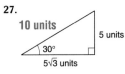
10 ft, 5 ft, 30°
$5\sqrt{3}$ or 8.660 ft

26.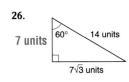
60°, 14 units, 7 units
$7\sqrt{3}$ units

27.
10 units, 30°, 5 units
$5\sqrt{3}$ units

28.
$\frac{\sqrt{3}}{2}$ m, $\frac{1}{2}$ m, 60°, 1 m

29.
2.5 yd, 60°, **$2.5\sqrt{3}$ yd**, 5 yd

Find the missing lengths for each 30°–60° right triangle described below.

	Hypotenuse	Side Opposite 30° Angle	Side Opposite 60° Angle
30.	6 m	? **3 m**	? **$3\sqrt{3}$ m**
31.	4.75 mm	? **2.375 mm**	? **$2.375\sqrt{3}$ mm**
32.	$3\frac{1}{2}$ in.	? **$1\frac{3}{4}$ in.**	? **$\frac{7}{4}\sqrt{3}$ in.**
33.	? **16 cm**	8 cm	? **$8\sqrt{3}$ cm**
34.	? **13 m**	6.5 m	? **$6.5\sqrt{3}$ m**
35.	? **$6\frac{1}{2}$ in.**	$3\frac{1}{4}$ in.	? **$\frac{13}{4}\sqrt{3}$ in.**
36.	? **4 m**	? **2 m**	$2\sqrt{3}$ m
37.	? **7 cm**	? **3.5 cm**	$3.5\sqrt{3}$ cm

38. In $\triangle ABC$ below, $\overline{AC}$ is 10 meters long, AB is $3\sqrt{3}$ meters long, and $\angle A$ measures 30°. Find the length of $\overline{BC}$. **$\sqrt{37}$ m**

C, 10, 30°, A, $3\sqrt{3}$, B

39. In $\triangle PQR$ below, $\overline{PS}$ is $8\sqrt{3}$ yards long. Find the perimeter of $\triangle PQR$.
$48 + 16\sqrt{3}$ yd or 75.71 yd

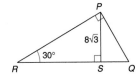
P, $8\sqrt{3}$, 30°, R, S, Q

40. Find the perimeter of the quadrilateral shown at the right.
$12 + 8\sqrt{3}$ in. or 25.86 in.

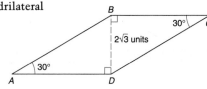
B, 30°, C, $2\sqrt{3}$ units, 30°, A, D

Critical Thinking
41. In rectangle $JKLM$ shown at the right, the measure of $\angle NJK$ is 30° and $\overline{KN}$ is 5 meters long. Find the perimeter of rectangle $JKLM$.
$\frac{60 + 20\sqrt{3}}{3}$ yd; 31.547 yd

J, 30°, 5 m, K, N, M, L

Applications

42. **Architecture** An A-frame house is one that looks like the letter A when viewed from the front. An architect is designing such a house. The sides of the building form an angle of 60° with the floor (base). If the house is to be 30 feet wide at the base, how high will it be? **15√3 ft or 25.98 ft**

43. **Construction** Rhonda wants to get a refrigerator into her house. She cannot lift it up the steps leading to her back door, so she decides to build a ramp. She decides that the ramp should make a 30° angle with the ground. If her back door is 2 feet above the ground, how long should Rhonda cut the boards to make the ramp? **4 ft**

Mixed Review

44. Find $-37.12 + 42.18 + (-12.6)$. **(Lesson 2-5)** **−7.54**

45. Factor $3y^2 + 5y - 2$. **(Lesson 7-5)** **$(3y - 1)(y + 2)$**

46. Solve $2x - y = 3x$ and $2x + y = 3y$ by using substitution. **(Lesson 11-3)** **no solution**

47. Simplify $-\sqrt{\frac{289}{100}}$. **(Lesson 12-2)** **$-\frac{17}{10}$**

48. Solve $2t^2 - t = 4$. **(Lesson 13-5)** **$\frac{1 \pm \sqrt{33}}{4}$**

49. What is the outlier in the box-and-whisker plot at the right? **(Lesson 14-5)** **34**

30 40 50 60 70 80 90 100

50. Find the complement of 17°. **(Lesson 15-1)** **73°**

Chapter 15, Quiz B, (Lesson 15-3), is available in the Evaluation Masters Booklet, p. 205.

Additional Answer to Mid-Chapter Review

11. The figure below shows the view from directly above the pins. Move the three pins as indicated in this figure.

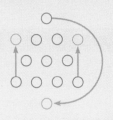

~~~~~~~~~~ **MID-CHAPTER REVIEW** ~~~~~~~~~~

Find both the complement and supplement of each angle measure. (Lesson 15-1)

1. 85° **5°, 95°**
2. 127° **none, 53°**
3. 65° **25°, 115°**
4. 108° **none, 72°**
5. x° **$(90 - x)°, (180 - x)°$**
6. $(3x + 5)°$ **$(85 - 3x)°, (175 - 3x)°$**

The length of the side opposite the 60° angle in a 30°–60° right triangle is given. Find the lengths of the other two sides. (Lesson 15-3)

7. $3\sqrt{3}$ m **3 m, 6 m**
8. $7\sqrt{3}$ yd **7 yd, 14 yd**
9. $9\sqrt{3}$ mm **9 mm, 18 mm**
10. $\frac{\sqrt{3}}{3}$ in. **$\frac{1}{3}$ in., $\frac{2}{3}$ in.**

11. **Solve by making a model. (Lesson 15-2)**

The bowling pin machine at Abbey Lanes is broken, making the pins point in the wrong direction. Can you make them face the opposite direction by moving just three pins? Explain. (*Hint:* All of the pins are exactly alike.) **See margin.**

Not this way   But this way

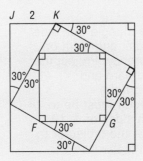

LESSON 15-3   30°–60° RIGHT TRIANGLES   **621**

EXTENDING THE LESSON

Math Power: Problem Solving

In the square shown, $\overline{JK}$ is 2 units long. Find the length of $\overline{FG}$. **$\frac{8}{1 + \sqrt{3}}$ units or about 2.9 units**

Enrichment Masters Booklet, p. 104

NAME _____ DATE _____

15-3 Enrichment Worksheet

Properties of Triangles

The 30°-60° right triangle appears frequently in mathematics. If the measure of the shorter leg of a 30°-60° right triangle is a, then the measure of the longer leg is $\sqrt{3}a$ and the measure of the hypotenuse is $2a$.

Other frequently-used triangles are the 3-4-5 right triangle, the equilateral triangle, and the 45°-45° right triangle. In an equilateral triangle, all three angles have the same measure and all three sides have the same length. The 45°-45° right triangle is also called an isosceles right triangle because its two legs have the same length.

Draw a model for each problem. Use a length of 1 inch for a. Then complete the statement that describes the properties of the triangle.
Triangles are shown in reduced size.

1. In a 45°-45° right triangle, if a is the measure of one of the legs, then find the measure of the other leg and of the hypotenuse. **$a; \sqrt{2}a$**

2. The sides of a triangle measure $\frac{3a}{2}, \frac{4a}{2}$, and $\frac{5a}{2}$. Find the measure of the angle opposite the longest side. **90°**

3. In an equilateral triangle with a side that measures a, find the measure of the altitude to each side. **$\frac{\sqrt{3}}{2}a$**

4. In an equilateral triangle with a side that measures a, find the area of the triangle. **$\frac{\sqrt{3}}{4}a^2$**

5. Find the area of an isosceles right triangle with a leg that measures a. **$\frac{a^2}{2}$**

Chapter 15   **621**

INTRODUCING THE LESSON

 5-Minute Check

(over Lesson 15-3)

The length of the side opposite the 30° angle in a 30° - 60° right triangle is given. Find the length of the hypotenuse in each triangle.

1. 17 m   34 m
2. 2.3 cm   4.6 cm
3. 27 m   54 m
4. 2.15 mm   4.30 mm
5. 7.9 m   15.8 m

Motivating the Lesson

Review student understanding of proportions by asking them to solve each of the following.

1. $\frac{3}{4} = \frac{x}{16}$ 12
2. $\frac{3}{12} = \frac{1}{y}$ 4
3. $\frac{15}{a} = \frac{25}{2}$ $\frac{6}{5}$
4. $\frac{m}{24} = \frac{5}{16}$ $7\frac{1}{2}$

TEACHING THE LESSON

Teaching Tip ❶ You may wish to review ratios and proportions before introducing this lesson. Similar triangles, along with ratios and proportions, are very important in the study of geometry.

Teaching Tip ❷ The angles in △ABC have the same measures as the angles in △NDR.

15-4 Similar Triangles Teaching Tip ❶

Objective
15-4

After studying this lesson, you should be able to:
- find the unknown measures of the sides of two similar triangles.

Application

Janet is an ichnologist. She studies dinosaur tracks to estimate their speeds and weights. She has taken a picture of a fossilized trail and wants to develop it.

△ABC is on a photo negative. △NDR is its image on the photo paper below. An angle and its image are called **corresponding angles**. The sides opposite corresponding angles are called **corresponding sides**.

Teaching Tip ❷

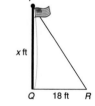

corresponding angles	corresponding sides
∠A and ∠N	$\overline{BC}$ and $\overline{DR}$
∠B and ∠D	$\overline{AC}$ and $\overline{NR}$
∠C and ∠R	$\overline{AB}$ and $\overline{ND}$

Two figures are **similar** if they have the same shape but not necessarily the same size. If corresponding angles of two triangles have equal measures, the triangles are similar. The two triangles in the example are similar. We write △ABC ~ △NDR. The order of the letters indicates the angles that correspond.

Compare the measures of the corresponding sides. Note that BC means the measure of $\overline{BC}$, DR means the measure of $\overline{DR}$, and so on.

$$\frac{BC}{DR} = \frac{14}{21} = \frac{2}{3} \qquad \frac{AC}{NR} = \frac{8}{12} = \frac{2}{3} \qquad \frac{AB}{ND} = \frac{20}{30} = \frac{2}{3}$$

When the measures of the corresponding sides form equal ratios, the measures are said to be **proportional**.

Similar Triangles	If two triangles are similar, the measures of their corresponding sides are proportional, and the measures of their corresponding angles are equal.

Example 1

If a tree 6 feet tall casts a shadow 4 feet long, how high is a flagpole that casts a shadow 18 feet long?

△JKL is similar to △PQR.

$\frac{JK}{PQ} = \frac{KL}{QR}$ *Corresponding sides of similar triangles are proportional.*

$\frac{6}{x} = \frac{4}{18}$

$4x = 6(18)$ *Cross multiply.*

$4x = 108$

$x = 27$ The flagpole is 27 feet high.

ALTERNATE TEACHING STRATEGIES

Using Manipulatives

Before class, draw a triangle with side lengths of 4 cm, 10 cm, and 8 cm on an overhead transparency. Project the triangle on the chalkboard and determine how far from the chalkboard the projector must be to obtain a triangle with sides of 4, 10, and 8 cm. Then move the projector to the right and back until the side lengths are 6, 15, and 12 cm and again note the position of the projector. In class, move the projector to the predetermined locations, trace the triangles with chalk, and have students give you the measures of the angles and sides of the two triangles. Show that the corresponding angles are congruent and the corresponding sides are proportional.

Similar triangles do not have to be positioned in the same way.

Example 2

Find the missing measures of the sides.

The measure of $\angle V = 180° - (120° + 38°)$ or $22°$.
The measure of $\angle W = 180° - (120° + 22°)$ or $38°$.

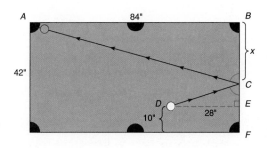

Since the corresponding angles have equal measures, $\triangle VMT \sim \triangle YWQ$. This means that the lengths of the corresponding sides are proportional.

$$\frac{VM}{YW} = \frac{MT}{WQ} \qquad\qquad \frac{VM}{YW} = \frac{VT}{YQ}$$

$$\frac{35}{14} = \frac{x}{6} \qquad\qquad \frac{35}{14} = \frac{y}{10}$$

$$14x = 35(6) \qquad\qquad 14y = 35(10)$$

$$14x = 210 \qquad\qquad 14y = 350$$

$$x = 15 \qquad\qquad y = 25$$

The missing measures are 15 and 25.

Example 3

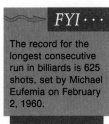

FYI · · ·

The record for the longest consecutive run in billiards is 625 shots, set by Michael Eufemia on February 2, 1960.

Eddie is playing billiards on a table like the one shown at the right. If he can make this next shot, he figures he will have no trouble winning. He wants to strike the cue ball at *D*, bank it at *C*, and hit another ball at the mouth of pocket *A*. Use similar triangles to find where Eddie's cue ball should strike the rail.

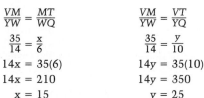

The ball bounces off the cushion at the same angle at which it hits. Since $\angle DCE$ has the same measure as $\angle ACB$, $\triangle ABC \sim \triangle DEC$.

$$\frac{BC}{EC} = \frac{AB}{DE} \qquad \overline{BC}, \overline{EC} \text{ and } \overline{AB}, \overline{DE} \text{ are pairs of corresponding sides.}$$

$$\frac{x}{32 - x} = \frac{84}{28} \qquad BC = x, EC = 32 - x, AB = 84, DE = 28$$

$$\frac{x}{32 - x} = \frac{3}{1} \qquad \textit{Simplify.}$$

$$x = 3(32 - x) \qquad \textit{Cross multiply.}$$

$$x = 96 - 3x \qquad \textit{Distributive property}$$

$$4x = 96$$

$$x = 24$$

Eddie should aim the cue ball 24 inches below pocket *B*.

RETEACHING THE LESSON

Have students move a mirror along the ground between an observer and an object until the top of the object is at the top of observer's line of sight reflected in the mirror. Then use similar triangles to find the height of the object.

Chalkboard Examples

For Example 1

Use similar triangles to solve the problem.

A tree 9 ft tall casts a shadow 5 ft long. How high is a flagpole that casts a shadow 15 ft long?   **27 ft**

For Example 2

Find the distance, *UV*, across the pond shown below. $\triangle STU$ is similar to $\triangle WVU$.   The pond is 105 meters across.

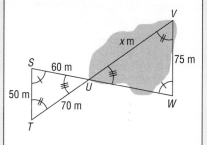

For Example 3

a. **Suppose in Chalkboard Example 2, $\overline{VW}$ is 90 meters long. Find x.   126 m**

b. **Suppose in Chalkboard Example 3, $\overline{ST}$ is 40 meters long. Find x.   131.25 m**

Reteaching Masters Booklet, p. 105

NAME _____ DATE _____

15-4 **Reteaching Worksheet**

Similar Triangles

Triangle *RST* is *similar* to triangle *XYZ*. The angles of the two triangles are congruent. They are called **corresponding angles**. The sides opposite corresponding angles are called **corresponding sides**. Proportions can be used to find the missing measures of similar triangles.

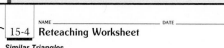

Similar Triangles	If two triangles are similar, the measures of their corresponding angles are equal and the measures of their corresponding sides are proportional.

Example: Find the height of the apartment building.
$\triangle ABC$ is similar to $\triangle AED$.

$$\frac{ED}{BC} = \frac{AD}{AC}$$

$$\frac{7}{x} = \frac{25}{300}$$

$$25x = 2100$$

$$x = 84$$

The apartment building is 84 meters high.

Refer to the triangles at the right to answer the questions.

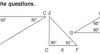

1. Which triangles are similar?
   $\triangle ABC$ and $\triangle HIG$
2. Name corresponding angles of the similar triangles.
   $\angle A$ and $\angle H$; $\angle B$ and $\angle I$; $\angle C$ and $\angle G$
3. Name corresponding sides of the similar triangles.
   $\overline{AB}$ and $\overline{HI}$; $\overline{AC}$ and $\overline{HG}$; $\overline{BC}$ and $\overline{IG}$

Solve.

4. Bruce likes to amuse his brother by shining a flashlight on his hand and making a shadow on the wall. How far is it from the flashlight to the wall?
   4.3 ft

EVALUATING THE LESSON

Checking for Understanding

Exercises 1-8 are designed to help you assess understanding through reading, writing, and speaking. You should work through Exercises 1-2 with your students, and then monitor their work on Exercises 3-8.

Error Analysis

In identifying similar triangles, students sometimes are careless in making sure corresponding vertices are given in same order. To check, make sure the angles at vertices given in corresponding order are congruent.

Closing the Lesson

Speaking Activity Have students explain how they can use proportions to find the missing measures of similar triangles.

Practice Masters Booklet, p. 119

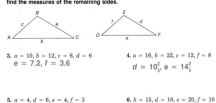

NAME _____ DATE _____

15-4 **Practice Worksheet**

Similar Triangles

Determine whether each pair of triangles is similar.

1. yes   2. no

$\triangle ABC$ and $\triangle DEF$ are similar. For each set of measures given, find the measures of the remaining sides.

3. $a = 10, b = 12, c = 6, d = 6$
   $e = 7.2, f = 3.6$

4. $a = 16, b = 22, c = 12, f = 8$
   $d = 10\frac{2}{3}, e = 14\frac{2}{3}$

5. $a = 4, d = 6, e = 4, f = 3$
   $c = 2, b = 2\frac{2}{3}$

6. $b = 15, d = 16, e = 20, f = 10$
   $c = 7\frac{1}{2}, a = 12$

7. $c = 4, d = 12, e = 16, f = 8$
   $a = 6, b = 8$

8. $e = 20, a = 24, b = 30, c = 15$
   $f = 10, d = 16$

9. $a = 2.5, b = 3, f = 5.5, e = 7$
   $c = 2\frac{5}{14}, d = 5\frac{5}{6}$

10. $c = 1.25, d = 6, e = 3.75, f = 2.50$
    $a = 3, b = 1.875$

CHECKING FOR UNDERSTANDING

Communicating Mathematics

Read and study the lesson to answer each question. **See margin.**

1. In Example 2, name the pairs of corresponding angles.

2. If two triangles are similar, list two things you know about the triangles.

Guided Practice

If $\triangle BIG \sim \triangle RED$, complete each of the following. 5. $\frac{BI}{RE} = \frac{IG}{ED}, \frac{BI}{RE} = \frac{BG}{RD}, \frac{IG}{ED} = \frac{BG}{RD}$

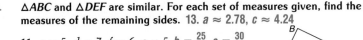

3. List the corresponding angles. $\angle B$ and $\angle R$, $\angle I$ and $\angle E$, $\angle G$ and $\angle D$

4. List the corresponding sides. $\overline{BI}$ and $\overline{RE}, \overline{IG}$ and $\overline{ED}, \overline{BG}$ and $\overline{RD}$

5. List three proportions that correspond to these triangles.

For each pair of similar triangles, name the triangle that is similar to $\triangle ABC$. Make sure you have the letters in the correct order.

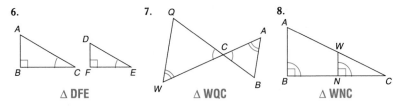

6. $\triangle DFE$ 7. $\triangle WQC$ 8. $\triangle WNC$

EXERCISES

Practice

Determine if each pair of triangles is similar.

A

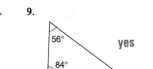

9. yes   10. no

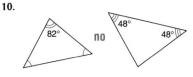

B

$\triangle ABC$ and $\triangle DEF$ are similar. For each set of measures given, find the measures of the remaining sides. 13. $a \approx 2.78, c \approx 4.24$

11. $a = 5, d = 7, f = 6, e = 5$ $b = \frac{25}{7}, c = \frac{30}{7}$

12. $c = 11, f = 6, d = 5, e = 4$ $a = \frac{55}{6}, b = \frac{22}{3}$

13. $b = 4.5, d = 2.1, e = 3.4, f = 3.2$

14. $a = 16, c = 12, b = 13, e = 7$ $d = \frac{112}{13}, f = \frac{84}{13}$

15. $a = 17, b = 15, c = 10, f = 6$ $d = \frac{51}{5}, e = 9$

16. $c = 18, f = 12, d = 18, e = 16$ $a = 27, b = 24$

C

17. $a = 4\frac{1}{4}, b = 5\frac{1}{2}, e = 2\frac{3}{4}, f = 1\frac{3}{4}$ $c = \frac{7}{2}, d = \frac{17}{8}$

18. $c = 7\frac{1}{2}, f = 5, a = 10\frac{1}{2}, b = 15$ $d = 7, e = 10$

19. $c = 5, f = 2.5, a = 12.6, e = 8.1$ $b = 16.2, d = 6.3$

Additional Answers

1. $\angle Y$ and $\angle V$, $\angle Q$ and $\angle T$, $\angle W$ and $\angle M$

2. The measures of their corresponding sides are proportional, and the measures of their corresponding angles are equal.

Critical Thinking

20. Find the value of x. $7\frac{1}{2}$

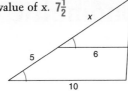

21. △ABC and △RST are similar. If the ratio of AC to RT is 2 to 3, what is the ratio of the area of △ABC to the area of △RST? **4:9**

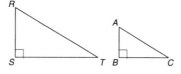

Applications

22. **Construction** In building a roof, a 5-foot support is to be placed at point B as shown on the diagram. Find the length of the support that is to be placed at point A. **13 ft 11 in.**

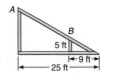

23. **Surveying** △ABC is similar to △EDC. Find the distance across the lake from point A to point B. **105 m**

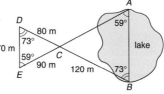

24. **Cinematography** When a movie theater is being designed, the size of the screen depends on the placement of the projector lens. Suppose a theater requires a screen 14 feet wide (DE). The distance from the projector to the screen (AC) is 90 feet. The film is 0.87 inches wide (FG). Find the focal length (AB) of the lens needed for this theater to the nearest tenth of an inch. **5.6 in.**

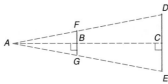

Mixed Review

25. Solve $13 - 8x = 5x + 2$. **(Lesson 3-6)** $\frac{11}{13}$

26. Find $\frac{6}{a^2 - 2ab + b^2} - \frac{6}{a - b}$. **(Lesson 8-7)** $\frac{6 - 6a + 6b}{a^2 - 2ab + b^2}$

27. Solve the system $2x + y = 8$ and $x - y = 3$. **(Lesson 11-4)** $\left(\frac{11}{3}, \frac{2}{3}\right)$

28. Simplify $\sqrt{48} - \sqrt{12} + \sqrt{300}$. **(Lesson 12-6)** $12\sqrt{3}$

29. Solve $x^2 - 4x + 1 = 0$ by completing the square. **(Lesson 13-4)** $2 \pm \sqrt{3}$

30. **Statistics** Olivia swims the 50-yard freestyle for the Wachung High School swim team. Her times in the last six meets were 26.89 seconds, 26.27 seconds, 25.18 seconds, 25.63 seconds, 27.16 seconds, and 27.18 seconds. Find the mean and median of her times. **(Lesson 14-3)** **26.385, 26.58**

31. The length of the side opposite the 60° angle in a 30°–60° right triangle is $5\sqrt{3}$ cm. Find the length of the other two sides. **(Lesson 15-3)** **5, 10**

EXTENDING THE LESSON

Math Power:
Problem Solving

Suppose a man is 180 cm tall. His image on the film of a camera is 1.5 cm tall. If the film is 2 cm from the lens of the camera, how far is the man from the camera? **240 cm**

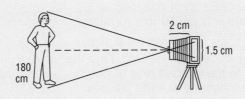

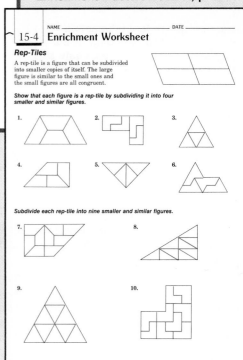

INTRODUCING THE LESSON

5-Minute Check
(over Lesson 15-4)

1. If △NBC ~ △FOX, then $\frac{BC}{?} = \frac{CN}{?}$.   OX; XF

2. Name the triangle that is similar to △SIM.   △LPM

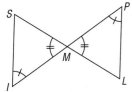

3. What is the value of x?   35

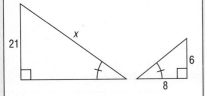

4. A tree five feet tall casts a shadow two feet long. At the same time, a flagpole casts a shadow nine feet long. How tall is the flagpole?   22.5 ft tall

Motivating the Lesson
The steepest streets in the U.S. are Filbert Street, 22nd Street, and Russian Hill in San Francisco. They rise 1 foot for every 3.17 feet. Using trigonometry, the students will be able to find the angle these streets form with the horizontal. approximately 17.5°

15-5 Trigonometric Ratios

Objectives   After studying this lesson, you should be able to:

15-5A   ▪ compute the sine, cosine, and tangent of an acute angle of a right triangle given the measures of its sides, and

15-5B   ▪ find the measure of an acute angle of a right triangle given a trigonometric value or the lengths of two of the sides.

If enough is known about a right triangle, certain ratios can be used to find the measures of the remaining parts of the triangle. These ratios are called **trigonometric ratios**.

A typical right triangle is shown at the right.

a is the measure of the side *opposite* ∠A, $\overline{BC}$.
b is the measure of the side *opposite* ∠B, $\overline{AC}$.
c is the measure of the side *opposite* ∠C, $\overline{AB}$.

a is *adjacent* to ∠B and ∠C.
b is *adjacent* to ∠A and ∠C.
c is *adjacent* to ∠A and ∠B.

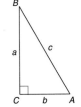

Recall that the side opposite ∠C, the right angle, is called the **hypotenuse**. The other two sides are called **legs**.

Teaching Tip ❶   Three common trigonometric ratios are defined as follows.

Definition of Trigonometric Ratios

$$\text{sine of } \angle A = \frac{\text{measure of side opposite } \angle A}{\text{measure of hypotenuse}}$$

$$\sin A = \frac{a}{c}$$

$$\text{cosine of } \angle A = \frac{\text{measure of side adjacent to } \angle A}{\text{measure of hypotenuse}}$$

$$\cos A = \frac{b}{c}$$

$$\text{tangent of } \angle A = \frac{\text{measure of side opposite } \angle A}{\text{measure of side adjacent to } \angle A}$$

$$\tan A = \frac{a}{b}$$

Notice that sine, cosine, and tangent are abbreviated as sin, cos, and tan, respectively.

ALTERNATE TEACHING STRATEGIES

Using Connections
The length in miles, ℓ, along the surface of Earth of one degree longitude is given by this formula. $\ell = \frac{2\pi (4000 \cos x)}{360}$, where x is the number of degrees latitude. Find the length to the nearest mile of one degree longitude at each latitude.
a. 30° latitude   60 miles
b. 60° latitude   35 miles
c. 90° latitude   0 miles

Example 1

Find the sine, cosine, and tangent of each acute angle. Round your answers to the nearest thousandth.

Use the Pythagorean Theorem to find the value of y.

$$7^2 + 24^2 = y^2$$
$$49 + 576 = y^2$$
$$625 = y^2$$
$$25 = y$$

$\sin N = \dfrac{\text{opposite leg}}{\text{hypotenuse}}$

$\sin N = \dfrac{7}{25}$ or 0.280

$\cos N = \dfrac{\text{adjacent leg}}{\text{hypotenuse}}$

$\cos N = \dfrac{24}{25}$ or 0.960

$\tan N = \dfrac{\text{opposite leg}}{\text{adjacent leg}}$

$\tan N = \dfrac{7}{24}$ or about 0.292

$\sin Q = \dfrac{\text{opposite leg}}{\text{hypotenuse}}$

$\sin Q = \dfrac{24}{25}$ or 0.960

$\cos Q = \dfrac{\text{adjacent leg}}{\text{hypotenuse}}$

$\cos Q = \dfrac{7}{25}$ or 0.280

$\tan Q = \dfrac{\text{opposite leg}}{\text{adjacent leg}}$

$\tan Q = \dfrac{24}{7}$ or about 3.429

Consider triangles *MTP* and *DFE*. Since corresponding angles have the same measure, $\triangle MTP \sim \triangle DFE$. In similar triangles, the corresponding sides are proportional.

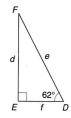
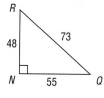

$$\frac{d}{m} = \frac{e}{p}$$

$$\frac{m}{e} \cdot \frac{d}{m} = \frac{m}{e} \cdot \frac{e}{p} \qquad \textit{Multiply each side by } \frac{m}{e}.$$

$$\frac{d}{e} = \frac{m}{p}$$

$$\sin D = \sin M$$

In general, the sine of a 62° angle of a right triangle will be the same number no matter how big or small the triangle is. A similar result holds for cosine and tangent.

Values of trigonometric functions can be found using the table on page 646 or by using a calculator.

Example 2

Find the value of sin 62° to the nearest ten thousandth.

Use a calculator.

Enter: 62 [SIN] 0.8829476   *The calculator must be in degree mode.*

Rounded to the nearest ten thousandth, sin 62° ≈ 0.8829.

Teaching Tip ① SOH-CAH-TOA is a helpful mnemonic device for remembering these ratios.

$\sin = \dfrac{\text{opposite}}{\text{hypotenuse}}$ or $s = \dfrac{o}{h}$

$\cos = \dfrac{\text{adjacent}}{\text{hypotenuse}}$ or $c = \dfrac{a}{h}$

$\tan = \dfrac{\text{opposite}}{\text{adjacent}}$ or $t = \dfrac{o}{a}$

Chalkboard Examples

For Example 1

Find the sine, cosine, and tangent of each acute angle to the nearest thousandth.

sin Q = 0.658
cos Q = 0.753
tan Q = 0.873
sin R = 0.753
cos R = 0.658
tan R = 1.146

For Example 2

For each exercise, the measures of the sides of triangle *ABC* are given. Express the sine, cosine, and tangent of angle *A* to the nearest thousandth.

a. $AC = 12$, $BC = 16$, $AB = 20$

$\sin A = \dfrac{16}{20} = 0.800$

$\cos A = \dfrac{12}{20} = 0.600$

$\tan A = \dfrac{16}{12} = 1.333$

b. $AC = 8$, $BC = 6$, $AB = 10$

$\sin A = \dfrac{6}{10} = 0.600$

$\cos A = \dfrac{8}{10} = 0.800$

$\tan A = \dfrac{6}{8} = 0.750$

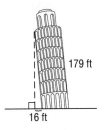
Example 3

Find the measure of ∠H to the nearest degree.

Use the cosine since the lengths of the side adjacent to ∠H and the hypotenuse are given.

$$\cos H = \frac{\text{adjacent leg}}{\text{hypotenuse}}$$

$$= \frac{8}{9}$$

Use a calculator.

Enter: 8 ÷ 9 = INV COS 27.266044   *The inverse key "undoes" the original function.*

To the nearest degree, the measure of ∠H is 27°.

Example 4

APPLICATION

Transportation

The steepest grade of any standard railway system in the world is in France between Chedde and Servoz. The slope of the track is $\frac{1}{11}$. Find the measure of the angle formed by the track between Chedde and Servoz with the horizontal.

Make a model.

$$\text{slope} = \frac{\text{rise}}{\text{run}} = \frac{1}{11}$$

Since the length of the opposite and adjacent sides are known, use the tangent.

$$\tan x° = \frac{\text{opposite leg}}{\text{adjacent leg}}$$

$$= \frac{1}{11}$$

$$= 0.090909 \quad \text{\textit{Use a calculator to find x.}}$$

$$x \approx 5.1944$$

To the nearest degree, the measure of the angle is 5°.

Example 5

APPLICATION

Physics

When a beam of light in air enters water, the beam is bent. According to Snell's Law, $\frac{\sin y°}{\sin x°} = 0.752$. If $x = 30$, find y to the nearest degree.

$$\frac{\sin y°}{\sin 30°} = 0.752 \quad \text{\textit{Use a calculator to find sin 30°.}}$$

$$\frac{\sin y°}{0.5} = 0.752$$

$$\sin y° = (0.5)(0.752)$$

$$\sin y° = 0.376 \quad \text{\textit{Use a calculator to find y.}}$$

$$y \approx 22.086$$

air

water

To the nearest degree, the measure of the angle is 22°.

RETEACHING THE LESSON

Given a trigonometric ratio of an angle, find the other two ratios for the angle by using a drawing of the relative lengths of a representative right triangle. For example, given $\sin A = \frac{3}{5}$, then the triangle at the right would be a representative right triangle.

$\cos A = \frac{4}{5}$; $\tan A = \frac{3}{4}$

CHECKING FOR UNDERSTANDING

Communicating Mathematics

Read and study the lesson to answer each question.

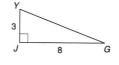

1. What is the measure of the leg opposite ∠Y? **8**

2. What is the measure of the leg adjacent to ∠Y? **3**

3. What trigonometric ratio or ratios involve the measure of the hypotenuse? **sine and cosine**

4. What trigonometric ratio or ratios do *not* involve the measure of the hypotenuse? **tangent**

Guided Practice

Using △NTK express each trigonometric ratio as a fraction.

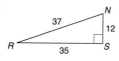

5. sin N $\frac{9}{41}$ 6. sin K $\frac{40}{41}$

7. cos N $\frac{40}{41}$ 8. cos K $\frac{9}{41}$

9. tan N $\frac{9}{40}$ 10. tan K $\frac{40}{9}$

11. Are ∠N and ∠K complementary angles? **yes**

12. What is true about the sine of an angle and the cosine of that angle's complement? **They are equal.**

Use a calculator to find the value of each trigonometric ratio to the nearest ten thousandth.

13. cos 25° **0.9063**   14. tan 31° **0.6009**   15. sin 71° **0.9455**

16. cos 64° **0.4384**   17. tan 9° **0.1584**   18. sin 2° **0.0349**

EXERCISES

See margin.

Practice

A

For each triangle, find sin N, cos N, and tan N to the nearest thousandth.

19.   20.   21.
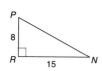   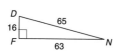

22.   23.   24.

Additional Answers

19. sin N = 0.246, cos N = 0.969, tan N = 0.254

20. sin N = 0.946, cos N = 0.324, tan N = 2.917

21. sin N = 0.600, cos N = 0.800, tan N = 0.750

22. sin N = 0.471, cos N = 0.882, tan N = 0.533

23. sin N = 0.724, cos N = 0.690, tan N = 1.050

24. sin N = 0.753, cos N = 0.658, tan N = 1.146

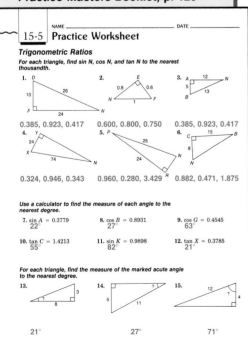

 Use a calculator to find the measure of each angle to the nearest degree. 25. 16° 26. 32° 27. 75°

25. $\sin A = 0.2756$ 26. $\cos B = 0.8480$ 27. $\cos W = 0.2598$
28. $\sin N = 0.6124$ **38°**   29. $\tan V = 0.956$ **44°**   30. $\tan Q = 7.84$ **83°**

For each triangle, find the measure of the marked acute angle to the nearest degree.

31.
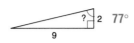
77°

32.
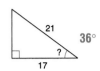
10°

33.
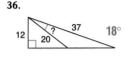
36°

 34.

53°

35.
49°

36.
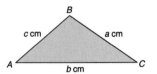
18°

37. The formula $\text{area} = \frac{1}{2}bc \sin A$ can be used to find the area of any triangle. Find the area of the triangle at the right to the nearest tenth of a square centimeter if $b = 16$, $c = 9$, and $\angle A$ is a 36° angle. **42.3 cm²**

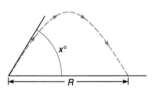

Critical Thinking

38. Use the triangle at the right to determine which of the following statements are true. Justify your answers. **a, d, e; See margin.**

   a. $\sin Z = \cos Y$

   b. $\cos Y = \frac{1}{\sin Y}$

   c. $\tan Z = \frac{\cos Z}{\sin Z}$

   d. $\tan Z = \frac{\sin Z}{\cos Z}$

   e. $\sin Y = (\tan Y)(\cos Y)$

Applications

39. **Physics** When an object is fired into the air, its path forms a parabola. The range of the object is given by $R = \frac{v^2}{g} \sin(2x)°$, where v is the velocity of the object when fired in feet/second, x is the angle at which the object is fired, and g is 32 feet/second². Find the range to the nearest foot of an object fired at 40 feet per second on an angle of 35°. **47 feet**

Additional Answers

Measures of sides and angles are rounded to the nearest tenth. Trigonometric ratios are rounded to the nearest thousandth.

42a. 5; 36.9°, 53.1°; sin A1 = 0.600, sin A2 = 0.800; cos A1 = 0.800, cos A2 = 0.600, tan A1 = 0.750, tan A2 = 1.333

42b. 13; 22.6°, 67.4°; sin A1 = 0.385, sin A2 = 0.923;

cos A1 = 0.923, cos A2 = 0.385, tan A1 = 0.417, tan A2 = 2.400

42c. 44.7; 26.6°, 63.4°; sin A1 = 0.447, sin A2 = 0.894; cos A1 = 0.894, cos A2 = 0.447, tan A1 = 0.500, tan A2 = 2.000

42d. 160.1; 51.3°, 38.7°; sin A1 = 0.781, sin A2 = 0.625; cos A1 = 0.625, cos A2 = 0.781, tan A1 = 1.250, tan A2 = 0.800

40. Meteorology The mean temperature in Chicago on the nth day of the year can be estimated using the formula

$$t = 25.5 \sin\left[\frac{360}{365}(n - 106)\right]^{\circ} + 50,$$

where t is the mean temperature for the day in degrees Fahrenheit. Find the mean temperature on October 1 (the 274th day of the year) to the nearest degree. **56°F**

41. Physics Refer to the diagram in Example 5. The following equation is also true.

$$\frac{\sin y^{\circ}}{\sin x^{\circ}} = \frac{\text{the speed of light in water}}{\text{the speed of light in air}}$$

The speed of light in air is about 3×10^8 meters/second. If $x = 40$, find y to the nearest degree using Snell's Law. Find the speed of light in water to two significant digits. **29°; 2.3×10^8 m/s**

Computer

42. Given the lengths of the legs of a right triangle, this BASIC program computes the length of the hypotenuse, the measures of the acute angles, and the values of the trigonometric ratios for each acute angle.

```
10 INPUT "ENTER THE LENGTHS OF
      THE LEGS: ";L1,L2
20 LET P = 3.1415927
30 LET H = SQR(L1^2 + L2^2)
40 LET A1 = ATN(L1/L2) * 180/P
50 LET A2 = ATN(L2/L1) * 180/P
60 PRINT "SIDES: ";L1;" , ";L2;" , ";H
70 PRINT "ANGLES: ";A1;" , ";A2;" , 90"
80 PRINT "SIN(";A1;") = ";L1/H
90 PRINT "SIN(";A2;") = ";L2/H
100 PRINT "COS(";A1;") = ";L2/H
110 PRINT "COS(";A2;") = ";L1/H
120 PRINT "TAN(";A1;") = ";L1/L2
130 PRINT "TAN(";A2;") = ";L2/L1
140 END
```

Given the lengths of the legs of each right triangle, use the program to find the length of the hypotenuse, the angle measures, and the trigonometric ratios of the acute angles. See margin. Teaching Tip ②

a. 3, 4   **b.** 5, 12   **c.** 20, 40   **d.** 125, 100

Mixed Review

43. Nineteen is what percent of 76? **(Lesson 4-1) 25%**

44. State the domain and range of $\{(1, 1), (2, 4), (-2, 4), (3, 9)\}$. **(Lesson 9-2) $\{1, 2, -2, 3\}$, $\{1, 4, 9\}$**

45. Solve the system $3x - 2y = 10$ and $x + y = 0$ by graphing. **(Lesson 11-1) $(2, -2)$**

46. Simplify $\sqrt{120a^3b}$. **(Lesson 12-5) $2|a|\sqrt{30ab}$**

47. Statistics The Goodwill Games were first held in Moscow in July 1985. The total number of medals won by the top eleven countries are 241, 28, 31, 18, 6, 10, 6, 142, 9, 11, and 6. Find the interquartile range. **(Lesson 14-4) 25**

LESSON 15-5 TRIGONOMETRIC RATIOS   631

EXTENDING THE LESSON

Math Power: Problem Solving

Use $\triangle DEF$ to find each value to the nearest thousandth.

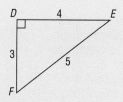

1. $\sin F + \tan F$ **2.13**
2. $(\tan E)(\sin E)$ **0.45**
3. $\tan F - \tan E$ **0.583**
4. $1 - (\tan E)(\tan F)$ **0**

Teaching Tip ② The program prints out the sides and angles so that the angles are opposite the respective sides. Point out to students that computers process angle measures in radians. In lines 40 and 50, the angle is calculated in radians by means of the ATN or arctan function and is multiplied by $\left(\frac{180}{\pi}\right)$ to convert to degrees. Note the use of the Pythagorean Theorem in line 30 to find the hypotenuse.

Enrichment Masters Booklet, p. 106

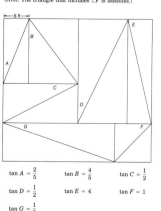

NAME _____ DATE _____

15-5   **Enrichment Worksheet**

Modern Art

Modern Art

The painting below, aptly titled, "Right Triangles," was painted by that well-known artist Two-loose La-Rectangle. Using the information below, find the dimensions of this masterpiece. (*Hint:* The triangle that includes $\angle F$ is isosceles.)

$\tan A = \frac{2}{5}$ $\tan B = \frac{4}{5}$ $\tan C = \frac{1}{2}$

$\tan D = \frac{1}{2}$ $\tan E = 4$ $\tan F = 1$

$\tan G = \frac{1}{3}$

1. What is the length of the painting?   33 ft

2. What is the width of the painting?   36 ft

Lesson Resources

- Reteaching Master 15-6
- Practice Master 15-6
- Enrichment Master 15-6
- Video Algebra, 59-60

 Transparency 15-6 contains the 5-Minute Check and a teaching aid for this lesson.

INTRODUCING THE LESSON

 5-Minute Check

(over Lesson 15-5)

For the triangle below, express each trigonometric ratio as a fraction in simplest form.

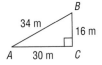

1. sin A $\frac{8}{17}$
2. sin B $\frac{15}{17}$
3. cos B $\frac{8}{17}$
4. cos A $\frac{15}{17}$
5. tan A $\frac{8}{15}$

Motivating the Lesson

The American Forestry Association recognizes a national champion of each species of tree in the United States. The size (T) of a tree is computed using the following formula.

$T = \frac{1}{2}$(circumference in inches measured $4\frac{1}{2}$ feet off the ground) + (total height in feet) + $\frac{1}{4}$(average crown spread in feet)

The national champion weeping willow is in Asheville, NC and is 114 feet tall. It would be difficult to measure this height directly. Using a sextant or other device to measure angles, it is possible to find the heights of objects indirectly without resorting to mirrors or shadows.

Objectives

15-6A
15-6B

After studying this lesson, you should be able to:
- use trigonometric ratios to solve verbal problems, and
- use trigonometric ratios to solve right triangles.

Solving a triangle means to find all of its missing measures.

Example 1

Solve △PQR.

The measure of ∠R is 90° − 36° or 54°.

$\sin 36° = \frac{x}{18}$

$0.5878 \approx \frac{x}{18}$

$10.6 \approx x$

Thus, $\overline{QR}$ is about 10.6 inches long.

$\cos 36° = \frac{y}{18}$

$0.8090 \approx \frac{y}{18}$

$14.6 \approx y$

Thus, $\overline{PQ}$ is about 14.6 inches long.

When using trigonometric ratios to solve problems, you will often deal with angles of elevation and depression. An **angle of elevation** is formed by a horizontal line and another line of sight above it. An **angle of depression** is formed by a horizontal line and another line of sight below it.

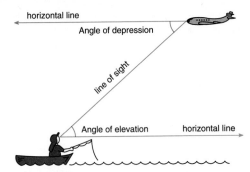

These concepts are used with trigonometric ratios to find missing measures of right triangles. Sometimes these measures are difficult to obtain directly.

ALTERNATE TEACHING STRATEGIES

Using Manipulatives

You can make an instrument which can measure angles of elevation or depression by attaching a weight to the center of a protractor. Students should be able to tell you that the angle measure at which the string crosses the protractor is the complement of the angle of elevation.

Example 2

The National Champion Elm Tree in Louisville, Kansas is 97 feet tall. As you are walking in your neighborhood, you notice a tall elm tree. Could this tree be taller than the National Champion? You walk 50 feet from the base of the tree. From this position, the angle of elevation to the top of the tree is 65°. Find the height of the tree to the nearest foot.

First, make a model. Notice that 50 feet is the length of the leg adjacent to the 65° angle and h is the length of the leg opposite the 65° angle. The tangent ratio should be used to solve this problem.

$$\tan 65° = \frac{\text{opposite leg}}{\text{adjacent leg}}$$

$$\tan 65° = \frac{h}{50}$$

$$2.1445 \approx \frac{h}{50}$$

$$2.1445(50) \approx h$$

$$107.225 \approx h \qquad \text{The tree is about 107 feet tall.}$$

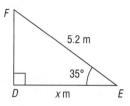

Example 3

Jack is fishing for salmon. He has 60 yards of line in the water, and the angle of depression to the lure is 20°. Find the lowest possible depth of the lure.

$$\sin 20° = \frac{\text{opposite leg}}{\text{hypotenuse}}$$

$$0.3420 \approx \frac{d}{60}$$

$$60\,(0.3420) \approx d$$

$$20.52 \approx d$$

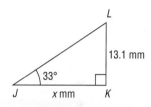

The lure could be at most about 21 yards below the surface.

Example 4

Alexis Martin has been hired to roof houses during the summer. She needs to purchase an extension ladder that reaches at least 24 feet off the ground. Ladder manufacturers recommend the angle formed by the ladder and the ground be no more than 75°. What is the shortest ladder she could buy to reach 24 feet safely?

$$\sin 75° = \frac{\text{opposite leg}}{\text{hypotenuse}}$$

$$0.9659 \approx \frac{24}{c}$$

$$0.9659c \approx 24$$

$$c \approx \frac{24}{0.9659}$$

$$c \approx 24.847$$

To the nearest foot, the ladder should be at least 25 feet long.

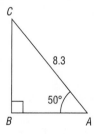

LESSON 15-6 SOLVING RIGHT TRIANGLES 633

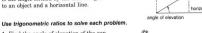
CHECKING FOR UNDERSTANDING

Communicating Mathematics

Read and study the lesson to answer each question.

1. In Example 1, once you know x is about 10.6, how could you find y without using trigonometry? **Use the Pythagorean Theorem.**

2. In all four examples you were given a right angle and the measures of two other parts of the triangle. Can you think of a right triangle in which you were given two other parts and could not solve the triangle? **If you were given the two acute angle measures only, you could not solve the triangle.**

Guided Practice Name the angles of elevation and depression in each drawing.

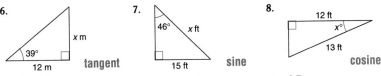

3. ∠FED; ∠EDG   4. ∠JKL; ∠MJK   5. ∠QRP; ∠SPR

State which trigonometric ratio you could use to find x.

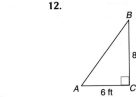

6. **tangent**   7. **sine**   8. **cosine**

9. Find the value of x in Exercise 6 to the nearest tenth. **9.7**
10. Find the value of x in Exercise 8 to the nearest degree. **23**

EXERCISES

Practice Solve each triangle. Give side lengths to the nearest tenth and angle measures to the nearest degree. **See margin.**

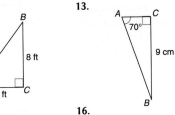

A   11.   12.   13.

14.   15.   16.

Use trigonometric ratios to solve each problem.

17. At a point 200 feet from the base of a flagpole, the angle of elevation is 62°. Find the height of the flagpole and the distance from the point to the top. **376 ft, 426 ft**

18. A guy wire is fastened to a TV tower 40 feet above the ground and forms an angle of 52° with the tower. How long is the wire? **65 ft**

19. A chimney casts a shadow 75 feet long when the angle of elevation of the sun is 41°. How tall is the chimney? **65 ft**

20. In a parking garage, there are 20 feet between each level. Each ramp to a level is 130 feet long. Find the measure of the angle of elevation of each ramp. **9°**

21. Find the area of a right triangle in which one acute angle measures 25° and the leg opposite that angle is 40 cm long. **1716 cm²**

22. From the top of a 70-meter lighthouse, an airplane was observed that was directly over a ship. The angle of elevation of the plane was 18°, while the angle of depression of the ship was 25°. Find the distance from the ship to the foot of the lighthouse and the height of the plane.

23. A weather balloon is directly above a tree. The angle of elevation is 60° when you are 100 meters from the tree. How high is the balloon?

24. A train in the mountains rises 15 feet for every 250 feet it moves along the track. Find the angle of elevation of the track.
22. 150.1 m, 118.8 m   23. 173.2 m   24. about 3.4°

Critical Thinking

25. Find the equation of this line in slope-intercept form.
y = 0.5543x + 5

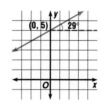

26. Solve the triangle. (*Hint:* Draw an altitude from *B*.)
∠B = 120°, AC = 20.1 m, BC = 16.4 m

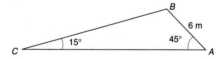

Applications

27. **Space Travel** An astronaut in a spacecraft *h* miles from Earth measures the angle (∠ABD) formed by the lines of sight to the Earth's horizon to be 80°. Use right triangle *ABC* to find *h* to the nearest mile. **2223 mi**

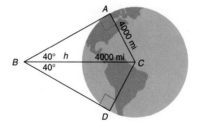

LESSON 15-6   SOLVING RIGHT TRIANGLES   635

Chapter 15, Quiz D, (Lessons 15-5 through 15-6), is available in the Evaluation Masters Booklet, p. 206.

Practice Masters Booklet, p. 121

NAME _____   DATE _____

15-6 | Practice Worksheet

Solving Right Triangles

Solve each triangle. Give side lengths to the nearest tenth and angle measures to the nearest degree.

1.
c = 50 ft,
∠A = 74°,
∠B = 16°

2.
c = 11.7 m,
b = 11.0 m,
∠A = 20°

3.
∠A = 45°,
a = 1 yd,
c = 1.4 yd

4.
b = 5.2 km,
a = 7.4 km,
∠A = 55°

5.
c = 12.8 in.,
∠A = 39°,
∠B = 51°

6.
∠A = 65°, b
c = 11.8 cm,
a = 10.7 cm

Use trigonometric ratios to solve each problem.

7. The guy wire supporting a utility pole is 3 meters long. If it makes an angle of 78° with the ground, how far up the pole is it attached?
2.9 m

8. A 20-foot ladder is leaning against the side of a house. The bottom of the ladder is about 8 feet from the wall. Find the angle the ladder forms with the ground.
66°

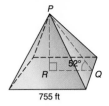

28. **Archaeology** The largest of the Pyramids of Egypt has a square base with sides 755 feet long. ∠RQP has a measure of 52°. The top of the pyramid is no longer there. What was the pyramid's original height ($\overline{PR}$) to the nearest foot? **483 ft**

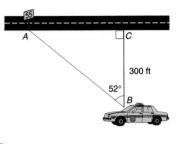

29. **Law Enforcement** A state trooper has positioned her car at point B, 300 feet from the road to be patrolled. She sights a road sign at point A so that the measure of ∠B is 52°. If the speed limit is 65 mph (95.3 feet per second), what is the shortest time a driver can get from A to C without exceeding the speed limit? Give your answer to the nearest tenth of a second. **4.0 seconds**

30. **Navigation** How far will a submarine travel when going to a depth of 300 feet if its course has an angle of depression of 25°? **709.9 ft**

Mixed Review

31. Solve $0.1x < 0.2x - 8$. **(Lesson 5-3)** $x > 80$

32. What is the slope of the line through $(12, -3)$ and $(14, -7)$? **(Lesson 10-1)** -2

33. Solve the system $2x + y = 3(x - 5)$ and $x + 5 = 4y + 2x$. **(Lesson 11-5)** $x = 13, y = -2$

34. Solve $\sqrt{2x + 7} = 5$. **(Lesson 12-7)** 9

35. How many real roots does $2p^2 - p - 3 = 0$ have? **(Lesson 13-6)** 2

36. Find P (a number divisible by 4) on a roll of a die. **(Lesson 14-7)** $\frac{1}{6}$

37. For what angle are the sine and cosine equal? **(Lesson 15-5)** $45°$

HISTORY CONNECTION

Pythagoras

About 540 B.C., Pythagoras of Samos (585–507 B.C.) founded a school for his followers, called the Pythagoreans, in what is now Italy. The Pythagorean Theorem had been discovered a thousand years earlier by the Babylonians, but the Pythagorean school is credited with proving it. Along with studying numbers, Pythagoras taught his disciples to worship them as well. The number one, they argued, was the generator of all numbers and not considered to be an odd number, all even numbers were considered to be feminine, and all odd numbers masculine. Five was the number for marriage, since it was the sum of the first even number and the first odd number. The holiest number of all was ten, for it was the number of the universe. Philolaus, a Pythagorean, once wrote that the number ten was "great, all-powerful and all-producing, the beginning and the guide of the divine as of the terrestrial life."

636 CHAPTER 15 TRIGONOMETRY

EXTENDING THE LESSON

Math Power: Problem Solving

Before *Apollo 11* descended to the surface of the moon, it made one orbit at a distance of 3 miles from the surface. At one point in its orbit, the onboard guidance system measured the angles of depression to the near and far edges of a crater. The angles measured 25° and 18°. Find the distance across the crater. **2.80 mi**

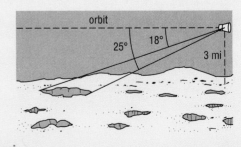

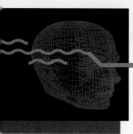

Technology

Trigonometric Functions

BASIC
Graphing calculators
▶ Graphing software
Spreadsheets

Using Technology

Objective This optional page shows how the graphing calculator can be used to perform mathematical computations and to enhance and extend mathematical concepts.

Teaching Suggestions

Explain to students that computers can be programmed to draw the graph mentioned in this feature. You may want to discuss the graphs only with your more advanced students.

A computer can calculate values of trigonometric functions very rapidly. Trigonometric functions usually available in BASIC include SIN, COS, and TAN. The program at the right uses the SIN function to print a table of sines.

The sine function generates ordered pairs. To graph the function, use the horizontal axis for the degree values and the vertical axis for the sine. After plotting the points, connect them with a smooth curve as shown below.

```
10 PRINT "ANGLE", "SINE
20 FOR D = 0 TO 360 STEP 30
30 LET R = D*3.1416/180
40 LET R1 = INT(SIN(R)*1000+.5)/1000
50 PRINT D, R1
60 NEXT D
70 END

RUN
ANGLE        SINE
0            0
30           .5
60           .866
90           1
120          .866
150          .5
180          0
210          -.5
240          -.866
270          -1
300          -.866
330          -.5
360          0
```

$y = \sin x$

EXERCISES

1. Modify the program to print a table of cosines. See margin.

State whether the value of each trigonometric ratio is *positive* or *negative*.

2. sin 30° pos.   **3.** cos 150° neg.   **4.** sin 330° neg.   **5.** cos 60° pos.

State which is greater.

6. cos 30° or cos 90°

7. sin 0° or sin 90°

Find the values of x for which each equation is true.

8. cos x = 1
   0°, 360°

9. sin x = 1
   90°

10. sin x = 0
   0°, 180°, 360°

11. cos x = −1
   180°

TECHNOLOGY: TRIGONOMETRIC FUNCTIONS 637

Additonal Answer

1. Change the following two lines in the program.

10 PRINT "ANGLE", "COSINE"
40 LET R1 = INT(COS(R)*1000+.5)/1000

VOCABULARY

Upon completing this chapter, you should be
familiar with the following terms:

angle of depression	632	626	tangent
angle of elevation	632	617	30°–60° right triangle
complementary angles	611	622	similar triangles
corresponding angles	622	626	sine
corresponding sides	622	610	supplementary angles
cosine	626	615	trigonometric ratios

SKILLS AND CONCEPTS

OBJECTIVES AND EXAMPLES	REVIEW EXERCISES
Upon completing this chapter, you should be able to:	Use these exercises to review and prepare for the chapter test.
■ find the complement and supplement of an angle **(Lesson 15-1)**	**Find both the complement and supplement of each angle measure.**
Find the complement and the supplement of an angle with a measure of 28°.	**1.** 66° 24°, 114°
	2. 62° 28°, 118°
complement: 90° − 28° or 62°	**3.** 148° no complement, 32°
supplement: 180° − 28° or 152°	**4.** y° (90 − y)°, (180 − y)°
■ find the measure of the third angle of a triangle given the measures of the other two angles **(Lesson 15-1)**	**Find the measure of the third angle of each triangle in which the measure of two angles of the triangle are given.**
The measures of two angles of a triangle are 38° and 41°. Find the measure of the third angle.	**5.** 16°, 72° 92°
	6. 41°, 121° 18°
180° − (38° + 41°) or 91°	**7.** 37°, 90° 53°
	8. y°, x° (180 − x − y)°

OBJECTIVES AND EXAMPLES	REVIEW EXERCISES

- find the measures of the sides of a 30°–60° right triangle given the measure of one side **(Lesson 15-3)**

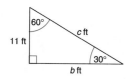

$b = 11\sqrt{3}$ $c = 22$

Find the missing lengths for each 30°–60° right triangle described below. Express irrational answers in simplest radical form.

	Hypotenuse	Side Opposite 30° Angle	Side Opposite 60° Angle
9.	8 cm	? 4 cm	? $4\sqrt{3}$ cm
10.	4.25 cm	? 2.125 cm	? $2.125\sqrt{3}$ cm
11.	? 6 in.	3 in.	? $3\sqrt{3}$ in.
12.	? 4 in.	? 2 in.	$2\sqrt{3}$ in.

- find the unknown measures of the sides of two similar triangles given the measures of four of the sides **(Lesson 15-4)**

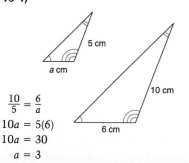

$\dfrac{10}{5} = \dfrac{6}{a}$

$10a = 5(6)$

$10a = 30$

$a = 3$

△ABC and △DEF are similar. For each set of measures, find the missing measures.

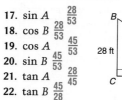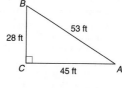

13. $a = 5$, $d = 11$, $f = 6$, $e = 14$ **See margin.**
14. $c = 16$, $b = 12$, $a = 10$, $f = 9$
15. $a = 8$, $c = 10$, $b = 6$, $f = 12$
16. $c = 12$, $f = 9$, $a = 8$, $e = 11$

- compute the sine, cosine, and tangent of an acute angle of a right triangle given the measures of its sides **(Lesson 15-5)**

$\sin A = \dfrac{\text{measure of leg opposite } \angle A}{\text{measure of hypotenuse}}$

$\cos A = \dfrac{\text{measure of leg adjacent to } \angle A}{\text{measure of hypotenuse}}$

$\tan A = \dfrac{\text{measure of leg opposite } \angle A}{\text{measure of leg adjacent to } \angle A}$

For △ABC, express each trigonometric ratio as a fraction in simplest form.

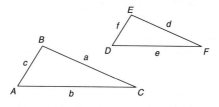

17. $\sin A$ $\dfrac{28}{53}$
18. $\cos B$ $\dfrac{28}{53}$
19. $\cos A$ $\dfrac{45}{53}$
20. $\sin B$ $\dfrac{45}{53}$
21. $\tan A$ $\dfrac{28}{45}$
22. $\tan B$ $\dfrac{45}{28}$

- find the measure of an acute angle of a right triangle given a trigonometric value **(Lesson 15-5)**

$\cos M = 0.3245$

Enter: 0.3245 [INV] [COS] 71.064715

The measure of $\angle M$ is about 71°

Use a calculator to find the measure of each angle to the nearest degree.

23. $\tan M = 0.8043$ **39°**
24. $\sin T = 0.1212$ **7°**
25. $\tan Q = 5.9080$ **80°**
26. $\cos F = 0.7443$ **42°**

Alternate Review Strategy

To provide a brief in-class review, you may wish to read the following questions to the class and require a verbal or written response.

1. Find the complement and supplement of an angle with a measure of 84°.   **6°, 96°**
2. The length of the side opposite the 30° angle in a 30° - 60° right triangle is 12 m. Find the length of the hypotenuse.   **24 m**
3. ∠ABC and ∠DEF are similar. For the set of measures, find the measure of the missing sides.
   $c = 18$, $f = 12$, $d = 18$, $e = 16$
   $a = 27$, $b = 24$
4. Express the sine, cosine, and tangent of each acute angle in each triangle to the nearest thousandth.
   $AC = 16$, $BC = 63$, $AB = 65$
   $\sin A = 0.969$, $\sin B = 0.246$
   $\cos A = 0.246$, $\cos B = 0.969$
   $\tan A = 3.938$, $\tan B = 0.254$

Additional Answers

13. $b = \dfrac{70}{11}$, $c = \dfrac{30}{11}$
14. $d = \dfrac{45}{8}$, $e = \dfrac{27}{4}$
15. $d = \dfrac{48}{5}$, $e = \dfrac{36}{5}$
16. $b = \dfrac{44}{3}$, $d = 6$

OBJECTIVES AND EXAMPLES	REVIEW EXERCISES
■ use trigonometric ratios to solve right triangles **(Lesson 15-6)**	Solve each triangle.

$m\angle B = 40°$ and $c = 6$

$m\angle a = 180° - (90° + 40°)$ or $50°$

$\cos 40° = \dfrac{a}{6}$ $\sin 40° = \dfrac{b}{6}$

$0.7660 \approx \dfrac{a}{6}$ $0.6428 \approx \dfrac{b}{6}$

$0.7660(6) \approx a$ $0.6428(6) \approx b$

$4.596 \approx a$ $3.857 \approx b$

27.
7 m, 62°

28.
9 in., 13 in.

$\angle B = 28°$, $AC \approx 3.7$ m, $AB \approx 7.9$ m

$AC \approx 9.4$ in., $\angle A \approx 46°$, $\angle B \approx 44°$

APPLICATIONS AND CONNECTIONS

Solve by making models. (Lesson 15-2)

29. Sam is making his family tree. He plans to include himself, his parents, his grandparents, his great grandparents, and his great-great grandparents. If Sam does not include any stepparents or stepgrandparents, how many people will he include in his family tree? **31 people**

30. A rectangular swimming pool is 4 meters by 10 meters. A walkway is 1 meter wide and goes around the pool. Find the area of the walkway. **32 m²**

Solve.

31. Find the area of an equilateral triangle if the length of each side is 12 feet. **(Lesson 15-3)** $36\sqrt{3}$ or 62.4 ft²

32. Without using a calculator or a table, find $\sin 30°$. **(Lesson 15-3)** $\dfrac{1}{2}$

33. **Broadcasting** A radio tower casts a shadow 120 meters long when the angle of elevation of the sun is 41°. How tall is the tower? **(Lesson 15-5)** **about 104 m**
x m, 41°, 120 m

34. **Forest Management** From the top of an observation tower 50 meters high, a forest ranger spots a deer at an angle of depression of 28°. How far is the deer from the base of the tower? **(Lesson 15-6)** **about 94 m**

35. **Navigation** An airplane, at an altitude of 2000 feet, is directly over a power plant. The navigator finds the angle of depression of the airport to be 19°. How far is the plane from the airport? How far is the power plant from the airport? **(Lesson 15-6)**
about 6143 ft; about 5808 ft

36. **Construction** A roof is constructed as shown in the diagram below. Find the pitch (angle of elevation) of the roof. **(Lesson 15-5)** **about 29°**

7.75 ft, 14 ft

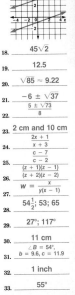

NAME _____ DATE _____

Cumulative Review (Chapters 1–15)

1. State the property shown in $3(4a + b) = 12a + 3b$.
2. Find $-\dfrac{3}{7} + \dfrac{1}{21}$.
3. Six is what percent of 80?
4. Solve $10y - 3(y + 4) \le 0$.
5. Simplify $\dfrac{-36a^2b^3c^4}{24ab^5c^3}$.
6. Peg is driving 30 mi/h. After Peg has driven 20 miles, Darren starts driving in the same direction. If Darren drives 45 mi/h, how long will it take him to catch up to Peg?
7. Factor $1 - 25m^2$.
8. Factor $8a^4 + 6a^2 - 2$.
9. Solve $9t^2 + 16 = 24t$.
10. Use the formula $h = vt - 16t^2$ to solve the following problem.
   A flare is launched with an initial velocity of 448 feet per second. How many seconds will it take the flare to return to the sea?
11. Draw a mapping for the relation $\{(-3, 8), (0, -5), (2, 3), (1, 3), (1, 1)\}$.
12. Graph $3y - x \le 3$.
13. Graph $-4x + 2y = 2$ using the slope-intercept method.
14. Find the coordinates of the midpoint of the line segment whose endpoints are $(8, 10)$ and $(-2, 7)$.
15. Solve the system of equations $3y - 2x = 4$ and $2y + 4x = 8$.
16. A can contains two different kinds of nuts, weighs 5 pounds, and costs $16. One type of nut costs $3.50 a pound. The other type costs $2.75 a pound. How many pounds of $2.75 nuts are there?

1. distributive
2. $-\dfrac{8}{21}$
3. 7.5%
4. $y \le \dfrac{12}{7}$
5. $-\dfrac{3ac}{2b}$
6. $1\dfrac{1}{3}$ hours
7. $(1 - 5m)(1 + 5m)$
8. $2(2a + 1)(2a - 1)(a^2 + 1)$
9. $\dfrac{4}{3}$
10. 28 seconds
11. (mapping)
12. (graph)
13. (graph) $b = 1, m = 2$
14. $\left(3, 8\dfrac{1}{2}\right)$
15. $(1, 2)$
16. 2 pounds at $2.75

NAME _____ DATE _____

Cumulative Review (Chapters 1–15)

17. Graph the equations $x - 3y = 3$ and $x - 3y = -9$. Then state the number of solutions of the system of equations.
18. Simplify $3\sqrt{3} \cdot 5\sqrt{6}$.
19. Solve and check $5 - \sqrt{2x} = 0$.
20. Find the distance between the pairs of points with coordinates $(2, -6)$ and $(8, 1)$.
21. Solve $k^2 + 12k - 1 = 0$ by completing the square.
22. Use the quadratic formula to solve $4n^2 - 5n - 3 = 0$.
23. Find the dimensions of the rectangle whose width is 8 cm less than its length and whose area is 20 cm².
24. Simplify $\dfrac{4x^2 - 8x - 5}{2x^2 + x - 15}$.
25. Find $\dfrac{c^2}{c^2 - 4} - \dfrac{5c + 14}{c^2 - 4}$.
26. Simplify $\dfrac{z - \dfrac{3}{z - 2}}{z - \dfrac{6}{z - 1}}$.
27. Solve $wx - w = \dfrac{x}{y}$ for w.
28. Find the mean, median, and mode of the data represented in the stem-and-leaf plot at the right.

Stem	Leaf
4	2 7
5	1 2 4
6	0 5 5

5 | 4 represents 54.

29. Find both the complement and the supplement for an angle of 63°.
30. The length of the side opposite the 30° angle in a 30°-60° right triangle is 5.5 cm. Find the length of the hypotenuse.
31. Solve right triangle ABC if $\angle C$ is the right angle, the measure of $\angle A = 36°$, and $a = 7$.
32. A picture measures 4 inches by 6 inches. A frame of uniform width is placed around the picture. How wide must the frame be if the area of the frame equals the area of the picture?
33. If $\tan D = 1.4213$ find the measure of $\angle D$ to the nearest degree.

17. no solutions
   (graph)
18. $45\sqrt{2}$
19. 12.5
20. $\sqrt{85} \approx 9.22$
21. $-6 \pm \sqrt{37}$
22. $\dfrac{5 \pm \sqrt{73}}{8}$
23. 2 cm and 10 cm
24. $\dfrac{2x + 1}{x + 3}$
25. $\dfrac{c - 7}{c - 2}$
26. $\dfrac{(z + 1)(z - 1)}{(z + 2)(z - 2)}$
27. $w = \dfrac{x}{y(x - 1)}$
28. $54\dfrac{1}{2}$; 53; 65
29. 27°; 117°
30. 11 cm
31. $\angle B = 54°$, $b = 9.6, c = 11.9$
32. 1 inch
33. 55°

Find both the complement and the supplement of each angle measure.

1. 28° **62°, 152°**   2. 69° **21°, 111°**   3. $(y + 20)°$ **$(70 - y)°$, $(160 - y)°$**

Find the measure of the third angle of each triangle in which the measures of two angles of the triangle are given.

4. 16°, 47° **117°**   5. 89°, 66° **25°**   6. 45°, 120° **15°**

Find the missing lengths for each 30°–60° right triangle described below. Express irrational answers in simplest radical form and in decimal form to the nearest thousandth.

	Hypotenuse	Side Opposite 30° Angle	Side Opposite 60° Angle
7.	17 in.	? **8.5 in.**	? **$8.5\sqrt{3}$ in.**
8.	? **16 ft**	8 ft	? **$8\sqrt{3}$ ft**
9.	? **18 m**	? **9 m**	$9\sqrt{3}$ m

$\triangle ABC$ and $\triangle JKH$ are similar. For each set of measures, find the missing lengths.

10. $c = 20$, $h = 15$, $k = 16$, $j = 12$ **$a = 16$, $b = \frac{64}{3}$**

11. $c = 12$, $b = 13$, $a = 6$, $h = 10$ **$j = 5$, $k = \frac{65}{6}$**

12. $k = 5$, $c = 6.5$, $b = 7.5$, $a = 4.5$ **$j = 3$, $h = \frac{13}{3}$**

13. $h = 1\frac{1}{2}$, $c = 4\frac{1}{2}$, $k = 2\frac{1}{4}$, $a = 3$ **$j = 1$, $b = \frac{27}{4}$**

Solve each triangle. **See margin.**

14.   15. 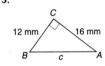   16.   17.

Solve.   19. **about 2923.8 ft**

18. **Recreation** A kite is flying at the end of a 300-foot string. Assuming the string is straight and forms an angle of 58° with the ground, how high is the kite? **about 254.4 ft**

19. **Navigation** A plane is 1000 feet above the ground. The angle of depression of the landing strip is 20°. Find the diagonal distance between the plane and the landing strip.

20. A 6-foot pole casts a 4-foot shadow. How tall is a tree that casts a 50-foot shadow? **75 ft**

Bonus Two buildings are separated by an alley. Joe is looking out of a window 60 feet above the ground in one building. He observes the measurement of the angle of depression of the base of the second building to be 50° and that of the angle of elevation of the top to be 40°. How high is the second building? **about 102 ft**

Test Generator Software is provided in both Apple and IBM versions. You may use this software to create your own tests, based on the needs of your students.

Additional Answers

14. $\angle B = 34°$, $b \approx 11.5$, $c \approx 20.5$
15. $\angle A \approx 37°$, $\angle B \approx 53°$, $c = 20$
16. $\angle A = 48°$, $a \approx 7.4$, $b \approx 6.7$
17. $\angle A \approx 44°$, $\angle B \approx 46°$, $a = 20$

Using the Chapter Test

This page may be used as a test or as a review. In addition, two multiple-choice tests and two free-response tests are provided in the Evaluation Masters Booklet. Chapter 15 Test, Form 1A is shown below.

Evaluation Masters Booklet, pp. 197-198

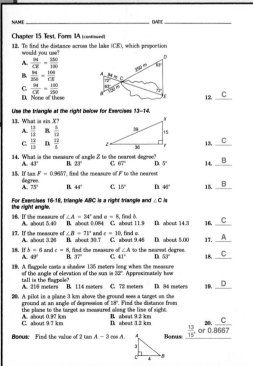

Using the College Entrance Exam Preview

The questions on these pages may be used to help students prepare for college entrance exams such as the SAT test. These questions require careful analysis and a thorough understanding of the concepts.

These pages can be used as an overnight assignment.

After students have completed the pages, discuss how each problem can be solved, or provide copies of the solutions from the *Merrill Algebra 1 Solutions Manual*.

The test questions on these pages deal with expression and equations.

Directions: Choose the best answer. Write A, B, C, or D.

1. What is the average of $70 - c$,
C $70 + 2c$, and $45 - c$?
   (A) 75 (B) $61\frac{2}{3} + \frac{2}{3}c$
   (C) $61\frac{2}{3}$ (D) $75 + c$

2. If $(1 - 2 + 3 - 4 + 5 - 6) = -3$,
A then $2(1 - 2 + 3 - 4 + 5 - 6) =$
   (A) -6 (B) 6 (C) 3 (D) -3

3. If $ab + 6 = 5abc$, then $b =$
D
   (A) $\frac{a + 6}{5c}$ (B) $\frac{6}{a - 5c}$
   (C) $\frac{-6}{5c - a}$ (D) $\frac{6}{5c - a}$

4. If $23(66 + x) = 2300$, then $x =$
C
   (A) 1185 (B) 728
   (C) 34 (D) 44

5. If $3y + 2$ is an odd integer, what is
A the next consecutive odd integer?
   (A) $3y + 4$ (B) $5y + 2$
   (C) $5y + 4$ (D) $y + 2$

6. $\frac{3(1.8 - 2.6) - (1.8 - 2.6)}{2} =$
C
   (A) 0.8 (B) -0.8
   (C) -1.6 (D) -3.4

7. If $\frac{x}{8} + 3 = 1$, the value of $\frac{x}{2}$ is
C
   (A) -32 (B) -16 (C) -8 (D) 4

8. If $2m - n = 8$ and $m + p = 14$, what is
C the value of n in terms of p?
   (A) $2p - 20$ (B) $10 - p$
   (C) $20 - 2p$ (D) $p - 10$

9. $-3(a - b) =$
A
   (A) $3(b - a)$ (B) $3(a \div b)$
   (C) $3(-b) + (-a)$ (D) $3ab$

10. If $x = 1$, $y = -2$, and $z = 2$, then
A $\frac{x^2 y}{(x - z)^2} =$
    (A) -2 (B) 2 (C) $\frac{-1}{3}$ (D) $\frac{1}{3}$

11. If $1 + \frac{c}{12} = 2\frac{3}{4}$, then $c =$
C
    (A) 33 (B) 32 (C) 21 (D) 12

12. A number added to one-third of itself
B results in a sum of 40. What is the number?
    (A) 32 (B) 30 (C) 10 (D) 27

13. How many dollars do you have if you
A have n nickels, d dimes, and k quarters?
    (A) $\frac{5n + 25k + 10d}{100}$
    (B) $\frac{25n + 10d + 4k}{100}$
    (C) $20n + 10d + 4k$
    (D) $\frac{20n + 10d + 4k}{100}$

14. If x, y, and z are three consecutive
A integers and $x > y > z$, then
    $(x - y)(x - z)(y - z) =$
    (A) 2 (B) -2 (C) -16 (D) 16

15. Emily, who is 24 years old, is three
D times as old as Barb. Barb is four years
younger than twice Pedro's age. How
old is Pedro?

(A) 2   (B) 12   (C) 10   (D) 6

16. If 20x cartons fill $\frac{x}{5}$ trucks, how many
D trucks are needed to hold 400 cartons?

(A) 20   (B) 8000

(C) 100   (D) 4

17. If $\frac{x}{2}$, $\frac{x}{5}$, and $\frac{x}{7}$ are whole numbers, x
D may be

(A) 20   (B) 35   (C) 50   (D) 70

18. If $\frac{1}{b-d} = 4$, then $d =$
A

(A) $b - \frac{1}{4}$ (B) $4b - 1$

(C) $\frac{b+1}{4}$ (D) $b + 4$

19. If $\frac{2a}{5b} = 6$, then $\frac{2a - 5b}{5b} =$
D

(A) 6   (B) $\frac{2}{5}$ (C) 15   (D) 5

20. If $3\frac{1}{5}c = 2\frac{1}{2}b$ and $c \neq 0$, then $\frac{b}{c} =$
A

(A) $\frac{25}{32}$ (B) $\frac{32}{25}$ (C) $\frac{7}{8}$ (D) $\frac{11}{10}$

21. Carrie's bowling scores for four games
A are $b + 2$, $b + 3$, $b - 2$, and $b - 1$.
What must her score be on her fifth
game to average $b + 2$?

(A) $b + 8$ (B) b

(C) $b - 2$ (D) $b + 5$

22. If $abc = 4$ and $b = c$, then $a =$
C

(A) c^2 (B) $\frac{1}{4c}$ (C) $\frac{4}{c^2}$ (D) $\frac{1}{c^2}$

23. The sum of six integers is what
D percent of the average of six integers?

(A) 0.001%   (B) 2%

(C) 10%   (D) 600%

24. Which of the following is an irrational
D number?

(A) 0.123 . . .   (B) $\sqrt{169}$

(C) $\sqrt{-8}$ (D) π

25. If r and s are roots of $x^2 + bx + c = 0$,
B then $r + s =$

(A) 0   (B) $-b$ (C) c (D) $b - c$

APPENDIX: USING TABLES

A table of squares and approximate square roots and a table of values of trigonometric functions are provided for use in case a scientific calculator is not available. This guide will show you how to use the tables to find squares, square roots, and values of trigonometric functions.

Example 1

Find the square and square root of 51.

Read across the row labeled 51.

SQUARES AND APPROXIMATE SQUARE ROOTS

n	n^2	$\sqrt{n}$	n	n^2	$\sqrt{n}$
1	1	1.000	51	2601	7.141
2	4	1.414	52	2704	7.211
3	9	1.732	53	2809	7.280
4	16	2.000	54	2916	7.348
5	25	2.236	55	3025	7.416

The n^2 column shows that the square of 51 is 2601.
The $\sqrt{n}$ column shows that the square root of 51 to the nearest thousandth is 7.141.

Example 2

Find the sine, cosine, and tangent of 37° to the nearest ten thousandth.

Read across the row labeled 37°.

TRIGONOMETRIC RATIOS

Angle	sin	cos	tan	Angle	sin	cos	tan
36°	0.5878	0.8090	0.7265	81°	0.9877	0.1564	6.3138
37°	0.6018	0.7986	0.7536	82°	0.9903	0.1392	7.1154
38°	0.6157	0.7880	0.7813	83°	0.9925	0.1219	8.1443
39°	0.6293	0.7771	0.8098	84°	0.9945	0.1045	9.5144
40°	0.6428	0.7660	0.8391	85°	0.9962	0.0872	11.4301

The sin column shows that the sine of 37° is 0.6018.
The cos column shows that the cosine of 37° is 0.7986.
The tan column shows that the tangent of 37° is 0.7536.

SQUARES AND APPROXIMATE SQUARE ROOTS

n	n^2	$\sqrt{n}$	n	n^2	$\sqrt{n}$
1	1	1.000	51	2601	7.141
2	4	1.414	52	2704	7.211
3	9	1.732	53	2809	7.280
4	16	2.000	54	2916	7.348
5	25	2.236	55	3025	7.416
6	36	2.449	56	3136	7.483
7	49	2.646	57	3249	7.550
8	64	2.828	58	3364	7.616
9	81	3.000	59	3481	7.681
10	100	3.162	60	3600	7.746
11	121	3.317	61	3721	7.810
12	144	3.464	62	3844	7.874
13	169	3.606	63	3969	7.937
14	196	3.742	64	4096	8.000
15	225	3.873	65	4225	8.062
16	256	4.000	66	4356	8.124
17	289	4.123	67	4489	8.185
18	324	4.243	68	4624	8.246
19	361	4.359	69	4761	8.307
20	400	4.472	70	4900	8.367
21	441	4.583	71	5041	8.426
22	484	4.690	72	5184	8.485
23	529	4.796	73	5329	8.544
24	576	4.899	74	5476	8.602
25	625	5.000	75	5625	8.660
26	676	5.099	76	5776	8.718
27	729	5.196	77	5929	8.775
28	784	5.292	78	6084	8.832
29	841	5.385	79	6241	8.888
30	900	5.477	80	6400	8.944
31	961	5.568	81	6561	9.000
32	1024	5.657	82	6724	9.055
33	1089	5.745	83	6889	9.110
34	1156	5.831	84	7056	9.165
35	1225	5.916	85	7225	9.220
36	1296	6.000	86	7396	9.274
37	1369	6.083	87	7569	9.327
38	1444	6.164	88	7744	9.381
39	1521	6.245	89	7921	9.434
40	1600	6.325	90	8100	9.487
41	1681	6.403	91	8281	9.539
42	1764	6.481	92	8464	9.592
43	1849	6.557	93	8649	9.644
44	1936	6.633	94	8836	9.695
45	2025	6.708	95	9025	9.747
46	2116	6.782	96	9216	9.798
47	2209	6.856	97	9409	9.849
48	2304	6.928	98	9604	9.899
49	2401	7.000	99	9801	9.950
50	2500	7.071	100	10000	10.000

TRIGONOMETRIC RATIOS

Angle	sin	cos	tan	Angle	sin	cos	tan
0°	0.0000	1.0000	0.0000	45°	0.7071	0.7071	1.0000
1°	0.0175	0.9998	0.0175	46°	0.7193	0.6947	1.0355
2°	0.0349	0.9994	0.0349	47°	0.7314	0.6820	1.0724
3°	0.0523	0.9986	0.0524	48°	0.7431	0.6691	1.1106
4°	0.0698	0.9976	0.0699	49°	0.7547	0.6561	1.1504
5°	0.0872	0.9962	0.0875	50°	0.7660	0.6428	1.1918
6°	0.1045	0.9945	0.1051	51°	0.7771	0.6293	1.2349
7°	0.1219	0.9925	0.1228	52°	0.7880	0.6157	1.2799
8°	0.1392	0.9903	0.1405	53°	0.7986	0.6018	1.3270
9°	0.1564	0.9877	0.1584	54°	0.8090	0.5878	1.3764
10°	0.1736	0.9848	0.1763	55°	0.8192	0.5736	1.4281
11°	0.1908	0.9816	0.1944	56°	0.8290	0.5592	1.4826
12°	0.2079	0.9781	0.2126	57°	0.8387	0.5446	1.5399
13°	0.2250	0.9744	0.2309	58°	0.8480	0.5299	1.6003
14°	0.2419	0.9703	0.2493	59°	0.8572	0.5150	1.6643
15°	0.2588	0.9659	0.2679	60°	0.8660	0.5000	1.7321
16°	0.2756	0.9613	0.2867	61°	0.8746	0.4848	1.8040
17°	0.2924	0.9563	0.3057	62°	0.8829	0.4695	1.8807
18°	0.3090	0.9511	0.3249	63°	0.8910	0.4540	1.9626
19°	0.3256	0.9455	0.3443	64°	0.8988	0.4384	2.0503
20°	0.3420	0.9397	0.3640	65°	0.9063	0.4226	2.1445
21°	0.3584	0.9336	0.3839	66°	0.9135	0.4067	2.2460
22°	0.3746	0.9272	0.4040	67°	0.9205	0.3907	2.3559
23°	0.3907	0.9205	0.4245	68°	0.9272	0.3746	2.4751
24°	0.4067	0.9135	0.4452	69°	0.9336	0.3584	2.6051
25°	0.4226	0.9063	0.4663	70°	0.9397	0.3420	2.7475
26°	0.4384	0.8988	0.4877	71°	0.9455	0.3256	2.9042
27°	0.4540	0.8910	0.5095	72°	0.9511	0.3090	3.0777
28°	0.4695	0.8829	0.5317	73°	0.9563	0.2924	3.2709
29°	0.4848	0.8746	0.5543	74°	0.9613	0.2756	3.4874
30°	0.5000	0.8660	0.5774	75°	0.9659	0.2588	3.7321
31°	0.5150	0.8572	0.6009	76°	0.9703	0.2419	4.0108
32°	0.5299	0.8480	0.6249	77°	0.9744	0.2250	4.3315
33°	0.5446	0.8387	0.6494	78°	0.9781	0.2079	4.7046
34°	0.5592	0.8290	0.6745	79°	0.9816	0.1908	5.1446
35°	0.5736	0.8192	0.7002	80°	0.9848	0.1736	5.6713
36°	0.5878	0.8090	0.7265	81°	0.9877	0.1564	6.3138
37°	0.6018	0.7986	0.7536	82°	0.9903	0.1392	7.1154
38°	0.6157	0.7880	0.7813	83°	0.9925	0.1219	8.1443
39°	0.6293	0.7771	0.8098	84°	0.9945	0.1045	9.5144
40°	0.6428	0.7660	0.8391	85°	0.9962	0.0872	11.4301
41°	0.6561	0.7547	0.8693	86°	0.9976	0.0698	14.3007
42°	0.6691	0.7431	0.9004	87°	0.9986	0.0523	19.0811
43°	0.6820	0.7314	0.9325	88°	0.9994	0.0349	28.6363
44°	0.6947	0.7193	0.9657	89°	0.9998	0.0175	57.2900
45°	0.7071	0.7071	1.0000	90°	1.0000	0.0000	∞

ALGEBRAIC SKILLS REVIEW

Integer Equations: Addition and Subtraction

Solve each equation.

1. $-5 + (-8) = x$ **−13**
2. $-7 + 4 = y$ **−3**
3. $-4 + 8 = t$ **4**
4. $9 + (-2) = a$ **7**
5. $6 + 6 = b$ **12**
6. $3 + (-8) = m$ **−5**
7. $-7 + (-9) = v$ **−16**
8. $-5 + 5 = z$ **0**
9. $-19 + 43 = c$ **24**
10. $51 + (-26) = w$ **25**
11. $-37 + (-48) = d$ **−85**
12. $-93 + 44 = e$ **−49**
13. $67 + (-82) = n$ **−15**
14. $28 + 46 = f$ **74**
15. $29 + (-37) = s$ **−8**
16. $-94 + (-58) = g$ **−152**
17. $-18 + 63 = p$ **45**
18. $28 + (-52) = j$ **−24**
19. $77 + 57 = r$ **134**
20. $47 + (-29) = x$ **18**
21. $-18 + 26 = a$ **8**
22. $-65 + (-75) = k$ **−140**
23. $21 + (-47) = h$ **−26**
24. $-15 + 52 = q$ **37**
25. $y = -13 + (-98)$ **−111**
26. $u = -5 + 82$ **77**
27. $s = -47 + 26 + (-18)$ **−39**
28. $a = -71 + (-85) + (-16)$ **−172**
29. $41 + 57 + (-32) = m$ **66**
30. $82 + (-14) + (-35) = c$ **33**
31. $-4 - (-2) = t$ **−2**
32. $5 - (-6) = p$ **11**
33. $-9 - 3 = x$ **−12**
34. $5 - (-5) = k$ **10**
35. $-3 - (-8) = m$ **5**
36. $3 - 9 = w$ **−6**
37. $-6 - 8 = w$ **−14**
38. $0 - 6 = v$ **−6**
39. $j = -10 - (-4)$ **−6**
40. $-23 - 45 = a$ **−68**
41. $28 - (-14) = z$ **42**
42. $-53 - (-61) = f$ **8**
43. $c = -16 - 47$ **−63**
44. $90 - 43 = g$ **47**
45. $71 - (-47) = q$ **118**
46. $-99 - (-26) = s$ **−73**
47. $38 - (-19) = t$ **57**
48. $-20 - (-92) = j$ **72**
49. $18 - 47 = y$ **−29**
50. $h = -15 - (-81)$ **66**
51. $-42 - 63 = b$ **−105**
52. $-84 - 47 = r$ **−131**
53. $42 - (-47) = d$ **89**
54. $y = -19 - (-63)$ **44**
55. $16 - (-84) = n$ **100**
56. $42 - (-26) = k$ **68**
57. $-52 - (-33) = x$ **−19**
58. $-35 - 86 = a$ **−121**
59. $v = -8 - (-47)$ **39**
60. $33 - 51 = t$ **−18**
61. $-2 + g = 7$ **9**
62. $9 + s = -5$ **−14**
63. $-7 + k = -2$ **5**
64. $-4 + y = -9$ **−5**
65. $m + 6 = 2$ **−4**
66. $t + (-4) = 10$ **14**
67. $h - (-2) = 6$ **4**
68. $v - 7 = -4$ **3**
69. $a - (-6) = -5$ **−11**
70. $r - (-3) = -8$ **−11**
71. $j - (-8) = 5$ **−3**
72. $x - 8 = -9$ **−1**
73. $-2 - x = -8$ **6**
74. $14 = -48 + b$ **62**
75. $c + (-26) = 45$ **71**
76. $z - (-57) = -39$ **−96**
77. $d + (-44) = -61$ **−17**
78. $n - 38 = -19$ **19**
79. $-77 = w + 23$ **−100**
80. $e - (-26) = 41$ **15**
81. $p - 47 = 22$ **69**
82. $-63 - f = -82$ **19**
83. $87 = t + (-14)$ **101**
84. $q + (-53) = 27$ **80**

Integer Equations: Multiplication and Division

Solve each equation.

1. $x = (-8)(-4)$ **32**
2. $(-3)5 = t$ **−15**
3. $(-7)(-2) = a$ **14**
4. $(-9)8 = b$ **−72**
5. $6(-5) = v$ **−30**
6. $k = 8(6)$ **48**
7. $14(-26) = s$ **−364**
8. $(-46)(-25) = g$ **1150**
9. $(-71)(-20) = y$ **1420**
10. $(-42)66 = h$ **−2772**
11. $(-97)47 = w$ **−4559**
12. $53(-32) = c$ **−1696**
13. $19(-46) = x$ **−874**
14. $(-82)0 = e$ **0**
15. $72(43) = m$ **3096**
16. $(-18)(-18) = d$ **324**
17. $24(-29) = u$ **−696**
18. $f = (-39)45$ **−1755**
19. $(-76)(-34) = s$ **2584**
20. $(-81)(-18) = q$ **1458**
21. $(-65)28 = t$ **−1820**
22. $71(-38) = p$ **−2698**
23. $j = 49(-92)$ **−4508**
24. $36(24) = a$ **864**
25. $(-42)78 = z$ **−3276**
26. $(-54)(-77) = r$ **4158**
27. $n = (-6)(-127)(-4)$ **−3048**
28. $(13)(-12)(95) = w$ **−14,820**
29. $(-1)(45)(-45) = v$ **2025**
30. $(-3)(61)(99) = y$ **−18, 117**
31. $72 \div (-8) = g$ **−9**
32. $-64 \div 8 = b$ **−8**
33. $-45 \div (-9) = y$ **5**
34. $56 \div (-7) = z$ **−8**
35. $42 \div 6 = e$ **7**
36. $-24 \div (-6) = m$ **4**
37. $992 \div (-32) = a$ **−31**
38. $-4428 \div 54 = k$ **−82**
39. $x = -600 \div (-24)$ **25**
40. $1472 \div (-64) = p$ **−23**
41. $-564 \div (-47) = h$ **12**
42. $-504 \div 14 = j$ **−36**
43. $-2201 \div 71 = r$ **−31**
44. $1512 \div (-28) = n$ **−54**
45. $765 \div (-85) = q$ **−9**
46. $-1591 \div (-37) = f$ **43**
47. $s = -1080 \div 36$ **−30**
48. $3432 \div (-52) = v$ **−66**
49. $2730 \div 78 = k$ **35**
50. $-3936 \div 96 = c$ **−41**
51. $-1476 \div 41 = z$ **−36**
52. $1496 \div (-22) = a$ **−68**
53. $2646 \div (-63) = t$ **−42**
54. $w = -4730 \div (-55)$ **86**
55. $-1092 \div (-26) = x$ **42**
56. $-2700 \div (-75) = e$ **36**
57. $1127 \div 49 = y$ **23**
58. $d = 1900 \div (-38)$ **−50**
59. $-845 \div 13 = w$ **−65**
60. $-1596 \div (-42) = a$ **38**
61. $-5p = 35$ **−7**
62. $7g = -49$ **−7**
63. $-3x = -24$ **8**
64. $a \div (-6) = -2$ **12**
65. $m \div (-8) = 8$ **−64**
66. $q \div 9 = -3$ **−27**
67. $41j = 1476$ **36**
68. $62y = -2356$ **−38**
69. $b \div (-21) = 13$ **−273**
70. $-33n = -1815$ **55**
71. $k \div 46 = -41$ **−1886**
72. $w \div 17 = 24$ **408**
73. $c \div (-59) = -7$ **413**
74. $-56h = 1792$ **−32**
75. $-42z = 1512$ **−36**
76. $j \div (-27) = 27$ **−729**
77. $89s = -712$ **−8**
78. $-18v = -1044$ **58**
79. $d \div (-34) = -43$ **1462**
80. $f \div 14 = -63$ **−882**
81. $45t = 810$ **18**
82. $-74w = 1554$ **−21**
83. $-49e = -2058$ **42**
84. $r \div (-16) = -77$ **1232**
85. $x \div (-26) = 47$ **−1222**
86. $-23 = t \div 44$ **−1012**
87. $-962 = -37g$ **26**
88. $-3040 = 95k$ **−32**
89. $84 = x \div 97$ **8148**
90. $-108 = m \div (-12)$ **1296**

Fraction Equations: Addition and Subtraction

Solve each equation and express answers in simplest form.

1. $\frac{3}{11} + \frac{6}{11} = x$ $\frac{9}{11}$

2. $\frac{4}{7} + \frac{5}{7} = a$ $\frac{9}{7} = 1\frac{2}{7}$

3. $\frac{5}{9} - \frac{2}{9} = t$ $\frac{1}{3}$

4. $\frac{17}{18} - \frac{5}{18} = w$ $\frac{2}{3}$

5. $\frac{1}{3} + \frac{2}{9} = b$ $\frac{5}{9}$

6. $\frac{1}{2} - \frac{1}{3} = v$ $\frac{1}{6}$

7. $\frac{3}{4} - \frac{9}{16} = s$ $\frac{3}{16}$

8. $\frac{2}{3} + \frac{8}{15} = r$ $1\frac{1}{5}$

9. $\frac{5}{6} - \frac{3}{4} = d$ $\frac{1}{12}$

10. $\frac{4}{9} + \frac{1}{6} = c$ $\frac{11}{18}$

11. $m = \frac{7}{9} + \frac{3}{8}$ $1\frac{11}{72}$

12. $\frac{11}{12} - \frac{7}{10} = j$ $\frac{13}{60}$

13. $\frac{5}{6} - \frac{5}{12} = p$ $\frac{5}{12}$

14. $4\frac{2}{3} + 1\frac{8}{15} = k$ $6\frac{1}{5}$

15. $5\frac{1}{2} - 2\frac{1}{3} = w$ $3\frac{1}{6}$

16. $8\frac{1}{12} - 5\frac{5}{12} = e$ $2\frac{2}{3}$

17. $7 - 1\frac{4}{9} = h$ $5\frac{5}{9}$

18. $n = \frac{3}{16} + \frac{7}{12}$ $\frac{37}{48}$

19. $4\frac{1}{2} - 2\frac{2}{3} = q$ $1\frac{5}{6}$

20. $7\frac{1}{12} - 4\frac{5}{8} = x$ $2\frac{11}{24}$

21. $11\frac{5}{6} + 9\frac{7}{15} = f$ $21\frac{3}{10}$

22. $y = 9\frac{2}{7} - 5\frac{5}{6}$ $3\frac{19}{42}$

23. $\frac{1}{4} + \frac{5}{6} + \frac{7}{12} = c$ $1\frac{2}{3}$

24. $\frac{5}{6} + \frac{2}{9} + \frac{3}{4} = z$ $1\frac{29}{36}$

25. $-\frac{2}{13} + \left(-\frac{3}{13}\right) = t$ $-\frac{5}{13}$

26. $-\frac{11}{18} + \frac{17}{18} = f$ $\frac{1}{3}$

27. $-\frac{9}{10} - \frac{7}{10} = n$ $-1\frac{3}{5}$

28. $-\frac{7}{11} - \left(-\frac{3}{11}\right) = a$ $-\frac{4}{11}$

29. $\frac{1}{12} - \left(-\frac{7}{12}\right) = w$ $\frac{2}{3}$

30. $\frac{17}{21} + \left(-\frac{10}{21}\right) = g$ $\frac{1}{3}$

31. $\frac{1}{4} + \left(-\frac{2}{3}\right) = p$ $-\frac{5}{12}$

32. $b = -\frac{1}{6} - \frac{8}{9}$ $-\frac{19}{18} = -1\frac{1}{18}$

33. $\frac{1}{3} - \frac{5}{6} = m$ $-\frac{1}{2}$

34. $-\frac{1}{2} + \left(-\frac{3}{5}\right) = a$ $-\frac{11}{10} = -1\frac{1}{10}$

35. $\frac{3}{7} + (-5) = s$ $-4\frac{4}{7}$

36. $-\frac{5}{9} - 2 = k$ $-2\frac{5}{9}$

37. $t = 1\frac{1}{2} - \left(-\frac{3}{4}\right)$ $2\frac{1}{4}$

38. $-\frac{3}{8} + \frac{4}{7} = c$ $\frac{11}{56}$

39. $\frac{3}{5} - \left(-3\frac{1}{4}\right) = v$ $3\frac{17}{20}$

40. $-8\frac{7}{8} - \left(-4\frac{5}{12}\right) = r$ $-4\frac{11}{24}$

41. $-3\frac{1}{6} + 5\frac{1}{15} = d$ $1\frac{9}{10}$

42. $-1\frac{8}{9} + \left(-5\frac{7}{12}\right) = h$ $-7\frac{17}{36}$

43. $7\frac{5}{6} + \left(-8\frac{7}{8}\right) = j$ $-1\frac{1}{24}$

44. $-3\frac{1}{2} - 4\frac{5}{9} = e$ $-8\frac{1}{18}$

45. $q = \frac{11}{16} - 12$ $-11\frac{5}{16}$

46. $-5\frac{11}{20} + 4\frac{7}{12} = z$ $-\frac{29}{30}$

47. $-1\frac{1}{12} - \left(-\frac{2}{3}\right) = w$ $-\frac{5}{12}$

48. $-4\frac{16}{21} + \left(-7\frac{5}{9}\right) = y$ $-12\frac{20}{63}$

49. $\frac{3}{13} + p = \frac{10}{13}$ $\frac{7}{13}$

50. $e + \frac{4}{15} = \frac{13}{15}$ $\frac{3}{5}$

51. $\frac{2}{5} + n = \frac{2}{3}$ $\frac{4}{15}$

52. $j - \frac{5}{18} = \frac{17}{18}$ $1\frac{2}{9}$

53. $r - \frac{1}{4} = \frac{5}{16}$ $\frac{9}{16}$

54. $b - \frac{1}{2} = \frac{2}{5}$ $\frac{9}{10}$

55. $s + \frac{2}{7} = 2$ $1\frac{5}{7}$

56. $\frac{7}{10} - a = \frac{1}{2}$ $\frac{1}{5}$

57. $1\frac{5}{6} + x = 2\frac{1}{4}$ $\frac{5}{12}$

58. $4\frac{1}{4} = w + 2\frac{1}{3}$ $1\frac{11}{12}$

59. $d - 1\frac{5}{7} = 6\frac{1}{4}$ $7\frac{27}{28}$

60. $h - \frac{3}{4} = 2\frac{5}{8}$ $3\frac{3}{8}$

61. $t - \frac{2}{3} = 1\frac{5}{8}$ $2\frac{7}{24}$

62. $g + \frac{5}{6} = \frac{4}{9}$ $-\frac{7}{18}$

63. $q - \frac{7}{10} = -\frac{11}{15}$ $-\frac{1}{30}$

64. $-\frac{3}{7} + c = \frac{1}{2}$ $\frac{13}{14}$

65. $-\frac{3}{4} = v + \left(-\frac{1}{8}\right)$ $-\frac{5}{8}$

66. $f - \left(-\frac{1}{8}\right) = \frac{3}{10}$ $\frac{7}{40}$

67. $m - \left(-1\frac{3}{8}\right) = -2\frac{1}{2}$ $-3\frac{7}{8}$

68. $-6\frac{5}{6} + y = 7\frac{7}{15}$ $14\frac{3}{10}$

69. $7\frac{1}{6} - z = -5\frac{2}{3}$ $12\frac{5}{6}$

70. $-2\frac{1}{3} + w = -5\frac{5}{6}$ $-3\frac{1}{2}$

71. $-6\frac{1}{7} + k = -\frac{4}{21}$ $5\frac{20}{21}$

72. $-4\frac{5}{12} = t - \left(-10\frac{1}{36}\right)$ $-14\frac{4}{9}$

Fraction Equations: Multiplication and Division

Solve each equation and express answers in simplest form.

1. $\frac{1}{7}\left(\frac{1}{3}\right) = x$ $\frac{1}{21}$

2. $\frac{2}{3}\left(\frac{1}{5}\right) = v$ $\frac{2}{15}$

3. $\frac{5}{6}\left(\frac{3}{10}\right) = y$ $\frac{1}{4}$

4. $2 \div \frac{1}{3} = j$ 6

5. $\frac{5}{6} \div \frac{1}{6} = f$ 5

6. $\frac{1}{4} \div \frac{5}{8} = c$ $\frac{2}{5}$

7. $\frac{2}{3}(9) = b$ 6

8. $\frac{5}{18}\left(\frac{3}{10}\right) = r$ $\frac{1}{12}$

9. $\frac{8}{15} \div \frac{1}{10} = k$ $\frac{16}{3} = 5\frac{1}{3}$

10. $g = \frac{1}{2} \div 8$ $\frac{1}{16}$

11. $\frac{3}{14} \div \frac{2}{7} = y$ $\frac{3}{4}$

12. $\frac{7}{12}\left(\frac{4}{5}\right) = w$ $\frac{7}{15}$

13. $\frac{6}{13} \div \frac{5}{7} = z$ $\frac{42}{65}$

14. $\frac{24}{25}\left(\frac{15}{32}\right) = a$ $\frac{9}{20}$

15. $\frac{7}{10}\left(\frac{5}{28}\right) = w$ $\frac{1}{8}$

16. $2\frac{2}{3}\left(\frac{4}{5}\right) = n$ $\frac{32}{15} = 2\frac{2}{15}$

17. $t = \frac{7}{8}\left(4\frac{1}{4}\right)$ $\frac{119}{32} = 3\frac{23}{32}$

18. $1\frac{3}{4} \div \frac{7}{12} = e$ 3

19. $1 \div 2\frac{3}{5} = d$ $\frac{5}{13}$

20. $2\frac{1}{10}\left(4\frac{2}{7}\right) = q$ 9

21. $1\frac{3}{5} \div 11\frac{1}{5} = s$ $\frac{1}{7}$

22. $3\frac{1}{8}\left(2\frac{4}{5}\right)\left(\frac{5}{7}\right) = p$ $\frac{25}{4} = 6\frac{1}{4}$

23. $3\frac{2}{3}\left(\frac{1}{8}\right)\left(1\frac{1}{11}\right) = h$ $\frac{1}{2}$

24. $m = 3\frac{1}{21} \div 1\frac{21}{35}$ $\frac{40}{21} = 1\frac{19}{21}$

25. $\frac{1}{5}\left(-\frac{1}{8}\right) = p$ $-\frac{1}{40}$

26. $-\frac{2}{9}\left(\frac{1}{3}\right) = w$ $-\frac{2}{27}$

27. $-\frac{5}{8}\left(-\frac{4}{5}\right) = c$ $\frac{1}{2}$

28. $-3 \div \frac{1}{2} = y$ -6

29. $-\frac{7}{9} \div \left(-\frac{1}{9}\right) = r$ 7

30. $\frac{2}{3} \div \left(-\frac{4}{9}\right) = t$ $-\frac{3}{2} = -1\frac{1}{2}$

31. $-\frac{2}{5}(-10) = m$ 4

32. $\frac{2}{3} \div \left(-\frac{7}{9}\right) = h$ $-\frac{6}{7}$

33. $-\frac{9}{15}\left(\frac{5}{9}\right) = s$ $-\frac{1}{3}$

34. $-\frac{9}{14} \div \left(-\frac{3}{7}\right) = a$ $\frac{3}{2} = 1\frac{1}{2}$

35. $\frac{7}{16} \div \left(-\frac{7}{11}\right) = z$ $-\frac{11}{16}$

36. $j = -\frac{4}{5}(30)$ -24

37. $-7 \div 4 = q$ $-\frac{7}{4} = -1\frac{3}{4}$

38. $-4\frac{9}{10}\left(-1\frac{5}{21}\right) = b$ $\frac{91}{15} = 6\frac{1}{15}$

39. $-5\frac{3}{5} \div 4\frac{1}{5} = g$ $-\frac{4}{3} = -1\frac{1}{3}$

40. $-5\frac{3}{5} \div \left(-4\frac{1}{5}\right) = e$ $\frac{4}{3} = 1\frac{1}{3}$

41. $v = 6\frac{1}{4}\left(-1\frac{7}{15}\right)$ $-\frac{55}{6} = -9\frac{1}{6}$

42. $3\frac{1}{3}\left(-4\frac{1}{2}\right) = w$ -15

43. $-2\left(1\frac{5}{18}\right) = k$ $-\frac{23}{9} = -2\frac{5}{9}$

44. $4\frac{2}{5} \div \left(-\frac{11}{15}\right) = p$ -6

45. $-2\frac{5}{8} \div 7\frac{1}{2} = x$ $-\frac{7}{20}$

46. $5 \div (-11) = n$ $-\frac{5}{11}$

47. $d = -2\frac{3}{10}\left(-\frac{5}{12}\right)$ $\frac{23}{24}$

48. $-9\frac{1}{3}\left(-3\frac{3}{4}\right) = f$ 35

49. $\frac{1}{3}a = 5$ 15

50. $\frac{4}{7}k = 4$ 7

51. $\frac{2}{5}x = \frac{4}{7}$ $\frac{10}{7} = 1\frac{3}{7}$

52. $w \div 5 = 3$ 15

53. $w \div \frac{1}{4} = \frac{3}{8}$ $\frac{3}{32}$

54. $c \div \frac{3}{10} = \frac{1}{2}$ $\frac{3}{20}$

55. $\frac{7}{11}t = \frac{4}{5}$ $\frac{44}{35} = 1\frac{9}{35}$

56. $h \div \frac{1}{8} = \frac{4}{11}$ $\frac{1}{22}$

57. $z \div 6 = \frac{5}{12}$ $\frac{5}{2} = 2\frac{1}{2}$

58. $1\frac{1}{2}d = \frac{6}{7}$ $\frac{4}{7}$

59. $\frac{10}{33} = b \div 4\frac{2}{5}$ $\frac{4}{3} = 1\frac{1}{3}$

60. $2\frac{1}{6}j = 5\frac{1}{5}$ $\frac{12}{5} = 2\frac{2}{5}$

61. $s \div 2\frac{1}{6} = 2\frac{2}{5}$ $\frac{26}{5} = 5\frac{1}{5}$

62. $1\frac{3}{24}g = 3\frac{1}{8}$ $\frac{25}{9} = 2\frac{7}{9}$

63. $3 = 1\frac{7}{11}q$ $\frac{11}{6} = 1\frac{5}{6}$

64. $n \div \frac{2}{3} = -\frac{4}{9}$ $-\frac{8}{27}$

65. $-1\frac{3}{4}p = -\frac{5}{8}$ $\frac{5}{14}$

66. $v \div \left(-\frac{7}{11}\right) = 1\frac{2}{7}$ $-\frac{9}{11}$

67. $-1\frac{3}{5} = e \div \left(-3\frac{1}{5}\right)$ $\frac{128}{3} = 5\frac{3}{25}$

68. $-\frac{5}{9}r = 7\frac{1}{2}$ $-\frac{27}{2} = -13\frac{1}{2}$

69. $3\frac{4}{7}x = -3\frac{3}{4}$ $-\frac{21}{20} = -1\frac{1}{20}$

70. $a \div 3\frac{2}{7} = -8\frac{3}{4}$ $-\frac{115}{4} = -28\frac{3}{4}$

71. $-2\frac{4}{7}m = -3\frac{3}{8}$ $\frac{21}{16} = 1\frac{5}{16}$

72. $f \div \left(-3\frac{1}{8}\right) = -3\frac{2}{5}$ $\frac{85}{8} = 10\frac{5}{8}$

Decimal Equations: Addition and Subtraction

Solve each equation. 15. 13.027 24. 17.216 30. 175.253 54. −85.225

1. $0.53 + 0.26 = x$ **0.79**

2. $14.756 + 0.185 = k$ **14.941**

3. $0.711 - 0.158 = z$ **0.553**

4. $12.01 - 0.83 = s$ **11.18**

5. $0.4 + 0.86 = n$ **1.26**

6. $1.4 - 0.12 = a$ **1.28**

7. $57.5 + 7.94 = m$ **65.44**

8. $10.04 - 0.18 = f$ **9.86**

9. $5 - 1.63 = r$ **3.37**

10. $5.92 + 7.3 = b$ **13.22**

11. $12 + 9.6 = y$ **21.6**

12. $28.05 - 9.95 = c$ **18.1**

13. $0.2 + 6.51 + 2.03 = y$ **8.74**

14. $4.4 + 30.6 + 11.2 = z$ **46.2**

15. $0.007 + 3 + 10.02 = h$

16. $w = 20.13 - 12.5$ **7.63**

17. $2.3 - 0.846 = t$ **1.454**

18. $11 - 1.1 = p$ **9.9**

19. $6.2 + 5.54 + 13.66 = g$ **25.4**

20. $a = 412 - 0.007$ **411.993**

21. $101.12 + 9.099 = s$ **110.219**

22. $66.4 - 5.288 = d$ **61.112**

23. $84.083 - 17 = m$ **67.083**

24. $q = 0.046 + 5.8 + 11.37$

25. $8 - 3.49 = n$ **4.51**

26. $8.77 + 0.3 + 52.9 = x$ **61.97**

27. $14.7 - 5.8364 = e$ **8.8636**

28. $66.68421 - 18.465 = v$
    48.21921

29. $y = 0.0013 + 2.881$ **2.8823**

30. $127.11 + 48 + 0.143 = u$

31. $-0.47 + 0.62 = h$ **0.15**

32. $-4.5 + (-12.8) = x$ **−17.3**

33. $-1.7 + 0.24 = p$ **−1.46**

34. $-6.831 - (-2.648) = c$
    −4.183

35. $-4.23 - 2.47 = b$ **−6.7**

36. $2.64 - (-5.9) = k$ **8.54**

37. $10 + (-0.43) = r$ **9.57**

38. $6.7 - (-0.64) = v$ **7.34**

39. $-6.71 - (-8) = e$ **1.29**

40. $14.14 + (-1.4) = a$ **12.74**

41. $1.2 - 6.73 = j$ **−5.53**

42. $-9.7 + (-0.86) = d$ **−10.56**

43. $-7 - 4.63 = w$ **−11.63**

44. $-0.17 - (-14.6) = g$ **14.43**

45. $m = 1.8 + (-14.14)$ **−12.34**

46. $5.003 + (-0.47) = f$ **4.533**

47. $0.88 - 42 = s$ **−41.12**

48. $-6.2 + (-27.47) = j$ **−33.67**

49. $n = -1.4962 + 2.118$
    0.6218

50. $2.4 - (-1.736) = q$ **4.136**

51. $4.16 + (-5.909) = t$ **−1.749**

52. $17 + (-0.45) = w$ **16.55**

53. $10 - 13.463 = a$ **−3.463**

54. $f = -82.007 - 3.218$

55. $-11.264 + (-8.2) = z$
    −19.464

56. $-56 + 2.783 = s$ **−53.217**

57. $-0.682 - (-0.81) = y$ **0.128**

58. $r = -23 + 4.093$ **−18.907**

59. $2.08 - (-0.094) = t$ **2.174**

60. $-51.34 + (-5.1346) = x$

61. $2.2 + a = 11.4$ **9.2**

62. $h + 1.83 = 8.42$ **6.59**

63. $c + 5.4 = -11.33$ **−16.73**

64. $m - 0.41 = 0.85$ **1.26**

65. $p - 1.1 = 14.9$ **16**

66. $r - 0.76 = -3.2$ **−2.44**

67. $t + (-6.47) = -22.3$ **−15.83**

68. $-6.11 + b = 14.321$ **20.431**

69. $k - (-4) = 7.9$ **3.9**

70. $k - 99.7 = -46.88$ **52.82**

71. $w + (-17.8) = -5.63$ **12.17**

72. $-5 = y - 22.7$ **17.7**

73. $13.475 + d = 4.09$ **−9.385**

74. $-5 - q = 1.19$ **−6.19**

75. $-3.214 + f = -16.04$

76. $-88.9 = s - 6.21$ **−82.69**

77. $2 + e = 1.008$ **−0.992**

78. $n + (-4.361) = 59.78$ **64.141**

79. $4.8 - j = -5.834$ **10.634**

80. $w - 0.73 = -1.8$ **−1.07**

81. $-8 = g - (-4.821)$ **−12.821**

82. $-2.315 + x = -15$ **−12.685**

83. $m + (-1.4) = 0.07$ **1.47**

84. $v - 5.234 = -1.051$ **4.183**

85. $7.1 = v - (-0.62)$ **6.48**

86. $s + 6.4 = -0.11$ **−6.51**

87. $t - (-46.1) = -3.673$

88. $k + (-1.604) = -0.45$ **1.154**

89. $81.6 + p = -6.73$ **−88.33**

90. $-0.1448 - z = -2.6$ **2.4552**

60. **−56.4746** 75. **−12.826** 87. **−49.773**

Decimal Equations: Multiplication and Division

Solve each equation. 30. 0.06   60. −0.101   84. 0.01802   90. −0.000945

1. $46(0.5) = e$ 23

2. $108(0.9) = b$ 97.2

3. $g = 6.47(39)$ 252.33

4. $0.04(197) = f$ 7.88

5. $r = 67(5.892)$ 394.764

6. $2.8(4.27) = d$ 11.956

7. $0.061(5.5) = m$ 0.3355

8. $0.62(0.13) = c$ 0.0806

9. $4.007(1.95) = q$ 7.81365

10. $6.25 \div 5 = w$ 1.25

11. $t = 91.8 \div 27$ 3.4

12. $7.31 \div 43 = h$ 0.17

13. $5.91 \div 0.3 = a$ 19.7

14. $167.5 \div 2.5 = k$ 67

15. $4.7208 \div 0.84 = v$ 5.62

16. $p = 278.1 \div 6.18$ 45

17. $30{,}176 \div 9.43 = n$ 3200

18. $0.1001 \div 0.77 = j$ 0.13

19. $2.11(0.059) = w$ 0.12449

20. $s = 0.4484 \div 1.18$ 0.38

21. $0.0062(84.7) = x$ 0.52514

22. $0.03912 \div 1.63 = z$ 0.024

23. $230.4 \div 0.072 = m$ 3200

24. $w = 59.8(100.23)$ 5993.754

25. $v = 432 \div 9.6$ 45

26. $0.008(0.0045) = x$ 0.000036

27. $1.21(0.47)(9.3) = s$ 5.28891

28. $0.0418 \div 0.19 = x$ 0.22

29. $0.032(13)(2.6) = t$ 1.0816

30. $0.0001926 \div 0.00321 = y$

31. $-5(0.2) = x$ −1

32. $-1.7(-44) = f$ 74.8

33. $72(1.01) = c$ 72.72

34. $627(-0.14) = a$ −87.78

35. $-2.3(7.81) = n$ −17.963

36. $r = -1.02(-4.4)$ 4.488

37. $57.6 \div (-12) = b$ −4.8

38. $160.8 \div 24 = h$ 6.7

39. $-16.38 \div (-0.7) = t$ 23.4

40. $m = -15.54 \div 2.1$ −7.4

41. $-0.405 \div (-0.27) = a$ 1.5

42. $-598 \div 0.13 = p$ −4600

43. $0.45(-0.0016) = k$
−0.00072

44. $y = -0.002052 \div 0.054$
−0.038

45. $6.7284 \div 1.08 = d$ 6.23

46. $-0.0066(-91.8) = w$
0.60588

47. $455 \div (-1.82) = q$ −250

48. $-0.905(0.208) = g$ −0.18824

49. $-2.4827 \div (-6.71) = e$ 0.37

50. $0.153 \div (-0.017) = z$ −9

51. $j = -462.1(0.0094)$ −4.34374

52. $56.1(2.3) = y$ 129.03

53. $0.07553 \div 0.0083 = v$ 9.1

54. $-1.7(-0.121) = s$ 0.2057

55. $t = -0.6612 \div (-0.114)$ 5.8

56. $-0.026(45.1) = x$ −1.1726

57. $59(-0.00042) = w$ −0.02478

58. $7.93(-5.036) = c$ 39.93548

59. $9.2397 \div 1.9 = t$ 4.863

60. $-0.000101 \div 0.001 = m$

61. $7c = 4.2$ 0.6

62. $37p = 81.4$ 2.2

63. $57k = 0.1824$ 0.0032

64. $1.5m = 9.9$ 6.6

65. $1.296 = 0.48d$ 2.7

66. $0.0022b = 0.1958$ 89

67. $t \div 110 = 2.8$ 308

68. $x \div 71 = 0.33$ 23.43

69. $r \div 0.85 = 10$ 8.5

70. $h \div 1.98 = 6.7$ 13.266

71. $a \div 0.002 = 0.109$ 0.000218

72. $n \div 40.6 = 0.021$ 0.8526

73. $100.8x = 9374.4$ 93

74. $2.61 = f \div 9.5$ 24.795

75. $1.7118 = 0.317e$ 5.4

76. $0.0603g = 0.0043416$ 0.072

77. $w \div 0.0412 = 60$ 2.472

78. $q \div 1.07 = 0.088$ 0.09416

79. $5j = -32.15$ −6.43

80. $-1.2v = 112.8$ −94

81. $-0.013s = -0.00923$ 0.71

82. $w \div (-2) = -2.48$ 4.96

83. $z \div 2.8 = -6.2$ −17.36

84. $a \div (-0.53) = -0.034$

85. $k \div (-0.013) = -0.7$ 0.0091

86. $-4.63t = -125.473$ 27.1

87. $7.9y = 1583.16$ 200.4

88. $6.05p = -1573$ −260

89. $g \div 9.9 = 12$ 118.8

90. $x \div (-0.063) = 0.015$

Forms of Real Numbers

Write each fraction in simplest form.

1. $\frac{13}{26}$ $\frac{1}{2}$
2. $\frac{9}{12}$ $\frac{3}{4}$
3. $-\frac{36}{42}$ $-\frac{6}{7}$
4. $\frac{5}{60}$ $\frac{1}{12}$

5. $-\frac{24}{32}$ $-\frac{3}{4}$
6. $-\frac{10}{35}$ $-\frac{2}{7}$
7. $\frac{54}{63}$ $\frac{6}{7}$
8. $-\frac{45}{60}$ $-\frac{3}{4}$

9. $\frac{48}{84}$ $\frac{4}{7}$
10. $-\frac{28}{42}$ $-\frac{2}{3}$
11. $-\frac{72}{96}$ $-\frac{3}{4}$
12. $\frac{75}{105}$ $\frac{5}{7}$

13. $-\frac{16}{100}$ $-\frac{4}{25}$
14. $\frac{24}{60}$ $\frac{2}{5}$
15. $\frac{15}{27}$ $\frac{5}{9}$
16. $-\frac{99}{111}$ $-\frac{33}{37}$

17. $\frac{126}{700}$ $\frac{9}{50}$
18. $-\frac{198}{462}$ $\frac{3}{7}$
19. $-\frac{84}{1080}$ $-\frac{7}{90}$
20. $-\frac{525}{1155}$ $-\frac{5}{11}$

Write each fraction as a decimal.

21. $\frac{1}{4}$ 0.25
22. $-\frac{3}{10}$ -0.3
23. $\frac{1}{50}$ 0.02
24. $\frac{2}{3}$ $0.\overline{6}$

25. $-\frac{1}{9}$ $-0.\overline{1}$
26. $-\frac{16}{25}$ -0.64
27. $-\frac{9}{20}$ -0.45
28. $\frac{1}{11}$ $0.\overline{09}$

29. $\frac{5}{9}$ $0.\overline{5}$
30. $-\frac{5}{8}$ -0.625
31. $\frac{43}{100}$ 0.43
32. $-\frac{5}{6}$ $-0.8\overline{3}$

33. $-\frac{7}{11}$ $-0.6\overline{3}$
34. $\frac{3}{7}$ 0.4286
35. $\frac{4}{5}$ 0.8
36. $-\frac{7}{12}$ $-0.58\overline{3}$

37. $-\frac{15}{16}$ 0.9375
38. $-\frac{8}{15}$ $-0.5\overline{3}$
39. $\frac{1}{6}$ $0.1\overline{6}$
40. $-\frac{11}{32}$ -0.34375

41. $\frac{9}{11}$ $0.\overline{81}$
42. $\frac{11}{16}$ 0.6875
43. $-\frac{11}{15}$ $-0.7\overline{3}$
44. $\frac{124}{125}$ 0.992

Write each mixed numeral as a decimal.

45. $-5\frac{1}{2}$ -5.5
46. $14\frac{17}{100}$ 14.17
47. $6\frac{3}{25}$ 6.12
48. $-7\frac{1}{3}$ $-7.3\overline{3}$

49. $4\frac{3}{25}$ 4.12
50. $-20\frac{2}{9}$ $-20.2\overline{2}$
51. $12\frac{3}{4}$ 12.75
52. $-10\frac{5}{6}$ $-10.8\overline{3}$

53. $-1\frac{4}{9}$ $-1.\overline{4}$
54. $-9\frac{16}{50}$ -9.32
55. $-2\frac{2}{11}$ $-2.\overline{18}$
56. $13\frac{13}{40}$ 13.325

57. $3\frac{5}{12}$ $3.41\overline{6}$
58. $-8\frac{5}{7}$ -8.7143
59. $2\frac{3}{5}$ 2.6
60. $11\frac{1}{12}$ $11.08\overline{3}$

61. $-44\frac{3}{8}$ -44.375
62. $19\frac{8}{15}$ $19.5\overline{3}$
63. $-67\frac{7}{10}$ -67.7
64. $5\frac{3}{16}$ 5.1875

65. $78\frac{2}{9}$ $78.\overline{2}$
66. $-108\frac{1}{20}$ -108.05
67. $-51\frac{6}{7}$ -51.8571
68. $8\frac{1}{15}$ $8.0\overline{6}$

Write each decimal as a fraction in simplest form.

69. 0.3 $\frac{3}{10}$
70. 0.14 $\frac{7}{50}$
71. 0.013 $\frac{13}{1000}$
72. -1.25 $-\frac{5}{4}$ or $-1\frac{1}{4}$

73. 4.2 $4\frac{1}{5}$ or $\frac{21}{5}$
74. -20.05 $-20\frac{1}{20}$ or $-\frac{401}{20}$
75. $0.\overline{3}$ $\frac{1}{3}$
76. -14.50 $-14\frac{1}{2}$ or $-\frac{29}{2}$

77. $-12.\overline{7}$ $-12\frac{7}{9}$ or $-\frac{115}{9}$
78. 6.125 $6\frac{1}{8}$ or $\frac{49}{8}$
79. -8.6 $-8\frac{3}{5}$ or $-\frac{43}{5}$
80. $-8.\overline{6}$ $-8\frac{2}{3}$ or $-\frac{26}{3}$

81. 23.15 $23\frac{3}{20}$ or $\frac{463}{20}$
82. -0.37 $-\frac{37}{100}$
83. -33.85 $-33\frac{17}{20}$ or $-\frac{677}{20}$
84. 1.16 $1\frac{4}{25}$ or $\frac{29}{25}$

85. -2.27 $-2\frac{27}{100}$ or $-\frac{227}{100}$
86. 16.75 $16\frac{3}{4}$ or $\frac{67}{4}$
87. -5.375 $-5\frac{3}{8}$ or $-\frac{43}{8}$
88. 4.26 $4\frac{13}{50}$ or $\frac{213}{50}$

89. 7.1875 $7\frac{3}{16}$ or $\frac{115}{16}$
90. -9.45 $-9\frac{9}{20}$ or $-\frac{189}{20}$
91. $5.2\overline{6}$ $5\frac{4}{15}$ or $\frac{79}{15}$
92. -0.324 $-\frac{81}{250}$

Percents

Write each decimal as a percent.

1. 0.71 **71%**
2. 0.4 **40%**
3. 0.835 **83.5%**
4. 1.05 **105%**
5. 0.009 **0.9%**
6. 0.27 **27%**
7. 2.5 **250%**
8. 0.706 **70.6%**

Write each fraction as a percent.

9. $\frac{31}{100}$ **31%**
10. $\frac{1}{2}$ **50%**
11. $\frac{4}{5}$ **80%**
12. $\frac{3}{10}$ **30%**
13. $\frac{1}{8}$ **12.5%**
14. $\frac{5}{4}$ **125%**
15. $\frac{2}{3}$ **$66\frac{2}{3}$%**
16. $\frac{4}{11}$ **$36\frac{4}{11}$%**

Write each percent as a decimal.

17. 14% **0.14**
18. 10% **0.10**
19. 450% **4.50**
20. 6% **0.06**
21. 27.5% **0.275**
22. 4.2% **0.042**
23. 190.5% **1.905**
24. 0.3% **0.003**

Write each percent as a fraction in simplest form.

25. 17% $\frac{17}{100}$
26. 40% $\frac{2}{5}$
27. 8% $\frac{2}{25}$
28. 75% $\frac{3}{4}$
29. 0.9% $\frac{9}{1000}$
30. 2.5% $2\frac{1}{2}$ or $\frac{5}{2}$
31. 45.6% $\frac{57}{125}$
32. 1.05% $\frac{21}{20}$

Solve.

33. 10% of 70 is __. **7**
34. 20% of 35 is __. **7**
35. 4% of 250 is __. **10**
36. 255% of 160 is __. **408**
37. 115% of 24 is __. **27.6**
38. 130% of 60 is __. **78**
39. __ is 3.7% of 300. **11.1**
40. __ is 22.5% of 260. **58.5**
41. __ is 52.6% of 150. **78.9**
42. 5 is __% of 20. **25%**
43. 3 is __% of 10. **30%**
44. 17 is __% of 68. **25%**
45. __% of 500 is 55. **11%**
46. __% of 96 is 12. **12.5%**
47. __% of 81 is 27. **$33\frac{1}{3}$%**
48. 40% of __ is 12. **30**
49. 10% of __ is 16. **160**
50. 65% of __ is 26. **40**
51. 25 is $33\frac{1}{3}$% of __. **75**
52. 54 is 108% of __. **50**
53. 1.28 is 16% of __. **8**
54. 6.3% of 400 is __. **25.2**
55. __% of 40 is 25. **62.5%**
56. 68% of __ is 85. **125**
57. 44% of __ is 37.4. **85**
58. 53% of 62 is __. **32.86**
59. __% of 16 is 56. **350%**
60. __ is 235% of 270. **634.5**
61. __ is 5.8% of 45. **2.61**
62. 28 is __% of 21. **$133\frac{1}{3}$%**
63. 2.5% of __ is 1. **40**
64. __% of 20 is 26.2. **131%**
65. 420% of __ is 336. **80**
66. __% of 45 is 30. **$66\frac{2}{3}$%**
67. $87\frac{1}{2}$% of __ is 14. **16**
68. $66\frac{2}{3}$% of 81 is __. **54**
69. __ is 12.4% of 15. **1.86**
70. 135 is 675% of __. **20**
71. 45 is __% of 36. **125%**
72. 14.5% of 18 is __. **2.61**
73. 180.5% of 200 is __. **361**
74. 98.1 is __% of 90. **109%**
75. __% of 85 is 102. **120%**
76. 3% of __ is 18. **600**
77. 44% of __ is 37.4. **85**
78. __% of 170 is 153. **90%**
79. 738 is 72% of __. **1025**
80. $266\frac{2}{3}$% of 561 is __. **1496**

Evaluating Expressions

Evaluate each expression if $a = 3$, $b = 5$, $c = 12$, and $d = 9$.

1. $8 + c$ **20**
2. $d - 4$ **5**
3. $b \cdot d$ **45**
4. $c \div a$ **4**
5. $a + c + d$ **24**
6. $c - d$ **3**
7. $a \cdot b \cdot c$ **180**
8. $d - a$ **6**
9. $a \cdot c$ **36**
10. $\frac{d}{a}$ **3**
11. $\frac{13 + c}{b}$ **5**
12. $\frac{a + d}{4}$ **3**

Evaluate each expression if $e = 2$, $f = 5$, $g = 6$, and $h = 10$.

13. $8g$ **48**
14. fh **50**
15. g^2 **36**
16. e^5 **32**
17. $7f^2$ **175**
18. g^2h^3 **36,000**
19. $\frac{h^4}{f^2}$ **400**
20. $3e^2g$ **72**
21. $8g^2f^2$ **7200**
22. $e^4f^2h^3$ **400,000**
23. $20e^3f^3g$ **120,000**
24. $\frac{3e^2f^3}{g}$ **250**

Evaluate each expression if $x = 3$, $j = 4$, $k = 9$, and $m = 20$.

25. $k^2 - 4k + 6$ **51**
26. $(m + j) \div 3$ **8**
27. $x^3j^2 - 4m$ **352**
28. $(xj + k) \div x$ **7**
29. $5j^2 \div m + k^2$ **85**
30. $j^3 + mk + 4x^4$ **568**
31. $(j^3 + m)k - 4x$ **744**
32. $(xj)^2 + km^2$ **3744**
33. $k^3 + m \div j - 5j^2$ **654**
34. $(5 + j)^2 \div k + m^2$ **409**
35. $(m - k)^3 \div (2j + 3)$ **121**
36. $(x^4 + k)m^2 - kx$ **35,973**

Evaluate each expression if $n = -1$, $p = 6$, $q = -8$, $r = 15$, and $s = -24$.

37. $pr + 2q$ **74**
38. $pn^4 + s$ **−18**
39. $r^2 - q + 5s$ **113**
40. $pq^2 \div ns$ **16**
41. $(p + 2q)n - r$ **−5**
42. $(p + q)^5n^5 + s$ **8**
43. $pr^2 + ns - 6q$ **1422**
44. $p(r^2 + ns) - 6q$ **1542**
45. $(q + r + s)p + n$ **−103**
46. $\frac{4(p^2 + q^2)}{2q} - s$ **−1**
47. $(p + n)^3 + \left(\frac{s}{p}\right)q$ **157**
48. $[(r + s)q]p$ **432**

The formula for the total surface area of a rectangular solid is $T = 2\ell w + 2wh + 2\ell h$, where T is the total surface area of the solid, ℓ is its length, w is its width, and h is its height. Find the total surface area of each rectangular solid.

49. $\ell = 8$, $w = 5$, $h = 14$ **444**
50. $\ell = 4$, $w = 2.5$, $h = 3$ **59**
51. $\ell = 7$, $w = 7$, $h = 16$ **546**
52. $\ell = 14$, $w = 17$, $h = 11$ **1158**
53. $\ell = 21$, $w = 18$, $h = 6$ **1224**
54. $\ell = 3.7$, $w = 1.2$, $h = 3.5$ **43.18**

The formula to change Fahrenheit degrees to Celsius degrees is $C = \frac{5}{9}(F - 32)$, where C is the temperature in Celsius degrees and F is the temperature in Fahrenheit degrees. Change each temperature in Fahrenheit degrees to Celsius degrees.

55. $86°F$ **30°C**
56. $5°F$ **−15°C**
57. $-13°F$ **−25°C**
58. $41°F$ **5°C**
59. $-40°F$ **−40°C**
60. $23°F$ **−5°C**
61. $-58°F$ **−50°C**
62. $374°F$ **190°C**

Inequalities

Replace each ▓ with >, <, or = to make each sentence true.

1. $9 \; \underset{<}{▓} \; 12$ **2.** $14 \; \underset{>}{▓} \; 7$ **3.** $-3 \; \underset{<}{▓} \; 0$ **4.** $-7 \; \underset{<}{▓} \; -3$

5. $-5 \; \underset{<}{▓} \; 3$ **6.** $7 + 8 \; \underset{=}{▓} \; 15$ **7.** $-8 + 5 \; \underset{>}{▓} \; -6$ **8.** $-24 \div (-8) \; \underset{>}{▓} \; -3$

9. $-3 - (-9) \; \underset{>}{▓} \; -12$ **10.** $-9 \; \underset{<}{▓} \; -3 + (-4)$ **11.** $-6 \cdot 3 \; \underset{=}{▓} \; -18$ **12.** $10 \; \underset{>}{▓} \; 36 \div 4$

13. $8 \; \underset{>}{▓} \; -40 \div 5$ **14.** $5 - (-4) \; \underset{=}{▓} \; 9$ **15.** $27 \; \underset{<}{▓} \; 4 \cdot 7$ **16.** $4 - 7 \; \underset{<}{▓} \; 3$

Solve each inequality.   **56.** all real numbers   **58.** $-\frac{1}{2} \le p < \frac{1}{2}$

17. $x + 4 < 10$ $x < 6$ **18.** $a + 7 \ge 15$ $a \ge 8$ **19.** $g + 5 > -8$ $g > -13$

20. $c + 9 \le 3$ $c \le -6$ **21.** $z - 4 > 20$ $z > 24$ **22.** $h - (-7) > -2$ $h > -9$

23. $m - 14 \le -9$ $m \le 5$ **24.** $d - (-3) < 13$ $d < 10$ **25.** $\frac{g}{-8} < 4$ $g > -32$

26. $\frac{w}{3} > -12$ $w > -36$ **27.** $\frac{p}{5} < 8$ $p < 40$ **28.** $\frac{t}{-4} \ge -10$ $t \le 40$

29. $7b \ge -49$ $b \ge -7$ **30.** $-5j < -60$ $j > 12$ **31.** $-8f < 48$ $f > -6$

32. $-2 + 9n \le 10n$ $n \ge -2$ **33.** $-5e + 9 > 24$ $e < -3$ **34.** $3y - 4 > -37$ $y > -11$

35. $7s - 12 < 13$ $s < \frac{25}{7}$ **36.** $-6v - 3 \ge -33$ $v \le 5$ **37.** $-2k + 12 < 30$ $k > -9$

38. $-2x + 1 < 16 - x$ $x > -15$ **39.** $15t - 4 > 11t - 16$ $t > -3$ **40.** $13 - y \le 29 + 2y$ $y \ge -\frac{16}{3}$

41. $5q + 7 \le 3(q + 1)$ $q \le -2$ **42.** $2(w + 4) \ge 7(w - 1)$ $w \le 3$ **43.** $-4t - 5 > 2t + 13$ $t < -3$

44. $9m + 7 < 2(4m - 1)$ **45.** $3\left(a + \frac{2}{3}\right) \ge a - 1$ $a \ge -\frac{3}{2}$ **46.** $3(3y + 1) < 13y - 8$ $y > \frac{11}{4}$
     $m < -9$

47. $2 + x < -5$ or $2 + x > 5$ $x < -7$ or $x > 3$ **48.** $-4 + t > -5$ or $-4 + t < 7$ all real numbers

49. $3 \le 2g + 7$ and $2g + 7 \le 15$ $-2 \le g \le 4$ **50.** $7 - 3s < 13$ and $7s < 3s + 12$ $-2 < s < 3$

51. $2x + 1 < -3$ or $3x - 2 > 4$ $x < -2$ or $x > 2$ **52.** $2v - 2 \le 3v$ and $4v - 1 \ge 3v$ $v \ge 1$

53. $3b - 4 \le 7b + 12$ and $8b - 7 \le 25$ **54.** $-9 < 2z + 7 < 10$ $-8 < z < \frac{3}{2}$
     $-4 \le b \le 4$

55. $5m - 8 \ge 10 - m$ or $5m + 11 < -9$ **56.** $12c - 4 \le 5c + 10$ or $-4c - 1 \le c + 24$
     $m \ge 3$ or $m < -4$

57. $2h - 2 \le 3h \le 4h - 1$ $h \ge 1$ **58.** $3p + 6 < 8 - p$ and $5p + 8 \ge p + 6$

59. $4a + 3 < 3 - 5a$ or $a - 1 \ge -a$ $a < 0$ or $a \ge \frac{1}{2}$ **60.** $d - 4 < 5d + 14 < 3d + 26$ $-\frac{9}{2} < d < 6$

61. $2r + 8 > 16 - 2r$ and $7r + 21 < r - 9$ $\emptyset$ **62.** $-4j + 3 < j + 22$ and $j - 3 < 2j - 15$ $j > 12$

63. $3n \ne 9$ and $6n - 5 \le 2n + 7$ $n < 3$ **64.** $7e \ne -21$ and $5e + 8 \ge e + 6$ $e \ge -\frac{1}{2}$

65. $2(q - 4) \le 3(q + 2)$ or $q - 8 \le 4 - q$ **66.** $\frac{1}{2}w + 5 \ge w + 2 \ge \frac{1}{2}w + 9$ $w \le 6$
     $q \ge -14$ or $q \le 6$

67. $|g + 6| > 8$ **68.** $|t - 5| \le 3$ **69.** $|a + 5| \ge 0$ **70.** $|y - 9| < 19$
   $g > 2$ or $g < -14$ $2 \le t \le 8$ all real numbers $-10 < y < 28$

71. $|2m - 5| > 13$ **72.** $|14 - w| \ge 20$ **73.** $|3p + 5| \le 23$ **74.** $|6b - 12| \le 36$
   $m > 9$ or $m < -4$ $w \le -6$ or $w \ge 34$ $-\frac{28}{3} \le p \le 6$ $-4 \le b \le 8$

75. $|25 - 3x| < 5$ **76.** $|7 + 8x| > 39$ **77.** $|4c + 5| \ge 25$ **78.** $|4 - 5s| > 46$
   $\frac{20}{3} < x < 10$ $x > 4$ or $x < -\frac{23}{4}$ $c \ge 5$ or $c \le -\frac{15}{2}$ $s < -\frac{42}{5}$ or $s > 10$

Polynomials: Addition and Subtraction

Find each sum. 12. $8x + 5y - 13z$ 16. $-3x^2 + 3x + 20$ 18. $6g + 5h - 6k - 9$

1. $(3x - 4y) + (8x + 6y)$ $11x + 2y$

2. $(12b + 2a) + (7b - 13a)$ $19b - 11a$

3. $(7m - 8n) + (4m - 5n)$ $11m - 13n$

4. $(5x^2 + 3x) + (4x^2 + 2x)$ $9x^2 + 5x$

5. $(-6s - 11t) + (5s - 6t)$ $-s - 17t$

6. $(-14g - h) + (-8g + 5h)$ $-22g + 4h$

7. $(4p - 7q) + (5q - 8p)$ $-4p - 2q$

8. $(5y^2 - 7y) + (7y - 3y^2)$ $2y^2$

9. $(9b^3 - 3b^2) + (12b^2 + 4b)$ $9b^3 + 9b^2 + 4b$

10. $(2r + 8s) + (-3s - 9t)$ $2r + 5s - 9t$

11. $(2a^2 + 4a + 5) + (2a^2 - 10a + 6)$
$4a^2 - 6a + 11$

12. $(7x - 2y - 5z) + (x + 7y - 8z)$

13. $(-3m + 9mn - 5n) + (14m - 2n - 5mn)$
$11m + 4mn - 7n$

14. $(5x + 8y + 3z) + (-6z + 6y)$ $5x + 14y - 3z$

15. $(6 - 4g - 9h) + (12g - 4h - 6j)$
$6 + 8g - 13h - 6j$

16. $(x^2 - 4x + 8) + (12 + 7x - 4x^2)$

17. $(-7t^2 + 4ts - 6s^2) + (3s^2 - 12ts - 5t^2)$
$-12t^2 - 8ts - 3s^2$

18. $(7g + 8h - 9) + (-g - 3h - 6k)$

19. $(8a^2 - 4ab - 3b^2 + a - 4b) + (3a^2 + 6ab - 9b^2 + 7a + 9b)$ $11a^2 + 2ab - 12b^2 + 8a + 5b$

20. $(-3v + 14w - 12x - 13y + 6z - 8) + (16 - 6v + 2x - 5y - 2z)$
$-9v + 14w - 10x - 18y + 4z + 8$

21. $(3y^2 - 7y + 6) + (3 - 2y^2 - 5y) + (y^2 - 8y - 12)$ $2y^2 - 20y - 3$

22. $(4a^2 - 10b^2 + 7c^2) + (2c^2 - 5a^2 + 2b) + (7b^2 - 7c^2 + 7a)$ $-a^2 - 3b^2 + 2c^2 + 7a + 2b$

23. $(5x^2 + 3) + (4 - 7x - 9x^2) + (2x - 3x^2 - 5) + (2x - 6)$ $-7x^2 - 3x - 4$

24. $(9p - 13p^2) + (7p^2 + 5q^2) + (-6p - 12q) + (3q - 8q^2)$ $-6p^2 + 3p - 3q^2 - 9q$

Find each difference. 36. $4v - 20w + 8x$ 42. $-3x^2 - 8y^2 + 11z^2 + 12$ 44. $15j^4k^2 - 15j^2k - 3$

25. $(5g + 3h) - (2g + 7h)$ $3g - 4h$

26. $(2e - 5f) - (7e - f)$ $-5e - 4f$

27. $(-3m + 8n) - (6m - 4n)$ $-9m + 12n$

28. $(6a^2 - 9a) - (4a^2 + 2a)$ $2a^2 - 11a$

29. $(-11k + 6) - (-6k - 8)$ $-5k + 14$

30. $(9y^2 - 4y) - (-6y^2 - 8y)$ $15y^2 + 4y$

31. $(-r - 3s) - (2s - 5r)$ $4r - 5s$

32. $(13c^2 - 4c) - (5c - 12c^2)$ $25c^2 - 9c$

33. $(g^3 - 2g^2) - (5g^2 - 7)$ $g^3 - 7g^2 + 7$

34. $(7a + 4b) - (7b - 6c)$ $7a - 3b + 6c$

35. $(z^2 + 6z - 8) - (4z^2 - 7z - 5)$ $-3z^2 + 13z - 3$

36. $(6v - 12w - 2x) - (2v + 8w - 10x)$

37. $(6a^2 - 7ab - 4b^2) - (6b^2 + 2a^2 + 5ab)$
$4a^2 - 12ab - 10b^2$

38. $(3r - 7t) - (2t + 2s + 9r)$ $-6r - 2s - 9t$

39. $(7ax^2 + 2ax - 4a) - (5ax - 2ax^2 + 8a)$
$9ax^2 - 3ax - 12a$

40. $(h^3 + 4h^2 - 7h) - (3h^2 - 7h - 8)$ $h^3 + h^2 + 8$

41. $(4d + 3e - 8f) - (-3d + 10e - 5f + 6)$
$7d - 7e - 3f - 6$

42. $(-3z^2 + 4x^2 - 8y^2) - (7x^2 - 14z^2 - 12)$

43. $(2b^2 + 7b - 2) - (2b^2 + 3b - 16)$ $4b + 14$

44. $(15j^4k^2 - 7j^2k + 8) - (8j^2k + 11)$

45. $(9x^2 - 11xy - 3y^2) - (12y^2 + x^2 - 16xy)$
$8x^2 + 5xy - 15y^2$

46. $(17z^4 - 5z^2 + 3z) - (4z^4 + 2z^3 + 3z)$
$13z^4 - 2z^3 - 5z^2$

47. $(-4p - 7q - 3t) - (-8t - 5q - 8p)$
$4p - 2q + 5t$

48. $(-14h + 16j - 7k) - (-3j + 5h - 6k - 3)$
$-19h + 19j - k + 3$

49. $(14a + 9b - 2x - 11y + 4z) - (8a + 8b + 6x - 5y - 7z)$ $6a + b - 8x - 6y + 11z$

50. $(7m^2 - 3mn + 4n^2 - 2m - 8n) - (4m^2 + 3m - 4n^2 - 13n + 4mn)$
$3m^2 - 7mn + 8n^2 - 5m + 5n$

Polynomials: Multiplication and Division

Find each product.

1. $t^3 \cdot t^6$ t^9

2. $g^5 \cdot g^9$ g^{14}

3. $(3x^2y)(-5x^3y^8)$ $-15x^5y^9$

4. $(7p^4q^7r^2)(4p^5r^7)$ $28p^9q^7r^9$

5. $(2a^2b)(-b^2c^3)(-8ab^2c^4)$ $16a^3b^5c^7$

6. $(e^4f^6g)^5$ $e^{20}f^{30}g^5$

7. $(-2m^6n^2)^6$ $64m^{36}n^{12}$

8. $(-3h^2k^3)^3(5hj^6k^8)^2$ $-675h^8j^{12}k^{25}$

9. $(v^4w)^6(-1v^3w^2)^8$ $v^{48}w^{22}$

10. $5y(y^2 - 3y + 6)$ $5y^3 - 15y^2 + 30y$

11. $-ab(3b^2 + 4ab - 6a^2)$ $-3ab^3 - 4a^2b^2 + 6a^3b$

12. $4st^2(-4s^2t^3 + 7s^5 - 3st^3)$ $-16s^3t^5 + 28s^6t^2 - 12s^2t^5$

13. $(d + 2)(d + 3)$ $d^2 + 5d + 6$

14. $(z + 7)(z - 4)$ $z^2 + 3z - 28$

15. $(m - 5)(m - 8)$ $m^2 - 13m + 40$

16. $(2x - 5)(x + 6)$ $2x^2 + 7x - 30$

17. $(7a - 4)(2a - 5)$ $14a^2 - 43a + 20$

18. $(t + 7)^2$ $t^2 + 14t + 49$

19. $(q - 4h)^2$ $q^2 - 8hq + 16h^2$

20. $(w - 12)(w + 12)$ $w^2 - 144$

21. $(2b + 4d)(2b - 4d)$ $4b^2 - 16d^2$

22. $(4x + y)(2x - 3y)$ $8x^2 - 10xy - 3y^2$

23. $(7v + 3)(v + 4)$ $7v^2 + 31v + 12$

24. $(4e + 3)(4e + 3)$ $16e^2 + 24e + 9$

25. $(7s - 8)(3s - 2)$ $21s^2 - 38s + 16$

26. $(5b - 6)(5b + 6)$ $25b^2 - 36$

27. $(4g + 3h)(2g - 5h)$ $8g^2 - 14gh - 15h^2$

28. $(5c - 2d)^2$ $25c^2 - 20cd + 4d^2$

29. $(10x + 11y)(10x - 11y)$ $100x^2 - 121y^2$

30. $(12r - 4s)(5r + 8s)$ $60r^2 + 76rs - 32s^2$

Simplify.

31. $\dfrac{24x^5}{8x^2}$ $3x^3$

32. $\dfrac{s^7t^4}{s^5}$ s^2t^4

33. $\dfrac{-9h^2k^4}{18h^5j^3k^4}$ $\dfrac{-1}{2h^3j^3}$

34. $\dfrac{3m^7n^2p^4}{9m^2np^3}$ $\dfrac{m^5np}{3}$

35. $\dfrac{9a^2b^7c^3}{12a^5b^4c}$ $\dfrac{3b^3c^2}{4a^3}$

36. $\dfrac{-15xy^5z^7}{-10x^4y^6z^4}$ $\dfrac{3z^3}{2x^3y}$

37. $\dfrac{-5w^4v^2 - 3w^3v}{w^3}$ $-5wv^2 - 3v$

38. $\dfrac{8g^4h^4 + 4g^3h^3}{2gh^2}$ $4g^3h^2 + 2g^2h$

39. $\dfrac{x^2 - 2x - 15}{x - 3}$ $x + 1$ R -12

40. $\dfrac{q^2 - 10q + 24}{q - 4}$ $q - 6$

41. $\dfrac{2j^2 + 10j + 12}{j + 3}$ $2j + 4$

42. $\dfrac{12d^2 + d - 6}{3d - 2}$ $4d + 3$

43. $\dfrac{4s^3 + 4s^2 - 9s - 18}{2s + 3}$ $2s^2 - s - 3$ R -9

44. $\dfrac{z^3 - 27}{z - 3}$ $z^2 + 3z + 9$

45. $\dfrac{6n^3 + 7n^2 - 29n + 12}{3n - 4}$ $2n^2 + 5n - 3$

46. $\dfrac{3e^2 + 3e - 80}{e - 5}$ $3e + 18$ R10

47. $\dfrac{-6k^2 + 3k + 12}{2k + 3}$ $-3k + 6$ R -6

48. $\dfrac{t^3 + 3t}{t - 1}$ $t^2 + t + 4$ R4

49. $\dfrac{4g^3 - 4g - 20}{2g - 4}$ $2g^2 + 4g + 6$ R4

50. $\dfrac{9a^3 - 3a^2 + 7a + 2}{3a + 1}$ $3a^2 - 2a + 3$ R -1

51. $\dfrac{8c^3 - 2c^2 + 2c - 4}{2c - 2}$ $4c^2 + 3c + 4$ R4

52. $\dfrac{8y^3 - 1}{2y + 1}$ $4y^2 - 2y + 1$ R -2

53. $\dfrac{12m^3 + m^2 - 20}{4m - 5}$ $3m^2 + 4m + 5$ R5

54. $\dfrac{5b^3 - 2b^2 + 7b + 4}{5b + 3}$ $b^2 - b + 2$ R -2

Factoring

Find the prime factorization of each integer. Write each negative integer as the product of -1 and its prime factors. 12. $-1 \cdot 2 \cdot 2 \cdot 2 \cdot 3 \cdot 3 \cdot 5$ 15. $-1 \cdot 2 \cdot 2 \cdot 3 \cdot 3 \cdot 3 \cdot 7 \cdot 7$

1. 35 $5 \cdot 7$
2. 12 $2 \cdot 2 \cdot 3$
3. 72 $2 \cdot 2 \cdot 2 \cdot 3 \cdot 3$
4. 64 $2 \cdot 2 \cdot 2 \cdot 2 \cdot 2 \cdot 2$

5. -75 $-1 \cdot 3 \cdot 5 \cdot 5$
6. 70 $2 \cdot 5 \cdot 7$
7. 85 $5 \cdot 17$
8. -92 $-1 \cdot 2 \cdot 2 \cdot 23$

9. -117 $-1 \cdot 3 \cdot 3 \cdot 13$
10. -114 $-1 \cdot 2 \cdot 3 \cdot 19$
11. 243 $3 \cdot 3 \cdot 3 \cdot 3 \cdot 3$
12. -360

13. 405 $3 \cdot 3 \cdot 3 \cdot 3 \cdot 5$
14. 605 $5 \cdot 11 \cdot 11$
15. -5292
16. 5076 $2 \cdot 2 \cdot 3 \cdot 3 \cdot 3 \cdot 47$

Factor. 22. $6g^4h^3(g - 2h^3k - 3g^2h^2)$

17. $10g + 35h$ $5(2g + 7h)$
18. $t^3s^2 - t^2$ $t^2(ts^2 - 1)$

19. $15a^2b - 24a^5b^2$ $3a^2b(5 - 8a^3b)$
20. $18c^4d - 30c^3e$ $6c^3(3cd - 5e)$

21. $36m^4n^2p + 12m^5n^3p^2$ $12m^4n^2p(3 + mnp)$
22. $6g^5h^3 - 12g^4h^6k - 18g^6h^5$

23. $p^2 - q^2$ $(p + q)(p - q)$
24. $144x^2 - 49y^2$ $(12x + 7y)(12x - 7y)$

25. $75r^2 - 48$ $3(5r + 4)(5r - 4)$
26. $64v^2 - 100w^4$ $(8v + 10w^2)(8v - 10w^2)$

27. $g^2 + 4g + 4$ $(g + 2)^2$
28. $t^2 - 22t + 121$ $(t - 11)^2$

29. $9n^2 - 36nm + 36m^2$ $9(n - 2m)^2$
30. $2a^2b^2 + 4ab^2c^2 + 2b^2c^4$ $2b^2(a + c^2)^2$

31. $g^2 - 14g + 48$ $(g - 6)(g - 8)$
32. $z^2 + 15z + 36$ $(z + 3)(z + 12)$

33. $12 - 13b + b^2$ $(12 - b)(1 - b)$
34. $x^2 + 17xy + 16y^2$ $(x + 16y)(x + y)$

35. $g^2 - 4g - 32$ $(g - 8)(g + 4)$
36. $h^2 + 12h - 28$ $(h - 2)(h + 14)$

37. $s^2 - 13st - 30t^2$ $(s + 2t)(s - 15t)$
38. $3a^2 + 11a + 10$ $(3a + 5)(a + 2)$

39. $6y^2 + 2y - 20$ $2(3y - 5)(y + 2)$
40. $12j^2 - 34j - 20$ $2(2j + 1)(3j - 10)$

41. $24a^2 - 57ax + 18x^2$ $3(8a - 3x)(a - 2x)$
42. $2sx - 4tx + 2sy - 4ty$ $(2s - 4t)(x + y)$

43. $8ac - 2ad + 4bc - bd$ $(2a + b)(4c - d)$
44. $2e^2g + 2fg + 4e^2h + 4fh$ $(2e^2 + 2f)(g + 2h)$

45. $5x^3 - 2x^2y - 5xy^2 + 2y^3$
$(5x - 2y)(x + y)(x - y)$
46. $4p^2 + 12pr + 9r^2$ $(2p + 3r)^2$

47. $169 - 16t^2$ $(13 - 4t)(13 + 4t)$
48. $b^2 - 11b - 42$ $(b - 14)(b + 3)$

49. $30g^2h - 15g^3$ $15g^2(2h - g)$
50. $3b^2 - 13bd + 4d^2$ $(3b - d)(b - 4d)$

51. $a^2x - 2a^2y - 5x + 10y$ $(x - 2y)(a^2 - 5)$
52. $s^2 + 30s + 225$ $(s + 15)^2$

53. $18v^2 + 42v + 12$ $6(3v + 1)(v + 2)$
54. $4k^2 + 2k - 12$ $2(2k - 3)(k + 2)$

55. $5z^3 - 8z^2 - 21z$ $z(5z + 7)(z - 3)$
56. $5g^2 - 20h^2$ $5(g - 2h)(g + 2h)$

57. $30x^2 - 125x + 70$ $5(3x - 2)(2x - 7)$
58. $a^2b^2 - b^2 + a^2 - 1$ $(b^2 + 1)(a + 1)(a - 1)$

59. $8t^4 + 56t^3 + 98t^2$ $2t^2(2t + 7)^2$
60. $3p^3q^2 + 27pq^2$ $3pq^2(p^2 + 9)$

61. $a^2c^2 + b^2c^2 - 4a^2d^2 - 4b^2d^2$
$(c - 2d)(c + 2d)(a^2 + b^2)$
62. $36m^3n - 90m^2n^2 + 36mn^2$
$18mn(2m^2 - 5mn + 2n)$

63. $4x^2z^2 + 7xyz^2 - 36y^2z^2$ $z^2(4x - 9y)(x + 4y)$
64. $4g^2j^2 - 25h^2j^2 - 4g^2 + 25h^2$
$(2g - 5h)(2g + 5h)(j - 1)(j + 1)$

Algebraic Fractions

Simplify.

1. $\dfrac{48a^2b^5c}{32a^7b^2c^3}$ $\dfrac{3b^3}{2a^5c^2}$

2. $\dfrac{-28x^3y^4z^5}{42xyz^2}$ $\dfrac{-2x^2y^3z^3}{3}$

3. $\dfrac{k+3}{4k^2+7k-15}$ $\dfrac{1}{4k-5}$

4. $\dfrac{t^2-s^2}{5t^2-2st-3s^2}$ $\dfrac{t+s}{5t+3s}$

5. $\dfrac{6g^2-19g+15}{12g^2-6g-18}$ $\dfrac{3g-5}{6(g+1)}$

6. $\dfrac{2d^2+4d-6}{d^4-10d^2+9}$ $\dfrac{2}{(d+1)(d-3)}$

Find each product or quotient.

7. $\dfrac{5m^2n}{12a^2} \cdot \dfrac{18an}{30m^4}$ $\dfrac{n^2}{4am^2}$

8. $\dfrac{25g^7h}{28t^3} \cdot \dfrac{42s^2t^3}{5g^5h^2}$ $\dfrac{15g^2s^2}{2h}$

9. $\dfrac{6a+4b}{36} \cdot \dfrac{45}{3a+2b}$ $\dfrac{5}{2}$

10. $\dfrac{x^2y}{18z} \div \dfrac{2yz}{3x^2}$ $\dfrac{x^4}{12z^2}$

11. $\dfrac{p^2}{14qr^3} \div \dfrac{2r^2p}{7q}$ $\dfrac{p}{4r^5}$

12. $\dfrac{3d}{2d^2-3d} \div \dfrac{9}{2d-3}$ $\dfrac{1}{3}$

13. $\dfrac{t^2-2t-15}{t-5} \cdot \dfrac{t+5}{t+3}$ $t+5$

14. $\dfrac{5e-f}{5e+f} \div (25e^2-f^2)$ $\dfrac{1}{(5e+f)^2}$

15. $\dfrac{8}{6c^2+17c+10} \div \dfrac{6}{c+2}$ $\dfrac{4}{3(6c+5)}$

16. $\dfrac{3v^2-27}{15v} \cdot \dfrac{v^2}{v+3}$ $\dfrac{v(v-3)}{5}$

17. $\dfrac{3k^2-10k+3}{5} \div \dfrac{3k-1}{15k}$ $3k(k-3)$

18. $\dfrac{3g^2+15g}{4} \cdot \dfrac{g^2}{g+5}$ $\dfrac{3g^3}{4}$

19. $\dfrac{x^2-2x-15}{2x^2-7x-15} \cdot \dfrac{4x^2-4x-15}{2x^2+x-15}$ 1

20. $\dfrac{a^2-16}{3a^2-13a+4} \div \dfrac{3a^2+11a-4}{a^3}$ $\dfrac{a^3}{(3a-1)^2}$

Find each sum or difference.

21. $\dfrac{j+4}{3} + \dfrac{j-7}{3}$ $\dfrac{2j-3}{3}$

22. $\dfrac{15n}{5n+3} + \dfrac{9}{5n+3}$ 3

23. $\dfrac{2a-3}{b} - \dfrac{a-5}{b}$ $\dfrac{a+2}{b}$

24. $\dfrac{25}{5-g} - \dfrac{g^2}{5-g}$ $5+g$

25. $\dfrac{s}{t^2} - \dfrac{r}{3t}$ $\dfrac{3s-rt}{3t^2}$

26. $\dfrac{7}{ab} + \dfrac{4}{bc}$ $\dfrac{7c+4a}{abc}$

27. $\dfrac{2}{2p+3} + \dfrac{p}{3p+2}$ $\dfrac{2p^2+9p+4}{(2p+3)(3p+2)}$

28. $\dfrac{x}{x+y} - \dfrac{5}{y}$ $\dfrac{xy-5x-5y}{y(x+y)}$

29. $\dfrac{c}{c^2-4c} - \dfrac{5c}{c-4}$ $\dfrac{1-5c}{c-4}$

30. $\dfrac{t+10}{t^2-100} + \dfrac{1}{t-10}$ $\dfrac{2}{t-10}$

31. $\dfrac{1}{g^2-6gh+9h^2} - \dfrac{3}{g-3h}$ $\dfrac{1-3g+9h}{(g-3h)^2}$

32. $\dfrac{x}{x+2} + \dfrac{x^2+3x}{x^2+5x+6}$ $\dfrac{2x}{x+2}$

33. $\dfrac{3d}{d^2-3d-10} + \dfrac{d+1}{d^2-8d+15}$ $\dfrac{4d^2-6d+2}{(d+2)(d-3)(d-5)}$

34. $\dfrac{k+2}{k^2-8k+16} - \dfrac{k+3}{k^2+k-20}$ $\dfrac{8k+22}{(k-4)^2(k+5)}$

Solving Equations

Solve each equation.

1. $2x - 5 = 3$ $x = 4$

2. $4t + 5 = 37$ $t = 8$

3. $7a + 6 = -36$ $a = -6$

4. $47 = -8g + 7$ $g = -5$

5. $-3c - 9 = -24$ $c = 5$

6. $5k - 7 = -52$ $k = -9$

7. $5s + 4s = -72$ $s = -8$

8. $6(y - 5) = 18$ $y = 8$

9. $-21 = 7(p - 10)$ $p = 7$

10. $2m + 5 - 6m = 25$ $m = -5$

11. $3z - 1 = 23 - 3z$ $z = 4$

12. $5b + 12 = 3b - 6$ $b = -9$

13. $\frac{e}{5} + 6 = -2$ $e = -40$

14. $\frac{d}{4} - 8 = -5$ $d = 12$

15. $\frac{p + 10}{3} = 4$ $p = 2$

16. $\frac{h - 7}{6} = 1$ $h = 13$

17. $\frac{5f + 1}{8} = -3$ $f = -5$

18. $\frac{4n - 8}{-2} = 12$ $n = -4$

19. $\frac{2a}{7} + 9 = 3$ $a = -21$

20. $\frac{-3t - 4}{2} = 8$ $t = -\frac{20}{3}$

21. $\frac{6v - 9}{3} = v$ $v = 3$

22. $|s - 4| = 7$ $s = 11$ or -3

23. $|5g + 8| = 33$ $g = 5$ or $-\frac{41}{5}$

24. $|16 - 3b| = 22$ $b = -2$ or $\frac{38}{3}$

25. $t(t - 4) = 0$ $t = 0$ or 4

26. $4p(p + 7) = 0$ $p = 0$ or -7

27. $7m(2m - 12) = 0$ $m = 0$ or 6

28. $(x - 5)(x + 8) = 0$
    $x = 5$ or -8

29. $(3s + 6)(2s - 7) = 0$
    $s = -2$ or $\frac{7}{2}$

30. $(4g + 5)(2g + 10) = 0$
    $g = -\frac{5}{4}$ or -5

31. $h^2 + 4h = 0$ $h = 0$ or -4

32. $3b^2 - 3b = 0$ $b = 0$ or 1

33. $m^2 - 16 = 0$ $m = 4$ or -4

34. $w^2 + w - 30 = 0$
    $w = -6$ or 5

35. $2c^2 - 14c + 24 = 0$
    $c = 4$ or 3

36. $6p^2 + 10p - 24 = 0$
    $p = -3$ or $\frac{4}{3}$

37. $5n^2 = 15n$ $n = 0$ or 3

38. $4x^2 + 20x + 25 = 0$ $x = -\frac{5}{2}$

39. $3y^2 = 75$ $y = 5$ or -5

40. $\frac{a}{3} - \frac{a}{4} = 3$ $a = 36$

41. $\frac{k}{6} + \frac{2k}{3} = -\frac{5}{2}$ $k = -3$

42. $\frac{r + 3}{r} + \frac{r - 12}{r} = 5$ $r = -3$

43. $\frac{2y}{y - 4} - \frac{3}{5} = 3$ $y = 9$

44. $\frac{2t}{t + 3} + \frac{3}{t} = 2$ $t = 3$

45. $\frac{2g}{2g + 1} - \frac{1}{2g - 1} = 1$ $g = 0$

46. $\frac{8n^2}{2n^2 - 5n - 3} = 4$ $n = -\frac{3}{5}$

47. $5 - \frac{5x}{x - 4} = \frac{2}{x^2 - 4x}$ $x = -\frac{1}{10}$

48. $\frac{2}{e + 1} - \frac{3}{e + 2} = 0$ $e = 1$

49. $\frac{1}{2d - 1} - \frac{12d}{6d^2 + d - 2} = \frac{-4}{3d + 2}$ $d = -2$

50. $\frac{4z}{2z + 1} - \frac{6 - z}{2z^2 - 5z - 3} = 2$ $z = 0$

51. $\frac{b + 1}{b - 2} - \frac{3b}{3b + 2} = \frac{20}{3b^2 - 4b - 4}$ $b = \frac{18}{11}$

52. $\frac{2s}{9s^2 - 3s - 2} + \frac{2}{3s + 1} = \frac{4}{3s - 2}$ $s = -2$

53. $\frac{m}{20} = \frac{9}{15}$ $m = 12$

54. $\frac{12}{21} = \frac{20}{f}$ $f = 35$

55. $\frac{4}{9} = \frac{16}{t + 8}$ $t = 28$

56. $\frac{4}{14} = \frac{2h - 1}{21}$ $h = 3.5$

57. $\frac{2 + c}{c - 5} = \frac{8}{9}$ $c = -58$

58. $\frac{2y + 4}{y - 3} = \frac{2}{3}$ $y = -\frac{9}{2}$ or -4.5

Radicals

Simplify. 46. $12\sqrt{2} + 6\sqrt{6}$ 47. $\frac{5(\sqrt{13} - \sqrt{7})}{3}$ 51. $\frac{15\sqrt{30} - 50\sqrt{2}}{7}$

1. $\sqrt{25}$ 5

2. $-\sqrt{64}$ −8

3. $\pm\sqrt{576}$ ±24

4. $\sqrt{900}$ 30

5. $\pm\sqrt{0.01}$ ±0.1

6. $\sqrt{1.44}$ 1.2

7. $-\sqrt{0.0016}$ −0.04

8. $\sqrt{4.84}$ 2.2

9. $\sqrt{\frac{36}{121}}$ $\frac{6}{11}$

10. $-\sqrt{\frac{16}{36}}$ $-\frac{2}{3}$

11. $\sqrt{\frac{81}{49}}$ $\frac{9}{7}$

12. $\pm\sqrt{\frac{64}{100}}$ $\pm\frac{4}{5}$

13. $\sqrt{75}$ $5\sqrt{3}$

14. $\sqrt{20}$ $2\sqrt{5}$

15. $\sqrt{162}$ $9\sqrt{2}$

16. $\sqrt{700}$ $10\sqrt{7}$

17. $\sqrt{4x^4y^3}$ $2x^2y\sqrt{y}$

18. $\sqrt{12ts^3}$ $2s\sqrt{3ts}$

19. $\sqrt{175m^4n^6}$ $5m^2n^3\sqrt{7}$

20. $\sqrt{99a^3b^7}$ $3ab^3\sqrt{11ab}$

21. $\sqrt{\frac{54}{g^2}}$ $\frac{3\sqrt{6}}{g}$

22. $\sqrt{\frac{32c^5}{9d^2}}$ $\frac{4c^2\sqrt{2c}}{3d}$

23. $\sqrt{\frac{27p^4}{3p^2}}$ $3p$

24. $\sqrt{\frac{243y^7}{3y^4}}$ $9y\sqrt{y}$

25. $\sqrt{7}$ $\sqrt{3}$ $\sqrt{21}$

26. $\sqrt{3}$ $\sqrt{15}$ $3\sqrt{5}$

27. $6\sqrt{2}$ $\sqrt{3}$ $6\sqrt{6}$

28. $5\sqrt{6} \cdot 2\sqrt{3}$ $30\sqrt{2}$

29. $\sqrt{5}(\sqrt{3} + \sqrt{10})$
$\sqrt{15} + 5\sqrt{2}$

30. $\sqrt{2}(\sqrt{6} + \sqrt{32})$
$2\sqrt{3} + 8$

31. $\sqrt{5}$ $\sqrt{t}$ $\sqrt{5t}$

32. $\sqrt{18}$ $\sqrt{g^3}$ $3g\sqrt{2g}$

33. $\sqrt{12k}$ $\sqrt{3k^5}$ $6k^3$

34. $\sqrt{15m^2}$ $\sqrt{6n^3}$
$3mn\sqrt{10n}$

35. $\frac{\sqrt{3}}{\sqrt{5}}$ $\frac{\sqrt{15}}{5}$

36. $\sqrt{\frac{2}{7}}$ $\frac{\sqrt{14}}{7}$

37. $\frac{3\sqrt{6}}{\sqrt{2}}$ $3\sqrt{3}$

38. $\sqrt{\frac{x}{8}}$ $\frac{\sqrt{2x}}{4}$

39. $\sqrt{\frac{t^2}{3}}$ $\frac{t\sqrt{3}}{3}$

40. $\sqrt{\frac{20}{a}}$ $\frac{2\sqrt{5a}}{a}$

41. $(5 + \sqrt{3})(5 - \sqrt{3})$ 22

42. $(\sqrt{17} + \sqrt{11})(\sqrt{17} - \sqrt{11})$ 6

43. $(2\sqrt{5} + \sqrt{7})(2\sqrt{5} - \sqrt{7})$ 13

44. $\frac{1}{3 + \sqrt{5}}$ $\frac{3 - \sqrt{5}}{4}$

45. $\frac{2}{\sqrt{3} - 5}$ $\frac{\sqrt{3} + 5}{-11}$

46. $\frac{12}{\sqrt{8} - \sqrt{6}}$

47. $\frac{10}{\sqrt{13} + \sqrt{7}}$

48. $\frac{14}{3\sqrt{2} + \sqrt{5}}$
$\frac{14(3\sqrt{2} - \sqrt{5})}{13}$

49. $\frac{\sqrt{3}}{\sqrt{3} - 5}$ $\frac{3 + 5\sqrt{3}}{-22}$

50. $\frac{\sqrt{6}}{7 - 2\sqrt{3}}$ $\frac{7\sqrt{6} + 6\sqrt{2}}{37}$

51. $\frac{5\sqrt{10}}{3\sqrt{3} + 2\sqrt{5}}$

52. $6\sqrt{13} + 7\sqrt{13}$
$13\sqrt{13}$

53. $9\sqrt{15} - 4\sqrt{15}$
$5\sqrt{15}$

54. $2\sqrt{11} - 8\sqrt{11}$
$-6\sqrt{11}$

55. $2\sqrt{12} + 5\sqrt{3}$ $9\sqrt{3}$

56. $2\sqrt{27} - 4\sqrt{12}$
$-2\sqrt{3}$

57. $4\sqrt{8} - 3\sqrt{5}$
$8\sqrt{2} - 3\sqrt{5}$

58. $8\sqrt{32} + 4\sqrt{50}$
$52\sqrt{2}$

59. $6\sqrt{20} + \sqrt{45}$ $15\sqrt{5}$

60. $2\sqrt{63} + 8\sqrt{45} - 6\sqrt{28}$
$-6\sqrt{7} + 24\sqrt{5}$

61. $10\sqrt{\frac{1}{5}} - \sqrt{45} - 12\sqrt{\frac{5}{9}}$
$-5\sqrt{5}$

62. $3\sqrt{\frac{1}{3}} - 9\sqrt{\frac{1}{12}} + \sqrt{243}$
$\frac{17\sqrt{3}}{2}$

Solve and check.

63. $\sqrt{t} = 10$ $t = 100$

64. $\sqrt{3g} = 6$ $g = 12$

65. $\sqrt{y} - 2 = 0$ $y = 4$

66. $5 + \sqrt{a} = 9$ $a = 16$

67. $\sqrt{2k} - 4 = 8$ $k = 72$

68. $\sqrt{5y + 4} = 7$ $y = 9$

69. $\sqrt{10x^2 - 5} = 3x$
$x = \sqrt{5}$

70. $\sqrt{2a^2 - 144} = a$
$a = 12$

71. $\sqrt{b^2 + 16} + 2b = 5b$
$b = \sqrt{2}$

72. $\sqrt{m + 2} + m = 4$ $m = 2$

73. $\sqrt{3 - 2c} + 3 = 2c$ $c = \frac{3}{2}$

Use the quadratic formula to solve each equation. 79. $w = \frac{4 \pm \sqrt{10}}{3}$ 81. $r = -1$ or $\frac{3}{2}$

74. $s^2 + 8s + 7 = 0$
$s = -7$ or -1

75. $d^2 - 14d + 24 = 0$
$d = 2$ or 12

76. $3h^2 = 27$ $h = 3$ or -3

77. $n^2 - 3n + 1 = 0$ $n = \frac{3 \pm \sqrt{5}}{2}$

78. $2z^2 + 5z - 1 = 0$ $z = \frac{-5 \pm \sqrt{33}}{4}$

79. $3w^2 - 8w + 2 = 0$

80. $3f^2 + 2f = 6$ $f = \frac{-1 \pm \sqrt{19}}{3}$

81. $2r^2 - r - 3 = 0$

82. $x^2 - 9x = 5$ $x = \frac{9 \pm \sqrt{101}}{2}$

Equations in Two Variables

Write an equation in slope-intercept form for each given slope and y-intercept.

1. $m = 2, b = 5$
$y = 2x + 5$

2. $m = -4, b = 1$
$y = -4x + 1$

3. $m = \frac{1}{2}, b = -3$
$y = \frac{1}{2}x - 3$

4. $m = -1, b = -6$
$y = -x - 6$

5. $m = \frac{3}{2}, b = 1$
$y = \frac{3}{2}x + 1$

6. $m = 5, b = \frac{1}{4}$
$y = 5x + \frac{1}{4}$

7. $m = \frac{2}{5}, b = -4$
$y = \frac{2}{5}x - 4$

8. $m = -\frac{3}{4}, b = \frac{1}{2}$
$y = -\frac{3}{4}x + \frac{1}{2}$

Write each equation in slope-intercept form.

9. $-3x + y = 2$
$y = 3x + 2$

10. $6x + y = -5$
$y = -6x - 5$

11. $2x - y = -3$
$y = 2x + 3$

12. $-x - y = 4$
$y = -x - 4$

13. $2x + 5y = 10$
$y = -\frac{2}{5}x + 2$

14. $x - 4y = -2$
$y = \frac{1}{4}x + \frac{1}{2}$

15. $-9x + 3y = -18$
$y = 3x - 6$

16. $4x + 7y = 3$
$y = -\frac{4}{7}x + \frac{3}{7}$

Write each equation in standard form.

17. $y = 3x + 6$
$-3x + y = 6$

18. $y = -4x + 1$
$4x + y = 1$

19. $y = \frac{2}{3}x - 7$
$2x - 3y = 21$

20. $y = \frac{1}{4}x + \frac{1}{2}$
$x - 4y = -2$

21. $y = -\frac{5}{3}x - \frac{1}{3}$
$5x + 3y = -1$

22. $y = 2x - \frac{1}{2}$
$-2x + y = -\frac{1}{2}$

23. $\frac{5}{6}y = \frac{1}{4}x + \frac{2}{3}$
$-3x + 10y = 8$

24. $\frac{1}{5}x = \frac{7}{10}y - \frac{3}{4}$
$4x - 14y = -15$

Write the equation of the line with each x-intercept and y-intercept. Use slope-intercept form.

25. x-intercept = 2; y-intercept = −1 $y = \frac{1}{2}x - 1$

26. x-intercept = −3; y-intercept = −2 $y = -\frac{2}{3}x - 2$

27. x-intercept = 1; y-intercept = 5 $y = -5x + 5$

28. x-intercept = $-\frac{1}{2}$; y-intercept = 3 $y = 6x + 3$

Write the equation of the line that passes through each pair of points. Use slope-intercept form.

29. (1, 3), (2, 7)
$y = 4x - 1$

30. (4, 8), (2, 4) $y = 2x$

31. (−2, 3), (3, 1)
$y = -\frac{2}{5}x + \frac{11}{5}$

32. (0, 0), (−2, −3) $y = \frac{3}{2}x$

33. (5, 1), (3, −2)
$y = \frac{3}{2}x - \frac{13}{2}$

34. (2, −1), (5, −4)
$y = -x + 1$

35. (8, 6), (10, 3)
$y = -\frac{3}{2}x + 18$

36. (−4, −1), (−1, −7)
$y = -2x - 9$

Solve each system of equations. 40. (−11, −4)   48. (−6, −3)

37. $y = 3x$
$4x + 2y = 30$ (3, 9)

38. $a = -2b$
$3a + 5b = 21$ (42, −21)

39. $n = m + 4$
$3m + 2n = 19 \left(\frac{11}{5}, \frac{31}{5}\right)$

40. $h = k - 7$
$2h - 5k = -2$

41. $s + 2t = 6$
$3s - 2t = 2$ (2, 2)

42. $c + 2d = 10$
$-c + d = 2$ (2, 4)

43. $3v + 5w = -16$
$3v - 2w = -2$ (−2, −2)

44. $e - 5f = 12$
$3e - 5f = 6$ (−3, −3)

45. $-3p + 2q = 10$
$-2p - q = -5$ (0, 5)

46. $2a + 5b = 13$
$4a - 3b = -13$ (−1, 3)

47. $5s + 3t = 4$
$-4s + 5t = -18$ (2, −2)

48. $2g - 7h = 9$
$-3g + 4h = 6$

49. $2c - 6d = -16$
$5c + 7d = -18$ (−5, 1)

50. $6m - 3n = -9$
$-8m + 2n = 4$ $\left(\frac{1}{2}, 4\right)$

51. $3x - 5y = 8$
$4x - 7y = 10$ (6, 2)

52. $9a - 3b = 5$
$a + b = 1$ $\left(\frac{2}{3}, \frac{1}{3}\right)$

Find the equation of the axis of symmetry and the maximum or minimum point for the graph of each quadratic function.

53. $y = -x^2 + 2x - 3$
$x = 1; (1, -2)$

54. $y = x^2 - 4x - 4$
$x = 2; (2, -8)$

55. $y = 3x^2 + 6x + 3$
$x = -1; (-1, 0)$

56. $y = 2x^2 + 12x$
$x = -3; (-3, -18)$

57. $y = x^2 - 6x + 5$
$x = 3; (3, -4)$

58. $y = 4x^2 - 1$ $x = 0; (0, -1)$

59. $y = -2x^2 - 2x + 4$
$x = -\frac{1}{2}; \left(-\frac{1}{2}, \frac{9}{2}\right)$

60. $y = \frac{1}{2}x^2 + 4x + \frac{1}{4}$
$x = -4; \left(-4, -\frac{31}{4}\right)$

61. $y = 6x^2 - 12x - 4$
$x = 1; (1, -10)$

GLOSSARY

absolute value   The absolute value of a number is the number of units that it is from zero on the number line.   (55)

addition property for inequalities   For all numbers *a*, *b*, and *c*,
  1. if $a > b$, then $a + c > b + c$, and
  2. if $a < b$, then $a + c < b + c$.   (176)

addition property of equality   For any numbers *a*, *b*, and *c*, if $a = b$, then $a + c = b + $ c.   (94)

additive identity   The number 0 is the additive identity since the sum of any number and 0 is equal to the number. (22)

additive inverse   Two numbers are additive inverses if their sum is zero. The additive inverse, or opposite, of *a* is $-a$.   (56)

algebraic expression   An expression consisting of one or more numbers and variables along with one or more arithmetic operations.   (8)

angle of depression   An angle of depression is formed by a line of sight along the horizontal and another line of sight below it.   (632)

angle of elevation   An angle of elevation is formed by a line of sight along the horizontal and another line of sight above it. (632)

associative property of addition   For any numbers *a*, *b*, and *c*,
  $(a + b) + c = a + (b + c)$.   (31)

associative property of multiplication   For any numbers *a*, *b*, and *c*,
  $(ab)c = a(bc)$.   (31)

axis of symmetry   A straight line with respect to which a figure is symmetric. (519)

base   In an expression of the form x^n, the base is x.   (9)
In the proportion $\frac{17}{25} = \frac{r}{100}$, the base is 25.   (138)

binomial   A polynomial with exactly two terms.   (226)

boundary   A line that separates a graph into half-planes.   (379)

box-and-whisker plot   In a box-and-whisker plot, the quartiles and extreme value of a set of data are displayed using a number line.   (579)

closed half-plane   A half-plane that includes the boundary.   (380)

coefficient   The numerical part of a term. (28)

commutative property of addition   For any numbers *a* and *b*,
  $a + b = b + a$.   (31)

commutative property of multiplication   For any numbers *a* and *b*, $ab = ba$.   (31)

comparison property   For any two numbers *a* and *b*, exactly one of the following sentences is true.
  $a < b$ $a = b$ $a > b$ (60)

comparison property for rational numbers   For any rational numbers $\frac{a}{b}$ and $\frac{c}{d}$, with $b > 0$ and $d > 0$,
  1. if $\frac{a}{b} < \frac{c}{d}$, then $ad < bc$, and
  2. if $ad < bc$, then $\frac{a}{b} < \frac{c}{d}$.   (65)

complementary angles   Two angles are complementary if the sum of their measures is 90°.   (611)

completeness property for points in the plane When plotting points, the following is true. (355)
1. Exactly one point in the plane is named by a given ordered pair of numbers.
2. Exactly one ordered pair of numbers names a given point in the plane.

completing the square Completing the square is a method of solving a quadratic equation where a perfect square trinomial is formed on one side of the equation. (532)

complex fraction If a fraction has one or more fractions in the numerator or denominator, it is called a complex fraction. (81)

composite number Any positive integer, except 1, that is not prime. (256)

compound event A compound event consists of two or more simple events. (600)

compound inequalities Two inequalities connected by *and* or *or*. (194)

compound interest The amount of interest paid or earned on the original principal plus the accumulated interest. (145)

compound sentence Two sentences connected by *and* or *or*. (185)

conjugates Two binomials of the form $a\sqrt{b} + c\sqrt{d}$ and $a\sqrt{b} - c\sqrt{d}$. (494)

conjunction A compound sentence where the statements are connected using *and*. (185)

consecutive even integers Numbers given when beginning with an even integer and counting by two's. (112)

consecutive numbers Numbers in counting order. (112)

consecutive odd integers Numbers given when beginning with an odd integer and counting by two's. (112)

consistent A system of equations is consistent and independent if it has one ordered pair as its solution. A system of equations is consistent and dependent if it has infinitely many ordered pairs as its solution. (443)

constant A monomial that does not contain variables. (213)

constant of variation In the direct variation equation $y = kx$, k is called the constant of variation. (162)

coordinate The coordinate of a point is the number that corresponds to it on the number line. (51)

coordinate plane The number plane formed by two perpendicular number lines that intersect at their zero points. (354)

corresponding angles In similar triangles, the measures of corresponding angles are equal. (622)

corresponding sides In similar triangles, the sides opposite corresponding angles are called corresponding sides. The measures of corresponding sides are proportional. (622)

cosine In a right triangle, the cosine of angle $A =$

$$\frac{\text{measure of side adjacent to angle } A}{\text{measure of hypotenuse}}. \quad (626)$$

cross product In the proportion $\frac{a}{b} = \frac{c}{d}$, the cross products are $a \times d$ and $b \times c$. (65)

data Numerical information. (560)

decimal notation A way of expressing numbers using a base ten system. 483.26 is expressed in decimal notation. (221)

degree The degree of a monomial is the sum of the exponents of its variables. The degree of a nonzero constant is 0. The degree of a polynomial is the greatest of the degrees of its terms. (227)

density property Between every pair of distinct rational numbers, there is another rational number. (137)(66)

difference of squares Two perfect squares separated by a subtraction sign.
$$a^2 - b^2 \quad (244)$$

direct variation A direct variation is described by an equation of the form $y = kx$, where k is not zero. (162)

discriminant In the quadratic formula, the expression $b^2 - 4ac$ is called the discriminant. (541)

disjoint sets Two sets that have no members in common. (51)

disjunction A compound sentence where the statements are connected using *or*. (185)

distance formula The distance between any two points (x_1, y_1) and (x_2, y_2) is given by the formula
$$d = \sqrt{(x_2 - x_1)^2 + (y_2 - y_1)^2}.$$ (506)

distributive property For any numbers a, b, and c:
1. $a(b + c) = ab + ac$ and $(b + c)a = ba + ca$.
2. $a(b - c) = ab - ac$ and $(b - c)a = ba - ca$. (26)

division property for inequalities For all numbers a, b, and c, with $c \neq 0$,
1. if c is positive and $a < b$, then $\frac{a}{c} < \frac{b}{c}$, and if c is positive and $a > b$, then $\frac{a}{c} > \frac{b}{c}$.
2. If c is negative and $a < b$, then $\frac{a}{c} > \frac{b}{c}$, and if c is negative and $a > b$, then $\frac{a}{c} < \frac{b}{c}$. (182)

division property of equality For any numbers a, b, and c, with $c \neq 0$, if $a = b$, then $\frac{a}{c} = \frac{b}{c}$. (104)

domain The domain of a relation is the set of all first components from each ordered pair. (359)

edge A line that separates a graph into half-planes. (379)

element One of the members of a set. (19)

elimination method A method for solving systems of equations in which the equations are added or subtracted to eliminate one of the variables. Multiplication of one or both equations may occur before the equations are added or subtracted. (452)

empty set A set with no elements. (19)

equally likely events Events that have an equal chance of occurring. (589)

equals sign The equals sign, $=$, between two expressions indicates that if the sentence is true, the expressions name the same number. (19)

equation A mathematical sentence that contains the equals sign. (19)

equivalent equations Equations that have the same solution. (94)

evaluate To find the value of an expression when the values of the variables are known. (13)

excluded value A value excluded from the domain of a variable because that value substituted for the variable would result in a denominator of zero. (306)

experimental probability Probability calculated by performing experiments. (594)

exponent A number used to tell how many times a number is used as a factor. In an expression of the form x^n, the exponent is n. (9)

extremes *See* proportion. (134)

factor In a multiplication expression, the quantities being multiplied are called factors. (8)

FOIL method for multiplying binomials To multiply two binomials, find the sum of the products of
F   the first terms,
O   the outer terms,
I   the inner terms, and
L   the last terms. (238)

formula An equation that states a rule for the relationship between certain quantities. (36)

function A function is a relation in which each element of the domain is paired with exactly one element of the range. (374)

functional notation The functional notation of the equation $y = x + 5$ is
$$f(x) = x + 5.$$ (376)

functional value The symbol $f(3)$ represents the functional value of f for $x = 3$. (376)

G

graph To graph a set of numbers means to locate the points by those numbers on a number line. (51)
To graph an ordered pair means to draw a dot at the point on a coordinate plane that corresponds to the ordered pair. (335)

greatest common factor (GCF) The GCF of two or more integers is the greatest factor that is common to each of the integers. (257)

grouping symbols Symbols used to clarify or change the order of operations in an expression. Parentheses, brackets, and the fraction bar are grouping symbols. (13)

H

half-plane The region of a graph on one side of a boundary. (379)

hypotenuse The side opposite the right angle in a right triangle. (482)

I

identity An equation that is true for every value of the variable. (118)

inconsistent A system of equations is inconsistent if it has no solution. (443)

inequality Any sentence containing $<$, $>$, $\neq$, $\leq$, or $\geq$. (60)

integers (Z) The set of numbers $\{\ldots, -3, -2, -1, 0, 1, 2, 3, \ldots\}$. (50)

intercept An intercept is a point where a graph crosses the x-axis or y-axis. (410)

interquartile range The difference between the upper quartile and the lower quartile of a set of data is called the interquartile range. It represents the middle half of the data in the set. (575)

intersection The intersection of two sets A and B ($A \cap B$) is the set of elements common to both A and B. (51)

inverse The inverse of any relation is obtained by switching the coordinates in each ordered pair of the relation. (360)

inverse operations Operations that undo each other, such as multiplication and division. (80)

inverse variation An inverse variation is described by an equation of the form $xy = k$, where k is not zero. (166)

irrational numbers (I) Numbers that cannot be expressed in the form $\frac{a}{b}$, where a and b are integers, $b \neq 0$. (487)

L

least common denominator (LCD) The least common multiple of the denominators of two or more fractions. (330)

least common multiple (LCM) The LCM of two or more integers is the least positive integer that is divisible by each of the integers. (329)

legs The adjacent sides of the right angle of a right triangle. (482)

like terms Terms that contain the same variables, with corresponding variables raised to the same power. (27)

linear equation A linear equation is an equation that may be written in the form $Ax + By = C$, where A, B, and C are any numbers and A and B are not both 0. (369)

line plot Numerical information displayed on a number line. (560)

lower quartile The lower quartile divides the lower half of the set of data into two equal parts. (575)

M

maximum point The highest point on the graph of a curve, such as a parabola, which opens down. (518)

mean The mean of a set of data is the sum of the elements in the set, divided by the number of elements in the set. (80)

means *See* proportion. (134)

median The median is the middle number of a set of data when the numbers are arranged in numerical order. (570)

midpoint The midpoint of a line segment is the point that is halfway between the endpoints of the segment. (428)

minimum point The lowest point on the graph of a curve, such as a parabola which opens up. (518)

mixed expression Algebraic expression which contain monomials and rational expressions. (334)

mode The mode is the number that occurs most often in a set of data. (570)

monomial A number, a variable, or a product of numbers and variables. (213)

multiplication property for inequalities For all numbers a, b, and c,
1. if c is positive and $a < b$, then $ac < bc$, and if c is positive and $a > b$, then $ac > bc$.
2. If c is negative and $a < b$, then $ac > bc$, and if c is negative and $a > b$, then $ac < bc$. (181)

multiplication property of equality For any numbers a, b, and c, with $c \neq 0$, if $a = b$, then $ac = bc$. (103)

multiplicative identity The number 1 is the multiplicative identity since the product of any number and 1 is equal to the number. (22)

multiplicative inverse Two numbers are multiplicative inverses if their product is 1. The multiplicative inverse, or reciprocal, of a is $\frac{1}{a}$. (81)(84)

multiplicative property of zero For any number a, $a \cdot 0 = 0$. (23)

natural numbers (N) The set of numbers $\{1, 2, 3, \ldots\}$. (51)

negative number A number that is graph-ed on the negative side of the number line. (50)

null set A set with no elements. (19)

number line A line with equal distances marked off to represent numbers. (50)

number theory The study of numbers. (112)

numerical coefficient The numerical part of a term. (28)(16)

odds The odds of an event occurring is the ratio of the number of ways the event can occur (successes) to the number of ways the event cannot occur (failures). (590)

open half-plane A half-plane that does not include the boundary. (379)

open sentence A sentence containing a symbol(s) to be replaced in order to determine if the sentence is true or false. (18)

opposite The opposite of a number is its additive inverse. (56)

ordered pair In mathematics, pairs of numbers used to locate points in the plane. (354)

order of operations
1. Simplify the expressions inside grouping symbols.
2. Evaluate all powers.
3. Then do all multiplications and divisions from left to right.
4. Then do all additions and subtractions from left to right. (13)

origin The point of intersection of the two axes of the coordinate plane. (354)

outlier Any element of a set of data that is at least 1.5 interquartile ranges above the upper quartile or below the lower quartile. (576)

parabola The general shape of the graph of a quadratic function. (518)

parallel lines Lines that have the same slope are parallel. All vertical lines are parallel. (423)

percent Per hundred, or hundredths. (138)

percentage A number which is compared to another number (base) in the percent proportion. (138)

percent of decrease The ratio of an amount of decrease to the previous amount, expressed as a percent. (146)

percent of increase The ratio of an amount of increase to the previous amount, expressed as a percent. (146)

percent proportion

$$\frac{\text{Percentage}}{\text{Base}} = \text{Rate or } \frac{P}{B} = \frac{r}{100}. \quad (139)$$

perfect square trinomial A perfect square trinomial is a trinomial of the form $(a + b)^2 = a^2 + 2ab + b^2$ or $(a - b)^2 = a^2 - 2ab + b^2$. (281)

perpendicular lines Two lines are perpendicular if the product of their slopes is -1. In a plane, vertical lines are perpendicular to horizontal lines. (424)

point-slope form For a given point (x, y) on a nonvertical line with slope m, the point-slope form of a linear equation is $y - y_1 = m(x - x_1)$. (405)

polynomial An expression that can be written as a sum of monomials. (226)

power An expression of the form x^n. (10)

prime factorization The expression of a composite number as the product of its prime factors. (256)

prime number An integer, greater than 1, whose only positive factors are 1 and itself. (256)

prime polynomial A polynomial that cannot be written as a product of two or more polynomials. (273)

principal square root The nonnegative square root of the expression. (477)

probability The ratio that tells how likely it is that an event will take place.

$$P(\text{event}) = \frac{\text{number of favorable outcomes}}{\text{number of possible outcomes}}$$

(589)

product The result of multiplication. (8)

product property of square roots For any numbers a and b, where $a \geq 0$ and $b \geq 0$, $\sqrt{ab} = \sqrt{a} \cdot \sqrt{b}$. (492)

properties Algebraic statements that are true for any number. (22)

proportion An equation of the form $\frac{a}{b} = \frac{c}{d}$ which states that two ratios are equal. The first and fourth terms (a and d) are called the extremes. The second and third terms (b and c) are called the means. (134)

Pythagorean Theorem In a right triangle, if a and b are the measures of the legs, and c is the measure of the hypotenuse, then $c^2 = a^2 + b^2$. (482)

quadrant One of the four regions into which two perpendicular number lines separate the plane. (256)

quadratic formula The solutions of a quadratic equation of the form $ax^2 + bx + c = 0$, where $a \neq 0$, are given by $x = \dfrac{-b \pm \sqrt{b^2 - 4ac}}{2a}$. (537)

quadratic function A quadratic function is a function described by an equation of the form $y = ax^2 + bx + c$, where $a \neq 0$. (518)

quotient property of square roots For any numbers a and b, where $a \geq 0$ and $b > 0$, $\sqrt{\dfrac{a}{b}} = \dfrac{\sqrt{a}}{\sqrt{b}}$. (493)

radical equations Equations containing radicals with variables in the radicand. (501)

radical expression An expression of the form $\sqrt{a}$. (477)

radical sign The symbol $\sqrt{}$ indicating the principal or nonnegative square root. (477)

radicand The expression under the radical sign. (477)

range The range of a relation is the set of all second components from each ordered pair. (259)
The difference between the greatest and the least values of a set of data. (575)

rate A ratio of two measurements having different units of measure. (135)
In the percent proportion, the rate is the fraction with a denominator of 100. (138)

ratio A comparison of two numbers by division. The ratio of a to b is $\frac{a}{b}$. (134)

rational equations Equations containing rational expressions. (338)

rational expression An algebraic fraction whose numerator and denominator are polynomials. (306)

rationalizing the denominator Rationalizing the denominator is a method used to eliminate radicals from the denominator of a fraction. (493)

rational numbers (Q) Numbers that can be expressed in the form $\frac{a}{b}$, where a and b are integers, $b \neq 0$. (61)

real numbers (R) Irrational numbers together with rational numbers form the set of real numbers. (51)

reciprocal The reciprocal of a number is its multiplicative inverse. (81)

reflexive property of equality For any number a, $a = a$. (23)

relation A set of ordered pairs. (359)

replacement set The set of numbers for which replacements for a variable may be chosen. (19)

right triangle A triangle that has a 90° angle. (612)

root of an equation A solution of the equation. (523)

scale A ratio that compares the size of a model to the actual size of the object being modeled. (135)

scatter plot In a scatter plot, two sets of data are plotted as ordered pairs in the coordinate plane. (583)

scientific notation A number is expressed in scientific notation when it is in the form $a \times 10^n$, where $1 \le a < 10$ and n is an integer. (221)

set A collection of objects or numbers. (19)

set-builder notation A notation used to describe the members of a set. For example, $\{y | y < 17\}$ represents the set of all numbers y such that y is less than 17. (177)

similar triangles If two triangles are similar, the measures of their corresponding angles are equal and the measures of their corresponding sides are proportional. (622)

simple interest The amount paid or earned for the use of money for a unit of time. $I = prt$ (142)

simplest form of an expression An expression in simplest form has no like terms and no parentheses. (27)

simplify To simplify an expression involving monomials, write an equivalent expression that has positive exponents and no powers of powers. Each base should appear only once and all fractions should be in simplest form. (218)

sine In a right triangle, the sine of angle
$$A = \frac{\text{measure of side opposite angle } A}{\text{measure of hypotenuse}}.$$
(626)

slope The slope of a line is the ratio of the change in y to the corresponding change in x.
$$\text{slope} = \frac{\text{change in y}}{\text{change in x}} \quad (400)$$

slope-intercept form The slope-intercept form of the equation of a line is $y = mx + b$. The slope of the line is m, and the y-intercept is b. (410)

solution A replacement for the variable in an open sentence which results in a true sentence. (18)

solution set The set of all replacements for the variable in an open sentence which make the sentence true. (19)

solve To solve an open sentence means to find all the solutions. (18)

spreadsheets Computer programs especially designed to create charts involving many calculations. (40)

square root If $x^2 = y$, then x is a square root of y. (477)

squaring Squaring a number means using that number as a factor two times. (477)

standard form of linear equation A linear equation in standard form is $Ax + By = C$ where A, B, and C are integers, and A and B are not both zero. (406)

statement Any sentence that is either true or false. (18)

statistics A branch of mathematics which provides methods for collecting, organizing, and interpreting data. (560)

stem-and-leaf plot In a stem-and-leaf plot, each piece of data is separated into two numbers that are used to form the stem and leaf. The data are organized into two columns. The column on the left is the stem and the column on the right is the leaf. (565)

subset A set that is made from the elements of another set. (19)

substitution method A method for solving systems of equations. One variable is expressed in terms of the other variable in one equation. Then the expression is substituted into the other equation. (447)

substitution property of equality For any numbers a and b, if $a = b$ then a may be replaced by b. (23)

subtraction property for inequalities For all numbers a, b, and c,

1. if $a > b$, then $a - c > b - c$, and
2. if $a < b$, then $a - c < b - c$. (176)

subtraction property of equality For any numbers a, b, and c, if $a = b$, then $a - c = b - c$. (99)

supplementary angles Two angles are supplementary if the sum of their measures is 180°. (610)

symmetric property of equality For any numbers a and b, if $a = b$ then $b = a$. (23)

system of equations A set of equations with the same variables. (442)

system of inequalities A set of inequalities with the same variables. (463)

tangent In a right triangle, the tangent of angle $A =$

$$\frac{\text{measure of side opposite angle } A}{\text{measure of side adjacent to angle } A}. (626)$$

term A number, a variable, or a *product* or *quotient* of numbers and variables. The terms of an expression are separated by the symbols $+$ and $-$. (27)

transitive property of equality For any numbers a, b, and c, if $a = b$ and $b = c$, then $a = c$. (23)

transitive property of order For all numbers a, b, and c,
1. if $a < b$ and $b < c$, then $a < c$, and
2. if $a > b$ and $b > c$, then $a > c$. (61)

tree diagram A diagram used to show all of the possibilities. (326)

trigonometric ratios Ratios in a right triangle that involve the measures of the sides and the measures of the angles. (626)

trinomial A polynomial having exactly three terms. (226)

uniform motion When an object moves at a constant speed, or rate, it is said to be in uniform motion. (158)

union The union of two sets A and B ($A \cup B$) is the set of all elements contained either in A or in B or in both. (51)

unit cost The cost of one unit of something. (66)

upper quartile The upper quartile divides the upper half of the set of data into two equal parts. (575)

variable In a mathematical sentence, a variable is a symbol used to represent an unspecified number. (8)

Venn diagram A diagram using circles or ovals inside a rectangle to show relationships of sets. (51)

vertex The vertex of a parabola is the maximum or minimum point of the parabola. (518)

vertical line test If any vertical line drawn on the graph of a relation passes through no more than one point of its graph, then the relation is a function. (375)

whole numbers (W) The set of numbers $\{0, 1, 2, 3, \ldots\}$. (50)

x-axis The horizontal number line which helps to form the coordinate plane. (354)

x-coordinate The first component of an ordered pair. (354)

x-intercept The value of x when y is 0. (410)

y-axis The vertical number line which helps to form the coordinate plane. (354)

y-coordinate The second component of an ordered pair. (354)

y-intercept The value of y when x is 0. (410)

zero product property For all numbers a and b, if $ab = 0$, then $a = 0$, $b = 0$, or both a and b equal 0. (290)

SELECTED ANSWERS

CHAPTER 1 AN INTRODUCTION TO ALGEBRA

Pages 11–12 Lesson 1-1

5. $7x$ **7.** $a + 19$ **9.** b^3 **11.** 5^3 **13.** $2m^3$ **15.** 16
17. 10,000 **19.** m minus 1 **21.** n to the fourth
power **23.** 8 times y squared **25.** $x + 17$ **27.** $2x^3$
29. $\frac{1x^2}{2}$ or $\frac{x^2}{2}$ **31.** $94 + 2x$ **33.** 15 m²
35. 56,800.236 **37.** 873,324 **39.** $a + b - ab$
43. 14,280 square feet

Pages 15–17 Lesson 1-2

7. 2 **9.** 316 **11.** 31 **13.** 75 **15.** 26 **17.** 14
19. 20 **21.** 408 **23.** 6 **25.** 16 **27.** 12.5 mm
29. 14 in. **31.** 12.56 ft **33.** 18 **35.** 13.2 **37.** 413
39. $\frac{11}{18}$; $0.6\overline{1}$ **41.** $2(a + b)$; 7 **43.** $b^2 + c$; $\frac{1}{4}$; 0.25
47. 13 year old: $R = 144.9$, 14 year old: $R = 144.2$,
15 year old: $R = 143.5$ **49.** $w - 7$ **50.** a number y
raised to the fifth power **51.** 4^4 **52.** $2n - 25$
53. 24 ft²

Pages 20–21 Lesson 1-3

7. false **9.** true **11.** 2 **13.** Foster, Winters, Gell,
Rath, or Gordon **15.** 11 **17.** 9 **19.** The capital of
the U. S. is not Houston; true. **21.** Birds do not
have wings; false. **23.** {1}, {2}, {1, 2}, Ø **25.** 5
27. 11.05 **29.** $\frac{7}{13}$ **31.** $\frac{7}{4}$ **33.** {6, 7, 8} **35.** {5}
37. {4, 5, 6, 7, 8} **41.** $614.54 **43.** h^3 **44.** $\frac{1}{2}a^2b^3$
45. 15 **46.** $\frac{11}{13}$ **47.** 25.7

Pages 24–25 Lesson 1-4

5. symmetric (=) **7.** substitution (=) **9.** 0 **11.** 7
13. 1 **15.** symmetric (=) **17.** multiplicative
identity **19.** reflexive (=) **21.** substitution (=)
23. multiplicative property of zero **25.** transitive
(=) **27.** 3 **29.** 7 **31.** 15 **33.** $4(20) + 7$; 87 years
35. $36.15 **36.** a number x squared **37.** 39
38. true **39.** 20

Page 25 Mid-Chapter Review

1. n^3 **2.** $n^2 + 7$ **3.** Divide 8 by 2. Multiply 2 by 6.
Then add. **4.** Square 3. Subtract 3. Then multiply
by 3. **5.** Add 8 and 6. Divide by 2. Then add 2.
6. $\frac{26}{3}$ **7.** 15 **8.** 2 **9.** 6.28 **10.** 4 **11.** 4
12. {4, 5, 6, 7, 8} **13.** {4, 5, 6} **14.** {8}
15. multiplicative property of zero
16. symmetric (=)

Pages 29–30 Lesson 1-5

3. 5 **5.** $\frac{1}{3}$ **7.** $6bc$, bc **9.** $4xy$, $5xy$ **11.** $5x$ **13.** in
simplest form **15.** 645 **17.** $24x + 56$ **19.** $18a$
21. $15am - 12$ **23.** $22y^2 + 3$ **25.** in simplest
form **27.** $3x + 4y$ **29.** $30a + 6b$ **31.** $14x + 14$
33. $8.827xy^3 - 0.012y^3$ **35.** $6336x^2$ **39a.** 172.4
cm **b.** 179.6 cm **41.** 3^2a^3 or $9a^3$ **42.** 7 **43.** 14.13
44. symmetric (=) **45.** 4

Pages 33–35 Lesson 1-6

3. associative (+) **5.** distributive **7.** commutative
(×) **9.** associative (×) **11.** commutative (+)
13a. commutative (+) **b.** associative (+)
c. distributive **d.** substitution (=)
15. commutative (+) **17.** associative (+)
19. commutative (×) **21.** additive identity
23. commutative (+) **25.** distributive
27. multiplicative identity **29.** $12a + 6b$
31. $5x + 10y$ **33.** $3a + 13b + 2c$ **35.** $14x + 3y$
37. $\frac{3}{4} + \frac{5}{3}x + \frac{4}{3}y$ **39.** $3.1x + 1.54$ **43a.** $7\frac{7}{8}$ in. ×
11 in. × 3 in. **c.** 6 ways **45.** 39 inches or 3 feet 3
inches **47.** $2x^2$ **48.** 10.69 **49.** 25.7 **50.** 15
51. $\frac{4}{5}$ **52.** $23a + 42$ **53.** substitution (=)
54. distributive

Pages 38–39 Lesson 1-7

3. $A = s^2$ **5.** $P = 4s$ **7.** 236 **9.** 584 **11.** 499
13. $2x + y^2 = z$ **15.** $(x + a)^2 = m$ **17.** $(abc)^2 = k$
19. $29 - xy = z$ **21.** 330 **23.** $33\frac{3}{4}$ **25.** 63.2
27. 13.68 **29.** 9 **31.** 2335 **33.** 18 **35.** 428
37. $A = s^2 + \frac{\pi}{2}s^2$ **41.** 19,800 ft **43.** 500 seconds or
8 minutes 20 seconds **44.** 6 **45.** $1\frac{1}{9}$ **46.** b^3, $4b^3$
47. $37a + 23b$ **48.** commutative (×)

Pages 42–43 Lesson 1-8

3a. $1 bills **b.** 7 **c.** $267 **d.** none **e.** $157 **f.** end
of the day **g.** $5n$ dollars **5a.** does not say **b.** 7¢
c. $7.18 **d.** more **e.** $(n - 7)$¢ or $(359 - n)$¢
7a. no **b.** yes **c.** rock **d.** 13 **e.** $n + 3$ **9. a.** 48
b. 72 **c.** no

Pages 44–46 Chapter 1 Summary and Review

1. $8y$ **3.** a^4 **5.** 320 **7.** 4 **9.** 2.2 **11.** additive
identity **13.** symmetric (=) **15.** $2a + 3b$
17. $9r + 7s$ **19.** associative (×) **21.** commutative
(×) **23.** $\frac{3a^2}{4} + \frac{5ab}{3}$ **25.** $c = (2x)^3$ **27.** 48 cm
29. Ostriches can fly; false **31.** less **33.** 59¢
35. $c = 3 \cdot 111$; 333 calories **37.** 8 bricks

CHAPTER 2   RATIONAL NUMBERS

Pages 52-54   Lesson 2-1

5. -7 **7.** -10 **9.** 2   **11.** -4 **13.** $\{3, 6, 9, 12\}$
15. $\{4, 6, 8, 10, 12\}$ **17.** $\{3, 4, 5, 6, 9, 12\}$
19. $\{3, 4, 5, 6, 8, 10, 12\}$ **21.** $-3 + 5 = 2$
23. $-1 + (-4) = -5$ **25.** $\{-3, -2, -1, 0\}$
27. $\{-1, 0, 1, 2, 3, 4, ...\}$

29.
-2 -1 0 1 2 3 4 5 6

33.
-5 -4 -3 -2 -1 0 1 2 3

35. 13   **37.** -20 **39.** -5 **41.** 0   **43.** 6   **45.** -5
47. 5   **49.** -22 **51.** $\varnothing$ **53.** $\{d, i, c, t, o, n, a, r, y, l\}$
57. 16 yd loss   **59.** $\frac{3}{4}xy^5$ **60.** 3   **61.** $55y^2$
62. $x + a^2 = n$

Pages 58-59   Lesson 2-2

5. $-8, 8$ **7.** 0, 0   **9.** $+$ **11.** 5   **13.** -4 **15.** -6
17. 40   **19.** 13   **21.** -5 **23.** 5   **25.** -29 **27.** $31m$
29. 22   **31.** 18   **33.** $33b$ **35.** -26 **37.** 8   **39.** 9
41. 0   **43.** 2   **45.** 2   **47.** -30 **49.** 926   **51.** -275
55. $s = 30 - 6 + 15$; \$39   **57a.** $2, -3, -8, ...$
b. $-15, -5, 5, ...$ **c.** $-5, -7, -9, ...$ **d.** The sum of
the steps between the addends is equal to the step
between the sums.   **58.** 1.32   **59.** 6   **60.** $3\frac{1}{4}x + \frac{3}{4}y$
61. associative $(+)$

62.
-4 -3 -2 -1 0 1 2 3 4

63. 9

Pages 63-64   Lesson 2-3

5. F   **7.** F   **9.** F   **11.** $\{4, 5, 6, ...\}$
13. $\{0, 1, 2, 3, 4, 5, 7, ...\}$ **15.** no   **17.** yes
19. $x \neq -3$ **21.** $x < -3$ **23.** $x \leq 2$

25.
-4 -3 -2 -1 0 1 2 3

29.
-15 -14 -13 -12 -11 -10 -9 -8

33. $y \geq -5$ **35.** $b < 0$ **37.** $>$ **39.** $<$ **41.** $=$ **43.** $>$

45.
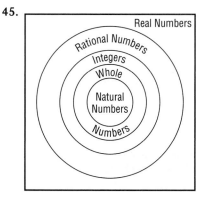

49. 4800 residents   **51.** 1955   **52.** 9.5
53. $\frac{m^2n}{2}$, $5m^2n$ **54.** 81, 243, 729
55. $4 + (-6) = -2$ **56.** 4   **57.** -20

Pages 67-68   Lesson 2-4

3. $\frac{4}{5}$ **5.** $\frac{10}{11}$ **7.** $\frac{6}{5}$ **9.** a 28-ounce can for 97¢   **11.** $<$
13. $>$ **15.** $=$ **17.** $\frac{20}{27}, \frac{19}{24}, \frac{17}{21}$ **19.** $\frac{9}{43}, \frac{3}{14}, \frac{5}{23}$
21. $\frac{79}{56}$; 1.411   **23.** $\frac{119}{180}$; $0.66\overline{1}$ **25.** 0   **29.** three liters
of soda for \$2.25   **31.** a dozen oranges for \$1.59
33. a 22-ounce bottle for \$1.09   **34.** $r + 7$ or $7 + r$
35. multiplicative identity   **36.** commutative $(+)$
37. $>$ **39.** $<$

Pages 71-73   Lesson 2-5

3. 4   **5.** 18   **7.** $\frac{4}{21}$ **9.** -153.8 **11.** $\frac{5}{14}$ **13.** -2
15. $-\frac{1}{6}$ **17.** -14.7 **19.** $\frac{1}{14}$ **21.** $\frac{4}{9}$ **23.** -0.3005
25. $-\frac{5}{24}$ **27.** -13.1 **29.** $-8\frac{5}{8}$ **31.** $-9m$ **33.** 2.2k
35. 8.9   **37.** -5.5 **39.** $-\frac{5}{8}$ **41.** $-28y$ **43.** $\frac{5}{6}$
45. $\frac{7}{32}$ **47.** 0.32   **53.** $2\frac{1}{2}$ points   **55.** $+30$ yards
57. $\frac{1}{8}$ **58.** $+650$ **59.** -25 **60.** $36 + (-11) = f$; 25th
floor

61.
-6 -5 -4 -3 -2 -1 0 1 2 3

62. a 184-gram can of peanuts for 91¢

Page 73   Mid-Chapter Review

1.
-3 -2 -1 0 1 2 3 4

4. -24 **5.** -70 **6.** -54 **7.** -18 **8.** -11 **9.** -82
10. $-\frac{19}{13}$ **11.** $-\frac{1}{6}$ **12.** -8.774 **13.** $=$ **14.** $>$
15. $>$ **16.** $>$ **17.** $=$ **18.** $<$ **19.** $+6\frac{3}{8}$ **20.** Brand X

Pages 77-78   Lesson 2-6

5. $+16$ **7.** $+24$ **9.** 60   **11.** 30   **13.** $\frac{7}{24}$
15. 0.00879   **17.** $-\frac{6}{5}$ **19.** 114.1482   **21.** -24
23. -6 **25.** 9   **27.** -332 **29.** -10 **31.** $98xy$
33. -68.416 **35.** $\frac{10}{7}$ **37.** $-21x$ **39.** $5.1x - 7.6y$
47. \$7.13   **49.** $6x^2 + 5x$ **50.** 3, 6, 9   **51.** 286
52. $\{-4, -3, -2, ...\}$ **53.** $\frac{1}{3}$ **54.** $82y$

Pages 83-84   Lesson 2-7

5. $\frac{1}{3}$ **7.** none   **9.** $\frac{3}{2}$ **11.** $\frac{4}{13}$ **13.** $-\frac{11}{71}$ **15.** -6
17. $5b$ **19.** $a + 3$ **21.** -5 **23.** $-45n$ **25.** $-7a$
27. -2 **29.** $-\frac{1}{12}$ **31.** $\frac{153}{10}$ **33.** $-\frac{35}{2}$ **35.** $a + 4$
37. $x + 2y$ **39.** $7\frac{1}{5}$ or 7.2   **41.** $1\frac{2}{5}$ or 1.4   **43.** $<$

45. < **47.** < **53.** 1543 airplanes **55.** 51,173 slices **56.** $b = x - m^3$ **57.** 5 **58.** true **59.** a 1-pound package of lunch meat for $1.98
60. 36m **61.** $-\frac{7}{2}$

Pages 86-87 Lesson 2-8

5. $49 - n$ **7.** $n - 8$ **9.** $5.65n **11.** Let k = Kimiko's age now; $k - 27 = 21$. **13.** Let x = number of years for a tree to become $33\frac{1}{2}$ feet tall; $17 + 1\frac{1}{2}x = 33\frac{1}{2}$. **15.** Let t = number of tapes; $t + \left(\frac{1}{2}t + 4\right) = 31$. **17.** Let q = number of quarters; $q + (q + 4) + (q + 4 - 7) = 28$. **19.** Twice Quincy's age 7 years ago was 58. How old is Quincy now?
21. Ramón's car weighs 250 pounds more than Seth's car. The sum of the weights of both cars is 7140 pounds. How much does each car weigh?
23. Reggie is 31 cm shorter than Soto. The sum of Soto's height and twice Reggie's height is 502 cm. How tall is Soto?

Page 88-90 Chapter 2 Summary and Review

1.

```
←—●—+—●—+—+—+—●—+—●—→
  -3 -2 -1  0  1  2  3  4  5
```

3. 8 **5.** −4 **7.** −22 **9.** 4 **11.** 6 **13.** −15
15.

```
←———————⊕———————————————→
  -5 -4 -3 -2 -1  0  1  2
```

17. < **19.** > **21.** > **23.** $\frac{71}{120}$ **25.** −1 **27.** 12.37
29. −99 **31.** $-\frac{3}{7}$ **33.** $-5a - 12b$ **35.** $-9b$
37. $-3a - 6$ **39.** {1, 3, 5} **41.** $38 **43.** −69
45. 1.25 liters of soda for $1.31 **47a.** $\frac{5}{12}; \frac{7}{12}$ **b.** 16 karats **49.** Let n = the number; $3n - 21 = 57$.

CHAPTER 3   EQUATIONS

Pages 97-98 Lesson 3-1

5. −13 **7.** 9 **9.** 13 **11.** −17 **13.** −12 **15.** 20
17. 1.4 **19.** −24 **21.** 58 **23.** 15 **25.** −10
27. −6 **29.** 21 **31.** −4 **33.** −2.8 **35.** 2.32
37. −32 **39.** 122 **41.** −32 **43.** 85 meters **45.** 63 cars **47.** 339.223 **48.** 31 **49.** −28.9 **50.** $-a - 5$
51. Let d = dimes; $d + (d + 8) + 15 = 51$.

Pages 101-102 Lesson 3-2

3. 16 **5.** 5 **7.** −3 **9.** $m - 8$ **11.** $z - 31$ **13.** −9
15. −23 **17.** −75 **19.** −0.8 **21.** −3 **23.** −21
25. 34 **27.** 24 **29.** −7 **31.** $\frac{5}{4}$; 1.25 **33.** −32
35. −26 **37.** −101 **41.** 126.1 seconds **43.** 443 cattle **44.** false

45.

```
←—+—●—+—●—+—+—+—+—●—+—→
 -1  0  1  2  3  4  5  6  7
```

46. A possible answer is 0. **47.** −26 **48.** 43
49. −16

Pages 106-107 Lesson 3-3

5. 3 **7.** $\frac{4}{3}$ **9.** $-\frac{1}{8}$ **11.** 4 **13.** 4 **15.** −8 **17.** 7
19. −9 **21.** $\frac{40}{9}; 4.\overline{4}$ **23.** $-\frac{11}{3}; -3.\overline{6}$ **25.** 0.188
27. −23 **29.** 48 **31.** 70 **33.** −1885 **35.** −25
37. $\frac{250}{3}; 83.\overline{3}$ **39.** $\frac{110}{13}; 8.462$ **41.** $\frac{14}{9}; 1.\overline{5}$ **43.** −8
45. 13 **47.** −65.3 **49.** 15 **51.** $7\frac{1}{2}$ **53.** 23 **55.** $-\frac{1}{3};$ $-0.\overline{3}$ **59.** 20 cans **60.** $4 + 80x + 32y$ **61.** 4, −7, −18 **62.** −3 **63.** −19

Page 107 Mid-Chapter Review

1. −1.9 **2.** 52 **3.** −25 **4.** −15 **5.** −60 **6.** −7
7. 104 **8.** −16 **9.** 6 **10.** $115.62 **11.** 6.25 kg

Pages 109-110 Lesson 3-4

3. 80 pounds **5.** $50 **7.** In the figure below, all sums are 11.

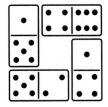

9. 981 **11.** top row: three-letter words; middle row: four-letter words; bottom row: five-letter words; the words in each row are in alphabetical order.
13. 15 **15.** Kevin, Kim, Maria, Marquita, and Paul

Pages 113-115 Lesson 3-5

5. −1 **7.** $-42\frac{1}{4}; -42.25$ **9.** 6, 8, 10
11. $x + (x + 1) = 17$ **13.** $x + (x + 2) = -36$
15. 3 **17.** 5 **19.** $-\frac{25}{3}; -8.\overline{3}$ **21.** 16 **23.** 4
25. 136 **27.** −38 **29.** −104 **31.** $\frac{65}{7}; 9.286$ **33.** 28, 29, 30 **35.** no solution **37.** 30, 32, 34, 36 **39.** 46 customers **41.** 88; no **43a.** They are multiples of 3 and odd. **b.** They are multiples of 3 and even.
c. They are not divisible by three. **44.** substitution (=) **45.** 11 **46.** $\frac{0.9}{5}$ **47.** −36 **48.** 7 **49.** 32 students

Pages 118-120 Lesson 3-6

5. Add 10 to each side. Add $3y$ to each side. Divide each side by 11. **7.** Multiply $x - 3$ by −7. Subtract 21 from each side. Divide each side by −7. **9.** 2
11. −2 **13.** 65 yd × 120 yd **15.** $-\frac{1}{2}; -0.5$ **17.** $\frac{7}{8};$

0.875   **19.** 5.6   **21.** −3   **23.** identity   **25.** no
solution   **27.** 8   **29.** 3   **31.** 42   **33.** identity
35. 43   **37.** 26, 28, 30   **39.** 38 vans   **41.** 65 yd by
120 yd   **43.** $a = m + n^2$ **44.** $\frac{1}{6}$ **45.** 0.00879
46. 12.4   **47.** −9   **48.** $-\frac{20}{3}$; $-6.\overline{6}$ **49.** 3

Pages 123–125   Lesson 3-7

5. 100; $817y = 420 - 370y$ **7.** 20;
$8x = 140 - 15x$ **9.** 49   **11.** $\frac{8}{5}$; 1.6   **13.** $\frac{11}{6}$; $1.8\overline{3}$
15. −17   **17.** $\frac{3}{2}$; 1.5   **19.** 4   **21.** −2   **23.** −1
25. $3c - a$ **27.** $\frac{3z + 2y}{e}$ **29.** $\frac{am - z}{a + n}$ **31.** $\frac{5}{3}(b - a)$
33. 120   **35.** 10   **37.** 18 and 30 or 150 and 162
39. 260 m   **41a.** identity   **b.** $\frac{5}{2}$; 2.5   **c.** 2   **d.** −5

e. no solution   **42.** >   **43.** $-\frac{1}{22}$ **44.** Yvette has 17
less pennies than nickels. Yvette has a total of 63
nickels and pennies. How many of each type of coin
does she have?   **45.** 3   **46.** −3

Page 126–128   Chapter 3 Summary and Review

1. 53   **3.** 6   **5.** 27   **7.** 77   **9.** −24   **11.** 38
13. −26   **15.** 55   **17.** 8   **19.** −6   **21.** −16
23. −16   **25.** 10   **27.** −18   **29.** 69   **31.** 7   **33.** 3
35. 43   **37.** 3   **39.** −0.5   **41.** $\frac{3b - 10a}{5}$ **43.** $\frac{3}{2}b$
45. 5.1   **47.** 900 mL   **49.** 25, 27, 29   **51.** 15.5 m ×
78.5 m   **53.** 36 ft, 38 ft, 40 ft, 42 ft

CHAPTER 4   APPLICATIONS OF RATIONAL NUMBERS

Pages 136–137   Lesson 4-1

5. $\frac{3}{11}$ **7.** $\frac{2}{1}$ **9.** $\frac{4}{1}$ **11.** 6   **13.** 14   **15.** $\frac{28}{3}$; $9.\overline{3}$
17. −2   **19.** $\frac{58}{3}$; $19.\overline{3}$ **21.** 23   **23.** $\frac{52}{41}$; 1.268
25. $-\frac{149}{6}$; $-24.8\overline{3}$ **27.** 2.28   **29.** 1.251
31. 63.368   **35.** 1127 deer   **37.** 267.9 km   **39.** 53
40. $14x + 14y$ **41.** $18px - 15bg$ **42.** 2 cups   **43.** 2

Pages 140–141   Lesson 4-2

3. 31%   **5.** 4%   **7.** $37\frac{1}{2}$%; 37.5%   **9.** 24   **11.** 60
13. 40%   **15.** $12\frac{1}{2}$%; 12.5%   **17.** 32   **19.** 25%
21. 80   **23.** $242.80   **25.** $50,000   **27.** $6.24
31. 40 questions   **33.** 7520 people
35. $2m + n^2 = y$ **36.** 52   **37.** $-\frac{17}{16}$ **38.** 18 weeks

Pages 143–145   Lesson 4-3

3. $480   **5.** $3\frac{1}{2}$ years   **7.** 12%   **9.** $2400   **11.** $6400
at 8%, $3600 at 12%   **13.** $3800   **15.** $3000
17. 11.5%   **19.** $18,000   **22.** 15   **23.** <   **24.** A

possible answer is 0.   **25.** 88 gallons in X, 40 gallons
in Y   **26.** 140

Pages 148–149   Lesson 4-4

5. D; $6; 6%   **7.** $172; $28   **9.** $47.89; 25.5%
11. 10   **13.** 28   **15.** 39   **17.** 20%   **19.** $3.00
21. $303.60   **23.** $41.18   **27.** $88.50   **29.** $307.80
30. $23a + 16b$ **31.** $-7b$ **32.** $\frac{19}{2}$ **33.** 30%   **34.** 4
years

Pages 152–153   Lesson 4-5

3. 4 hours   **5.** 3:30 P.M.   **7.** left: 7, middle: 3, right:
2, bottom: 5   **9.** 4

Pages 155–157   Lesson 4-6

3. $0.25x + 0.10(x + 8) = 2.55$
5. $0.10(5) + 1.00n = 0.40(5 + n)$ **7.** 5 adults, 16
children   **9.** 15 pounds   **11.** 15 pounds   **13.** 3.2
quarts   **15.** 20 liters   **17.** Let y = number of yards
Diego gained in both games; $134 + (134 - 17) = y$.
18. 13   **19.** 3.2 pounds   **20.** $41.95

Page 157   Mid-Chapter Review

1. 15   **2.** 14   **3.** 10.29   **4.** 30   **5.** 40   **6.** $12\frac{1}{2}$%
7. $800   **8.** $121.36   **9.** $40.81   **10.** $9.12

Pages 159–161   Lesson 4-7

3a. 120 mi   **b.** 180 mi   **c.** 10 mi   **d.** $\frac{2}{3}k$ mi   **5a.** 9
hours   **b.** 12 hours   **c.** $\frac{360}{x}$ hours   **7.** $3\frac{1}{2}$ hours
9. $2\frac{1}{2}$ hours   **11.** 11:30 A.M.   **13.** 46 mph   **15.** 240
km   **19.** $w - 5$ **20.** multiplicative property of
zero   **21.** 8   **22.** $12,500 at each rate

Pages 164–165   Lesson 4-8

3. 3   **5.** 7   **7.** 28   **9.** −5   **11.** 6   **13.** $26\frac{1}{4}$
15. $\frac{1}{5}$, $y = \frac{1}{5}x$ **17.** $-\frac{2}{3}$, $y = -\frac{2}{3}x$ **19.** $\frac{4}{5}$, $y = \frac{4}{5}x$
21. $\frac{567}{8}$ **25.** $13.33   **27.** $3\frac{1}{2}$ ft³   **28.** $\frac{6}{5}$ **29.** $11.66
30. 2^{17} or 131,072   **31.** 5 pounds   **32.** 5 hours

Pages 168–169   Lesson 4-9

5. direct, 3.14   **7.** direct, $\frac{1}{5}$ **9.** inverse, 14
11. inverse, 7   **13.** Emilio   **15.** 48   **17.** 99
19. 6.075   **23.** $21\frac{1}{3}$ m³   **25.** 720 cycles per second
27. $8\frac{1}{43}$ feet; about 8 ft $\frac{1}{4}$ in.   **29.** −15   **30.** 67
31. 16.6%   **32.** 1 liter   **33.** $467.50

Page 170–172   Chapter 4 Summary and Review

1. 18   **3.** 7   **5.** 16   **7.** 48   **9.** 87.5%   **11.** 0.1881
13. 12.5%   **15.** $189.86   **17.** $0.09x + 0.04 =$
$0.06(x + 1)$; 0.67 gal   **19a.** 40 mph   **b.** $\frac{240}{t}$ mph
21. 15   **23.** $\frac{75}{7}$; 10.714   **25.** 21   **27.** turkey -

12:30, potatoes - 3:45, yams - 3:30, green beans - 4:10, cranberry sauce - 4:55, gravy - 4:50, rolls - 4:45, jello - 12:45

CHAPTER 5   INEQUALITIES

Pages 178–180   Lesson 5-1

5. 17   **7.** 14.5   **9.** 1   **11.** -8 **13.** $\{r|r < -5\}$
15. $\{x|x \le 13\}$ **17.** $\{a|a < 9\}$ **19.** $\{r|r \ge 42\}$
21. $\{w|w \le 0\}$ **23.** $\{d|d < -7\}$ **25.** $\{x|x > -3\}$
27. $\{z|z < 23\}$ **29.** $\{x|x \ge 3\}$ **31.** $\{b|b \ge -1\}$
33. $\{s|s < -4.9\}$ **35.** $\left\{x|x \ge \frac{1}{5}\right\}$ **37.** $\{z|z \ge -1.654\}$
39. $\{x|x \ge -1\}$ **41.** $\{x|x < 8\}$ **43.** $\{x|x < 7\}$ **45.** 12
47. -5 **49.** 177 points   **51.** any score less than 9.9
53. $1.11y + 0.6$

54.

55. $-\frac{81}{4}$ **56.** \$31.00   **57.** 32

Pages 183–185   Lesson 5-2

5. 4; no   **7.** $\frac{1}{10}$; no   **9.** -10; yes   **11.** $\{x|x < -6\}$
13. $\left\{d|d \ge -\frac{5}{2}\right\}$ **15.** $\{x|x < 6\}$ **17.** $\{z|z \le 9\}$
19. $\{t|t > -36\}$ **21.** $\left\{c|c \ge -\frac{3}{2}\right\}$ **23.** $\{x|x > 0.6\}$
25. $\{a|a > 150\}$ **27.** $\{m|m \ge -33\}$ **29.** $\left\{y|y \le \frac{256}{3}\right\}$
31. $\left\{z|z < -\frac{7}{10}\right\}$ **33.** $d < 15$ **35.** $d < 144$
37. $\{x|x < 36\}$ **39.** $\{x|x \le 8\}$ **41.** $\{x|x > 30\}$
43. 48   **45.** $<$ **49.** at least 37.5 pounds   **51.** 37 shares   **53.** 12 ounces of orange juice at \$1.69
54. -9 **55.** $\{y|y < -6\}$ **56.** 26   **57.** $\frac{3}{5}$ **58.** $1\frac{11}{13}$

Pages 188–190   Lesson 5-3

5. $\{x|x > 5\}$ **7.** $\{n|n \ge 23\}$ **9.** $\{y|y \le -1\}$
11. $\{x|x > 2\}$ **13.** $\{a|a \ge -6\}$ **15.** $\{m|m \le 6\}$
17. $\{z|z \ge -48\}$ **19.** $\{d|d > -125\}$
21. $\{w|w < -6.5\}$ **23.** $\{r|r > 8\}$ **25.** $\{y|y \ge 15\}$
27. $\{g|g < -5\}$ **29.** $\{c|c > 2\}$ **31.** $\{x|x \le 12\}$
33. $\{x|x < 17\}$ **35.** 38 and 40   **37.** 7 and 9, 5 and 7, 3 and 5, 1 and 3   **39.** $y > \frac{9}{4}$ **41.** $c \le -4$ **43.** at least 90 points   **45.** more than 35 hours   **46.** Let x = number of points Megan scored in both games; $12 + (12 + 4) = x$.   **47.** 20   **48.** \$403.33
49. $\{z|z < 0.08\}$

Page 190   Mid-Chapter Review

1. $\{a|a < 8\}$ **2.** $\{s|s \ge -15\}$ **3.** $\{z|z < -3\}$
4. $\{b|b \ge 12\}$ **5.** $\left\{k|k < -\frac{18}{7}\right\}$ **6.** $\left\{a|a \le -\frac{65}{32}\right\}$
7. $\{x|x > -2\}$ **8.** $\left\{d|d \ge \frac{13}{10}\right\}$ **9.** $\left\{n|n > -\frac{5}{12}\right\}$
10. $\{n|n \ge 12\}$ **11.** $\{n|n < 120\}$ **12.** $\{n|n \le 42\}$

13. $\{n|n \le 1\}$ **14.** 63 newspapers or more   **15.** 33 or less

Page 193   Lesson 5-4

3. 25 thumbtacks   **5.** 1-Darryl, 2-Adrienne, 3-Allison, 4-Mr. Crawford, 5-Don, 6-Benito, 7-Chumani, 8-Belinda   **7.** $1^2 = 1$, $(25)^2 = 625$, or $(76)^2 = 5776$

Pages 197–198   Lesson 5-5

5. $0 \le m < 9$ **7.** $-\frac{4}{5} < z < \frac{2}{3}$

9.

13.

17.

21.

$\varnothing$

25. $\{$all numbers$\}$ **27.** $\varnothing$ **29.** $\{t|t < -2$ or $t > -1\}$
31. $\{x|x \le 4\}$ **33.** $\left\{x|x < \frac{3}{2}\right\}$ **35.** $x < -3$ or $x > 3$
37. $-3 \le x < 5$ **39.** $1 < n < 3$ **41.** $x < -\frac{5}{3}, x \ne 0$
43. $-4 < x < 1$ **47.** between \$131,250 and \$181,250   **49.** -7 **50.** 2.5   **51.** 4 adult, 12 children   **52.** $\{r|r < -6.6\}$ **53.** $\{x|x \ge -1\}$

Pages 202–203   Lesson 5-6

7. two   **9.** and   **11.** distance from 0 to y is more than 3 units; $y > 3$ or $y < -3$; $\{y|y > 3$ or $y < -3\}$
13. distance from 0 to $x - 12$ is less than 9 units; $x - 12 < 9$ and $x - 12 > -9$; $\{x|3 < x < 21\}$
15. distance from 0 to $7 - r$ is 4 units; $7 - r = 4$ or $7 - r = -4$; $\{3, 11\}$ **17.** $|s - 90| < 6$
19. $\{x|-3 < x < 5\}$ **21.** $\{a|a \le -9$ or $a \ge -7\}$
23. $\{y|y \le -4$ or $y \ge 22\}$ **25.** $\{z|z = -1$ or $z = 15\}$
27. $\{x|0 < x < 8\}$ **29.** $\{w|w < -10$ or $w > 8\}$
31. $\{$all numbers$\}$ **33.** $\varnothing$ **35.** $\left\{t|t \le -\frac{5}{3}$ or $t \ge 2\right\}$
37. $|x| = 1$ **39.** $|x| \ge 2$ **41.** $|x + 1| < 3$
43. $\{-2, -1, 0, 1, 2\}$ **45.** $2a + 1$ **49.** between $-259°C$ and $-255°C$ **51.** 1.96 cm to 2.04 cm, inclusive   **53.** $\frac{7n - 1}{3}$ **54.** 80   **55.** \$6350 at 8% and \$3650 at 10%   **56.** $333\frac{1}{3}\%$ **57.** 21 line segments
58. between 83 and 99, inclusive

Pages 204–206   Chapter 5 Summary and Review

1. $\{n|n < 13\}$ **3.** $\{a|a \ge -5.5\}$ **5.** $\{x|x > 7\}$
7. $\{n|n \ge 5\}$ **9.** $\{x|x \le 4\}$ **11.** $\{t|t > 1.2\}$
13. $\left\{k|k \ge \frac{1}{5}\right\}$ **15.** $\{n|n < -22\}$ **17.** $\{x|x < 6\}$
19. $\left\{y|y \le -\frac{9}{2}\right\}$ **21.** $\{z|z \le 20\}$ **23.** $\{n|n \le -5\}$

25.

29. $-2 \le x < 3$ **31.** $\{n|-4 \le n \le 6\}$ **33.** $\{p|p < -2$ or $p > \frac{5}{2}\}$ **35.** 32, 33, 34 **37.** Wednesday **39.** Jill: $208, Sung: $104 **41.** 17 to 19 books

CHAPTER 6 POLYNOMIALS

Pages 211-212 Lesson 6-1

3. 15,624 **5.** 21^2; 15^2 **7.** 1, 4, 9, 16, 25 **9.** 29 days **11.** You could never say this for the first time. The first time you say it, you would be lying. Therefore, only a Falsite could say it.

Pages 215-216 Lesson 6-2

5. no **7.** yes **9.** no **11.** p^{14} **13.** x^8 **15.** a^6
17. a^{13} **19.** m^4n^3 **21.** $(-4)^4$ or 256 **23.** r^7t^8
25. $-20x^5y$ **27.** $-343z^3$ **29.** $21y^7z$ **31.** $6x^4y^4z^4$
33. $a^{12}x^8$ **35.** $a^2b^2c^2$ **37.** $9a^2y^6$ **39.** $\frac{1}{8}x^3y^6$
41. $-54a^3b^6$ **43.** $90y^{10}$ **45.** $-6a^3b^5c^5$ **47.** $-30x^9y^3$
51. No, you will have $6908.22. **52.** $-1, -\frac{1}{2}, -\frac{1}{4}$
53. 1 daughter **54.** $\{x|x \le 4\}$ **55.** $\{x|x \ge 3\}$ **56.** 15 rectangles

Pages 219-220 Lesson 6-3

5. $-\frac{1}{8}$ **7.** $-\frac{1}{8}$ **9.** $\frac{1}{64}$ **11.** 81 **13.** $\frac{1}{b^2c}$ **15.** $\frac{5}{n^3}$ **17.** r^4
19. an **21.** r^3 **23.** m^6 **25.** b **27.** $3b$ **29.** y^3
31. $-s^6$ **33.** $-\frac{4b^3}{c^2}$ **35.** $-4y^4z^2$ **37.** $\frac{9ab^6}{5c^6}$ **39.** $\frac{s^3}{r^3}$
41. 1 **43.** $\frac{m}{7nr^2}$ **51.** $4597.87 **53.** 12 extra-large eggs weighing 27 ounces for $1.09 **54.** 2 **55.** $5\frac{7}{10}$ feet or 5 feet $8\frac{2}{5}$ in. **56.** Sam **57.** a^7

Pages 223-225 Lesson 6-4

5. 5000; 5.79×10^7 **7.** 12,760; 1.4959×10^8
9. 143,200; 7.782×10^8 **11.** 51,800; 2.87×10^9
13. 3000; 5.9×10^9 **15.** 2.4×10^5
17. 4.296×10^{-3} **19.** 3.17×10^{-9} **21.** 2.84×10^5
23. 3×10^2; 300 **25.** 6×10^2; 600 **27.** 5.5×10^{-9}, 0.0000000055 **29.** 6×10^{-3}; 0.006 **31.** 6.51×10^3; 6510 **33.** 7.8×10^8; 780,000,000 **35.** 2.1×10^{-1}, 0.21 **37.** 4×10^8; 400,000,000 **43.** 3000 calories
45. $886.38 **47a.** 1.416E + 7 **b.** 884,736
c. 5.706E + 14 **d.** 33,092 **48.** $-10a + 5b$ **49.** 8 legs **50.** 70 **51.** $\{q|q < 8\}$ **52.** $4a^6b^9$ **53.** $4a^7$

Pages 228-229 Lesson 6-5

5. not a polynomial **7.** yes, monomial **9.** yes, trinomial **11.** 0 **13.** 2 **15.** none **17.** 4 **19.** 29
21. 7 **23.** 4 **25.** 4 **27.** 3 **29.** 3 **31.** 7
33. $a^3 + 5ax + 2x^2$ **35.** $3xy^3 - 2x^2y + x^3$
37. $5b + \frac{2}{3}bx + b^3x^2$ **39.** $-3x^3 + 5x^2 + 2x + 7$
41. $7ax^3 + 11x^2 - 3x + 2a$

43. $\frac{1}{5}x^5 - 8a^3x^3 + \frac{2}{3}x^2 + 7a^3x$ **45.** yes **47.** 211 eggs

48.

49. -7 **50.** $4500 at 6.2%, $8000 at 8.6%
51. $\{p|p < -\frac{3}{2}\}$ **52.** 4.235×10^4 **53.** 6.28×10^{-6}

Pages 229 Mid-Chapter Review

1. 7 **2.** b^9 **3.** x^4y^4 **4.** $-6n^5y^7$ **5.** 15,625
6. $-48x^3y^2$ **7.** $9a^4b^{10}$ **8.** n^3 **9.** $-12ab^4$ **10.** $\frac{125}{r^3s^3}$
11. 2.85×10^7 **12.** 5×10^{-6} **13.** $\frac{1}{4}x - \frac{2}{5}s^4x^2 + \frac{1}{3}s^2x^3 + 4x^4$ **14.** $p^4 + 21p^2x + 3px^3$

Pages 232-233 Lesson 6-6

3. $-3x - 2y$ **5.** $-x^2 - 3x - 7$
7. $3ab^2 - 5a^2b + b^3$ **9.** 5m and $-3m$, 4mn and $-mn$, 2n and 8n **11.** $8a^2b$ and $16a^2b$, $11b^2$ and $-2b^2$ **13.** $7ax^2 - 5a^2x - 7a^3 + 4$
15. $9a - 3b - 4c + 16d$ **17.** $x^2y^2 - 5xy - 10$
19. $6m^2n^2 + 8mn - 28$ **21.** $7x + 14y$
23. $7x - 4y$ **25.** $13m + 3n$ **27.** $-2 - 6a$
29. $7ax^2 + 3a^2x - 5ax + 2x$ **31.** $x + y$
33. $5x^2 - 23x - 23$ **39.** 184 **40.** 2.1 **41.** 21 sports **42.** 8 hours, 4 hours **43.** $\{m|m < -7\}$ **44.** 3

Pages 236-237 Lesson 6-7

5. $24m^2 + 21m$ **7.** $10x - 6$ **9.** $35a^2b^3 + 7ab^3$
11. $7a^4 + 21a^3 - a + 25$ **13.** 0 **15.** $-24x - 15$
17. $15b^2 + 24b$ **19.** $2.2a^2 + 7.7a$ **21.** $15s^3t + 6s^2t^2$
23. $10a^4 - 14a^3 + 4a$ **25.** $40y^4 + 35y^3 - 15y^2$
27. $15x^4y - 35x^3y^2 + 5x^2y^3$ **29.** $-32x^2y^2 - 56x^2y + 112xy^3$ **31.** $-\frac{1}{4}ab^4 + \frac{1}{3}ab^3 - \frac{3}{4}ab^2$ **33.** $15t^2 + t$
35. $x^2 + 6x$ **37.** $50.6t^2 + 21t - 102$
39. $-3m^3 + 41m^2 - 14m - 16$
41. $21a^3 - 6a^2 - 46a + 28$ **43.** $\frac{29}{3}$ **45.** $\frac{58}{33}$ **47.** $\frac{1}{3}$
49. $-\frac{3}{2}$ **51.** 17 **55.** 4.5 ft **56.** -2 **57.** $-\frac{1}{5}$
58. $-\frac{14}{27}$ **59.** $7\frac{1}{2}\%$ **60.** $\{x|x \le 3$ or $x \ge 11\}$
61. $6a + 9b$

Pages 241-242 Lesson 6-8

3. $8x$ **5.** $22x$ **7.** $-b$ **9.** $a^2 + 10a + 21$
11. $x^2 + 7x - 44$ **13.** $c^2 + 10c + 16$
15. $y^2 - 4y - 21$ **17.** $8a^2 + 2a - 3$
19. $10x^2 + 19xy + 6y^2$ **21.** $40q^2 + qr - 6r^2$
23. $10r^2 - 0.1r - 0.03$ **25.** $18x^2 - \frac{1}{8}$
27. $2x^3 + 15x^2 - 11x - 9$ **29.** $12x^3 + 11x^2y - 11xy^2 - 3y^3$ **31.** $6x^3 - 5x^2 + 8x + 55$
33. $-24a^3 - 34a^2 + 19a + 15$ **35.** $20x^4 - 9x^3 + 73x^2 - 39x + 99$ **37.** $2x^4 - 17x^3 + 23x^2 + 30x - 24$ **39.** $-6x^4 - 5x^3 + 7x^2 + 71x + 40$
45. 21 ft by 47 ft **47.** 20, 35, 65 **48.** $11.66
49. $\{x|x < 14\}$ **50.** b^5 **51.** $4a^2 + 10a$

Pages 245–246   Lesson 6-9

5. $a^2 - 6ab + 9b^2$ 7. $9x^2 - 12xy + 4y^2$
9. $25a^2 - 9b^2$ 11. $4a^2 - 4ab + b^2$
13. $16x^2 - 72xy + 81y^2$ 15. $25x^2 + 60xy + 36y^2$
17. $25 - 10x + x^2$ 19. $1.21x^2 + 2.2xy + y^2$
21. $x^6 - 10x^3y^2 + 25y^4$ 23. $64a^2 - 4b^2$
25. $64x^4 - 9y^2$ 27. $2x^3 + 5x^2 - 8x - 20$
29. $x^4 - 25x^2 + 144$ 31. $8x^3 - 36x^2y + 54xy^2 - 27y^3$ 33. $16x^4 - 32x^3y + 24x^2y^2 - 8xy^3 + y^4$ 35. $a^5 - 5a^4b + 10a^3b^2 - 10a^2b^3 + 5ab^4 - b^5$ 37. 8 miles   39. $\frac{3}{8}$ 40. 110 at 95¢, 154 at \$1.25   41. false

Pages 248–250   Chapter 6 Summary and Review

1. y^7 3. $20a^5x^5$ 5. $576x^5y^2$ 7. $-\frac{1}{2}m^4n^8$ 9. y^4
11. $3b^3$ 13. $\frac{a^4}{2b}$ 15. 2.4×10^5 17. 3.14×10^{-4}
19. 6×10^{11} 21. 6×10^{-1} 23. 2   25. 4
27. $3x^4 + x^2 - x - 5$ 29. $-3x^3 + x^2 - 5x + 5$
31. $16m^2n^2 - 2mn + 11$ 33. $12a^3b - 28ab^3$
35. $10x^2 - 19x + 63$ 37. $r^2 + 4r - 21$
39. $4x^2 + 13x - 12$ 41. $x^3 + x^2 - 27x + 28$
43. $x^2 - 36$ 45. $16x^2 + 56x + 49$
47. $64x^2 - 80x + 25$ 49. Fibonacci sequence
51. $x^2 - 4$

CHAPTER 7   FACTORING

Pages 258–260   Lesson 7-1

5. prime   7. composite; $2^3 \cdot 3$ 9. 4   11. 5   13. 5
15. 1   17. $3 \cdot 7$ 19. $2^2 \cdot 3 \cdot 5$ 21. $3^2 \cdot 7$
23. $2^4 \cdot 7$ 25. $2^4 \cdot 19$ 27. $2^2 \cdot 3 \cdot 5^2$
29. $-1 \cdot 2 \cdot 2 \cdot 2 \cdot 2 \cdot 2 \cdot 2$
31. $-1 \cdot 2 \cdot 2 \cdot 2 \cdot 2 \cdot 3 \cdot 5$ 33. $2 \cdot 7 \cdot 7 \cdot a \cdot a \cdot b$
35. $2 \cdot 2 \cdot 3 \cdot 3 \cdot 3 \cdot 7 \cdot m \cdot m \cdot m \cdot n \cdot n \cdot n$ 37. 4
39. 5   41. 5   43. 1   45. $7y^2$ 47. $4ab$ 49. $10n^2$
51. $4a$ 53. 5   55. 6   57. 2   59. 3   61. $5a$ 63. $6y^2$
65. $-4x^2y^3$ 67. $6a^3b^2$ 71. 5 rows of 20 plants; 10 rows of 10 plants; 20 rows of 5 plants   73. 60×25 or 1500 squares of sod   75a. 16   b. 1   c. 12
76. -64 77. $x = 2d - r$ 78. 36 pounds
79. $\left\{x | x \geq -\frac{8}{5}\right\}$ 80. $\left\{y | y \geq \frac{9}{2} \text{ or } y \leq \frac{1}{2}\right\}$
81. $-40a^3 - 64a^2 + 24a$ 82. $25r^2 - 70rs + 49s^2$

Pages 263–264   Lesson 7-2

5. 2   7. 1   9. $7m$ 11. 1   13. r^2 15. $x(x^4y - 1)$
17. $3c^2d(1 - 2d)$ 19. $2x^2$ 21. $5ab$ 23. $8y(y + 1)$
25. $2mn(7n + 1)$ 27. $y^3(15x + y)$
29. $12pq(3pq - 1)$ 31. $2mn(m^2n - 8mn^2 + 4)$
33. $7abc(4abc + 3ac - 2)$ 35. $a(1 + ab + a^2b^3)$
37. $A = 3(4a + b + 12)$
39. $A = 8(a + b + c + 2d + 8)$
41. $y(y^4 + 5y^3 + 3y + 2)$ 43. $\frac{1}{5}ab(4a - 3b - 1)$
47. $(3x - 10)$ shares   48. $x \leq -3$ 49. \$1599

50. $\frac{61}{9}$ 51. 3×10^2, 300   52. $-3x^5 + 2mx^4 + 6x^3 + 4m^5$ 53. $2ab$

Pages 267–268   Lesson 7-3

5. $(t + s)(t - s)$ 7. $(8m + 1)(x + y)$ 9. $3x + 2y$
11. $2y - 5$ 13. $(a - c)(y - b)$ 15. $(5a + 2b) \cdot (1 + 2a)$ 17. $x^2 + 1$ 19. $5k - 7p$ 21. $(2m + r) \cdot (3x - 2)$ 23. $(m - b)(3y + a)$ 25. $(a + 1)(a - 2b)$
27. $(m^2 + p^2)(3 - 5p)$ 29. $(2x - 5y)(2a - 7b)$
31. $a(x + ax - 1 - 2a)$ 33. $(2x^2 - 5y^2)(x - y)$
35. $4z + 3m$ ft by $z - 6$ ft   37. $(4x + 3y)(a + b)$
39. $(7x + 3m - 4)(a + b)$ 41. $(x - 3y - z)(2a + b)$
45. $(s + 8)(2s - 3)$ 46. $\{2, 3\}$ 47. \$595.99   48. 61
49. $6x^2 - x - 40$ 50. $2x^2(5x^2 - 3xy - 4y^2)$

Pages 269–270   Lesson 7-4

3. $4 \cdot (5 - 2) + 7 = 19$

5.

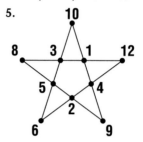

7. 631, 542   9. $3 \times 54 = 162$ 11. July 9 and September 7

Pages 274–275   Lesson 7-5

5. 2, 9   7. 2, 7   9. $-2, -6$ 11. 10   13. 9
15. $(x + 5)(x - 3)$ 17. $(b + 5)(b + 7)$ 19. -3
21. $2z, 3$ 23. $(y + 3)(y + 9)$ 25. $(c + 3)(c - 1)$
27. $(x - 8)(x + 3)$ 29. $(7a + 1)(a + 3)$
31. $(3y - 4)(2y - 1)$ 33. $(2x + 3)(x - 4)$
35. prime   37. $(9 - y)(4 - y)$ 39. $(a + 3b)(a - b)$
41. $(3s + 2t)(s - 4t)$ 43. prime   45. 7, -7, 11, -11 47. 12, -12 49. 1, -1, 11, -11, 19, -19, 41, -41 51. $4x^2(5x - 7)(2x - 3)$ 53. $(a - 3)(a - 4) \cdot (2x + 3y)$ 57. 60 m by 80 m   58. \$4300 at 5%, \$7400 at 7%   59. $\{n | n > 14.2\}$ 60. $12x^6y^8$
61. $x^2 - 15x + 10$ 62. $(5a + 2b)(3 + 2a)$ 63. 60 guests

Pages 278–280   Lesson 7-6

5. yes   7. yes   9. yes   11. d 13. a
15. $(x - 7)(x + 7)$ 17. $(x - 6y)(x + 6y)$
19. $(4a - 3b)(4a + 3b)$ 21. prime   23. $2(z - 7) \cdot (z + 7)$ 25. $2(2x - 3)(2x + 3)$ 27. $(5y - 7z^2) \cdot (5y + 7z^2)$ 29. $(0.1n - 1.3r)(0.1n + 1.3r)$
31. prime   33. $(7x - 4)(7x + 4)$
35. $\left(\frac{1}{4}x - 5z\right)\left(\frac{1}{4}x + 5z\right)$ 37. $\left(\frac{1}{2}n - 4\right)\left(\frac{1}{2}n + 4\right)$
39. prime   41. 5   43. $3a - 2, 3a + 2, a + 2$
45. $a - 5b, a + 5b, 5a + 3b$

47. $(2 - a)(2 + a)(4 + a^2)$
49. $3x(2x - y)(2x + y)(4x^2 + y^2)$ **51.** $(x - 1) \cdot$
$(x + 1)(x^2 + 1)(x^4 + 1)$ **57.** 12 in. by 12 in. **59.** $\frac{1}{6}$
60. 168 miles **61.** $\{x|-9 < x < 2\}$ **62.** $-8ab$
63. 7 **64.** $(8x - 5)(2x + 3)$

Page 280 Mid-Chapter Review

1. $13a^2$ **2.** $4ac^2$ **3.** $55m^2n$ **4.** $(y - 1)(y - 7)$
5. $5m^2n(5m + 3n)$ **6.** $(r + 6)(r - 3)$ **7.** prime
8. $5a(a^2 + 9a - 3)$ **9.** $(2p + 3)(3p - 1)$
10. $8(k + 3z)(k - 3z)$ **11.** $7ab^2(-a - 11a^2 + 11b)$
12. $(5x - 14)(x - 1)$ **13.** $(y + 2)(y - 2)(m + n)$
14. 41,312,432 or 23,421,314
15. $4x^2 + 36x - 115 \ m^2$

Pages 283-284 Lesson 7-7

5. 7 **7.** $8b$ **9.** $6x$ **11.** no **13.** yes, $(b - 7)^2$
15. no **17.** yes, $(p + 6)^2$ **19.** no **21.** yes, $(2a - 5)^2$
23. $(n - 4)^2$ **25.** $(2k - 1)^2$ **27.** prime
29. $(1 - 5z)^2$ **31.** $2(5x + 2)^2$ **33.** $(7m - 9)^2$
35. $(5x - 12)^2$ **37.** $(m + 8n)^2$ **39.** $(2x + z^2)^2$
41. $\left(\frac{1}{2}a + 3\right)^2$ **43.** yes; $11y + 1$ **45.** no **47.** 4
49. $4b^2$ **51.** 40 or -40
53. $(a + 2 - 3b)(a + 2 + 3b)$
55. $(m - k + 3)(m + k - 3)$ **57.** $(m - 2)(a + 3)^2$
59. $6y + 26$ **61.** 21 in. by 21 in. **63.** 37.5
64. 15.152 gallons **65.** 7, 8, or 9 **66.** $9x^2 - 4$
67. $16t^2 + 34t - 15$ **68.** $5(x - 4y^2)(x + 4y^2)$
69. $15x^2y(xy^3 - 2z)$

Pages 288-289 Lesson 7-8

5. greatest common factor **7.** perfect square
trinomial **9.** trinomial that has two binomial
factors **11.** $3(x^2 + 5)$ **13.** $(a - 3b)(a + 3b)$
15. $(a + 4)^2$ **17.** $6a(2a + 3y^2)$ **19.** $3(y - 7)(y + 7)$
21. $m(m + 3)^2$ **23.** $(3r + 2)(2r + 3)$
25. $(m^2 - p)(m^2 + p)$ **27.** $3x(x - 3)(x + 3)$
29. $2(5n + 1)(2n + 3)$ **31.** $(2a + 3b)^2$
33. $3t(3t - 2)(t + 8)$ **35.** $m(mn + 7)(mn - 7)$
37. $0.7(y - 2)(y - 3)$ **39.** $\frac{1}{12}(4m - 1)(3m + 2)$
41. $(x^2 + 8)(xy + 2)$ **43.** $(y^2 + z^2)(x + 1)(x - 1)$
45. $(x + y + a - b)(x + y - a + b)$ **47.** $x(x - 1)$
49. $(x^2 - 3y)(x + 3)^2$ **51.** $x - 3y, x + 3y, xy + 7$
53. 23 feet by 35 feet **55.** 29.4% **56.** \$21.60 or
less **57.** 28 games **58.** $-0.008x^9y^3$ **59.** ab^3
60. $12s - 28$

Pages 293-294 Lesson 7-9

5. $3r = 0$ or $r - 4 = 0$ **7.** $x - 6 = 0$ or $x + 4 = 0$
9. $4x - 7 = 0$ or $3x + 5 = 0$ **11.** $\{0, -4\}$
13. $\{0, 2\}$ **15.** $\left\{0, \frac{1}{2}\right\}$ **17.** $\{0, -6\}$ **19.** $\{3, 5\}$
21. $\{-1, -3\}$ **23.** $\left\{\frac{5}{3}\right\}$ **25.** $\{0, -36\}$ **27.** $\{0, -9\}$
29. $\{0, -8\}$ **31.** $\{0, -5\}$ **33.** $\{0, 2\}$ **35.** $\left\{0, \frac{1}{6}\right\}$
37. 16 years old **39.** 0, 1; $-3, -2$ **41.** 9 ft by 9 ft

43. 12 seconds **45.** 125 tickets
46. $\{s|s \le -6\}$ **47.** $8mn^2 + 3mn - n - 3n^3$
48. $2^2 \cdot 3^3 \cdot 5^2$ **49.** 15, -15, 6, -6, 0
50. $2(3c + 7d)(2c - 3d)$

Pages 297-299 Lesson 7-10

5. $\left\{-2, -\frac{1}{2}\right\}$ **7.** $\{4, -4\}$ **9.** $\{0, -1, -28\}$ **11.** Let
x = one of the integers; $x(15 - x) = 44$. **13.** Let
x = the amount the length and width should be
increased; $(7 + x)(4 + x) = 28 + 26$. **15.** $\{-8, 7\}$
17. $\{8, -8\}$ **19.** $\{12\}$ **21.** $\{9, -2\}$ **23.** $\left\{\frac{5}{3}, -7\right\}$
25. $\left\{\frac{5}{2}, -\frac{7}{3}\right\}$ **27.** $\left\{0, \frac{1}{5}, -7\right\}$ **29.** $\{-4, -5\}$
31. $\left\{-4, \frac{2}{3}\right\}$ **33.** 10, 12; $-12, -10$ **35.** 8, 11;
$-8, -11$ **37.** 6, 8; $-12, -10$ **39.** $\left\{2, -\frac{1}{3}, \frac{1}{3}\right\}$
41. $\left\{(p, z)|p = \frac{1}{4} \text{ or } z = -3\right\}$ **45.** 18 yd by 13 yd
47. 1.5 km **49.** 20 seconds **50.** 4133 points
51. -6 **52.** 16 **53.** $\{t|t > 2\}$
54. $56c^3d^3 - 8c^2d^3 + 8cd^4$ **55.** 16 or -16 **56.** 8
seconds

Pages 300-302 Chapter 7 Summary and Review

1. 5 **3.** 2 **5.** $4n$ **7.** mnp **9.** $6(x^2y + 2xy + 1)$
11. $2a(13b + 9c + 16a)$ **13.** $\frac{3}{5}(a - b + 2c)$
15. $(3a + 5b)(8m - 3n)$ **17.** $(4k - p^2)(4k^2 - 7p)$
19. $(y + 3)(y + 4)$ **21.** $(b - 1)(b + 6)$
23. $(3a - 7)(a - 2)$ **25.** $(a - b)(a - 9b)$
27. $(8m - 3n)(7m - 9n)$ **29.** $(5 - 3y)(5 + 3y)$
31. $2y(y - 8)(y + 8)$ **33.** $(9x^2 + 4)(3x - 2)(3x + 2)$
35. $(4x - 1)^2$ **37.** $2(4n - 5)^2$ **39.** $\left(y - \frac{3}{4}z^2\right)^2$
41. $(7y + 2)(4y - 3)$ **43.** $m(3m + 5)(2m - 3)$
45. $2r(r^2 - 9r + 15)$ **47.** $(x + 7)(x - 7)(m + b)$
49. $\{0, 5\}$ **51.** $\left\{0, \frac{9}{2}\right\}$ **53.** $\left\{0, \frac{3}{2}\right\}$ **55.** $\{7, -7\}$
57. $\left\{-\frac{2}{5}\right\}$ **59.** $\left\{0, -\frac{4}{3}, -\frac{7}{2}\right\}$ **61.** 5 of the 24 and 3 of
the 36 **63.** $16x$ **65.** 9, 11; $-11, -9$

CHAPTER 8 RATIONAL EXPRESSIONS

Pages 308-310 Lesson 8-1

5. $6y$; $x \ne 0, y \ne 0$ **7.** x: $x \ne 0, y \ne 2$ **9.** $a - b$;
$a \ne b$ **11.** $\frac{1}{3x}$; $x \ne 0$ **13.** $\frac{19a}{21b}$; $a \ne 0, b \ne 0$ **15.** $\frac{1}{2}$;
$m \ne -5$ **17.** $\frac{1}{y - 4}$; $y \ne 4, y \ne -4$ **19.** $-\frac{1}{w + 4}$;
$w \ne \frac{2}{3}, w \ne -4$ **21.** $\frac{c - 2}{c + 2}$; $c \ne -2$ **23.** m; $m \ne 2$
25. r^2; $r \ne 1$ **27.** $\frac{m^2}{2m - 1}$; $m \ne \frac{1}{2}, m \ne 0$ **29.** $\frac{2}{1 - 2y}$;
$y \ne \frac{1}{2}; y \ne 0$ **31.** $\frac{a^2b}{3a + 7b^2}$; $a \ne -\frac{7b^2}{3}, a \ne 0, b \ne 0$
33. $\frac{1}{x + y}$; $x \ne -y$ **35.** $\frac{6x}{x + 4}$; $x \ne -4$ **37.** $\frac{2}{x + 3}$;
$x \ne 7, x \ne -3$

39. $\frac{5}{3}$; $x \neq -1$ **41.** $\frac{2k+5}{2k-5}$; $k \neq \frac{5}{2}$ **43.** $\frac{1}{(b+3)(b+2)}$;
$b \neq 2, b \neq 3, b \neq -2, b \neq -3$ **45.** $\frac{n-2}{n(n-6)}$; $n \neq 0$,
$n \neq 6$ **47.** -1; $x \neq 3$ **49.** $\frac{x^2+4}{x^2-4}$; $x \neq 2, x \neq -2$
51. 36 seconds **53.** about 9.5°F **55.** $\frac{9}{17}$
56. 6 years **57.** $\left\{q | q \leq -\frac{27}{2}\right\}$ **58.** 7.124
59. $-20x^7$ **60.** $3a + 2b^2$ **61.** $\{-6, 6\}$

Pages 313-314   Lesson 8-2
3. $\frac{3b}{4a}$ **5.** $\frac{b}{d}$ **7.** 2 **9.** $\frac{a^2}{bd}$ **11.** $\frac{10ac}{3b^2}$ **13.** $\frac{4m^4}{15n^2}$ **15.** 15
17. 6 **19.** $\frac{3}{2}$ **21.** $4a - 4b$ **23.** 7 **25.** $\frac{x+y}{x+1}$
27. $\frac{3k}{k-3}$ **29.** $\frac{-xy - x^2}{y}$ **31.** $\frac{9m^2}{n}$ **33.** $\frac{1}{3}$
35. $\frac{x+5}{x^2 - 12x + 35}$ **37.** $-\frac{x}{xy^2 - y}$ **39.** $\frac{y^2}{y^2 - y - 2}$
41. $\frac{2y^2 + 11y - 21}{12y^3 + 19y^2 + 5y}$ **43.** $\frac{-2(a+b)(y+1)}{y}$
47. 742.5 ft³ **49.** 9, 25, 2500 **50.** $h < 450$
51. 7.6×10^6 **52.** $15x^2 + 32x - 7$
53. $6(y + 2x)(y - 2x)$ **54.** $\frac{x}{x^2 - 4}$

Pages 317-318   Lesson 8-3
3. $\frac{2}{m}$ **5.** $-\frac{3n}{8}$ **7.** $\frac{5}{2m^2}$ **9.** $\frac{x-y}{x+y}$ **11.** $\frac{-y}{5y+25}$ **13.** $\frac{a^4}{b^4}$
15. a **17.** $\frac{b+3}{4b}$ **19.** $2a$ **21.** $-\frac{x}{7}$ **23.** $\frac{ax + bx}{2}$
25. $\frac{3t+12}{2w-6}$ **27.** $\frac{x+3}{x}$ **29.** $\frac{2m-3}{3m-2}$ **31.** $\frac{x+5}{x+7}$
33. $\frac{4x^2 + 10x - 24}{2x^2 + 11x - 6}$ **35.** $8.50 **37.** 12.5%
39. $4500 **40.** $x < -20$ **41.** $9m^4 + 12m^2n + 4n^2$
42. $\frac{1}{4}x(2x - a)$ **43.** $2m + 4$

Pages 320-321   Lesson 8-4
3. a **5.** $4m^2$ **7.** x^2 **9.** $x + 4$ **11.** $a + 5$
13. $c + 3 + \frac{9}{c+9}$ **15.** $r - 5$ **17.** $2x + 3$
19. $x^2 + 2x - 3$ **21.** $t^2 + 4t - 1$
23. $3c - 2 + \frac{4}{9c - 2}$ **25.** $3n^2 - 2n + 3 + \frac{3}{2n+3}$
27. $3s^2 + 2s - 3 - \frac{1}{s+2}$ **29.** $5t^2 - 3t - 2$
31. $8x^2 - 9$ **35.** 9 football fields
37a. $3x + 11 + \frac{24}{x-2}$ **b.** $3x - 1 + \frac{4}{x+2}$
c. $x^2 + 4x + 4$ **d.** $x^2 + 4$
e. $2x^3 + 3x^2 + x + 4 + \frac{5}{x-1}$ **f.** $2x^3 - x + 2$
38. $9\frac{3}{5}$ ft **39.** 9 days **40.** $\frac{9yz^5}{x^3}$ **41.** $(p+5)(p+5)$
42. $\frac{y^2}{a^2}$

Pages 324-325   Lesson 8-5
5. $\frac{7}{a}$ **7.** $-\frac{1}{z}$ **9.** $-\frac{1}{16}$ **11.** $\frac{k}{m}$ **13.** $\frac{a}{4}$ **15.** -1
17. $\frac{2m+3}{5}$ **19.** 1 **21.** $\frac{-y}{b+6}$ **23.** $\frac{2y}{y-2}$ **25.** 0
27. $\frac{r^2 + s^2}{r - s}$ **29.** $m + n$ **31.** 4 **33.** $a + b$ **35.** $\frac{x+1}{x-1}$
37. 0 **39.** $\frac{1}{x+1}$ **41.** $-\frac{1}{t+1}$ **43.** $P = -2x - 4$
47. $1,506,167,664 **48.** 12:00 noon

49. $-\frac{1}{2} < r < \frac{8}{3}$ **50.** $56m + 16$ **51.** $2^3 \cdot 5^3$
52. $m^2 - 2m - 9 + \frac{-4}{m-4}$

Page 325   Mid-Chapter Review
1. $\frac{1}{a+1}$; $a \neq -1, a \neq 7$ **2.** $\frac{1}{y+3}$; $y \neq 3, y \neq -3$
3. $\frac{4y-1}{8y-1}$; $y \neq \frac{1}{8}, y \neq -2$ **4.** $\frac{y-2}{y-1}$ **5.** $\frac{m^2 + 16}{m^2 + 8m + 16}$
6. $\frac{x}{x^2 + 8x + 16}$ **7.** b **8.** $\frac{1}{q(y-2)}$ **9.** $\frac{2m + 2n}{3m^2 - 3n}$
10. $2m - 1$ **11.** $t^2 - 4t - 9 + \frac{16}{3t+1}$

Pages 327-328   Lesson 8-6
3. 24, 48 **5.** 27 **7.** $180,000 **9.** Since Ed was
freshly shaved and neatly trimmed and there are
only two barbers, we can assume that Floyd did it.
Therefore, the visitor went to Floyd's. **11.** 5 people
13a. It is also happy. **b.** 1, 7, 10, 13, 19, 23, 28, 31,
32, 44, 49, 68, 70, 79, 82, 86, 91, 94, 97

Pages 331-332   Lesson 8-7
3. a^2 **5.** $120a^2b^3$ **7.** $392ax^3y$ **9.** $n(m+n)$
11. $\frac{m^2 - 2mn + n^2 - 1}{m^2 - n^2}$ **13.** $\frac{13t}{21}$ **15.** $\frac{2}{a}$ **17.** $\frac{5z + 6x}{xyz}$
19. $\frac{2s + t^2 + 3t}{st}$ **21.** $\frac{2a + 3}{a+3}$ **23.** $\frac{y^2 + 12y + 25}{y^2 - 25}$
25. $\frac{2(x^3 + 1)}{x^2 - 1}$ or $\frac{2(x^2 - x + 1)}{x - 1}$ **27.** $\frac{-7y - 39}{y^2 - 9}$
29. $\frac{-x^3 + x^2 + 3xy - 3y}{9xy^2}$ or $\frac{(3y - x^2)(x - 1)}{9xy^2}$
31. $\frac{2x^2 + 5x^2 - 3x}{(2x-3)(2x+3)^2}$ **33.** $\frac{x^2 + 6x - 11}{x^2 - 2x - 3}$
35. $\frac{9m + 6}{(m+2)^2(m+1)}$ **37.** $\frac{x^2 + 12x + 2}{(x-1)^2(x+4)}$ **39a.** 360; 2;
180; 360 **b.** 768; 16; 48; 768 **c.** The product of
the numbers is equal to the product of their GCF
and LCM. **d.** Divide the product of the two
numbers by their LCM. **41.** eldest: 9 cows; second:
6 cows; youngest 2 cows **43.** 3 tables of 5 people
and 8 tables of 8 people or 11 tables of 5 people and
3 tables of 8 people **45.** 16 **46.** 160 balls **47.** 7
48. $3.16, $1.50, $1.25, $1.20 **49.** 1 **50.** 6 ways

Pages 336-337   Lesson 8-8
3. $\frac{4x+2}{x}$ **5.** $\frac{2m^2 + m + 4}{m}$ **7.** $\frac{b^3 - 2b^2 + 2}{b - 2}$ **9.** $\frac{14}{19}$
11. $\frac{y^3(x+4)}{x^2(y-2)}$ **13.** $\frac{a-b}{x-y}$ **15.** $\frac{x+y}{x-y}$ **17.** $\frac{x+1}{x-2}$
19. $\frac{1}{y+4}$ **21.** $\frac{a+2}{a+3}$ **23.** $\frac{(x+3)(x-1)}{(x-2)(x+4)}$
25. $\frac{8x^2 - 27y^2}{x^2 - 4y^2}$ **27.** $\frac{x+1}{x+5}$ **29.** 1 **31.** 1888 **33.** 45
pounds **34.** $\frac{6}{9}, \frac{57}{99}, \frac{253}{999}, \frac{6001}{9999}$ **35.** $12(a+1)(a-1)$
36. $\frac{15bx + 3a}{21x^2}$

Pages 341-342   Lesson 8-9
3. 6 **5.** 8 **7.** $r^2 - 1$ **9.** $(k+5)(k+3)$
11. $3(2x+1)(2x-1)$ **13a.** $\frac{1}{n}$ **b.** $\frac{4}{n}$ **c.** $\frac{x}{n}$ **15.** -3

17. $-\frac{9}{4}$ 19. 5 21. $\frac{1}{4}$ 23. $-\frac{3}{2}$ 25. $\frac{1}{2}$ 27. 20, 10
29. -3 31. 2 33. $\frac{27}{7}$ 35. 7 37. 3, 1 41. 30
hours 43. 12 mph 45. 30 mph 47. 4.355 minutes
or about 4 minutes 21 seconds 48. 8.8 ft
49. $6a + 9b$ 50. $(a + 6)^2$ 51. $\frac{xy + x}{x}$

Pages 345-347 Lesson 8-10
5. 3.429 ohms 7. 4 ohms 9. 8 ohms, 4 ohms
11. $t = \frac{v}{a}$ 13. $v = \frac{2s - at^2}{2t}$ 15. $M = \frac{Fd^2}{Gm}$
17. $p = \frac{A}{1 + rt}$ 19. $P = \frac{36,500}{IR + 365}$ 21. $y = \frac{r}{2a + 0.5}$
23. $R = \frac{H}{0.24I^2t}$ 25. $R_1 = \frac{R_T R_2}{R_2 - R_T}$ 27. $n = \frac{IR}{E - Ir}$
29. $m = \frac{y - b}{x}$ 31. $y_2 = mx_2 - mx_1 + y_1$
33. $R = P - DQ$ 35. $2.91\overline{6}$ ohms 37. $7.\overline{6}$ ohms
39. 96 ohms 41. 12.632 ohms 44. 15°C
45. $\left\{x \mid -\frac{9}{2} \le x \le \frac{5}{2}\right\}$ 46. $8405.68 47. 50 hours or
about 2 days 48. $2(m + 4n)(m - 4n)$ 49. 60
minutes

Pages 348-350 Chapter 8 Summary and Review
1. $\frac{x}{4y^2z}$ 3. $\frac{a - 5}{a - 2}$ 5. $\frac{7a^2}{9b}$ 7. $\frac{(x + 4)^2}{(x + 2)^2}$ 9. $-2p$
11. $\frac{7ab(x + 9)}{3(x - 5)}$ 13. $x^2 + 4x - 2$
15. $2a^2 + 18a + 159 + \frac{1422}{a - 9}$ 17. $\frac{7 + a}{x^2}$ 19. 2
21. $\frac{2 - x}{x - y}$ 23. $\frac{8x - 9}{x^2 - 4}$ 25. $\frac{3x}{y}$ 27. $\frac{(x - 5)(x + 13)}{(x + 2)(x + 6)}$ or
$\frac{x^2 + 8x - 65}{x^2 + 8x + 12}$ 29. $-2, -\frac{5}{2}$ 31. 0 33. $\frac{xy}{r}$ 35. $\frac{a}{c + cb}$
37. $\frac{x - 2}{x + 2}$ 39. 33, 66, 99

CHAPTER 9 FUNCTIONS AND GRAPHS

Pages 357-358 Lesson 9-1
5. (1, 4) 7. (-1, -2) 9. (3, -1) 11. I 13. II
15. none 17. (-1, 1) 19. (3, -2) 21. (1, 1)
23. (-1, -1) 25. (2, -3) 27. (-4, 1) 29. IV
31. II 33. IV 35. II 37. none

55.

57.
airplane or jet
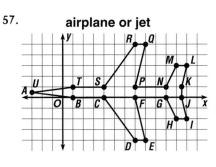

61. Irving 63. (B, 4), (B, 5), (C, 4), (C, 5) 65. (A, 3),
(B, 3), (C, 3), (D, 3), (E, 3), (E, 4), (F, 4)
66. $10x^2 + 3y + z^2$ 67. 540 seats
68. $25a^2 - 10ab + b^2$
69.

70. 5×10^5; 500,000 71. $4(x + 4y)(x - 4y)$
72. $\frac{1}{z + 6}$

Pages 361-363 Lesson 9-2
5. {5, 0, -9}; {2, 0, -1} 7. {7, -2, 4, 5, -9};
{5, -3, 0, -7, 2} 9. $\left\{\frac{1}{2}, 1\frac{1}{2}, -3, -5\frac{1}{4}\right\}$;
$\left\{\frac{1}{4}, -\frac{2}{3}, \frac{2}{5}, -6\frac{2}{7}\right\}$ 11. {(1, 3), (2, 2), (4, 9), (6, 5)};
{1, 2, 4, 6}; {3, 2, 9, 5}; {(3, 1), (2, 2), (9, 4), (5, 6)}
13. {(1, 7), (2, 2), (-3, 1), (5, 2)} 15. {(5, 4), (5, 8),
(2, 9), (-7, 2), (3, 2), (3, 4)} 17. {(1, 3), (2, 4), (3, 5),
(4, 6), (5, 7)}; {(3, 1), (4, 2), (5, 3), (6, 4), (7, 5)}
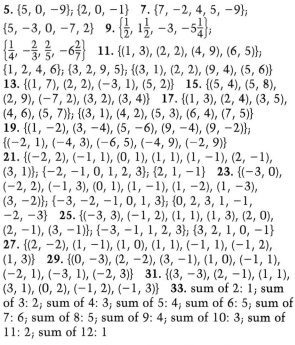
19. {(1, -2), (3, -4), (5, -6), (9, -4), (9, -2)};
{(-2, 1), (-4, 3), (-6, 5), (-4, 9), (-2, 9)}
21. {(-2, 2), (-1, 1), (0, 1), (1, 1), (1, -1), (2, -1),
(3, 1)}; {-2, -1, 0, 1, 2, 3}; {2, 1, -1} 23. {(-3, 0),
(-2, 2), (-1, 3), (0, 1), (1, -1), (1, -2), (1, -3),
(3, -2)}; {-3, -2, -1, 0, 1, 3}; {0, 2, 3, 1, -1,
-2, -3} 25. {(-3, 3), (-1, 2), (1, 1), (1, 3), (2, 0),
(2, -1), (3, -1)}; {-3, -1, 1, 2, 3}; {3, 2, 1, 0, -1}
27. {(2, -2), (1, -1), (1, 0), (1, 1), (-1, 1), (-1, 2),
(1, 3)} 29. {(0, -3), (2, -2), (3, -1), (1, 0), (-1, 1),
(-2, 1), (-3, 1), (-2, 3)} 31. {(3, -3), (2, -1), (1, 1),
(3, 1), (0, 2), (-1, 2), (-1, 3)} 33. sum of 2: 1; sum
of 3: 2; sum of 4: 3; sum of 5: 4; sum of 6: 5; sum of
7: 6; sum of 8: 5; sum of 9: 4; sum of 10: 3; sum of
11: 2; sum of 12: 1

35.

39.

43.
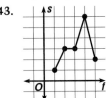

45. no solution 46. 200 mL 47. $7a^6b^2 - 35a^4b^3 +$
$42a^2b^4$ 48. $(12n + 7)^2$ 49. $2\frac{2}{29}$ ohms

50.
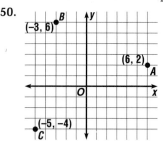

Pages 367-368 Lesson 9-3

5. $-1, (-4, -1); \frac{1}{3}, \left(-2, \frac{1}{3}\right); \frac{5}{3}, \left(0, \frac{5}{3}\right); \frac{7}{3}, \left(1, \frac{7}{3}\right); \frac{11}{3},$ $\left(3, \frac{11}{3}\right)$ **7.** b, c **9.** $y = 5 - x$ **11.** $b = 3 + 5a$

13. a, b, c **15.** a **17.** $y = 4 - 2x$ **19.** $s = \frac{2 - 6r}{5}$

21. $b = \frac{3a - 8}{7}$ **23.** $r = \frac{4 + 5n}{7}$ **25.** $\{(-2, -3),$ $(-1, -1), (0, 1), (2, 5), (5, 11)\}$ **27.** $\{(-2, -6),$ $(-1, -5), (0, -4), (2, -2), (5, 1)\}$ **29.** $\left\{\left(-2, \frac{17}{3}\right),\right.$ $\left.(-1, 5), \left(0, \frac{13}{3}\right), (2, 3), (5, 1)\right\}$ **31.** $\left\{\left(-2, \frac{13}{2}\right), (-1, 4),\right.$ $\left.\left(0, \frac{3}{2}\right), \left(2, -\frac{7}{2}\right), (5, -11)\right\}$ **33.** $\left\{\left(-2, -\frac{11}{2}\right), (-1, -4),\right.$ $\left.\left(0, -\frac{5}{2}\right), \left(2, \frac{1}{2}\right), (5, 5)\right\}$ **35.** $\left\{(-2, 5), \left(-1, \frac{31}{6}\right),\right.$ $\left.\left(0, \frac{16}{3}\right), \left(2, \frac{17}{3}\right), \left(5, \frac{37}{6}\right)\right\}$ **37.** $\left\{\left(-\frac{4}{5}, -3\right), \left(-\frac{2}{5}, -1\right),\right.$ $\left.\left(-\frac{1}{5}, 0\right), \left(\frac{1}{5}, 2\right), \left(\frac{2}{5}, 3\right)\right\}$ **39.** $\left\{\left(\frac{11}{2}, -3\right), (4, -1),\right.$ $\left.\left(\frac{13}{4}, 0\right), \left(\frac{7}{4}, 2\right), (1, 3)\right\}$ **41.** $\left\{(-1, -3), \left(-\frac{2}{3}, -1\right),\right.$ $\left.\left(-\frac{1}{2}, 0\right), \left(-\frac{1}{6}, 2\right), (0, 3)\right\}$ **45.** 4 m by 4 m

47. $\{s | s < -6.9\}$ **48.** $-3x^2y + 6xy^2 - 2y^2$
49. $3a(14bc - 4ab^2 + ac^2)$ **50.** $\{-1, 0\}$ **51.** 3 hours
52. $\{8, 4, 6, 5\}; \{1, 2, -4, -3, 0\}; \{(1, 8), (2, 4),$ $(-4, 6), (-3, 5), (0, 6)\}$

Pages 371-373 Lesson 9-4

5. yes **7.** no **9.** yes **11.** no **13.** yes

15. $y = 8x - 16$ **17.** $y = \frac{12 - 3x}{4}$ **19.** $y = \frac{3}{4}x - 15$

21. yes **23.** no **25.** yes **27.** yes

29.
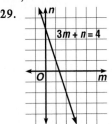

33.
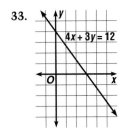

37.
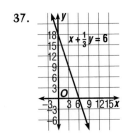

41.
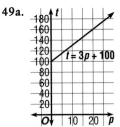

45. $y = -3x$ or $3x + y = 0$

49a.
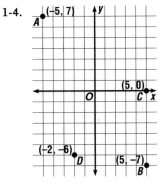

49b. 250 people **51.** $2nxy^5 + 12n^4xy^3 - 4n^2x^3$
52. $-\frac{9m^7}{n^2}$ **53.** $\frac{k - 1}{k + 1}$ **54.** $5x^2 - 4x + 7$ **55.** 8 m by
19 m **56.** $\left\{\left(-3, \frac{22}{3}\right), \left(-1, \frac{14}{3}\right), \left(0, \frac{10}{3}\right), (1, 2), (4, -2)\right\}$

Page 373 Mid-Chapter Review

1-4.

5. $\{(4, 2), (1, 3), (3, 3), (6, 4); \{4, 1, 3, 6\}; \{2, 3, 4\};$ $\{(2, 4), (3, 1), (3, 3), (4, 6)\}$ **6.** $\{(4, 2), (-3, 2), (8, 2),$ $(8, 9), (7, 5)\}; \{4, -3, 8, 7\}; \{2, 9, 5\}; \{(2, 4), (2, -3),$ $(2, 8), (9, 8), (5, 7)\}$ **7.** $\{(-2, 2), (-1, 1), (1, 1),$ $(1, -1), (2, 2), (2, -2)\}; \{-2, -1, 1, 2\}; \{2, 1, -1, -2\};$ $\{(2, -2), (1, -1), (1, 1), (-1, 1), (2, 2), (-2, 2)\}$
8. $\{(-5, -22), (-2, -7), (0, 3), (1, 8), (3, 18)\}$
9. $\{(-5, -17), (-2, -11), (0, -7), (1, -5), (3, -1)\}$
10. $\left\{\left(-5, -\frac{4}{3}\right), \left(-2, \frac{8}{3}\right), \left(0, \frac{16}{3}\right), \left(1, \frac{20}{3}\right), \left(3, \frac{28}{3}\right)\right\}$
11. $\left\{\left(-5, -\frac{41}{5}\right), \left(-2, -\frac{23}{5}\right), \left(0, -\frac{11}{5}\right), (1, -1),\right.$ $\left.\left(3, \frac{7}{5}\right)\right\}$ **12.** yes **13.** yes

684

14. no **15.** yes

Pages 377-378   Lesson 9-5

5. no **7.** yes **9.** no **11.** yes **13.** -9 **15.** 0
17. yes **19.** yes; $\{(1, 3), (1, 5), (1, 7)\}$; no **21.** no;
$\{(4, -2), (3, 1), (2, 5), (4, 1)\}$; no **23.** yes; $\{(4, 5),$
$(5, -6), (5, 4), (4, 0)\}$; no **25.** yes **27.** yes **29.** no
31. yes **33.** -14 **35.** $-\frac{2}{9}$ **37.** 11.5 **39.** 12
41. $12a - 5$ **43.** $18n - 15$ **45.** $12m^2 - 6m$
47. $3a + 4$ **53.** $\$59.60$ **55a.** $(0, 2)$ **b.** The
coefficients of x are the additive inverses of those in
Exercise **a.** **56.** 88x **57.** 28 m by 38 m
58. $(7n - 1)(n - 3)$ **59.** $\frac{3a + 20}{a^2 - 25}$

60.
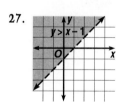

Pages 381-383   Lesson 9-6

5. yes **7.** c **9.** b **11.** a, b **13.** half-plane to left of
line **15.** half-plane to right of line **17.** half-plane
to left of line

19.
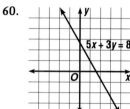

23.
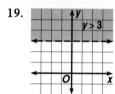

27.
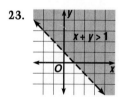

31.
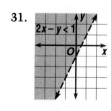

35.
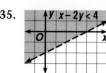

39.
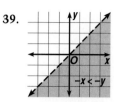

43.
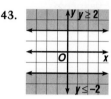

47.
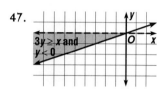

49a.
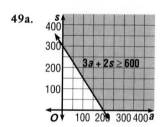

49b. Answers will vary; typical answers are 200
adult and 0 student tickets, 0 adult and 300 student
tickets, and 100 adult and 200 student tickets.
51. $\{x|x \geq -1\}$ **52.** $4r^8x^3y$ **53.** 4 **54.** $\frac{b - a}{x - y}$
55. $(3a + 4c)(5a - 7b)$ **56.** No; after 4 seconds, the
ball will be $100 - 4.9(4)^2$ or 21.6 meters above the
ground.

Pages 387-388   Lesson 9-7

5. d **7.** b **9.** 0, -3 **11.** 10, 20 **13.** 11.25, 10.75
15. 16, 32 **17.** $-4, \frac{1}{2}$ **19.** $n = 2m + 1$; 1, 3
21. $b = 4a + 3$; 11, 19 **23.** $n = 11 - m$; 9, 8, 7
25. $y = 18 - 2x$; 10, 6, 2 **27.** $d = \frac{1}{3}c - 2$; 6, 8, 12
29. $y = x^3 + 1$ **31.** $y = 15 - x^2$
35. a. $y = \$0.34x + \$0.36$ **b.** $\$0.70$; $\$0.34$
36. $\$8200$ at 5%, $\$4000$ at 6.5% **37.** 4x
38. $3x(x + 11y)(x - 3y)$ **39.** $\frac{x^2 + x - 12}{x^2 - 3x - 18}$

40.

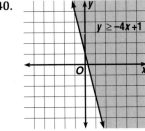

$y \geq -4x + 1$

Pages 390-391 Lesson 9-8

7. yes **9.** In Graph A, Restaurant III does not appear as unpopular as it does in Graph B.
11. Graph A **13.** 512 **15.** Al, 12 years old; Betty, 14 years old; Carmelita, 7 years old; Dwayne, 4 years old

Pages 392-394 Chapter 9 Summary and Review

5. I **7.** II **9.** {4}; {1, −2, 6, −1}; {(1, 4), (−2, 4), (6, 4), (−1, 4)} **11.** {−2, −5 −7}; {1}; {(1, −2), (1, −5), (1, −7)} **13.** $y = 7 - 3x$ **15.** $y = \frac{12 - x}{6}$
17. {(−4, −13), (−2, −11), (0, −9), (2, −7), (4, −5)}
19. $\left\{\left(-4, -\frac{16}{3}\right), \left(-2, -\frac{8}{3}\right), (0, 0), \left(2, \frac{8}{3}\right), \left(4, \frac{16}{3}\right)\right\}$

21.

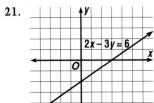

$2x - 3y = 6$

25. no **27.** yes **29.** 3 **31.** $a^2 + a + 1$

33.

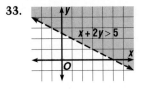

$x + 2y > 5$

37. $y = 3x + 5$ **39.** 4.5 seconds

41a.

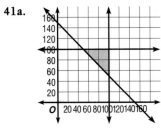

b. Answers will vary; typical answers are 74 and 73, 80 and 67, and 100 and 47.

Pages 403-404 Lesson 10-1

5. -1; 1; $\frac{-1}{1} = -1$ **7.** -4; 3; $\frac{-4}{3} = -\frac{4}{3}$

9.

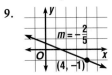

$m = -\frac{2}{5}$

$(4, -1)$

15. -1 **17.** 0 **19.** $-\frac{1}{5}$ **21.** -2 **23.** $-\frac{3}{2}$ **25.** $\frac{3}{2}$
27. 0 **29.** 0.5 **31.** $-\frac{3}{4}$ **33.** $\frac{25}{3}$ **35.** 7 **37.** 7
39. 2, 3 **43.** 11,160 feet **45.** 9.8%
46. associative (+) **47.** 7
48. $(5a + 3b)(a + b)(a - b)$ **49.** $\frac{6x - 5}{x^2}$
50. 16, 21, 31

Pages 408-409 Lesson 10-2

5. 3; (5, 2) **7.** $-\frac{3}{2}$; (−5, −6) **9.** 0; (0, 3)
11. $2x - y = -6$ **13.** $2x - 3y = -1$
15. $2x + 3y = 22$ **17.** $2x - 3y = 15$
19. $3x + y = -2$ **21.** $y = 6$ **23.** $x + y = 9$
25. $x = 4$ **27.** $x + 2y = -4$ **29.** $3x + 11y = -4$
31. $4x + 10y = 13$ **33.** $2x + 3y = 6$
37. $y = -5x + 90$, where x = the number of weeks that have passed and y = the amount of money he has left **38.** $56a^2 + 77a$ **39.** $(x - 7)(x - 2)$
40. $\frac{y^2}{y^2 - y - 2}$ **41.** Quadrant I **42.** 1015 feet

Pages 413-414 Lesson 10-3

5. 5, 3 **7.** $\frac{1}{3}$, 0 **9.** $-\frac{2}{3}$, $\frac{5}{3}$ **11.** 6, 5 **13.** $-\frac{8}{5}$, $-\frac{2}{5}$
15. $y = -3x + 5$ **17.** $y = \frac{1}{2}x + 5$ **19.** $y = 14$
21. 2, 10 **23.** 14, −4 **25.** −2, none **27.** none, 4
29. $-\frac{2}{5}$, 2; $y = -\frac{2}{5}x + 2$ **31.** $-\frac{7}{4}$, 2; $y = -\frac{7}{4}x + 2$
33. $-\frac{4}{3}$, $\frac{5}{3}$; $y = -\frac{4}{3}x + \frac{5}{3}$ **35.** −6, 15; $y = -6x + 15$
37. −4, 12; $y = -4x + 12$ **39.** $-\frac{5}{2}$, 4; $y = -\frac{5}{2}x + 4$
41. $\frac{11}{2}$, −16; $y = \frac{11}{2}x - 16$ **43.** −9, −2;
$y = -9x - 2$ **45.** $-\frac{11}{3}$, $\frac{25}{3}$; $y = -\frac{11}{3}x + \frac{25}{3}$
47. $y = \frac{4}{5}x + \frac{3}{2}$ **49.** $y = \frac{2}{5}x + 12$ **55. a.** $56 **b.** $5
57. 4 tennis balls **58.** $-6x^8y^3$ **59.** $(m^2 + 6n^2)^2$
60. y **61.** 4 **62.** $y = 7$

Pages 417-418 Lesson 10-4

3. 2, 8 **5.** 4, −8 **7.** $\frac{10}{7}$, 5 **9.** Possible answers are (1, 3) and (2, 5). **11.** Possible answers are (4, 2) and (2, 2). **13.** Possible answers are (7, 3) and (9, 4).

15.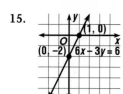

19.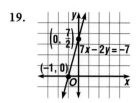

23.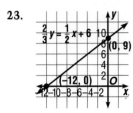

27.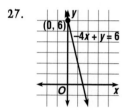

31.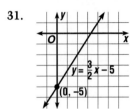

37a.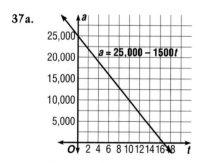

37b. $16\frac{2}{3}$ minutes or 16 minutes 40 seconds

39. 152 feet **40.** $3y^2 - 7y - 6$ **41.** 2 **42.** $\frac{5}{4}$

43. 41, 51, 61 **44.** 3, 6

Page 418 Mid-Chapter Review

1. 2 **2.** $-\frac{1}{2}$ **3.** -1 **4.** $3x - 4y = 16$

5. $3x - 2y = -20$ **6.** $x = -2$ **7.** $x + y = 10$

8. $x = 5$ **9.** $3x - 10y = -6$ **10.** 3, 5 **11.** $-\frac{5}{3}, \frac{5}{2}$

12. $\frac{8}{3}$, 16 **13.** $-\frac{3}{4}$, 3; $y = -\frac{3}{4}x + 3$ **14.** $\frac{5}{7}, -\frac{3}{2}$;
$y = \frac{5}{7}x - \frac{3}{2}$ **15.** 11, 14; $y = 11x + 14$

Pages 421-422 Lesson 10-5

5. 14 **7.** $-\frac{7}{2}$ **9.** 2, -2, $y = 2x - 2$ **11.** -4, 4,
$y = -4x + 4$ **13.** $-\frac{2}{3}$, 2, $y = -\frac{2}{3}x + 2$

15. $y = \frac{2}{3}x + \frac{2}{3}$ **17.** $y = \frac{3}{4}x - \frac{5}{2}$ **19.** $y = \frac{1}{4}x + 8$

21. $y = -\frac{2}{3}x + 4$ **23.** $y = -x + 1$

25. $y = -\frac{7}{9}x - \frac{8}{3}$ **27.** $y = -0.515x + 5.551$

29. $y = -1.595x - 7.429$ **31.** $y = 0.556x - 9.110$

33. $d = \frac{50}{3}h + 15$, where h = the number of hours
worked and d = the total charge **35.** 8.21×10^7

36. $9(2x - 3y^2)(2x + 3y^2)$ **37.** -1 **38.** $\{(-2, -13),$
$(-1, -8), (0, -3), (2, 7), (5, 22)\}$

39.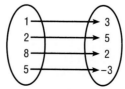

Pages 425-426 Lesson 10-6

5. 5, $-\frac{1}{5}$ **7.** $\frac{2}{3}, -\frac{3}{2}$ **9.** undefined, 0 **11.** $\frac{2}{3}, -\frac{3}{2}$

13. -1, 1 **15.** $y = \frac{3}{4}x$ **17.** $y = -\frac{2}{3}x + \frac{14}{3}$

19. $y = \frac{4}{3}x - \frac{16}{3}$ **21.** $y = x - 9$ **23.** $y = \frac{8}{3}x + 4$

25. $y = \frac{1}{3}x + 2$ **27.** $y = -\frac{3}{2}x - \frac{9}{2}$ **29.** $y = -\frac{1}{2}x - 4$

31. no **33.** 75% **34.** $16x^6 - 24x^3y^2 + 9y^4$

35. T = 5, W = 4, E = 6, Y = 0, H = 9, I = 3,
S = 1, V = 8, and either N = 7 and R = 2 or N = 2
and R = 7 **36.** $\frac{x + 7}{x + 5}$ **37.** yes

Pages 429-431 Lesson 10-7

3. 6 **5.** 5 **7.** $\frac{3}{2}$ **9.** (2, 2) **11.** (7, 4.5)

13. $(-1, -1)$ **15.** $(-2, 3.5)$ **17.** (10, 3) **19.** (14, 3)

21. $(6, -2)$ **23.** $\left(6, \frac{1}{2}\right)$ **25.** $\left(\frac{1}{2}, 7\right)$ **27.** $(4x, 2y)$

29. $B(19, 9)$ **31.** $P(-1, 6)$ **33.** $A(13, 11)$

35. $B(6, -7)$ **37.** $P(-2, -3)$ **39.** $B(9, -18)$

41. $(6, -4)$ **43.** (9, 6) **45.** $\left(-1, \frac{5}{2}\right)$ **49. a.** yes

b. no **c.** no **d.** no **51.** $\left(\frac{1}{2}, 2\right)$ **53.** $\left(\frac{9}{2}, -\frac{1}{2}\right)$

55. (4, 1) **57.** $\left(-\frac{3}{2}, 1\right)$ **59.** $\{y|y \geq -1\}$

60. $3x + 2y$ **61.** $5(x^2 + 4y^2)$ **62.** 10 ways

63.

7. over 65 **9.** Ana and Carl, Betty and Frank, Daisy and Ed

Pages 434-436 Chapter 10 Summary and Review

1. $-\frac{1}{3}$ **3.** $\frac{1}{3}$ **5.** $-\frac{5}{3}$ **7.** $5x - 2y = -10$ **9.** $y = 2$

11. $\frac{1}{4}$, 3 **13.** $\frac{1}{2}$, $\frac{7}{2}$ **15.** -2, 12 **17.** $\frac{1}{2}$, 4 **19.** 8, $-\frac{8}{3}$

21.

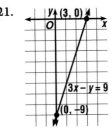

25. $y = 4x - 26$ **27.** $y = -\frac{5}{2}x + 7$ **29.** $y = 4x - 9$

31. $y = -\frac{7}{2}x - 14$ **33.** (6, 1) **35.** $\left(1, -\frac{5}{2}\right)$

37. (3, 3) **39.** $y = 45(x - 2) + 80$, where x = time and y = distance

CHAPTER 11 SYSTEMS OF OPEN SENTENCES

Page 441 Lesson 11-1

5. 2100 rings **7.** 3041 digits

Pages 445-446 Lesson 11-2

5. (6, 3) **7.** (1, 3) **9.** (2, 1) **11.** $m = -1$, $b = 6$; $m = 1$, $b = -2$; one solution **13.** $m = -\frac{1}{2}$, $b = \frac{5}{2}$; $m = -\frac{1}{2}$, $b = \frac{5}{2}$; infinitely many solutions
15. $m = \frac{3}{8}$, $b = -\frac{1}{2}$; $m = \frac{3}{8}$, $b = -\frac{21}{8}$; no solution
17. one, (3, 3) **19.** one, (9, 1) **21.** one, (6, 2)
23. (0, 0) **25.** (2, −6) **27.** infinitely many solutions **29.** (3, 1) **31.** (−1, −5) **33.** (−3, 1)
35. (1, −5) **37.** (−2, −3) **39.** infinitely many solutions **41.** (0, 3), (2, 4), (−1, 10) **45.** 0.3 mile
47. < **48.** $a^2m^3n^3$ **49.** 8 mph **50.** (−7, −3)

Pages 450-451 Lesson 11-3

5. $x = 5 - y$; $y = 5 - x$ **7.** $x = 3 - \frac{3}{2}y$; $y = 2 - \frac{2}{3}x$

9. $x = -\frac{0.8}{0.75}y - 8$; $y = -\frac{0.75}{0.8}x - 7.5$

11. $x + (3 + 2x) = 7$; $x = \frac{4}{3}$ **13.** $5x = 12x$; $x = 0$

15. $\left(-6 + \frac{2}{3}y\right) + 3y = 4$; $y = \frac{30}{11}$ **17.** (−3, −9)

19. $\left(3, \frac{3}{2}\right)$ **21.** (13, 30) **23.** $\left(\frac{12}{5}, \frac{1}{15}\right)$

25. no solution **27.** (0, 0) **29.** (3, 3) **31.** (50, 4)
33. (4, 2) **35.** 24 **37.** 35 **39.** (−1, 5, −4)
43. $1000 at 10% and $3000 at 12%
45. 125 tapes **46.** $\{y|2 < y < 11\}$ **47.** $(x + 2)^2(x - 2)$
48. $460 **49.** $3x + 11y = -4$ **50.** (3, 1)

Pages 455-456 Lesson 11-4

5. subtraction, (1, 3) **7.** addition, $\left(\frac{5}{2}, \frac{9}{2}\right)$

9. $-x = -9$; (9, −12) **11.** $10x = 40$; $\left(4, -\frac{3}{2}\right)$

13. (8, −1) **15.** (23, 14) **17.** $\left(\frac{11}{2}, -\frac{1}{2}\right)$ **19.** $\left(-1, \frac{9}{2}\right)$

21. (3, 4) **23.** $\left(2, \frac{1}{2}\right)$ **25.** $\left(\frac{14}{9}, -\frac{16}{3}\right)$ **27.** (24, 4)
29. (2, 5) **31.** 11, 53 **33.** (4, 2, 3) **35.** (2, 3, −4)
39. math: 760 points, verbal: 580 points
41. $y + n^3 = 2x$ **42.** $-\frac{1}{6}$, $-\frac{3}{2}$ **43.** {5, −3, 4, 2};
{1, 2, 0}; {(1, 5), (2, −3), (2, 4), (0, 5), (2, 2)}
44. 4.4% or $\frac{11}{250}$ **45.** (5, −2)

Page 456 Mid-Chapter Review

1. 375 games **2.** (1, −2) **3.** no solution
4. infinitely many **5.** (3, 3) **6.** (2, 10) **7.** (1, −1)
8. (−9, −7) **9.** (4, 3) **10.** 8 mph

Pages 460-461 Lesson 11-5

5. Multiply the second equation by −4, then add; (2, 0). **7.** Multiply the first equation by 3, multiply the second equation by −2, then add; (3, 0).
9. Multiply the first equation by 2, then add; $\left(\frac{11}{9}, \frac{8}{9}\right)$. **11.** Multiply the first equation by 2, multiply the second equation by −5, then add;
(2, 2). **13.** $\left(\frac{2}{3}, \frac{22}{3}\right)$ **15.** $\left(\frac{3}{5}, 3\right)$ **17.** (4, 1)
19. (4, −28) **21.** (−9, −2) **23.** (10, 25)
25. (4, 16) **27.** 16 **29.** (11, 12) **31.** $\left(\frac{1}{3}, \frac{1}{6}\right)$
33a. 21 mph **b.** 3 mph **35.** 475 mph
37a. no solution **b.** infinite number of solutions
c. (−9, −7) **d.** infinite number of solutions
38. 18 **39.** 34 ft by 22 ft **40.** $\frac{4}{(m + 2)(m - 4)}$
41. (−14, −13)

Pages 465-467 Lesson 11-6

5. no **7.** yes **9.** A **11.** D

13.

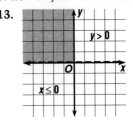

17.

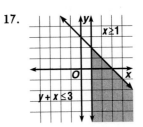

21.

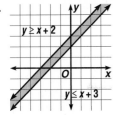

$y \geq x + 2$
$y \leq x + 3$

25.

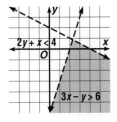

$2y + x < 4$
$3x - y > 6$

29.

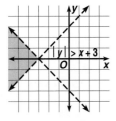

$|y| > x + 3$

33. yes **35.** $x > 1, y > -2$ **37.** $y \geq -x, y < 3 - x$
39. $y < 3 - x, y < 3 + x$ **41.** $x \geq 0, y \geq 0,$
$x + 2y \leq 6$

43.

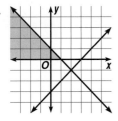

47.

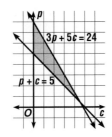

$3p + 5c = 24$
$p + c = 5$

Answers will vary. Possible solutions: 1 lb of
cashews, 6 lb of peanuts; 3 lb of cashews, 3 lb of
peanuts; 4 lb of cashews, 1 lb of peanuts
49. Answers will vary. Possible solutions: 2 light,
8 dark; 6 light, 8 dark; 7 light, 4 dark **50.** 30%
51. $(4 + 3x)(-4 + 3x)$ **52.** $\frac{2x + 1}{(x + 1)^2}$ **53.** $\left\{\left(-2, -\frac{1}{4}\right),\right.$
$\left(-1, \frac{1}{4}\right), \left(0, \frac{3}{4}\right), \left(1, \frac{5}{4}\right), \left.\left(3, \frac{9}{4}\right)\right\}$ **54.** $y = -\frac{4}{5}x - \frac{1}{5}$
55. 20 small and 10 large

Pages 468-470 Chapter 11 Summary and Review
1. $(4, 2)$ **3.** $(-2, -7)$ **5.** no solution
7. one, $(2, -2)$ **9.** $(3, -5)$ **11.** $\left(\frac{1}{2}, \frac{1}{2}\right)$ **13.** $(2, -1)$
15. $(5, 1)$ **17.** $\left(\frac{14}{5}, \frac{4}{5}\right)$ **19.** $(-4, 6)$

21.

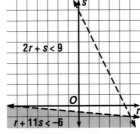

$2r + s < 9$
$r + 11s < -6$

23.

25. 16 cm by 9 cm **27.** \$15, \$9 **29.** $\frac{35}{2}$ mph, $\frac{5}{2}$ mph

CHAPTER 12 RADICAL EXPRESSIONS

Pages 475-476 Lesson 12-1
3a. Boston **b.** March **c.** 8.86 in., July, Mobile
d. 3.26 in., October **5.** 10 **7.** 3, for the units digit
of 7^3 **9.** 79 years old

Pages 479-481 Lesson 12-2
5. 144 **7.** 0.09 **9.** $\frac{121}{16}$ **11.** -9 **13.** 0.04
15. -12.21 **17.** 7.77 **19.** 16 **21.** $\frac{6}{14}$ or $\frac{3}{7}$
23. 0.05 **25.** 1.8 **27.** -10 **29.** 22 **31.** ±31
33. 45 **35.** -3.2 **37.** $\pm\frac{12}{39}$ **39.** -13.251
41. 23.052 **43.** 1.521 **45.** ±0.097 **47.** 11.36 in.
49. 3 **51.** 2 **55.** 18.4 meters per second **57.** 40
58. $5a^2(2c + 3)^2$ **59.** 35 mph

60.

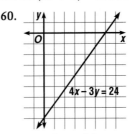

$4x - 3y = 24$

61. $y = -\frac{1}{8}x + \frac{15}{4}$

62.

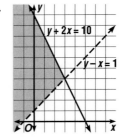

$y + 2x = 10$
$y - x = 1$

Pages 484–486 Lesson 12-3

5. false **7.** 10 **9.** 8 **11.** 16 **13.** 15 **15.** 2
17. 34 **19.** 20 **21.** 5 **23.** $\sqrt{45}$ or about 6.71
25. $\sqrt{28}$ or about 5.29 **27.** $\sqrt{21}$ or about 4.58
29. no **31.** yes **33.** no **35.** 14 cm **37.** $\sqrt{89}$ or about 9.43 m **41.** $\sqrt{31}$ or about 5.57 ft **43.** 56 m

44. 7.25 **45.** $\dfrac{2x+5}{2x+1}$

46.

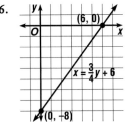

47. 75 gallons of 50% solution, 25 gallons of 30% solution **48.** ±66

Pages 489–491 Lesson 12-4

9. N, W, Z, Q **11.** Q **13.** N, W, Z, Q **15.** I
17. 6.32 **19.** −9.43 **21.** Q **23.** I **25.** Q
27. 4.47 **29.** −8.12 **31.** −5.57 **33.** 10.34
35. Q; 95 **37.** I; 86, 87 **39.** 362.24 ft² **41.** 7.9 ft by 23.7 ft **43.** 10.3 cm² **47.** No, since the rain will end at about 12:50 A.M. **48.** $9x^2 - 0.25$

49. $d = \pm\sqrt{\dfrac{GMn}{F}}$ **50.** $m = \dfrac{7}{3}, b = -\dfrac{10}{3}$ **51.** $\left(\dfrac{5}{2}, -\dfrac{1}{8}\right)$
52. No, she needs about 17.2 meters of wire.

Page 491 Mid-Chapter Review **1.**

Temperature in Degrees Fahrenheit	Number of Days	Temperature in Degrees Fahrenheit	Number of Days
0	1	16	4
1	0	17	2
2	1	18	2
3	0	19	0
4	1	20	0
5	3	21	0
6	1	22	1
7	0	23	2
8	1	24	1
9	0	25	1
10	0	26	1
11	0	27	2
12	2	28	0
13	0	29	3
14	0	30	1
15	0		

2. 16°F **3.** 10 days **4.** −21 **5.** 3.3 **6.** ±0.29
7. $\dfrac{8}{9}$ **8.** 35 **9.** 1.2 **10.** 8 **11.** no

Pages 495–496 Lesson 12-5

5. $2\sqrt{5}$ **7.** $4\sqrt{3}$ **9.** 2 **11.** $\sqrt{5}+7; -44$
13. $2\sqrt{8} - 3\sqrt{5}; -13$ **15.** $\dfrac{\sqrt{2}}{\sqrt{2}}$ **17.** $\dfrac{4+\sqrt{3}}{4+\sqrt{3}}$
19. $3\sqrt{5}$ **21.** $6\sqrt{2}$ **23.** $2\sqrt{70}$ **25.** $10\sqrt{10}$
27. $\dfrac{\sqrt{2}}{2}$ **29.** $\dfrac{\sqrt{22}}{8}$ **31.** 10 **33.** $84\sqrt{5}$ **35.** $\dfrac{\sqrt{11}}{11}$
37. $2b^2\sqrt{10}$ **39.** $4|x|y\sqrt{5y}$ **41.** $7x^2y^3\sqrt{3xy}$
43. $\dfrac{3\sqrt{3}}{|r|}$ **45.** $\dfrac{|x|\sqrt{3xy}}{2|y^3|}$ **47.** $\dfrac{5\sqrt{5}+45}{-38}$
49. $\dfrac{54b - 9b\sqrt{b}}{36-b}$ **51.** $\dfrac{3\sqrt{35} - 5\sqrt{21}}{-15}$
53. $\dfrac{a - 2\sqrt{ab} + b}{a-b}$ **57a.** $2s\sqrt{10}$ miles
b. 31.62 miles **58.** $(a+b)^2 = a^2b^2$
59. $(2r+s)(6r-11s)$ **60.** yes; no **61.** (20, −5)
62. (2, 3) **63.** about 18.26 amperes

Pages 499–500 Lesson 12-6

5. $4\sqrt{2}, 7\sqrt{2}$ **7.** $-3\sqrt{7}, 2\sqrt{28}$ **9.** none
11. $11\sqrt{6}$ **13.** in simplest form **15.** $21\sqrt{2x}$
17. $9\sqrt{3}, 15.59$ **19.** $-10\sqrt{5}, -22.36$
21. $13\sqrt{3} + \sqrt{2}, 23.93$ **23.** $4\sqrt{3}, 6.93$
25. $-2\sqrt{2}, -2.83$ **27.** $8\sqrt{2} + 6\sqrt{3}, 21.71$
29. $\dfrac{8\sqrt{7}}{7}, 3.02$ **31.** $4\sqrt{3} - 3\sqrt{5}, 0.22$
33. $4\sqrt{7} + 2\sqrt{14}, 7 + 7\sqrt{7}$
35. $2\sqrt{2} + 8\sqrt{3}, 5 - \sqrt{6}$ **37.** $19\sqrt{5}$
39. $15\sqrt{2} + 11\sqrt{5}$ **43.** $6.\overline{2}$ or $6\dfrac{2}{9}$ feet **44.** $n \geq \dfrac{23}{3}$
45. $\dfrac{k^2 - 2k + 1}{3k + 15}$ **46.** $0.22 per mile
47. $y = -4x - 3$ **48.** $18\sqrt{6}$

Pages 503–504 Lesson 12-7

5. $x = 25$ **7.** $121 = 2a - 5$ **9.** no real solution
11. 5 **13.** 39 **15.** 10 **17.** $4\sqrt{2}$ **19.** −112
21. no real solution **23.** $\dfrac{121}{9}$ **25.** 3 **27.** 144
29. $\dfrac{3}{25}$ **31.** 11 **33.** 7 **35.** 6 **37.** −6, −4 or 4, 6
39. 0 **41.** no real solution **43.** $\left(\dfrac{1}{4}, \dfrac{25}{36}\right)$
47. 1.6 meters per second squared **49.** 6
50. 2.5 feet **51.** $\left\{(-4, 7), \left(-2, \dfrac{23}{5}\right), \left(0, \dfrac{11}{5}\right), (1, 1), \left(5, -\dfrac{19}{5}\right)\right\}$ **52.** $\left(-\dfrac{1}{2}, 4\right)$ **53.** (6, −2) **54.** $26\sqrt{3}$ or about 45.03

Pages 508–509 Lesson 12-8

5. 5 **7.** 13 **9.** $3\sqrt{2}$ or 4.24 **11.** $4\sqrt{5}$ or 8.94
13. $2\sqrt{13}$ or 7.21 **15.** $\dfrac{\sqrt{74}}{7}$ or 1.23
17. $2\sqrt{14}$ or 7.48 **19.** 7 or 1 **21.** −2 or −12

23. The distance between (0, 0) and (7, 4) is $\sqrt{65}$ units. The distance between (7, 0) and (1, 4) is $\sqrt{52}$ units. Thus, the trapezoid is not isosceles. **25.** $22 + 4\sqrt{10}$ or about 34.65 units **27.** $8\sqrt{3}$
31. 2290 miles **33.** $\frac{2m + 1}{m - 2}$ **34.** 13
35. $4x - 3y = 23$ **36.** 425 mph **37.** 1

Pages 510–512 Chapter 12 Summary and Review
1. 13 **3.** -0.17 **5.** -7.85 **7.** ±4.8 **9.** 34
11. $\sqrt{125}$ or about 11.18 **13.** irrational
15. rational **17.** $6\sqrt{3}$ **19.** $2\sqrt{6} - 4\sqrt{3}$ **21.** $\frac{2\sqrt{35}}{7}$
23. $4x^2\sqrt{6}$ **25.** $\frac{2\sqrt{15}}{|y|}$ **27.** $5\sqrt{13} + 5\sqrt{15}$ or about 37.39 **29.** $-6\sqrt{2} - 12\sqrt{7}$ or about -40.23
31. 12 **33.** 3 **35.** 17 **37.** 18 or -8
39. 1985, 1990 **41.** 6.1 cm **43.** 24.85 units
45. No; it should skid about 201.7 feet.

CHAPTER 13 QUADRATICS

Pages 521–522 Lesson 13-1
5. up **7.** down **9.** $x = -\frac{1}{2}$ **11.** $x = -1$ **13.** $\left(\frac{3}{2}, \frac{9}{4}\right)$
15. $x = \frac{5}{2}$; $\left(\frac{5}{2}, \frac{49}{4}\right)$ **17.** $x = -1$; $(-1, -1)$
19. $x = -4$; $(-4, 32)$
21. $x = 2$; $(2, -9)$

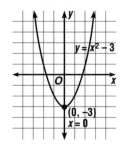

23. $x = 3$; $(3, 14)$
25. $x = 0$; $(0, -3)$

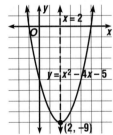

27. $x = 0$; $(0, 3)$
29. $x = 8$; $\left(8, -\frac{49}{4}\right)$

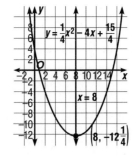

31. $x = 2$; $(2, 1)$ **33.** $(-1, 1)$ **35.** $(4, 0)$ **37.** a
39. $x = -\frac{3}{2}$

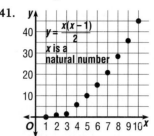

43. 196 ft **44.** 9 weeks **46.** $700
47.

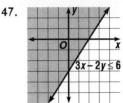

48. $-5x + 6y = -2$ **49.** $(1, 3)$ **50.** 5 or -3

Pages 525–526 Lesson 13-2
5. 0, 2 **7.** 2 **9.** $-3, -4$ **11.** 3, 7 **13.** no real roots **15.** 4 **17.** $-5 < x < -4, -2 < x < -1$
19. $2 < x < 3, -4 < x < -3$ **21.** $-13, -7$ or 7, 13
23. b
25.

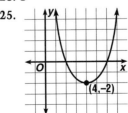

33. $1 < y < 2, 2 < y < 3$ **35.** $-2, -6$ **37.** between 4 meters and 5 meters **39.** $2b + 3$ **40.** $y = x^2 - 4$
41. $\frac{2}{3}$, $-\frac{13}{3}$; $\frac{13}{2}$ **42.** $12\sqrt{5}$ **43.** 1800 m²

Pages 528–529 Lesson 13-3

3. 10 dogs **5.** 19 numbers **7.** 1, 2, 4, 5, 8, 11
9. 19 handshakes **11.** his 13th season

Pages 534–535 Lesson 13-4

5. no **7.** no **9.** yes **11.** 16 **13.** $\frac{49}{4}$ **15.** 1, 7
17. $\frac{49}{4}$ **19.** 9 **21.** −3, −4 **23.** $\frac{5}{2}$ **25.** $3 \pm \sqrt{5}$
27. $5 \pm 4\sqrt{3}$ **29.** 3, $\frac{1}{2}$ **31.** $\frac{2}{3}$, −1 **33.** $\frac{5 \pm \sqrt{17}}{4}$
35. 6.5 yd by 12 yd **37.** 60 or −60 **39.** $\frac{9}{4}$
41. $\frac{-b \pm \sqrt{b^2 - 4c}}{2}$ **45.** 9 in. by 6 in. **47.** 2300
cards **48.** 52 **49.** $30\sqrt{2} + \sqrt{5}$ **50.** $0 < x < 1$,
$2 < x < 3$ **51.** 63

Pages 539–540 Lesson 13-5

5. 1, 7, 6 **7.** 2, 7, 3 **9.** 4, 8, 0 **11.** 49 **13.** 144
15. 2500 **17.** $-2 \pm \sqrt{2}$; −0.56, −3.41
19. $\frac{-4 \pm \sqrt{10}}{3}$; −0.28, −2.39 **21.** −1, −9
23. 5, −5 **25.** $\frac{5}{2}$, −3 **27.** $-\frac{1}{2}$, −3 **29.** $\frac{13 \pm 3\sqrt{33}}{2}$;
15.12, −2.12 **31.** $\frac{2}{3}$, $-\frac{1}{4}$ **33.** $\frac{3}{7}$, $-\frac{2}{3}$ **35.** $-3 \pm 2\sqrt{3}$;
0.46, −6.46 **37.** $\frac{4 \pm \sqrt{29}}{2}$; 4.69, −0.69 **39.** −2.1,
0.1 **41.** 0.2, 1.4 **43.** −0.5, −2.9 **45.** $x^2 + 3x +$
$1 = 0$ **47.** $3x^2 - 8x + 3 = 0$ **51.** 8.1%
52. $\frac{5}{4}a^2 + 5ab$ **53.** $\frac{a^3 - a^2b + a^2 + ab}{(a + b)(a - b)^2}$
54.

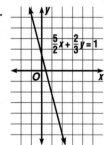

55. $3x + y = 11$ **56.** 4 seconds **57.** $\frac{3 \pm \sqrt{19}}{2}$

Page 540 Mid-Chapter Review

1. $x = \frac{1}{2}$; $\left(\frac{1}{2}, -\frac{49}{4}\right)$ **2.** $x = 0$; $(0, -9)$ **3.** $x = -1$;
$(-1, 8)$ **4.** no real roots
5. $-1 < x < 0$, $2 < x < 3$ **6.** 6, −1 **7.** $3 \pm \sqrt{2}$
8. $\frac{7}{2}$, −3 **9.** −5, −3 **10.** $\frac{-5 \pm \sqrt{13}}{2}$ **11.** 13.5 days

Pages 544–545 Lesson 13-6

5. 25; 2 real roots **7.** 0; 1 real root **9.** −11; no real
roots **11.** 5; 2 real roots **13.** 0; 1 real root
15. −20; no real roots **17.** $2 \pm \sqrt{3}$; 3.73, 0.27
19. 2, −6 **21.** $-\frac{1}{2}$, −1 **23.** $\frac{5 \pm \sqrt{193}}{12}$; 1.57, −0.74
25. $\frac{1}{3}$ **27.** 1, $\frac{2}{3}$ **29.** $\frac{7 \pm \sqrt{69}}{10}$; 1.53, −0.13
31. $\frac{1 \pm \sqrt{133}}{22}$; 0.57, −0.48 **33.** 0 **35.** 2 **37.** 1

39. 12, −12 **41.** $k < -\frac{25}{4}$ **43a.** 72.5 seconds
b. yes **45a.** no real roots **b.** 0.5 **c.** 0.7142857,
−1 **d.** 10, 1 **e.** no real roots **f.** 6, 0 **46.** $18.50
47. yes **48.** $c = 34h + 15$, where $h =$ the number of
hours for the repair job and $c =$ the total charge
49.

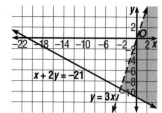

50. 7.7 **51.** 3.4 meters by 0.6 meters

Pages 548–549 Lesson 13-7

5. factoring or quadratic formula **7.** quadratic
formula **9.** quadratic formula or completing the
square **11.** $-5 \pm 3\sqrt{3}$; 0.20; −10.20 **13.** $-\frac{2}{3}$, 3
15. $\frac{7 \pm \sqrt{85}}{6}$; 2.70, −0.37 **17.** $\frac{-1 \pm \sqrt{41}}{4}$; 1.35,
−1.85 **19.** $\frac{5 \pm \sqrt{13}}{6}$; 1.43, 0.23 **21.** 1.5, −0.4
23. $2 \pm \sqrt{6}$; 4.45, −0.45 **25.** 5, 7 **27.** 21 in. by
42 in. **29a.** 1 second, 5.25 seconds **b.** 6.25
seconds **31.** 80 ft by 100 ft **34.** 11 **35.** 2 hours
36. (10, 4) **37.** no **38.** 56; 2 real roots

Pages 552–553 Lesson 13-8

5. −2, −1 **7.** $\frac{13}{6}$, $-\frac{5}{2}$ **9.** no **11.** yes **13.** no
15. $x^2 + 5x - 6 = 0$ **17.** $x^2 + 0.3x - 0.18 = 0$
19. 5, −24 **21.** $-\frac{13}{2}$, $-\frac{9}{4}$ **23.** $\frac{1}{3}$, $-\frac{1}{12}$ **25.** $\frac{1}{15}$, $-\frac{1}{300}$
27. $x^2 - 11x + 28 = 0$ **29.** $x^2 + 9x - 10 = 0$
31. $2x^2 - 9x + 10 = 0$ **33.** $6x^2 + 5x - 6 = 0$
35. $x^2 - 2 = 0$ **37.** $x^2 - 4x + 1 = 0$ **39.** $x^2 -$
$(8 + \sqrt{3} + \sqrt{5})x + (15 + 5\sqrt{5} + 3\sqrt{3} + \sqrt{15})$
41. 4 **43.** 35 **45.** $x^2 - (q + r)x + qr = 0$ **49.** yes
50. $\frac{2}{7}a^2 - \frac{5}{4}a + 1$ **51.** $\frac{1}{n - 6}$
52.

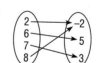

$\{(2, -2), (6, 5), (7, 3), (8, -2)\}$;
$\{(-2, 2), (5, 6), (3, 7), (-2, 8)\}$

53. 1 mph **54.** 7 **55.** 2.1 seconds

Pages 554–556 Chapter 13 Summary and Review

1. $x = \frac{3}{2}$; $\left(\frac{3}{2}, -\frac{25}{4}\right)$ **3.** $x = \frac{9}{4}$; $\left(\frac{9}{4}, \frac{9}{8}\right)$
5.

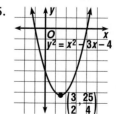

9. −3, 4 **11.** −5 < x < −4, 0 < x < 1 **13.** 16
15. 8 ± 4√2; 13.66, 2.34 **17.** $-\frac{3}{2}, -\frac{5}{2}$
19. $\frac{-9 \pm \sqrt{21}}{10}$; −0.44, −1.36 **21.** $\frac{3}{4}, \frac{2}{3}$ **23.** 2 real
roots **25.** 1 real root **27.** 6, 15 **29.** −8, −14
31. $\frac{1}{2}$, −3 **33.** $2x^2 + 5x - 12 = 0$ **35.** 99
37. $22.50

CHAPTER 14   STATISTICS AND PROBABILITY

Pages 562–564   Lesson 14-1

5. from 10 to 50, intervals of 10 **7.** from 1000 to
11,000, intervals of 1000 **9a.** 50 **b.** 22 **c.** 30
students **d.** 9 students **e.** 26

11a.
```
            X  XX X
         X  XXXX     X
        XXXX XXXX   X   X
   XX  XXXXXXX XXXXX XXX XX   XX
 ◄─┼┼┼┼┼┼┼┼┼┼┼┼┼┼┼┼┼┼┼┼┼┼┼┼┼┼┼┼►
   40   45   50   55   60   65   70
```

b. 41 **c.** yes; 54 years old to 57 years old **13a.** Mr.
Jebson's **b.** No; the number of hours of television
watched for Ms. Lee's students is more spread out
while the number of hours watched for Mr. Jebson's
students is more clustered between 15 and 30 hours.
15. 91°F, 92°F, 98°F

```
           XX X X
          XX XXXXXX  X
          XXX XXXXXX XX
    X   X  XXX XXXXXXXXXX XXX X        X
 ◄─┼┼┼┼┼┼┼┼┼┼┼┼┼┼┼┼┼┼┼┼┼┼┼┼┼┼┼┼┼┼┼┼►
   80  85  90  95 100 105 110 115 120
```

17. 15

```
           X
         X  XX
         X XXXXXX X     X
        XX XXXXXXX XX   X X X
 ◄─┼┼┼┼┼┼┼┼┼┼┼┼┼┼┼┼┼┼┼┼┼┼┼┼►
    5   10  15  20  25  30
```

18. 43.2 mph **19.** $3a^2 + 6a + 1$ **20.** 8150 covers
21. 18 **22.** $3x^2 + 2x - 21 = 0$

Pages 567–569   Lesson 14-2

5. 1, 2, 3, 4, 5 **7.** 19, 20, 21, 22, 23, 24, 25, 26
9. 46, 45 **11.** 43, 43 **13a.** 85°F **b.** 49°F **c.** 11
days **d.** 77°F

15a.

Stem	Leaf
1	6 7 7 8 8 8 8 8 9 9 9 9
	9 9 9
2	0 0 2 3 4 4 5 5 7 7
3	0 2 3 3 5 6
4	5 8 4|8 =
5	5 48 years old

b. 35 people
c. 39 years
d. 19 years old
e. teens
f. 12 students

Pages 572–574   Lesson 14-3

5. 7; 6; no mode **7.** 8; 7; 7 **9.** 17.5; 17.5; 12 and
23 **11.** 4; 2 **13.** 94; 82 **15.** 218; 219 **19.** 140.5
yards **21.** 8.3; 6.5; 4 **23.** 40.61; 40.2; 43.4
25. 4.45; 4; 3 and 5 **27.** $5.14; $5.05; $4.75

29.

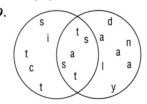

30. $(8x - 7y)(3x - 5y)$ **31.** $3x + y = 16$ **32a.** 3
seconds **b.** 269 feet

33.

Stem	Leaf (rounded)
36	5
37	39|2 = 39.15 to
38	2 3 39.24 seconds
39	2 4
40	1 2 2 3
41	
42	
43	1 2 4 4 4

17a.

Stem	Leaf
13	9 9 9
14	0 3 3 4 5 7 9 9
15	1 1 3 3 6 7 8 9 9 9
16	1 1 2 2 2 3 4 8
17	1
18	6 15|1 = 151 mph

b. 150-159 mph

19a.

Stem	Leaf		Stem	Leaf
6	5 8 9		14	5
7	3 4 4 6 7		15	7
8	0 2 2 3 5		17	4
	5 9		18	2
9	4 8		21	2
10	4		26	2
11	2		29	0
13	6 9|4 = $94,000			

b. $225,000
c. $80,000-
$89,000

22. $b + 8$ **22.** $\frac{x(2x + 3)}{2(x + 2)}$ **24.** 280 miles **25.** $\sqrt{185}$
or about 13.6 units **26.** $2 \pm \sqrt{7}$
27. 63 in.

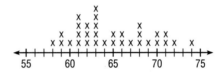

```
                 X
            X  X
            X  X  X          X
        X  X X X   XX  X   X  XX
      X X X X X X X X X X X X X X X   X
 ◄─┼┼┼┼┼┼┼┼┼┼┼┼┼┼┼┼┼┼┼┼┼┼┼┼┼┼┼┼►
    55      60      65      70      75
```

Pages 577–578   Lesson 14-4

5. 11   **7.** 34   **9.** 77   **11.** 40; 45; 34   **13.** 65; 85; 45
15. 37; 73, 77, 62; 15   **17.** 49; 208, 212, 204.5; 7.5
19. 4.6; 8.7, 10.05, 7.9; 2.15   **23a.** $0.26, $0.09
b. $0.32   **25.** $\{x|-3 < x < 3\}$ **26.** $\{(3, -3), (-2, 2), (1, -1), (0, 0), (-1, 1)\}$ **27.** $\sqrt{35}$ or about 5.92 in.
28. $\frac{3}{5}, -\frac{2}{7}$ **29.** $363; $364

Pages 581–582   Lesson 14-5

5. 25%   **7.** 85   **9.** 90   **11.** 75%   **13.** X   **15.** Y

17.

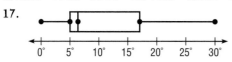

21.

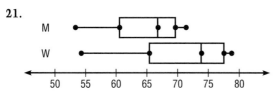

23. $\frac{34}{9}$

24.

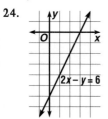

25. (10, −6)   **26.** $\frac{7 + \sqrt{3}}{46}$ **27.** 61, 2 real roots
28. 19.2; 33.0, 34.6, 36.8; 3.8; 44.8, 50.4

Pages 585–587   Lesson 14-6

5. positive   **7.** negative or positive   **9.** none
11. positive   **13.** none

15a.

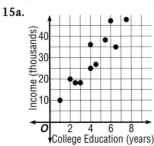

b. the more years of college education, the greater the income   **17b.** positive   **c.** Yes; you could estimate the number of assists by using the points in the scatter plot.   **d.** Yes; some players have more opportunities to score points because of the position they play for the team.   **e.** Yes, since more playing time provides a player with more opportunities to score points.

19a.

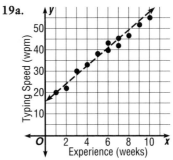

b. $y = \frac{13x}{3} + \frac{43}{3}$ **c.** about 66 words per minute
21. $6x^2 - 25$ **22.** 20 mph

23.

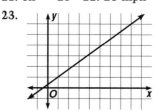

24. 3.2 cm by 4.5 cm

25.

Page 587   Mid-Chapter Review

1. 18.6 in., summer, New Orleans; 0.3 in., summer, San Francisco

2.

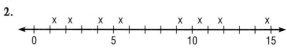

3. Stem	Leaf
1	8
2	6
4	8
6	5
7	1
10	8
12	1 5

$6|5 = 6.5$ inches

4. 8.45 in.; 10.15 in.; no mode
5. 18.3 in.; 4.15 in., 9.9 in., 11.2 in.; 7.05 in.; no outliers

6.

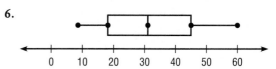

7.

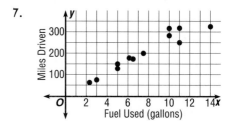

Pages 591–593 Lesson 14-7

7. 1 **11.** yes **13.** no **15.** yes **17.** $\frac{1}{6}$ **19.** $\frac{1}{2}$

21. 1:2 **23.** 5:1 **25.** $\frac{1}{2}$ **27.** 1:3 **29.** $\frac{4}{13}$ **31.** 4:3

33. $\frac{14}{23}$ **35.** 0.7 **39.** 1:24 **41.** 11 days

42.

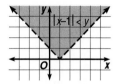

43. 240 feet **44.** no real roots

45a.

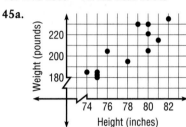

b. the taller the player, the greater the weight

Pages 596–597 Lesson 14-8

5b. Expected probability is $\frac{2}{36}$ or about 0.056.

c. Expected probability is $\frac{6}{36}$ or about 0.167.

d. Expected probability is $\frac{6}{36}$ or about 0.167.

e. Expected probability is $\frac{21}{36}$ or about 0.583.

f. Sum that should occur most often is 7. **g.** Sums that should occur least often are 2 and 12.

7a. $\frac{1}{42} \approx 0.02$ **b.** $\left(\frac{1}{42}\right)^2 \approx 0.0006$ **c.** 1.1×10^{-11}

9. 5:3 **12.** $y = 1 - \frac{1}{2}x$ **13.** 6 **14.** 24

15. $56\sqrt{2}$ or about 79.20 **16.** 10:3

Page 599 Lesson 14-9

3. 1027 pages **5.** Take the cat across first. Then go back, pick up either the dog or the bird, and take it across the bridge. Now, go back with the cat, leave it, pick up the remaining animal, and take it across. Finally, go back, pick up the cat again, and take it across. **7.** 10 peaches at $0.32 each and 2 pears at $0.29 each or 2 peaches at $0.34 each and 10 pears at $0.31 each **9.** 12 hens

Pages 602–603 Lesson 14-10

3a. 0.5 **b.** 0.25 **c.** 0.25 **d.** 0.125 **5.** $\frac{15}{16} = 0.9375$

7a. 0.125 **b.** 0.375 **c.** 0.875 **9a.** $\frac{3}{10} = 0.3$

b. $\frac{9}{10} = 0.9$ **c.** man and woman **11.** $\frac{1}{4} = 0.25$

13. $135,575 **14.** $\frac{7}{5-p}$ **15.** 4.5 ft

16. P(heads) should be approximately $\frac{1}{2}$ or 0.50. If not, then the results do not necessarily imply that the coin is not fair because of the low number of trials. More trials must be done in order to determine whether or not the coin is fair.
17. 4850 diagonals

Pages 604–606 Chapter 14 Summary and Review

1. Philip Morris **3.** Percents are rounded to the nearest tenth. Exxon: 4.0%, Ford Motor: 3.9%, General Electric: 7.1%, General Motors: 3.3%, IBM: 6.0%, Mobil: 7.4%, Philip Morris: 7.4%; Philip Morris; no

5.

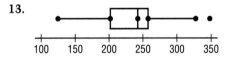

7.

Rounded	Stem	Truncated
8 6 5 1	3	1 4 6 8
4 3	4	2 4 9
8 7 6 0	5	6 6 8
8	6	7

rounded data: 3|1 = 4250-4349
truncated data: 3|1 = 4300-4399

9. 12.92; 10; 10 **11.** 34.7; 254.8 in.

13.

15. $\frac{11}{20} = 0.55$ **17.** $\frac{9}{13}$ or about 0.692 **19.** Expected probability is $\frac{1}{2}$ or 0.5. **21.** $\frac{7}{15} = 0.4\overline{6}$ **23.** 207 games

CHAPTER 15 TRIGONOMETRY

Pages 612–614 Lesson 15-1

5. 77° **7.** 66° **9.** 14° **11.** $(50 - 2x)°$ **13.** 50°
15. 93° **17.** 148° **19.** $(180 - y)°$ **21.** $(200 - x)°$
23. 3°, 93° **25.** none, 20° **27.** 22°, 112° **29.** none, 6° **31.** $(90 - a)°$, $(180 - a)°$ **33.** $(60 - x)°$, $(150 - x)°$ **35.** $(90 - 5x)°$, $(180 - x)°$ **37.** $(y - 90)°$, $y°$ **39.** 70° **41.** 60° **43.** 105° **45.** 138°
47. $(160 - 2x)°$ **49.** $(179 - 3m)°$ **51.** 58°, 60°, 62°
53. 90° **55.** 15°, 75° **57.** 75° **59.** 60° **61.** 43°, 48°, 89° **65.** 120° **67.** $R = am - z$ **68.** $-35a^5b^2c$
69. $x \le 2, y \ge 2$ **70.** $\sqrt{29}$ or about 5.39 units
71. $x = \frac{3}{2}, \left(\frac{3}{2}, \frac{137}{4}\right)$ **72.** −12, −28 **73.** $\frac{1}{3} = 0.\overline{3}$

Page 616 Lesson 15-2

5. 660 in² **7.** Hong: 7, Dora: 5 **9.** $62

Pages 619–621   Lesson 15-3

5. 8 cm   **7.** 4.5 mi   **9.** $1\frac{11}{16}$ in.   **11.** 2.315 cm   **13.** 2 cm, 4 cm   **15.** 1 mi, 2 mi   **17.** 12.4 cm   **19.** 9 mi   **21.** 26 m   **23.** $15\frac{1}{2}$ in.   **25.** $5\sqrt{3}$ or about 8.660 ft   **27.** 10 units   **29.** $2.5\sqrt{3}$ or about 4.330 yd   **31.** 2.375 mm, $2.375\sqrt{3}$ or about 4.114 mm   **33.** 16 cm, $8\sqrt{3}$ or about 13.856 cm   **35.** $6\frac{1}{2}$ in., $\frac{13}{4}\sqrt{3}$ or about 5.629 in.   **37.** 7 cm, 3.5 cm   **39.** $48 + 16\sqrt{3}$ or about 75.71 yd   **43.** 4 ft   **44.** -7.54 **45.** $(3y - 1)(y + 2)$ **46.** no solution   **47.** $-\frac{17}{10}$ **48.** $\frac{1 \pm \sqrt{33}}{4}$ **49.** 34   **50.** 73°

Page 621   Mid-Chapter Review

1. 5°, 95°   **2.** none, 53°   **3.** 25°, 115°   **4.** none, 72°   **5.** $(90 - x)°$, $(180 - x)°$ **6.** $(85 - 3x)°$, $(175 - 3x)°$ **7.** 3 m, 6 m   **8.** 7 yd, 14 yd   **9.** 9 mm, 18 mm   **10.** $\frac{1}{3}$ in., $\frac{2}{3}$ in.   **11.** The figure below shows the view from directly above the pins. Move the three pins as indicated in this figure.

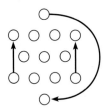

Pages 624–625   Lesson 15-4

3. $\angle B$ and $\angle R$, $\angle I$ and $\angle E$, $\angle G$ and $\angle D$ **5.** $\frac{BI}{RE} = \frac{IG}{ED}$, $\frac{BI}{RE} = \frac{BG}{RD}$, $\frac{IG}{ED} = \frac{BG}{BD}$ **7.** $\triangle WQC$ **9.** yes   **11.** $b = \frac{25}{7}$, $c = \frac{30}{7}$ **13.** $a \approx 2.78$, $c \approx 4.23$ **15.** $d = \frac{51}{5}$, $e = 9$

17. $c = \frac{7}{2}$, $d = \frac{17}{8}$ **19.** $b = 16.2$, $d = 6.3$ **23.** 105 m   **25.** $\frac{11}{13}$ **26.** $\frac{6 - 6a + 6b}{a^2 - 2ab - b^2}$ **27.** $\left(\frac{11}{3}, \frac{2}{3}\right)$ **28.** $12\sqrt{3}$ **29.** $2 \pm \sqrt{3}$ **30.** 26.385, 26.58   **31.** 5, 10

Pages 629–631   Lesson 15-5

5. $\frac{9}{41}$ **7.** $\frac{40}{41}$ **9.** $\frac{9}{40}$ **11.** yes   **13.** 0.9063   **15.** 0.9455   **17.** 0.1584   **19.** $\sin N = 0.246$, $\cos N = 0.969$, $\tan N = 0.254$ **21.** $\sin N = 0.600$, $\cos N = 0.800$, $\tan N = 0.750$ **23.** $\sin N = 0.724$, $\cos N = 0.690$, $\tan N = 1.050$ **25.** 16°   **27.** 75°   **29.** 44°   **31.** 77°   **33.** 36°   **35.** 49°   **37.** 42.3 cm²   **39.** 47 feet   **41.** 29°; 2.3×10^8 meters per second   **43.** 25%   **44.** {1, 2, −2, 3}, {1, 4, 9}   **45.** (2, −2)   **46.** $2|a|\sqrt{30ab}$ **47.** 25

Pages 634–636   Lesson 15-6

3. $\angle FED$; $\angle EDG$ **5.** $\angle QRP$; $\angle SPR$ **7.** sine   **9.** 2.3   **11.** $\angle B$: 69°, $\overline{AB}$: 13.9 in., $\overline{BC}$: 5.0 in.   **13.** $\angle B$: 20°, $\overline{AB}$: 9.6 cm, $\overline{AC}$: 3.3 cm   **15.** $\angle B$: 50°, $\overline{AC}$: 12.3 m, $\overline{BC}$: 10.3 m   **17.** 376 ft, 426 ft   **19.** 65 ft   **21.** 1716 cm²   **23.** 173.2 m   **27.** 22 miles   **29.** 4.0 seconds   **31.** $\{x|x > 80\}$ **32.** -2 **33.** $x = 13$, $y = -2$ **34.** 9   **35.** 2   **36.** $\frac{1}{6}$ **37.** 45°

Pages 638–640   Chapter 15 Summary and Review

1. 24°, 114°   **3.** none, 32°   **5.** 92°   **7.** 53°   **9.** 4 cm, $4\sqrt{3}$ or about 6.928 cm   **11.** 6 in., $3\sqrt{3}$ or about 5.196 in.   **13.** $b = \frac{70}{11}$, $c = \frac{30}{11}$ **15.** $d = \frac{48}{5}$, $e = \frac{36}{5}$ **17.** $\frac{28}{53}$ **19.** $\frac{45}{53}$ **21.** $\frac{28}{45}$ **23.** 39°   **25.** 80°   **27.** $\angle B$: 28°, $\overline{AC}$: 3.7 m, $\overline{AB}$: 7.9 m   **29.** 31 people   **31.** $36\sqrt{3}$ or about 62.4 ft²   **33.** about 104 m   **35.** about 6143 ft, about 5808 ft

INDEX

A

Absolute values, 55–58, 69–70, 89, 492
    open sentences involving, 199–203, 206, 464, 466
Acute angles, 182
Acute triangles, 612
Addition
    additive identity, 22–24
    additive inverse property, 74–75
    associative property of, 31–35, 45, 70, 230
    commutative property of, 31–34, 70, 230, 497
    elimination using, 453–459, 469
    of integers, 52–59, 88
    of polynomials, 230–233, 497
    properties of, 22–24, 31–34
    of radical expressions, 497–500, 511
    of rational expressions, 322–325, 330–332, 335, 349
    of rational numbers, 69–72, 79, 89, 322
    in solving equations, 94–98, 100, 112, 126
    in solving inequalities, 176–179, 187
    symbol in BASIC, 10
    words used to indicate, 9
Addition property for inequality, 176
Addition property of equality, 94, 99–100
Additive identity property, 22–24
Additive inverse property, 74–75
Additive inverses, 56–58, 230–232, 266–267, 322, 453–454
Adjacent sides, 626–629, 633, 639
A'h-Mose, 165
Algebraic expressions, 8–17, 36
    evaluating, 10–16, 45
    rational, 306–325, 330–351
    simplifying, 27–30, 45
Al-Khwarizmi, Muhammed ibn Musa, 93, 549

Analytic geometry, 383
Angles
    acute, 182
    complementary, 611–613, 638
    corresponding, 622–624
    of depression, 632–634
    of elevation, 632–634
    measures of, 610–614, 638
    supplementary, 610, 612–613, 638
    of triangles, 233, 611–614, 638
Applications
    in automobile safety, 353
    in biology, 209
    black holes, 225
    compound interest, 145
    in construction, 517
    in consumer awareness, 133
    escape velocity, 486
    formulas, 343–347
    in history, 93
    in literature, 439
    in marine biology, 255
    meteorology, 54
    mixtures, 154–157, 171
    in nature, 473
    in optics, 609
    in physics, 305
    in probability, 559
    Punnett squares, 246
    in recreation, 49
    simple interest, 142–144
    in skiing, 399
    solving quadratic equations, 546–549
    in sports, 7
    in statistics, 175
    travel agents, 161
    uniform motion, 158–161, 171
Area, 36–40
    of circles, 37, 479
    cross-sectional, 12
    of rectangles, 37, 105, 166, 213, 215, 234, 238, 240, 243, 256, 261–265, 272, 276–277, 287, 295, 312–313, 368, 498, 546, 555
    of squares, 10, 38, 243, 245–246, 276, 282, 480
    surface, 37, 247
    of trapezoids, 38, 40, 237, 246, 343
    of triangles, 36, 39–40, 446, 630
Arrays, 242

Ascending order, 227–228
Associative properties
    of addition, 31–35, 45, 70, 230
    of multiplication, 31–35, 75–76, 214, 223
Automorphic numbers, 193
Averages
    batting, 7
    means, 80, 188, 570–576, 605
    medians, 570–581, 605
    modes, 570–575, 605
Axes
    of symmetry, 519–522, 554
    x, 354, 356
    y, 354, 356

B

Back-to-back stem-and-leaf plots, 566–568
Balanced numbers, 109
Banneker, Benjamin, 409
Bar graphs, 389–390, 432
Base functions, 530
Bases
    percents, 138–139
    of powers, 9, 213, 218
BASIC, 12
    DATA statements, 40
    FOR/NEXT loops, 378
    IF-THEN statements, 180
    programs, 12, 30, 40, 59, 78–79, 115, 125, 144, 150, 185, 225, 247, 260, 321, 378, 431, 461, 509, 545, 597, 631, 637
    READ statements, 40
    symbol for exponents, 12, 225
Batting averages, 7
Bernoulli, Jacob, 593
Bimodal data, 571
Binomials, 226
    conjugates, 494–495
    difference of squares, 276–280, 286, 301
    dividing by, 319–321, 349
    factoring, 261–263, 276–279, 286, 300–301
    multiplying, 238–246
Boundaries, 379–381, 463–464

Box-and-whisker plots, 579–582, 605
Boyle's Law, 169

CALC commands, 121, 191, 315, 427, 505
Calculators, 227, 533, 538
  change-sign keys, 57
  degree mode, 627
  graphing, 384, 462, 530, 588
  inverse keys, 628
  parentheses keys, 420
  percent keys, 139
  power keys, 215
  raising numbers to powers, 10
  recall keys, 420
  reciprocal keys, 84
  scientific, 15
  scientific notation, 223–224
  square root keys, 478–480, 488–489, 498
  store keys, 420
  for trigonometric ratios, 627–630, 639
Capture-recapture method, 134–135
Carroll, Lewis, 439
Cartesian coordinate system, 383
Catenaries, 517
Celsius, 36, 78, 120, 199, 347, 373
Centers, 428, 430
Central tendencies
  means, 570–576, 605
  medians, 570–581, 605
  modes, 570–575, 605
Change-sign keys, 57
Ch'ang Ts'ang, 467
Chapter reviews, 44–46, 88–90, 126–128, 170–172, 204–206, 248–250, 300–302, 348–350, 392–394, 434–436, 468–470, 510–512, 554–556, 604–606, 638–640
Chapter tests, 47, 91, 129, 173, 207, 251, 303, 351, 395, 437, 471, 513, 557, 607, 641
Charles' Law, 165
Circle graphs, 141, 432–433
Circles
  area of, 37, 479
  centers of, 428, 430
  circumferences of, 16, 38
  diameters of, 414, 428, 430

Circumferences, 16, 38
Closed half-planes, 380–381
Coefficients, 28–29, 242
  of one, 94
College entrance exams previews, 130–131, 252–253, 296–297, 514–515, 642–643
Collinear points, 431
Common denominators, 322–323
  least, 330–331
Common factors, 257–258
  greatest, 257–263, 277, 286–288, 291, 300–301
Common monomial factors, 265, 271, 286, 301
Commutative properties
  of addition, 31–34, 70, 230, 497
  of multiplication, 31–34, 75, 214, 223
Comparative graphs, 432
Comparison property, 65, 82
Comparisons of numbers, 60, 65–68, 89
Complementary angles, 611–613, 638
Complete graphs, 384
Completeness properties
  for points in the plane, 355–356
  for points on the number line, 488
Completing the square, 531–536, 555
Complex fractions, 81, 334–337, 349
Composite numbers, 256, 258
Compound events, 600–603, 606
Compound inequalities, 175, 194–198, 200–203, 205–206
Compound interest, 226–227, 325
Compound sentences, 185, 199
Computers
  BASIC, 12, 40, 225, 321, 637
  CALC commands, 121, 191, 315, 427, 505
  E notation, 225
  Mathematics Exploration Toolkit, 121, 191, 315, 427, 505
  programs, 12, 30, 40, 59, 78–79, 115, 125, 144, 150, 180, 185, 225, 247, 260, 321, 378, 431, 461, 509, 545, 597, 631, 637
  spreadsheets, 40, 247
Conjugates, 494–495

Conjunctions, 185
Connections
  geometry, 10, 14, 32, 36–37, 105, 117, 166, 182, 213, 231, 243, 262, 272, 278, 287, 312, 323, 343, 423, 428, 444, 494, 497–498, 507, 543
  history, 35, 78, 125, 165, 180, 233, 260, 310, 383, 409, 467, 481, 549, 593
  number theory, 449, 453, 502–503, 525
  probability, 361
  sequences, 76
  set theory, 51
  stratistics, 188
Consecutive numbers, 112–115
  even, 112–115
  odd, 112–115
Consistent equations, 443–444
Constants, 213
  of variation, 162
Cooperative learning activities, 43, 87, 110, 153, 193, 212, 270, 328, 391, 433, 441, 476, 529, 599, 616
Coordinate planes, 354–358, 392
  origins, 354, 380
  quadrants, 356–357, 392
  x-axis, 354, 356
  y-axis, 354, 356
Coordinates, 354, 359–361
  on number lines, 51–52
  x, 354–356, 381
  y, 354–356, 381
Corresponding angles, 622–624
Corresponding sides, 622–624
Cosine, 626–632, 639–640
Counting numbers, 487
Cross products, 65, 134, 163
Cross-sectional area, 12
Cubes, 10

Data, 560
  bimodal, 571
  box-and-whisker plots of, 579–582, 605
  interquartile ranges of, 575–578, 580, 605
  line plots of, 560–564, 604
  means of, 80, 188, 570–576, 605
  medians of, 570–581, 605
  modes of, 570–575, 605
  outliers, 576–578, 580

quartiles of, 575–581, 605
ranges of, 575, 577–578, 605
scatter plots of, 583–587, 606
stem-and-leaf plots of,
565–570, 572–573,
576–579, 582, 605
DATA statements, 40
Decimal notation, 221–224, 249
Decimals
in equations, 122–125
repeating, 487–488, 511
terminating, 487, 511
Degree mode, 627
Degrees
of monomials, 227, 249
of polynomials, 227–228, 249
Denominators
common, 322–323, 330–331
least common, 330–332,
338–341, 343
rationalizing, 493–496
Density property, 66–67
Dependent equations, 443–444
Descartes, René, 383
Descending order, 227–228, 249,
282
Diameters, 414, 428, 430
Differences
of squares, 244, 276–280, 286,
301
squares of, 244–245
Diophantus, 93, 125
Direct variations, 162–165, 172
Discounts, 133, 146–150, 171
successive, 150
Discriminants, 541–545, 555
Disjoint sets, 51
Disjunctions, 185
Distance formula, 506–509, 512
Distributive property, 26–30,
32–34, 45, 57, 74–75, 82, 122,
135, 187, 230, 234, 238–239,
494, 497
factoring using, 261–264, 271,
300
Dividends, 319–320
Division
dividends, 319–320
divisors, 319–320
of monomials, 217–219
of polynomials, 319–321, 349
of powers, 217–219
quotients, 319–321
of rational expressions,
316–318, 334, 348
of rational numbers, 80–84, 99
remainders, 319–321
in solving equations, 104–107,
111, 121, 127

in solving inequalities,
182–187, 200
symbol in BASIC, 12
words used to indicate, 9
by zero, 123
Division property for inequalities,
182–183
Division property of equality,
104–105, 111
Divisors, 319–320
binomials, 319–321, 349
proper, 328
Dodgson, Charles Lutwidge, 439
Domains, 359–362, 364–366,
368–369, 376, 392

Edges, 379
Einstein, Albert, 233
Elements, 19–20
Elimination, 452–461, 469
Empirical probability, 594
Empty set, 19, 51, 195
E notation, 225
Equally likely events, 589, 591,
600
Equations, 19–22
with absolute values, 199
of axes of symmetry, 519–522,
554
checking solutions, 95–98,
100–101, 104, 112, 123, 124,
291, 296, 407, 444, 447, 452,
457, 501–504
consistent, 443–444
with decimals, 122–125
dependent, 443–444
equivalent, 94
formulas, 36–40
with fractions, 122–124, 127
identities, 118–119
inconsistent, 443–444
independent, 443–444
linear, 369–373, 375, 393,
405–427, 434–436,
442–461, 468–469
with more than one variable,
123–124, 128
percents, 139–140
point-slope form, 405–407, 410
quadratic, 290–299, 302,
523–526, 531–557
radical, 501–505, 512
rational, 338–347, 350
as relations, 364–373
from relations, 385–388, 394

slope-intercept form, 410–414,
416–422, 424–426, 435, 444
solving, 94–107, 111–129,
290–299, 302, 338–347, 350,
501–504, 512, 523–526,
531–540, 546–549, 554–555
standard form, 406–409,
411–412, 416, 420–421
systems of, 442–461, 468–469
in two variables, 364–373, 375
with variables on both sides,
116–121, 127
writing, 85–87
Equilateral triangles, 611, 617
Equivalent equations, 94
Eratosthenes, 260
Escalante, Jaime, 481
Escape velocity, 486
Even numbers, 636
consecutive, 112–115
Events
compound, 600–603, 606
equally likely, 589, 591, 600
simple, 589–592, 600, 606
Excluded values, 306–309
Experimental probability,
594–597, 606
Exponents, 9–12, 44, 213–214,
217–223, 227
negative, 218–219, 222–224,
248
symbol in BASIC, 12, 225
zero, 218–219
Expressions, 8–17, 36
evaluating, 10–16, 45
mixed, 334
radical, 477–500, 511
rational, 306–325, 330–351
simplest form of, 27–30, 45
simplifying, 218–219,
492–500, 511
Extra, 242, 318
Extremes, 134–136

Factors, 8, 256–268, 271–303,
319
of binomials, 261–263,
276–279, 286, 300–301
checking, 265–267, 271
common, 257–258
common monomial, 265, 271,
286, 301
of differences of squares,
276–280, 286, 301
using distributive property,
261–264, 271, 300

greatest common, 257–263, 277, 286–288, 291, 300–301, 307–308, 322–323
by grouping, 265–268, 287, 300
of monomials, 257–259, 300
of perfect square trinomials, 281–288, 296, 301
of polynomials, 257–259, 261–268, 271–289, 300–301
prime, 256–258, 478, 492–493
in solving equations, 290–299, 302, 546–547
of trinomials, 262–264, 271–275, 281–288, 301
Fahrenheit, 36, 54, 78, 120, 347, 373
Fibonacci sequence, 212
Figurate numbers, 153, 270
FOIL method, 238–241, 244, 265, 271–272, 277, 287, 498
Formulas, 36–40, 343–347, 350
for acceleration, 481
for area of circles, 37, 479
for area of rectangles, 105, 213, 312
for area of squares, 38
for area of trapezoids, 38, 40, 237, 246, 343
for area of triangles, 36, 40, 446, 630
for changing Celsius to Fahrenheit, 36, 120, 373
for changing Fahrenheit to Celsius, 78, 347
for circumferences, 38
for compound interest, 145, 226
distance, 506–509, 512
for distance, 39, 158–159, 161, 171, 339, 342
for earned-run average, 46
for escape velocity, 486
for focal length, 343
for height of projectile, 255, 290, 294, 299, 368, 376, 522–523, 526, 536, 540, 548, 551, 553, 556
for interest, 142–143, 145, 170
for length of storm, 491
for monthly payments, 220
for perimeters of parallelograms, 38
for perimeters of rectangles, 117, 323, 497
for perimeters of squares, 38
for periods of pendulums, 496
for pitch of roofs, 105
for power, 481
to predict time of storm, 35
quadratic, 537–547, 555
for range of projectiles, 630

for resistance, 344–345, 363
for Schwarzschild radius, 225
for simple interest, 142–143, 170
Snell's Law, 609, 628, 631
for speed, 501, 512
for surface area of rectangular solids, 37
for terms of arithmetic sequences, 76
for time to fall to Earth, 504
for visible distance, 504
for voltage, 489, 491
for volume of rectangular prisms, 32
for volume of trapezoidal prisms, 314
FOR/NEXT loop, 378
Fractions
adding, 79, 322–325, 330–332, 335, 349
algebraic, 306–325, 330–351
bars, 13–15
complex, 81, 334–337, 349
dividing, 316–318, 334, 348
in equations, 122–124, 127
history of, 310
improper, 104, 334
least common denominators, 330–332, 338–341, 343
mixed numbers, 334
multiplying, 311–316, 348
to percents, 138
simplifying, 307–309, 311, 323, 348
subtracting, 322–324, 331–332, 335, 349
unit, 165, 528
Functional notation, 376–378
Functional values, 376–378, 393
Functions, 374–378, 393
base, 530
families of, 530
functional notation, 376–378
functional values, 376–378, 393
graphs of, 375, 377, 518–526, 542, 554
greatest integer, 260
quadratic, 518–526, 542, 554
Trace, 462
vertical line test, 375, 377

Geometric means, 502–503
Geometry

analytic, 383
angles, 182, 610–614, 632–634, 638
area, 10, 36–40, 105, 166, 446, 479, 498, 546, 555, 630
circles, 16, 37–38, 414, 428, 430, 479
circumferences, 16, 38
collinear points, 431
cubes, 10
midpoints, 428–431, 436
parallel lines, 423–426
parallelograms, 423
perimeters, 14, 16, 38, 40, 117–118, 497, 543, 555
perpendicular lines, 354, 424–426, 436
quadrilaterals, 423
rectangles, 105, 117, 166, 497–498, 543, 555
rectangular prisms, 32, 37, 247
squares, 10, 40
surface area, 37, 247
trapezoids, 38, 40, 507
triangles, 36, 39–40, 185, 446, 473, 482–486, 494, 510, 611–614, 617–641
volume, 10, 32, 247, 278–279, 547
Grade, 400, 402
Graphing calculators, 384, 462, 530, 588
standard viewing window, 384
Trace functions, 462
Graphs, 353
bar, 389–390, 432
boundaries, 379–381, 463–464
circle, 141, 432–433
comparative, 432
complete, 384
distance formula, 506–509, 512
of functions, 375, 377, 518–526, 542, 554
graphing calculators, 384, 462, 530, 588, 637
of inequalities, 195–198, 200–202, 205–206, 379–384, 394, 463–466, 470
intercepts, 443
line, 389–390, 436
line plots, 560–564, 604
of lines, 369–373, 375, 384, 393, 400–405, 410–418, 421–427, 435, 442–447, 468
misleading, 390
number lines, 50–53, 55, 62–63, 69, 88–89, 195–202, 205–206, 354
of ordered pairs, 354–360, 369–371
of parabolas, 517–526, 530, 542, 554
pictographs, 432

of points, 354–360, 369–371
of quadratic functions,
518–526, 542, 554
of relations, 359–360, 362,
369–375, 377, 379–383,
393–394
scatter plots, 583–587, 606
slopes, 399–414, 416–427,
431, 434–435, 443–444, 448,
584, 606, 628
of solution sets, 195–202,
205–206
of systems of equations,
442–447, 468
of systems of inequalities,
463–466, 470
of trigonometric functions, 637
using, 389–391, 432–433
x-intercepts, 384, 410,
412–413, 415, 417–419, 435,
523–524, 541–542, 544
y-intercepts, 384, 410–422,
424, 435
Graunt, John, 593
Greatest common factors,
257–263, 277, 286–288, 291,
300–301, 307–308, 322–323
Greatest integer function, 260
Guess and check, 269–270

Half-planes, 379–382, 463
closed, 380–381
open, 379
Hamilton, Sir William Rowan, 35
Happy numbers, 328
Harriot, Thomas, 180
History connections
A'h-Mose, 165
Benjamin Bannaker, 409
Diophantus, 125
Emmy Noether, 233
Eratosthenes, 260
fractions, 310
Graunt and Bernoulli, 593
Jaime Escalante, 481
K'iu-ch'ang Suan-shu, 467
Muhammed ibn Musa al
Khwarizmi, 549
Pythagoras, 636
Recorde, Harriott, and
Oughtred, 180
René Descartes, 383
Sir William Rowan Hamilton,
35
Sonya Kavalevskaya, 78
Horizontal lines, 401–402, 407

Identities, 118–119
additive, 22–24
multiplicative, 22–24, 28
IF-THEN statements, 180
Improper fractions, 104, 334
Inches
united, 230
Inconsistent equations, 443–444
Independent equations, 443–444
Inequalities, 60–64, 89
addition property for, 176
checking solutions, 176
compound, 175, 194–198,
200–203, 205–206
division property for, 182–183
graphs of, 195–198, 200–202,
205–206, 379–384, 394,
463–466, 470
involving absolute values,
200–203, 206, 464, 466
with more than one operation,
186–191, 196, 200, 205
multiplication property for,
181–182, 186
phrases for, 177
solving, 176–191, 195–198,
200–207
subtraction property for, 176,
186
systems of, 463–467, 470
in two variables, 379–383
Integers, 50–60, 487, 489
absolute values of, 55–58, 89
adding, 52–59, 88
consecutive even, 112–115
consecutive odd, 112–115
factoring, 256–259
subtracting, 57–58, 88
Intercepts, 410, 443
x, 410, 412–413, 415,
417–419, 435, 523–524,
541–542, 544
y, 410–422, 424, 435
Interest, 216
compound, 145, 226–227, 325
principals, 142, 145, 170
rates, 142, 145, 170
simple, 142–144, 170
Interquartile ranges, 575–578,
580, 605
Intersecting lines, 442–447

Hypotenuse, 473, 482–483, 485,
494, 510, 617–618, 626–629,
631, 633, 639

Intersections, 51–52, 194–195
Inverse keys, 628
Inverse operations, 80
Inverses, 99
additive, 266–267, 322,
453–454
multiplicative, 316
of relations, 360–363, 392
Inverse variation, 166–169, 172
product rule for, 167–168
proportions, 167, 172
Irrational numbers, 487–489, 511
Isosceles trapezoids, 507
Isosceles triangles, 612–613

Jefferson, Thomas, 409

K'iu-ch'ang Suan-shu, 467
Kovalevskaya, Sonya, 78

Least common denominators,
330–332
Least common multiples,
329–330
Legs, 482–483, 494, 626–629,
631
adjacent, 626–629, 633, 639
opposite, 626–629, 633, 639
L'Enfant, Pierre, 409
Levers, 167, 169
Like terms, 27–29, 230–232, 234,
239–240, 262, 323
Linear equations, 369–373, 375,
393, 405–427, 434–436
point-slope form, 405–407, 410
slope-intercept form, 410–414,
416–422, 424–426, 435, 444
standard form of, 406–409,
411–412, 416, 420–421
systems of, 442–461, 468–469
Line graphs, 389–390, 436
Line plots, 560–564, 604

Lines
   graphs of, 369–373, 375, 393,
     400–405, 410–418,
     421–427, 435, 442–447, 468
   horizontal, 401–402, 407
   intersecting, 442–447
   number, 354, 560–564,
     579–582
   parallel, 423–426, 443–444,
     448
   perpendicular, 354, 424–426,
     436
   regression, 588
   slopes of, 399–414, 416–427,
     431, 434–435, 443–444, 448,
     584, 606, 628
   vertical, 401–402, 407
   x-axis, 354, 356
   y-axis, 354, 356
Line segments
   midpoints of, 428–431, 436
Logic, 18
   compound sentences, 185, 199
   conjunction, 185
   disjunctions, 185
   negations, 18
   statements, 18
Lower quartiles, 575–577,
   579–581, 605

Magic squares, 59
Mappings, 359–360, 362, 374
Maps, 356, 358, 431, 433
Mathematics Exploration Toolkit,
   121, 191, 315, 427, 505
Matrix, 151–152
Maximum points, 518, 520–522
McKinley, William, 475
Means
   averages, 80, 188, 570–576,
     605
   geometric, 502–503
   of proportions, 134–136
Means-extremes property of
   proportions, 134–135, 402, 527
Measurement
   of angles, 610–611
   area, 10, 36–40, 105, 166, 446,
     479, 498, 546, 555, 630
   circumferences, 16, 38
   ohms, 344–347
   perimeters, 14, 16, 38, 40,
     117–118, 497, 543, 555
   protractors, 610–611
   surface area, 37, 247

   temperature, 36–37, 54, 78,
     120, 199, 347
   united inches, 230
   volume, 10, 32, 247, 278–279,
     314, 547
Measures of central tendency,
   570–575
   means, 80, 188, 570–576, 605
   medians, 570–581, 605
   modes, 570–575, 605
Measures of variation, 575–578
   interquartile ranges, 575–578,
     580, 605
   ranges, 575, 577–578, 605
Medians, 570–581, 605
Meteorology, 54
Mid-chapter reviews, 25, 73, 107,
   157, 190, 229, 280, 325, 373,
   418, 456, 491, 540, 587, 621
Midpoints, 428–431, 436
Minimum points, 518–521, 554
Misleading graphs, 390
Mixed expressions, 334
Mixed numbers, 104, 334
Mixture problems, 154–157, 171
Modes, 570–575, 605
Money
   commissions, 140
   consumer awareness, 133
   discounts, 133, 146–150, 171
   interest, 142–145, 170, 216,
     226–227, 325
   taxes, 146–149
Monomials, 213–220, 226–228
   adding, 497
   constants, 213
   degrees of, 227
   dividing, 217–219
   factoring, 256–259, 300
   greatest common factors of,
     258–259, 261–262, 300
   multiplying by, 234–237, 250
   powers of, 214–216
   simplifying, 218–219, 248
   subtracting, 497
Multiples
   least common, 329–330
Multiplication
   associative property of, 31–35,
     75–76, 214, 223
   of binomials, 238–246
   commutative property of,
     31–34, 75, 214, 223
   elimination using, 457–461,
     469
   factors, 8, 256–268, 271–303
   FOIL method, 238–241, 244,
     250, 265, 271–272, 277, 287,
     498

   multiplicative identity, 22–24,
     28
   of polynomials, 234–246, 250
   of powers, 213–216, 234, 348
   product, 8–9
   properties of, 22–24, 31–34
   of radical expressions, 498, 500
   of rational expressions,
     311–316, 348
   of rational numbers, 74–78, 89
   in solving equations, 103–107,
     112, 116–117, 127
   in solving inequalities,
     181–186, 188, 205
   symbol in BASIC, 12
   words used to indicate, 9
   zero product property,
     290–293, 295–296, 302
Multiplication property for
   inequalities, 181–182, 186
Multiplication property of
   equality, 103, 105, 122
Multiplicative identity property,
   22–24, 28
Multiplicative inverse property,
   81
Multiplicative inverses, 81–82,
   316
Multiplicative property of zero,
   23–24, 32, 74

Nasty numbers, 289
Natural numbers, 51, 487, 489,
   598
Negations, 18
Negative numbers, 50
   as exponents, 218–219,
     222–224, 348
   factoring, 257
   as slopes, 401–402, 584, 606
Noether, Emmy, 233
Null set, 19
Number lines, 50–53, 55, 354
   in adding, 52–53, 55, 69
   box-and-whisker plots,
     579–582, 605
   comparing numbers on, 61
   completeness property, 488
   graphing inequalities, 62–63,
     89, 195–198, 200–202,
     205–206
   graphing sets of numbers,
     51–53, 88
   line plots, 560–564, 604
   x-axis, 354, 356
   y-axis, 354, 356

Numbers
  absolute values of, 55–58,
    69–70, 89
  additive inverses, 56–58,
    453–454
  automorphic, 193
  balanced, 109
  comparing, 60, 65–68, 89
  composite, 256, 258
  consecutive, 112–115
  counting, 487
  decimal notation, 221, 249
  even, 636
  factors of, 256–259
  Fibonacci, 212
  figurate, 153, 270
  happy, 328
  integers, 50–60, 88, 487, 489
  inverses, 99
  irrational, 487–489, 511
  mixed, 104, 334
  multiplicative inverses, 81–82
  nasty, 289
  natural, 51, 487, 489, 598
  negative, 50
  odd, 636
  ordered pairs, 354–374,
    392–393, 442–445,
    463–465, 583
  palindromes, 528
  perfect, 328
  perfect squares, 281
  persistence of, 433
  prime, 256, 258, 260
  prime factorization of, 256–259
  rational, 61–84, 487–489, 511
  real, 51, 369, 488–489,
    523–524
  rounded, 566–568
  scientific notation, 221–225,
    249
  square roots of, 474, 477–513,
    531–532
  squares of, 477, 479, 501–502
  triangular, 153
  truncated, 566–567
  twin prime, 259
  whole, 50–52, 487, 489
Number theory, 112, 212, 328
  automorphic numbers, 193
  balanced numbers, 109
  composite numbers, 256, 258
  consecutive numbers, 112–115
  figurate numbers, 153, 270
  geometric means, 502–503
  happy numbers, 328
  nasty numbers, 289
  palindromes, 528
  perfect numbers, 328
  persistence of numbers, 433
  prime numbers, 256, 258, 260
  triangular numbers, 153
  twin primes, 259

Numerical coefficient, 28–29

Obtuse triangles, 612
Odd numbers, 636
  consecutive, 112–115
Odds, 590–593, 606
Ohm, Georg Simon, 344
Ohms, 344–347
Open half-planes, 379
Open sentences, 18–21
  with absolute values, 199–203,
    206
  equations, 19–22, 94–107,
    111–129, 338–347, 350,
    369–373, 375, 393, 405–427,
    434–436
  inequalities, 60–64, 89,
    176–191, 194–198,
    200–207, 379–383, 394
Operations
  inverse, 80
  order of, 13–14, 19
Opposites, 56
Opposite sides, 617–620,
  626–629, 633, 639
Ordered pairs, 354–374,
  392–393, 442–445, 463–465,
  583
  graphing, 354–360, 369–371
  relations, 359–374, 392
Order of operations, 13–14, 19
Origins, 354, 380
Oughtred, William, 180
Outliers, 576–578, 580

Palindromes, 528
Parabolas, 517–526, 530, 542,
  554
  axes of symmetry, 519–522,
    554
  maximum points, 518,
    520–522
  minimum points, 518–521, 554
  vertices, 518–522
Parallel lines, 423–426, 443–444,
  448
  slopes of, 423–425
Parallelograms, 423
  perimeters of, 38

Parentheses, 9, 13–17, 27, 220
Parentheses keys, 420
Percentages, 138–139
Percent keys, 139
Percents, 138–150
  of change, 146–150, 171
  commissions, 140
  of decrease, 146–150, 171
  discounts, 146–150, 171
  fractions to, 138
  of increase, 146–149, 171
  interest, 142–145, 170
  mixture problems, 155–157
  sales taxes, 146–149
  solving using equations,
    139–140
  solving using proportions,
    138–140, 170
Perfect numbers, 328
Perfect squares, 281, 487
  trinomials, 281–288, 296, 301,
    531–535
Perimeters, 14, 16, 231
  of parallelograms, 38
  of rectangles, 40, 117–118,
    323, 325, 368, 497, 543, 555
  of squares, 38
Perpendicular lines, 354,
  424–426, 436
  slopes of, 424–425
Persistence, 433
Philolaus, 636
Pictographs, 432
Planes
  completeness property for
    points in, 355–356
  coordinate, 354–358, 392
  half, 379–382
Points, 354
  collinear, 431
  graphing, 354–360, 369–371
  maximum, 518, 520–522
  midpoints, 428–431, 436
  minimum, 518–521, 554
  origins, 354, 380
  vertices, 518–522
Point-slope form, 405–407, 410
Polynomials, 226–246, 306
  adding, 230–233, 249, 497
  ascending order, 227–228
  binomials, 226, 261–263,
    276–279, 286, 300–301,
    494–495
  degrees of, 227–228
  descending order, 227–228,
    249, 282
  dividing, 319–321, 349
  factoring, 257–259, 261–268,
    271–289, 300–301,
    306–308, 323, 330

monomials, 213–220, 226–228, 257–259, 300
multiplying, 234–246, 250
prime, 273–274, 286
subtracting, 230–233, 249, 497
trinomials, 226–228, 262–264, 271–275, 281–288, 301, 531–535

Positive numbers
as slopes, 401–402, 584

Power keys, 215

Powers, 9–13, 44, 213–228
of monomials, 214–216
of powers, 214–216
of products, 214–216
products of, 213–216, 234, 248
quotients of, 217–219
reading, 220
symbols in BASIC
zero, 218–219

Prime factorization, 256–258
to find least common multiples, 329
to find square roots, 478
to simplify radical expressions, 492–493

Prime factors, 256–258

Prime numbers, 256, 258
sieve of Eratosthenes, 260
twin, 259

Prime polynomials, 273–274, 286

Principals, 142, 145, 170

Principal square roots, 477–480, 492

Prisms
rectangular, 32, 247
trapezoidal, 314
volume of, 32, 214, 247, 547

Probability, 198, 559, 589–597, 599–603
of compound events, 600–603, 606
experimental, 594–597, 606
of one, 590–591
of simple events, 589–592, 606
of zero, 590–591

Problem-solving strategies
check for hidden assumptions, 440–441
explore verbal problems, 41–43
guess and check, 269–270
identify subgoals, 527–529
list possibilities, 326–328
look for a pattern, 210–212
make a diagram, 192–193
make a model, 615–616
make a table or chart, 151–153
solve a simpler problem, 210–211, 598–599

use a graph, 389–391, 432–433
use a table, 474–476
work backwards, 108–110
write an equation, 85–87

Product property of square roots, 492–493, 495

Product rule for inverse variations, 167–168

Products, 8–9
cross, 65, 134, 163
factors of, 256–268, 271–303
of powers, 213–216, 234
powers of, 214–216
of roots, 550–553, 556
special, 243–246
of sums and differences, 244–245

Programs, 12, 30, 40, 59, 78–79, 115, 125, 144, 150, 185, 225, 260, 321, 378, 431, 461, 509, 545, 597, 631
DATA statements, 40
FOR/NEXT loops, 378
IF-THEN statements, 180
READ statements, 40
spreadsheets, 40, 247

Proper divisors, 328

Properties, 22–35
of addition, 22–24, 31–34, 497
additive identity, 22–24
additive inverse, 74–75
associative, 70, 75–76, 214, 223, 230
commutative, 31–34, 70, 75, 214, 223, 230, 497
comparison, 65, 82
completeness, 355–356, 488
density, 66–67
distributive, 26–30, 32–34, 45, 57, 74–75, 82, 122, 135, 187, 230, 234, 238–239, 261–262, 271, 300, 494, 497
of equalities, 23–24, 94, 99–101, 103–105
for inequalities, 176, 181–182
of levers, 167, 169
means-extremes, 134–135, 402, 527
of multiplication, 22–24, 31–34
multiplicative identity, 22–24, 28
multiplicative inverse, 81
product, 492–493, 495
of proportions, 134
quotient, 493
reflexive, 23–24, 60
of square roots, 492–493
substitution, 23–24, 28, 31–33, 45, 55, 74–76, 230

symmetric, 23–24, 27, 60
transitive, 23–24, 60–61
zero product, 290–293, 295–296, 302, 306–307, 340, 502

Proportions, 134–140, 170, 622–623, 627, 639
capture-recapture method, 134–135
direct variations, 163–165, 172
extremes, 134–136
inverse variations, 167, 172
means, 134–136
means-extremes property of, 134–135, 402
percents, 138–140
scales, 135

Protractors, 610–611

Punnett squares, 246

Puzzles, 59, 115, 120

Pythagoras, 636

Pythagorean Theorem, 473, 482–486, 494, 506, 508, 510, 618, 627, 636

Quadrants, 356–357, 392

Quadratic equations, 523–526, 531–557
applications, 546–549
completing the square, 531–536, 555
discriminant, 541–545, 555
nature of roots, 541–545, 555
products of roots, 550–553, 556
quadratic formula, 537–547, 555
solving by factoring, 290–299, 302, 546–547
solving by graphing, 523–526, 554
sums of roots, 550–553, 556

Quadratic formula, 537–547, 555
discriminant, 541–545, 555

Quadratic functions, 518–526, 542, 554

Quadrilaterals, 423

Quartiles, 575–581
lower, 575–577, 579–581, 605
upper, 575–577, 579–581, 605

Quotient property of square roots, 493

Quotients, 319–321
of powers, 217–219

Radical equations, 501–505, 512

Radical expressions, 477–500, 511
  adding, 497–500, 511
  multiplying, 498, 500
  rationalizing denominators, 493–496
  simplifying, 492–500, 511
  subtracting, 497–500, 511

Radical signs, 477–480, 487

Radicands, 477, 479

Radii
  Schwarzschild, 225

Ranges
  of data, 575, 577–578, 605
  interquartile, 575–578, 580, 605
  of relations, 359–362, 364, 368, 384, 392

Rates
  of interest, 142, 145, 170
  percents, 138–140
  ratios, 135–136
  of speed, 158
  tax, 147–148

Rational equations, 338–347, 350

Rational expressions, 306–325, 330–351
  adding, 322–325, 330–332, 335, 349
  complex, 334–337, 349
  dividing, 316–318, 334, 348
  excluded values, 306–309
  least common denominators, 330–332, 338–341, 343
  mixed expressions, 334
  multiplying, 311–316, 348
  simplifying, 307–309, 311, 323, 348
  subtracting, 322–324, 331–332, 335, 349

Rationalizing denominators, 493–496

Rational numbers, 61–84, 487–489, 511
  adding, 69–72, 79, 89, 322
  comparing, 65–68, 89
  comparison property for, 65, 82
  dividing, 80–84, 99
  multiplying, 74–78, 89
  subtracting, 70–72

Ratios, 134–138, 146
  cosine, 626–632, 639–640
  percents, 138–150, 155–157
  rates, 135–136
  scales, 135

sine, 609, 626–633, 639–640
tangent, 626–631, 633, 639
trigonometric, 626–636, 639–640

Reading algebra, 17, 185, 220

READ statements, 40

Real numbers, 51, 369, 488–489, 523–524

Real roots, 523–525, 537–545, 555

Recall keys, 420

Reciprocal keys, 84

Reciprocals, 81–83, 182, 316–317, 334–336

Recorde, Robert, 180

Rectangles
  area of, 37, 105, 166, 213, 215, 234, 238, 240, 243, 256, 261–265, 272, 276–277, 287, 295, 312–313, 368, 498, 546, 555
  perimeters of, 40, 117–118, 323, 325, 368, 497, 543, 555

Rectangular prisms
  surface area of, 37
  volume of, 32, 247, 278–279, 547

Reflexive property, 23–24, 60

Regression lines, 588

Relations, 359–388, 392–395
  domain of, 359–362, 364–366, 368–369, 376, 392
  equations as, 364–373
  equations from, 385–388, 394
  functions, 374–378, 393
  graphs of, 359–360, 362, 369–375, 377, 379–383, 393–394
  inverses of, 360–363, 392
  mappings, 359–360, 362, 374
  ordered pairs, 359–374, 392
  range of, 359–362, 364, 368, 384, 392
  tables, 359–362

Remainders, 319–321

Repeating decimals, 487–488, 511

Replacement sets, 19

Reviews
  chapter, 44–46, 88–90, 126–128, 170–172, 204–206, 248–250, 300–302, 348–350, 392–394, 434–436, 468–470, 510–512, 554–556, 604–606, 638–640
  mid-chapter, 25, 73, 107, 157, 190, 229, 280, 325, 373, 418, 456, 491, 540, 587, 621

Right triangles, 473, 482–486, 612
  hypotenuse, 473, 482–483, 485, 494, 510, 617–618, 626–629, 631, 633, 639
  legs, 482–483, 494, 626–629, 631, 633, 639
  Pythagorean Theorem, 473, 482–486, 494, 506, 508, 510, 618, 627, 636
  solving, 632–636, 640
  30°-60°, 617–621, 639
  trigonometric ratios, 626–636, 639–640

Roosevelt, Theodore, 475

Roots, 523–526, 533–557
  nature of, 541–545, 555
  products of, 550–553, 556
  real, 523–525, 537–545, 555
  square, 474, 477–513, 531–532
  sums of, 550–553, 556

Rotations, 424

Rounded numbers, 566–568

Sales taxes, 146–149

Samples, 175

Scales, 135

Scatter plots, 583–587, 606

Schwarzschild radius, 225

Scientific calculators, 15

Scientific notation, 221–225, 249
  E notation, 225

Sequences, 76–77
  Fibonacci, 212

Set-builder notation, 177

Sets, 19–21
  disjoint, 51
  elements of, 19–20
  empty, 19, 51, 195
  intersections of, 51–52, 194–195
  replacement, 19
  set-builder notation, 177
  solutions, 19, 176–177, 182, 186–187, 195–196, 199–201
  subsets, 19–20, 51
  unions of, 51–52, 195–196
  universal, 51

Sides
  adjacent, 626–629, 633, 639
  corresponding, 622–624
  opposite, 617–620, 626–629, 633, 639

Sieve of Eratosthenes, 260
Similar triangles, 622–625, 627, 639
Simple events, 589–592, 600, 606
Simple interest, 142–144, 170
Simplest form, 27–30
Sine, 609, 626–633, 639–640
Slope-intercept form, 410–414, 416–422, 424–426, 435, 444
Slopes, 399–414, 416–427, 431, 434–435, 443–444, 448, 628
  of horizontal lines, 401–402, 407
  negative, 401–402, 584, 606
  of parallel lines, 423–425
  of perpendicular lines, 424–425
  positive, 401–402, 584
  of vertical lines, 401–402, 407
Snell, Willebrord, 609
Snell's Law, 609, 628, 631
Solutions, 18–19
  checking, 95–98, 100–101, 104, 112, 123–124, 176, 291, 296, 407, 444, 447, 452, 457, 501–504
  of equations in two variables, 364–373
  roots, 523–526, 533–557
Solution sets, 19, 176–177, 182, 186–187, 195–196, 199–201
Spreadsheets, 40, 247
Square root keys, 478–480, 488–489, 498
Square roots, 474, 477–513, 531–532
  principal, 477–480, 492
  product property of, 492–493, 495
  quotient property of, 493
  simplifying, 492–496, 511
Squares
  area of, 10, 38, 243, 245–246, 276, 282, 287, 480
  completing, 531–536, 555
  of differences, 244–245
  differences of, 244
  magic, 59
  of numbers, 477, 479, 501–502
  perfect, 281–288, 296, 301, 487
  perimeters of, 38
  Punnett, 246
  of sums, 243–245
Standard form, 406–409, 411–412, 416, 420–421
Standard viewing window, 384
Statements, 18
Statistics, 175, 560–587, 604–606
  bar graphs, 389–390, 432

box-and-whisker plots, 579–582, 605
circle graphs, 141, 432–433
comparative graphs, 432
interquartile ranges, 575–578, 580, 605
line graphs, 389–390, 436
line plots, 560–564, 604
means, 80, 188, 570–576, 605
medians, 570–581, 605
modes, 570–575, 605
outliers, 576–578, 580
pictographs, 432
quartiles, 575–581, 605
ranges, 575, 577–578, 605
regression lines, 588
samples, 175
scatter plots, 583–587, 606
stem-and-leaf plots, 565–570, 572–573, 576–579, 582, 605
tolerance, 175
Stem-and-leaf plots, 565–570, 572–573, 576–579, 582, 605
  back-to-back, 566–568
Store keys, 420
Subsets, 19–20, 51
Substitution, 447–451, 469
Substitution property, 23–24, 28, 31–33, 45, 55, 74–76, 230
Subtraction
  elimination using, 452, 454–456
  of integers, 57–58, 88
  of polynomials, 230–233, 497
  of radical expressions, 497–500, 511
  of rational expressions, 322–324, 331–332, 335, 349
  of rational numbers, 70–72, 322
  in solving equations, 99–102, 111–112, 116, 126
  in solving inequalities, 176–179, 186–188, 200–201, 204
  symbol in BASIC, 10
  words used to indicate, 9
Subtraction property for inequality, 176, 186
Subtraction property of equality, 99, 111
Summaries, 44–46, 88–90, 126–128, 170–172, 204–206, 248–250, 300–302, 348–350, 392–394, 434–436, 468–470, 510–512, 554–556, 604–606, 638–640
Sums
  of roots, 550–553, 556
  squares of, 243–246
Supplementary angles, 610, 612–613, 638

Surface area, 37, 247
Symmetric property, 23–24, 27, 60
Symmetry, 519–522, 554
Systems of equations, 442–461, 468–469
  elimination, 452–461, 469
  graphing, 442–447, 468
  number of solutions, 443–446, 448, 450, 468
  substitution, 447–451, 469
Systems of inequalities, 463–467, 470

Tangent, 626–631, 633, 639
Taxes, 146–149
Technologies
  adding fractions, 79
  formulas, 40
  graphing linear equations, 427
  graphing linear relations, 384
  quadratic equations, 530
  radical equations, 505
  rational expressions, 315
  regression lines, 588
  solving equations, 121
  solving inequalities, 191
  successive discounts, 150
  systems of equations, 462
  trigonometric functions, 637
  volume and surface area, 247
Temperature
  Celsius, 36, 78, 120, 199, 347, 373
  Fahrenheit, 36, 54, 78, 120, 347, 373
  windchill factors, 54
Terminating decimals, 487, 511
Terms, 27–29
  coefficients of, 28–29
  like, 27–29, 230–232, 234, 239–240, 262, 323
Tests
  chapter, 47, 91, 129, 173, 207, 251, 303, 351, 395, 437, 471, 513, 557, 607, 641
  college entrance, 130–131, 252–253, 296–297, 514–515
  vertical line, 375, 377
Theorems
  Pythagorean, 473, 482–486, 494, 506, 508, 510, 618, 627, 636
  unique factorization, 256
Tolerance, 175
Trace functions, 462

Trajectory, 518

Transitive property, 23–24
 of order, 60–61

Trapezoidal prisms, 314

Trapezoids
 area of, 38, 40, 237, 246, 343
 diagonals of, 507
 isosceles, 507

Tree diagrams, 326–327,
 600–602

Triangles
 acute, 612
 area of, 36, 39–40, 446, 630
 equilateral, 611, 617
 isosceles, 612–613
 obtuse, 612
 perimeters of, 231
 right, 339–340, 473, 482–486,
  494, 510, 612, 617–621,
  626–636
 sides of, 185
 similar, 622–625, 627, 639
 sum of angles of, 233,
  611–614, 638

Triangular numbers, 153

Trigonometric ratios, 626–636,
 639–640
 using calculators, 627–630, 639
 cosine, 626–632, 639–640
 graphs of, 637
 sine, 609, 626–633, 639–640
 tangent, 626–631, 633, 639

Trinomials, 226–228
 factoring, 262–264, 271–275,
  281–288, 301
 perfect square, 281–288, 296,
  301, 531–535

Truncated numbers, 566–567

Twin primes, 259

Uniform motion problems,
 158–161, 171, 339–340, 342,
 454, 456, 459, 461

Unions, 51–52, 195–196

Unique Factorization Theorem,
 256

Unit cost, 66

United inches, 230

Unit fractions, 165, 528

Universal sets, 51

Upper quartiles, 575–577,
 579–581, 605

Variables, 8
 in BASIC, 10

Variations
 constants of, 162
 direct, 162–165, 172
 interquartile ranges, 575–578,
  580, 605
 inverse, 166–169, 172
 ranges, 575, 577–578, 605

Venn diagrams, 51

Vertical lines, 401–402, 407

Vertical line test, 375, 377

Vertices, 518–522

Volume
 of cubes, 10
 of rectangular prisms, 32, 247,
  278–279, 547
 of trapezoidal prisms, 314

Washington, George, 409

Whole numbers, 50–52, 487, 489

Windchill factors, 54

x-axis, 354, 356

x-coordinates, 354–356, 381

x-intercepts, 384, 410, 412–413,
 415, 417–419, 435, 523–524,
 541–542, 544

y-axis, 354, 356

y-coordinates, 354–356, 381

y-intercepts, 384, 410–422, 424,
 435

Zero
 division by, 123
 exponent, 218–219
 multiplicative property of,
  23–24, 32, 74
 opposite of, 56
 probability of, 590–591
 product property, 306–307,
  340
 slope of, 401–402, 407, 434

Zero product property, 290–293,
 295–296, 302, 502

PHOTO CREDITS

Cover, Photo courtesy of Digital Equipment Corporation, Photo Design, Skolos-Wedell, Inc.

v, (t) Rick Rickman/Duomo, (b) Skip Comer Photography; **vi,** Aaron Haupt; **vii,** (t) Art Resource, (b) Skip Comer Photography; **viii,** (t) © Doug Watzstein, FPG, (b) Carl K. Sams II/Peter Arnold, Inc.; **ix,** (t) COMSTOCK, INC., (b) Tim Cairns/Cobalt Productions; **x,** Aaron Haupt; **xi,** (t) Romilly Lockyer/The Image Bank, (b) COMSTOCK, INC.; **xii,** (t) Coco McCoy/Rainbow, (b) COMSTOCK, INC.; **xiii,** (t) COMSTOCK, INC., (b) David Lissy/The Photo File; **xiv,** Aaron Haupt; **xv,** Ted Mahieu/The Stock Market; **6,** Rick Rickman/Duomo; **7,** Stephen Wilkes/The Image Bank; **8–9,** Official White House Photo; **10,** Latent Image; **12,** Kul Bhatia/Photo Researchers; **13,** Skip Comer Photography; **14,** Skip Comer Photography; **18,** Howard Sochurck/Photo Researchers; **20,** Kenneth Fink/Photo Researchers; **21,** Doug Martin; **25,** Cobalt Production; **26–27,** Skip Comer Photography; **30,** The Bettmann Archive; **31,** John McDermott/Tony Stone Worldwide/Chicago; **35,** Ralph Wetmore/Tony Stone Worldwide/Chicago; **36,** Skip Comer Photography; **39,** Sheila Goode-Green; **42,** Latent Image; **48–49,** Skip Comer Photography; **54,** Brian Parker/Tom Stack & Associates; **56,** Mitchell Layton/Duomo; **60,** © Howard Zyrb, FPG; **64,** Bo Zaunders/The Stock Market; **65,** Randy Scheiber; **68–69,** Skip Comer Photography; **72,** Heinz Kluetmeier/Sports Illustrated/© Time, Inc.; **73,** Pete Saloutos/The Stock Market; **74,** The Bettmann Archive; **78, 80,** Latent Image; **84,** Reinhard Kunkel/The Image Bank; **85,** Latent Image; **87,** Superstock, Inc.; **92,** Art Resource; **93,** Al Assid/The Stock Market; **96,** Latent Image; **98,** Robert Garvey/The Stock Market; **99,** Latent Image; **102,** Richard Price/Westlight; **103,** © Tom Tracy, FPG; **108,** Latent Image; **109,** George Hunter/Tony Stone Worldwide/Chicago; **110,** Pictures Unlimited; **111,** Dave Wilhelm/The Stock Market; **115,** Henley & Savage/The Stock Market; **116,** (l) Howard Millard/The Stock Market, (r) Superstock, Inc.; **120,** © Carl Purcell, FPG; **122,** Skip Comer Photography; **123,** Image First; **132,** Skip Comer Photography; **133,** © Martin Rogers, FPG; **134,** Mark Albin; **135,** Image First; **136,** Steve Vidler/Superstock, Inc.; **138,** Ben Simmons/The Stock Market; **139,** Ron Dahlquist/Superstock, Inc.; **141,** Ted Mahieu/The Stock Market; **144,** Skip Comer Photography; **147,** Latent Image; **148,** John H. Curtis/The Stock Market; **149,** Skip Comer Photography; **152,** Brownie Harris/The Stock Market; **154–155,** Latent Image; **156,** Pictures Unlimited; **160,** Barney Oldfield; **162,** NASA; **165,** British Museum/Superstock, Inc.; **166,** Skip Comer Photography; **174,** © Doug Watzstein, FPG; **175,** Comstock, Inc./Mike & Carol Werner; **177,** Latent Image; **178,** Dan Helms/Duomo; **180,** Focus on Sports, Inc.; **181,** Sheila Goode-Green; **184,** Skip Comer Photography; **186,** (t) Doug Martin, (r) Courtesy: D.C. Comics/Movie Still Archives; **190,** Doug Martin; **198,** Skip Comer Photography; **199,** Gerard Photography; **201,** Randy Scheiber; **203,** © Art Montes de Oca, FPG; **208,** Carl K. Sams II/Peter Arnold, Inc.; **209,** Gary Griffen/Animals Animals; **212,** Rod Planck/Photo Researchers; **216,** © C. Simpson, FPG; **220,** file photo; **221,** NASA; **222,** Tom Dietrich/Tony Stone Worldwide/Chicago; **223,** NASA; **224,** Heinz Kluetmeier/Sports Illustrated/© Time, Inc.; **226,** Bud Fowle; **229,** Stan Osolinski/The Stock Market; **230,** Skip Comer Photography; **240,** Superstock, Inc.; **246,** David Frazier; **254,** Comstock, Inc./Bruce Hands; **255,** Dan McCoy/Rainbow; **260,** Larry Hamill; **264,** Randy Duchaine/The Stock Market; **268,** Comstock, Inc./David Lokey; **270,** Tim Davis/Photo Researchers; **275,** Serraillier/Rapho/Photo Researchers; **280,** David Stoecklein/The Stock Market; **282,** Donald Johnson/The Stock Market; **289,** Clyde H. Smith/Peter Arnold, Inc.; **294,** Tim Courlas; **295,** (1) Doug Martin, (r) James Westwater; **299,** COMSTOCK, INC.; **304,** Tim Cairns/Cobalt Production; **309,** Spencer Swanger/Tom Stack & Associates; **314,** SV & B Productions/The Image Bank; **318,** Comstock, Inc./Sharon Chester; **321,** John Iacono/Sports Illustrated/© Time, Inc.; **325,** COMSTOCK, INC.; **326,** Brian Heston; **327,** Robert Kligge/The Stock Market; **329,** Ted Rice; **332,** Larry Hamill; **337,** Aaron Haupt; **338,** Tim Courlas; **339,** David Stoecklein/The Stock Market; **341,** Doug Martin; **342,** David Frazier; **344,** ITTC Productions/The Image Bank; **346,** Murray Alcosser/The Image Bank; **347,** Jean Anderson/The Stock Market; **352,** Romilly Lockyer/The Image Bank; **358,** Larry Hamill; **359,** Steve Elmore/Tom Stack & Associates; **361, 363,** Latent Image; **364,** Cobalt Productions; **366,** Skip Comer Photography; **368,** David Cavagnaro; **372,** Craig Hammell/The Stock Market; **376,** NASA; **379,** Ted Rice; **383,** Michael Furman/The Stock Market; **385,** Skip Comer Photography; **388,** Ron Dahlquist/Tony Stone Worldwide/Chicago; **391,** Elyse Lewin/The Image Bank; **398,** Comstock, Inc./A. Hurtman; **399,** Comstock, Inc./David Lokey; **400,** (t) David Frazier, (b) David Barnes/The Stock Market; **404,** Doug Martin; **407,** Lawrence Migdale/Photo Researchers; **409,** Michel Tcherevkoff/The Image Bank; **410,** Tim Courlas/Milepost; **411,** Skip Comer Photography; **414,** Latent Image; **416,** Skip Comer Photography; **418,** Manfred Gottschalk/Tom Stack & Associates; **419,** Pictures Unlimited; **423,** Doug Martin; **426,** Ed Block/The Stock Market; **431,** Howard J. Millard/The Stock Market; **438,** Coco McCoy/Rainbow; **446,** Gary McMichael/Photo Researchers; **447,** Bob Pool/Tom Stack & Associates; **449,** Ken Frick; **451,** Andy Levin/Photo Researchers; **452,** Stanley Tess, Jr./The Stock Market; **454,** Karl Weatherly/Tony Stone Worldwide; **459,** Michael Melford/The Image Bank; **467,** William J. Weber; **472,** Comstock, Inc./R. Michael Stuckey; **473,** Comstock, Inc./R. Michael Stuckey; **475,** The Bettmann Archive; **477,** Latent Image; **482,** © J. Blank, FPG; **486,** Steve Lissau; **491,** Marc Romanelli/The Image Bank; **496,** Doug Martin; **504,** COMSTOCK, INC.; **506,** Jon Feingersh/Tom Stack & Associates; **509,** Washnik Studio/The Stock Market; **516,** Comstock, Inc./Mark Ippolito; **517,** Albert Normandin/The Image Bank; **518,** Tim Courlas; **520,** UPI/